The Greek Alphabet

A	α	alpha		N	ν	nu
B	β	beta		Ξ	ξ	xi
Γ	γ	gamma		O	o	omicron
Δ	δ	delta		Π	π	pi
E	ϵ	epsilon		P	ρ	rho
Z	ζ	zeta		Σ	σ	sigma
H	η	eta		T	τ	tau
Θ	θ	theta		Υ	υ	upsilon
I	ι	iota		Φ	ϕ	phi
K	κ	kappa		X	χ	chi
Λ	λ	lambda		Ψ	ψ	psi
M	μ	mu		Ω	ω	omega

Ron Craig
&
Sheryl Snow

MOLECULAR
CELL BIOLOGY

MOLECULAR CELL BIOLOGY

Charlotte J. Avers
Rutgers University

ADDISON-WESLEY PUBLISHING COMPANY

Reading, Massachusetts ▪ Menlo Park, California ▪ Don Mills, Ontario ▪ Wokingham, England
Amsterdam ▪ Sydney ▪ Singapore ▪ Tokyo ▪ Madrid ▪ Bogotá ▪ Santiago ▪ San Juan

Sponsoring editor: Bruce Spatz
Art development editor: James Funston
Production supervisor: Margaret Pinette
Copy editor: Connie Day
Text designer: Catherine Dorin
Illustrators: Oxford Illustrators
Art consultant: Loretta Bailey
Production coordinator: Janet Davis Castro
Manufacturing supervisor: Ann DeLacey

On the cover: A schematic dissection of globin into the product of the separate exons, with color added for effect. Copyright by the Nobel Foundation, Stockholm, Sweden.

Library of Congress Cataloging in Publication Data

Avers, Charlotte J.
    Molecular cell biology.

    Includes bibliographies and index.
    1. Cytology.   2. Molecular biology.   I. Title.
QH581.2.A96 1985   574.87   85-3908
ISBN 0-201-10307-9

ABCDEFGHIJK-MU-89876

To Ron and Paula

Preface

We are in the midst of a revolution in biological studies due mainly to the development of precise methods of analysis at the molecular level. The growing excitement in molecular cell biology stems from important new information and insights concerning the elegant and sophisticated worlds within worlds that make up the living cell. The dynamic nature of the cell is evident from its varied responses to many kinds of stimuli, its repertory of regulation mechanisms for coping with a constantly changing internal and external environment, its ability to manage alone or in accommodation with other cells in the test tube or organism, and its properties of repair, growth, reproduction, and flexibility to evolve.

Biology itself is undergoing unification as cell biologists, developmental biologists, geneticists, biochemists, immunologists, and others direct and focus their efforts toward common objectives and the solutions of basic problems. In this book I have tried to convey the ongoing challenge and excitement of current research, the debts we owe to seminal studies of the recent past in paving the way to present-day understanding, and the convergence of ideas, methods, and intellectual approaches of different life sciences.

About This Book

I have written *Molecular Cell Biology* for students with a college-level background in biology and chemistry who are taking a first, one-term course in modern cell biology. In my writing I made every effort to provide discussions and explanations of complex phenomena, data, and processes. In collaboration with members of the publishing staff I assembled an extensive set of photographs and illustrations to provide graphic accompaniment to the written word, and the electron micrographs have been reproduced in their original size for full pedagogical effect. Other aids for the student and the instructor include summaries and extensive sets of readings and references for each chapter, and a glossary of more than 800 terms, all of which are highlighted in boldface type in the text.

A Flexible Organization

To permit the greatest flexibility I have designed the chapter contents to allow for alternative sequences of instruction. The book is subdivided into six parts. Part I contains chapters on cellular structures and molecules and the major biochemical and genetic processes and units of life. With these four chapters as an introduction, the remaining fourteen chapters can be rearranged to suit individual preferences and course organizations. For example, Part IV (Organization of the Genome) and Part V (Reproduction and Development) could be covered prior to Part II (Cell Boundaries and Surfaces) and Part III (Organization of the Cytoplasm) if that order is preferred. Some may wish to assign Chapter 4, Genetic Processes, in conjunction with Part IV, Organization of the Genome. Part VI (Evolution), however, was deliberately written as a summarizing evolutionary perspective of molecular cell biology. I believe this perspective to be the one that brings together any or all of biology in its most basic content and highly recommend that this material be the final, capstone section of the course.

Topic Coverage

Given the massive amounts of information required in an up-to-date text in modern cell biology, a key challenge facing the author of such a book is to keep it to a length that is suitable for an undergraduate first course. I have answered this challenge by setting as my goal the need to avoid overwhelming introductory students with excessive detail or material that should come in a later course. Thus, I have discussed some topics more briefly than is done in other texts, but in all cases I have given at least the flavor and major significance of the subject in sketching the picture of the living cell in all its varied features. I am comfortable with the decisions that I have made in allocating more space to some topics than to others, but I welcome comments and suggestions from the readers.

Acknowledgments

It is a pleasure to acknowledge my debt to many friends and colleagues who generously provided excellent photographs, offered useful comments and suggestions to improve the book, and reviewed all or part of the text and art manuscripts. In particular I wish to thank the following reviewers for their helpful comments:

William Bradshaw
Brigham Young University

Robert P. Donaldson
George Washington University

Gideon Dreyfuss
Northwestern University

Edwin V. Gaffney
The Pennsylvania State University

Mary Lee S. Ledbetter
College of the Holy Cross

Albert P. Torzilli
George Mason University

Sara McCowen
Virginia Commonwealth
University

Margaret Waterman
Emory University

I could not have managed the many phases of preparation and production of this book without the cheerful encouragement of my editor, Bruce Spatz; the efficiency of the production staff, Margaret Pinette and Judy Ullman in particular; and the prodigious efforts of James Funston and Dr. Mary Lee S. Ledbetter in writing and revising the summaries and carefully developing and editing the entire set of illustrations. I believe the book has benefited greatly by all these inputs and that the students will be as enthusiastic as I am about the story now emerging in molecular cell biology—a story of the cell as a dynamic and elegant unit of life.

New Brunswick, New Jersey   C. J. A.

Abridged Contents

Contents

CHAPTER **6**

The Cell Surface   183

PART **III**   Organization of the Cytoplasm

CHAPTER **7**

Endoplasmic Reticulum and Golgi Apparatus   227

CHAPTER **8**

Lysosomes and Microbodies   267

CHAPTER **9**

Mitochondria   305

490 →

CHAPTER **10**

Chloroplasts   363

CHAPTER 11

Cytoskeletal Systems and Movement   413

PART IV   Organization of the Genome

CHAPTER 12

Molecular Nature of the Genome   479

CHAPTER **13**

Gene Expression: Transcription and Translation   529

CHAPTER **14**

Regulation of Gene Expression   585

485 - see
refs + 606-611

PART **V**   Reproduction and Development

PART **VI**

Evolution

CHAPTER **18**

Cellular and Molecular Evolution   765

PART I

Introduction to the Cell

CHAPTER 1

Cells in Perspective

Historical Highlights

The historical and modern basis for cell biology is microscopy. In the modern discipline of cell biology, however, the methods of biochemistry, genetics, and molecular biology have merged with microscopic methods to produce a broader perspective for the study of cells as dynamic living units. Cell biologists are as concerned with molecules as with cellular structures made from these molecules, which has contributed to our analysis of cells from a most comprehensive and dynamic view. The cell biologist attempts to observe, understand, and explain how structure and function are correlated and how function is regulated within the framework of space and time in a living system.

The brief historical synopsis that follows may give the impression that we accumulate knowledge and understanding in a simple stepwise progression. On the contrary, as will be demonstrated throughout this text, a significant step forward is often made possible because different kinds of information are brought together to permit us to develop a new and more inclusive perspective on a subject or a phenomenon. New methods or new applications of existing methods provide the means by which we seek answers to questions on the basis of hypotheses, or working ideas. Questions that lead only to philosophical debate may be interesting, but they are not particularly productive. Hypotheses that generate new research based on one or more testable predictions have proved to be the most valuable foundations for expanding our comprehension of the world around us. A few of the historical landmarks that have contributed to the modern view of living cells are discussed in the following sections. These and many other original studies have shown us a little of the astonishingly complex nature of the interacting systems of structure, function, and regulation that underlie the cellular basis of life.

1.1
Microscopy and the Cell Theory

The beginnings of cell study can be traced to the invention of lenses and microscopes that allowed early scientists to magnify living materials and see details invisible to the naked eye. We cannot see most cells with the naked eye, because cells are too small to be visible as individual units and because we cannot distinguish the individual cells from one another within a group even though the whole group may be large enough to see without magnification. The human eye cannot resolve two objects as separate entities if they are closer together than 200 micrometers (μm). No matter how great the enlargement achieved by magnification, we would still see a fuzzy single object rather than two separate objects, unless the magnifying lenses also provide adequate *resolution* to distinguish the separate objects. The early microscopes could resolve individual cells ranging in average size between 1 and 100 μm (Table 1.1). Modern microscope lenses allow us to achieve a resolution of 0.2 μm using ordinary white light as a source of illumination and a resolution of 0.001 μm or less using a beam of electrons to illuminate objects with the electron microscope (Fig. 1.1).

The first useful microscope was invented in 1590 by Z. and H. Janssen. They built a **compound microscope**—that is, a magnifying system containing two lenses whose individual magnification factors are multiplied to produce the total enlargement of the image observed. Their microscope could magnify an object 30 times its actual size, and with good resolution of individual entities. A microscope with two lenses usually provides a less distorted magnified image than is seen with a simple microscope (one lens) because there is less optical aberration in the compound instrument.

Robert Hooke is credited with reporting the first important information using a compound microscope. He described "cells" or "pores" in cork and other plant tissues (Fig. 1.2). In addition to these observations,

TABLE 1-1
Units of Measurement

A. LENGTH				
Meter (m)	Millimeter (mm)	Micrometer (μm)	Nanometer (nm)	Ångstrom (Å)
1	1,000 (1×10^3)	1,000,000 (1×10^6)	1,000,000,000 (1×10^9)	1×10^{10}
0.001	1	1,000	1,000,000	1×10^7
0.000001	0.001	1	1,000	1×10^4
1×10^{-9}	1×10^{-6}	0.001	1	10
1×10^{-10}	1×10^{-7}	1×10^{-4}	0.1	1
B. WEIGHT				
Gram (g)	Milligram (mg)	Microgram (μg)	Nanogram (ng)	Picogram (pg)
1	1,000	1,000,000	1×10^9	1×10^{12}
0.001	1	1,000	1×10^6	1×10^9
1×10^{-6}	0.001	1	1×10^3	1×10^6
1×10^{-9}	1×10^{-6}	0.001	1	1×10^3
1×10^{-12}	1×10^{-9}	1×10^{-6}	0.001	1

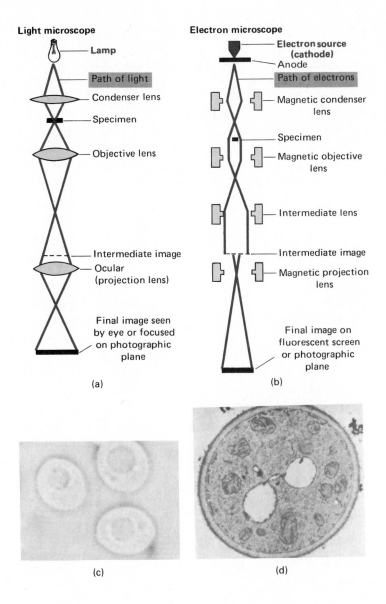

(a) (b)

(c) (d)

FIGURE 1-1
The basic features of optical systems for (a) the light microscope and (b) the electron microscope are shown schematically. The longer wavelengths of visible light allow less magnification and resolution of detail with light microscopy than can be obtained when a beam of electrons, radiation of shorter wavelengths, is used in electron microscopy. Much less detail is apparent in yeast cells photographed (c) through a light microscope (×2100) than (d) through an electron microscope (×16,000).

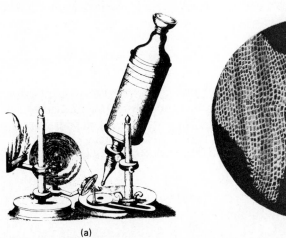

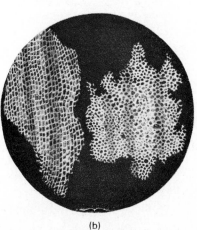

(a) (b)

FIGURE 1-2
In the seventeenth century Robert Hooke used (a) a relatively crude compound microscope to view plant tissues, including (b) cork tissue in which he described boxlike compartments he called "cells."

which were published in his book *Micrographia* in 1665, Hooke also noted that some kinds of cells were filled with "juices." He drew particular attention, however, to the highly visible, thick cell wall, and cell walls rather than cell contents remained the focus of cell studies for about 150 years.

Although the earliest studies were made of plants, animals were scrutinized by microscopy shortly afterward. Plant and animal cells looked quite different, however, leading to the general belief that plants and animals were constructed differently. Plant cell walls exhibit conspicuous boundaries, whereas individual animal cells are difficult to see distinctly in a tissue sample. The fundamental similarity between plant and animal construction was made clear when Theodor Schwann showed that animal cartilage cells had well-defined outlines that were similar to cell wall boundaries in plant tissues. Individual cell boundaries in cartilage tissue are delineated by thick deposits of collagen fibers, just as thick deposits of cellulose outline the average plant cell in a tissue. On the basis of their studies of plant and animal tissues by microscopy, Matthew Schleiden and Schwann proposed a simple and unifying **cell theory** for all organisms. In 1838–1839 Schleiden and Schwann postulated that the cell is the basic unit of structure in all life and that all organisms are constructed from one or more cells. The cell theory was further refined in 1855 when Rudolf Virchow presented the important idea that *all cells arise from pre-existing cells.* This idea helped to direct attention to the cell as an important factor in the transmission of inherited traits from one generation to the next.

Although the cell nucleus had been described earlier, it was not until the 1870s that its importance was firmly established as the physical basis for continuity between generations. The significance of the nucleus in reproduction was demonstrated dramatically in 1875–1876 when Oskar Hertwig showed that two nuclei must fuse if an egg is to develop into an embryo. He also showed that one nucleus was present in the egg cell of the animal and that the second nucleus was introduced by the sperm when the egg was fertilized. Similar events were shown to characterize reproduction in plants, which further confirmed the fundamental similarity between plant and animal organisms.

By the turn of the century chromosomes had been identified and counted, and the nuclear division processes of mitosis and meiosis had been described. These and other studies established that continuity between generations depended on the cell nucleus. Cells arise only from other cells like themselves because of nuclear constancy based on the transmission of a set of chromosomes from parent to offspring cells and individuals.

These and other discoveries during the nineteenth century provided enough information to support a unifying cell theory that embraced the entire living world known at that time. The cell theory states that

1. All living organisms are made up of one or more living units or cells.

2. Each cell can maintain its living properties independently of the rest, but the properties of life of any organism are based on the properties of life of its individual cells.

3. The smallest clearly defined unit of life is the cell.

4. Cells arise only from other cells.

1.2
Genetic and Biochemical Aspects of the Cell

Various proposals were made in the late 1800s to relate particular nuclear factors with the control of heredity. None of these proposals took into account Gregor Mendel's studies of inheritance in garden peas, and his 1866 publication went largely unnoticed in his lifetime. Biologists were poorly prepared at that time to appreciate an abstract approach to heredity. By 1900 the state of biology had progressed enough for Mendel's concepts to be eagerly accepted when they were quoted in independently conducted studies reported by Hugo de Vries, Carl Correns, and Ernst von Tschermak. The study of genetics as a biological discipline is dated as beginning in 1900. In 1902 Walter Sutton formally proposed the **chromosome theory of heredity**, which stated that the hereditary factors, or genes, were located in chromosomes in the nucleus (Fig. 1.3). Supporting evidence for this theory was collected by various geneticists in the years that followed, and by 1916 the theory was widely accepted. Particularly critical experimental evidence for the theory was provided by the group of *Drosophila* geneticists under the leadership of

FIGURE 1-3
Photograph of the 46 chromosomes from a human body cell undergoing nuclear division. The cells were treated in such a way that they would burst and allow the individual chromosomes to spread over a large area on the microscope slide. A deeply stained nondividing nucleus at the bottom of the photograph has not burst, and no detail is visible within the structure. ×3250.

Thomas Hunt Morgan at Columbia University. They showed that the transmission of certain genes paralleled the transmission of the chromosome in which these genes had been mapped, meaning that genes were parts of the chromosome.

Studies of the chemical basis of heredity can be dated as beginning in 1871 when Friedrich Miescher described "nuclein" (later renamed deoxyribonucleic acid, or DNA), an unusual acidic substance he had isolated from nuclei of white blood cells. It was not until the early 1950s, however, that DNA was generally acknowledged to be the genetic material. Before 1950 many scientists held to the belief that genes were proteins, because only proteins were then known to exist in sufficient variety to account for the great diversity of genes in organisms. DNA was considered a relatively invariant molecule made up of equal parts of the four kinds of nucleotides in a repeating tetranucleotide sequence. Because chromosomes consisted of proteins as well as DNA, there was little reason at the time to favor DNA over proteins as the genetic material.

By the early 1950s the scientific community was more disposed to consider DNA rather than protein as the genetic material. Biochemical studies by Erwin Chargaff in particular showed that DNA was a variable molecule, and physical studies by Maurice Wilkins, Rosalind Franklin, and others provided crucial details of DNA molecular structure. In 1953 James Watson and Francis Crick published two brief articles in *Nature*, in which they proposed the double-helix model of the DNA molecule and pointed out features that made the molecule eminently suitable to act as the genetic material. The molecular model provided a basis for numerous experimental tests, and progress in molecular genetics has proceeded at a dizzying pace ever since. Genes have been purified, they are transferred almost at will from one cell or organism to another in the laboratory, and the sequence of tens of thousands of nucleotides can be readily determined for individual genes or even entire genomes in various organisms.

Advances in chemistry were crucial to the development of the cell theory and in relating cell structure and function. Friedrich Wöhler revolutionized biology as well as chemistry in 1828 when he showed that an organic compound, urea, could be synthesized from an inorganic compound, ammonium cyanate. Before this it was generally believed that the living and nonliving worlds were entirely different and that the laws of physics and chemistry did not apply to living systems. Wöhler showed that the same substance known to be made in living systems could also be made from inorganic raw materials in the laboratory and that both processes adhered to the same basic laws of physics and chemistry. From this and later studies, scientists gradually came to accept the thesis that organic compounds were formed in ordinary chemical reactions in cells rather than by vague and mystical "vital" processes.

In 1871 Louis Pasteur demonstrated that fermentation of sugar to form alcohol would take place under natural conditions only if living yeast cells were present. His experiments clearly showed that living organisms were associated with organic chemical reactions. On the other hand, Pasteur's work also helped to revive the belief that such reactions represented vital processes unique to living cells. In 1897, however, Hans and Eduard Büchner accidentally discovered that sugars could be fermented by extracts made from yeast cells; that is, the yeasts did not have to be alive in order to carry out the process. The factors in the yeast extracts that were responsible for the chemical activities were enzymes (earlier called "ferments"). Enzymes are unique protein catalysts of living cells, and enzyme activity can be retained in cell extracts that are obtained carefully and then placed in suitable conditions. During the 1920s Otto Warburg, David Keilin, and others contributed substantially to our understanding of cellular metabolism by their experimental studies of enzymatically catalyzed respiratory activities during the breakdown of sugars and other foods in the cytoplasm and mitochondria of cells. From these and later studies we have obtained exquisitely detailed information on the role played by each part of the cell in the interplay of energy and enzymes required to sustain the living state.

As more has become known about the interrelationship of form and function, biologists and chemists have gradually come to analyze both of these aspects of the cell. Cell chemistry and cell structure are studied by cytologists (microscopists), biochemists, physiologists, and geneticists from a broader perspective than any had taken earlier. The blurring of boundaries between scientific disciplines is one positive indication of advances in our understanding of the complexity and interaction that characterize the living system at every level of its organization. Just as the study of biology allows us to see fundamental similarities among plants, animals, and microorganisms, which we might miss if we studied botany, zoology, or microbiology separately, the union of biological studies allows us to seek fundamental features common to all life rather than a mere catalogue of their superficial differences.

Structural Organization of the Cell

In traditional systems of classification, all organisms are assigned to either the plant or the animal kingdom. Although many species can easily be accommodated within these two major categories, others pose difficulties because they have both plantlike and animal-like features. For example, *Euglena* is a unicellular organism with chloroplasts but without the typically rigid cell wall of plants. Bacteria and fungi lack chloroplasts, but these organisms are classified as plants in traditional systems because they possess rigid cell walls. The difficulty of sorting organisms in evolutionarily related groups has prompted attempts to modify kingdom classifications. These modifications emphasize evolutionary relationships rather than selected structural traits such as cell walls (Table 1.2).

Some recent revisions in kingdom classifications are based on the radically different cellular plans found in **prokaryotes** and **eukaryotes**. A prokaryotic cell lacks a membrane-bounded nucleus, whereas a eukaryotic cell has a nucleus that is separated by a membrane system

TABLE 1-2
Kingdom Classification Systems

"traditional"	Dodson, 1971	Whittaker, 1969

Plantae
  bacteria
  blue-green algae
  chrysophytes
  green algae
  red algae
  brown algae
  slime molds
  true fungi
  bryophytes
  tracheophytes
Animalia
  protozoa
  metazoa
	Monera
	  bacteria
	  blue-green algae
	Plantae
	  chrysophytes
	  green algae
	  red algae
	  brown algae
	  slime molds
	  true fungi
	  bryophytes
	  tracheophytes
	Animalia
	  protozoa
	  metazoa
		Monera
		  bacteria
		  blue-green algae
		  grass-green algae
		Protista
		  chrysophytes
		  protozoa
		Fungi
		  slime molds
		  true fungi
		Plantae
		  green algae
		  red algae
		  brown algae
		  bryophytes
		  tracheophytes
		Animalia
		  metazoa

Data from E. O. Dodson, 1971. The kingdoms of organisms. *Systematic Zoology* **20**: 265–281; and R. H. Whittaker, 1969. New concepts of the kingdoms of organisms. *Science* **163**:150–160.

from the surrounding cytoplasm in living cells. The difference in nuclear organization is the primary distinction, but other features also identify an organism as prokaryotic or eukaryotic (Table 1.3). The fundamental evolutionary divergence of prokaryotes and eukaryotes is an important aspect of modern cell studies. The terms *prokaryote* (*pro*: before; *karyon*: nucleus), for pre-nuclear life, and *eukaryote* (*eu*: true), for nucleated

TABLE 1-3
Some Major Differences Between Prokaryotes and Eukaryotes

Characteristic	Prokaryotes	Eukaryotes
Cell size	Mostly small (1–10 μm)	Mostly larger (10–100 μm)
Genetic system	DNA not associated with proteins in chromosomes	DNA complexed with proteins in chromosomes
	Nucleoid not membrane-bounded	Membrane-bounded nucleus
	One linkage group	Two or more linkage groups
	Little or no repetitious DNA	Repetitious DNA
Internal membranes (organelles)	Transient, if present	Numerous types, e.g., mitochondrion, chloroplast, lysosome, Golgi, etc.
Tissue formation	Absent	Present in many groups
Cell division	Binary fission, budding, or other means; no mitosis	Various means, associated with mitosis
Sexual system	Unidirectional transfer of genes from donor to recipient, if present	Complete nuclear fusion of equal gametic genomes; associated with meiosis
Motility organelle	Simple flagella in bacteria, if present	Complex cilia or flagella, if present
Nutrition	Principally absorption, some photosynthesizers	Absorption, ingestion, photosynthesis

organisms, were suggested by Hans Ris in the early 1960s and have been widely accepted since then.

1.3
Prokaryotic Cell Organization

Blue-green algae and bacteria are the two major prokaryotic groups. These organisms have been put into the kingdom Monera by several authorities. This classification has been widely accepted, because the plan of prokaryotic cell organization distinguishes monerans from all other cellular life forms.

The average size of a prokaryotic cell is 1–10 μm, but bacteria of the mycoplasma, rickettsia, and psittacosis groups are as small as 0.2–0.3 μm, and cells of the blue-green alga *Oscillatoria princeps* are 60 μm in diameter. In some cases, the products of cell division remain associated in chains, filaments, or other groupings, but many prokaryotic species exist as single, ungrouped cells. In either situation we still consider prokaryotes unicellular rather than multicellular organisms, because each cell can exist independently of all others and there is no difference between cells in a group. Each prokaryotic cell can produce new cells like itself, usually by binary fission. Some species produce spores and a few reproduce by a budding process.

The living material of a cell is called **protoplasm**. The protoplasmic contents of a prokaryotic cell include an enveloping **plasma membrane**, or **plasmalemma**, surrounding two recognizable regions called **cytoplasm** and **nucleoid**. The living protoplasm in turn is surrounded by a rigid or semirigid **cell wall**, which provides support and shape. The cell wall is usually considered to be a secretion of the living material within the cell and not to be protoplasmic in nature (Fig. 1.4).

The mycoplasmas are unusual prokaryotes because they have no cell wall. However, even these tiny prokaryotes have a plasma membrane as the cell boundary. Every living cell must have and must maintain an intact plasma membrane if it is to survive. The plasma membrane of a cell is about 10 nanometers (nm) thick, and, when seen in cross section (view of the cut edge), it displays a characteristic three-layered staining pattern in photographs taken with the electron microscope (Fig. 1.5). In

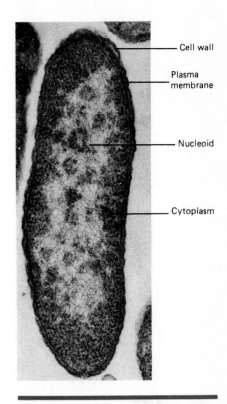

FIGURE 1-4
Electron micrograph of a thin section of the rod-shaped bacterium *Pseudomonas aeruginosa*. The central nucleoid is surrounded by dense cytoplasm, and the entire living protoplast is enclosed within a rather thin cell wall. (Photograph by H. -P. Hoffmann.)

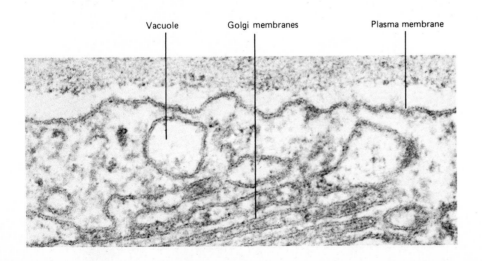

Vacuole   Golgi membranes   Plasma membrane

FIGURE 1-5
Electron micrograph of a section through part of a cell from the plant *Potamogeton natans* showing the typical three-layered staining pattern of cell membranes. The plasma membrane appears the same in cells from prokaryotes and eukaryotes, but eukaryotic cells contain a variety of other membranes, including ones that delimit vacuoles and form part of the Golgi system that packages cell secretions. ×151,000. (Photograph courtesy of M. C. Ledbetter.)

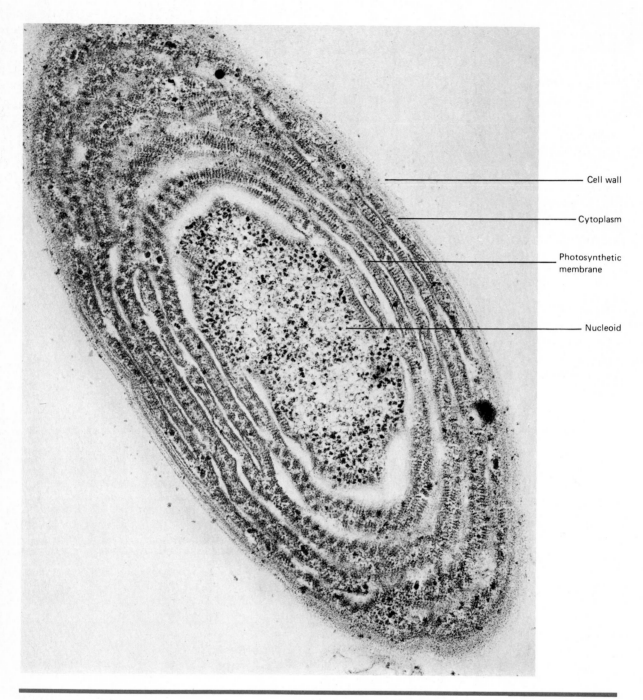

Cell wall

Cytoplasm

Photosynthetic
membrane

Nucleoid

FIGURE 1-6
Electron micrograph of a section
through the cell of the blue-green
alga *Synechococcus lividus*. A
concentrically folded photosynthetic
membrane fills the cytoplasmic area
between the central nucleoid and the
cell wall boundary. Numerous granules
of a special light-sensitive pigment
are attached to the photosynthetic
membrane, which itself is constructed
from a variety of lipid and protein
molecules. The photosynthetic membrane is believed to be an infolded
and differentiated portion of the plasma
membrane. ×62,400. (Courtesy
of E. Gantt, from Edwards, M. E.,
and E. Gantt, 1971, *J. Cell Biol.*
50: 896–900, Fig. 1.)

certain prokaryotic groups the plasmalemma is infolded at some locations, and these infoldings extend into the cytoplasm. In photosynthetic prokaryotes, such as the blue-green algae and purple bacteria, the infolded membrane regions contain tightly bound pigments and enzymes involved in the light-capturing reactions of photosynthesis (Fig. 1.6). Another type of plasmalemma infold, called a **mesosome**, appears to function in cellular activities such as respiration and cell division. In all these cases it is generally assumed that membranous infolds are attached at one or more sites to the plasma membrane, with which they are continuous. Some difference of opinion on this matter does exist, however, at least in certain cases involving photosynthetic membranes. The significance of the difference in opinions is that attached infolds represent differentiated regions of a single plasma membrane system, whereas separated membranes represent internal compartments of the cell and thus the occurrence of two or more separate membrane systems. In the former case the prokaryotic cell is noncompartmentalized; in the latter case the cell has compartments. The majority opinion is that prokaryotic cells are noncompartmentalized, but there are few data in support of either opinion.

Except for the plasma membrane and its occasional infolded regions, there is no other *permanent* membrane system in prokaryotic cells (with the possible exception of photosynthetic membranes in certain species). Localized concentrations of chemicals or cellular activities are not set apart by membranes from other regions of the cell. This feature represents another major distinction between prokaryotic and eukaryotic cellular organization.

The cytoplasm of the prokaryotic cell contains many kinds of chemicals, including enzymes that are active in metabolism, and numerous ribosomes. A **ribosome** is a tiny particle measuring 15–20 nm in diameter, so it is visible only at the high magnification of electron microscopy. Despite its morphological simplicity, the ribosome is a complex structure consisting of at least three RNA molecules and more than fifty different proteins. Ribosomes are essential components of protein synthesis in the processes of translating encoded genetic information in the cell.

The genetic material is localized in the nucleoid region of the prokaryotic cell. The nucleoid is visible in electron micrographs as an irregularly shaped area of lower density than the cytoplasm surrounding it. One or more nucleoids may be present in a cell, depending on the activity level of the cell, but each nucleoid contains a copy of the same DNA molecule in which all the genes of the species are located. DNA is not intimately complexed with proteins in prokaryotes, and the naked duplex DNA molecule appears as a dense fibrillar tangle in sectioned cells (see Fig. 1.4). From various kinds of analysis, including direct measurements of DNA spilled out of burst cells, we know that the single DNA molecule is about 2 nm wide, thousands of nanometers long, and probably circular in conformation in all or most species (Fig. 1.7).

All prokaryotic cells thus contain a ribosome-rich cytoplasm, naked duplex DNA in the nucleoid, and an enclosing plasma membrane. Except for the mycoplasmas, the smallest of all known cells, all prokaryotes have a semirigid cell wall boundary. Various other features

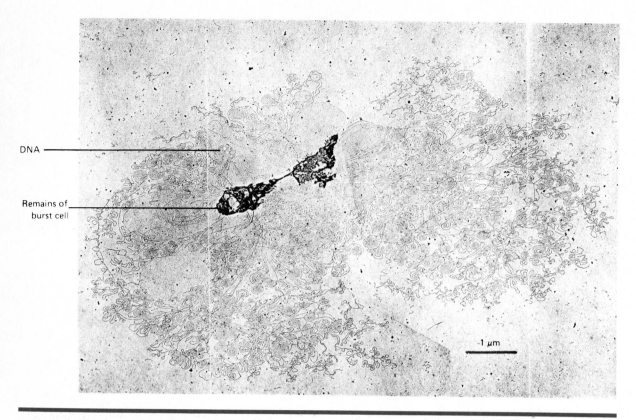

DNA ————

Remains of
burst cell

·1 μm

FIGURE 1-7
When the cell bursts, the highly folded
duplex DNA molecule of the *E. coli*
nucleoid spills out and reveals the very
great length (1300 μm) of the single
molecule. Some of the twists and
whorls of the folded DNA are visible
throughout the cloud of spilled DNA.
(From Delius, H., and A. Worcel, 1974,
J. Mol. Biol. **82**: 107.)

characterize some but not all prokaryotes. Some prokaryotes have a
surrounding sheath or capsule outside the cell wall, some produce
spores, some are motile by means of flagella, and some produce storage
granules or gas vacuoles. Prokaryotes are relatively simple in construction and cellular organization, but they are highly diversified in their
metabolic activities.

1.4
Eukaryotic Cell Organization

The major trademark of the eukaryotic cell is its membrane-bounded
compartments, all of which are physically separate from the enveloping
plasma membrane (Fig. 1.8). The **nucleus** is the most conspicuous
compartment and it contains the chromosomes, which are complex
nucleoprotein structures. Each **chromosome** is made up of one molecule
of DNA intimately associated with various proteins. In contrast to the
single DNA molecule that comprises the genome in prokaryotes, eukaryotes have two or more different chromosomes in the genome. Some
eukaryotic species have hundreds of different chromosomes comprising a
genome, or full set of genes.

The nuclear envelope consists of two membranes pockmarked with
nuclear openings called pores. The outer surface of the outer nuclear
membrane is studded with ribosomes and shows occasional continuities
with cytoplasmic membranes. A nucleus always includes at least one
nucleolus, but two or more nucleoli may be present. A **nucleolus** is a
globular structure produced at a specific region of certain chromosomes

and is essential for cell existence because it is the center for the synthesis of ribosomes. Unless a cell can maintain its ribosomal machinery, replacing used ribosomes and making new ones for new cells, proteins lost by wear and tear cannot be replenished and new proteins cannot be made. Apart from the structurally defined chromosomes and nucleoli, the remainder of the nucleus consists of a chemically complex but shapeless material called nucleoplasm. Recent studies using electron microscopy have provided evidence for the existence of a fibrous framework distributed throughout the amorphous nucleoplasm. The nature and function of this ribonucleoprotein framework is under investigation. Of all the parts of the nucleus just listed, only the chromosomes are regularly and precisely transmitted from one cell generation to the next during reproduction.

Between the plasma membrane boundary and the nuclear envelope is the cytoplasm with its profusion of membranes and particles all bathed in a granular **cytosol**. Occasional continuities probably occur

FIGURE 1-8
Numerous internal structures characterize eukaryotic cells, as seen in this electron micrograph of a section through part of a rat liver cell. Membrane-bounded compartments include the nucleus (only a portion is visible), mitochondria, rough and smooth endoplasmic reticulum (ER), microbodies, lysosomes, and others. Opaque granules of glycogen, a stored carbohydrate food reserve, are distributed throughout the cytoplasm. ×24,300. (Photograph courtesy of K. R. Porter.)

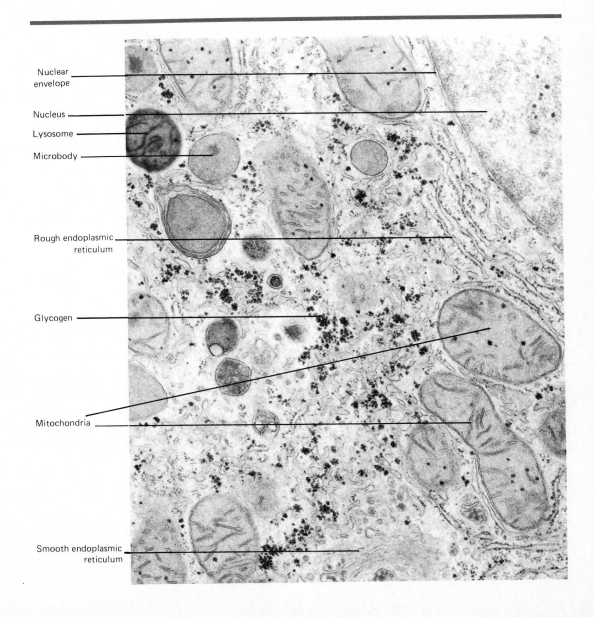

Nuclear envelope
Nucleus
Lysosome
Microbody
Rough endoplasmic reticulum
Glycogen
Mitochondria
Smooth endoplasmic reticulum

among all the membranous compartments of the cytoplasm, but none of these compartments is continuous with the plasma membrane. One of the more extensive cytoplasmic membranous systems is the **endoplasmic reticulum (ER)**, which consists of a system of channels and passageways that branch throughout the cytoplasm. When seen in cross section in an electron micrograph, the ER usually appears to be multilayered or to have tubular regions here and there. This image is somewhat deceptive, because we actually see only the cut ends of a sheet of membrane folded back on itself many times (Fig. 1.9). Ribosomes may be attached on one surface of the folded membrane sheet; we refer to such a region as **rough ER**. Regions of ER lacking attached ribosomes are called **smooth ER**. The endoplasmic reticulum, including its attached ribosomes, forms the structural basis for synthesis and distribution of proteins within the cell.

The **Golgi apparatus** is a subcellular compartment composed of smooth membranes. The main function of the Golgi apparatus is to process and package certain proteins made at the rough ER in the same cells. Some of these proteins are **secretions**, which are molecules destined for export from the cells in which they are made. In addition to processing proteins by adding sugar residues or by other means, the Golgi apparatus packages the modified proteins in vesicles (membrane "bubbles"). Secretion vesicles move toward the cell surface after passing through the Golgi region, and their contents are ultimately discharged into the surrounding extracellular space (Fig. 1.10). Other kinds of vesicles formed within the Golgi apparatus may remain within the cells in which they were produced. The **lysosome** is a major example of such a vesicle. It is formed in the Golgi apparatus but remains within the cell, where it functions in intracellular digestion processes. The lysosome is a membranous package of powerful digestive enzymes that can break down virtually any known organic substance of biological importance. Digestion takes place within the lysosome after it has fused with cellular or foreign material. In addition to its role in intracellular metabolism, the lysosome provides one line of defense against invasion by bacteria and other foreign agents. Lysosomes may also function in the dissolution

FIGURE 1-9

The rough endoplasmic reticulum. (a) In the two-dimensional perspective of an electron micrograph, the reticulum membrane appears to be composed of separate elements that define ribosome-studded lumens, or channels, alternating with ribosome-free lumens. ×85,000. (b) In a three-dimensional reconstruction, the endoplasmic reticulum is shown in its true form as a folded membrane sheet whose facing ribosome-studded surfaces define cytosolic lumens and whose facing ribosome-free surfaces define endoplasmic reticulum lumens. (Photograph courtesy of K. R. Porter.)

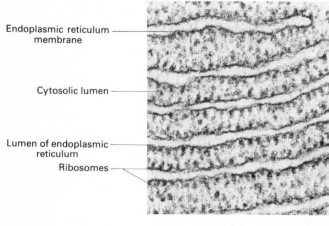

Endoplasmic reticulum membrane

Cytosolic lumen

Lumen of endoplasmic reticulum

Ribosomes

(a)

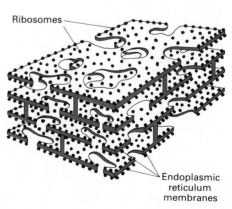

Ribosomes

Endoplasmic reticulum membranes

(b)

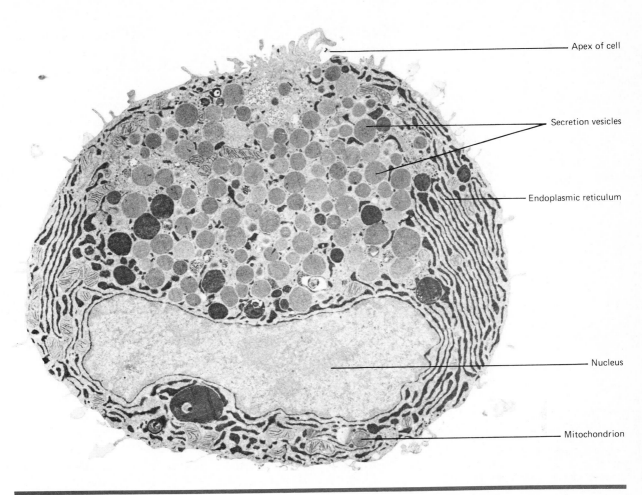

Apex of cell

Secretion vesicles

Endoplasmic reticulum

Nucleus

Mitochondrion

FIGURE 1-10
Electron micrograph of a section
through a secretory cell isolated from a
rat lacrimal gland. The cell interior
is filled with numerous secretion
vesicles, as well as a prominent
nucleus, endoplasmic reticulum, and
mitochondria. After their formation from
the Golgi apparatus, the secretion
vesicles move from the cell interior to
the cell apex, where the secretions are
released. ×7400 (Photograph
courtesy of V. Herzog, from Herzog, V.,
H. Sies, and F. Miller, 1976, *J. Cell Biol.*
70: 692, Fig. 10.)

of cells or tissues during metamorphosis in amphibians, in the break-down of the corpus luteum during the menstrual cycle, and in other normal developmental events.

The **mitochondrion** is found in all eukaryotic cells except certain unusual anaerobic protozoa. Mitochondria have two enveloping mem-branes around a granular, unstructured matrix (Fig. 1.11). The outer membrane has a smooth outline, and the inner membrane infolds into numerous tubular projections called **cristae** (sing., crista), which serve as the major identifying structural feature of the organelle. Enzymes located in the matrix and inner membrane of the mitochondrion participate in the energy-yielding reactions of food breakdown during aerobic respiration. The major product of respiration is ATP (adenosine triphosphate), the most important energy-storing molecule in cells. During respiration in mitochondria, a significant fraction of the energy extracted during food breakdown is conserved in ATP synthesis. ATP can then subsidize many kinds of biosynthetic reactions in cells by providing the energy necessary for these reactions to proceed. All aerobic life derives the bulk of its energy for all cellular activities from the processes of mitochondrial respiration in eukaryotes and from the respiratory reactions catalyzed by equivalent enzymes situated within the plasmalemma and cytoplasm in prokaryotes.

FIGURE 1-11
Electron micrograph showing mitochondrial profiles in a section of rat
spermatogonial cell. The outer mitochondrial membrane is a relatively
smooth envelope, whereas the inner
membrane infolds into tubular elements
called cristae. The infolded nature of
the cristae is particularly evident in
favorable planes (at arrows) of the
section. Mitochondria are centers of
aerobic respiration, in which most of the
ATP is made for numerous cellular
activities. ×65,000. (Photograph
courtesy of H. H. Mollenhauer.)

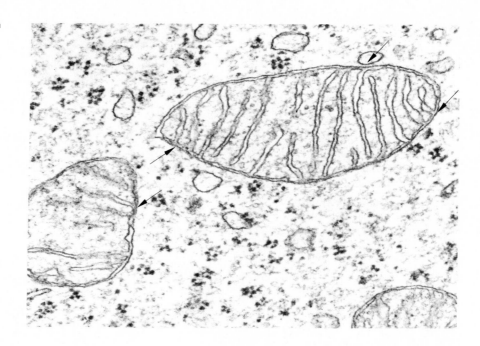

The **chloroplast** is another kind of organelle, in addition to the mitochondrion, that engages in processes involving energy transformation. Chloroplasts, however, are present only in eukaryotic algae, in certain unicellular protists, and in tissue-forming plants, whereas mitochondria are ubiquitous. The chloroplast is constructed of two closely appressed encircling membranes and a third set of internal membranes bathed in a granular stroma or matrix (Fig. 1.12). The processes of photosynthesis, by which foods are manufactured from carbon dioxide and water using light energy, take place in chloroplasts of eukaryotic species. Photosynthetic species are essential to the existence of virtually all life on Earth for two reasons: (1) Oxygen in our atmosphere is continuously replenished by photosynthetic cells, which release this gas as a byproduct of their light-capturing activities. (2) Organic foods required for life are provided by green cells, which alone are able to convert light energy to chemical energy and to use this chemical energy to manufacture food molecules. Photosynthetic species are the foundation of the food chain for life on Earth.

In addition to a variety of membranous subcellular compartments that carry out unique functions, eukaryotic cells contain nonmembranous structures of several types. Among these are ribosomes, centrioles, and systems of microtubules and filaments dispersed within the cytoplasm. We have already mentioned that ribosomes are essential for the synthesis of proteins translated from encoded genetic information. The **centriole** acts as a microtubule organizing center in processes of nuclear division, in the formation of cilia and flagella, and in certain aspects of cell division in a few protist species. The centriole itself is made up of 27 microtubules arranged in a particular pattern, which is evident in cross-sectional views in electron micrographs (Fig. 1.13). Centrioles are present in almost all eukaryotic cells at least at some stage of cellular development. Centrioles are lacking entirely, however, in certain amoebae, unicellular red algae, pine trees and their relatives, and all the

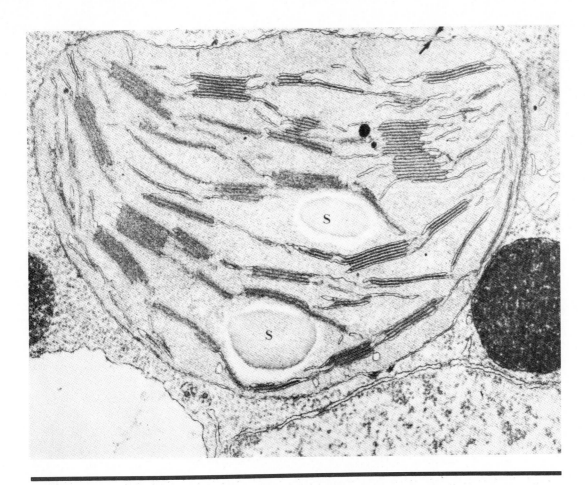

FIGURE 1-12

Electron micrograph of a section through a mesophyll cell of tobacco leaf, showing one of the chloroplasts. The two closely appressed outer membranes of the chloroplast (at arrows) enclose a third system of stacked membranes. Photosynthetic reactions take place on and in these stacked membranes and in the amorphous matrix in which they are suspended. Two sites of starch deposit can be seen in the chloroplast matrix. × 33,300. (Photograph courtesy of E. H. Newcomb, from Frederick, S. E., and E. H. Newcomb, 1969, *J. Cell Biol.* **43**: 343.)

FIGURE 1-13

Electron micrograph showing in cross section two centrioles and some cytoplasmic microtubules in the protozoan *Paramecium tetraurelia*. Each centriole consists of 27 microtubules arranged in 9 sets of 3 microtubules each. Each microtubule resembles a long straw, whose thick wall and central opening are clearly seen in cross section. Centriolar and cytoplasmic microtubules are identical in structure and chemical composition. ×105,000. (Photograph courtesy of R. V. Dippell.)

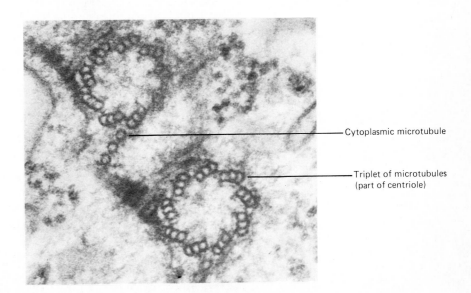

Cytoplasmic microtubule

Triplet of microtubules (part of centriole)

flowering plants. These same organisms also have no ciliated or flagellated cells of any type.

   Microtubules, intermediate filaments, and **microfilaments** contribute to cellular movements involving whole cells or parts of cells. One or more of these three major fibrous systems underlies such motility phenomena as cytoplasmic streaming, chromosome movement to the poles of the dividing cell, and cell propulsion through liquids by means of cilia and flagella. In addition, changes in cell shape, modifications in cell surface properties, and migration of subcellular structures within the cytoplasm are all made possible through the agency of microtubular and filamentous systems. The structural basis for muscular contraction resides in the systems of filaments that fill the cytoplasmic volume in striated muscle fibers.

   The algae, true fungi, and land plants characteristically have a thick **cell wall** that surrounds the living cellular material. These walls may remain and function as a structural framework after cells have died, as occurs in woody plants. The woody parts are composed of dead cells for the most part, but their cell walls provide structural support as well as a system for the transport of water from the roots to upper parts of the plant. Another feature common to algae, true fungi, and land plants is the occurrence of large **vacuoles** containing various substances in dilute solution or in suspension (Fig. 1.14). Almost the entire volume of a mature plant cell may be filled by a vacuole that is surrounded by a

FIGURE 1-14
Electron micrograph of a mature root cell from the plant *Potamogeton natans* showing large vacuoles, a prominent nucleolus in the centrally situated nucleus, mitochondria, starch-filled plastids, endoplasmic reticulum, and ribosomes, all enclosed within the boundary of a thick cell wall. Large vacuoles are a distinctive feature of mature plant cells. ×8350. (Photograph courtesy of M. C. Ledbetter.)

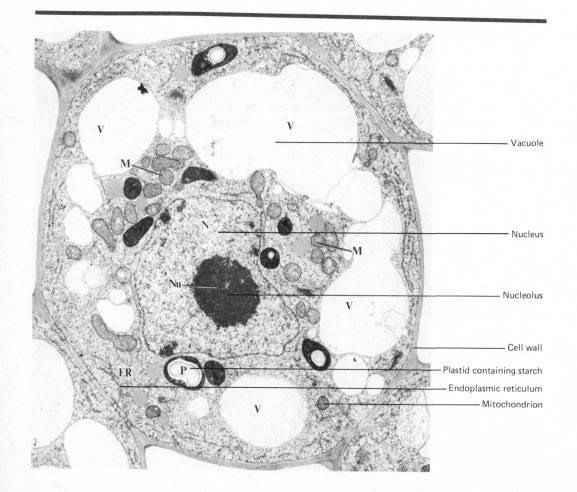

narrow band of protoplasm. Animal cells often contain small vacuoles, but more typically the cytoplasm is densely packed with cellular components and fills the volume of the cell. The appearance of animal cells is thus quite different from that of plant cells.

The cell surface in animal tissues provides a remarkable system that contributes to many kinds of interactions between adjacent cells. The cell surface can establish close contact and communication with a neighboring surface, because there is no wall covering the plasma membrane as there is in plants. The animal cell surface may be folded into fingerlike protrusions called **microvilli**, which greatly increase the cell surface area and undoubtedly contribute to more effective transport of molecules between cells in a tissue (Fig. 1.15). The plasma membranes of adjacent cells often show structurally modified regions called **junctions**. Different kinds of junctions provide special properties to the locally differentiated area of plasma membrane in which they occur. Some junctions seal off the intercellular space and prevent the flow of molecules between adjacent cells, and other junctions enhance the flow of substances between neighboring cells and from one cell into another. The **desmosome** is a junctional region shared by adjacent cells, and it serves to bind the cells together by adhesion. Desmosomes are particularly evident in tissues subjected to mechanical stresses, such as skin, and they help maintain the integrity of such tissues despite mechanical trauma due to stress. Component molecules of the cell surface membrane provide systems by which one cell can recognize another and systems by which a cell can recognize specific molecules and interact appropriately with them, as in immune responses. The surface of animal cells is thus a dynamic system and not merely a wrapping for the protoplasm within.

1.5
Evolutionary Relationships

All modern life forms are descended from particular ancestral species, which themselves arose during evolution by diversification from a common primordial ancestor that presumably appeared on Earth some 4 billion years ago. Although the nature of the first life forms on Earth is not known in any detail, they or their later descendants were probably prokaryotes. We might infer that prokaryotes are more ancient than eukaryotes because prokaryotes are the simpler of the two in structure and organization. Confirming evidence for this inference has come from the fossil record. Fossilized prokaryotes have been found in rock deposits as old as 3.5 billion years, whereas the earliest record of eukaryotes has been found in deposits only 1.3 billion years old. The fossil record provides an evolutionary timetable and a reasonable sampling of former life, so we can conclude that prokaryotes are the more ancient group.

Prokaryotes and eukaryotes have in common many kinds of molecules and functions, including DNA as genetic material, a ribosomal machinery for protein synthesis, enzymes that catalyze metabolic reactions, various similar metabolic pathways, and membranes consisting of similar or identical molecules and organization. These and other basic similarities are far more likely to be due to descent, from common

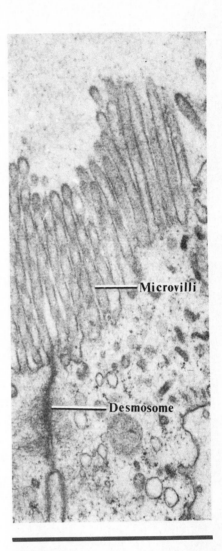

FIGURE 1-15
Electron micrograph of cells from a proximal tubule of frog kidney. Microvilli provide increased surface area for absorption, and desmosomes serve as adhesive junctions between contiguous cells. ×30,000.

FIGURE 1-16

The five-kingdom system of classification proposed by R. H. Whittaker groups all the prokaryotes in the single kingdom Monera and separates eukaryotes into the unicellular Protista and the multicellular (or multinucleate) plants, fungi, and animals. Heterotrophic monerans absorb nutrients in solution from their surroundings, and autotrophic monerans (blue-green algae and certain bacteria) make their own foods by photosynthesis. In addition to photosynthesis and absorption by some protists, other protists can ingest solid foods and digest them internally. The multicellular eukaryotes differ in organization and life style according to the particular mode of nutrition characteristic of each kingdom. The five-kingdom system emphasizes evolutionary relationships and postulates a moneran ancestor of the protists, which later gave rise from different lineages to the three kingdoms of multicellular eukaryotes. (From Whittaker, R. H., *Science* **163**: 150–160, Fig. 3, 10 January 1969. Copyright © 1969 by the American Association for the Advancement of Science.)

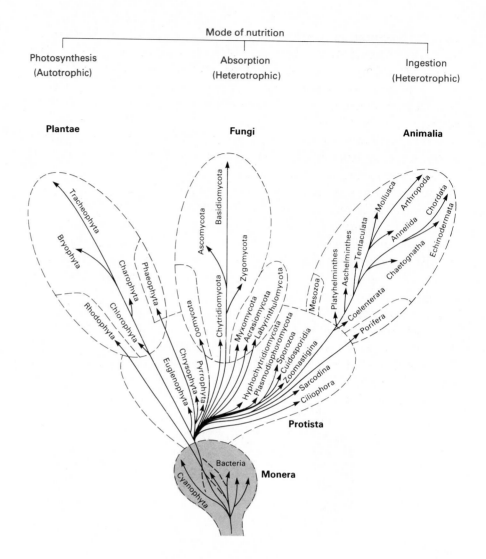

ancestors, than to coincidental developments in unique life forms that arose independently of each other.

The evolutionary origin of eukaryotes from prokaryotes is widely accepted, but the particular pathways leading to modern groups of organisms are the subject of lively controversy. Biologists do not even agree on the number of kingdoms of organisms now in existence (see Table 1.2). Richard Whittaker has proposed a detailed lineage for the five kingdoms of organisms that he recognizes (Fig. 1.16). His scheme takes into account many metabolic as well as structural features of cellular life forms. All the bacteria, blue-green algae, and grass-green algae are included in the kingdom Monera, which thus includes all known prokaryotic organisms. All the grass-green and blue-green algae and several groups of bacteria are **autotrophic**, meaning that they make organic compounds using energy from light or from inorganic molecules and that they obtain carbon from carbon dioxide. Most of the bacteria, however, are **heterotrophic**. They derive energy and carbon for growth from the metabolic breakdown of organic foods, which they absorb in solution from their environment. None of the monerans can ingest solid foods. Protists are the simplest and most ancient group of eukaryotes. They include organisms that can obtain nutrients through photosynthesis, by absorption of organic substances from the surroundings, or by ingestion of solids. It is uncertain whether protists arose from a single ancestral prokaryote and subsequently diversified or arose from more than one prokaryotic lineage. Many of the evolutionary scenarios postulate a unitary origin for eukaryotes, but the nature of this ancestral prokaryote is highly controversial.

Whittaker and others have proposed that different kinds of protists gave rise to new eukaryotic lineages that are represented today by three different kingdoms of organisms: plants, animals, and fungi. With few exceptions, plants are photosynthetic, fungi absorb organic nutrients in solution, and animals ingest their foods. Plants are thus autotrophic, whereas fungi and animals are heterotrophic in their nutrition.

A strikingly different proposal for the classification and evolutionary origin of modern organisms has been made by Carl Woese, George Fox, and their colleagues. On the basis of new information from molecular studies, these investigators suggest that the division of all cellular life into prokaryotes and eukaryotes is unacceptable. Instead they propose the existence of three distinct groups of organisms, which they put into three kingdoms. They believe that the bacteria should be separated into a kingdom including the grass-green algae, blue-green algae, and the true bacteria, or *eubacteria*, and a separate kingdom of *archaebacteria*; all eukaryotic species are lumped into a third kingdom (Fig. 1.17). Woese

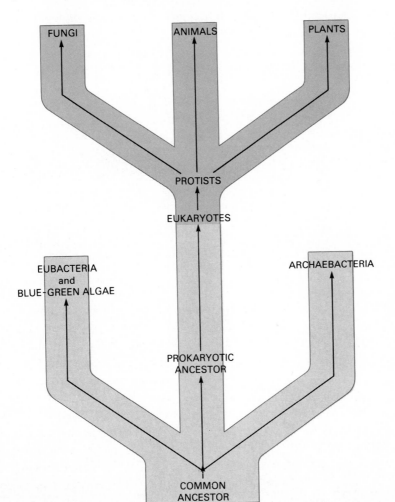

FIGURE 1-17
The evolutionary scheme proposed by C. R. Woese and G. E. Fox separates the prokaryotic archaebacteria from the prokaryotic eubacteria and blue-green algae on the basis of important molecular differences between the two groups. The archaebacteria have some features in common with eukaryotes, some features in common with eubacteria and blue-green algae, and other features of a unique nature. On this basis, Woese and Fox have proposed a common ancestor that diverged to produce three prokaryotic lineages. Two of these lineages remained prokaryotic in cellular organization but evolved molecular distinctions, and the third prokaryotic lineage ultimately evolved into the eukaryotic protists from which plants, fungi, and animals are derived.

and Fox suggest that the ancestor that gave rise to all extant life was far simpler than any known prokaryotic form. During evolution this unspecified ancestor diverged to produce three different prokaryotic lineages. The eubacterial and archaebacterial lineages retained the prokaryotic pattern of cellular organization, and the eukaryotes evolved from the third prokaryotic lineage via modifications that included a compartmented cellular plan.

It is too early to choose between evolutionary scenarios, no matter how compelling any one may seem to be, but considerable new information from further molecular and biochemical studies may enable us to make a reasonable choice in the not-too-distant future. It is clear from current studies, however, that we should not rely too heavily on morphological data alone in constructing genealogies.

Viruses

Because viruses are not cellular, they are neither prokaryotic nor eukaryotic. They are quite a varied group, however, and range in size between 30 and 3000 nm, or from about the size of a ribosome to about the limit of visibility in the light microscope. The simpler viruses are made only of nucleic acid and protein, but more complex viruses have additional kinds of organic molecules in their construction. The nucleic acid is either DNA or RNA, but never both (Table 1.4). Viruses are sometimes enclosed within a membrane, but it is a membrane derived from the host cell and not a membrane made or specified by the virus. Viral shapes are specific for each species, some being spherical, or rodlike, or dodecahedral, among others (Fig. 1.18). Viruses tend to be

TABLE 1-4
Some Characteristics of Representative Viruses

Nucleic acid	Virus	Main host	Comments
DNA			
single-stranded	fd, ϕX174	*Escherichia coli*	
double-stranded	T2, T4, T6	*Escherichia coli*	
	P22	*Salmonella typhimurium*	
	herpes simplex	human	type 1 causes "fever blisters" type 2 causes genital herpes (a venereal disease)
	variola	human	caused smallpox (virus now extinct)
	Epstein-Barr	human	causes infectious mononucleosis; associated with Burkitt's lymphoma
	cauliflower mosaic	cauliflower	transmitted by aphids
	simian virus 40 (SV40)	monkeys	
RNA			
single-stranded	Qβ	*Escherichia coli*	
	tobacco mosaic	tobacco	
	polio	human	
	measles	human	
	mumps	human	
	influenza A, B, C	human	
double-stranded	reovirus	human	causes mild illness of respiratory and GI tracts
	wound tumor	plants	transmitted by leafhoppers

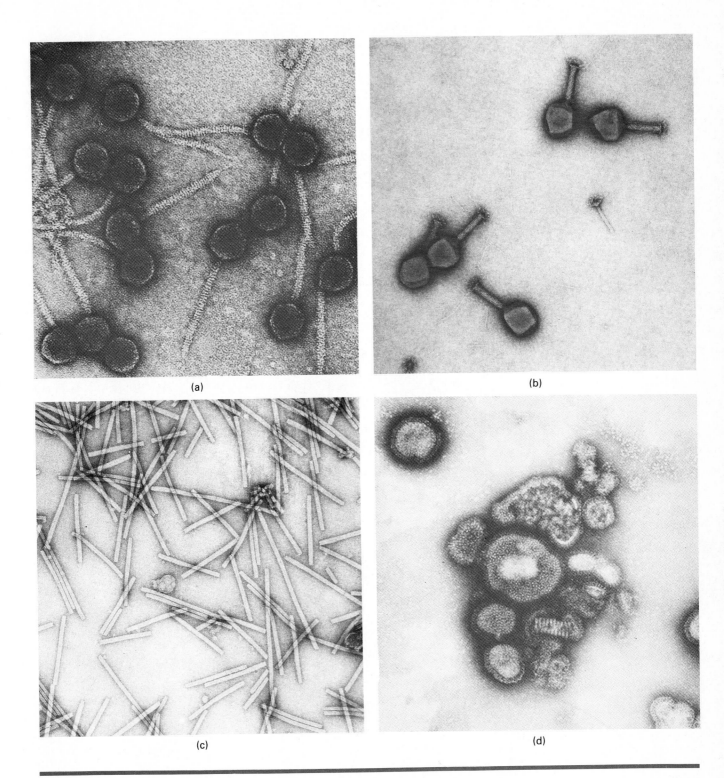

(a)

(b)

(c)

(d)

FIGURE 1-18
Electron micrographs of representative viruses. Both (a) phage lambda and (b) phage T4 infect and reproduce in the bacterium *Escherichia coli* and carry their DNA genomes in the head portion of the tailed viral particles. (c) Tobacco mosaic virus is a plant pathogen, and its single-stranded RNA genome is wound within the rodlike protein coat of the particles. (d) Influenza virus is an RNA-containing species that has a lipoprotein envelope derived largely from its human host cells and enclosing the viral capsid. (Photograph (a) courtesy of R. Hendrix, (b) and (c) courtesy of L. D. Simon, and (d) courtesy of N. Wrigley.)

named in a random fashion according to the disease caused (polio virus), the tissue affected (adenoviruses infect adenoid tissue), the host organism (bacterial virus, or **bacteriophage**, or **phage**), or some coded system (T1, T2, P1 phages of the colon bacillus *Escherichia coli*).

Whether or not viruses are life forms is still a debatable issue. Viruses are inert outside a living host cell, and many viruses can be purified or even crystallized like many chemicals. Upon gaining entry into a host cell, many kinds of viruses become active and begin to direct molecular syntheses leading to production of new virus particles. To do this they must rely partly on their own programmed genetic information and partly on the genetic and biosynthetic capacities of their host. Viral multiplication is very different from cell replication. Cells produce their own chromosomes, proteins, membranes, and other constituents, and these materials are partitioned into progeny cells after a division process in the parent cell. As stated in the cell theory, cells arise only from pre-existing cells. Viruses, on the other hand, provide only the genetic information for some or all of the molecules required to make progeny viruses. These progeny particles are *assembled* from molecules made in the host cell by host cell machinery. The assembled viruses are then released from their host, and each virus is able to initiate another cycle like the one in which it was produced (Fig. 1.19). It is this striking distinction in its mode of replication that clearly identifies a virus and distinguishes it from all cellular species.

FIGURE 1-19
Viral reproduction involves the assembly of mature viruses from protein and nucleic acid molecules synthesized in host cells according to viral genetic instructions brought into host cells during viral infection. In the life cycle of a virulent phage (a bacterial virus that kills its host), viral DNA (color) enters the host cell and is replicated there. Viral coat proteins are made from viral genetic instructions. The newly synthesized proteins and nucleic acid then assemble into mature viruses, which are released for new cycles of infection when host cell lysis occurs. Although events vary from one kind of virus to another, all viruses share the common feature of having their component molecules synthesized and assembled in a living host cell.

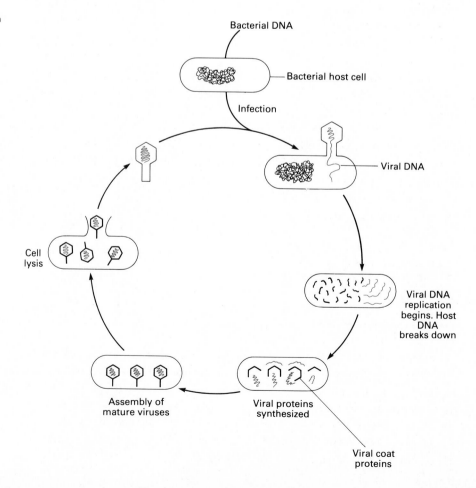

Living cells share three basic features that permit them to live independently of one another, or at least to possess the *potential* for an independent existence:

1. A cell has *a set of genes* that constitutes the blueprints for making new cells with all their components and parts.

2. There is *a cell membrane* around each cell, acting as a physical boundary between the cell and its surroundings but permitting controlled exchange of matter and energy with the outside world.

3. Each cell has *a metabolic machinery* by which energy can be obtained and by which this energy can be used to subsidize living processes such as those involved in growth, reproduction, and repair or replacement of parts.

Viruses have only one of these characteristics and must therefore rely on host cells for the other requirements for virus multiplication. Viruses certainly are not cellular, but are they living entities? There is no universally accepted answer to this question, because no single definition of life satisfies everyone. If living is defined as being cellular, then viruses are not alive. If living is defined as being capable of making new life directly through one's own metabolic efforts, then viruses are not living. If living is defined as being able to specify each new generation according to one's own genetic instructions, then viruses are living systems. Each new crop of viruses is made specifically according to a set of genetic instructions that is unique for each and every kind of virus. Each cellular life form also has a unique set of genes. A system may borrow a membrane or borrow metabolism, but it cannot borrow a set of genes from another species. The one indispensable and unique feature of every life form is its genes, so most biologists would agree that viruses are living organisms—of an unusual type to be sure, but with the full potential for continuity of the species and for evolutionary change.

Genetic mechanisms are very similar in viruses and in cellular life. Viruses undergo mutations, their genes undergo recombination, and they use the same genetic code as prokaryotes and eukaryotes. The basic similarities between viral and cellular genetic mechanisms provide strong evidence for biological relationships among all life forms on Earth, including viruses.

Summary

Although cell biology as a discipline is still in its youth, it has its roots in several much older scientific traditions. With the invention of the compound microscope in the sixteenth century, it became possible to observe the cellular structure of plant and animal tissues, and in the nineteenth century the unified cell theory became the accepted basis for understanding the organization of living systems. In the twentieth century, further developments in microscopy, along with our growing understanding of the genetic and biochemical processes in living systems, brought us to the contemporary discipline of cell biology. Modern cell biology makes use of the methods and principles bridging these diverse fields of study and concentrates on an interdisciplinary approach to the study of form and function at the cellular level.

Many structural features are shared by all cells, but there is a clear distinction between the organization of prokaryotic cells and that of eukaryotic cells. In particular, cells of prokaryotes (bacteria, blue-green algae, and grass-green algae) are small and simple. They have a plasma membrane, usually bounded by a rigid cell wall; a nucleoid consisting of a single, circular DNA molecule that represents all the genes (genome) of the organism; and cytoplasm that contains ribosomes and a variety of molecules that mediate metabolism but lack any permanent internal membranes. All prokaryotes are unicellular organisms.

By contrast, cells of all four kingdoms of eukaryotic organisms (protists, fungi, animals, and plants) are larger and are characterized by many membranous compartments. The nucleus with its chromosomes is the primary trademark of eukaryotic cells. The cytoplasm around the membrane-bounded nucleus includes a host of organelles, each kind having its own characteristic structural organization and particular function(s) in the cell. In addition to membranous organelles, such as endoplasmic reticulum, Golgi apparatus, mitochondria, lysosomes, chloroplasts (in photosynthetic cells), and others, there are ribosomes, centrioles, microfilaments, microtubules, and a multitude of proteins suspended in the cytosolic portion of the cytoplasm. A plasma membrane surrounds the cytoplasm and itself may be bounded by a rigid cell wall or by surface coatings of other sorts. In many cells the cell surface includes characteristic specializations, such as cilia or flagella, microvilli, and junctions with other cells in tissues. Eukaryotes may be unicellular or multicellular, they may be sexual or asexual, and they vary considerably in external form.

The evolutionary relationships among the types of modern cells are not clearly understood, but prokaryotes are undoubtedly older and share a common ancestry with eukaryotic organisms. All cells have similar membrane structure, mechanisms for information storage and transfer, and metabolism, so these aspects must have evolved very early and must have been retained thereafter in all descendant lineages. New methods of molecular analysis may illuminate these fundamental evolutionary issues.

Viruses are not cellular, but they are generally considered to be living systems because they possess unique sets of genes that specify viral characteristics. Viruses are dependent on the metabolic machinery of a host cell to synthesize new proteins and nucleic acids for reproduction of progeny particles by processes of molecular assembly. Their mode of reproduction distinguishes viruses from all cellular life.

Readings and References

Butler, P. J. G., and A. Klug. November 1978. The assembly of a virus. *Sci. Amer.* **239**:62.

Campbell, A. M. December 1976. How viruses insert their DNA into the DNA of the host cell. *Sci. Amer.* **235**:102.

Claude, A. 1975. The coming of age of the cell. *Science* **189**:433 (Nobel lecture).

Fawcett, D. W. 1981. *The Cell: Its Organelles and Inclusions.* 2nd ed. Philadelphia: Saunders.

Jensen, W. A., and R. B. Park. 1967. *Cell Ultrastructure.* Belmont, Calif.: Wadsworth.

Kessel, R. G., and R. H. Kardon. 1979. *Tissues and Organs: A Text–Atlas of Scanning Electron Microscopy.* San Francisco: Freeman.

Ledbetter, M. C., and K. R. Porter. 1970. *Introduction to the Fine Structure of Plant Cells.* New York: Springer-Verlag.

Mirsky, A. E. June 1968. The discovery of DNA. *Sci. Amer.* **218**:78.

Porter, K. R., and A. B. Novikoff. 1974. The 1974 Nobel prize for physiology or medicine. *Science* **186**:516.

Roland, J.-C., A. Szöllösi, and D. Szöllösi. 1977. *Atlas of Cell Biology.* Boston: Little, Brown.

Simons, K., H. Garoff, and A. Helenius. February 1982. How an animal virus gets into and out of its host cell. *Sci. Amer.* **246**:58.

Whittaker, R. H. 1969. New concepts of kingdoms of organisms. *Science* **163**:150.

Wilson, E. B. 1928. *The Cell in Development and Heredity.* 3rd ed. New York: Macmillan.

Woese, C. R. June 1981. Archaebacteria. *Sci. Amer.* **244**:98.

CHAPTER 2

Organic Molecules

Basic Features of Organic Molecules

Chemistry is a basic feature of the living world as well as of the nonliving. The uniqueness of organic molecules is due in large measure to special properties of the carbon atom. In fact, modern organic chemistry is the chemistry of carbon. Although organic chemistry is concerned with all classes of compounds containing carbon, modern biochemistry deals with the chemical dynamics of living systems and of those few classes of organic compounds that are biologically important.

2.1
Chemical Bonds

Two or more atoms are held together in an aggregate by chemical bonds. Any chemical bond has a certain chance of being broken at any time in any system, but some bonds are more stable than others. A stable bond is one that requires higher bond energies to be broken than other chemical bonds. It is convenient to refer to more stable bonds as strong and to less stable bonds as weak.

In biological systems, we refer to covalent bonds as strong chemical bonds, and to other chemical bonds as weaker than, or secondary to, covalent bonds. A **covalent bond** is formed when two atoms share one or more pairs of electrons. An atom has a certain stable number of electrons, and when two or more atoms share electrons, each participant becomes more stable than before the covalent bond formed. A hydrogen atom has one electron in its orbital, but two electrons is the more stable state of the atom. When two hydrogen atoms share their electrons, each atom assumes the more stable state, even though the unit has a total of only two electrons (Fig. 2.1). It is conventional to indicate a single covalent bond, or one pair of shared electrons between atoms, by a dash between the two atomic symbols (for example, H—H and H—O—H). A covalent double bond (such as O=C=O) forms when two atoms share

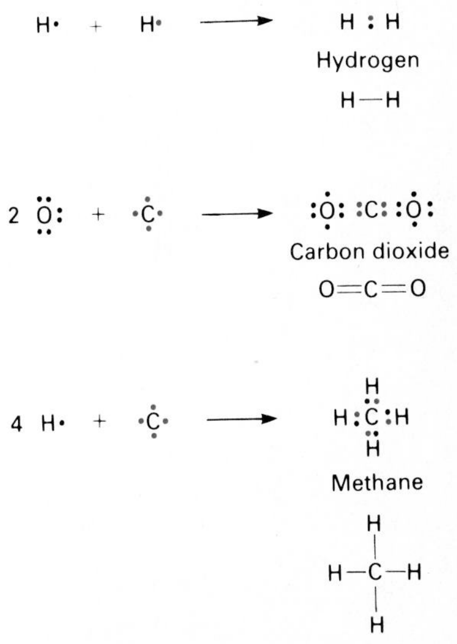

FIGURE 2-1
Covalent bonds form when two atoms share one or more pairs of electrons, which leads to a more stable state for each participating atom in the molecule. The number of dashes between two atoms indicates the number of pairs of shared electrons. Carbon compounds are very stable when the outer electron orbital of the carbon atom is completely filled with eight electrons.

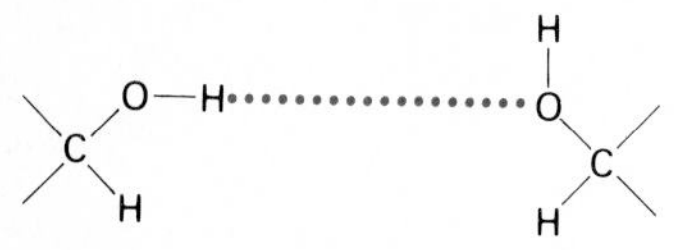

(a)

(b)

FIGURE 2-2
Hydrogen bonds (color) involve proton sharing between two nitrogen atoms, (a) two oxygen atoms, or (b) one nitrogen and one oxygen. The hydrogen bond holds together two covalently bonded units, but the shared proton (hydrogen nucleus) is covalently bonded to only one of the two participating atoms in the interacting units.

two pairs of electrons, and a triple bond involves three pairs of shared electrons between two atoms (such as $H—C\equiv N$). Covalent bonds are **nonpolar** if the negative charge of symmetrically distributed electrons is shared equally by the bonded atoms. They are **polar** if the electrical charge is closer to one atomic nucleus than to another in the electron-sharing unit.

The most important weak bonds in biological systems are hydrogen bonds, ionic bonds, and van der Waals bonds or forces. A fourth type of atomic association is the hydrophobic bond or interaction, which is not a true chemical bond but is instead a recognized tendency of certain groups of atoms to associate and to exclude any water that may be present. A **hydrogen bond** forms when two atoms share a hydrogen atomic nucleus (proton). The shared proton is usually found between two nitrogen atoms or two oxygens or between one atom of each of these two elements. The hydrogen nucleus itself is covalently bonded to an atom of nitrogen or oxygen, so the shared proton or hydrogen bond holds two covalently bonded units together (Fig. 2.2). An **ionic bond** involves electron transfer from one atom to another. Electrostatic forces begin to operate between atoms or groups of atoms of opposite electrical charge—for example, between a cation and an anion (such as Na^+ and Cl^-) or between a carboxyl and an amino group (COO^- and NH_3^+). Ionic units of opposite charge attract each other, and their outermost electron orbitals become stabilized when one to three electrons are lost or gained by each unit. A **van der Waals bond** forms as a result of attractive forces produced when two atoms or groups of atoms come near each other. Binding forces are sufficiently low at cell temperatures for van der Waals bonds to develop only when several atoms in a molecule interact with several atoms in a nearby molecule. Under these conditions, the energy of interaction is greater than the tendency to dissociate in response to thermal movements. Because size and shape of interacting units are more important than the particular atoms involved, van der Waals bonds are relatively nonspecific and can thus be formed between many kinds of molecules.

The amount of energy required to break a covalent bond varies between 70 and over 100 kilocalories (kcal) per mole, and still higher amounts are needed to break double and triple covalent bonds involving carbon atoms (Table 2.1). In contrast to strong covalent bonds, hydrogen bonds have a bonding energy of about 3 to 7 kcal/mole, ionic bonds have a bonding energy of about 5 kcal/mole, and van der Waals

TABLE 2-1
Values for Some Covalent Bond Energies*

Single Bonds		Double Bonds		Triple Bonds	
O—H	110				
H—H	104				
C—H	99				
C—O	84	C=O	170		
C—C	83	C=C	146	C≡C	195
C—N	70	C=N	147	C≡N	212

* Energy (kcal/mole) required to break the bond.

bonds break when the energy input is 1 to 2 kcal/mole. More energy is needed to break stable covalent bonds than weaker chemical bonds, so covalent bonds are the principal source of molecular stability at cell temperatures. Organic molecules do not easily dissociate into their constituent atoms under normal cellular conditions. On the other hand, weak chemical bonds allow a substantial level of molecular modification in chemical reactions, which is important in the ebb and flow of metabolism. The combination of strong and weak chemical bonds in an organic molecule thus provides a basis for some flexibility in rearranging atoms in organic molecules during metabolism. As organic compounds are made and degraded, are assembled and disassembled, and interact with one another in various ways, each type of chemical bond provides some advantage in the spectrum of cellular activities.

2.2
The Chemistry of Carbon Atoms

Organic compounds are versatile, which is evident from their occurrence in virtually unlimited numbers and from their varied properties. Organic molecules are also quite stable, as shown by their relatively sluggish reactions with molecular oxygen or water. These trademarks of versatility and stability are due to particular features of the carbon atom. One feature already mentioned is that carbon atoms form covalent bonds with one another and with hydrogen, oxygen, nitrogen, phosphorus, sulfur, and the few other elements generally found in cellular molecules. The "skeleton" of carbon atoms forms the basic framework of organic compounds, and these covalently bonded atoms can exist in chains, rings, networks, and other arrangements or combinations.

The structural diversity of organic molecules is due to the fact that carbon has a valency of 4. That is, only four electrons are present in the outer electron orbital, which can hold a maximum of eight electrons. The tetravalent carbon atom can form covalent bonds with one to four other carbon atoms as well as with electrically charged atoms of H, O, N, P, and S. Organic molecules can occur in various sizes and shapes because carbon atoms can interact with each other. And, because carbons also interact with other elements of biological importance, many different combinations of a few kinds of atoms are possible in organic molecules of diverse size. Other features of carbon enhance molecular versatility. Carbon atoms can form single, double, and triple covalent bonds with each other and with other atoms. The organic molecule or some portion of it has different properties depending on whether nitrogen and carbon form single, double, or triple bonds, even though the combination involves the same two elements. The same holds true for other elements with a valency greater than 1. For example, higher bond energies are required to break double and triple bonds than to break single covalent bonds (see Table 2.1). Molecules with double or triple bonds are thus more stable than molecules or parts of molecules with single-bond construction.

Because the carbon atom is tetravalent, its outer electron orbital becomes filled when four covalent bonds are formed. The filled electron orbital leads to the energetically most favorable configuration—that is,

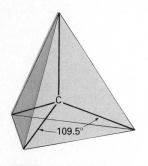

FIGURE 2-3
The individual tetravalent carbon atom is geometrically symmetrical due to the tetrahedral distribution in space of its valency of 4 in specific angles and lengths.

to the most stable state. Stability of the entire carbon framework of an organic molecule is thus largely due to the energetically satisfying configuration of its individual carbon atoms. The tetrahedral distribution in space of the valency of 4 in the carbon atom endows the atom with a basic symmetry (Fig. 2.3). This geometrical symmetry also contributes to greater stability of bonding between carbon atoms or with other atoms.

2.3
Isomers

The tetrahedral nature of the carbon valency can lead to asymmetry at the *molecular* level. When a carbon atom is bonded to four different atoms or groups of atoms, two spatial arrangements of the molecule can occur such that one alternative arrangement is the mirror image of the other (Fig. 2.4). The alternative forms of the same compound are called **isomers**. These may be *stereoisomers*, differing in configuration, or *optical isomers*, differing in the direction in which each isomer in solution can rotate the plane of polarized light.

The potential asymmetry of *each* carbon atom in an organic molecule is a significant feature; the same compound may occur in a number of isomeric forms, each having different properties. This feature also contributes to the versatility of carbon compounds. Organic molecules in biological systems usually assume only a fraction of the number of possible isomeric configurations, however, and these are the most energetically favorable alternatives.

2.4
Biologically Important Carbon Compounds

The four major classes of organic compounds of importance in biological systems are carbohydrates, lipids, proteins, and nucleic acids. Except for lipids, many of these organic molecules are **polymers** made up of repeating **monomer** subunits, or building blocks. Certain carbohydrates, such as starch, glycogen, and cellulose, are polymers constructed only from monomeric glucose units. Nucleic acids are polymers comprised of four kinds of nucleotides, and proteins may be built from as many as twenty different kinds of amino acid monomeric units.

FIGURE 2-4
A carbon atom that is covalently bonded to four different atoms or groups of atoms is asymmetric and can exist in two alternative arrangements that are mirror images of each other. The alternative forms are isomers of the same molecule.

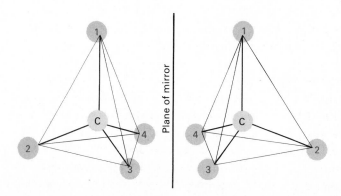

The four classes of cellular organic compounds contribute to cell structure and function and to the regulation of cellular activities. Each class makes some unique contribution, however, so all these groups must be present to sustain the living state. Carbohydrates provide the major source of molecules involved in energy transformations and other aspects of metabolism, as well as stored foods and materials for cell structure. Lipids are vital components of cellular membranes, and they also serve as food storage forms. Proteins, perhaps the most diversified molecules, participate in virtually all processes of function, construction, and regulation in cells. Nucleic acids, of course, are genetic molecules in all cellular life forms. The major characteristics and the importance of these compounds in biological systems are discussed in the remainder of this chapter.

Carbohydrates

Carbohydrates are compounds that have the general formula $(CH_2O)_n$. Some biologically important carbohydrates also contain nitrogen or sulfur atoms. The most commonly occurring carbohydrate in cells is glucose, a six-carbon sugar. Glucose and other simple sugars that are single units are called **monosaccharides**.

2.5
Monosaccharides

Monosaccharides are classified according to the number of carbon atoms in the molecule. A hexose (such as glucose) has six carbon atoms, a pentose sugar has five carbons, a triose has three, and so on. Monosaccharides can occur in a number of isomeric forms because one or more of the carbon atoms is usually asymmetric. Glucose has four asymmetric carbon atoms, so sixteen different stereoisomers are theoretically possible, depending on the orientation of the hydroxyl bound to each asymmetric carbon atom. Only three of these isomers, however, are found in nature (Fig. 2.5).

Monosaccharides are identified as D or L forms according to a convention based on the configuration of the triose D-glyceraldehyde. A monosaccharide is of the D variety if the hydroxyl group on the bottommost asymmetric carbon atom is on the right (when the carbonyl group, $>C=O$, is at the top of the formula) as in D-glyceraldehyde (Fig. 2.6). If this hydroxyl group is on the left, then the molecule is of the L variety. Glucose in its naturally occurring form is a D-hexose according to this convention.

Pentose and hexose sugars in solution exist largely in a ring form in equilibrium with a small amount of the linear form of the molecule (Fig. 2.7). When the oxygen bridge is located between carbons 1 and 5 (pyranose form), it is conventional to depict the molecule as a hexagon. When the oxygen bridge is a 1,4 bond (furanose form), the molecule is drawn as a pentagon. A heavier line is drawn across the bottom of the pentagon or hexagon to indicate that this is the part of the molecule

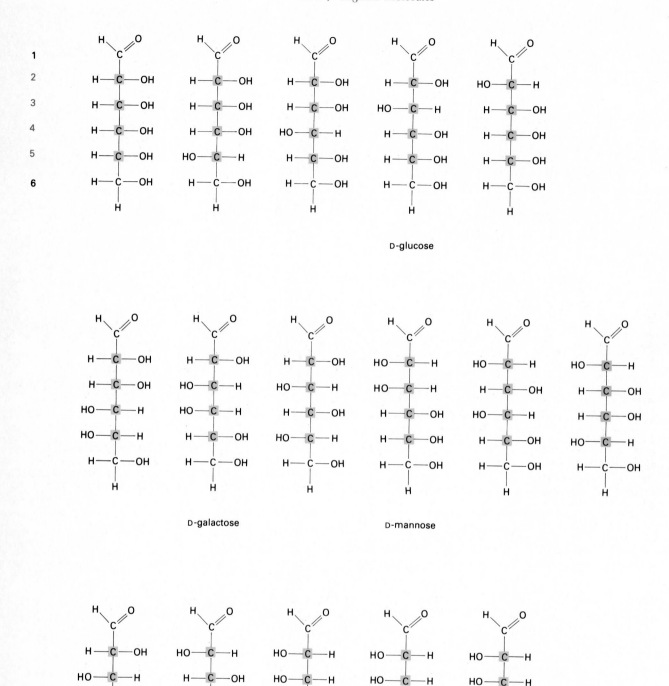

D-glucose

D-galactose   D-mannose

FIGURE 2-5

In its linear form a hexose molecule has **4** asymmetric carbon atoms (color), and **16** different isomers are possible depending only on the orientations of the hydrogen and hydroxyl residues of the asymmetric carbons. Of these isomers only glucose, galactose, and mannose are found in nature.

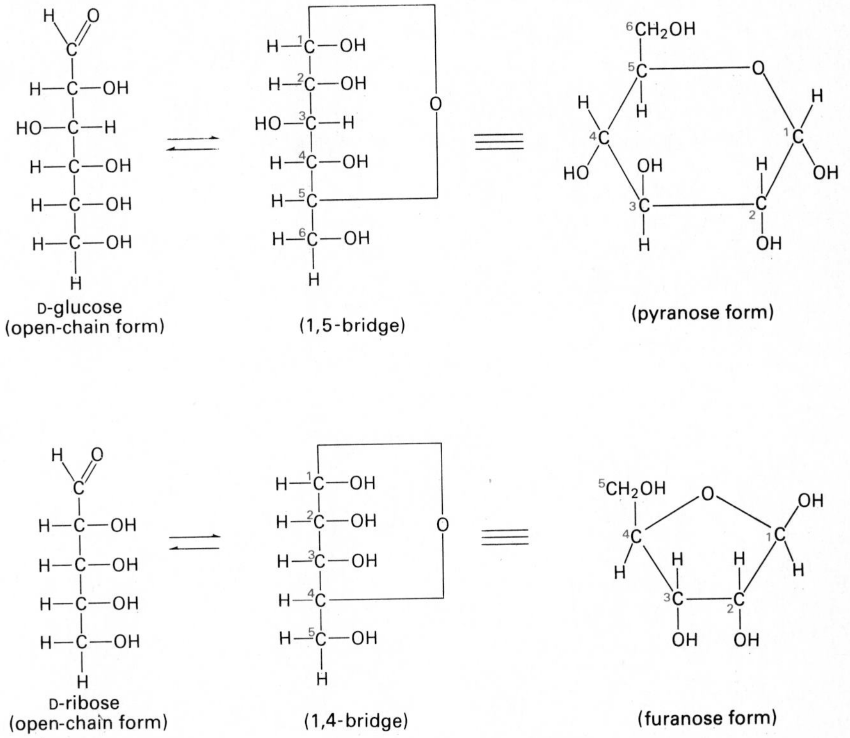

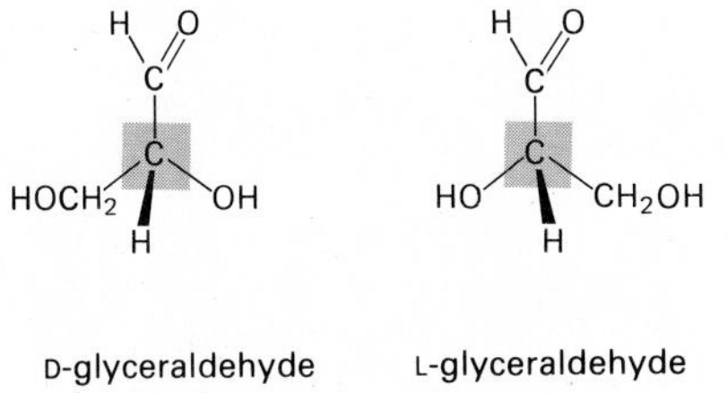

FIGURE 2-6
The orientation of the hydroxyl bound
to the asymmetric carbon is the
determining feature for designating the
D- and L-isomers of glyceraldehyde,
and of other compounds as well.

FIGURE 2-7
Sugars in solution exist in equilibrium
mixtures consisting of a predominant
ring form and a small amount of the
linear open-chain form of the molecule.
When carbons 1 and 5 are joined by an

oxygen bridge, this pyranose form of
the molecule is conventionally drawn as
a hexagon; the furanose form produced
by a 1,4-oxygen bridge is drawn as a
pentagon.

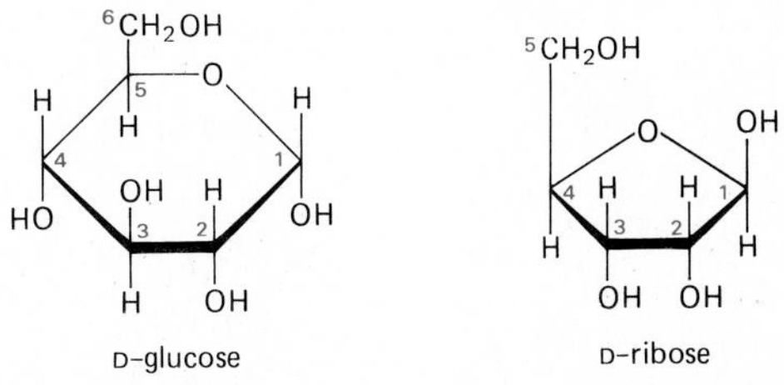

FIGURE 2-8
Haworth formulas of glucose and ribose
are conventionally drawn showing the
plane of the molecule perpendicular to
the paper. The heavier line across the
bottom of the formula indicates that
this portion is closer to the viewer.
Hydrogens and hydroxyls that are
covalently bonded to carbons associated with an oxygen bridge are
conventionally shown in a vertical
orientation at each of these carbons in
the ring.

nearest the viewer, and the plane of the molecule is perpendicular to the
plane of the paper. The hydrogens and hydroxyls are oriented up or
down and are indicated by vertical lines at each of the carbons (Fig. 2.8).
These conventional representations, called Haworth formulas, make it
very simple to specify a particular isomer and to recognize it at a glance.
Monosaccharide rings can have only five or six carbon atoms because of
spatial restrictions. A carbon chain with seven members would be
subject to excessive strain if bent into a ring.

With the formation of the oxygen bridge, the cyclic molecule gains
asymmetry at carbon atom 1. The hydroxyl of carbon-1 is either
adjacent to the hydroxyl of carbon-2 or is rotated 180° relative to it

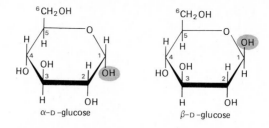

FIGURE 2-9
Upon ring formation, carbon-1 becomes asymmetric and may exist in the α or the β isomeric form, depending on the position of the hydroxyl at carbon-2 relative to the hydroxyl at carbon-1. The two hydroxyls are adjacent in the α isomer but not in the β isomer of the cyclic molecule.

(Fig. 2.9). These isomers are designated as the α and β forms of the cyclic monosaccharides. Polymers made up of α units are profoundly different from polymers constructed of β units of the same monosaccharide building block.

2.6
Polysaccharides

Polysaccharides have the general formula $(C_6H_{10}O_5)_n$, and these polymers are formed by condensation of smaller units. Each link between monomeric units is a **glycosidic bond**. These may be α- or β-glycosidic bonds, depending on whether the hydroxyl group at carbon-1 is in the α or β conformation in the monosaccharide monomers. Monomers can be joined more directly by α linkages, because a β-glycosidic bond requires the hydroxyl of one unit to be rotated 180° in order to be in appropriate spatial relationship with the hydroxyl of its neighboring monomer (Fig. 2.10). These linkages are physiologically important for at least three reasons.

1. They provide a means by which two or more subunits can be joined in the construction of a variety of larger molecules with different functions and specificities.

2. Different enzymes attack α- and β-glycosidic bonds, which allows the cell additional means of discriminating among compounds used in structure and function.

3. Molecules with α-glycosidic bonds are readily mobilized for metabolism, whereas β-glycosides are stable molecules used in cell construction and are quite resistant to modification or breakdown.

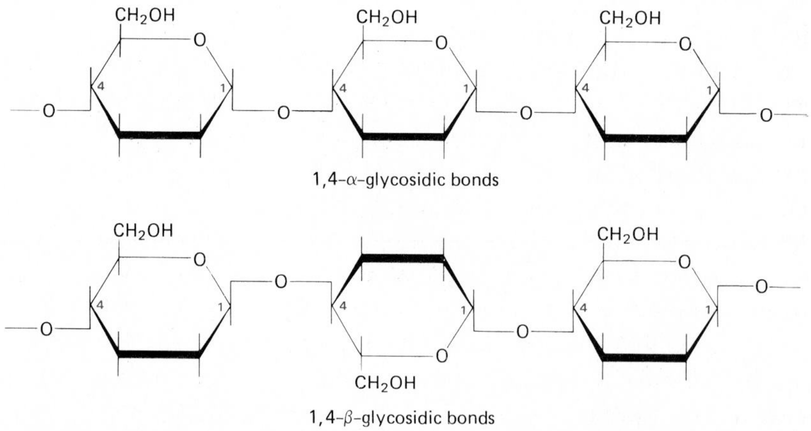

FIGURE 2-10
Polysaccharide fragments showing α- and β-glycosidic bonds. In these examples glycosidic bonds are shown as 1,4-links. That is, they are shown between carbon-1 and carbon-4 of adjacent monomer units.

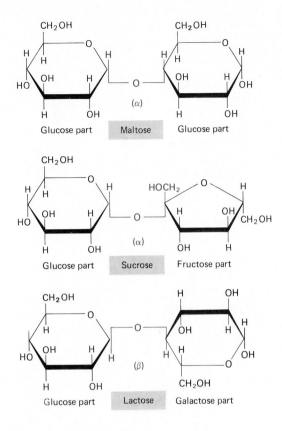

FIGURE 2-11
Three metabolically important disaccharide sugars are sucrose, lactose, and maltose. Monomer units of
sucrose and maltose are joined by
1,4-α-glycosidic bonds, whereas a
1,4-β-glycosidic link joins the glucose
and galactose monomer units of
lactose.

Polysaccharides are usually made of hundreds or thousands of monosaccharide residues. Compounds made of two to about eight or nine monosaccharide units are called **oligosaccharides** (Gr. *oligos*: few). The most important oligosaccharides in metabolism are the two-sugar compounds, or **disaccharides**, such as sucrose (table sugar), lactose (milk sugar), and maltose (malt sugar, a degradation product of starch) (Fig. 2.11).

The major functions served by polysaccharides in cells are concerned with food storage and with cellular structures. In eukaryotes the main polysaccharide food reserves are *starch* and *glycogen*, both of which can be hydrolyzed to their constituent glucose units by specific enzymes. Starch is deposited in large granules in the chloroplasts of some green cells or in colorless plastids (leucoplasts) in root, stem, and other plant tissues. Starch granules can be seen with the light microscope and can be identified using an iodine solution in a simple staining test. Two kinds of polymers are incorporated into starch granules, but both are α-glycosides. One kind of starch molecule consists of an unbranched chain of 250 to 300 glucose units; the second kind of starch molecule has approximately 1000 glucose residues in a long chain with occasional branches.

Although starch is a major form of stored food in algae and land plants, glycogen is the principal food reserve in animals and fungi. Glycogen granules are deposited directly in the cytoplasm and not in organelles (see Fig. 1.8). Particularly large amounts of glycogen are present in animal liver cells. The liver glycogen polymer is a long branched chain containing about 30,000 glucose units joined by α-

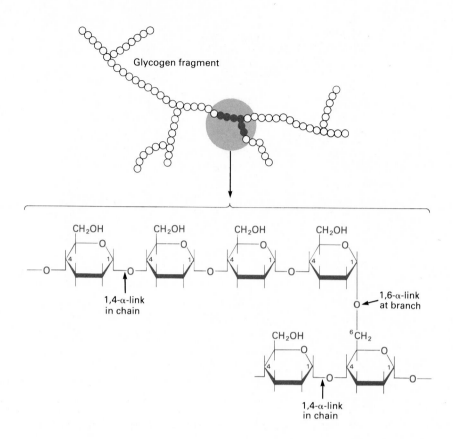

FIGURE 2-12
Glycogen molecules in liver cells are branched-chain polymers made up entirely of about 30,000 glucose monomer units. Monomers are joined by 1,4-α-glycosidic links except at branch points of the chains, where 1,6-α-glycosidic links occur. Glycogen is a major form of stored food in fungi as well as in animals, and it occurs in granules in the cytoplasm (see Fig. 1.8).

glycosidic bonds between carbon atoms 1 and 4 in the main chain and by 1,6-links at points of branching along the main chain (Fig. 2.12).

The two common structural polysaccharides in eukaryotes are *cellulose* and *chitin*, both of which are β-glycosides. Cellulose is found along with other materials in the cell wall of many algae and all the higher plants, as well as in certain fungi and protists. About 8000 glucose units are joined by 1,4-β-glycosidic links in the long unbranched cellulose chain. These chains fold by hydrogen bonding in a way that produces bundles of long fibrils that can readily be seen with the electron microscope (Fig. 2.13). Chitin is a polysaccharide with nitrogen atoms as well as C, H, and O. Residues of *N*-acetylglucosamine are linked by β-glycosidic bonds in long unbranched chains. These residues are derivatives of glucose. Chitin found in cell walls of many fungi is chemically identical to chitin in the rigid exoskeleton of insects, crustacea, and certain other invertebrate animals.

Polysaccharide chains in bacterial cell walls are long unbranched molecules made of disaccharide units that are joined through 1,4-β-glycosodic bonds. The disaccharide repeating unit is invariably composed of two sugar derivatives, *N*-acetylglucosamine and *N*-acetylmuramic acid. Individual polysaccharide chains are connected by cross-links of four to five covalently bonded amino acid units, so that the basic wall construction consists of a **peptidoglycan** sheet (Fig. 2.14). Although the polysaccharide component of the sheet is essentially the same in bacterial species, the short peptide cross-links vary considerably from one species to another. As much as 90% of the cell wall in Gram-positive bacteria consists of peptidoglycan, but as little as 5% of

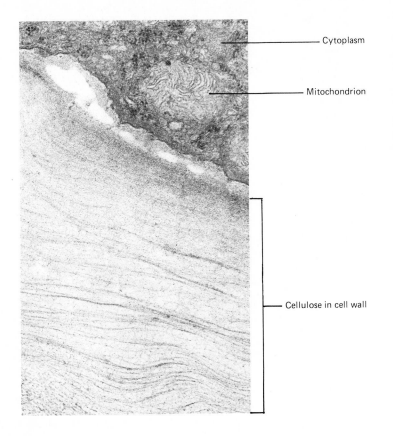

Cytoplasm

Mitochondrion

Cellulose in cell wall

FIGURE 2-13
Electron micrograph of part of a wheat cell, showing the cell wall largely composed of parallel bundles of cellulose fibers. Each fiber is made up of numerous unbranched cellulose polymer molecules, and each cellulose molecule consists of about 8000 glucose monomer units joined by 1,4-β-glycosidic links. ($\times$37,000) (Photograph courtesy of M. C. Ledbetter.)

the wall in some Gram-negative species is made of this substance. In addition to the peptidoglycan sheet, other polysaccharides, proteins, and lipids are usually present in the bacterial cell wall. The bacterial cell wall is far more complex in its organization and function than equivalent structures in plants and fungi.

FIGURE 2-14
The peptidoglycan sheet of bacterial cell walls is constructed from repeating disaccharide units, each composed of N-acetylglucosamine (NAG) and N-acetylmuramic acid (NAM). The sugar derivatives are joined by 1,4-β-glycosidic links to form long unbranched chains, which are connected by short cross-links of four or five covalently bonded amino acids (filled circles). The detail in (a) represents the circled section (color) of the peptidoglycan in (b).

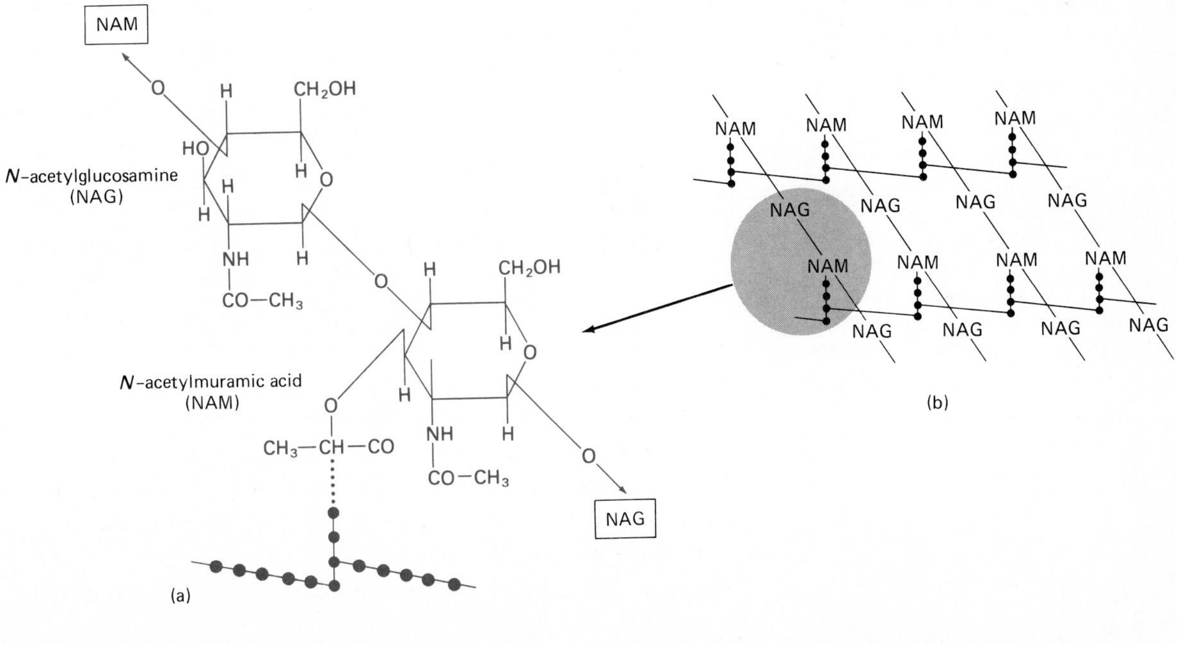

Lipids

Lipids are a diverse group of substances that have the common property of solubility in nonpolar, organic solvents such as ether and alcohol. Among the many types of lipids we can cite fats, fatty acids, waxes, steroids, phospholipids, glycolipids, and terpenes as examples of biologically important substances.

2.7
Fatty Acids

Naturally occurring **fatty acids** are unbranched hydrocarbon chains with a carboxyl group at one end. Because fatty acids are synthesized from two-carbon acetyl units, they usually have an even number of carbon atoms, the most common numbers being 16 and 18. When all the carbon atoms of a fatty acid chain are joined by single covalent bonds, the compound is "saturated" (with hydrogens at both sites not involved in the —C—C— chain). An "unsaturated" fatty acid has one or more double bonds between carbons in the backbone of the chain (Fig. 2.15).

The carboxyl end of the fatty acid molecule is water-soluble and highly polar, whereas the hydrocarbon portion of the chain is water insoluble and highly nonpolar. When fatty acids interact with water, the soluble carboxyl end is contained as a layer within the water while the hydrocarbon tails of these molecules remain outside the water surface (Fig. 2.16). Although fatty acids occur in trace amounts in cells and tissues, they are important as building blocks of several classes of lipids.

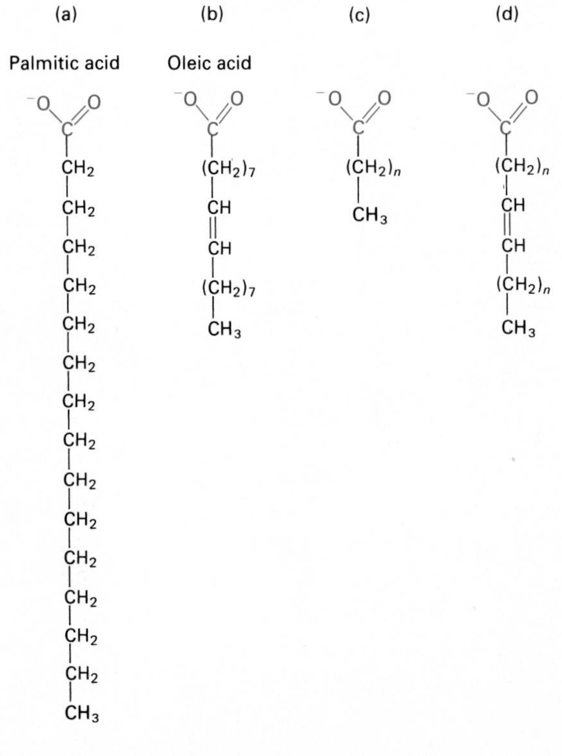

FIGURE 2-15
Fatty acids are unbranched hydrocarbon chains that usually contain an even number of carbon atoms, such as (a) palmitic acid, a C_{16} saturated fatty acid lacking double bonds in the hydrocarbon chain, and (b) oleic acid, a C_{18} unsaturated fatty acid with one double bond in the chain. (c) Saturated fatty acids of any kind have —C—C— construction throughout the hydrocarbon chain, whereas (d) any unsaturated fatty acid has one or more —C=C— links in the chain. The carboxyl terminus (color) of a fatty acid is water soluble and highly polar, whereas the remainder of the molecule is water insoluble and nonpolar.

(a) Palmitic acid (b) Oleic acid (c) (d)

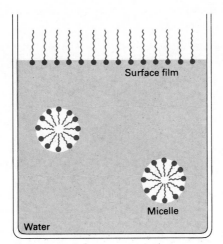

FIGURE 2-16
When fatty acids interact with water, the aggregated molecules may form a surface film with their polar heads in water. When completely surrounded by water, fatty acids aggregate to form a micelle in which the nonpolar tails, or hydrocarbon chains, are sequestered away from water and only their polar heads make contact with water molecules.

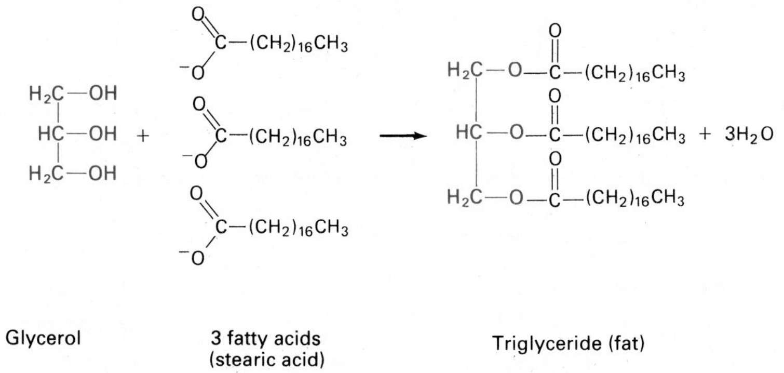

Glycerol   3 fatty acids (stearic acid)   Triglyceride (fat)

FIGURE 2-17
Glycerides, or neutral fats, are fatty acid esters of the alcoholic compound glycerol. In a dehydration reaction between glycerol and three fatty acids, which may be all alike or not, a triglyceride is produced and may be stored as a reserve food in the cell.

2.8
Neutral Fats

Fatty acid esters of the alcohol *glycerol* are **neutral fats**, or glycerides (Fig. 2.17). One, two, or three different kinds of fatty acids can combine with the hydroxyl groups of glycerol to form a molecule of fat. These fats are the major storage form of lipids in both plants and animals. They may be formed from excess carbohydrate, protein, or lipid in cells and tissues. When fats are oxidized they provide more than twice as much energy (in calories per gram) as carbohydrates or proteins, because the overall state of oxidation of the long hydrocarbon chains of the fatty acids is very low. Fats, therefore, have much further to go before they are completely processed to carbon dioxide and water.

Neutral fats are nonpolar molecules and insoluble in water because the carboxyl groups of the constituent fatty acids are no longer accessible for molecular interactions. Neutral fats in cells are hydrolyzed by digestive enzymes called lipases, but they can be hydrolyzed outside the living system when boiled with acids or bases. Animal fats can be converted to soap when boiled in the presence of alkali. This practical method for home manufacture is still used in some societies.

Oils are fats that liquefy at room temperature. The melting point of a particular oil depends on the degree of saturation of the constituent fatty acids; more highly saturated oils have higher melting points. Vegetable oils are saturated to convert them to the "hard" fat form of margarine.

TABLE 2-2
Some of the Major Types of Lipids in Cells

Lipid Groups	Compounds	Important Cellular Location of Compounds
Fatty acids	Oleic acid, palmitic acid, stearic acid	Cytosol, mitochondria, glyoxysomes of fatty seeds
Neutral fats	Coconut oil, beef tallow	Fat storage depots
Phospholipids	Phosphatidylethanolamine, phosphatidylcholine, phosphatidylserine, phosphatidylinositol	Membranes
Sphingolipids	Sphingomyelin	Membranes
Glycolipids	Cerebrosides, gangliosides	Membranes
Steroids	Cholesterol	Membranes
Terpenes	Essential oils, carotenoids	Plant cytosol, chloroplasts

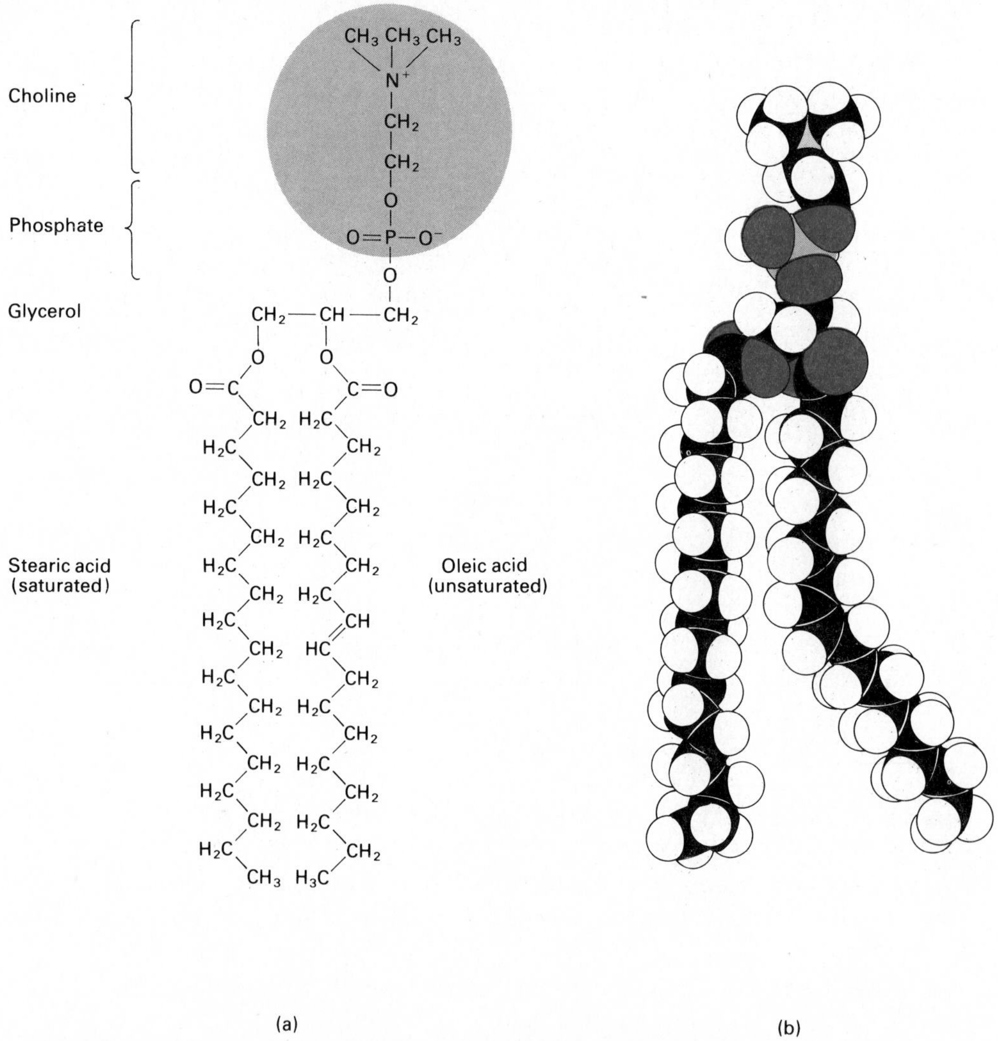

FIGURE 2-18

A typical phospholipid, such as the phosphatidylcholine shown here, consists of (a) a hydrophilic head (color) bonded to one hydroxyl of the glycerol residue, and two hydrophobic fatty acids ("tails") bonded to the other two hydroxyls of the glycerol residue in the molecule. (b) A space-filling model of phosphatidylcholine showing a kink in the unsaturated fatty acid tail, produced as a result of the double bond in the oleic acid chain. Fatty acid chains are usually packed parallel to each other in a membrane, but an unsaturated chain has more mobility (fluidity) and may undergo a greater degree of displacement than is possible for a saturated hydrocarbon chain. Phosphatidylcholines have the same head component (choline and phosphate) but may have different fatty acids, one of which is usually unsaturated.

(a)

(b)

2.9
Phospholipids

Phospholipids are a major constituent of cellular membranes (Table 2.2). In a phospholipid molecule, a fatty acid is bonded to each of two hydroxyl groups of glycerol and a phosphoric acid residue is bonded to the third hydroxyl, instead of a third fatty acid being there, as in a neutral fat (Fig. 2.18). All phospholipids thus have a hydrophobic "tail" consisting of two fatty acid chains and a hydrophilic "head" made up of a negatively charged phosphoric acid residue to which a positively charged group is bonded in turn. Phospholipids are therefore amphipathic molecules; they have both hydrophobic and hydrophilic regions in the same molecule. Because of its amphipathic nature, a phospholipid can interact with both watery and nonwatery phases and thus serve as a link between the cell and its surroundings.

When phospholipids interact with water, they spontaneously aggregate into two layers, each of which is one molecule thick. In such bimolecular sheets of phospholipids, the hydrophilic heads of the molecules are in the water and the hydrophobic tails are excluded from water (Fig. 2.19). Such bimolecular aggregates strongly resemble phospholipid arrangements in cellular membranes. They resemble membranes even more closely when a mixture of proteins and phospholipids is added to a system with water and air phases. The amphipathic properties of phospholipids are thus important in membrane *conformation* as well as in membrane *functions* in interactions involving water, lipids, and proteins.

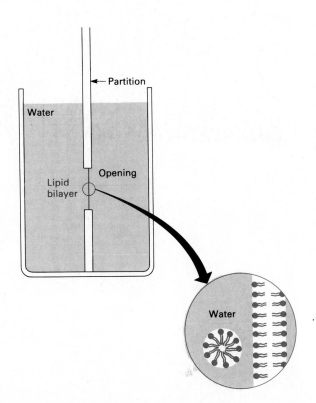

FIGURE 2-19
When two aqueous compartments are separated by a partition in which an opening is present, any phospholipids added to the system aggregate spontaneously to form a planar bilayer across the opening. The polar heads interact with water on each side of the opening, but water is excluded from the hydrophobic region of fatty acids oriented end to end. When completely surrounded by water, a phospholipid micelle may aggregate spontaneously. In such a micelle the polar head groups are in contact with water and the hydrophobic fatty acid tails are sequestered inside the structure, away from water.

2.10
Sphingolipids and Glycolipids

Sphingolipids and glycolipids are also amphipathic molecules, because they have two hydrophobic residues in a "tail" and one hydrophilic residue in a "head" region. These two kinds of lipids also occur in membranes, but they are more restricted than phospholipids in cellular distribution. Sphingolipids and glycolipids are particularly prominent components of cell membranes in brain and nervous tissues, though they occur elsewhere as well.

Sphingolipids lack a glycerol component, and they have a **sphingosine** residue in place of one of the two fatty acid chains (Fig. 2.20). The fatty acid and sphingosine chains make up the hydrophobic region of the molecule, and the polar head consists of some kind of hydrophilic residue bound to sphingosine. *Sphingomyelin* is the most abundant of the known sphingolipids.

FIGURE 2-20
Sphingolipids such as (a) sphingomyelin are amphipathic molecules that have one fatty acid tail and sphingosine in place of a second fatty acid in the hydrophobic region of the molecule. The polar head of sphingomyelin consists of a choline residue bonded to a phosphate residue, just like the hydrophilic head of phosphatidylcholine (see Fig. 2.18). (b) A space-filling model of sphingomyelin.

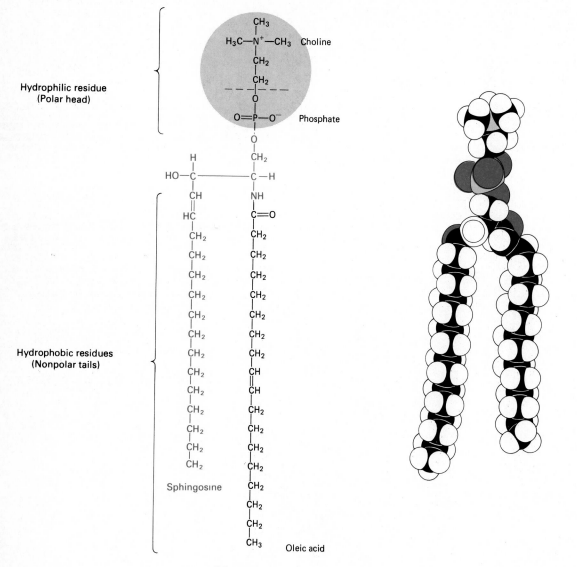

(a)   (b)

Glycolipids are distinguished by having a polar hydrophilic carbohydrate residue in the head of the molecule, usually D-glucose or D-galactose. Two important classes of these compounds are *cerebrosides* and *gangliosides*. Cerebrosides are found particularly in the myelin sheath of nervous tissue. Gangliosides are abundant in the outer surface of the plasma membrane of nerve cells and are important factors in immune responses and other cell-surface phenomena. Gangliosides are unusual glycolipids; they have an oligosaccharide rather than a monosaccharide residue as a polar head group. Cerebrosides are actually glycosphingolipids because they have a sugar head group but the hydrophobic tail includes a sphingosine chain.

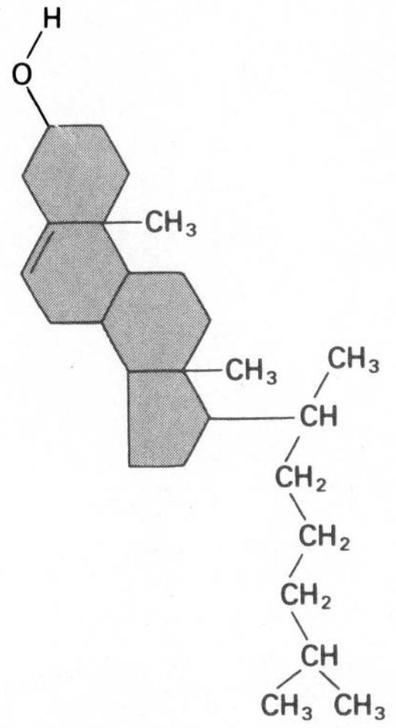

2.11
Steroids and Terpenes

Lipids that cannot be converted to soaps (nonsaponifiable) include steroids and terpenes. Both types are derived from common five-carbon building blocks and are therefore related groups of compounds. The most familiar steroids are cholesterol, bile acids, and sex hormones in vertebrates. Most of the steroids occur in trace amounts, but *sterols* are a relatively abundant class of these compounds. Sterols are steroids that occur as free alcohols or as long-chain fatty acid esters. The most common sterol is cholesterol, which is a plasma membrane component in animal tissues (Fig. 2.21). Plants and fungi contain other kinds of sterols; sterols have not been found in bacteria.

Terpenes are especially evident constituents of certain plants and are responsible for characteristic odors and flavors. They are a major component of "essential oils" derived from such plants; for example, the terpenes camphor, limonene, and menthol occur in oil of camphor, lemon, and mint, respectively. A terpenoid alcohol called *phytol* is part of the chlorophyll molecule (Fig. 2.22). Other terpenoids include natural rubber and the carotenoid pigments that absorb light energy in photo-

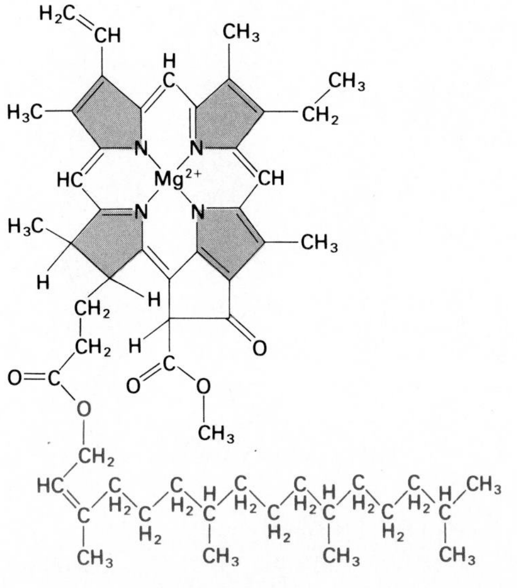

FIGURE 2-21
Cholesterol is an amphipathic component of animal cell plasma membranes. The hydroxyl terminus is hydrophilic, and the planar ring structure and hydrocarbon chain are hydrophobic components of the molecule. Cholesterol is a sterol member of the steroid group of lipids.

Phytol side-chain

FIGURE 2-22
The chlorophyll *a* molecule, a photosynthetic green pigment, consists of a complex ring structure coordinated with a magnesium ion, and the terpenoid alcohol phytol as a side chain (color).

synthesis and contribute to the yellow and orange colors of carrots, autumn foliage, and other plant materials. The fat-soluble vitamins A, D, E, and K are synthesized from the same five-carbon precursors as the terpenes. Plant carotenes are precursors of vitamin A, which is found only in animals.

Proteins

The enormous variety of proteins serve as major building materials and as regulatory molecules that control the diverse activities of living systems. Major types of fibrous proteins that act as structural elements include **actin** and **myosin** of muscle and other contractile systems, **collagens** of connective ligaments in the body, **keratins** in protective coverings such as skin, hair, claws, horns, feathers, and other structures of land vertebrates, and a number of other compounds. Proteins that regulate the numerous processes and activities of the organism include **enzymes**, which modulate chemical reactions of metabolism; **antibodies**, which provide immunity against infection; and **hormones**, and various other substances that make each life form respond appropriately to the constantly changing internal and external environments. Regulatory proteins are globular in shape, in contrast to fibrous structural proteins. These conformations have an important bearing on the character of the molecule and on its activity or function.

2.12
Amino Acids

The thousands of kinds of proteins in living systems share a common plan of construction. The 20 kinds of naturally occurring **amino acid** monomers are strung together in unbranched, linear polymer chains of proteins. These are the 20 amino acids specified in the genetic code common to all life. Some other kinds of amino acids are also found in cells, but they are either degradation products or residues that have been modified from one or more of the 20 commonly occurring amino acids after the latter have been inserted into the polymer chain. Hydroxyproline is a major amino acid constituent of collagen, but proline residues are initially included in the protein and become hydroxylated after polymerization. Hydroxyproline is not one of the encoded amino acids, but proline is. Many proteins contain fewer than 20 kinds of amino acids. The relative proportions and the absolute numbers of the amino acid repertory vary from one protein to another, as a reflection of the specific information in genes, which are the blueprints for protein construction.

All 20 amino acids have the same basic structure (Fig. 2.23). A carboxyl group ($-COO^-$) and an amino group ($-NH_3^+$) are joined to the first carbon, or α-carbon, atom, and a hydrogen atom is found as a third unit bonded to this carbon in all amino acids. Except for glycine, which has a second hydrogen joined to the α-carbon, the other 19 amino acids have a fourth group that differs from the other three bonded to the

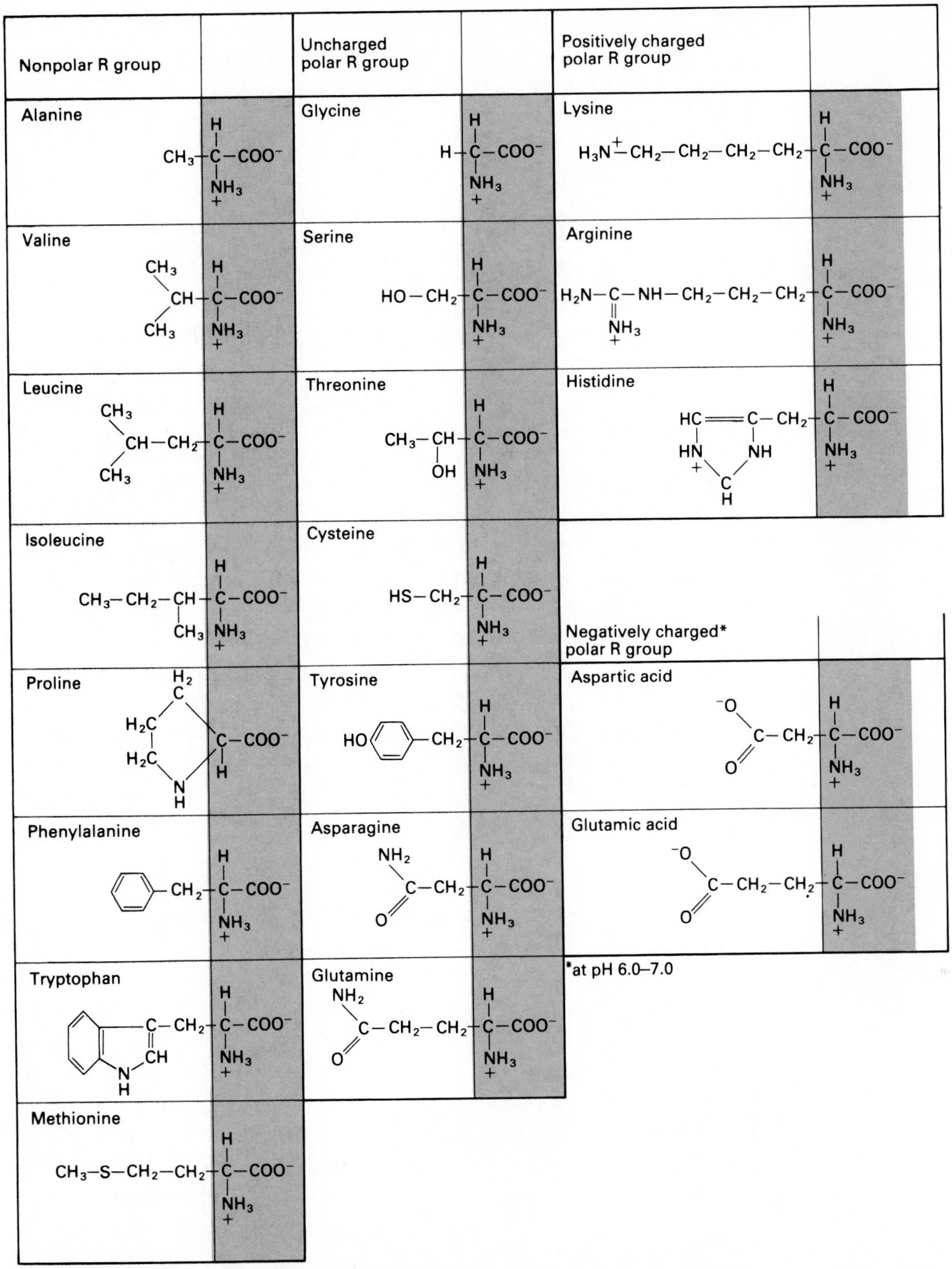

Nonpolar R group		Uncharged polar R group		Positively charged polar R group	
Alanine	$CH_3-\underset{\underset{+}{NH_3}}{\overset{H}{\underset{\|}{C}}}-COO^-$	Glycine	$H-\underset{\underset{+}{NH_3}}{\overset{H}{\underset{\|}{C}}}-COO^-$	Lysine	$H_3N^+-CH_2-CH_2-CH_2-CH_2-\underset{\underset{+}{NH_3}}{\overset{H}{\underset{\|}{C}}}-COO^-$
Valine		Serine	$HO-CH_2-\underset{\underset{+}{NH_3}}{\overset{H}{\underset{\|}{C}}}-COO^-$	Arginine	$H_2N-\underset{\underset{+}{NH_3}}{\overset{\|}{C}}-NH-CH_2-CH_2-CH_2-\underset{\underset{+}{NH_3}}{\overset{H}{\underset{\|}{C}}}-COO^-$
Leucine		Threonine	$CH_3-CH-\underset{\underset{+}{NH_3}}{\overset{H}{\underset{\|}{C}}}-COO^-$	Histidine	
Isoleucine	$CH_3-CH_2-CH-\underset{\underset{+}{NH_3}}{\overset{H}{\underset{\|}{C}}}-COO^-$	Cysteine	$HS-CH_2-\underset{\underset{+}{NH_3}}{\overset{H}{\underset{\|}{C}}}-COO^-$	Negatively charged* polar R group	
Proline		Tyrosine	$HO-\langle\rangle-CH_2-\underset{\underset{+}{NH_3}}{\overset{H}{\underset{\|}{C}}}-COO^-$	Aspartic acid	
Phenylalanine	$\langle\rangle-CH_2-\underset{\underset{+}{NH_3}}{\overset{H}{\underset{\|}{C}}}-COO^-$	Asparagine		Glutamic acid	
Tryptophan		Glutamine		*at pH 6.0–7.0	
Methionine	$CH_3-S-CH_2-CH_2-\underset{\underset{+}{NH_3}}{\overset{H}{\underset{\|}{C}}}-COO^-$				

FIGURE 2-23

In all twenty amino acids specified in the genetic code the α-carbon atom is bonded to a carboxyl group, an amino group, and a hydrogen atom (colored column), but the fourth group (R) varies from one amino acid to another. The R side-chain determines the electrical and polar or nonpolar nature of the amino acid. Except for glycine, all the other amino acids may exist in the D- and L-isomeric forms because the α-carbon is asymmetric. L-amino acids are the predominant or only Isomers in virtually all natural proteins.

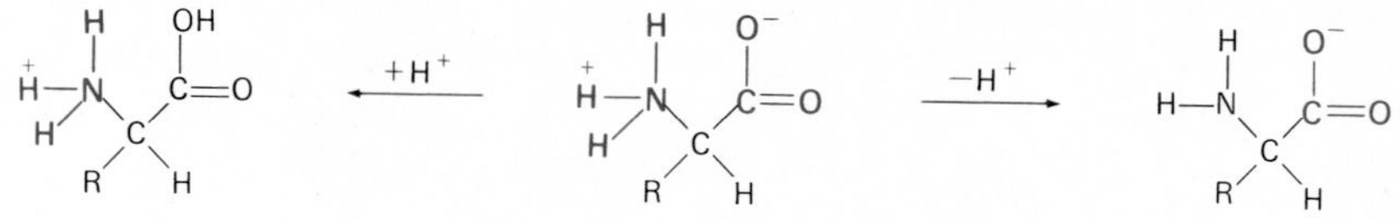

FIGURE 2-24
Free amino acids are zwitterions, because negative and positive electrically charged residues (color) are both present in the same molecule. Such zwitterions can neutralize added H^+ in acid solutions or added OH^- in basic solutions.

first carbon atom. Except for glycine, therefore, the amino acids have an asymmetric α-carbon atom. They are also optically active molecules. The L-isomer of these 19 amino acids occurs in almost all natural proteins, though some D-amino acids have been found in certain molecules from plants and bacteria. For example, D-alanine and D-glutamic acid are constituents of the peptidoglycan in bacterial cell walls.

The side-chain differences are responsible for the varying properties of different amino acids and for particular properties of the proteins in which they occur. When individual amino acids are in solution at pH 7.0, added alkali or acid is neutralized by the amino acid. The amino acid is a "zwitterion" with both negatively and positively charged groups in the same molecule (Fig. 2.24). These effects disappear when amino acids condense to form a *peptide* unit because of the nature of the bond that joins amino acid monomers into a linear chain in dehydration reactions. The formation of a **peptide bond** or **amide linkage** involves covalent bonding between an amino group of one amino acid and the carboxyl group of the adjoining amino acid (Fig. 2.25). Because this amide linkage involves one charged group of each amino acid, the "zwitterion" property no longer exists for individual amino acids in the chain.

An amino acid polymer may still display acidic or basic properties because of the presence of acidic or basic side-chains in its constituent amino acid units. At pH 7.0, aspartic acid and glutamic acid residues confer acidic properties on a polymer region, and the positively charged polar groups of histidine, arginine, and lysine contribute basic properties to a protein.

When acid is added to proteins in solution, a net positive charge develops because $-COO^-$ changes to $-COOH$. Addition of a base causes $-NH_3^+$ to change to $-NH_2$, leaving the protein with a net negative charge. At a particular intermediate pH called the **isoelectric point**, equal numbers of positive and negative charges occur in the protein, and the net charge is zero (Fig. 2.26). Positively and negatively charged proteins migrate in an electrical field, but proteins at their

FIGURE 2-25
When the carboxyl group (color) of one amino acid joins in a dehydration reaction with the amino group (color) of another amino acid, the two amino acids are held together by a peptide bond (color). Once the peptide bond, or amide linkage, has formed, the individual aminoacyl residues no longer possess zwitterion properties, but the dipeptide molecule has both negatively and positively charged components at its termini.

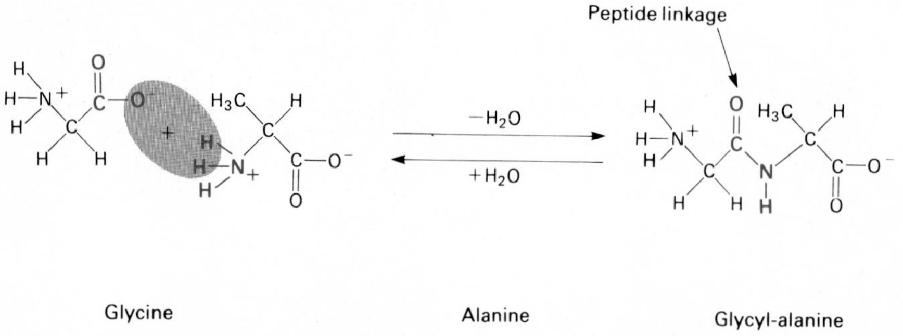

Glycine   Alanine   Glycyl-alanine

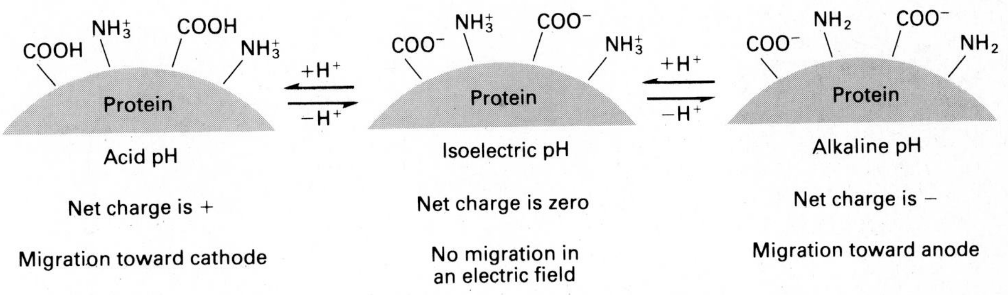

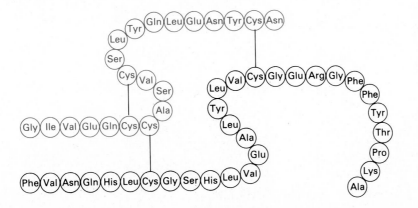

COOH NH$_3^+$ COOH   NH$_3^+$ COO$^-$ NH$_3^+$ COO$^-$ NH$_3^+$ COO$^-$ NH$_2$ COO$^-$ NH$_2$

Protein   Protein   Protein

+H$^+$ +H$^+$
$\rightleftharpoons$ $\rightleftharpoons$
−H$^+$ −H$^+$

Acid pH   Isoelectric pH   Alkaline pH

Net charge is +   Net charge is zero   Net charge is −

Migration toward cathode   No migration in an electric field   Migration toward anode

FIGURE 2-26
Migration of proteins in an electrical field depends on the net charge of the molecule. The net charge is zero at the isoelectric pH, even though the number of charges is at the maximum for the molecule, because the number of positive charges equals the number of negative charges in the molecule.

isoelectric point do not move toward either the cathode or the anode. Proteins are most easily precipitated by appropriate solvents when in solution at their isoelectric pH, the pH at which the protein is at its minimum solubility. Most proteins have an isoelectric point on the acid side and therefore carry a net negative charge at physiological pH. Basic proteins, such as histones in chromosomes, carry a net positive charge under normal cellular conditions. Relatively high amounts of lysine and arginine contribute to the positive charge and to chromosome structure, because positively charged histones readily combine with negatively charged DNA to form highly stable nucleoprotein complexes.

2.13
Polypeptides

The formation of a peptide bond is one part of the complex sequence of events during protein synthesis at the ribosomes. These events will be discussed in Chapter 13. A dipeptide forms when two amino acids are joined by a covalent amide linkage; a tripeptide involves three amino acids; and a **polypeptide** contains a large number of amino acids, perhaps as many as 1000. Identical peptide bonds join all the amino acids in a polypeptide molecule (Fig. 2.27).

Proteins may consist of one or more polypeptide chains held together by various forces in the functional protein molecule. The individual polypeptides are identical in some proteins, whereas other proteins include two or more different polypeptide chains. The molecular weight of an individual polypeptide is usually in the range of 15,000 to 100,000, and a whole protein may be as large as several million daltons. The hormone insulin is an unusually small protein (its molecular weight is 6000), yet it is made of two polypeptide chains constructed of 21 and 30 amino acids, respectively (Fig. 2.28). Insulin was the first

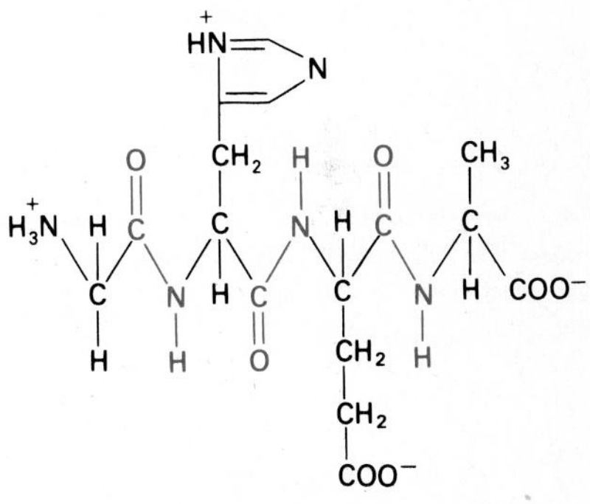

glycyl–histidyl–glutamyl–alanine
(at pH 7)

FIGURE 2-27
The peptide bond (color) is identical throughout the length of a peptide chain, and it joins any amino acid to any other amino acid in any unbranched sequence.

FIGURE 2-28
The hormone insulin consists of two short polypeptide chains of 21 and 30 amino acid residues, respectively. The two chains are held together by disulfide (—S—S—) bridges formed by interactions between sulfhydryl (—SH) groups in cysteine residues in the same or in different chains of the protein molecule.

protein to have its composition and sequence of amino acids described. The study was reported in 1953 by Frederick Sanger, a Nobel laureate, and it opened the way to detailed analyses of other proteins and to our understanding of the relationship of protein structure to cell function and gene action.

2.14
Protein Structure

Protein structure is usually described in terms of different aspects of molecular organization. The unique sequence of amino acids in a polypeptide is called the **primary structure** of the chain. Secondary, tertiary, and quaternary structure, which we will discuss shortly, all refer to three-dimensional aspects of a polypeptide or a whole protein. The primary structure of a molecule is important for at least two reasons. First, primary structure determines the three-dimensional conformation of the molecule and, therefore, its cellular role. Second, the primary structure of a polypeptide or protein is a linear translation of the sequence of nucleotides in DNA (or RNA) and thus provides crucial information about genetic input to protein synthesis and cellular potential.

A change in even one amino acid in the primary structure of a polypeptide may produce a drastic effect in the organism. Human hemoglobin is a protein comprised of two α-globin chains and two β-globin chains. People suffering from the inherited disorder called sickle-cell anemia have β-globins in which one of the 146 amino acid

FIGURE 2-29
(a) In the β-globin chain of normal adult hemoglobin, the sixth amino acid from the amino terminus is glutamic acid. Valine is substituted for glutamic acid at this position in the β-globin chain of sickle-cell hemoglobin, but the remaining 145 amino acids of β-globin remain unchanged. (b) Scanning electron micrographs of normal human red blood cells (left) and sickled red blood cells (right). The biconcave discoid shape of normal cells becomes distorted in cells containing sickle-cell hemoglobin, especially in conditions of low oxygen. Sickling of red blood cells is due to the altered shape and properties of sickle-cell hemoglobin molecules.

	1	2	3	4	5	6	7	8	146
Hb A	Val	His	Leu	Thr	Pro	Glu	Glu	Lys	His
Hb S	Val	His	Leu	Thr	Pro	Val	Glu	Lys	His

(a)

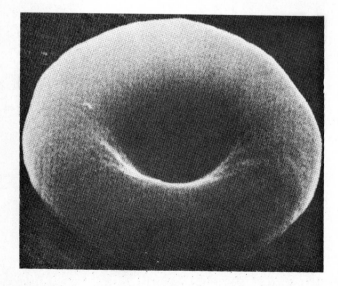

(b)

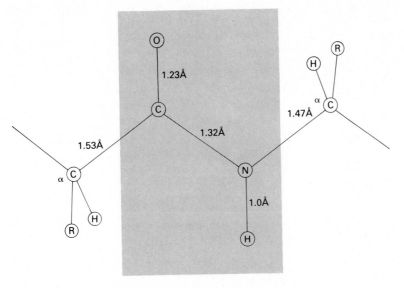

Peptide bond

(a)

FIGURE 2-30
Nature of the peptide bond. (a) The peptide bond is planar in shape (color), and the individual atoms are held at specific distances (shown in angstroms) and at specific angles as a consequence of the covalent bonds between them. (b) Because of the partial double-bond character of the C—N link, rotation around this bond is not possible. Rotations of atoms in a polypeptide chain can thus occur only between (arrows) adjacent planar elements (color) at the α carbons.

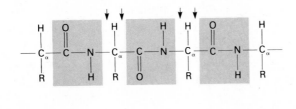

(b)

residues is different from the normal (Fig. 2.29). Valine is substituted for glutamic acid in the sixth position along the amino acid chain, which leads to altered interactions and to altered protein shape. The change in molecular shape causes interference in binding molecular oxygen to hemoglobin in the bloodstream, leading to an assortment of metabolic problems that reduce the life expectancy of the individual.

Such a profound effect because of one amino acid substitution is not typical of modifications in proteins. For example, the respiratory protein cytochrome c differs in yeast and human cells by about 40 out of 104 amino acids in the chain, yet the protein carries out its function equally well in both species. In this case the amino acid substitutions do not involve those critical regions of the molecule that are responsible for its three-dimensional shape. These and many other studies have shown that protein shape depends on interactions between some—but not all—of the amino acid residues in a molecule.

The standard dimensions of the polypeptide backbone are determined by lengths and angles of the covalent chemical bonds in the peptide linkage (Fig. 2.30). The restrictions imposed by the zigzag, rigid polypeptide backbone, whose amide groups are planar in shape, lead to restrictions in the way in which this linear chain can fold into a three-dimensional structure in space. From physical studies it is clear that proteins are rigid, compact molecules that must be folded, because

a protein molecule is much shorter than we would expect from the
lengths of its constituent polypeptides. Interactions between neighboring amino acid residues contribute to **secondary structure** of a
polypeptide chain, whereas interactions between residues at some distance from each other in the chain lead to **tertiary structure**. The
three-dimensional character of a polypeptide is a consequence of both
these levels of spatial organization.

One principal mode of secondary structure, called the **α helix**, was
first postulated in 1951 by Linus Pauling and Robert Corey (Fig. 2.31).
The **α** helix is a natural conformation for linear polymers having
regularly repeated monomeric units, because each monomer occupies an
identical orientation within the molecule. This leads to formation of the
same group of secondary bonds for each monomer in the polymer, and to
a more stable state because each set of bonds is as strong as any other set
of secondary bonds (secondary to covalent bonds of the polymeric
backbone). Many polymers, particularly proteins, contain different kinds
of monomeric units and are therefore not regular in construction. Even

FIGURE 2-31

Secondary structure in proteins. (a) The
α-helix structure of a polypeptide chain,
or part of a chain, is stabilized by
hydrogen bonds (dotted lines) between
the oxygen (color) of one peptide bond
and the hydrogen of another. (b) The
β-sheet structure of all or part of a
polypeptide chain is characterized by
hydrogen bonds (dotted lines) between
every peptide bond and its neighbor.
The stability of α-helix and β-sheet
secondary structures is due to identical
hydrogen bonding between all monomers, which are thus equally strong.

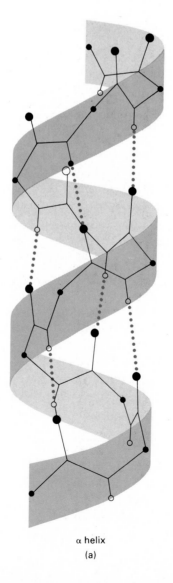

α helix

(a)

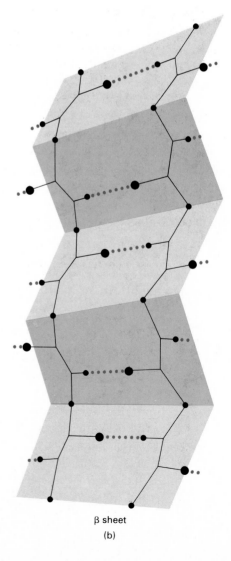

β sheet

(b)

though the polypeptide backbone is regular (repeated peptide bonds), the side-chains of the amino acids are irregular; they vary from one amino acid to another. A helical structure may be energetically satisfactory for the backbone but unsatisfactory for the side-chains of the amino acid monomers. The three-dimensional shape of a protein, therefore, is usually the result of some compromise between the tendency of the regular backbone to form a regular helix and the tendency of the amino acid side-chains to twist the backbone into a different energetically satisfactory configuration. Proteins usually assume the three-dimensional shape dictated more by interactions between the side-chains of widely separated amino acids (tertiary structure) than by interactions between neighboring residues (secondary structure).

Fibrous proteins exhibit a high degree of secondary structure, leading to highly ordered cables and sheets of molecules involved in cellular construction. Interactions between distant side-chains predominate in globular proteins, such as enzymes, thus producing the extensive molecular folding typical of tertiary structure. Globular proteins usually have a considerable amount of unordered *random coil* regions, along with regions of ordered α helix and other types of secondary structure.

Quaternary structure refers to the spatial organization assumed when two or more polypeptides are part of a single protein molecule (Fig. 2.32). The polypeptides are held together by weak chemical bonds, as shown by their ready dispersion in the presence of reagents known to break only noncovalent bonds. The absolute number of polypeptides and the number of different kinds of polypeptides in a protein vary considerably. Hemoglobin molecules consist of two α chains and two β chains, each of which has a molecular weight of about 16,000. Ferritin, a protein that stores iron atoms in mammals, consists of 20 identical polypeptide chains of about 200 amino acids each. The ferritin molecule has a molecular weight of about 480,000, compared with 64,000 for hemoglobin. Disruption of any level of molecular organization, including quaternary structure, leads to protein malfunction.

FIGURE 2-32
Four levels of structural organization in a protein as exemplified by the hemoglobin molecule. (a) Primary structure consists of amino acids joined in sequence by peptide bonds. (b) Secondary structure develops through interactions between neighboring residues, as by hydrogen bonds between adjacent monomer units in an α-helix region. (c) Tertiary structure depends on interactions between more distant residues, leading to folding and to a more globular conformation of the polypeptide chain. (d) Quaternary structure is the consequence of interactions between two or more polypeptide chains in a protein molecule (four chains in hemoglobin). Each globin chain in hemoglobin is bonded to a heme group (color), which functions in oxygen transport to body tissues.

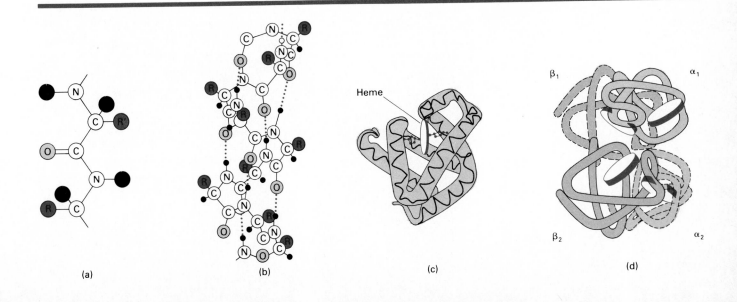

(a) (b) (c) (d)

Proteins are extremely stable in the watery environment of the cell. One major reason for this feature is that the polypeptide backbone is strongly polar and readily forms hydrogen bonds with the surrounding water molecules. Hydrogen bonding with water contributes to an energetically satisfactory state and results in considerable molecular stability. Hydrogen bonds are much weaker than covalent bonds, however, which allows ample metabolic flexibility for proteins in chemical reactions.

Nucleic Acids

As Friedrich Miescher noted over a century ago, nucleic acids are unusual biological compounds for several reasons, including their high phosphorus content. We study nucleic acids today because of their fundamental importance in the genetic apparatus and their participation in protein synthesis and in reactions involving energy exchange during metabolism. We must have an appreciation of the basic features of nucleic acid molecules in order to deal knowledgeably with those cellular properties and activities that involve these molecules.

2.15
Nucleotides

A mononucleotide is made up of one nitrogenous organic base, one pentose sugar, and a phosphate residue (Fig. 2.33). Mononucleotides

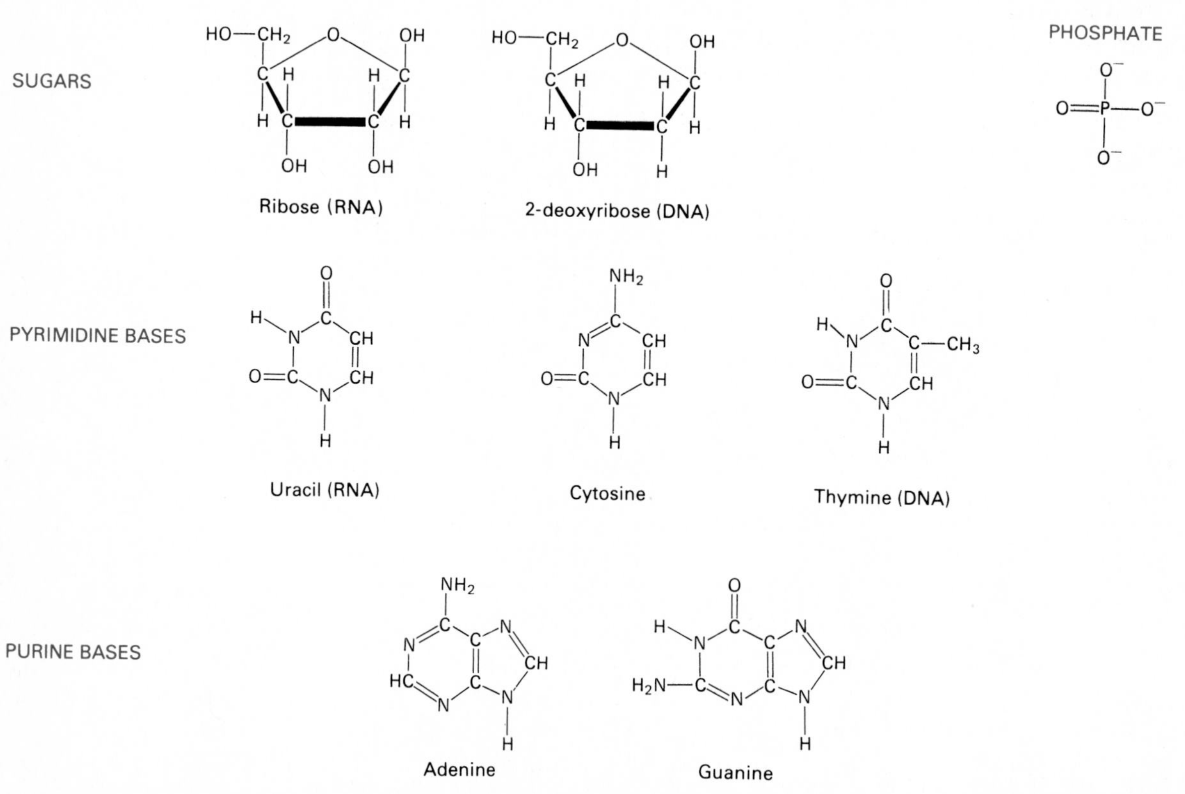

FIGURE 2-33
The building blocks of nucleic acid molecules are nucleotides, which consist of a phosphate group, a pentose sugar, and a nitrogenous purine or pyrimidine base. The sugar residue in DNA is 2-deoxyribose; in RNA it is ribose. Four kinds of bases are present in a DNA or RNA molecule, two kinds of purines and two kinds of pyrimidines. The purines adenine and guanine occur in both DNA and RNA, as does the pyrimidine cytosine. The second kind of pyrimidine is thymine in DNA but uracil in RNA.

SUGARS

Ribose (RNA)   2-deoxyribose (DNA)   PHOSPHATE

PYRIMIDINE BASES

Uracil (RNA)   Cytosine   Thymine (DNA)

PURINE BASES

Adenine   Guanine

TABLE 2-3
Constituent Units of Nucleic Acids

Base	Nucleoside	Nucleotide	Nucleic Acid
Purines:			
Adenine	Adenosine	Adenylic acid	RNA
	Deoxyadenosine	Deoxyadenylic acid	DNA
Guanine	Guanosine	Guanylic acid	RNA
	Deoxyguanosine	Deoxyguanylic acid	DNA
Pyrimidines:			
Cytosine	Cytidine	Cytidylic acid	RNA
	Deoxycytidine	Deoxycytidylic acid	DNA
Thymine	Thymidine	Thymidylic acid	DNA
Uracil	Uridine	Uridylic acid	RNA

participate in at least two major cellular functions: (1) they are monomers for the construction of DNA and RNA polymers, and (2) they are agents for energy transfer in many metabolic reactions.

The combination of a sugar and base, without the phosphate residue, is a nucleoside. Nucleotides are therefore called nucleoside phosphates. More specifically we may refer to nucleoside mono-, di-, or triphosphate when the molecule includes one, two, or three phosphate groups, respectively.

The nitrogenous bases commonly found in nucleic acids and their nucleotide building blocks are derivatives of the heterocyclic compounds purine and pyrimidine. Both DNA and RNA contain the purines adenine and guanine, and the pyrimidine derivative cytosine. The second kind of pyrimidine in DNA is thymine, whereas its demethylated form, uracil, is present in RNA. Because a unique pyrimidine distinguishes DNA from RNA, it is convenient to study nucleic acid synthesis and activity using isotopically labeled precursors containing one or the other of these two bases. Either of the nucleosides thymidine or uridine, or its nucleotide form, is usually provided to the biological system under study (Table 2.3).

The pentose sugar in nucleosides is either **D-ribose** (ribonucleosides) or **2-deoxy-D-ribose** (deoxyribonucleosides). The presence of a hydroxyl group at carbon atom-2 of D-ribose in RNA, but a hydrogen at carbon-2 of 2-deoxy-D-ribose in DNA, is partly responsible for profound differences in stability, pairing potential, and function of DNA and RNA.

Polynucleotides of both the DNA and the RNA variety are built from mononucleotides that are linked covalently by **phosphodiester bridges**. These bridges extend between the 3′ position of one sugar unit and the 5′ position of the next sugar unit in the chain (Fig. 2.34). There is no restriction in either DNA or RNA on the *vertical* sequence of adjacent mononucleotides linked by these 3′,5′-phosphodiester bridges. A considerable variety of molecules is therefore possible even though only four kinds of mononucleotide occur in ribonucleic acid (containing the bases A, G, C, and U) and in deoxyribonucleic acid (containing the bases A, G, C, and T). The theoretical variety is calculated as 4^n, where 4 is the number of different kinds of nucleotides and n is the number of monomers in the polymer. For a molecule made up of only 75

FIGURE 2-34
Region of a nucleic acid chain showing the phosphodiester link between carbon-3 of one sugar and carbon-5 of the adjacent sugar residue in a polynucleotide. The same 3',5'-phosphodiester linkage connects all the nucleotides in a single chain of DNA or RNA. The nitrogenous base of the nucleotide unit is bonded to carbon-1 of the sugar.

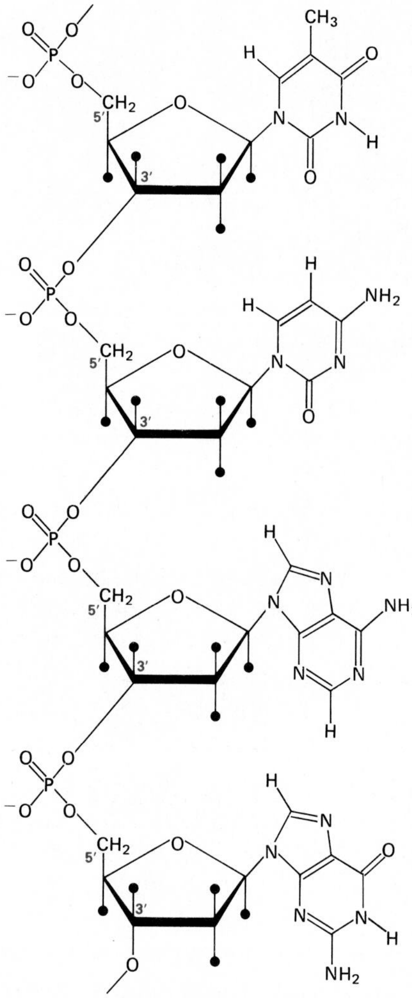

monomeric units, as in some of the smallest RNAs, there may be 4^{75} different arrangements of the constituent units. Each arrangement theoretically constitutes a molecule of different specificity. Where an average gene may include about 500 nucleotides in a DNA sequence, 4^{500} different sequences are theoretically possible and, therefore, 4^{500} different and specific genes. Despite the apparently meager number of monomer types, an astronomically large number of possible genes can be constructed. Such variety of genetic material can easily account for all past and present life forms and still provide infinite variation for future evolutionary change.

2.16
The Double Helix

DNA molecules usually have regular helical configurations because most DNA molecules consist of two *complementary* polynucleotide strands. The two strands are held together by hydrogen bonds between each complementary pair of purine and pyrimidine (Fig. 2.35). Adenine binds with thymine, and guanine binds with cytosine. This repeated hydrogen bonding within the double helix and bonding between virtually all the surface atoms in the sugar and phosphate groups with water molecules serve to stabilize the structure.

Because purine–pyrimidine pairs are found in the center of the molecule, their flat surfaces can stack on top of each other and thereby limit their contact with water. A regular structure is possible in a double helix because the complementary base pairs are exactly the same size. A regular backbone structure is impossible for single chains because pyrimidines are smaller than purines, which would cause the angle of helical rotation to vary with the sequence of bases.

DNA double-helix molecules are very stable at physiological temperatures because (1) disruption of the double helix breaks hydrogen bonds and brings hydrophobic purines and pyrimidines into contact with water, which is energetically unsatisfactory; and (2) many weak bonds occur within the DNA molecule, arranged so that most of them cannot break without many others breaking at the same time. Even though some hydrogen bonds may be broken by thermal motion, hydrogen bonds in the rest of the molecule remain intact and the molecule does not fall apart. In fact, when held together by more than 10 nucleotide pairs, the duplex is quite stable at room (or cellular) temperature. The cooperative result of a number of weak bonds is stability of molecular shape, in proteins as well as nucleic acids. At abnormally high temperatures weak chemical bonds break more frequently, and stability decreases as temperatures rise above physiological levels. Once a significant number of weak bonds has been broken, a protein or nucleic acid molecule usually loses its original form (in the process of denaturation) and changes to an inactive, or denatured, form.

FIGURE 2-35
Region of a duplex DNA molecule showing hydrogen bonding (dotted lines) between complementary purine and pyrimidine bases of the two polynucleotide chains. Adenine and thymine are joined by two hydrogen bonds, whereas guanine and cytosine are held together by three hydrogen bonds. The two chains of a duplex DNA molecule are antiparallel in orientation, as indicated by the arrow alongside each chain and by the relative positions of the constituents in each chain.

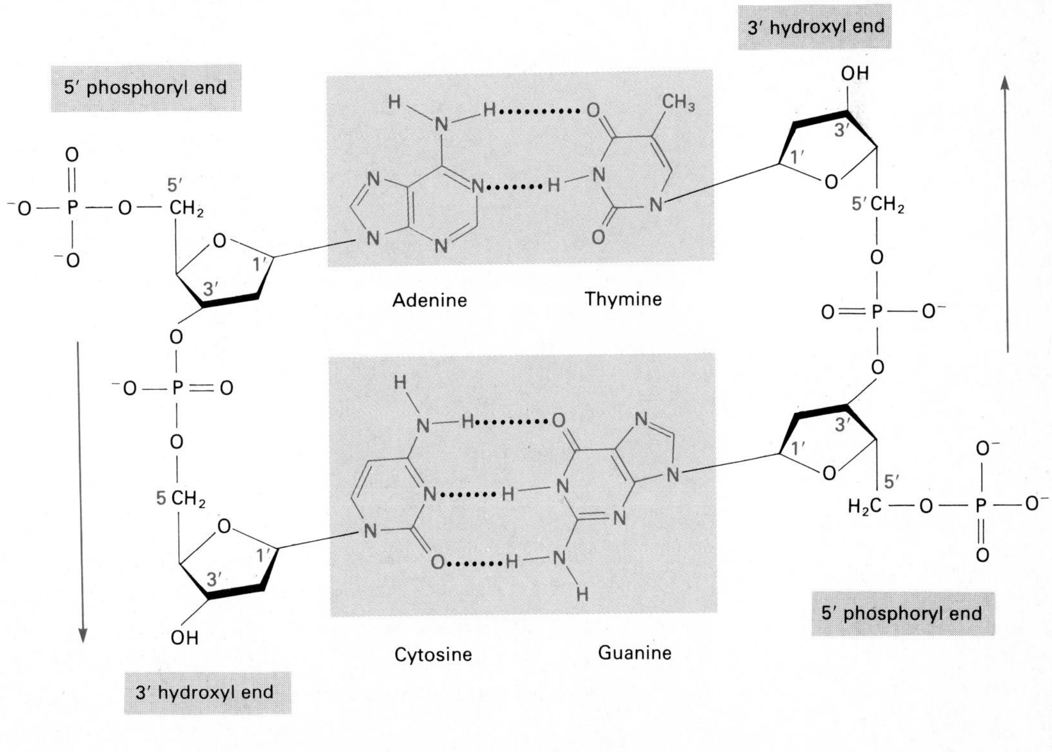

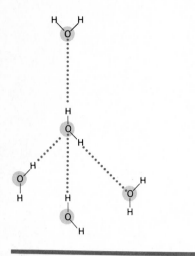

FIGURE 2-36
Because hydrogen bonds (dotted lines) between oxygen atoms in water molecules are directed tetrahedrally, each water molecule tends to have four nearest neighbors. Nearest neighbors change continually in liquid water because of the energy of thermal motion, but water molecules at any given instant are held together nevertheless by four hydrogen bonds. Very few water molecules ionize to produce H^+ and OH^-.

Water

Life depends on water. Cells usually consist of 60% to 95% water, and even dormant seeds and spores contain from 10% to 30% water. Water has a number of important properties which make it distinctive and uniquely suitable as the medium of cellular activities.

2.17
Properties of Water

Water molecules exist as polar H—O—H units, whose shared electrons are closer to the oxygen than to the hydrogen nuclei. Furthermore, water molecules are **dipoles**; there is a net positive charge at the end of the molecule carrying the two hydrogens and a net negative charge at the oxygen end of the molecule.

Under physiological conditions, very few water molecules ionize to form H^+ and OH^- ions. Instead, the hydrogen and oxygen atoms of the polar water molecules form strong hydrogen bonds. These bonds are directed tetrahedrally, so that each water molecule tends to have four nearest neighbors (Fig. 2.36). The arrangement of molecules is fixed in ice, because the bonds between neighbors are very rigid. In the liquid state, between 0 and 100°C, there is enough energy of thermal motion to break hydrogen bonds, which allows continual change of nearest neighbors. At any given instant, however, water molecules are held by four strong hydrogen bonds, even in the liquid state.

Water will dissolve an appreciable quantity of almost any molecule that carries a net electrical charge or that has polar (especially dipole) groups. Any part of a molecule with an asymmetrically distributed electron cloud, or a permanent dipole such as O—H, is likely to be soluble in water because of attractive forces between it and the permanently dipolar water molecules. Hydrogen bonds or other non-covalent bonds usually form between the water molecules in the **solvent** phase and the **solute** molecules that are added to the water. The relative degree of solubility depends on how many water–water bonds can be disrupted when solute–water bonds replace them. Water–water bonds are usually more energetically favorable (that is, at a lower energy state) than solute–water bonds, so many compounds have only limited solubility in water. Compounds that readily form bonds with water molecules are hydrophilic. Hydrophobic compounds cannot readily form hydrogen bonds with water and are, therefore, poorly soluble in that medium.

When a nonpolar molecule, such as benzene, is mixed with water, there is a rapid separation of the water and benzene molecules. The water molecules form hydrogen bonds among themselves, while the benzene molecules bind to each other by hydrophobic interactions or by other relatively weak forces. The hydrophobic molecules are effectively separated in space from the water molecules. Each compound exists in its own space and does not mingle with the other.

If some electrically charged group, such as a phosphate residue, is added to a hydrophobic molecule, that molecule becomes more readily soluble in water. The increased solubility is due to a greater capacity for the formation of hydrogen bonds and other weak bonds between the electrically charged residue and the dipolar water molecules. Because water molecules are dipolar, either or both of their charged regions can undergo bonding, depending on the particular charge(s) of the solute molecules. In this same way, it is clear that water is an excellent solvent for electrically charged ions, or for charged inorganic molecules even when these are in the crystalline state.

2.18
The pH Scale

Water can enhance the dissociation of substances such as weak acids or bases that already exist in partially dissociated or ionized form. In addition, water itself can undergo slight dissociation to ionized components. Although conventionally expressed as $H_2O \rightleftarrows H^+ + OH^-$, naked protons (nuclei of hydrogen atoms, or hydrogen ions) do not occur among the small number of ionized components of water. Instead, water dissociates into H_3O^+ (hydronium ions) and OH^- ions. For practical purposes, however, this can be ignored, and H^+ and OH^- ions are usually referred to as **dissociation products of water**.

Dissociation of water is an equilibrium process and, at constant temperature, can be expressed by

$$K_{eq} = \frac{[H^+][OH^-]}{[H_2O]}$$

where K_{eq} is the equilibrium constant, and the concentrations of water molecules and their ionized components are expressed in moles per liter (signified by enclosure in brackets [ ]). The molar concentration (M) of water in pure water is 55.5 M (number of grams of water in a liter divided by gram molecular weight of water, or 1000/18), and H^+ and OH^- ion concentrations in pure water are very low ($1 \times 10^{-7} M$ at 25°C). Hence, we can simplify the equilibrium constant to $55.5 \times K_{eq} = [H^+][OH^-]$. The term $55.5 \times K_{eq}$ is called the **ion product of water** or the constant K_w.

$$K_w = [H^+][OH^-]$$

K_w is the basis for the **pH scale**, which is a means of designating the actual concentration of H^+ ions (and thus of OH^- ions as well) in any aqueous solution in the biologically significant acidity range between 1.0 M H^+ and 1.0 M OH^- (Table 2.4). The term **pH** is defined as

$$pH = -\log_{10}[H^+]$$

It is convenient to use a logarithmic scale for pH values because of the wide variations in H^+ ion concentrations. The negative logarithm to the base 10 is used so that a positive scale of readings can be obtained. In a precisely neutral solution at 25°C, $[H^+] = [OH^-] = 1 \times 10^{-7} M$, and the pH of such a solution is

$$pH = -\log_{10}[H^+] = -\log_{10}(10^{-7}) = 7.0$$

TABLE 2-4
The pH Scale and the Molar Concentrations of H^+ and OH^- Ions

H^+ ions (M)	pH	OH^- ions (M)
1.0	0	10^{-14}
0.1	1	10^{-13}
0.01	2	10^{-12}
0.001	3	10^{-11}
0.0001	4	10^{-10}
10^{-5}	5	10^{-9}
10^{-6}	6	10^{-8}
10^{-7}	7	10^{-7}
10^{-8}	8	10^{-6}
10^{-9}	9	10^{-5}
10^{-10}	10	0.0001
10^{-11}	11	0.001
10^{-12}	12	0.01
10^{-13}	13	0.1
10^{-14}	14	1.0

The value of pH 7.0 for a neutral solution is thus derived from the ion product of water at 25°C and not from some arbitrary standard. In an acidic solution the pH is less than 7.0 because the H^+ ion concentration is high, whereas in an alkaline solution the pH is more than 7.0 because the solution has a low H^+ ion concentration.

Because the pH scale is logarithmic, there is a 10-fold difference between one pH unit and the next, a 100 times difference in H^+ ion concentration between any two whole pH units, a 1000 times difference in H^+ ion concentration for a span of three pH units, and so forth. Measurements of H^+ ion concentration are made rapidly and routinely by using a pH meter.

Cellular activities are extremely sensitive to slight changes in internal pH, primarily because *enzyme activity* is affected by H^+ ion concentration. An enzyme is maximally active at a characteristic pH called the **optimum pH**, and its activity declines sharply above and below this optimum value. The striking effects of pH on enzyme activity reflect electrical changes at the surface of an enzyme molecule. Such changes lead to a modified shape of the enzyme molecule, and to reduced enzyme activity at inappropriate pH values.

Variations in fractions of a pH unit may be damaging or even lethal to some cells. These fluctuations in pH are modulated by the powerful *buffering action* of coupled H^+ ion donors (acids) and H^+ ion acceptors (bases) that are present in intracellular and extracellular fluids of living organisms. Buffered systems tend to resist changes in pH on the addition of H^+ and OH^- ions. The principal buffering system in blood plasma of vertebrate species is the donor–acceptor pair H_2CO_3—HCO_3^-. The pH of human blood plasma is closely regulated to about pH 7.40. Irreparable damage may occur if plasma pH falls below 7.0 or rises higher than 7.8. The difference between pH 7.4 and 7.8 in blood reflects a change in H^+ ion concentration of only 3×10^{-8} M. The small magnitude of this change emphasizes the importance of pH-regulating mechanisms as precise modulators of acidity and alkalinity of cellular fluids.

Summary

Organic chemistry focuses on the chemistry of carbon atoms, which interact with each other and with a number of other elements by means of strong covalent chemical bonds and weaker hydrogen bonds, ionic bonds, van der Waals bonds, and by hydrophobic interactions, to form molecular building blocks for cellular structure, function, and regulation. The chemistry of carbon is central to biological processes. The ability of a carbon atom to bond covalently to four other substituents makes organic molecules versatile. The most common substituents are atoms of carbon, hydrogen, oxygen, nitrogen, phosphorus, and sulfur, but metals and some other elements may also be involved. Organic compounds with apparently identical structures are nevertheless distinguishable by biological systems as stereoisomers because of another property of carbon—its asymmetry when bonded to four different substituents in a tetrahedral array.

Organic molecules of biological importance belong to four major classes: carbohydrates, lipids, proteins, and nucleic acids. Except for lipids, organic compounds may exist as polymers of one or more kinds of monomeric units: monosaccharide units for polysaccharide carbohydrates, amino acids for polypeptide or protein polymers, and nucleotides for the nucleic acids DNA and RNA. Lipids also form large aggregates, but the forces holding these aggregates together are hydrophobic interactions rather than covalent chemical bonds.

Carbohydrates have the structural formula CH_2O_n. They are commonly formed of monosaccharides—chains of carbon atoms between three and seven units long. Each of these carbons is covalently bonded to an oxygen atom through a carbonyl group ($C{=}O$) or an alcohol group (—OH). Pentose (five-carbon) and hexose (six-carbon) monosaccharides may assume numerous stereoisomeric alternatives, and the number doubles because of the tendency of these molecules to form ring structures in solution, introducing a new site of asymmetry. Monosaccharides may be covalently joined via glycosidic bonds to form oligosaccharides (two to eight or nine units in length) and polysaccharides (hundreds or thousands of monomers long). Polysaccharides function as food-storage molecules, particularly starch and glycogen, and as structural elements such as cellulose and chitin.

Lipids have in common a hydrophobic tendency—they are nonpolar and insoluble in water. They are structurally quite diverse. Fatty acids are saturated or unsaturated unbranched chains of hydrocarbons terminating in a carboxyl group (COO^-). Neutral fats (glycerides) are produced when one, two, or all three of the hydroxyl groups of glycerol are esterified to the carboxyls of fatty acids. These fats are a storage form of foods, and they represent a concentrated store of energy. Depending on the degree of saturation of the fatty acids, the fat may be solid or liquid (oil) at room temperature. Phospholipids, which are important in membrane structure, are diglycerides with a phosphoric acid derivative bonded to the third hydroxyl of the glycerol component; they are thus amphipathic, having both hydrophilic (phosphoric acid) and hydrophobic (fatty acids) regions in the same molecule. Other amphipathic lipids include sphingolipids and glycolipids, found chiefly in the membranes of the nervous system. Steroids and terpenes are chemically unrelated to other types of lipids but share their nonpolarity and aversion to water.

Proteins serve as structural, functional, and regulatory components of the cell. They are composed of a linear, unbranched combination of any or all of 20 kinds of amino acids, linked together by peptide bonds. Each kind of amino acid has an asymmetric α-carbon atom to which is bonded an amino group, a carboxyl group, a hydrogen, and a unique side-chain. The nature of the side chains determine to a great extent the properties of the protein molecule. A typical protein may contain up to 1000 amino acid units; the number of units, their composition, and their sequence in the polypeptide chains uniquely define the primary structure of the protein molecule. Interactions between neighboring amino acids determine secondary structure, and interactions between side chains of distant amino acids determine tertiary structure. These features underlie the precise three-dimensional folding of a polypeptide chain. Where a protein consists of more than one polypeptide chain, the association between chains (subunits) is referred to as quaternary structure. Structural proteins tend to have a regular repeating conformation, such as the α helix or β sheet, whereas regulatory proteins tend to assume a more globular conformation with areas of random coil interspersed among more regular regions.

Nucleic acids are built up as linear arrays of nucleotide monomers. Each nucleotide consists of a phosphate group, a pentose sugar, and one of a group of nitrogenous, heterocyclic bases. The bases are purines (adenine and guanine) or pyrimidines (cytosine, thymine, and uracil). In RNA the pentose sugar is D-ribose and the pyrimidine bases are cytosine and uracil, whereas in DNA the sugar is 2-deoxy-D-ribose and thymine replaces uracil. In a nucleic acid, nucleotides of the appropriate series are linked together by covalent phosphodiester bridges between the successive sugars. There is no chemical restriction on the sequence of nucleotides, but the sequence is specified genetically and it in turn specifies the sequence of proteins. The DNA double-helical molecule consists of two polynucleotide strands held together by hydrogen bonding between complementary bases—adenine in one strand bonds with thymine in the other, and cytosine bonds with guanine. The additive effect of the large number of weak chemical bonds between complementary strands makes duplex DNA a very stable molecule under physiological conditions.

All cellular processes take place in aqueous solution, and it is essential to understand the properties of water in order to understand biological processes. Water molecules are dipoles, the negatively charged oxygen and the positively charged hydrogens being positioned at opposite ends of each molecule. They thus attract other water molecules as well as other negatively charged or positively charged molecules. The solubility of such molecules in water brands them as hydrophilic, by contrast to nonpolar, hydrophobic molecules. Only a small fraction of the water actually dissociates into H^+ and OH^- ions in an equilibrium process. The ion product of water, or the constant K_w, is the basis for the pH scale that designates the actual H^+ concentration of any aqueous solution in the biologically significant acidity range between pH 0 (1.0 M H$^+$, 10^{-14} M OH$^-$) and pH 14 (10^{-14} M H$^+$, 1.0 M OH$^-$). Cellular activities are very sensitive to H$^+$ concentration, and enzyme activity in particular may decline or cease when the pH is not optimal for the catalyst's function.

Readings and References

Albersheim, P. April 1975. The walls of growing plant cells. *Sci. Amer.* **232**:80.

Dickerson, R. E., and I. Geis. 1969. *The Structure and Action of Proteins.* Menlo Park, Calif.: Benjamin-Cummings.

Doolittle, R. F. December 1981. Fibrinogen and fibrin. *Sci. Amer.* **245**:126.

DuPraw, E. J. 1972. *The Biosciences: Cell and Molecular Biology.* Stanford: Cell and Molecular Biology Council.

Lambert, J. B. January 1970. The shapes of organic molecules. *Sci. Amer.* **222**:58.

Lehninger, A. L. 1982. *Principles of Biochemistry.* New York: Worth.

Morell, P., and W. T. Norton. May 1980. Myelin. *Sci. Amer.* **242**:88.

Pauling, L., R. B. Corey, and H. R. Branson. 1951. The structure of proteins: Two hydrogen-bonded helical configurations of the polypeptide chain. *Proc. Natl. Acad. Sci. U. S.* **37**:729.

Pauling, L., R. B. Corey, and R. Hayward. July 1954. The structure of protein molecules. *Sci. Amer.* **191**:51.

Perutz, M. F. December 1978. Hemoglobin structure and respiratory transport. *Sci. Amer.* **239**:92.

Perutz, M. F. December 1978. Electrostatic effects in proteins. *Science* **201**:1187.

Sanger, F., and E. O. P. Thompson. 1953. The amino acid sequence in the glycyl chain of insulin. *Biochem. J.* **53**:353.

Scholander, P. F. 1972. Tensile water. *Amer. Sci.* **60**:584.

Sharon, N. May 1974. Glycoproteins. *Sci. Amer.* **230**:78.

Sharon, N. November 1980. Carbohydrates. *Sci. Amer.* **24**:90.

Stryer, L. 1981. *Biochemistry.* 2nd ed. San Francisco: Freeman.

Watson, J. D., and F. H. C. Crick. 1953. Molecular structure of nucleic acids. A structure for deoxyribose nucleic acid. *Nature* **171**:737.

Zubay, G. 1983. *Biochemistry.* Reading, Mass.: Addison-Wesley.

CHAPTER 3

Energy and Enzymes

Cellular chemistry, or **metabolism**, differs in several ways from the chemistry of the nonliving world. To see how metabolism operates, we need basic information concerning (1) the *nature of energy* needed to do work in the mild environment within the cell, (2) the coordinated systems responsible for *energy transfer* between energy-consuming and energy-requiring reactions, and (3) the *catalysts* that influence reaction rates and direct the ebb and flow of metabolism. We can then examine a metabolic pathway to illustrate how these cellular features interact.

Bioenergetics

Energy is broadly defined as the capacity to do work. Energy may exist in different forms and do different kinds of work. For example, the thermal energy of steam can be transformed into mechanical energy by a steam engine, and the mechanical energy thus produced can be used to perform mechanical work. The application, movement, and transformation of energy ultimately underlie all physical and chemical processes. The area of physical science that deals with exchanges of energy in collections of matter is called **thermodynamics**, a term based on early studies in which heat was the focus of measurement. The equivalent term applied more specifically to the study of energy transformations in living systems is **bioenergetics**.

3.1
Free Energy

In thermodynamic and bioenergetic studies we distinguish between the *system*, or collection of matter, and the *surroundings*, or all other matter in the universe apart from the system under study. We can measure the total energy content of a system in its *initial state*, before the reaction begins, and in its *final state* of equilibrium at the conclusion of the reaction. It is much simpler, however, to measure the amount of energy that has been exchanged between the system and its surroundings during the reaction. This amount represents the difference (Δ) in energy content between the initial reactants and the end products of the reaction. The only significant form of useful energy in biological systems is **free energy**, or Gibbs free energy, designated as G. Free energy can be used to do work in living systems. Although heat energy is released during many biological reactions, it cannot be used to perform useful work in the cell. Heat can do work only if it acts through a temperature differential from warmer to cooler, and living cells have little or no temperature differential between their parts. We usually regard heat as energy wasted or lost from a biological system, because it is not useful for cellular work.

We can measure the energy difference between initial reactants and end products of a reaction in the laboratory by recording the kilocalories of heat released to the surroundings as one mole of a substance is burned completely in air. For example, 686 kcal of heat are released when a mole of glucose is burned (oxidized) in air to its end products CO_2 and H_2O. We expect that the same energy difference will characterize the oxidation of glucose to CO_2 and H_2O in the cell, but that only some of the energy will be lost as heat and the rest retained as free energy within the cell. From various calculations, we know that 411 kcal are lost as heat and 275 kcal are retained in the cell as free energy. We thus state that $\Delta G = -411$ kcal/mole of glucose. Reactions in which energy is released, or **exergonic** reactions, are signified by a negative ΔG value ($-\Delta G$). An **endergonic** reaction, however, requires energy to be added to the system; it is signified by a positive ΔG value ($+\Delta G$). In the case of glucose synthesis from $CO_2 + H_2O$ in a cell, the change in free energy is $\Delta G = 411$ kcal/mole, because the same amount of energy is involved in making or degrading the same molecule. Cells are obviously not totally efficient in conserving all the free energy of a molecule during its degradation in metabolism. The process of glucose oxidation to CO_2 and H_2O in the cell is only 40% efficient, because only 275 kcal of the possible 686 kcal/mole are not dissipated as heat ($275/686 \times 100 = 40\%$).

3.2
Change in Free Energy

The First Law of Thermodynamics states the principle of the conservation of energy in the universe (system + surroundings): *energy can be neither created nor destroyed*. Energy can be transformed, however, without violating the First Law because the energy content of the universe remains unchanged. We usually deal only with changes in free energy in biological systems, but we assume that there is a compensating change in the surroundings such that the First Law is satisfied.

The Second Law of Thermodynamics tells us that *all systems tend toward an equilibrium state*; that is, all systems tend to minimize their free-energy content. When this minimum is reached, the system is in equilibrium; that is, $\Delta G = 0$. A reaction can proceed in a specific direction only when energy is exchanged—when $\Delta G > 0$ or $\Delta G < 0$. Energy-requiring endergonic reactions run "uphill" (against the natural tendency to minimize free-energy content), whereas exergonic reactions run "downhill" (toward their states of minimum free energy). Endergonic reactions require the addition of energy to the system if they are to proceed, whereas exergonic reactions release energy from a system to the surroundings or to another system that is part of the surroundings. The thermodynamic laws permit us to make predictions about the energetics and direction of a reaction, but not about its rate. Catalysts are the primary factors that determine reaction rates, as we shall soon see.

The *actual* free-energy change of a reaction, ΔG, varies from one time to another in living cells. Differences in reagent concentrations, temperature, pH, and other factors all have some influence on the specific ΔG for a particular reaction. For the sake of consistency in characterizing reactions and in making meaningful predictions concerning reactions, we routinely use the thermodynamic constant $\Delta G°$, called the **standard free-energy change**. Measurement of $\Delta G°$ is made under standard conditions of temperature (25°C), pressure (1 atmosphere), and concentration (1.0 M) of reactants and products. In biological reactions it is also necessary to standardize the pH (7.0). Living cells rarely if ever exist at any moment under these standard conditions, but we more or less pretend they do anyway.

The simplest way to measure $\Delta G°$ for a reaction is to calculate the equilibrium constant, K_{eq}, which is equal to the ratio of the molar concentration of the final product(s) to the molar concentration of the initial reactant(s) at equilibrium:

$$K_{eq} = \frac{[\text{final product at equilibrium}]}{[\text{initial reactant at equilibrium}]}$$

At equilibrium there is no further change in free energy because $\Delta G = 0$, or

$$\Delta G = \Delta G° + RT \ln K_{eq}$$

where R is the gas constant (1.987 cal/mole·degree), T is the absolute temperature in kelvins, $\ln K_{eq}$ is the natural logarithm of the equilibrium constant, and $\Delta G°$ is the standard free-energy change. The relationship of K_{eq} to $\Delta G°$ is shown by

$$\Delta G° = -RT \ln K_{eq}$$

Once K_{eq} has been analytically determined, the standard free-energy change of a reaction can be calculated. The relationship between the two sets of values is shown in Table 3.1. The equilibrium constant and the standard free-energy change provide information concerning the energetics of a reaction. When $K_{eq} > 1$ ($\Delta G°$ is negative), we know that the reaction was exergonic and we know the amount of the decrease in free energy under standard conditions. When $K_{eq} < 1$ ($\Delta G°$ is positive), we know that energy was added to the system and we know the amount of free-energy increase at the end of the reaction. The higher the K_{eq} value,

TABLE 3-1
Relationship Between the Equilibrium Constant and the Standard Free-Energy Change at 25°C and pH 7.0

K_{eq}	$\Delta G°$ (kcal/mole)
0.001	+4.09
0.01	+2.73
0.1	+1.36
1.0	0
10.0	−1.36
100.0	−2.73
1000.0	−4.09

the greater the decrease in free energy of the system and the greater the speed of progress toward equilibrium.

These points can be illustrated by the following example. During sugar oxidation in the cell, glucose 1-phosphate is converted to glucose 6-phosphate in the presence of a specific enzyme. If we add this enzyme to a solution of 0.020 M glucose 1-phosphate at pH 7 and 25°C (298 K), we can determine the concentrations of the initial reactant and the final reaction product at equilibrium. Suppose we find that glucose 1-phosphate has decreased to 0.001 M and that glucose 6-phosphate has increased from zero to 0.019 M. The equilibrium constant is

$$K_{eq} = \frac{[\text{glucose 6-phosphate}]}{[\text{glucose 1-phosphate}]} = \frac{0.019}{0.001} = 19$$

and the standard free-energy change can be calculated as follows:*

$$\begin{aligned} \Delta G° &= -RT \ln K_{eq} \\ &= -1.987 \times 298 \times \ln 19 \\ &= -1.987 \times 298 \times 2.303 \times \log_{10} 19 \\ &= -1363 \times 1.28 \\ \Delta G° &= -1745 \text{ cal/mole, or } -1.745 \text{ kcal/mole} \end{aligned}$$

From the positive K_{eq} we know that the reaction is energy-releasing. From the standard free-energy change we know the difference in free energy between the compounds in this exergonic reaction. After a reasonable number of repeat experiments, the specific thermodynamic constants can thereafter be used to characterize this particular reaction. In addition, from a large body of data derived from many such analyses we can make generalizations about chemical reactions in metabolism.

3.3
Open Systems and Steady States

Classical thermodynamics is concerned with **closed systems**, which do not exchange matter with the surroundings. In living cells, however, we find **open systems** that do exchange both matter and energy with the surroundings. Furthermore, living cells exist in different **steady states**, in which the rate of input equals the rate of output at each given moment, but a different pair of input–output rates may lead to a different steady state from moment to moment. Because cells exist in a state of constant flux, they do not usually achieve thermodynamic equilibrium where $\Delta G = 0$. A nonequilibrium open system that exists in different steady states has two significant features:

1. An open system can perform work precisely because it does not attain equilibrium; equilibrium is a state of no work.

2. Systems that are not at equilibrium can be subject to control and regulation of their activities.

---

* It is often convenient to change from base e natural logarithms (ln) to base 10 logarithms (log or $\log_{10}$) in working with equations. The conversion is 2.303 log x = ln x.

The flexibility and variety of living systems are due in large measure to these thermodynamic characteristics. In addition to the two features stated above, we should note that cells proceed toward minimal free-energy levels more slowly than closed systems. The open system existing in different steady states moves more slowly toward the disorderly state sometimes called *entropic doom*. The total universe moves inexorably from greater to lesser orderliness (to greater randomness). Cells, on the other hand, maintain internal order at the expense of their surroundings, which become thermodynamically more disorderly. Once the cell dies, its progress toward greater disorder proceeds rapidly. The Second Law is in effect at all times, but its outcome is minimized by the maintenance of steady states in living cells.

Energy Transfer in Coupled Metabolic Reactions

Metabolism consists of energy-releasing and energy-requiring reactions. Energy must be provided for endergonic reactions, which are otherwise thermodynamically unfavorable. Similarly, "downhill" reactions of food breakdown in cells must be exploited in such a way that the released energy can be applied toward work of different kinds. Living systems manage these problems through the device of *coupled* metabolic reactions. In this way, energy released during food breakdown can be tapped to drive energy-requiring biosynthesis reactions. Coupled exergonic–endergonic reaction systems predominate in the living world, but they are quite rare in the nonliving world. The energy obtained during breakdown reactions (**catabolism**) must be free energy, stored as chemical energy for immediate or future use in cellular work, including biosyntheses (**anabolism**). Cellular efficiency is based in large measure on the ability to retain and use energy that might otherwise be wasted as unusable heat.

In biological systems, energy transfer is mediated by substances that can donate or accept chemical-bond energy or electrons. The existence of several energy-transfer mechanisms and of various energy-transferring agents all combine to make living systems more flexible in responding to changes inside and outside the cell. Two major mechanisms for energy transfer exist in cells: phosphoryl group transfer and electron transfer. The general or particular chemical agents that mediate energy transfers will be described in each case.

3.4
Phosphoryl Group Transfer and ATP

When ATP (adenosine triphosphate) is hydrolyzed, the terminal *phosphoryl group*

$$-\overset{\displaystyle O^-}{\underset{\displaystyle O^-}{P}}\!\!=\!\!O, \text{ or } -PO_3{}^{2-}$$

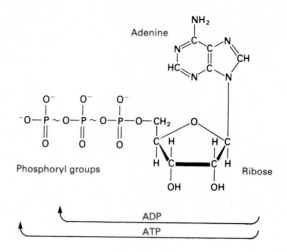

72   CHAPTER 3 / Energy and Enzymes

FIGURE 3-1
The nucleoside adenosine (adenine—ribose) may be linked to one, two, or three phosphoryl groups. Phosphoryl group transfer in cells is usually accomplished in reactions coupled to the hydrolysis of ATP to form ADP ($\Delta G° = -7.3$ kcal/mole) or to the phosphorylation of ADP to produce ATP ($\Delta G° = 7.3$ kcal/mole).

is removed, and ADP (adenosine diphosphate) is formed (Fig. 3.1). The free-energy difference or $\Delta G°$ of the reaction is about -7.3 kcal/mole. Conversely, when a phosphoryl group is added onto ADP in a **phosphorylation** reaction producing ATP, about 7.3 kcal more free energy are present per mole of ATP than of ADP; that is, $\Delta G° = +7.3$ kcal/mole. If ATP hydrolysis is coupled to energy-requiring work, such as biosynthesis or movement, 7.3 kcal of free energy is available to sponsor this work for every mole of ATP hydrolyzed to lower-energy ADP.

Energy transfer is accomplished as the terminal phosphoryl group is transferred from ATP to some molecule, which in turn becomes phosphorylated and therefore exists at a higher energy level than before the transfer. These phosphorylated molecules can then engage in reactions or other work because they now have a higher free-energy level and can proceed in a thermodynamically favorable "downhill" direction. Such phosphorylated metabolites are *intermediates* in reaction sequences. Each step in the sequence takes place under energetically favorable conditions because some molecule is temporarily raised to a high enough energy level to take part in the next reaction step. As it participates in the next reaction, the molecule is dephosphorylated. In some cases, dephosphorylation is coupled to ATP synthesis from ADP, thus regenerating ATP for other rounds of work in the cell.

In effect we have said that ATP acts as a *common intermediate* in biological energy transfer. The ATP–ADP cycle acts as a link between energy-releasing and energy-requiring reactions through the mechanism of **phosphoryl group transfer**. For example, consider two reactions in which ADP and ATP interact with compounds X and Y and their phosphorylated forms X—P and Y—P (P signifies a phosphoryl group here).

$$X—P + ADP \longrightarrow X + ATP; \quad \Delta G° = -5 \text{ kcal/mole} \tag{3.1}$$

and

$$Y + ATP \longrightarrow Y—P + ADP; \quad \Delta G° = -1 \text{ kcal/mole} \tag{3.2}$$

In each case we are really summing up a pair of reactions.

X—P $\longrightarrow$ X + P	$\Delta G° = -12$ kcal/mole
ADP + P $\longrightarrow$ ATP	$\Delta G° = +\ 7$ kcal/mole
X—P + ADP $\longrightarrow$ X + ATP	$\Delta G° = -\ 5$ kcal/mole

[3.3]

and

ATP $\longrightarrow$ ADP + P	$\Delta G° = -7$ kcal/mole
Y $\longrightarrow$ Y—P	$\Delta G° = +6$ kcal/mole
Y + ATP $\longrightarrow$ Y—P + ADP	$\Delta G° = -1$ kcal/mole

[3.4]

In reaction [3.3] dephosphorylation of X—P is *coupled* to formation of ATP by phosphorylation of ADP. In reaction [3.4] formation of Y—P is coupled to dephosphorylation of ATP, with transfer of this phosphoryl group from ATP to Y, making Y—P (and leaving ADP as the other product). Each pair of coupled reactions is thermodynamically favorable because an energetically unfavorable reaction (such as Y $\rightarrow$ Y—P or ADP $\rightarrow$ ATP) is coupled with an energy-releasing reaction that drives them both. These two separate pairs of reactions can be shown as

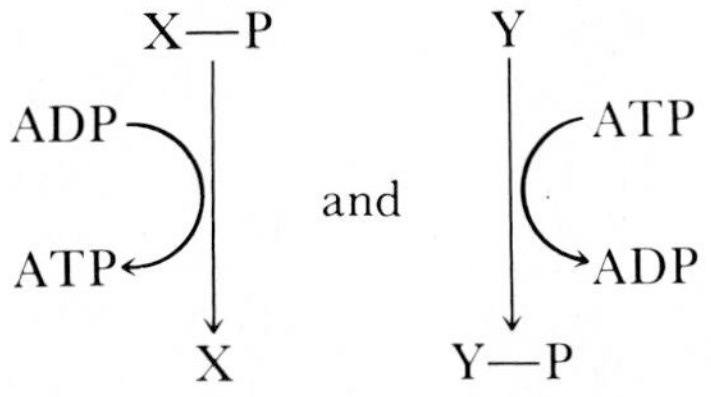

[3.5]

Instead of two unrelated sequences, suppose these two sets of coupled reactions were part of a biochemical pathway in which energy transfers depended on one of these reactions preceding the other; for example, when X—P is a precursor of Y—P. We can show these relationships in a pathway as follows:

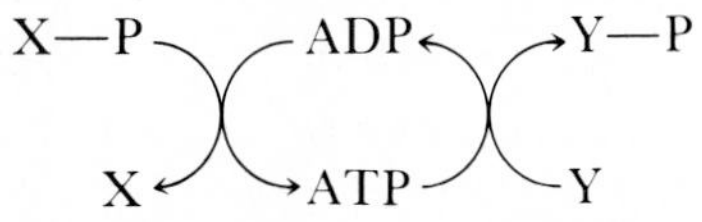

[3.6]

In reaction system [3.6] coupled reactions are involved in the transfer of phosphoryl-bond energy from a higher-potential compound, via a common ADP–ATP cyclic link. By "phosphoryl-bond energy" we really mean the free-energy difference between the reactants and products of the reaction, indicated by $\Delta G°$. In other words, we are not referring to energy localized to the chemical bond itself, although references to bond energy may seem to imply this. We use bond energy as a colloquial expression in energetics, but we actually mean the free-energy difference between reactants in the initial state and products in the final state of a reaction.

We may note two important features of ATP in relation to energy flow.

1. The standard free-energy change of ATP hydrolysis is intermediate between the $\Delta G°$ values for a group of so-called *high-energy*

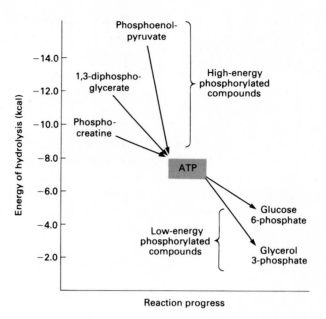

FIGURE 3-2
Energy transfer from compounds of high free-energy level to those of low free-energy level occurs through the mediation of ATP, whose free-energy level is intermediate in value. Energy transfer does not occur directly between high free-energy and low free-energy compounds. (From A. L. Lehninger. *Bioenergetics: The Molecular Basis of Biological Energy Transformations*, 2d ed. Menlo Park, Calif.: W. A. Benjamin, Inc., 1971.)

phosphorylated compounds and so-called *low-energy* phosphorylated compounds.

2. ATP and ADP participate in almost all phosphoryl group transfers in metabolism.

Because ATP occupies an intermediate position in the thermodynamic scale, it connects reactions involving high-potential and low-potential compounds. ATP is produced when ADP accepts a phosphoryl group from some high-potential compound. ATP subsequently donates its terminal phosphoryl group to some acceptor molecule. Once it is phosphorylated by interaction with ATP, the acceptor is raised to a sufficiently high energy level to participate in the favorable "downhill" direction dictated by the standard free energies of the reactants and products.

Because ATP and ADP participate in nearly all phosphoryl group transfers, ATP serves as a general energy carrier in the cell; that is, it is the energy "currency" for a multitude of unrelated activities in cells. Enzymes that function in energy transfer catalyze phosphoryl group transfer from higher-energy compounds to ATP and from ATP to lower-energy compounds (Fig. 3.2). No enzymes are known to transfer phosphoryl groups directly from a high-energy to a low-energy compound.

3.5
Electron Transfer and Oxidation–Reductions

Energy transfer can be accomplished by coupled reactions involving *gain and loss of electrons*, as well as by phosphoryl group transfer. In some cases the electron itself is involved in transfer; in other cases **electron transfer** is achieved when hydrogen atoms (including their electron) are gained or lost. Reactions involving electron loss, called **oxidations**, are coupled with reactions in which there is a gain of electrons, called **reductions**. In such coupled **oxidation–reduction** reactions the substance accepting electrons is an **oxidizing agent**, or **oxidant**, whereas the substance that loses electrons is a **reducing agent**, or **reductant**. Oxidation–reductions are also known as **redox reactions**.

The ability to donate or accept electrons varies among oxidants and reductants. The tendency to lose electrons can be quantitatively compared and expressed as a positive or negative value in a **redox series**, arranged according to the oxidation–reduction potential (**redox potential**) of various substances. These values are obtained from measurements of electrode potential made against the standard of hydrogen, according to the reaction

$$H_2 \rightleftharpoons 2\,H^+ + 2\,e^-$$

In this reaction molecular hydrogen is in equilibrium with its oxidation products, hydrogen ions (protons) and electrons, under standard conditions.

When electrons of a substance are donated to the standard hydrogen electrode, the potential has a negative value (< 0); when the substance accepts electrons, its potential registers as positive (> 0). The **standard electrode potential** of a substance, or E_0, is its potential relative to a hydrogen electrode, expressed in volts (V). Stronger oxidizing agents have a higher positive potential, or a greater affinity for electrons, than weaker oxidants and reductants that have negative potential.

The redox series represents a range of increasing electron affinity, going from negative to positive E_0 values (Table 3.2). The redox series has great predictive value for determining which reactions are theoretically possible, just as the $\Delta G°$ series permits predictions for direction of energy flow and thermodynamically possible reactions. An oxidant can be reduced by a substance with a lower E_0 value than its own, and conversely, a reductant can be oxidized by a substance with a higher E_0 value than its own. In coupled oxidation–reductions, therefore, electron transfer occurs spontaneously in predictable directions according to E_0 values.

TABLE 3-2
Standard Redox Potentials of Biochemical Systems at pH 7.0 and 25–37°C*

Reductant	Oxidant	E_0 (volts)
Pyruvate	Acetate	−0.70
H_2	$2H^+$	−0.42
NADH	NAD^+	−0.32
Lactate	Pyruvate	−0.19
Cytochrome c (reduced)	Cytochrome c (oxidized)	+0.26
H_2O	$\frac{1}{2}O_2$	+0.82

* Systems having more negative standard reduction potential than the H_2–$2H^+$ couple have a greater tendency to lose e^- than H_2. Those with more positive potential than the H_2–$2H^+$ couple have a lesser tendency to lose e^- than H_2.

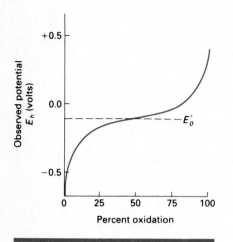

FIGURE 3-3
Titration curve (color) of a biological substance showing that its standard redox potential (E_0') is determined from the inflection point of the curve, at which the reaction is 50% complete.

Standard redox potentials for biochemical systems, at the physiological pH of 7.0, are usually determined by potentiometric titrations in which an oxidizing agent is added to the completely reduced form of a system. The difference in potential is then determined at various stages of oxidation by reference to a standard electrode. The process can be carried out in reverse, by adding reducing agent to the completely oxidized form of a substance. The inflection point of the titration curve is the point at which 50% of the reaction is complete, and this point is taken as E_0', the standard redox potential (Fig. 3.3).

The standard free-energy change ($\Delta G°$) is related to the difference in redox potentials (ΔE_0) between the oxidation and reduction half-reactions as follows:

$$\Delta G° = -nF\Delta E_0 \tag{3.7}$$

where n is the number of electrons that move, F is the Faraday (23,040 cal/V), and ΔE_0 is the redox potential difference (in volts). The interconvertibility of $\Delta G°$ and ΔE_0 is illustrated in the following hypothetical scheme for the reaction $AH_2 + B \rightleftarrows BH_2 + A$, shown as oxidation and reduction half-reactions.

$$AH_2 \rightleftarrows A + 2\ H^+ + 2\ e^- \qquad E_0 = 0.20\ V \tag{3.8}$$
$$B + 2\ H^+ + 2\ e^- \rightleftarrows BH_2 \qquad E_0 = -0.10\ V \tag{3.9}$$

Reaction [3.8] proceeds by being coupled to reaction [3.9], so that

$$\Delta E_0 = 0.20\ V - (-0.10\ V) = 0.30\ V$$

and, according to equation [3.7],

$$\Delta G° = -2 \times 23,040\ cal/V \times 0.30\ V$$
$$= -13,824\ cal\ or\ -13.8\ kcal/mole$$

3.6
Energy Transfer by Electron Carriers

Redox couples act in energy transfers involving electrons (or hydrogens containing these electrons) just as the ADP–ATP system does in phosphoryl group transfers. A **redox couple** is the oxidized and reduced form of an electron-transferring compound. The standard reduction potential E_0 of a redox couple is compared with the E_0 of the reduced-substrate–oxidized-substrate couple with which it interacts. From this comparison one can predict the direction and equilibrium composition of the oxidation–reduction system (Table 3.3).

The neutral term *reducing equivalent* is often used to refer to an electron or a hydrogen atom that is transferred, because either electrons, or hydrogens, or both may be involved in transfers. Hydrogens may be involved, so a dehydrogenation reaction is an oxidation, and a reaction in which hydrogens are added is a reduction.

Three principal groups of electron-transferring substances are of major importance in cell chemistry: **pyridine nucleotide** couples, **riboflavin** derivative couples, and **iron–porphyrin** couples. These redox couples generally function as parts of enzymes and are thus considered *coenzyme* or *prosthetic group* components bound to the protein portion of the enzyme.

TABLE 3-3
Redox Potentials of Redox and Substrate Couples

Redox Couple (red/ox)	E_0	Substrate Couple (red/ox)	E_0
$NADH/NAD^+ + H^+$	-0.32	α-ketoglutarate/succinate	-0.67
$FMNH_2/FMN$	-0.12	Ethanol/acetaldehyde	-0.20
Cytochrome c, red/ox	$+0.26$	Lactate/pyruvate	-0.19
Cytochrome a, red/ox	$+0.29$	Malate/oxaloacetate	-0.17
Fe^{2+}/Fe^{3+} (nonprotein)	$+0.77$	Succinate/fumarate	$+0.03$
		Hydrogen peroxide/oxygen	$+0.30$
		Water/oxygen	$+0.82$

The pyridine nucleotide **nicotinamide adenine dinucleotide**, or **NAD**, and its relative **NADP** exist as NAD^+—NADH and $NADP^+$—NADPH redox couples (Fig. 3.4). Redox couples interact with substrate couples (oxidized and reduced forms of a substrate) according to the general reaction.

reduced substrate + NAD^+ (or $NADP^+$)

$$\Updownarrow$$

oxidized substrate + NADH (or NADPH) + H^+

Each NAD^+ or $NADP^+$ accepts two electrons from a substrate; one of these electrons is part of a hydrogen atom. The proton remaining after removal of the electron from a second hydrogen atom is released into the medium as a free H^+ ion. When protons are required in two-electron

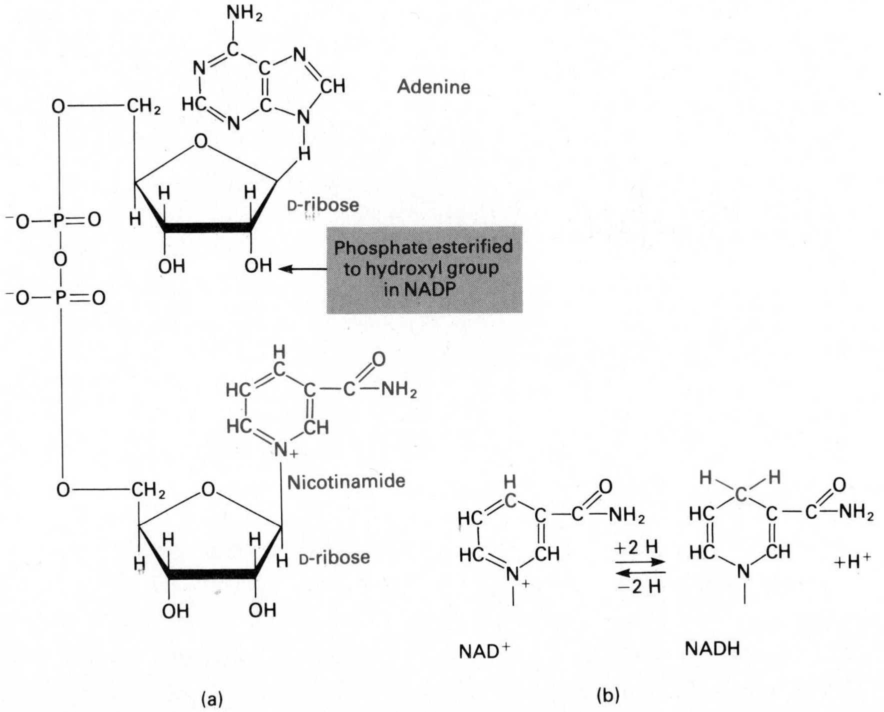

(a)

(b)

FIGURE 3-4
(a) Structural formula of the energy-transferring electron carrier nicotinamide adenine dinucleotide (NAD). (b) NAD exists as a redox couple, because oxidation and reduction of the nicotinamide residue produce electrically charged NAD^+ and electrically neutral NADH, respectively.

transfers producing NAD^+ (or $NADP^+$) and reduced substrate, any H^+ ion in the medium can provide the proton to be added to the substrate, along with a hydrogen atom and an electron from NADH (or NADPH). In both of these pyridine nucleotide redox couples, it is the pyridine ring in the nicotinamide portion that undergoes oxidation–reduction (see Fig. 3.4).

The NAD system can also transfer electrons from one substrate couple to another substrate couple, because $NAD^+/NADH$ (or $NADP^+/NADPH$) can act as a *common intermediate* shared by two NAD-linked, coupled reactions, each catalyzed by a specific enzyme. For example,

$$H_2X \quad NAD^+ \quad H_2Y$$
$$X \quad NADH + H^+ \quad Y$$

NAD is usually bound to an enzyme protein as its coenzyme. Coenzymes are generally nonprotein, organic molecules essential for activity of various enzymes. NAD-linked enzymes usually participate in breakdown (catabolic) reactions, whereas NADP-linked enzymes engage in biosynthetic (anabolic) reactions in metabolism.

Flavoproteins often act as electron-carrier enzymes in mixed reactions where electron flow is from a two-electron donor to a one-electron acceptor, or vice versa. The electron-carrier component is a riboflavin derivative bound to a protein as a coenzyme. The more common derivative is **flavin adenine dinucleotide (FAD)**, but **riboflavin 5′-phosphate** (also called **flavin adenine mononucleotide**, or **FMN**) also acts as an electron-carrier component in certain enzymes.

Many compounds transfer one electron at a time; these usually are metal-containing compounds, and iron is the most common of these metals. The valency state of the metal changes in oxidation–reduction, not the structure of the molecule. Electron carriers containing a **heme** (iron–porphyrin) group, such as **cytochromes**, transfer single electrons between the Fe^{2+} and Fe^{3+} valency states. The cytochromes act sequentially to transfer electrons from flavoproteins to molecular oxygen in the respiratory chain of aerobic cells. They are parts of the plasma membrane of prokaryotes and of the inner membrane of the mitochondrion (see Chapter 9).

Both electron transfer and phosphoryl transfer contribute to cellular energetics. In general, greater energy release can be achieved by electron transfer than by phosphoryl transfer. Each of these modes, however, performs a particular function in the overall cellular economy.

Enzymes: Catalysts of Life

Catalysts are substances that modulate or influence reaction rates without altering the equilibrium point of the reaction. The unique catalysts of the living world are **enzymes**, all of which appear to be globular proteins. Nonliving systems, on the other hand, rely entirely on inorganic catalysts such as iron atoms and hydrogen ions.

Although these inorganic catalysts can also act in living systems, enzymes are particularly suited to cellular chemistry because they possess both catalytic and regulatory properties. Organic chemical reactions are notoriously slow under the mild conditions of temperature and pressure of the average cell. Enzymes not only accelerate these reaction rates, but they also exert a fine control over the actual rate at which a reaction proceeds. Enzymes themselves are subject to regulation, both by external factors and by particular qualities of their own.

There are several thousand different enzymes in an average cell's repertory, so regulation of enzyme activity and regulation of rates of reactions in progress are important aspects of the order that distinguishes the open system of the cell from its disordered surroundings. Cellular activities may undergo profound and rapid changes under the catalytic direction of enzymes. The distinctiveness of the chemistry of different cells or of different compartments of a cell can be traced to differential enzyme content and activity. These features, in turn, are the outcome of gene action and of the regulation of the activity of enzymes produced according to genetic instructions in certain cells at certain times.

Although first formulated in the 1850s, the concept of catalysis was not expanded to include proteins as catalysts until the 1930s. The first enzyme to be purified in crystalline form was *urease*, which catalyzes the hydrolysis of urea to carbon dioxide and ammonia.

$$\begin{matrix} H_2N \\ \diagdown \\ \qquad C{=}O + H_2O \longrightarrow CO_2 + 2NH_3; \ \Delta G° = -13.8 \ kcal/mole \\ \diagup \\ H_2N \end{matrix}$$

Beginning with analysis of urease in 1926, it was suggested that all other enzymes were proteins. This proposal was strongly opposed by leading chemists of the day. Their opposition was overcome by the mid-1930s, as other enzymes were purified and found to be proteins. In addition to about 100 different enzymes that have been crystallized and many more that have been purified in noncrystalline form, we now know the complete structure of a number of enzymes.

Enzyme nomenclature has been formalized by international agreement. Many common names remain in general use, however, because of their greater familiarity and their less cumbersome character. Enzymes are divided into six classes, and each class is subdivided into particular categories (Table 3.4). The suffix -*ase* identifies almost all enzymes. A few enzymes are still called by their original names because these names are very familiar and occurred often in the extensive older literature of chemistry and medicine. Pepsin and trypsin, which digest proteins, are examples of enzymes whose older names remain in wide use today even though the suffix -ase is not included.

3.7
Enzyme Activity

The complexity of cellular biochemistry is based ultimately on simple chemical reactions that are catalyzed at each step by a specific enzyme. Enzyme-catalyzed reactions follow the same basic rules of chemistry as

TABLE 3-4
International System of Enzyme Classification*

Enzyme Class	Type of Reaction Catalyzed	Code Number**
Oxido–reductases	Oxidation–reduction reactions	1.
	Acting on —CH—OH	1.1
	Acting on —C=O	1.2
	Acting on NADH; NADPH	1.6
Transferases	Transfer of functional groups	2.
	One-carbon groups	2.1
	Phosphate groups	2.7
	Sulfur-containing groups	2.8
Hydrolases	Hydrolysis reactions	3.
	Esters	3.1
	Peptide bonds	3.4
Lyases	Addition to double bonds	4.
	—C=C—	4.1
	—C=O	4.2
Isomerases	Isomerization reactions	5.
	Racemases	5.1
Ligases	Formation of bonds, with ATP cleavage	6.
	C—O	6.1
	C—N	6.3
	C—C	6.4

* Only some examples of specific reaction types are shown in column 2.
** A specific enzyme is identified by two additional numbers. For example, hexokinase is the trivial name of the enzyme catalyzing the reaction ATP + glucose → glucose 6-phosphate + ADP. Its formal name is ATP : hexose phosphotransferase. Its Enzyme Commission code number is EC 2.7.1.1.

any other chemical reactions in our world. The hydrolysis of urea can occur whether or not a catalyst is present, yielding the same end products and energy. The spontaneous, uncatalyzed reaction rate can be speeded up if H^+ ions are provided as a catalyst. The rate of hydrolysis is much faster when the enzyme urease is added instead of H^+ ions. In all three instances, the difference is only in the rate of reaction, not in the end products, the energy balance sheet, the direction of reaction, or the point at which equilibrium is reached.

The basis for these differences in rate of urea hydrolysis, and other reaction rates, is the relative ease with which reactant molecules pass over the **energy of activation barrier** (Fig. 3.5). In order for urea to react with water, there must be sufficient energy for urea and water molecules to form an *activated complex* and enter a transition state between reactant and product. The activation-energy barrier is reduced to the greatest extent in an enzyme-catalyzed reaction system. For this reason, the reaction proceeds more rapidly when urease is present than when H^+ ions are present or in the complete absence of a catalyst.

The main function of an enzyme, therefore, is to lower the activation-energy barrier to a chemical reaction. Reactions proceed spontaneously in the direction of lower energy potential (higher ΔG) because molecules possess thermal energy. Some molecules have more thermal energy than others, and there is a statistical probability at all times of some molecules interacting after random collisions, thus

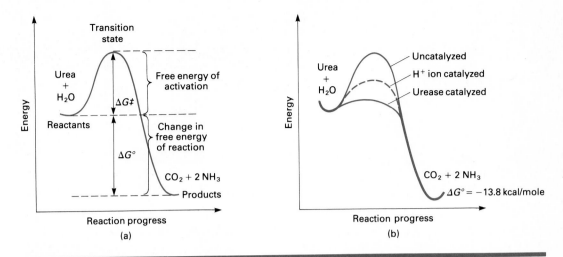

FIGURE 3-5
The energy of activation barrier. (a) The
energy relations are shown for the
reaction in which urea is hydrolyzed to
carbon dioxide and ammonia, and for
the reverse reaction. The difference in
free energy ($\Delta G°$) between reactants
and end products is -13.8 kcal/mole,
but the additional activation energy is
required to raise the molecule to a
transition state before the reaction can
occur. (b) The activation-energy barrier
is reduced by catalysts, thereby
speeding up the rate of reaction. The
enzyme urease is a more effective
catalyst than H^+. Whether the reaction is catalyzed or not, the free-
energy change remains the same:
-13.8 kcal/mole.

overcoming the activation-energy barrier. If we add thermal energy to a system by raising the temperature, molecules gain additional energy and more easily hurdle the activation-energy barrier, because molecules will interact more frequently. The reaction rates are therefore accelerated at higher temperatures. Cells, however, experience little change in temperature.

Enzymes increase the probability that reactant molecules will pass the barrier and go on to completion of a reaction. An enzyme does this by combining with the reactant, or **substrate** (molecule changed in the reactions) in *temporary* association. The enzyme–substrate activated complex has a lower activation-energy requirement, so more substrate molecules can pass over the activation-energy barrier *per unit time*. Some enzymes can handle millions of substrate molecules per second, repeatedly dissociating from the temporary enzyme–substrate complex. A relatively few enzyme molecules can therefore process numerous substrate molecules.

Enzymes show a high level of *specificity* for particular substrates. Inorganic catalysts such as iron or H^+ ions are relatively nonspecific in their interactions with substrates. Because a particular enzyme has a highly specific affinity for a particular substrate, it is highly *efficient* in catalyzing the particular reaction in question. Each enzyme handles its own share of the workload, and many different reactions can therefore proceed simultaneously within the confines of an organelle or a cell.

For their activity some enzymes require a nonprotein cofactor, which may be a complex organic molecule, a metal ion, or both. Intact protein–cofactor complexes are called holoenzymes. When the cofactor is removed, the protein remaining is called the apoenzyme, and the cofactor component itself is a coenzyme. If a coenzyme is covalently bound or otherwise tightly associated with the apoenzyme, it may be referred to as a prosthetic group. The heme cofactor of cytochrome enzymes in the respiratory electron-transport system is a prosthetic group that is difficult to dissociate from the apoenzyme portion.

Many coenzymes readily dissociate from the apoenzyme and act almost like substrates in the chemical reaction. The coenzyme undergoes no permanent change during the reaction and is thus a catalytic component in the true sense of the definition. Coenzymes such as NAD and FAD usually function as electron carriers. Other kinds of coenzymes carry specific atoms or functional groups of the substrate involved in the reaction.

Enzymes usually work only within narrow limits of pH, known as their *optimum pH* for the reaction. The large majority of enzymes have pH optima well within the physiological range of most cells, about pH 6.0–7.0. Some enzymes, such as pepsin in the stomach, have pH optima of 1.5–2.0 for particular substrates, whereas others work best at alkaline values, which may be near pH 10.0 in some systems. The same enzyme usually shows a different pH optimum for different substrates if it has the capacity to act on more than one substrate.

Like any chemical reaction, an increase in temperature leads to an increase in an enzyme-catalyzed reaction rate. But because enzymes are proteins, they are subject to denaturation (unfolding of tertiary structure), resulting in inactivation when many weak bonds are broken at elevated temperatures. Many enzymes are inactivated at 45°C, and most of them are rapidly denatured at 55°C and above. Organisms that live at unusually high temperatures, such as thermophilic bacteria and blue-green algae that inhabit hot springs, obviously possess enzymes with a tolerance for high temperature. These cell types are often useful in providing enzymes and other proteins that can be analyzed in experiments conducted at temperatures that would denature ordinary proteins.

3.8
Substrate Specificity

The mechanism of enzyme action was described by Emil Fischer in 1894 as a "lock and key" relationship. This analogy was appropriate; many enzymes are so discriminating between substrates that virtually identi-

FIGURE 3-6
Both chymotrypsin and trypsin digest peptide bonds in proteins, but each enzyme cleaves only particular peptide bonds according to the projecting side-chain of the amino acid. Chymotrypsin acts only on peptide bonds that follow large, hydrophobic side-chains, such as those in phenylalanine. Trypsin acts only on peptide bonds that follow either lysine or arginine, which have positively charged side-chains.

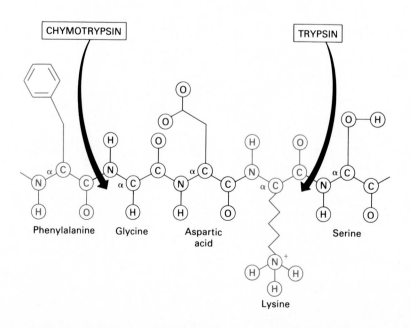

cal molecules may be handled by different enzymes in chemical reactions. For example, different enzymes catalyze reactions involving different isomers of the same compound. Some enzymes, however, can interact with a group of molecules rather than with a single substance. For example, trypsin and chymotrypsin disrupt peptide links in many proteins, and some phosphatases hydrolyze several kinds of phosphate compounds. Even in these cases, however, the different substrates have a similar molecular site with which the enzyme interacts (Fig. 3.6).

Specificity is apparently determined largely by the catalytic site, or **active site**, of the enzyme. It is this part of the enzyme that combines specifically with the substrate molecule. The active site of an enzyme contains the particular functional groups that can bind the substrate (or its relevant portion) and then bring about the catalytic event. Much of our knowledge of enzyme specificity has come from studies of enzymes whose amino acid sequence and three-dimensional structure are known. From such molecular models it is clear that side-chains on the protein backbone that participate in catalysis are not necessarily very close together in the protein chain. Folding brings these groups into closer proximity (Fig. 3.7). When an enzyme is denatured, unfolding separates the component side-groups of the active site, preventing their coordi-

FIGURE 3-7
Folding of the main chain of α-chymotrypsin brings distant amino acid residues (numbered within the circles according to the primary sequence of chymotrypsinogen) into proximity at the active site of the enzyme. The amino acids at positions 102 (aspartate), 57 (histidine), and 195 (serine) are catalytically important and are shown as black circles. (Reprinted by permission from *The Structure and Action of Proteins*, by R. E. Dickerson and I. Geis. W. A. Benjamin, Inc., Menlo Park, California. Copyright © 1969 by R. E. Dickerson and I. Geis.)

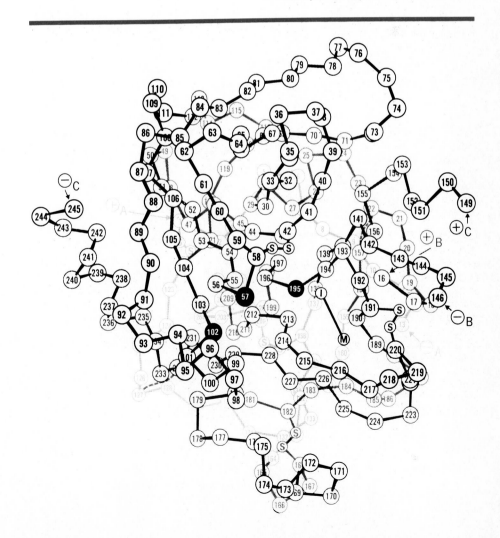

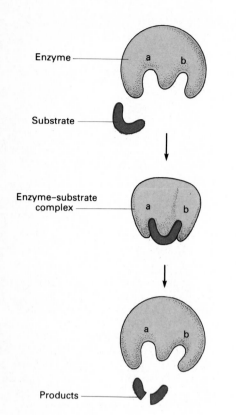

Enzyme

Substrate

Enzyme–substrate complex

Products

RNA

Ribonuclease

Polypeptide

Chymotrypsin

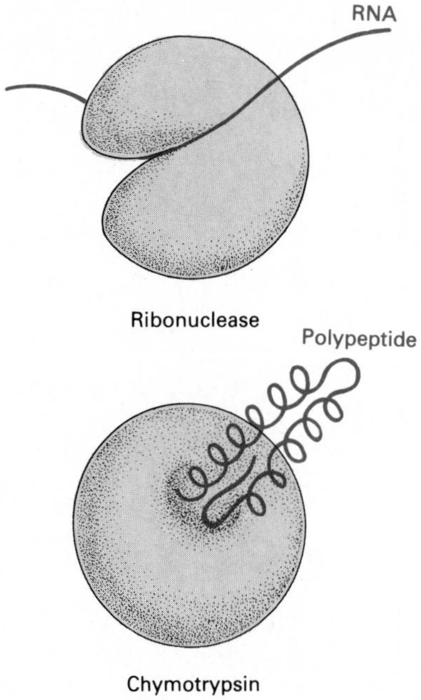

FIGURE 3-9
Diagram illustrating the relationship between active-site geometry and conformation of the substrate in relation to the way the substrate is processed. Ribonuclease, a crevice enzyme, snips exposed regions along the RNA chain, whereas chymotrypsin, a pit enzyme, attacks the accessible portions of the polypeptide chain that is its substrate.

FIGURE 3-8
The substrate molecule binds to the active site of the enzyme, forming a transient enzyme–substrate (ES) complex. According to one prevalent viewpoint, binding is facilitated by a distortion of the active-site geometry so there is "induced fit" between enzyme and substrate. Once the chemical reaction has occurred, the products of the catalyzed reaction move away and the enzyme is once again available for catalysis. The shift in positions of the letters a and b are meant to emphasize the shape change in "induced fit."

nated participation in a chemical reaction. Enzyme inactivation is caused by these gross events of denaturation, but it may also occur in some cases when only one side-group is displaced or substituted.

The substrate molecule is oriented to the enzyme by the active site of the enzyme, and the making and breaking of chemical bonds are enhanced by enzyme–substrate complexing (Fig. 3.8). Physical interaction between the enzyme and substrate molecules leads to "induced fit" through distortion of the molecular surfaces. Although the three-dimensional shape and organization of only a handful of enzymes have been studied, it has been suggested that the active site of an enzyme is in a *crevice*, a *shallow depression*, or a *pit* in the surface of the protein. The geometry of the active site is closely related to the conformation of the particular substrate molecule and to the way in which this molecule is processed in the catalytic reaction. Examples of two of these situations may help to illustrate the concept.

Ribonuclease and some others are crevice enzymes. Ribonuclease acts on RNA chains to cut bonds that are located in relatively exposed positions. The RNA substrate chain appears to fit into the cleft containing the active site of the enzyme, very much like a thread that can be snipped anywhere in the middle of its length by a pair of scissors.

Chymotrypsin has its active site in a pit. In this case, the enzyme can fit up against the substrate molecule and cut away at the bond near the end of the substrate chain. Because polypeptides in fibrous proteins are tightly packed, exposed strands are rare, so it would be difficult for an enzyme to interact with the chain except at the occasional exposed ends. An active site shaped like a crevice would be ineffective in this case, whereas the end of a folded polypeptide chain can easily be brought into appropriate juxtaposition if the active site is in a pit (Fig. 3.9).

The active site occupies a relatively small area of the surface of the rather large enzyme molecule. This means that only a small portion of the enzymatic surface actually engages in catalysis. Other surface regions bind molecules that are involved in regulation of enzyme activity and in subunit associations of enzymes with quaternary structure.

3.9
Enzyme Kinetics

Quantitative analysis of enzyme activity, or **enzyme kinetics**, can provide useful information about the mode of enzyme action. Such kinetic analysis also allows us to make comparisons between different enzymes or for the same enzyme under varied conditions. For many enzymes the rate of catalysis, or **velocity of reaction**, V, varies according to substrate molar concentration (Fig. 3.10). At a constant level of enzyme, V is nearly linearly proportional to substrate concentration when [S] is low. When [S] is high, V is virtually independent of [S]. A simple model to account for these kinetic characteristics was proposed in 1913 by Leonor Michaelis and Maud Menten. The so-called **Michaelis–Menten equation**

$$V = V_{max} \frac{[S]}{[S] + K_M}$$

accounts for the kinetic data shown in Fig. 3.10. V_{max} *is the maximal velocity of reaction*, and K_M (the Michaelis constant) *is equal to the substrate concentration at which the reaction rate is half of its maximal value*; that is, when $[S] = K_M$, then $V = V_{max}/2$. At low substrate concentration, when [S] is much less than K_M, the reaction rate is directly proportional to the substrate concentration. At high substrate concentration, when [S] is much greater than K_M, the rate is maximal; that is, it is independent of substrate concentration.

Both the V_{max} and K_M values provide useful information about an enzyme. Depending on factors influencing enzyme kinetics, such as pH and the particular substrate present, K_M indicates the *affinity* of enzyme E for substrate S. A higher K_M indicates a lower affinity, meaning there is weaker binding between enzyme and substrate during formation of the ES intermediate in catalysis (see Fig. 3.8). K_M values range widely, but for most enzymes K_M lies between 10^{-1} and 10^{-6} M.

The maximal rate, V_{max}, can reveal the *turnover number* for an enzyme when a number of specified conditions exist for the incubation mixture. The turnover number of an enzyme is the number of substrate molecules converted into product per unit time, when the enzyme is fully saturated with substrate. It is usually expressed as the number of substrate molecules that can be converted to product by one enzyme molecule per second. One of the highest values known is for the enzyme carbonic anhydrase, which catalyzes the formation of H_2CO_3 from CO_2; the turnover number is 600,000 per second. The turnover numbers of most enzymes for their principal substrates range in general from 1 to 10^4 per second (Table 3.5).

Values for K_M and V_{max} can readily be obtained from rates of catalysis at different substrate concentrations, if the enzyme obeys

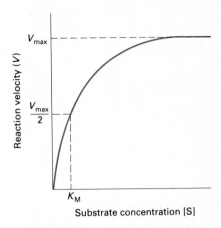

FIGURE 3-10
Relationship between reaction velocity and substrate concentration for a reaction that follows Michaelis–Menten kinetics. When [S] is low, V is linearly proportional to [S]. When [S] is high, V is essentially independent of [S]. The Michaelis constant K_M is numerically equal to the substrate concentration when the reaction rate is one-half its maximal value ($V_{max}/2$).

TABLE 3-5
Maximum Turnover Numbers of Selected Enzymes

Enzyme	Turnover Number (per second)
Carbonic anhydrase	600,000
Acetylcholinesterase	25,000
Penicillinase	2,000
Chymotrypsin	100
DNA polymerase I	15
Lysozyme	0.5

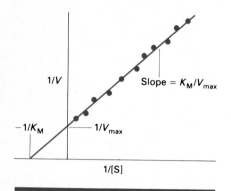

1/V

Slope = K_M/V_{max}

$-1/K_M$ $1/V_{max}$

1/[S]

FIGURE 3-11
Lineweaver–Burk double reciprocal
straight-line plot of velocity and
substrate concentration. The slope and
intercepts for the two coordinate axes
are shown. K_M and V_{max} can be derived
more accurately from a straight-line plot
than from a hyperbolic plot, and from a
relatively few points of data.

Michaelis–Menten kinetics. Instead of generating a hyperbolic curve, however, it is easier and more accurate to transform the Michaelis–Menten equation into one that gives a straight-line plot. As formulated by Lineweaver and Burk, a straight-line plot is obtained using the reciprocals $1/V$ and $1/[S]$ of velocity and substrate concentration (Fig. 3.11). When $1/V$ is plotted as a function of $1/[S]$, the points of data can be connected by a straight line. The slope is K_M/V_{max}, the intercept of the vertical axis is $1/V_{max}$, and the intercept of the horizontal axis is $1/K_M$. A relatively few points can therefore provide information to derive K_M and V_{max} on a more accurate basis from a double-reciprocal plot than from a hyperbolic plot.

3.10
Inhibition of Enzyme Activity

Inhibition of enzymatic activity serves as an important control in biological systems. It can also provide significant information on the mechanism of enzyme action. In general, inhibition may be either a reversible or an irreversible process. In **reversible inhibition** the functional regions of the enzyme molecule do not change, and the enzyme and inhibitor equilibrate rapidly. The inhibiting effects can be removed rather readily by appropriate remedies, such as increasing the substrate concentration in the mixture. Enzymatic activity is thereby restored. In **irreversible inhibition**, on the other hand, the inhibitor modifies the enzyme molecule. Furthermore, the inhibitor is bound so tightly to the enzyme that the two molecules dissociate very slowly. In these circumstances, enzymatic activity is severely reduced or even abolished. Various nerve poisons, including the active agents in a number of insecticides, act as irreversible inhibitors of enzymatic activity. Even after the inhibitor has been removed, enzymatic activity may not be restored if there has been substantial or crucial modification of the enzyme molecule, such as modifying cysteine residues that participate in —S—S— bridges in molecular construction.

Reversible inhibition may be accomplished by either of two general types of inhibitors: competitive or noncompetitive. In **competitive inhibition**, the inhibitor competes with the substrate for the same active site of the enzyme, because inhibitor and substrate usually resemble one another (Fig. 3.12). Less substrate binds to available enzyme, so the rate of catalysis is reduced. In **noncompetitive inhibition**, which is also

FIGURE 3-12
Competitive inhibitors bind to the active
site of an enzyme, competing with
the substrate for the same physical
space on the enzymatic surface.
Noncompetitive inhibitors bind to some
site other than the enzymatic active
site. Both kinds of inhibition are
reversible.

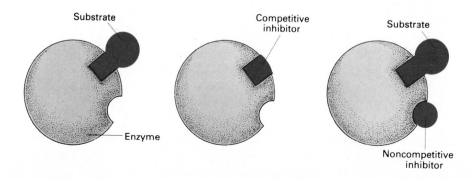

Substrate

Competitive
inhibitor

Substrate

Enzyme

Noncompetitive
inhibitor

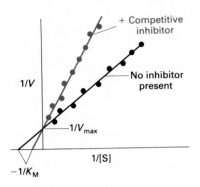

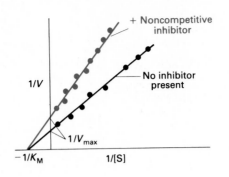

FIGURE 3-13
Effects of inhibitors on enzyme kinetics. A competitive inhibitor increases K_M but does not alter V_{max} of a reaction. A noncompetitive inhibitor, on the other hand, reduces V_{max} but has no effect on K_M of a reaction. From these relationships we can predict that a sufficiently high [S] will reverse the effect of a competitive inhibitor but will not affect noncompetitive inhibitors.

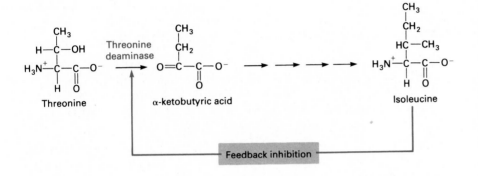

FIGURE 3-14
Feedback inhibition. At high concentration, isoleucine, the end product of a five-step reaction sequence, inhibits activity of the regulatory enzyme threonine deaminase, the enzyme that catalyzes the first reaction. Further production of isoleucine is shut down until its concentration is substantially reduced. Isoleucine thus regulates its own level in the cell through its action as an allosteric modulator of threonine deaminase activity.

reversible, inhibitor and substrate can bind simultaneously to the enzyme molecule, which means the two must occupy different binding sites on the enzymatic surface. A noncompetitive inhibitor decreases the turnover number of an enzyme, whereas a competitive inhibitor diminishes the proportion of enzyme molecules that have bound substrate.

Competitive and noncompetitive inhibitors can be distinguished kinetically by measuring the rates of catalysis at different concentrations of substrate and inhibitor. From double-reciprocal plots we can see that in competitive inhibition V_{max} is unchanged but K_M is increased; in noncompetitive inhibition V_{max} is reduced but K_M is unchanged (Fig. 3.13). We can thus predict that competitive inhibition can be overcome at a sufficiently high substrate concentration, whereas noncompetitive inhibition cannot be reversed by increasing the substrate concentration.

3.11
Regulation of Enzyme Activity

Changes in enzyme shape usually affect the activity of an enzyme and influence reaction rates in metabolism. These conformational changes generally occur as the result of binding between a substrate or another metabolite and some portion of the surface residues of the enzyme molecule. In the phenomenon of **feedback inhibition**, the end product of a multistep reaction sequence inhibits an enzyme that catalyzes an early reaction in the sequence, usually the first enzyme in the series of enzymes governing each step (Fig. 3.14). The enzyme that is inhibited is called a regulatory enzyme, and the inhibitory metabolite is called a **modulator**. The substrate of the regulatory enzyme is structurally

FIGURE 3-15
Two views of the interaction between allosteric modulators and enzymes composed of two or more subunits. (a) Binding of modulator to one subunit leads to a conformational change in the remaining subunits in unison. (b) Conformational changes are induced in each enzymatic subunit only upon binding between modulator and subunit. Other subunits are not perturbed indirectly.

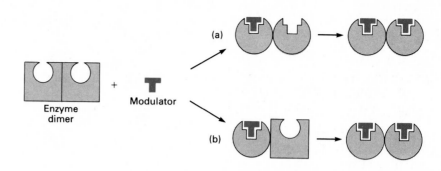

different from the inhibitor, so the term **allostery** (meaning "different structure") is used to describe the modification of an enzymatic reaction by a compound that differs in shape from the true substrate. Allosteric modulators must bind to the enzyme elsewhere than its active site, because there is strict specificity of fit between the substrate molecule and the active site of the enzyme.

An allosteric modulator may be an activator or an inhibitor of enzyme activity, which is why the neutral term is more appropriate than the other two in a general discussion. Once it binds to the enzyme, an allosteric modulator induces a change in the conformation or shape of the enzyme. The precise mechanism by which the conformational change is induced is uncertain, but two hypotheses have been proposed. One hypothesis states that binding between the modulator and one subunit of the enzyme leads to a conformational change of all the enzymatic subunits in unison. Another hypothesis postulates that only the enzymatic subunit to which the modulator binds changes shape, leaving other subunits unchanged (Fig. 3.15). In either case the modulator molecules are not consumed in the reaction with the enzyme.

An important system of allosteric modulation of enzyme activity involves calcium ions and the ubiquitous calcium-binding protein *calmodulin*. Neither component is active alone, but once Ca^{2+} binds to calmodulin, the Ca^{2+}–calmodulin complex binds to kinases and a few other kinds of enzymes. Enzyme activation is the usual result of these allosteric interactions. Kinases catalyze transfer of a phosphoryl group from ATP to another molecule, the latter determining the particular kinase involved. For example, NAD kinase catalyzes NAD + ATP → NADP + ADP, and protein kinases catalyze phosphorylation of proteins. Other calcium-binding proteins are known, such as troponin C in skeletal muscle, but all of these are tissue-specific and species-specific. Calmodulin is found in almost every type of eukaryotic cell, and it appears to have been preserved virtually unchanged for over a billion years of evolution. These features alone imply that calmodulin plays a central role in regulating a broad spectrum of cellular activities.

Modulators participate in regulating enzyme activity via conformational changes but are otherwise still available in the cell for metabolism. Inhibitory modulators distort the enzyme shape; activators restore the proper conformation of the enzyme. Modulator molecules do not undergo chemical changes during binding with the enzyme protein. Once released from the complex with the enzyme, the modulator returns to the metabolic pool in the cell. Using the same set of enzymes and modulators, the cell regulates its metabolism through this system of switching catalysis off and on.

Another way in which enzymatic activity is regulated in the cell is **cooperativity**. The binding patterns of nonregulatory enzymes and substrates form a hyperbolic curve, indicating an increase in enzyme activity as concentration of substrate bound to the enzyme increases (Fig. 3.16). A binding pattern indicating an increase in enzyme activity level to the same extent but with much less substrate required identifies an enzyme that exhibits *positive* cooperativity. An enzyme that does not reach its maximum activity level even at saturating concentrations of substrate is one that exhibits *negative* cooperativity. These features of regulatory enzyme activity have also been explained on the basis of conformational flexibility of the protein upon binding with substrate molecules. In positive cooperativity, binding of the substrate to the active site of one subunit of the enzyme leads to a conformational change that makes the next subunit more receptive to the substrate, and it therefore binds more readily. A kind of "domino" effect leads to more efficient enzyme–substrate interaction, and enzyme activity reaches high levels at relatively lower substrate concentrations than in noncooperative systems. In the case of negative cooperativity, it is assumed that binding of the substrate to the enzyme induces a conformational change in the protein such that additional binding to the substrate is less likely. Activity levels remain lower in this case, even when very high concentrations of substrate exist in the cell.

The regulation of enzyme activity by cooperativity helps explain the different degrees of sensitivity of enzymes to the actual concentration of substrates in the cell. Positively cooperative enzymes are extremely sensitive to minor fluctuations in substrate concentration, whereas negatively cooperative enzymes appear rather insensitive to such fluctuations. Each type of cooperativity provides an advantage—especially in relation to the amount of available substrate at any one time in the cell.

Systems involving activators and inhibitors (positive and negative modulators) are different but complementary to systems involving positive and negative cooperativity. Activators turn on regulatory

FIGURE 3-16
Cooperativity. (a) A standard increase in enzyme activity relative to substrate concentration produces a hyperbolic curve, which represents the binding pattern with substrate of an enzyme that is not self-regulatory. (b) A self-regulating enzyme with properties of positive cooperativity requires far less substrate than a noncooperative enzyme to reach the same activity level. (c) A self-regulating enzyme with properties of negative cooperativity does not achieve the same high levels of activity as a noncooperative enzyme, even at saturating concentrations of substrate. For comparison, all three curves are shown to reach the same activity level at a substrate concentration of 10.

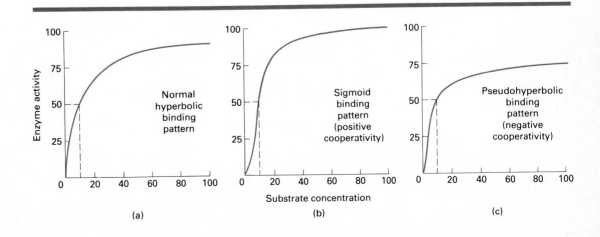

FIGURE 3-17
The kind of enzyme protein synthesized in a cell is determined by genetic instructions encoded in DNA, but the amount synthesized is often subject to control over transcription of DNA into a complementary messenger-RNA copy of the gene. Each triplet of bases (codon) attached to the sugar–phosphate backbone of the nucleic acid molecule specifies a particular one of the twenty amino acids included in the genetic code. (Here S represents sugar and P phosphate.) If transcription is blocked or reduced, little or no messenger RNA is available for translation into protein, even though the gene is present.

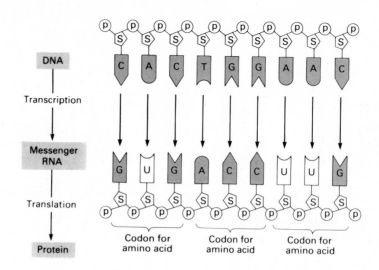

enzymes, and inhibitors turn them off. Cooperativity increases or decreases the sensitivity of regulatory enzymes to the environmental fluctuations in substrate concentration. Activators and inhibitors play a major role in regulation, but cooperativity allows fine-tuning of the catalytic system. All or most of these regulations depend on the ability of an enzyme to undergo changes in shape, some of which involve a displacement of only a few angstroms.

Regulation of enzyme activity provides a fine control over cell metabolism and is effective at the level of the enzyme protein itself. The important but coarser controls over catalysis, however, are those determining the *kind* of enzyme and the *amount* of enzyme synthesized in the cell. These latter two aspects of regulation are influenced by the genes. The gene codes for enzyme protein, thus determining the kind of enzyme that can be synthesized in cells. If the gene for the enzyme threonine deaminase is absent, that protein will not be manufactured. If the gene mutates and either fails to direct synthesis of the enzyme or directs synthesis of a defective enzyme, the catalyst is not available for its specified reaction. If the gene is present, the enzyme may be synthesized but the amount of enzyme manufactured is controlled by processes that take place at the level of the gene itself. Amounts of enzyme protein are generally regulated by transcriptional controls—that is, by control over the manufacture of messenger RNA (Fig. 3.17).

3.12
Isozymes

Multiple molecular forms of a single species of enzyme, differing principally in their net electrical charge, are known as isoenzymes or **isozymes**. Isozymes of an enzyme catalyze the same chemical reaction but have different properties and can be distinguished by appropriate activity assays. According to current information, different proportions of a common set of subunits combine to form the isozymic varieties of a particular enzyme.

One of the best studied of these isozymic groups is lactate dehydrogenase from rat tissues. There are five isozymes, each of which is

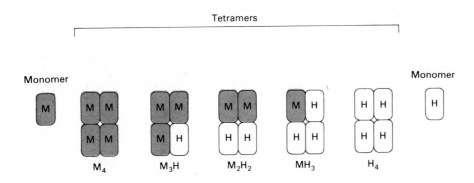

FIGURE 3-18
The enzyme lactate dehydrogenase occurs in five isozymic forms, each made up of a tetramer of monomer polypeptide units of the M and/or H types in different numerical combinations.

made up of four subunit polypeptide chains arranged in a tetramer quaternary structure (Fig. 3.18). The individual polypeptides have a molecular weight of 35,000, and the whole enzyme protein has a molecular weight of 140,000. Only two kinds of polypeptide subunits occur in the enzyme molecule, the M chain and the H chain.

Lactate dehydrogenase occurs in all or most cells in its five isozymic forms. M_4 is made up of 4 M chains exclusively, H_4 has 4 H chains in the tetramer, and the other possible combinations are M_3H, M_2H_2, and MH_3. These isozymic forms do not necessarily occur in equal proportions in all cells. In fact, muscle tissue contains the M_4 isozyme predominantly, whereas heart tissue has been found to contain the H_4 isozyme predominantly. These locations led to the naming of the subunits as M (muscle) and H (heart).

The relative proportions of the five isozymes depend on random combinations of subunits, but some cells produce more of one kind of subunit than the other. The M and H subunits are translations of two different genes. If these genes are equally active in a cell, then M and H subunits may be produced in equal proportions and all five isozymes will occur in amounts that correspond to random combinations. If one gene is more active than the other, the ratio of isozymic types reflects the greater abundance of one subunit over the other. The high amounts of M_4 and M_3H in white skeletal muscle and the high proportions of MH_3 and H_4 isozymes in tissues that have higher aerobic respiratory activities are probably explained in this way.

Isozyme synthesis is genetically programmed and the regulation of reactions involving different isozymes varies according to cell differentiation, or the stage of cell and tissue development. Regulation of metabolism by isozymic forms of an enzyme extends the influence of cellular controls over chemical reactions.

3.13
Multienzyme Systems

Multienzyme systems are sequential chains of catalysts involved in reactions in which the product of one reaction becomes the substrate of the next in the sequence. Three levels of complexity of molecular organization have been recognized for multienzyme systems. The simplest involves individual enzymes in suspension in the cytosol, existing as independent molecular entities that are not physically associated at any time during their action. The small substrate molecules move

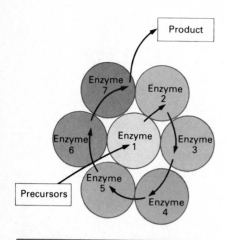

FIGURE 3-19
Mode of action and organization of the fatty acid synthetase enzyme complex. The reaction intermediates remain sequestered within the physically associated enzymes of the cluster during steps that process precursors into the final fatty acid product, which is then released from the complex.

rapidly among the enzyme molecules due to high rates of diffusion. Enzymes of glycolysis provide an example of such a simple system.

Groups of individual enzymes that are physically associated and function together are known as *enzyme complexes*. The individual enzymes are inactive if separated, but when they are present in a tightly bound cluster, the entire complex functions to guide the synthesis of a molecule from smaller precursors. One well-known system of this kind is the fatty acid synthetase complex that catalyzes synthesis of fatty acids from two-carbon precursors (Fig. 3.19). The metabolic intermediates remain sequestered within the enzyme cluster and are released only after the completed fatty acid has been formed by coordinated action of the seven enzymes in this particular complex.

The most intricate and highly organized multienzyme systems are those associated with cellular structures, especially membranes and ribosomes. Certain enzymes of aerobic respiration are an integral part of membrane structure. In prokaryotes they are part of the surrounding plasma membrane, and in eukaryotes the same respiratory enzymes are incorporated within the structure of the inner membrane of the mitochondrion, as we will see in Chapter 9. Multienzyme systems are particularly difficult to study by conventional biochemical methods because relatively intact membrane structure is required for the retention of their catalytic activities, at least in the region housing the enzymes.

Glycolysis: A Metabolic Pathway

The hexose sugar glucose is the most widely used fuel molecule in cells. Glucose can be obtained directly from foods, and it can be derived after suitable chemical processing from stored foods and carbohydrate metabolites. The breakdown of glucose by **glycolysis** ("dissolution of sugar") consists of ten reactions that are essentially the same in all cells, from the simplest bacteria to the most complex plants and animals. Glycolysis is also known as the Embden–Meyerhof pathway in honor of Gustav Embden and Otto Meyerhof, two German chemists who provided important information and insight into the pathway during the 1920s and 1930s.

3.14
An Overview of Glycolysis _____

During glycolysis, ATP is produced when a molecule of glucose is split into two molecules of pyruvate in reactions that can take place in the presence or absence of molecular oxygen. The intermediates in glycolysis have either six carbons or three carbons, and all the intermediates are phosphorylated.

All ten reactions take place in the cell cytosol, and each is catalyzed by a specific enzyme. The ADP–ATP cycle serves as a common intermediate in phosphoryl group transfer, and the redox couple $NAD^+/NADH$ is a common intermediate in oxidation–reduction dur-

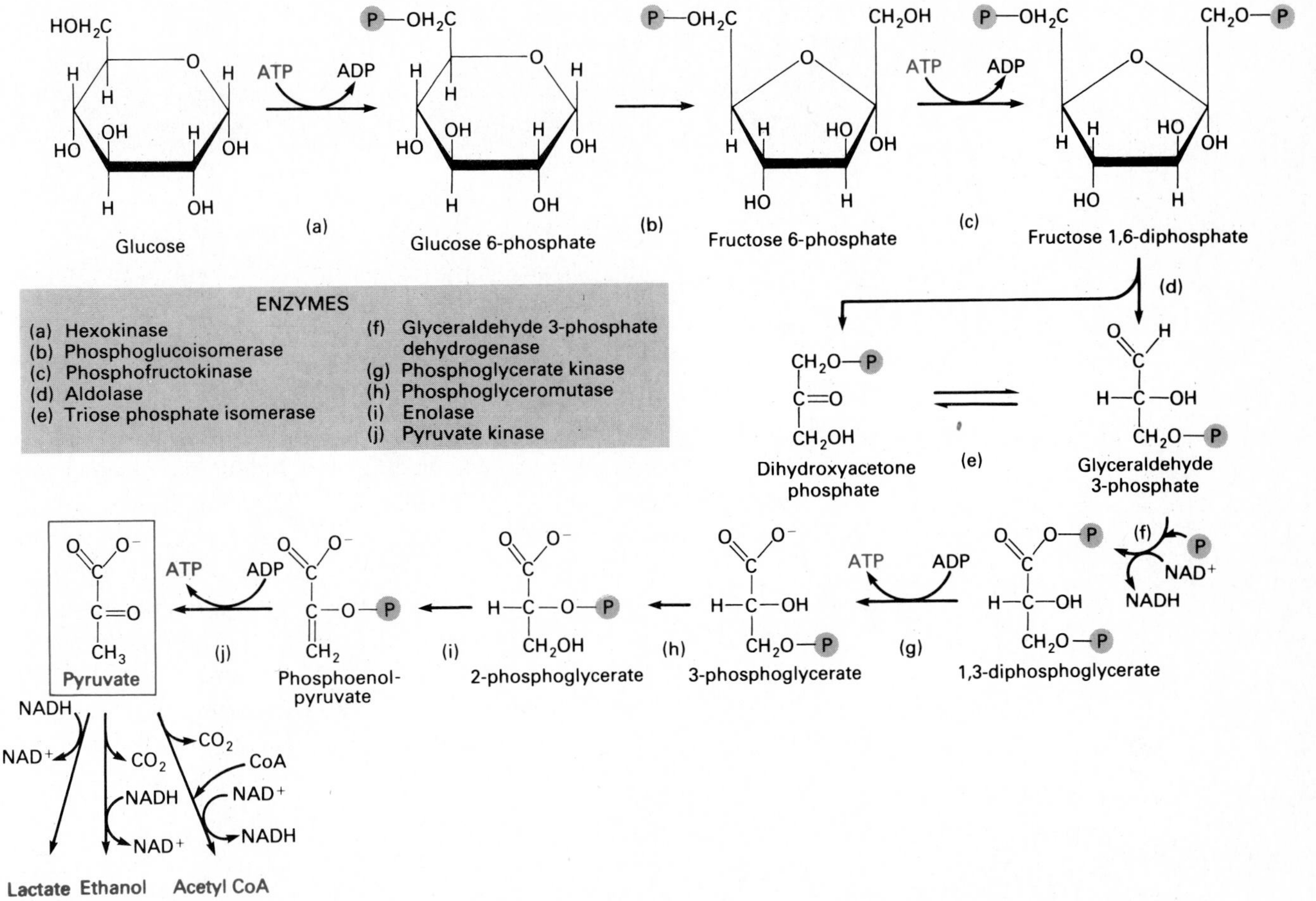

ENZYMES

(a) Hexokinase
(b) Phosphoglucoisomerase
(c) Phosphofructokinase
(d) Aldolase
(e) Triose phosphate isomerase
(f) Glyceraldehyde 3-phosphate dehydrogenase
(g) Phosphoglycerate kinase
(h) Phosphoglyceromutase
(i) Enolase
(j) Pyruvate kinase

FIGURE 3-20
The oxidation of glucose to pyruvate in glycolysis occurs in two stages. In stage 1, glucose is phosphorylated and then rendered into two C_3 compounds. Two ATPs are used in these events. In stage 2, each half of the original glucose molecule is processed in the same reaction pathway, which is an economical metabolic device. At the end of the reaction, pyruvate has been formed. A total of four ATPs are produced in stage 2, but the net yield per glucose is only two ATPs because two ATPs were utilized in stage-1 events. The fate of pyruvate varies according to the enzymatic capacity of the species and the amount of molecular oxygen present. The end products of anaerobic reactions are lactate or ethyl alcohol. In the presence of molecular oxygen, however, pyruvate is decarboxylated and acetyl CoA is formed. In eukaryotes, the conversion of pyruvate to acetyl CoA takes place within the mitochondrion. The enzymes involved at each step are shown in the box, identified by a lower-case letter.

ing particular coupled reactions in the sequence leading from glucose to pyruvate. Although there is a net gain in free energy during the breakdown of glucose, the more significant feature of the pathway is the formation of pyruvate, from which substantial amounts of free energy can be derived during subsequent oxidation in aerobic respiration. Under anaerobic conditions pyruvate is converted to lactate or to ethanol, with the release of considerably less free energy than occurs in aerobic processes in cells.

The glycolytic pathway can be divided into two general stages (Fig. 3.20). In the first stage the glucose molecule is energized by phosphorylation, at the expense of two molecules of ATP. The phosphorylated six-carbon compound can be readily split into two three-carbon units, each of which is a phosphorylated molecule. The phosphorylated trioses, in the form of glyceraldehyde 3-phosphate, are then processed to yield pyruvate and ATP during the second stage of glycolysis. The net gain in free energy is realized by the formation of two molecules of ATP for each glucose molecule that is processed to pyruvate. Although four ATPs per glucose are made in the glycolytic pathway, two ATPs are used when glucose is phosphorylated in the first stage of the sequence (Table 3.6).

TABLE 3-6
Changes in ATP During Glycolysis

Reaction	ATP Change (per Glucose)
Glucose → glucose 6-phosphate	−1
Fructose 6-phosphate → fructose 1,6-diphosphate	−1
2 1,3-diphosphoglycerate → 2 3-phosphoglycerate	+2
2 Phosphoenolpyruvate → 2 pyruvate	+2
Net change	+2

The initial step in glucose breakdown is to modify the molecule to a form that can be metabolized in the thermodynamically favorable "downhill" direction. The conversion of glucose to fructose 1,6-diphosphate consists of three reactions. The first reaction is the phosphorylation of glucose by ATP to form glucose 6-phosphate, catalyzed by *hexokinase*. A kinase is an enzyme that transfers a phosphoryl group from ATP to an acceptor. Hexokinase is thus an enzyme that transfers a phosphoryl group from ATP to hexoses. In the second step, glucose 6-phosphate is converted to its isomer fructose 6-phosphate under the catalytic direction of *phosphoglucoisomerase*. In the third reaction, fructose 6-phosphate is phosphorylated by ATP to fructose 1,6-diphosphate. This reaction is catalyzed by the allosteric enzyme *phosphofructokinase*, which regulates the rate of glycolysis by a feedback inhibition mechanism. We will discuss this feature in the last section of the chapter.

The formation of a diphosphate costs the cell two molecules of ATP. The second phosphorylation is an economical reaction whose cost is repaid twice over to the cell, for a simple reason. When fructose 1,6-diphosphate is cleaved to form *two* phosphorylated three-carbon units, *each* of these triose compounds can be coupled to two ATP-synthesizing reactions in stage 2 of glycolysis. The cell thus derives a net gain of two ATPs for each glucose molecule. If fructose 6-phosphate instead of a diphosphate were split in two, only one of the two triose products would be energetically capable of taking part in stage-2 reactions. The nonphosphorylated triose could not participate in an energy-releasing reaction because of thermodynamic constraints. If only half the glucose molecule were processed to pyruvate, only two molecules of ATP would be made. The net yield from a glucose molecule would then be only one ATP (one ATP used in stage 1 and two ATPs made later in stage 2). Less efficient reactions of this kind are characteristic of glycolysis in certain bacteria.

Fructose 1,6-diphosphate is cleaved to yield two three-carbon compounds, glyceraldehyde 3-phosphate and dihydroxyacetone phosphate. Dihydroxyacetone phosphate is not on the direct pathway of glycolysis, but it is readily converted to its isomer glyceraldehyde 3-phosphate. We can thus say that two molecules of glyceraldehyde 3-phosphate are formed from one molecule of fructose 1,6-diphosphate in a sequence of two enzymatically catalyzed reactions: (1) the split of fructose 1,6-diphosphate into dihydroxyacetone phosphate and glyceraldehyde 3-phosphate catalyzed by *aldolase*, and (2) isomerization of dihydroxyacetone phosphate to glyceraldehyde 3-phosphate catalyzed by *triose phosphate isomerase*. The remaining steps in glycolysis are stage-2 reactions, which only involve three-carbon intermediates derived from glyceraldehyde 3-phosphate.

The energy invested in making glyceraldehyde 3-phosphate in stage-1 reactions is returned with interest during stage 2 of glycolysis, when energy is extracted from this intermediate. The initial reaction is complex and it involves a coupled oxidation and phosphorylation, catalyzed by *glyceraldehyde 3-phosphate dehydrogenase*. In this reaction, glyceraldehyde 3-phosphate is converted to the high-energy phosphate compound 1,3-diphosphoglycerate. At the same time, the coenzyme NAD^+ is reduced to NADH. The reaction is an oxidation–reduction because the diphosphate product is in an oxidized state and NADH is the reduced form of the NAD^+ coenzyme of the dehydrogenase. The high-energy phosphoryl bond in 1,3-diphosphoglycerate is used to generate ATP in the next step of the sequence. *Phosphoglycerate kinase* catalyzes the transfer of the high-energy phosphoryl bond from 1,3-diphosphoglycerate to ADP, with the formation of ATP and 3-phosphoglycerate.

In the last three steps of glycolysis, a second molecule of ATP is generated and 3-phosphoglycerate is converted to pyruvate. In the first of these three reactions the phosphoryl group is shifted from the 3' carbon to the 2' carbon atom. This intramolecular rearrangement produces 2-phosphoglycerate from 3-phosphoglycerate and it is catalyzed by *phosphoglyceromutase*. In the next reaction *enolase* catalyzes the dehydration of 2-phosphoglycerate to form phosphoenolpyruvate, a high-energy molecule (see Fig. 3.2). In the last reaction, the enzyme *pyruvate kinase* catalyzes the transfer of a phosphoryl group from phosphoenolpyruvate to ADP, with the formation of ATP and pyruvate.

The *net reaction* in the transformation of glucose to pyruvate in glycolysis is

$$\text{Glucose} + 2\,HPO_4^{2-} + 2\,\text{ADP} + 2\,NAD^+ \longrightarrow$$
$$2\,\text{pyruvate} + 2\,\text{ATP} + 2\,\text{NADH} + 2\,H^+ \qquad [3.10]$$

3.15
The Fate of Pyruvate

In contrast to the relatively universal sequence of glycolytic reactions in virtually all cells, various reactions lead to the generation of free energy from pyruvate. Three particular reactions of pyruvate will be briefly described here.

1. In yeast and several other microorganisms, pyruvate is decarboxylated in one reaction and the intermediate is reduced to ethanol in the second step of the sequence. Each of the two steps is catalyzed by a specific enzyme.

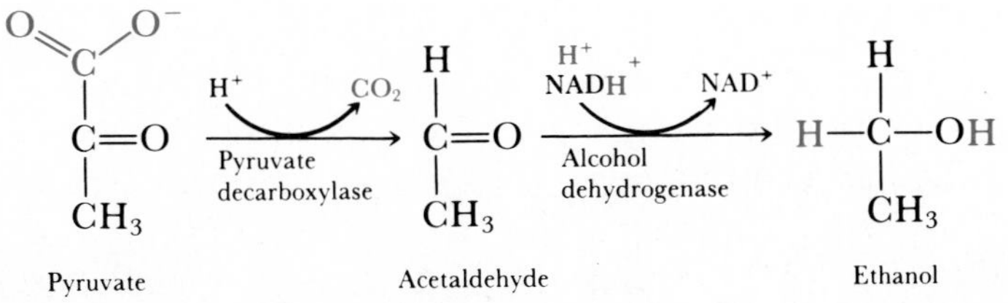

Pyruvate   Acetaldehyde   Ethanol

The conversion of glucose to ethanol is an anaerobic process called *alcoholic fermentation*. The net reaction of this process is

$$\text{Glucose} + 2\,HPO_4^{2-} + 2\,ADP \longrightarrow 2\,\text{ethanol} + 2\,CO_2 + 2\,ATP \qquad [3.11]$$

Alcoholic fermentation is a biological process of considerable importance in the brewing and baking industries. Alcohol production is the desired feature of yeasts used in the manufacture of beer, wine, and liquor, and gaseous CO_2 is the principal end product required of yeasts used in baking.

2. The conversion of pyruvate to lactate is catalyzed by *lactate dehydrogenase* in many microorganisms and in cells of higher organisms, under relatively anaerobic conditions. Pyruvate is reduced by NADH, the coenzyme of the dehydrogenase, to form lactate.

The net reaction in the conversion of glucose to lactate in the anaerobic process of *lactic acid fermentation* is

$$\text{Glucose} + 2\,HPO_4^{2-} + 2\,ADP \longrightarrow 2\,\text{lactate} + 2\,ATP \qquad [3.12]$$

Neither NAD^+ nor NADH appears in reactions [3.11] and [3.12], as they do in the overall glycolysis reaction [3.10]. NAD^+ is regenerated in the reduction of pyruvate to ethanol or lactate. In fact, this regeneration of NAD^+ allows glycolysis to continue under anaerobic conditions. If NAD^+ were not regenerated, glycolysis would not proceed into stage-2 reactions beyond glyceraldehyde 3-phosphate, and ATP would not be synthesized (see Fig. 3.20).

3. In the presence of molecular oxygen, pyruvate is drawn into mitochondria and it is there converted to acetyl CoA in an oxidative decarboxylation reaction catalyzed by the *pyruvate dehydrogenase* complex.

$$\text{Pyruvate} + CoA + NAD^+ \longrightarrow \text{acetyl CoA} + CO_2 + NADH + H^+$$

Acetyl CoA is the entry point to the oxidative pathway in which the bulk of glucose energy is extracted as glucose is completely oxidized to CO_2 and H_2O. These processes of aerobic respiration will be discussed in Chapter 9. The NAD^+ required for the conversion of pyruvate to acetyl CoA and for the oxidation of glyceraldehyde 3-phosphate in glycolysis is regenerated when NADH later transfers its electrons to molecular oxygen in mitochondrial aerobic respiration.

3.16
Regulation of the Rate of Glycolysis

The ten glycolytic enzymes comprise a multienzyme complex that functions in the cytosol. The enzymes are not grouped, nor are they part of any known cellular structure. Reactants and products encounter little hindrance as they diffuse toward and away from the enzyme molecules.

In common with other multienzyme systems, at least one regulatory enzyme is allosteric and interacts with one or more modulators, in addition to its catalytic function in guiding a reaction in the pathway. Phosphofructokinase is one of the regulatory enzymes of glycolysis, as well as the catalyst for the formation of fructose 1,6-diphosphate from fructose 6-phosphate in stage 1.

The pace of glycolysis is critically dependent on the ratio of ADP to ATP in the cell. The catalytic action of phosphofructokinase increases when ADP is in excess relative to ATP. ADP acts as a positive modulator (activator) of the enzyme. When ATP is in relative excess, however, the regulatory enzyme shows reduced activity. ATP thus acts as a negative modulator (inhibitor) of phosphofructokinase action. Because the *sum* of the concentrations of ADP and ATP in the cell is constant, a high charge of ATP favors inhibition of the enzyme, whereas a high charge of ADP favors activation and a higher rate of reaction and of glycolysis as a whole.

ATP is an end product of glycolysis, so the glycolytic reactions slow down when this end product inhibits an enzyme that catalyzes an early step in the pathway. These features are characteristic of the regulatory phenomenon of feedback inhibition of enzyme activity.

Summary

Living cells can promote orderly structure and function in apparent violation of the Second Law of thermodynamics, which requires that all processes tend toward an equilibrium state of minimum free energy (maximum disorder). The study of bioenergetics deals with the thermodynamics of biological systems, by which cells extract energy and use energy in their ongoing activities. Of the total energy released in exergonic processes or required in endergonic processes, only a portion—the free energy—is available to do useful work in the cell. As an open system that exchanges both energy and matter with its environment, the cell can replenish its energy reserves even as these are used in biosynthetic and other endergonic processes. By entering different steady states, the cell is never at equilibrium. Thus it can continue to function and also be subject to regulation of its activities.

Cells obtain their usable free energy primarily via the breakdown of fuel molecules. As nutrient molecules are broken down during metabolism, a portion of the free-energy difference between the original and the product molecules is conserved in the form of intermediates that can transfer it to reactions requiring energy. Among the most important intermediates are those transferring phosphoryl groups and those transferring reducing equivalents (electrons and hydrogen atoms) in oxidation–reduction reactions. By transferring the phosphoryl groups to ADP to make ATP or the electrons to reduce NAD^+ (for example), cells conserve a portion of the original food energy. The phosphoryl groups or reducing equivalents can be transferred from ATP or NADH to energy-requiring processes. Energy-yielding reactions are therefore coupled to energy-requiring processes through ATP/ADP, NAD$^+$/NADH, and other common intermediates of metabolism.

Enzymes are proteins that serve as the unique catalysts of these metabolic reactions in living systems. Like all catalysts, they accelerate a reaction without influencing its equilibrium position or its energy requirements. By providing a surface to which the reactants bind, enzymes increase the likelihood of effective collisions with reactants and thereby lower the activation energy requirement for reactions to proceed. The selectivity of enzyme–reactant interaction allows specific reactions to occur in solutions containing many other potentially competing molecules. Enzymes may have nonprotein components associated with them as cofactors either temporarily (coenzyme) or permanently (prosthetic group).

Substrates are reactants that bind to enzymes and are modified in the reaction that occurs. The binding ability of a particular substrate for its enzyme is determined by the enzyme's three-dimensional conformation in a region called the active site. As with all proteins, this conformation may be affected by environmental conditions, such as pH or temperature, or by the presence of molecules that bind to other surface regions of the enzyme, thereby influencing the conformation of the active site and, in turn, the catalytic activity.

Enzyme kinetics is the study of enzyme activity and the factors that modify this activity. Inhibitors can block activity by irreversibly altering the structure of the active site or by reversibly binding either to the active site (competitive inhibition) or elsewhere on the enzyme molecule (noncompetitive inhibition). Many drugs and toxic substances act as inhibitors, but natural constituents of the cell also modify enzyme activity, usually by binding to specific sites other than the active site in the process of allosteric modulation. The modulation may be positive (activation) or negative (inhibition) and serves to regulate the reaction catalyzed by the enzyme. Enzymes that consist of several polypeptides may exhibit cooperativity, a phenomenon whereby substrate binding to one subunit changes the affinity for substrate of the other subunits. In addition to these forms of regulation, the cell may regulate the amount of enzyme available by controlling the synthesis of messenger RNA from the gene encoding the enzyme protein. Such control may involve induction (stimulation of mRNA synthesis) or repression (inhibition of mRNA synthesis) in response to appropriate stimuli. Enzymes may also be produced constitutively, without regard for variations in growth conditions.

Additional regulatory possibilities are afforded by isozymes, where several different kinds of subunits associate in different proportions to form enzymes with related but different kinetic properties. Multienzyme systems are associations between a series of enzymes each of which relies for its substrate on the product of a previous enzyme. Multienzyme systems are the foundation of metabolic pathways. They may be free in solution or physically associated in particles or membranes.

An important multienzyme system carries out the process of glycolysis, wherein a glucose molecule is broken down into two pyruvate molecules in a series of ten enzyme-catalyzed reactions. In the process, free energy is conserved by the generation of two ATP molecules and two molecules of NADH. The breakdown occurs in two stages. The first stage activates the glucose by phosphorylation and results in two 3-carbon units, each with an attached phosphoryl group. The second stage extracts energy from these activated units by oxidizing the carbons and recovering the phosphoryl groups in ATP. The resulting pyruvate has several alternative fates. In anaerobic yeast and microorganisms, it may be decarboxylated and reduced to ethanol. In many cells deprived of oxygen, it is reduced to lactate. In both cases, NAD^+ is regenerated from NADH during the reduction step, permitting continuation of the glycolytic pathway. When oxygen is available, a third alternative is aerobic respiration; the pyruvate is oxidized and decarboxylated to acetyl coenzyme A and enters the mitochondrion (in eukaryotes) or cytoplasm (in prokaryotes). There it becomes completely oxidized to CO_2 and the NADH is reoxidized by oxygen. The rate of glycolysis is regulated by the activity of the enzyme phosphofructokinase, which has allosteric modulators, including ATP (an inhibitor) and ADP (an activator).

Readings and References

Anderson, C. M., F. H. Zucker, and T. A. Steitz. 1979. Space-filling models of kinase clefts and conformation changes. *Science* **204**:375.

Breslow, R. 1982. Artificial enzymes. *Science* **218**:532.

Changeux, J.-P. April 1965. The control of biochemical reactions. *Sci. Amer.* **212**:36.

Dickerson, R. E., and I. Geis. 1969. *The Structure and Action of Proteins.* Menlo Park, Calif.: Benjamin-Cummings.

Erecinska, M., and D. F. J. Wilson. 1982. Regulation of cellular energy metabolism. *J. Membr. Biol.* **70**:1.

Fruton, J. S. 1976. The emergence of biochemistry. *Science* **192**:327.

Hess, B. 1977. Oscillating reactions. *Trends Biochem. Sci.* **2**:193.

Hill, T. L. 1977. Biochemical cycles and free-energy transduction. *Trends Biochem. Sci.* **2**:204.

Hinkle, P. C., and R. E. McCarty. March 1978. How cells make ATP. *Sci. Amer.* **238**:104.

Koshland, D. E., Jr. October 1973. Protein shape and biological control. *Sci. Amer.* **229**:52.

Lehninger, A. L. 1971. *Bioenergetics.* Menlo Park, Calif.: Benjamin-Cummings.

Lieber, C. S. March 1976. The metabolism of alcohol. *Sci. Amer.* **234**:25.

Masters, C. J. 1978. Interactions between soluble enzymes and subcellular structure. *Trends Biochem. Sci.* **3**:206.

Neurath, H. December 1964. Protein-digesting enzymes. *Sci. Amer.* **211**:68.

Ochoa, S. 1985. Carl Ferdinand Cori, 1896–1984. *Trends Biochem. Sci.* **10**:147.

Phillips, D. C. November 1966. The three-dimensional structure of an enzyme molecule. *Sci. Amer.* **215**:78.

Racker, E. 1980. From Pasteur to Mitchell: A hundred years of bioenergetics. *Fed. Proc.* **39**:210.

Stroud, R. M. July 1974. A family of protein-cutting enzymes. *Sci. Amer.* **231**:74.

Stryer, L. 1981. *Biochemistry.* 2nd ed. San Francisco: Freeman.

Zubay, G. 1983. *Biochemistry.* Reading, Mass.: Addison-Wesley.

CHAPTER 4

Genetic Processes

The Genetic Material

The blueprints for development of a cell or organism are contained in the set of genes that is unique to each species. The science of genetics began in 1900 with the rediscovery of Gregor Mendel's mid-nineteenth-century studies on inheritance in garden peas, and it expanded steadily during the first half of this century. The molecular nature of the gene and of genetic processes, however, remained unknown or uncertain until the early 1950s. Despite our poor understanding of the molecular nature of genetic systems in those years, the analysis of gene transmission patterns and of gene behavior provided essential information about the location and organization of genes in chromosomes, about interactions between genes in the development of the individual, and about many important features of inheritance. Those studies provided the firm foundations, then and now, for modern molecular approaches to analyzing genes and genetic processes.

During the second half of this century we have been treated to dazzling new discoveries and insights into the nature of genetic materials and processes at the molecular level. This chapter briefly examines selected basic features of genetic systems. We will explore these topics more thoroughly in later chapters.

4.1
DNA Is the Genetic Material

The first meaningful evidence to show that genes are made of DNA came from studies of the pneumococcal bacterium *Diplococcus pneumoniae*, reported in 1944 by Oswald Avery, Colin MacLeod, and Maclyn McCarty. They showed that highly purified DNA extracted from one genetic strain could genetically *transform* a different genetic strain of the pneumococcus. The recipients of the DNA extract were genetically altered: They expressed the inherited trait of the DNA donor strain and

FIGURE 4-1
Diagrammatic representation of the classic 1944 experiments by O. T. Avery and co-workers, who provided the first significant evidence that DNA was the genetic material. Transformation of genetically avirulent type III cells to genetically virulent type II cells was accomplished only when DNA from virulent type II cells was added to the type III culture. Virulent cells have a capsule (color), but avirulent cells are not encapsulated.

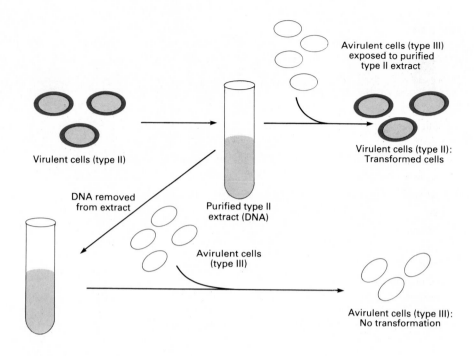

Virulent cells (type II)

DNA removed from extract

Purified type II extract (DNA)

Avirulent cells (type III)

Avirulent cells (type III) exposed to purified type II extract

Virulent cells (type II): Transformed cells

Avirulent cells (type III): No transformation

transmitted the altered trait to descendant generations (Fig. 4.1). In control experiments Avery and co-workers showed that transformation took place neither in the absence of DNA (the transforming principle) nor when proteins were substituted for DNA in donor extracts.

Although these experimental results seem overwhelmingly convincing to us today and stand as a milestone achievement, the majority of the scientific community remained unconvinced at the time. The consensus of opinion in the 1940s was that genes probably were made of proteins rather than of DNA. Proteins were known to be highly diverse and highly specific, as are genes, and it seemed the simplest posture to view proteins as the agents responsible for the diversity and specificity of both the metabolic and the genetic processes leading to development of cells and organisms. In addition, a number of people accepted the tetranucleotide hypothesis, which postulated that DNA molecules were constructed of repeating sets of the four kinds of nucleotides, such as —TAGCTAGCTAGC—, and were therefore relatively invariant and monotonous molecules that could hardly dictate the diversity and specificity of genes.

The case for DNA as the genetic material gained strength during the next few years as the result of biochemical and biological studies. The tetranucleotide hypothesis lost favor as data accumulated to show that the base composition of DNA varied among species rather than being identical, as predicted by the tetranucleotide viewpoint. Particularly important studies by Erwin Chargaff demonstrated that the absolute percentages of the four kinds of bases differed from one species to another but that the percentage of adenine equalled the percentage of thymine and that guanine and cytosine occurred in equal amounts in the DNAs examined (Table 4.1). The rule of A = T and G = C helped Watson and Crick to formulate their molecular model of DNA a few years later.

TABLE 4-1
Molar Proportions of Bases (as Moles of Nitrogenous Constituents per 100 g-atoms P) in DNAs from Various Sources

Source of DNA	A	T	G	C	$\dfrac{A + T}{G + C}$	$\dfrac{A + G}{T + C}$	A:T	G:C
human liver	30.3	30.3	19.5	19.9	1.53	0.99	1.00	0.98
human sperm	30.7	31.2	19.3	18.8	1.62	1.00	0.98	1.03
human thymus	30.9	29.4	19.9	19.8	1.52	1.03	1.05	1.00
bovine sperm	28.7	27.2	22.2	21.9	1.27	1.04	1.06	1.01
rat bone marrow	28.6	28.5	21.4	21.5	1.33	1.00	1.00	1.00
wheat germ	27.3	27.2	22.7	22.8	1.20	1.00	1.00	1.00
yeast	31.3	32.9	18.7	17.1	1.79	1.00	0.95	1.09
Escherichia coli	26.0	23.9	24.9	25.2	1.00	1.04	1.09	0.99
Mycobacterium tuberculosis	15.1	14.6	34.9	35.4	0.42	1.00	1.03	0.98
bacteriophage T2, T4, or T6	32.5	32.5	18.3	16.7*	1.86	1.03	1.00	1.10
bacteriophage T3	23.7	23.5	26.2	26.6	0.89	1.00	1.01	0.98
bacteriophage T5	30.3	30.7	19.5	19.5	1.56	0.99	0.99	1.00

* The T-even phages have hydroxymethyl cytosine in place of cytosine in their DNA.

In 1952 Alfred Hershey and Martha Chase used newly available radioactive isotopes to label DNA and protein differentially and thereby to follow the fate of these molecules during the infection of *E. coli* by phage T2. The aim of the experiments was to determine which of these labeled molecules behaved like genetic material—that is, whether [^{32}P]DNA or [^{35}S]protein of phage T2 entered the host cells and there directed the synthesis of progeny T2 viruses. Labeled molecules that remained outside the host cells could hardly function as the genes of phage T2, because such molecules would not influence the reproduction and genetic specification of progeny T2 during the infection cycle. When viruses labeled with [^{35}S]proteins were used, most of the labeled protein remained outside the host cells during infection and phage reproduction. On the other hand, infection with phage T2 containing [^{32}P]DNA yielded infected host cells that the labeled DNA had entered (Fig. 4.2). DNA but not protein entered the host cells during infection. Hence DNA must be the genetic material that contained the specific instructions for the synthesis of new viruses exactly like the infecting parental viruses.

By 1953 it was possible for James Watson and Francis Crick to propose a molecular model for DNA that incorporated information derived from biochemical studies such as Chargaff's; from x-ray diffraction studies of physical properties of DNA by Maurice Wilkins, Rosalind Franklin, and others; from genetic studies by Hershey and Chase and other investigators; and from their own theoretical analysis of the molecular components of DNA, the binding properties of these components, and other features. Watson and Crick pointed out important features of the DNA molecular model that could explain mutation and replication, two fundamental properties of genetic material. Together with the more favorable climate of opinion in 1953, their suggestions concerning the suitability of DNA as a genetic molecule had a profound impact on the scientific community. In addition, many features of the

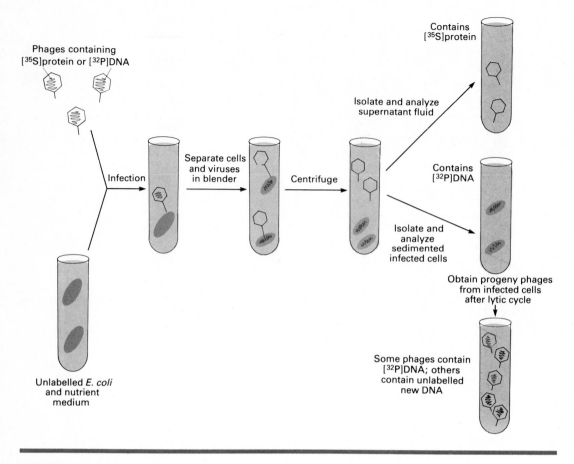

FIGURE 4-2
Illustration of the main features in the Hershey–Chase experiments. T2 phages containing labeled protein *or* labeled DNA (color) were allowed to infect *E. coli*. After infection was initiated, the viruses and their host cells were separated mechanically in a blender. The mixture was centrifuged and each component was then analyzed. Labeled DNA was found inside the host while labeled protein occurred primarily outside the *E. coli* cells. DNA must therefore be the genetic material, directing virus reproduction during the infection cycle in host cells.

molecular model were open to experimental verification. The era of molecular genetics was begun.

4.2
DNA Replication

One of the compelling features of the Watson–Crick molecular model was their suggestion that each strand of the double helix might act as a template for the synthesis of a new, complementary partner strand. Because of the inherent property of *complementary base pairing*, each strand of the duplex would guide the formation of an exactly complementary partner strand, and therefore each parental duplex would guide the synthesis of two identical progeny duplex molecules (Fig. 4.3). Because only one strand of the parental duplex is conserved in each new duplex formed, the pattern is that of **semiconservative replication**. The DNA molecules in every new generation are identical to the parental molecules and to each other, thereby ensuring genetic continuity from each generation to the next.

Virtually nothing was known about the actual processes of DNA replication, other than the proposed end products of identical duplexes, and other theoretical modes of replication were soon suggested. In particular, it was proposed that DNA might replicate by a conservative mode or by a dispersive mode, rather than semiconservatively. By **conservative replication** each parental duplex would remain intact

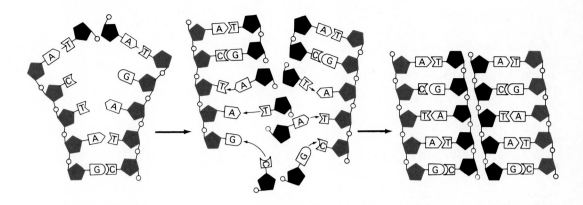

FIGURE 4-3
Each strand of the DNA duplex guides synthesis of a new complementary partner strand, making two molecules identical to each other and to the original parental DNA. Genetic continuity is thus ensured from generation to generation.

and would somehow guide the synthesis of two new duplex DNA molecules exactly like the original. **Dispersive replication** was proposed to occur via breakdown of the original duplex and synthesis of new duplex parts, all of which reassembled correctly, somehow, to produce new duplexes containing parts that were new and parts of the original duplex DNA (Fig. 4.4).

In 1958 Matthew Meselson and Franklin Stahl provided strong evidence that supported the semiconservative mode and refuted the two alternative possibilities. Their experiments were elegantly designed to obtain data that fit the predictions made on the basis of only one of the possible replication modes, while excluding the other two modes at the same time. They took advantage of the availability of the heavy nitrogen

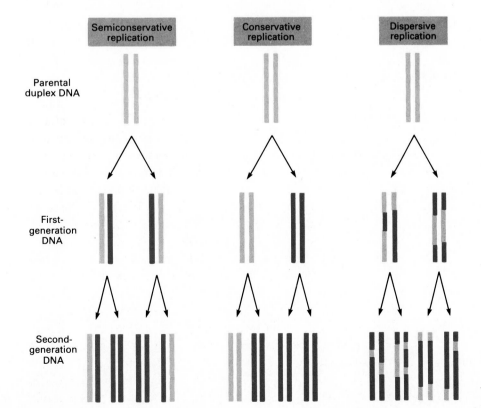

FIGURE 4-4
Three possible modes of DNA replication. The predicted distribution of original parental DNA (black) and newly synthesized strands of DNA (color) are shown for two rounds of replication. The distribution of original and new DNA in progeny duplex molecules is unequivocally different for conservative, semiconservative, and dispersive modes of replication in each generation.

Equilibrium density gradient centrifugation. Samples of experimental material can be sedimented in a preparative centrifuge, from which the material can be collected in individual fractions for subsequent analysis in various assays. Alternatively, materials may be centrifuged to the point of equilibrium in a density gradient in an analytical ultracentrifuge and analyzed directly in the centrifuge tube or cell. After centrifugation of DNA in a CsCl density gradient, for example, the contents of the tube may be photographed to show UV absorption bands representing the separated DNAs in the gradient. Tracings by densitometer from the photographs show the position and relative amounts of each band of sedimented DNA, and interpretations can then be made of the nature of the experimental material.

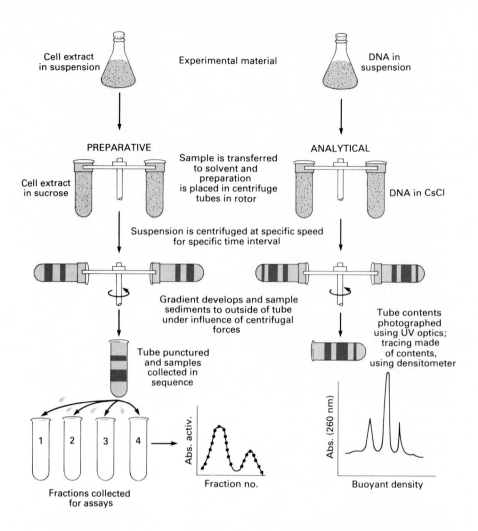

isotope ^{15}N and of the new method of **equilibrium density gradient centrifugation** by which DNAs of different isotopic composition could be identified according to the different regions of a cesium chloride gradient in which the molecules settled at equilibrium after high-speed centrifugation (Fig. 4.5). The distribution of original and new DNA in first- and second-generation molecules would be quite different for each of the three possible modes of replication (see Fig. 4.4), and the patterns observed after centrifugation would indicate which of the three sets of predictions was fulfilled—and, therefore, which mode was correct and which were incorrect.

Meselson and Stahl grew cultures of *E. coli* in media containing ^{15}N-labeled nutrients so that their DNA became uniformly labeled with the isotope by the beginning of the experiments. These ^{15}N-labeled cells were then transferred to media containing ordinary ^{14}N for continued growth and reproduction during the experiments. At selected times over a period of four cell generations, samples were removed and the DNA was extracted and centrifuged to identify the kinds of isotope-labeled molecules that had been synthesized in the cells growing in ^{14}N-containing media.

According to the semiconservative replication hypothesis, all first-generation DNA molecules were predicted to be half-heavy (^{15}N–^{14}N).

One strand would be the original parental ^{15}N-labeled strand, and the new partner would be ^{14}N-labeled because it was synthesized from [^{14}N]precursors in the growth medium. Similarly, second-generation DNA would include 50% half-heavy (^{15}N–^{14}N) and 50% unlabeled, light duplexes (^{14}N–^{14}N). This would occur because each first-generation ^{15}N–^{14}N duplex would replicate semiconservatively such that the ^{15}N-strand would guide the synthesis of a new partner ^{14}N-strand, and the ^{14}N-strand of the first-generation duplexes would also guide the synthesis of a new partner ^{14}N-strand. On the other hand, if DNA replicated conservatively, 50% of the first-generation molecules would be intact ^{15}N–^{15}N parental duplexes and 50% would be newly synthesized ^{14}N–^{14}N duplexes. That is, 50% of first-generation DNA would be heavy and 50% light. In the second generation, 25% of the DNA would be the original intact ^{15}N–^{15}N heavy duplexes and 75% would be ^{14}N–^{14}N light molecules. Finally, if replication were dispersive, the populations of DNA molecules in any generation would consist of varying amounts of original ^{15}N-pieces and newly made ^{14}N-pieces, depending on how much original DNA and how much new DNA had been incorporated into progeny duplexes.

When the extracted DNA was sedimented by high-speed centrifugation and came to rest at equilibrium in the regions of the CsCl density gradient that corresponded to their own buoyant density in CsCl, the contents of the centrifuge tubes were photographed. These were then interpreted from the tracings made with a densitometer (Fig. 4.6). The distributions of DNA from all of the times sampled were the distributions and proportions predicted according to semiconservative replication. These results, and many other lines of evidence obtained for DNA from many different organisms and sources, have shown semiconservative replication to be the pattern by which DNA increases in successive generations.

In the years since 1958, we have learned a great deal about the enzymes that catalyze the synthesis of new DNA and about the processes that ensure the remarkable fidelity of DNA replication. Replication is not error-free, but mistakes in copying new strands from template strands are very rare—on the order of one per million bases incorporated into the sequence specified by the complementary template strand. The accuracy of new-strand synthesis is due to many factors, including a "proofreading" function of one of the replication enzymes. The enzyme *DNA polymerase I* is able to remove incorrect bases and guide their replacement with correct bases for a sequence. We will discuss these and other features of DNA replication in some detail in Chapter 12.

4.3
Mutation

Mutations are defined as sudden, heritable changes. All of our information concerning mutations up to the early 1950s was obtained on the basis of operational criteria centering on observed changes in inheritance patterns and in phenotypes of mutants. We knew from decades of genetic studies that both spontaneous and induced mutations were

FIGURE 4-6
Experimental demonstration of semi-conservative replication of *E. coli* DNA. Cells initially labeled with ^{15}N were grown for specified times in [^{14}N]medium to distinguish original [^{15}N]DNA from newly synthesized [^{14}N]DNA in progeny cells. Photographs were taken of sedimented DNA (bands) in tubes after equilibrium density gradient centrifugation in an analytical ultracentrifuge and were traced by densitometry to allow measurement of the amount of DNA in each absorption band. Interpretations of these data fit the predictions made for the amount and distribution of original [^{15}N]DNA (black) and newly synthesized [^{14}N]DNA (color) according to the semiconservative mode of replication (see Fig. 4.4). Controls shown in the bottom two panels indicate the reliability of identifying specific bands as representing DNA of specific density and isotopic composition, in known amounts. This is illustrated for a mixture of 0 generation and 1.9 generation DNA in one panel and for 0 generation and 4.1 generation DNA in the bottom panel. (From Meselson, M., and F. W. Stahl, 1958, *Proc. Nat. Acad. Sci. U.S.* **44**:671.)

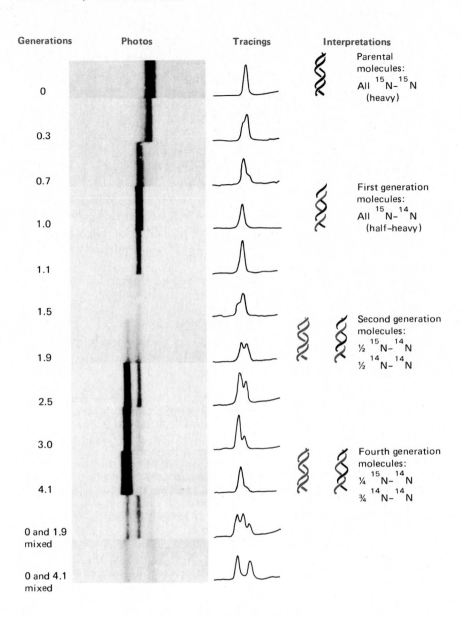

aspects of the same genetic phenomena leading to altered traits that were transmitted from generation to generation. But we did not know the molecular basis of these inherited changes, nor did we know how the genes were altered by chemical and physical agents or how a spontaneous change occurred in the absence of known mutation-inducing agents (mutagenic agents, or **mutagens**).

In their 1953 publication pointing out the genetical implications of the molecular model for DNA, Watson and Crick correctly suggested that mutations could arise as the result of **base substitution** during DNA replication. During new-strand synthesis, thymine is incorporated opposite its adenine complement in the template strand. If a hydrogen shifts to a different location in the adenine residue, thereby producing a tautomeric form of adenine, the adenine **tautomer** pairs with a cytosine and not with a thymine. Once the cytosine residue is incorporated into the new strand, the base sequence has been changed and the cytosine guides the incorporation of a guanine residue in the new strand formed

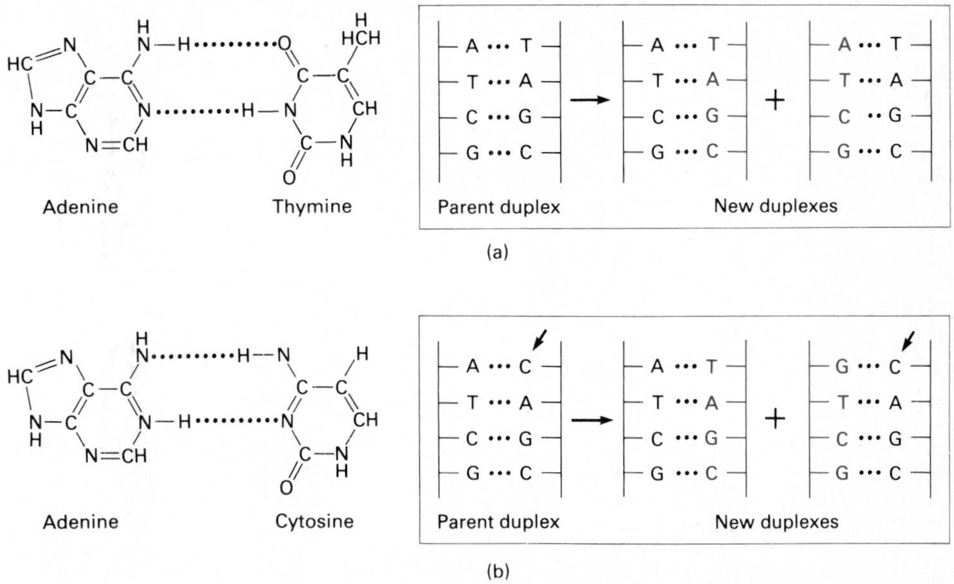

(a)

(b)

FIGURE 4-7
Spontaneous mutation by base substitution. (a) In its more stable tautomeric form, adenine pairs with thymine, and new complementary strands (color) are identical to strands in the original duplex DNA. (b) In another tautomeric form, adenine pairs with cytosine, and one of the new duplexes contains a G–C base pair instead of the original A–T base pair. Mutation by such base substitution during replication was first suggested by Watson and Crick and was later verified by experiments.

in the next replication (Fig. 4.7). The net result of the base substitution is the replacement of an AT base pair with a GC base pair, and the new sequence is transmitted to subsequent generations via preponderantly accurate copying of DNA sequences during semiconservative replication. Occasional miscopying during DNA replication is known to be the principal cause of spontaneous mutation and of the great majority of mutations induced by many chemical mutagens. Such mutagens cause an increase in miscopying errors and thereby cause an increase over the spontaneous value for the mutation rate of a given gene. For example, **base analogs** such as 5-bromouracil resemble a naturally occurring base in DNA and may be incorporated into replicating DNA in place of the usual base. The analog 5-bromouracil (5-BU) resembles thymine (5-methyluracil) except that it has a bromine atom instead of a methyl group at carbon-5. In its more stable keto form, 5-BU pairs with adenine, as does thymine, but in its rarer enol tautomeric form, 5-BU pairs with guanine (Fig. 4.8). Base-pair substitution takes place during replication of DNA with 5-BU in its sequence because of the miscopying due to altered pairing properties of the 5-BU enol tautomer. Other mutagens may act directly on DNA by chemically altering a base so that its pairing properties are changed and base-pair substitution will occur. Nitrous acid oxidatively deaminates adenine to produce hypoxanthine, which pairs with cytosine rather than thymine, and the mutagen also oxidatively deaminates cytosine to produce uracil, which pairs with adenine rather than guanine. Mutations arise in either case when base substitution occurs during DNA replication (Fig. 4.9).

Certain kinds of chemical mutagens alter DNA by adding or deleting one or more bases in a sequence, and physical mutagens such as ultraviolet light and x-rays damage DNA in various ways. The altered molecules faithfully replicate the new sequences, and mutant genes are thereby transmitted to successive generations. In some situations,

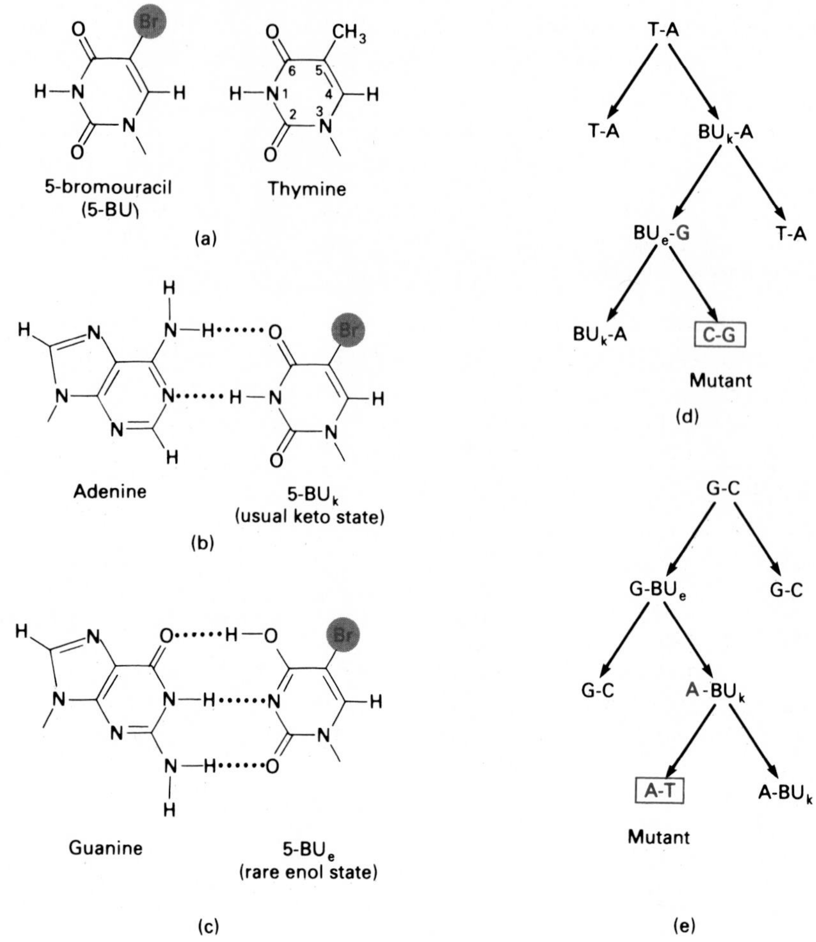

FIGURE 4-8
Induced mutation by base substitution.
(a) 5-Bromouracil is a mutagenic base
analog of thymine, differing only in the
residue at carbon-5. (b) The common
keto tautomer of 5-bromouracil (5-BU_k)
pairs with adenine, as does thymine,
whereas (c) the rare enol tautomer 5-BU_e
pairs with guanine instead of adenine.
(d) Because 5-BU_k and thymine both
pair with adenine, no base substitution
occurs during replication with 5-BU_k,
whereas 5-BU_e pairs with guanine and
thus induces mutation by substitution of
a C–G pair for the normal T–A base
pair. (e) When 5-BU_e pairs with guanine
during replication of a G–C base pair,
mutation may occur if 5-BU_e assumes
the more common 5-BU_k tautomeric
form and pairs with adenine, thereby
causing A–T substitution for the original
G–C base pair during replication.

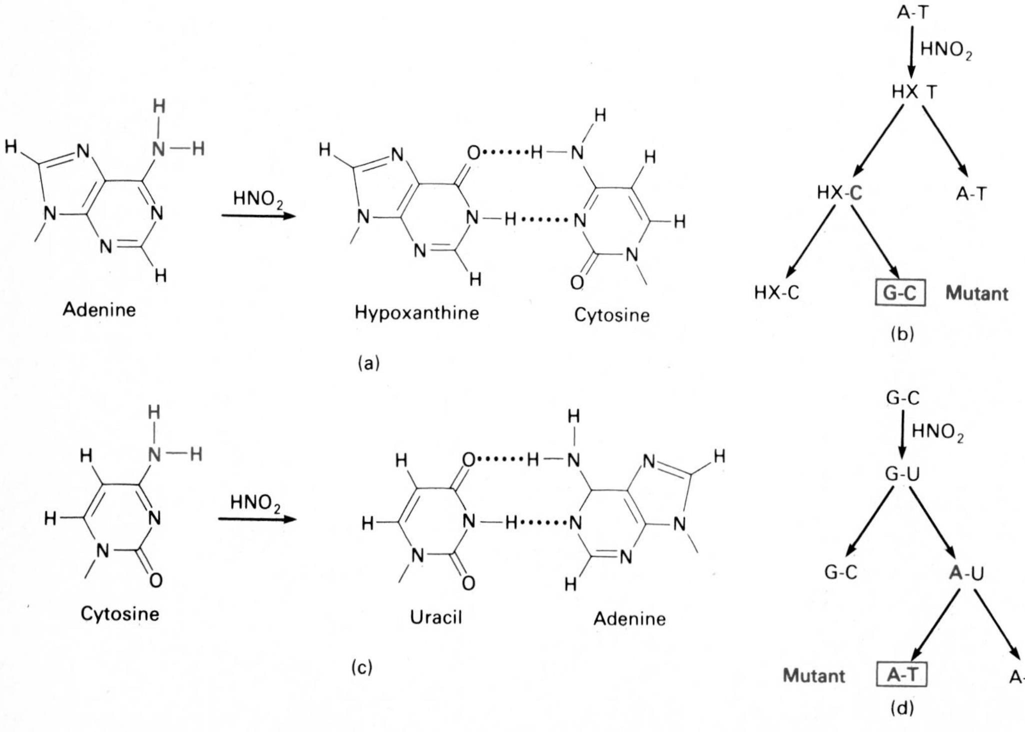

5-bromouracil
(5-BU)   Thymine

(a)

Adenine   5-BU_k
(usual keto state)

(b)

Guanine   5-BU_e
(rare enol state)

(c)

(d)

(e)

Adenine   Hypoxanthine   Cytosine

(a)

Cytosine   Uracil   Adenine

(c)

(b)

(d)

FIGURE 4-9
Mutation induction by
nitrous oxide (HNO_2).
(a) HNO_2 oxidatively
deaminates adenine to
produce hypoxanthine,
which pairs with cytosine
rather than thymine and
thereby (b) causes
mutation by base-pair
substitution of G–C for
A–T during replication.
(c) HNO_2 oxidatively
deaminates cytosine to
produce uracil, which
pairs with adenine but not
with guanine, and there-
by (d) causes mutation
by A–T base-pair
substitution for G–C
during replication.

however, an altered sequence may be repaired in reactions that involve many of the same enzymes that catalyze DNA replication. Such *DNA repair* is an important process in normally occurring phenomena as well, particularly in gene recombination, as we will see in later chapters.

Information Storage and Flow

DNA has the four main properties expected of genetic material: the capacity for *replication* of exact copies, the capacity to undergo *mutation* and to transmit mutations to successive generations, the capacity to *store genetic information* that specifies the characteristics of cells and organisms, and the capacity to *transfer* this information to molecules that can carry the genetic blueprints to the sites of protein synthesis. Genetic information is stored in coded form in the DNA molecular structure itself and is transferred to complementary messenger-RNA copies made in *transcription*. These messenger-RNA transcripts then guide the synthesis of encoded polypeptides during *translation* at the ribosomes in the cytoplasm. The same basic rules of complementary base pairing that ensure the accuracy of DNA replication are also responsible for the accuracy of recognition between DNA and RNA in transcription and for RNA and RNA in translation (Fig. 4.10).

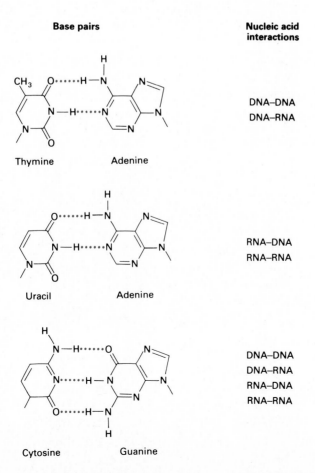

Base pairs

Nucleic acid interactions

DNA–DNA
DNA–RNA

Thymine   Adenine

RNA–DNA
RNA–RNA

Uracil   Adenine

DNA–DNA
DNA–RNA
RNA–DNA
RNA–RNA

Cytosine   Guanine

FIGURE 4-10
Complementary base pairing is the basic feature of the recognition system that provides for the high accuracy of translation at the ribosome. Thymine in DNA pairs with adenine in either DNA or RNA molecules. Uracil in RNA pairs with adenine in either DNA or RNA. Cytosine and guanine pair in any combination of DNA and RNA molecules (DNA–DNA, DNA–RNA, RNA–RNA).

4.4
The Genetic Code

During the 1940s it was evident from biochemical genetic studies of *Neurospora* and other organisms that genes specified proteins, particularly enzymes, and thereby specified the wealth of phenotypic traits programmed in the organism. With the introduction of the molecular model for DNA, it became possible to ask specific questions about the relationship between a gene and its specified protein product at the level of the molecules themselves. It was clear that the genetic information existed in coded form in DNA and that the coded information was used to guide the synthesis of proteins through specification of the kinds of amino acids from which the proteins were constructed. Deciphering the genetic code was a spectacular achievement of the 1960s.

The central problem was to identify the codewords, or **codons**, in DNA that specified the 20 different kinds of amino acids that were incorporated into proteins during synthesis at the ribosomes. The codons were generally believed to exist as triplets of nucleotides, or bases, because 64 unique triplet permutations of the four kinds of bases (4^3) were more than adequate to specify the 20 naturally occurring amino acids in proteins. A doublet coding dictionary would include only 16 unique permutations (4^2), which was inadequate.

In the 1960s, unlike today, it was much easier to analyze the code using RNA transcripts than using DNA sequences directly. Most of our information was obtained with RNA, and the generally recognized coding dictionary that emerged from these studies was based on RNA codons. Furthermore, the messenger RNA codons are directly involved in translation, and all information derived from studies with RNA can be related directly to the complementary triplets in DNA. In 1961 Marshall Nirenberg and Heinrich Matthaei made the first breakthrough in deciphering the code when they showed that artificial messenger RNA containing only uracil residues [**poly(U)**, or polyuridylic acid] directed the synthesis *in vitro* of polypeptide chains made up only of phenylalanines. The *in vitro* test system contained all the ingredients required for protein synthesis, including amino acids, but a different one of these amino acids was radioactively labeled in each test system. The aim was to find the system with radioactively labeled polypeptide and thereby to identify the amino acid encoded in the poly(U) messenger. Polyphenylalanine would be made in all the test systems, because phenylalanine was present in all of them, but the polypeptides would not be labeled except in the system containing radioactively labeled phenylalanine and the other amino acids without a label. When the labeled polypeptide was hydrolyzed, it was confirmed that phenylalanine was the only amino acid in the polymer. The codon UUU thus specified the amino acid phenylalanine (Fig. 4.11).

Between 1961 and 1967 the remaining 63 codons were deciphered and their specifications determined. Of the total 64 codons, 61 specified a particular amino acid and the remaining three served as **termination codons**, which marked the Stop point of a genetic message. One of the amino-acid-specifying codons, AUG, acted as an **initiation codon** for the beginning of a genetic message *and* as the codon that specified the amino

Second Nucleotide

	U	C	A	G	
U	UUU UUC Phe UUA UUG Leu	UCU UCC UCA Ser UCG	UAU UAC Tyr UAA UAG Stop	UGU UGC Cys UGA Stop UGG Trp	U C A G
C	CUU CUC CUA Leu CUG	CCU CCC CCA Pro CCG	CAU CAC His CAA CAG Gln	CGU CGC CGA Arg CGG	U C A G
A	AUU AUC AUA Ile AUG Met	ACU ACC ACA Thr ACG	AAU AAC Asn AAA AAG Lys	AGU AGC Ser AGA AGG Arg	U C A G
G	GUU GUC GUA Val GUG	GCU GCC GCA Ala GCG	GAU GAC Asp GAA GAG Glu	GGU GGC GGA Gly GGG	U C A G

First Nucleotide (left), Third Nucleotide (right)

Abbreviation	Amino acid
Ala	Alanine
Arg	Arginine
Asn	Asparagine
Asp	Aspartic acid
Cys	Cysteine
Gln	Glutamine
Glu	Glutamic acid
Gly	Glycine
His	Histidine
Ile	Isoleucine
Leu	Leucine
Lys	Lysine
Met	Methionine
Phe	Phenylalanine
Pro	Proline
Ser	Serine
Thr	Threonine
Trp	Tryptophan
Tyr	Tyrosine
Val	Valine

FIGURE 4-11
The genetic coding dictionary, showing messenger RNA codons and the amino acids and Stop punctuations they specify. As little as one codon (for Met and Trp) and as many as six codons (for Leu, Ser, and Arg) may specify a particular one of the 20 amino acids included in the genetic code. Three of the 64 triplets serve as Stop codons that terminate a genetic message, and the codon AUG specifies Met at the initiation of a genetic message.

acid methionine. These studies and others showed that the genetic code had the following features.

1. The code is *triplet*, and each of the 64 codons consists of a unique combination or permutation of 3 nucleotides drawn from the set of 4 kinds of nucleotides in DNA or RNA.

2. The code includes specific Start and Stop codons, or *punctuations*, that mark the beginning and end of each genetic message.

3. Codon *synonyms* exist for 18 of the 20 encoded amino acids—only methionine and tryptophan are specified by one codon each—so the code is degenerate.

4. The code is *consistent*; each of the 61 codons is specified for only one amino acid in the set of 20.

5. The code is essentially *universal*, because the same codons specify the same amino acids in viruses, prokaryotes, and eukaryotes, and the same punctuation codons serve in all organisms. A few codons have been found to have a different meaning in mitochondrial genes, but 60 or more of the 64 codons have exactly the same meaning in mitochondria as in all life forms. The few exceptions in mitochondria do not invalidate the general theme of code universality.

Because the codons in a gene sequence specify the amino acids in a protein sequence, we would expect that certain base substitutions might alter a codon so that a different amino acid was specified in the mutant protein from that specified in the normal protein. The first example of a difference in a single amino acid between normal and mutant protein products of a gene was described for the β chain of normal adult hemoglobin (Hb A) and sickle-cell hemoglobin (Hb S) in humans. Amino acid 6 in the β chain of 146 amino acids of β globin is *glutamic acid* in

FIGURE 4-12
(a) In the gene coded for the β-globin chain of normal adult hemoglobin (Hb A), the codon corresponding to position 6 specifies glutamic acid in the amino acid sequence of the chain.
(b) The β-globin gene for sickle-cell hemoglobin (Hb S) contains a base substitution in codon 6 and thus specifies valine instead of glutamic acid in the sequence. The remaining 145 amino acids of the β-globin chain are identical in Hb A and Hb S proteins.

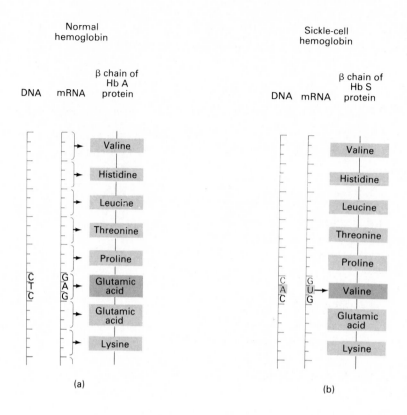

Hb A but *valine* in Hb S (Fig. 4.12). Although the codons were unknown in the mid-1950s when this study by Vernon Ingram was published, we now know that a single base substitution in the triplet codon for amino acid 6 is responsible for the amino acid difference in the globin chain. In this particular example, the mutation has a profound effect on the oxygen-carrying capacity of hemoglobin and on the consequences for the person who has sickle-cell anemia, because Hb S instead of Hb A is in the bloodstream. Not all mutations, whether or not they arise from base substitution, have such a severe effect on the individual. In fact, many mutations have no observable or detectable effect on the individual. Such silent or *neutral mutations* may be due to the replacement of one codon synonym for another, both of which specify the same amino acid, or to a new codon that specifies a different amino acid that does not alter the behavior or conformation of the protein in any consequential way. During the evolution of cytochrome *c*, for example, as many as 44 of the 112 amino acids in the protein have been changed in humans (as compared with yeast), but the protein carries out the same respiratory function in both species.

A number of amino acids are not included in the genetic code. In each case we know that the uncoded amino acid either is a product of protein degradation or arises by modification of a coded amino acid after the latter has been incorporated into the polypeptide chain during translation. For example, collagen contains a substantial amount of hydroxyproline residues that result from the hydroxylation of proline after proline has been incorporated into the polypeptide. The twenty encoded amino acids are the only ones to be included directly in a growing polypeptide chain as synthesis proceeds at the ribosomes.

4.5
Transcription and Translation of Stored Information _____

The encoded genetic instructions in DNA are spatially separated from the sites of protein synthesis in the cytoplasm, which means that there must be an intermediary to carry DNA instructions to the sites of translation. The logical candidate for this intermediary, or messenger, is RNA. It also is a polynucleotide and can interact specifically with DNA through complementary base pairing.

In the process of **transcription** one strand of the DNA duplex serves as the template for synthesis of a complementary single-stranded RNA polymer consisting of covalently bonded ribonucleotides. The reactions are catalyzed by the enzyme DNA-dependent RNA polymerase, or **RNA polymerase** for short. The resulting transcript molecule is **messenger RNA**, or **mRNA**, which moves from its site of synthesis along the DNA template out to the cytoplasm. The mRNA binds at its 5′ end to a group of complementary bases located at the 3′ end of **ribosomal RNA (rRNA)** in the smaller of the two subunits of the ribosome. In this way the mRNA is oriented appropriately to the ribosome, and the first part of the encoded message is in position to be translated into the first part of the polypeptide, which will be its amino terminus.

For **translation** to occur, however, the correct amino acids must be brought to the mRNA–ribosome aggregate, and they must be incorporated into the polypeptide in the precise sequence corresponding to the sequence of codons in mRNA. Translation must therefore involve an appropriate means of recognition between mRNA codons and amino acids. Once again the recognition system involves complementary base pairing between nucleic acid molecules. Each amino acid is bound to a **transfer RNA (tRNA)** molecule, which includes in its sequence a triplet of nucleotides called an **anticodon**. The complex of amino acid and its tRNA carrier, or **aminoacyl–tRNA**, interacts at the ribosome by complementary base pairing between mRNA codon and tRNA anticodon (Fig. 4.13).

Once codon–anticodon base pairing has occurred, a sequence of events follows in which the incoming aminoacyl residue is added to the growing polypeptide chain and the tRNA component is recycled in the cytoplasm. The same process is repeated for each amino acid added to the growing chain, until a stop codon in mRNA signals the carboxy terminus of the polypeptide. In translation, therefore, the genetic message transcribed into mRNA is read off in codon triplets, in sequence, and the message translation consists of a polypeptide whose primary structure of amino acid sequence corresponds to the specific encoded genetic information.

All three kinds of RNA are transcripts of specific genes. Polypeptide-specifying genes are transcribed into mRNA, which is then translated, but genes for rRNA and tRNA are only transcribed and are

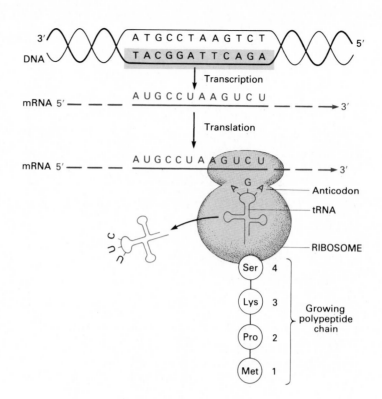

FIGURE 4-13
Complementary base pairing is the mechanism by which different components of the genetic apparatus recognize each other and interact appropriately. During transcription an exact complementary copy of messenger RNA (mRNA) is synthesized from the template (coding) strand (gray screen) of duplex DNA in nucleus or nucleoid, catalyzed by the enzyme RNA polymerase. The single-stranded mRNA copy of the genetic message is translated into a particular polypeptide during interactions at the ribosome, where mRNA binds. The correct amino acids in the correct sequence are brought to the mRNA–ribosome complex by transfer-RNA (tRNA) molecules, whose anticodon recognizes and pairs with the complementary mRNA codon in the message copy. One tRNA carries the growing polypeptide chain during translation, and other tRNAs are recycled. Note that the chain grows in accordance with the sequence of codons in mRNA (AUG = Met, CCU = Pro, AAG = Lys, UCU = Ser, and so on).

not translated. The products of rRNA and tRNA genes, therefore, are rRNA and tRNA transcripts. Various methods can be used to show that all these RNAs are transcribed from DNA and that each kind of RNA is encoded in unique sets of genes. One method, called **molecular hybridization**, is based on the specificity and discrimination of complementary base pairing. When duplex DNA is melted to single strands at high temperature or high alkaline pH, the separated strands can be recovered and mixed with single-stranded RNA. The formation of DNA–RNA **hybrid duplexes** signifies the complementarity of the nucleic acid strands, which could only be the case if the RNA were transcribed from the DNA with which it pairs (Fig. 4.14).

The location of genes specifying tRNA or rRNA can be determined by the method of ***in situ* hybridization**, which utilizes molecular hybridization and autoradiography to make direct observations of chromosomes on microscope slide preparations. Radioactively labeled rRNA extracted from ribosomes or tRNA extracted from cytoplasm is applied to chromosome preparations on a slide, after pretreatment to partially melt chromosomal DNA and allow base pairing to occur. The preparation is covered with a photographic emulsion and autoradiographs are later developed to reveal the silver grains in the emulsion, which indicate the sites where radioactively labeled RNA has bound to complementary DNA sequences in the chromosomes (Fig. 4.15). If enough of a particular mRNA is available, particular genes specifying a polypeptide can also be located by this very useful method. Other methods have become available in recent years by which specific genes can be isolated and specific mRNAs identified in molecular assays. We will discuss these methods later.

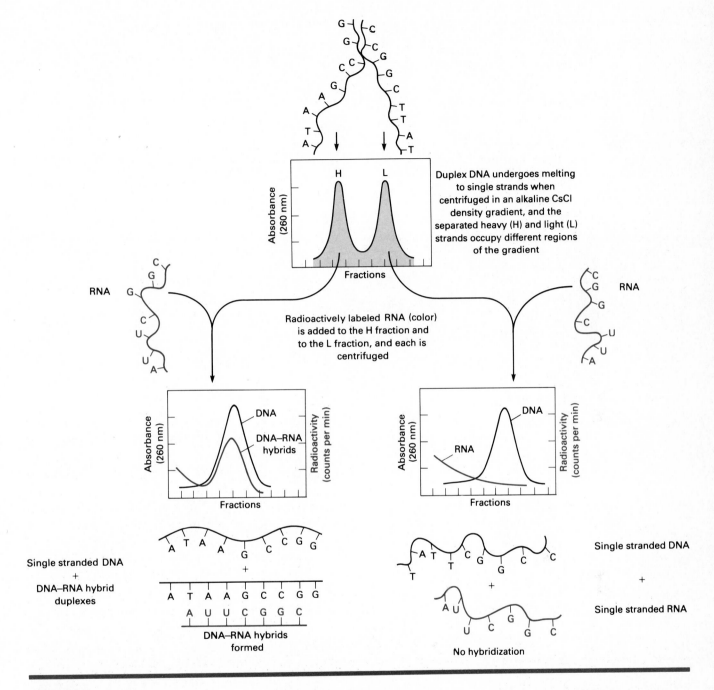

FIGURE 4-14

Molecular hybridization. Single strands of melted duplex DNA can be separated by centrifugation in CsCl density gradients if one strand is heavier (contains more A and G, the larger purines) than its complement (which contains more C and T, the smaller pyrimidines). Melting, or denaturation, may be achieved by prior heating or directly in alkaline CsCl gradients during centrifugation. Fractions of heavy (H) and light (L) strands are mixed with radioactively labeled RNA (color) and the mixtures are centrifuged to determine whether the RNA and DNA strands are complementary and therefore have undergone base pairing to produce DNA–RNA molecular hybrid duplexes. Unhybridized single-stranded DNA and double-stranded DNA–RNA molecular hybrids occur in large amounts in the same region of the gradient, but molecular hybrids are distinguished by their radioactively labeled RNA. If hybridization has not occurred, the radioactively labeled RNA molecules are scattered across the gradient because of their varied lengths, but the long single strands of DNA appear in the same region of the gradient in each case. Even if unhybridized RNA were to occupy a confined region of the gradient, it could be distinguished from DNA–RNA hybrids by its response to ribonuclease. The enzyme digests single-stranded RNA but has no effect on DNA–RNA molecular hybrids.

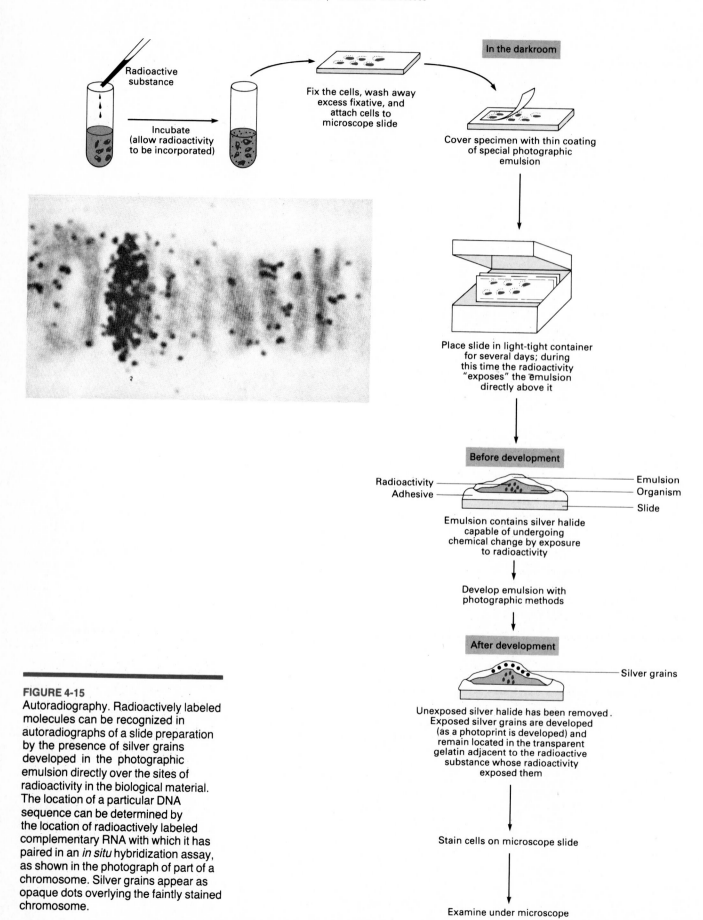

In the darkroom

Radioactive substance

Incubate (allow radioactivity to be incorporated)

Fix the cells, wash away excess fixative, and attach cells to microscope slide

Cover specimen with thin coating of special photographic emulsion

Place slide in light-tight container for several days; during this time the radioactivity "exposes" the emulsion directly above it

Before development

Radioactivity — Emulsion
Adhesive — Organism
— Slide

Emulsion contains silver halide capable of undergoing chemical change by exposure to radioactivity

Develop emulsion with photographic methods

After development

Silver grains

Unexposed silver halide has been removed. Exposed silver grains are developed (as a photoprint is developed) and remain located in the transparent gelatin adjacent to the radioactive substance whose radioactivity exposed them

Stain cells on microscope slide

Examine under microscope

FIGURE 4-15
Autoradiography. Radioactively labeled molecules can be recognized in autoradiographs of a slide preparation by the presence of silver grains developed in the photographic emulsion directly over the sites of radioactivity in the biological material. The location of a particular DNA sequence can be determined by the location of radioactively labeled complementary RNA with which it has paired in an *in situ* hybridization assay, as shown in the photograph of part of a chromosome. Silver grains appear as opaque dots overlying the faintly stained chromosome.

4.6
Gene Organization and Transcript Processing

Until the mid-1970s most of our information about the organization of the gene was derived indirectly from studies of natural and artificial mRNAs and from amino acid sequences in the polypeptide products encoded in the DNA sequences. By direct sequencing of the DNA itself and by molecular and electron microscopic analysis of DNA–mRNA hybrid duplexes, it soon became apparent that genes were organized differently in prokaryotes and eukaryotes. In prokaryotes the information in DNA consists of an uninterrupted sequence of triplet codons extending from the initiation codon TAC at the 3′ end of the message to the 5′ termination codon; the gene and polypeptide are *colinear*. Transcribed mRNA is virtually unchanged from its synthesis to its utilization in translation. In eukaryotes, however, the initial transcript is considerably longer than the final mRNA molecule that guides polypeptide synthesis at the ribosomes. Through direct nucleotide sequencing and other methods, it soon became clear that the gene in eukaryotes is composed of coding and noncoding segments interspersed between the beginning and the end of the genetic message. The initial transcript, or **pre-mRNA**, is an exact copy of the DNA sequence, but pre-mRNA is processed to its mature mRNA form by a series of reactions that includes excision of noncoding segments (**introns**) and splicing together of the coding segments (**exons**) to yield the final sequence of contiguous codons colinear with the polypeptide (Fig. 4.16).

FIGURE 4-16
The DNA sequence of a gene includes coding regions, or exons (black), which are expressed in the polypeptide translation, and intervening sequences, or introns (color), which are noncoding and are not expressed. The entire gene sequence is transcribed into a precursor of messenger RNA (pre-mRNA). Noncoding introns are excised precisely, and the exons are then spliced together precisely to yield the mature mRNA whose sequence of codons is colinear with the sequence of amino acids in the polypeptide translation. A region at the 5′ end and a region at the 3′ end of mature mRNA are not translated, but they have other functions in the translation process. Translation proceeds in the 5′ to 3′ direction along mRNA, and amino acids are added from the first residue at the amino terminus to the last residue at the carboxy terminus of the polypeptide chain.

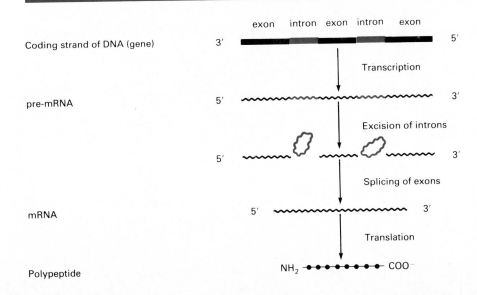

The existence of **split genes**, also called mosaic or interrupted genes, came as a complete surprise. We now know that virtually every gene in eukaryotes and its viruses are organized in this same fashion, although the numbers of exons and introns and the relative lengths of these segments obviously vary from one gene to another. The gene that encodes the major chicken egg protein, *ovalbumin*, has been intensively analyzed for several years. By direct DNA sequencing, the 7564 nucleotide pairs of the gene have been identified and 8 coding segments have been found to include the codons for the 386 amino acids of the protein. All 7 of the intervening noncoding segments are excised during pre-mRNA processing, and the exons are spliced together to make the continuous reading frame for ovalbumin. When ovalbumin DNA and mature mRNA are hybridized, the duplexes observed in electron micrographs consist of paired regions separated by unpaired loops of the DNA strand (Fig. 4.17). The paired regions represent complementary DNA and mRNA coded segments. The noncoding DNA introns remain unpaired because the complementary sequences were excised from pre-mRNA during its processing to mature mRNA.

FIGURE 4-17
The chicken ovalbumin gene consists of 8 exons alternating with 7 introns over a length of 7564 nucleotide pairs. (a) Tracing taken from an electron micrograph of a hybrid duplex molecule made up of DNA (black) and mature mRNA (color) strands that encode the ovalbumin protein. The 8 exons of the gene are all that remain in the complementary RNA strand, as shown by the pairing geometry. The 7 introns (A–G) are missing in mRNA but are evident from the size and location of the unpaired loops of DNA in the duplex molecule. (With permission from F. Gannon et al., 1979, *Nature* **278**:428–434, Fig. 3b. Copyright © 1979 Macmillan Journals Limited.) (b) The numbers of nucleotides in different parts of the gene are shown in tabulated form. Exons 1–8 contain a total of 1872 nucleotides (color), and excised introns A–G contain a total of 5692 nucleotides (black). The polypeptide of 386 amino acids is specified by only 1161 nucleotides (1158 + 3 for Stop). The remaining 711 nucleotides of the total of 1872 occur at the 3′ and 5′ ends of the gene and are not translated.

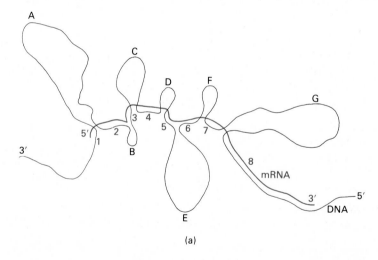

(a)

Coding sequences (exons)	Intervening sequences (introns)	Location in gene (nucleotide nos.)	Sequence size (no. nucleotides)
1		1–47	47
	A	48–1636	1589
2		1637–1821	185
	B	1822–2072	251
3		2073–2123	51
	C	2124–2704	581
4		2705–2833	129
	D	2834–3233	400
5		3234–3351	118
	E	3352–4309	958
6		4310–4452	143
	F	4453–4783	331
7		4784–4939	156
	G	4940–6521	1582
8		6522–7564	1043
			7564

(b)

The significance of split-gene organization in eukaryotes is uncertain, although much interesting speculation has emerged. The evolutionary origin of split genes also remains speculative. According to some viewpoints, the prokaryotic gene organization may represent the ancestral pattern from which the eukaryotic pattern evolved later on. According to others, the eukaryotic pattern may be the original one that was altered during subsequent prokaryotic evolution by losses of introns and the eventual appearance of modern-day unsplit genes. In either of these scenarios we must still seek explanations for the relative advantages of the different patterns of gene organization during evolution. Some progress is being made, but these questions remain among the most challenging in current biological studies.

4.7
Recombinant DNA Technology

In order for a particular gene or DNA sequence to be analyzed, it must first be isolated from the entire set of genes, or **genome**, in the cell or organism. Once isolated, the desired DNA must be obtained in pure form and in adequate amounts for molecular analysis. These objectives can be realized by procedures collectively referred to as **recombinant DNA technology**.

Part or all of a genome can be cut into pieces of useful size by the use of one or more **restriction enzymes**, or restriction endonucleases, which break both strands of duplex DNA at sites specific for each of the known enzymes (Table 4.2). The cut pieces, called **restriction fragments**, are separated according to their lengths by migration in a gel under the influence of an electrical field. During such **gel electrophoresis**, progressively shorter fragments move progressively faster through the gel, and the restriction fragments can then be isolated and analyzed (Fig. 4.18).

The individual sets of restriction fragments in the genomic collection are incubated with *vector DNA*, which has also been cut with restriction enzymes. Some of the molecules in the mixture will be **recombinant DNA**, which is genomic DNA spliced to vector DNA through base pairing between exposed single-stranded ends that have resulted from staggered breaks due to restriction enzyme action on the duplexes. Vector DNA serves several essential functions: (1) It provides a means of entry for the desired gene into a host cell. (2) It provides a replicating system to make many copies of the desired gene that is spliced to it. (3) It can carry suitable marker genes to indicate whether or not recombinant DNA is present in the host cells. The principal vectors are viral DNA or plasmids, which are dispensable DNA molecules that can exist and replicate independently of the host genome in the host cell (Fig. 4.19).

Through appropriate methods of examining colonies of host cells, the desired colonies carrying recombinant DNA can be identified and isolated. In this way the entire genome of an organism can be obtained as a collection of bits and pieces in a collection of host colonies or clones carrying recombinant DNA. From such a *genomic library of cloned DNA*, searches can be made for a specific gene or DNA sequence. The search is

TABLE 4-2
A Selection of Site-Specific Restriction Endonucleases Isolated from Bacteria

Enzyme	Bacterial Source	Restriction Site
EcoRI	Escherichia coli RY13	5′—G↓A-A-T-T-C—3′ 3′—C-T-T-A-A↑G—5′
EcoRII	Escherichia coli R245	5′—↓C-C-T-G-G—3′ 3′—G-G-A-C-C↑—5′
BamI	Bacillus amyloliquefaciens	5′—G↓G-A-T-C-C—3′ 3′—C-C-T-A-G↑G—5′
HpaII	Hemophilus parainfluenza	5′—C↓C-G-G—3′ 3′—G-G-C↑C—5′
HaeIII	Hemophilus aegyptius	5′—G-G↓C-C—3′ 3′—C-C↑G-G—5′
Hind II	Hemophilus influenza Rd	5′—G-T-Py↓Pu-A-C—3′ 3′—C-A-Pu↑Py-T-G—5′
Hind III	Hemophilus influenza Rd	5′—A↓A-G-C-T-T—3′ 3′—T-T-C-G-A↑A—5′
PstI	Providencia stuartii	5′—C-T-G-C-A↓G—3′ 3′—G↑A-C-G-T-C—5′
SmaI	Serratia marcescens	5′—C-C-C↓G-G-G—3′ 3′—G-G-G↑C-C-C—5′
HhaI	Hemophilus haemolyticus	5′—G-C-G↓C—3′ 3′—C↑G-C-G—5′
Bgl II	Bacillus globiggi	5′—A↓G-A-T-C-T—3′ 3′—T-C-T-A-G↑A—5′

All known restriction sites are 4 to 6 nucleotide pairs long and have a twofold rotational symmetry. Arrows indicate specific sites of cleavage on each strand of the duplex DNA.

FIGURE 4-18
Gel electrophoresis of restriction fragments. A sample of restriction fragments is placed at the top of a gel column, and they migrate through the gel when power is applied to produce an electrical field from cathode (−) to anode (+) terminals in buffer. Smaller fragments move faster than larger fragments through the gel, and fragments of different size (length) come to rest in different parts of the gel when the power supply is turned off. The separated fragment populations can be analyzed afterward in sequencing or other assays.

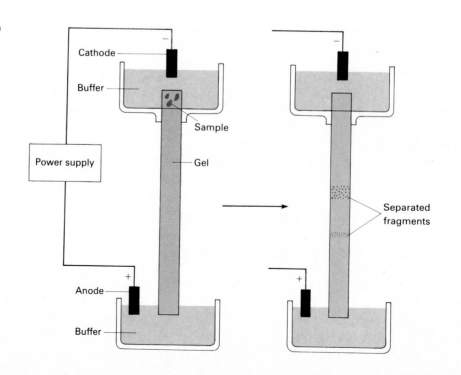

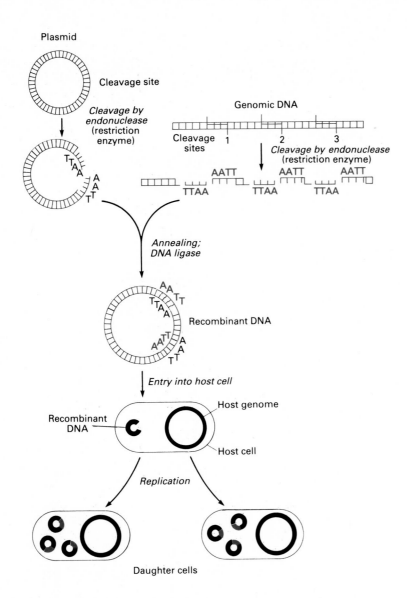

Plasmid

Cleavage site

Cleavage by endonuclease (restriction enzyme)

Genomic DNA

Cleavage sites 1 2 3

Cleavage by endonuclease (restriction enzyme)

AATT   AATT   AATT
TTAA   TTAA   TTAA

Annealing; DNA ligase

Recombinant DNA

Entry into host cell

Host genome

Recombinant DNA

Host cell

Replication

Daughter cells

FIGURE 4-19
Recombinant DNA technology. A fraction of genomic DNA that has been cut into restriction fragments by a restriction enzyme (endonuclease) and isolated by gel electrophoresis is incubated with vector DNA (plasmid or viral DNA) that has also been cut by the same restriction enzyme. After the vector DNA and genomic restriction fragments in the mixture have had time to undergo base pairing, or annealing, and the broken ends have been sealed by DNA ligase action, any recombinant (spliced) DNA that has formed can be identified and isolated for incubation with host cells. Once recombinant DNA has entered the host cytoplasm, it can replicate independently of the host genome and thereby be amplified during host cell reproduction, producing larger amounts of the molecules for subsequent experiments or assays.

simplified by the use of *probes* consisting of known DNA or RNA that can pair with the unique gene sequence under study. For example, large quantities of radioactively labeled mRNA can be obtained from cells that make an abundance of one particular polypeptide, such as reticulocytes that make globins for hemoglobin or oviduct cells that make ovalbumin egg protein. Isolated globin or ovalbumin mRNA or other known probes can then be applied to samples of cells or cloned DNA from any or all of the collection of host colonies or DNA fragments in order to find the colony or DNA with the desired sequence in the genomic library. One of the most widely used of these procedures is the **Southern blot assay**, which was developed in 1975 by E. M. Southern. Purified genomic fragments are transferred by surface contact, or "blotting," to cellulose nitrate paper, and the adhering DNA is denatured in order to facilitate base pairing. The radioactively labeled probe molecules are applied to the "blots" and allowed to undergo molecular hybridization. The desired genomic DNA retains bound radioactive probe in hybrid duplexes, whereas unbound probe is washed away. The target DNA is revealed by its radioactivity in an autoradiograph, and the reference DNA in the collection can then provide the material to transfer to cells for growth in culture and consequent amplification of the desired DNA for further study (Fig. 4.20).

An important follow-through in analyzing an identified cloned DNA is to determine its base sequence. DNA sequencing methods developed in the mid-1970s by Frederick Sanger and by Alan Maxam and Walter Gilbert are now used routinely in many laboratories, as are the methods for cloning specific genes. These methods have revolutionized molecular biology. The Maxam–Gilbert chemical method for DNA sequencing of restriction fragments of appropriate lengths utilizes a ^{32}P radioactive label to identify the 5′ ends of the two strands of duplex DNA. Once labeled, the duplexes are melted to single strands and one of the two complementary strands is sequenced. The preparation of 5′-labeled single strands is divided into four equal portions, or aliquots, and each of these is treated to identify one of the four kinds of bases (G, A, T, and C). Each of the four chemical treatments causes the DNA strand to *break* at the site of one particular kind of the four bases, and the reagent concentrations are adjusted so that an average of one break is made per restriction fragment in each of the four aliquots. In this way a single break will occur at random along the fragment length, but only at the

FIGURE 4-20
Southern blot assay. (a) In order to identify a particular sequence of genomic DNA from a library of cloned DNA, samples of different cloned DNAs are transferred by surface contact ("blotting") to cellulose nitrate paper, and the adhered DNA is denatured to facilitate base pairing through molecular hybridization with added probe molecules of known DNA or RNA containing a radioactive label. The paper is then washed to remove any unhybridized probe molecules, which do not stick to the paper, and an autoradiograph is made of the paper and its contents. Hybrid molecules with the radioactive label are the only ones to appear in the developed autoradiograph, thus indicating which of the cloned DNAs is complementary to the known probe—and is therefore identified. The identified cloned DNA in the reference collection may then be used in various studies. (b) Southern blot showing hybridization of a radioactively labeled probe of spleen focus-forming virus DNA with DNA restriction fragments from different strains of murine erythroleukemia cells. Two DNA bands present in gel lanes B to F but absent in lanes A and G correspond to 3.3 kilobase (kb)- and 3.0 kb-long fragments representative of viral DNA integrated into mouse chromatin. (Photograph courtesy of D. E. Axelrod.)

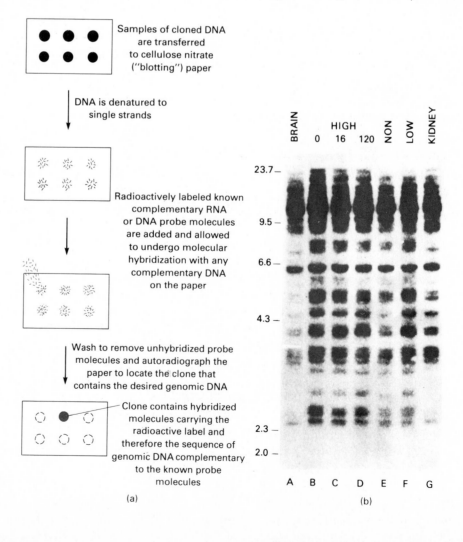

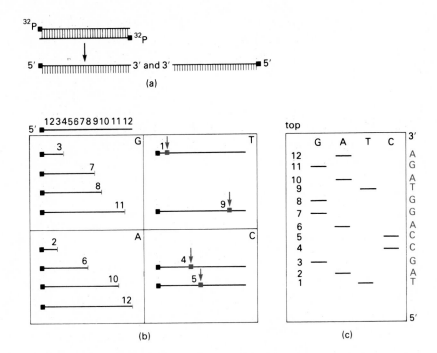

FIGURE 4-21
The Maxam–Gilbert method for sequencing DNA. (a) A pure preparation of DNA, such as a population of a particular restriction fragment 12 base-pairs long, is labeled with ^{32}P at the 5′ ends of both strands of the duplexes. Duplexes are separated into two fractions of complementary single strands, and one of these fractions is then sequenced. (b) The fraction of single strands is divided into four approximately equal portions and each of these aliquots is treated specifically to identify one of the four bases (G, A, T, or C). Each treatment causes breakage of the DNA strand at the site of the base in question, but the concentration of reagents is adjusted so that each strand experiences an average of one break. The break may occur by chance at any of the sites occupied by the base involved, and a break will occur at one or another of these sites in the many fragments making up the aliquot of DNA. The different lengths of the broken 12-base-long fragments are shown in panels for G and A; the site of a break in the 12-base-long fragments is indicated by an arrow in the panels for T and C. Each usable fragment retains its original 5′ end, as determined by autoradiographic detection of the radioactive ^{32}P marker. Fragments lacking the 5′ end are not visible in the autoradiograph, and thus confusion is avoided. (c) Each of the four aliquots migrates in a separate lane in a gel that is subjected to an electrical field in a gel electrophoresis apparatus. Fragments migrate at rates proportional to their length, with the shorter fragments migrating more rapidly toward the bottom of the gel from the origin at the top. By comparing the autoradiographic patterns of the 12 different-sized fragments in the four gel lanes, we can read the entire sequence of 12 bases directly. Reading proceeds from the shortest to the longest pieces, going from the 5′ to the 3′ end of the sequence, upward from the bottom to the top of the gel.

site of the particular base that is sensitive to the chemical treatment. If this were not the case, the restriction fragments would be cut into tiny bits that would be useless for sequencing. Thus, in the aliquot to identify adenine, for example, some fragments are broken at one adenine site and some fragments at other adenine sites, but in the entire population of treated fragments every adenine site experiences a break in some of the fragments. A series of radioactively labeled fragments is thereby generated in each aliquot, the four sets of fragments are run in four separate lanes in a gel electrophoresis system, and the fragments form distinct bands in the gel in proportion to fragment length. Each band of fragments is visible by autoradiography, because of the ^{32}P-labeled 5′ end, and each lane in the gel contains DNA treated to reveal one of the four kinds of bases. The sequence is read from the bottom to the top of the gel (that is, from the shortest 5′-labeled pieces to the longest 5′-labeled pieces), taking one band at a time across all the four gel lanes (Fig. 4.21).

About 150 or more bases can be read from a single gel run, and when all the data are collected from sequences of all the restriction fragments obtained from the original cloned DNA, the entire base sequence of that DNA is assembled. Sequences of many thousands of nucleotides can be obtained in this way, which may encompass the entire genome in the smaller viruses and whole genes in other organisms, such as the 7564 nucleotides of the ovalbumin gene (see Fig. 4.17). The electrophoretic method is sensitive enough to resolve nucleotide chains that differ by only one residue, thus providing a high degree of accuracy in sequence analysis. Furthermore, we can obtain results in days or weeks via rapid sequencing methods, instead of the years required for the earlier tedious and time-consuming analyses.

The facility with which genes can be cloned and DNA can be sequenced does not mean that we can expect to dissect any genome of interest down to the minutest detail. A typical mammalian genome may consist of 3 billion base pairs (3×10^9 bp) of DNA. Even with restriction fragments 20,000 to 50,000 bp long it would be necessary to establish 20,000 to 50,000 different clones, each carrying one unique restriction fragment in a recombinant-DNA molecule. The useful size of a restriction fragment depends on the amount of DNA that can be spliced to the vector and still permit entry into the host cell. These realities make it clear that molecular analysis of the genome is an enormous and formidable task. We must seek additional means by which to understand the organization and qualities of the gene and the genome in relation to development of an organism according to its genetic program.

4.8
Regulation of Information Flow

Each cell contains a complete set of genes, yet the genetically identical cells of a multicellular organism are structurally and functionally differentiated into blood, skin, liver, and numerous other cell types. When one sample from an *E. coli* culture is grown in media with lactose, the cells synthesize β-galactosidase and utilize the sugar in metabolism, whereas another sample of cells grown in media without lactose does not synthesize the enzyme even though the *lac* genes are present. Clearly, the flow of instructions from DNA must be regulated such that some genes are active only at certain times in certain cells. Genes specify the *kinds* of proteins the cell can produce, but the *amounts* made of these proteins are determined by various control systems, most of which act on the genes themselves. The most common and best understood controls are ones that turn transcription on and off; that is, they regulate the synthesis of mRNA without which translation cannot occur.

Transcriptional control can be demonstrated more readily in cells devoted to the synthesis of one particular protein in large amounts, such as in reticulocytes that make hemoglobin or in oviduct cells that make ovalbumin to the exclusion of all or most of the other proteins encoded in their DNA. If control over protein synthesis is exerted at the level of transcription, active cells should have mRNA transcripts and inactive cells should lack them. Molecular hybridization provides a specific and sensitive assay for mRNA transcripts, because hybrid duplexes are formed only by base pairing between hemoglobin or ovalbumin DNA probes and their respective complementary mRNAs. When virgin oviduct tissue is assayed for ovalbumin pre-mRNA or mRNA, less than one molecule of RNA hybridizes with ovalbumin probe DNA. If the oviduct tissue is stimulated by hormones such as estrogen, large quantities of pre-mRNA and mRNA then hybridize with probe DNA. Virgin oviduct does not synthesize ovalbumin whereas hormonally induced oviduct carries out synthesis, therefore, because transcription is turned off in virgin tissue but is turned on in induced tissue. Hormonal treatment has no effect on reticulocytes, which do not synthesize ovalbumin under any conditions. Transcription of ovalbumin DNA is permanently turned off in reticulocytes, but the process can be activated in oviduct cells that respond to hormonal induction. Similarly, globin transcripts are found only in reticulocytes and only when the cells are actively synthesizing hemoglobin, whereas globin mRNA is not found in oviduct cells under any experimental condition tested.

Quite different transcriptional controls are responsible for *differential gene action* in prokaryotes, although the end result is also for transcription to be switched on and off in response to regulatory proteins acting on the genes. In the case of β-galactosidase synthesis in *E. coli*, for example, lactose acts as an inducer of enzyme synthesis through its interaction with a **repressor protein**, which is itself the encoded product of a *lac* repressor gene. In the absence of lactose, the repressor protein binds to *lac* DNA and prevents transcription by blocking the movement of RNA polymerase along the DNA template (Fig. 4.22). When lactose is present, the sugar molecules bind to repressor protein and alter its ability to bind to DNA. With the removal of bound repressor, RNA polymerase is no longer hindered and it proceeds along the gene sequence catalyzing the synthesis of *lac* mRNA transcripts. Once mRNA is available, β-galactosidase is translated and the enzyme participates in

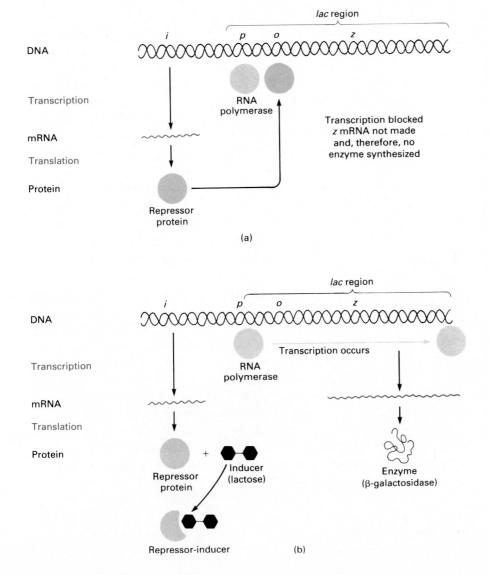

FIGURE 4-22
Differential gene action in *E. coli*.
(a) When lactose is absent, the repressor protein product of repressor gene *i* can bind to DNA at the special *o* (operator) site immediately adjacent to gene *z*, which codes for the enzyme β-galactosidase. Transcription is blocked by the repressor, which is bound to DNA between the binding site *p* (promoter) of RNA polymerase and gene *z*, and the enzyme cannot move past the repressor to catalyze transcription of gene *z*. Without mRNA, no enzyme is synthesized. (b) When the inducer lactose is present, it binds to repressor protein and so alters its conformation that repressor–inducer cannot bind to the *o* site of DNA. Because it is not blocked by repressor, RNA polymerase is able to move along the DNA strand and catalyze transcription of the mRNA for the β-galactosidase gene *z*, which is translated. The inducible enzyme is then available to process lactose in cellular metabolism.

lactose utilization in the induced cells. If lactose is depleted in the medium, enzyme synthesis comes to a halt because repressor protein is once again in a conformationally suitable form to bind to DNA and prevent further transcription. These mRNA transcripts obviously have a relatively short half-life, and new transcripts must be made in order for enzyme synthesis to continue.

Transcriptional controls are only one of the means by which gene action is regulated. Gene action may also be influenced by mechanisms that modulate processing of pre-mRNA transcripts at any of the steps that lead to the mature mRNA molecules, or by mechanisms that act during or after translation, or by direct alteration of the genes themselves. We will discuss these mechanisms in Chapter 14.

Packaging of the Genome in Chromosomes

The entire genome of a bacterial species is contained within a single naked duplex DNA molecule that is circular in conformation. In eukaryotes the genome is partitioned among a set of chromosomes, each chromosome consisting of one linear duplex DNA molecule in association with particular proteins, including **histones**. The eukaryotic chromosome is a **nucleoprotein fiber** whose great length is folded and condensed into a structure that may be only a few micrometers long in its most contracted state (Fig. 4.23). The replication and distribution of the eukaryotic genome to progeny cells pose quite different problems from the replication and distribution of a single DNA molecule in prokaryotic species. The synthesis of new chromosomes during the eukaryotic *cell cycle* and the distribution of whole genomes during *mitosis* are the underlying features of the remarkable accuracy with which eukaryotic cells solve these problems in every cell generation.

FIGURE 4-23
The highly folded nature of the chromosomal nucleoprotein fiber is evident in this electron micrograph of a condensed chromosome from a human cell in the metaphase stage of mitosis. The two halves of the replicated chromosome are held together at the common centromere region, which appears as a constriction. ×21,000. (Photograph courtesy of G. F. Bahr.)

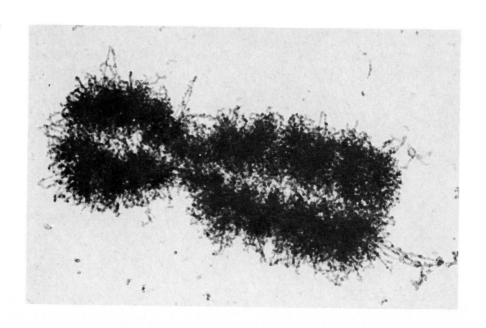

4.9
Structural Organization of the Chromosome

We have known for a long time that the chromosome retains its linear integrity only so long as it retains an intact DNA molecule. If chromosomes are exposed to proteolytic enzymes, the nucleoprotein fiber is eroded but not degraded. But exposure to deoxyribonuclease (**DNAase**) causes the chromosome to break up because its DNA is cut into pieces by enzyme action. These general observations provided the basis for more detailed biochemical and electron microscopic studies, first reported in 1974 by Roger Kornberg and by Ada and Donald Olins.

Kornberg found that controlled nuclease digestion of chromosomal nucleoprotein, or **chromatin**, yielded subchromosomal particles that consisted of about 200 base pairs of duplex DNA complexed to all five kinds of histones (two molecules each of histones H2A, H2B, H3, and H4 and one molecule of histone H1). Further digestion yielded a particle consisting of about 140 base pairs of DNA complexed to an octamer of H2A, H2B, H3, and H4 histones, two of each. The interpretations of these results led to the **nucleosome** concept of chromosome organization (Fig. 4.24). The chromosome is conceived to be organized as a

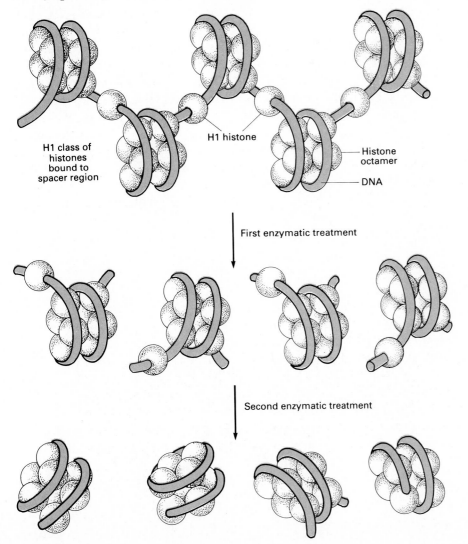

H1 class of histones bound to spacer region

H1 histone

Histone octamer

DNA

First enzymatic treatment

Second enzymatic treatment

FIGURE 4-24
The nucleosome model of chromosome organization was first proposed on the basis of controlled digestion experiments. Mild digestion of the chromatin preparation yielded particles consisting of about 200 base pairs of DNA complexed to 1 molecule of histone H1 and an octamer composed of two molecules each of histones H2A, H2B, H3, and H4. Upon further digestion of these particles, the resulting smaller particles consisted of about 140 base pairs of DNA complexed to a histone octamer but lacking histone H1. These results were interpreted as showing that the chromatin fiber is organized as a chain of repeating nucleosome subunits such that a continuous duplex DNA molecule is wound around histone octamers at regular intervals along its length and such that histone H1 is bound to a spacer region of DNA between octamers.

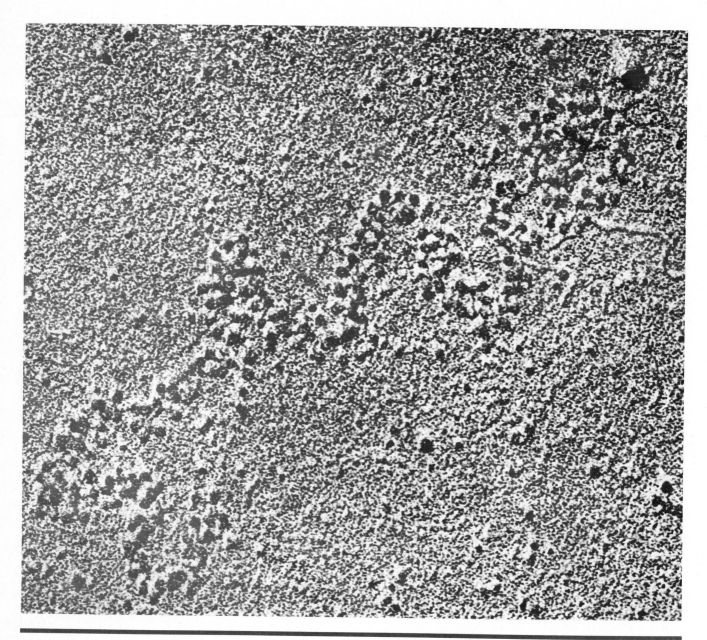

FIGURE 4-25
Electron micrograph of chromatin
from chicken liver nuclei, showing
nucleosomal particles strung out along
a continuous length of DNA. The
chromatin fiber has been stretched
somewhat during preparations for
microscopy. ×252,000. (Photograph
courtesy of P. Oudet and P. Chambon,
from Oudet, P., *et al.*, 1975, *Cell*
4:281–300, Fig. 13.)

continuous duplex DNA molecule that is wound around histone octamers along its length, and to which histone Hl is bound in the spacer
portion between octamers. The two-step digestion treatment presumably cuts DNA in the spacer region first, producing the units that are
200 base pairs long, and the second step releases the spacer DNA (plus
histone H1) from the DNA wound around the histone octamer. Electron
micrographs of stretched chromatin fibers reveal the repeating nucleosome units, which appear as beads on a string (Fig. 4.25).

The organization of the chromatin fiber as a chain of repeating
nucleosome subunits provides a satisfactory explanation for the capacity
of a rather stiff nucleoprotein fiber to be folded back on itself repeatedly
and thereby occupy a space that may be little more than a few
micrometers of chromosome length. Even a chromatin fiber that is

20,000 μm long can readily be folded into a tiny condensed chromosome such as we see in dividing nuclei in most eukaryotic cells. One of the great challenges today is to discover how parts of the folded chromosome can be accessible to RNA polymerase so that transcription can occur, whereas other parts of the same or different chromosomes are not accessible for transcription. We must relate the geometry of the chromosome to differential gene action if we are to understand fully how the genome guides the program of development in cells and organisms.

Chromosomes are not merely strings of genes lined up from one end to another; chromosomes are differentiated into regions that carry out specific functions. One such differentiated region is the centromere, without which the chromosome cannot move directionally during nuclear division. The **centromere** is the single site for attachment of spindle fibers, which are essential for directional movements of chromosomes. Chromosomes that have lost their centromere (acentric chromosomes) usually lag behind and are not incorporated into new nuclei at the conclusion of nuclear division (Fig. 4.26). Gross rearrangements that lead to dicentric (two-centromere) chromosomes also cause problems in the distribution of the genome to progeny cells and often lead to the loss of genes or to other genetic distortions. The behavior of acentric and dicentric chromosomes clearly indicate the importance of the centromere in the process of chromosome distribution to progeny cells during nuclear division. No other region of a chromosome can substitute for the centromere should it be lost, which emphasizes the unique nature of the differentiated region.

The centromere may be located anywhere along the length of a chromosome, but each chromosome of a set has its centromere in a fixed, constant location. Particular chromosomes are readily identified according to several criteria, including the position of the centromere, the relative length of the whole chromosome, and the relative lengths of the arms to either side of the centromere. In many cases, however, more than one chromosome may have the same morphology. Then identification can be made only if, in addition, the chromosomes are stained to reveal their unique banding patterns (Fig. 4.27). Because each chromosome of the genome can be recognized, many detailed studies can be made of gene locations in chromosomes; similarities and differences between genomes of related species; and site-specific effects of structural rearrangements, breaks induced by viruses or other agents, and other phenomena.

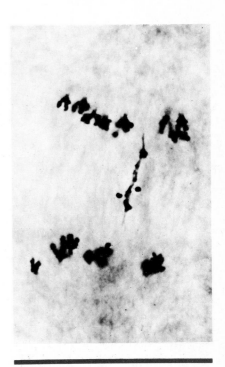

FIGURE 4-26
Nucleus in the anaphase stage of division, showing a dicentric chromosome bridging the space between the two groups of chromosomes at the poles of the cell because each centromere of the aberrant chromosome moved toward an opposite pole. Two acentric chromosomes lie alongside the chromosome bridge, not having moved to the poles because each lacked a centromere for spindle fiber attachment. (Photograph courtesy of M. M. Rhoades.)

4.10
Synthesis of New Chromosomes and Their Distribution to Progeny Cells ____

Life arises from pre-existing life, and each new generation of cells is the result of reproduction. Progeny resemble or are identical to their parents, so mechanisms must exist by which whole new genomes are made and are subsequently distributed to the new generation. Both the *increase* and the *transfer* of the full set of genetic information must be accomplished with great accuracy and must be repeated countless times in the life of a cell population, regardless of the actual number of chromosomes in a genome. We would expect the same processes to

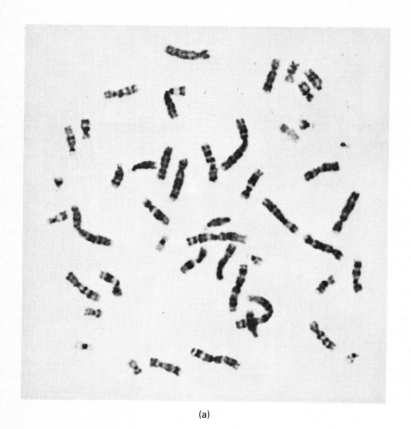

(a)

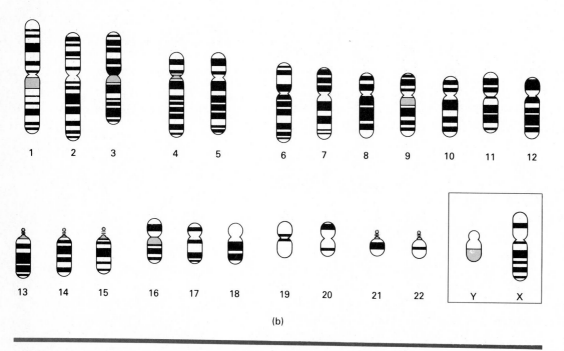

(b)

FIGURE 4-27

The human chromosome complement. (a) All 23 pairs of chromosomes can be identified by their relative length, centromere location, and unique bands revealed by staining. (b) The 22 different nonsex chromosomes and the X and Y sex chromosomes are conventionally arranged in order of decreasing size and by centromere location (constriction). Chromosomes of the same size and shape are readily distinguished by their stained band patterns.

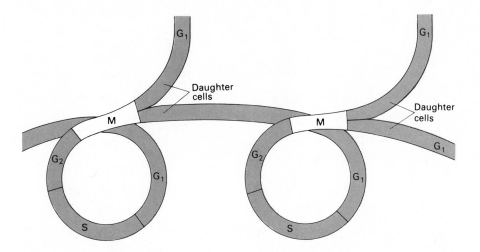

FIGURE 4-28
The cell cycle consists of interphase, subdivided into phases G_1, S, and G_2, and the phase of mitosis (M). Biosyntheses in preparation for chromosome replication take place during G_1, chromosomes replicate during S, and biosyntheses in preparation for mitosis take place during G_2. Delivery of the replicated chromosomes to daughter nuclei occurs during mitosis. Upon completion of mitosis and cell division, the daughter cells enter G_1 if each proceeds through a new cell cycle and prepares to divide again.

underlie the synthesis and distribution of a genome of two chromosomes or two hundred chromosomes, because cells utilize economy and simplicity in their varied activities and because fundamental processes undergo relatively little profound change during the evolution of species groups.

The increase and transfer of genomes during cellular reproduction take place in a sequence of events that comprise the cell cycle. A **cell cycle** consists of three phases in which macromolecular syntheses take place, plus the phase of mitosis in which the genomes are delivered to daughter cells. The three phases of biosyntheses are G_1, when preparations are initiated for chromosome replication; **S**, when chromosomes replicate; and G_2, when preparations are made for the actual delivery of the genomes, which occurs in the **M** phase of mitosis (Fig. 4.28). Although we know very few of the specific structural and catalytic molecules that are made or called into action during G_1 and G_2, we know that DNA replicates during the S phase and that histone proteins are synthesized at the same time and in stoichiometric amounts relative to DNA. The activities during S phase have been analyzed by various molecular methods, including autoradiographic analysis of the incorporation of labeled thymidine into new DNA and quantitative biochemical assays of DNA and histones before, during, and after S phase.

Upon completion of preparations in G_2, mitosis begins and whole sets of chromosomes are partitioned equally into the daughter cells. The remarkable accuracy and efficiency of mitosis leads to trillions of genetically identical cells in the human being who develops from a single fertilized egg—and to the replacement of old cells with new cells during the lifetime of the organism. The continuous sequence of events in **mitosis** is conventionally divided into stages of **prophase** (*pro*, before), **metaphase** (*meta*, between), **anaphase** (*ana*, back), and **telophase** (*telo*, end). The interval between mitotic divisions is called **interphase**, and it includes the G_1, S, and G_2 phases of the cell cycle (Fig. 4.29).

As prophase begins, the stringy tangle of chromosomes in the interphase nucleus begins to condense into shorter and thicker strands. Individual chromosomes can be recognized by mid-prophase, and they continue to condense until the beginning of metaphase, when the chromosomes line up on the equatorial plane of the **spindle**. Each

FIGURE 4-29

Mitosis. Preparations for chromosome replication and delivery are made during interphase (see Fig. 4-28), and mitosis commences as the chromosomes begin to condense in prophase. The nuclear membrane and nucleoli disappear by the end of prophase. The spindle occupies a central position in the cell as prometaphase begins and the chromosomes move toward the equatorial plane of the spindle. Chromosomes are aligned on the spindle equator in metaphase. During anaphase, sister chromatids of each replicated chromosome separate and move to opposite poles of the cell. Nuclear reorganization takes place during telophase, and each nucleus enters the interphase state upon completion of telophase. The new nuclei may or may not proceed through other mitotic divisions.

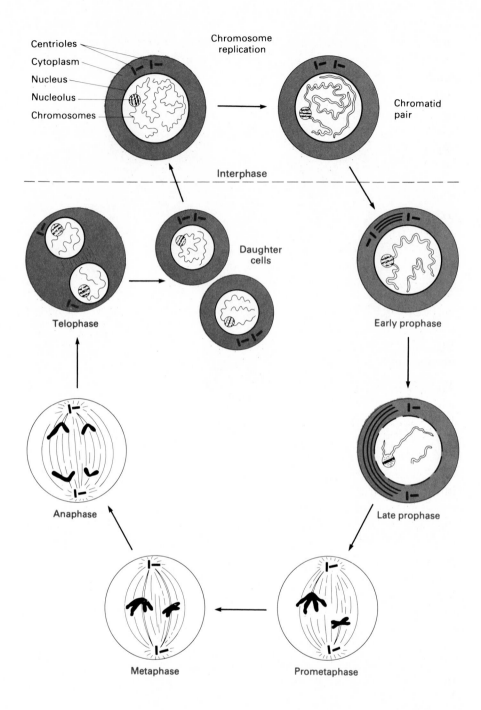

chromosome is a replicated structure consisting of two sister **chromatids**, but these remain associated in a common *centromere region* aligned on the spindle equator. The individual *kinetochore* of each sister chromatid in the common centromere region is oriented toward an opposite pole of the spindle figure, and when anaphase begins the sister chromatids separate and move toward their respective poles, guided by the spindle fibers inserted into the kinetochore (Fig. 4.30). Once separated, each chromatid becomes a full-fledged chromosome that acts independently of its sister. During the final stage of telophase, the condensed chromosomes in each daughter nucleus unfold and gradually assume their extended interphase conformation. Nuclear reorganization takes place, and the sequence ends with two new interphase nuclei produced from the original parental nucleus. The fidelity of distribution ensures the genetic identity of the daughter genomes in the new nuclei and therefore accounts for the *genetic constancy* in mitotic cell generations.

Although each descendant cell in a particular mitotic lineage is genetically identical to its sisters, differences may (and usually do) appear later in the history of the population. These differences in function and behavior, as well as in morphology, result from the differential action of the genes during development and differentiation. The regulation of gene action governs the differences in *expression of the genetic potential* encoded in the genome, such that a variety of cells, tissues, and organs arise in a multicellular individual whose cells all have identical genomes. Mitosis delivers identical sets of genes to daughter nuclei, but different factors and influences then guide these genes toward their varied destinies in the organism or population.

Summary

The biochemical basis of heredity is DNA, a fact established from work with microorganisms and bacteriophage accomplished in the 1940s and 1950s, culminating in Watson and Crick's model for the double-helical structure of DNA. Many features of DNA are implicit in the model and have been verified by subsequent experimentation. These include the mechanisms of replication, mutation, and the storage and transfer of information specifying cellular characteristics.

Replication occurs by a semiconservative mechanism, each strand of the parent DNA molecule serving as a template to direct the assembly of its complementary partner strand in a daughter molecule. DNA polymerases and other enzymes catalyze the process. Mutation (the occurrence of sudden, heritable change in the properties of a cell or organism) often involves a change in the sequence of bases of the DNA that may occur spontaneously or may be induced by chemical or physical mutagens. Unless corrected by repair mechanisms, such alterations are faithfully propagated in future generations.

Genetic information is stored by means of the genetic code, whereby the sequence of bases in the DNA specifies the sequence of amino acids in a polypeptide chain. Codons consist of triplets of bases in the linear DNA molecule. Each codon specifies one and only one amino acid or acts as a signal for termination of protein synthesis. All the 64 possible combinations of the 4 kinds of bases taken 3 at a time are meaningful; 61 represent one or another of the 20 kinds of amino acids used in protein synthesis, and the other 3 represent Stop signals. One of the amino acid codons also signals the start of protein synthesis. The code is universal to all cells, both prokaryotic and eukaryotic, and to viruses. Mutation can thus be understood as an alteration of a DNA base that alters the meaning of the codon and leads to a protein whose function may be affected by the changed amino acid.

The coded information in the DNA template is transcribed into a messenger RNA (mRNA) intermediate via reactions catalyzed by RNA

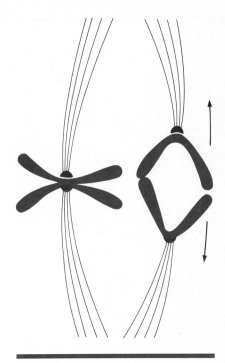

FIGURE 4-30
Each replicated metaphase chromosome consists of two sister chromatids held together in a common centromere region. The kinetochore, or centromere, of each chromatid in a pair is attached to spindle fibers oriented toward opposite poles of the cell. When sister chromatids separate at anaphase, each moves toward its respective pole of the cell unerringly in the vast majority of mitotic divisions.

polymerases. Particular regions of the DNA are transcribed into ribosomal RNA (rRNA) or transfer RNA (tRNA). The three sorts of RNA collaborate in the process of translation, where protein is synthesized according to the coded information in mRNA. Successive codons are "read" at the ribosome, which mediates base pairing between the codons in bound mRNA and their complementary anticodons of tRNA molecules that carry the appropriate amino acids to the sites of translation. The ribosomes also promote the addition of amino acids to the growing polypeptide chains, with successive amino acids being added in the linear sequence specified by mRNA until a Stop codon is reached.

In prokaryotes the informational DNA is uninterrupted, so the genes in the DNA are colinear with the mRNA and the resulting protein. In eukaryotes, however, the gene consists of coding segments (exons) interspersed with noncoding segments (introns). The entire gene sequence is transcribed into pre-mRNA in the nucleus, but before it enters the cytoplasm, the introns are excised and the exons are spliced into a continuous sequence colinear with the encoded protein. Molecular hybridization of DNA with cytoplasmic mRNA reveals this phenomenon, the evolutionary significance and origin of which are uncertain.

Advances in recombinant DNA technology permit detailed analysis of genetic fine structure. Individual segments of DNA can be excised with restriction enzymes and combined with DNA vectors that carry them into host cells and allow their replication and expression. A library of cloned DNA in host cells can contain representatives of the complete genome of an organism, and individual DNA sequences can be selected and purified in sufficient quantity to study. DNA base sequence determination permits prediction of the amino acid sequence and also provides insight into the regulation of gene expression. A typical cell expresses different genes to different extents. In prokaryotes this regulation is mediated principally by repressor proteins that influence transcription by binding to operator DNA. Eukaryotes have no repressor proteins, but they otherwise regulate transcription and processing of pre-mRNA, modify the protein posttranslationally, or alter the structure of the chromatin containing the genes.

The basic structural organization of eukaryotic chromatin is as a series of beadlike nucleosomes, each a core particle of 8 histones (4 kinds, 2 molecules each) around which are wrapped 146 base pairs of DNA. Each nucleosome is connected to the next by a more exposed stretch of about 60 base pairs of DNA associated with a fifth kind of histone. Additional levels of packaging confer characteristic specializations on the regions of particular chromosomes, including the centromere (where spindle fibers attach during mitosis) and differential banding patterns (reflecting the affinity of different regions of the chromosome for dyes). The cell-division cycle includes a phase during which DNA synthesis occurs (S), the actual period of mitosis (M), and two "gap" periods: G_1 (before S) and G_2 (after S). Mitosis is a continuous process but may be subdivided into prophase, metaphase, anaphase, and telophase, each with characteristic features. Differences arise among progeny cells in the same mitotic lineage due to changes in gene expression, an important feature of differentiation.

Readings and References

Anderson, W. F., and E. G. Diakumakos. July 1981. Genetic engineering in mammalian cells. *Sci. Amer.* **245**:106.

Avers, C. J. 1984. *Genetics.* 2nd ed. Boston: Willard Grant.

Avery, O. T., C. M. MacLeod, and M. McCarty. 1944. Studies on the chemical nature of the substance inducing transformation of pneumococcal types. *J. Exp. Med.* **79**:137.

Berg, P. 1981. Dissections and reconstructions of genes and chromosomes. *Science* **213**:296 (Nobel lecture).

Brenner, S., F. Jacob, and M. Meselson. 1961. An unstable intermediate carrying information from genes to ribosomes for protein synthesis. *Nature* **190**:576.

Brown, D. D. August 1973. The isolation of genes. *Sci. Amer.* **229**:20.

Chambon, P. May 1981. Split genes. *Sci. Amer.* **244**:60.

Chargaff, E. 1951. Structure and function of nucleic acids as cell constituents. *Fed. Proc.* **10**:654.

Chilton, M.-D. June 1983. Vectors for introducing new genes into plants. *Sci. Amer.* **248**:50.

Crick, F. H. C. October 1966. The genetic code. III. *Sci. Amer.* **215**:55.

Dickerson, R. E. December 1983. The DNA helix and how it is read. *Sci. Amer.* **249**:94.

Drake, J. W., B. W. Glickman, and L. S. Ripley. 1983. Updating the theory of mutation. *Amer. Sci.* **71**:621.

Drets, M. E., and M. W. Shaw. 1971. Specific banding patterns of human chromosomes. *Proc. Natl. Acad. Sci. U. S.* **68**:2073.

DuPraw, E. J. 1970. *DNA and Chromosomes.* New York: Holt.

Felsenfeld, G. 1978. Chromatin. *Nature* **271**:115.

Fiddes, J. C. December 1977. The nucleotide sequence of a viral DNA. *Sci. Amer.* **237**:54.

Fiers, W., *et al.* 1978. Complete nucleotide sequence of SV40 DNA. *Nature* **273**:113.

Gall, J. G., and M. L. Pardue. 1969. Formation and detection of RNA–DNA hybrid molecules in cytological preparations. *Proc. Natl. Acad. Sci. U. S.* **63**:378.

Gilbert, W. 1981. DNA sequencing and gene structure. *Science* **214**:1305 (Nobel lecture).

Gilbert, W., and L. Villa-Komaroff. April 1980. Useful proteins from recombinant bacteria. *Sci. Amer.* **242**:74.

Hall, B. D., and S. Spiegelman. 1961. Sequence complementarity of T2-DNA and T2-specific RNA. *Proc. Natl. Acad. Sci. U. S.* **47**:137.

Hershey, A. D., and M. Chase. 1952. Independent functions of viral protein and nucleic acids in growth of bacteriophage. *J. Gen. Physiol.* **36**:39.

Howard-Flanders, P. November 1981. Inducible repair of DNA. *Sci. Amer.* **245**:72.

Ingram, V. I. 1956. A specific chemical difference between the globins of normal human and sickle-cell anaemia haemoglobin. *Nature* **178**:792.

Ingram, V. I. January 1958. How do genes act? *Sci. Amer.* **198**:68.

Itakura, K. 1980. Synthesis of genes. *Trends Biochem. Sci.* **5**:114.

Khorana, H. G. 1979. Total synthesis of a gene. *Science* **203**:614.

Kornberg, A. 1980. *DNA Replication.* San Francisco: Freeman.

Kornberg, A. 1984. DNA replication. *Trends Biochem. Sci.* **9**:122.

Kornberg, R. D. 1974. Chromatin structure: A repeating unit of histones and DNA. *Science* **184**:868.

Kornberg, R. D., and A. Klug. February 1981. The nucleosome. *Sci. Amer.* **244**:52.

Landy, A., and W. Ross. 1977. Viral integration and excision: Structure of the lambda *att* sites. *Science* **197**:1147.

Maniatis, T., and M. Ptashne. January 1976. A DNA operator–repressor system. *Sci. Amer.* **234**:64.

Maxam, A. M., and W. Gilbert. 1977. A new method for sequencing DNA. *Proc. Natl. Acad. Sci. U. S.* **74**:560.

Mazia, D. January 1974. The cell cycle. *Sci. Amer.* **230**:54.

Meselson, M., and F. W. Stahl. 1958. The replication of DNA in *E. coli. Proc. Natl. Acad. Sci. U. S.* **44**:671.

Mirsky, A. E. June 1968. The discovery of DNA. *Sci. Amer.* **218**:78.

Nathans, D. 1979. Restriction endonucleases, simian virus 40, and the new genetics. *Science* **206**:903 (Nobel lecture).

Nirenberg, M. W., and J. H. Matthaei. 1961. The dependence of cell-free protein synthesis in *E. coli* upon naturally occurring or synthetic polyribonucleotides. *Proc. Natl. Acad. Sci. U. S.* **47**:1588.

Novick, R. P. December 1980. Plasmids. *Sci. Amer.* **243**:102.

Olins, D. E., and A. L. Olins. 1978. Nucleosomes: The structural quantum in chromosomes. *Amer. Sci.* **66**:704.

Pardue, M. L., and J. G. Gall. 1970. Chromosomal localization of mouse satellite DNA. *Science* **168**:1356.

Pestka, S. August 1983. The purification and manufacture of human interferons. *Sci. Amer.* **249**:36.

Ptashne, M., and W. Gilbert. June 1970. Genetic repressors. *Sci. Amer.* **222**:36.

Ptashne, M., A. D. Johnson, and C. O. Pabo. November 1982. A genetic switch in a bacterial virus. *Sci. Amer.* **247**:128.

Reddy, V. B., *et al.* 1978. The genome of simian virus 40. *Science* **200**:494.

Sanger, F. 1981. Determination of nucleotide sequences in DNA. *Science* **214**:1205 (Nobel lecture).

Sanger, F., *et al.* 1977. Nucleotide sequence of bacteriophage ϕX174. *Nature* **265**:687.

Smith, H. O. 1979. Nucleotide sequence specificity of restriction endonucleases. *Science* **205**:455 (Nobel lecture).

Smith, M. 1979. The first complete nucleotide sequencing of an organism's DNA. *Amer. Sci.* **67**:57.

Smith, M. 1982. Site-directed mutagenesis. *Trends Biochem. Sci.* **7**:440.

Spiegelman, S. May 1964. Hybrid nucleic acids. *Sci. Amer.* **210**:48.

Watson, J. D. 1976. *Molecular Biology of the Gene*. 3rd ed. Menlo Park, Calif.: Benjamin-Cummings.

Watson, J. D., and F. H. C. Crick. 1953. Molecular structure of nucleic acids. A structure for deoxyribose nucleic acid. *Nature* **171**:737.

Watson, J. D., and F. H. C. Crick. 1953. Genetical implications of the structure of deoxyribose nucleic acid. *Nature* **171**:964.

Wetzel, R. 1980. Application of recombinant DNA technology. *Amer. Sci.* **68**:664.

White, M. J. D. 1973. *The Chromosomes*. 6th ed. London: Chapman & Hall.

Wilkins, M. H. F., A. R. Stokes, and H. R. Wilson. 1953. Molecular structure of deoxypentose nucleic acids. *Nature* **171**:738.

Yanofsky, C. May 1967. Gene structure and protein structure. *Sci. Amer.* **216**:80.

Yanofsky, C., *et al.* 1967. The complete amino acid sequence of the tryptophan synthetase A protein (α subunit) and its colinear relationship with the genetic map of the A gene. *Proc. Natl. Acad. Sci. U. S.* **57**:296.

Yunis, J. J., and O. Prakash. 1982. The origin of man: A chromosomal pictorial legacy. *Science* **215**:1525.

Cell Boundaries and Surfaces

CHAPTER 5

Membrane Structure and Function

The membranes of prokaryotic and eukaryotic cells have a common overall structure, which consists of assemblies of lipids and proteins held together by noncovalent forces. The membrane framework is a *lipid bilayer*, and the proteins are distributed at the surfaces or completely traversing the basic two-layered structure.

A membrane separates the internal contents of a cell or organelle from its surroundings. The membrane is a dynamic barrier, however; it regulates the movement of substances across the lipid bilayer by virtue of its property of *selective permeability*. The protein molecules of a membrane are responsible for many of its functions and account in large part for differing specific properties of different membranes. Various membrane proteins catalyze particular reactions that occur at the membrane, aid in the transport of specific substances across the membrane, act as receptors of chemical information from the surroundings, and link molecular structural systems associated with membrane surfaces.

Molecular Organization of Membranes

About sixty years ago the plasma membrane was described as a lipid bilayer, on the basis of relatively indirect evidence showing that all the extracted lipids of the red blood cell plasma membrane occupied a surface area on water that was twice the surface area of the original cell. The conclusion based on these data was that the lipid molecules in the plasma membrane were arranged as a continuous structure that was two molecules thick. The surface properties of a simple lipid bilayer were quite different from those of a living cell, however, and other membrane models were proposed afterward that accounted for membrane proteins as well as lipids.

In 1935 and later, James Danielli and Hugh Davson postulated that the lipid bilayer was coated on each surface by a continuous monolayer

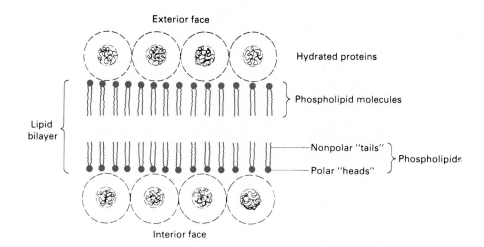

of hydrated globular proteins (Fig. 5.1). The membrane displayed hydrophobic properties due to its "lipoid" interior, which was created by hydrophobic fatty acid chains of the two facing layers of phospholipid molecules. Hydrophilic properties of the membrane were attributed to the coatings of hydrated proteins bound to the hydrophilic residues of the phospholipid layers. In the early 1960s, J. David Robertson proposed a modified version of the Danielli–Davson model, which assumed that the proteins were in an extended rather than globular conformation on both surfaces of the phospholipid bilayer. Robertson's model drew on information obtained by electron microscopy, as well as criteria based on membrane functions. He proposed that the uniform thickness of 7.5 nm and the consistent dark–light–dark staining pattern of the cellular membranes could be explained if each protein coat was 2 nm thick and the phospholipid bilayer sandwiched in between was about 3.5 nm thick. In order to accommodate a thickness of 2 nm, each protein coat had to consist of molecules in extended conformation (Fig. 5.2).

Various objections to the available models stimulated new kinds of studies using mitochondrial and chloroplast membranes as well as plasma membranes. In the late 1960s, S. Jon Singer and Garth Nicolson proposed the **fluid mosaic membrane** model, according to which a mosaic of protein molecules was distributed in and on a fluid phospholipid bilayer. The fluid mosaic membrane is widely accepted today, although certain details of the model have been changed since its inception or still remain controversial.

5.1
The Fluid Mosaic Membrane

The Singer–Nicolson model postulates that the lipid bilayer exists in a relatively fluid state, with the consistency of a light oil, and that lipids in each monolayer can move laterally within the plane of the membrane. Various protein molecules are distributed on each surface of the lipid bilayer, and other proteins penetrate the thickness of the bilayer but protrude from one or both of its surfaces (Fig. 5.3). The surface proteins are *peripheral* and the proteins that extend into or through the bilayer are *integral*. Protein molecules can move laterally within the plane of the

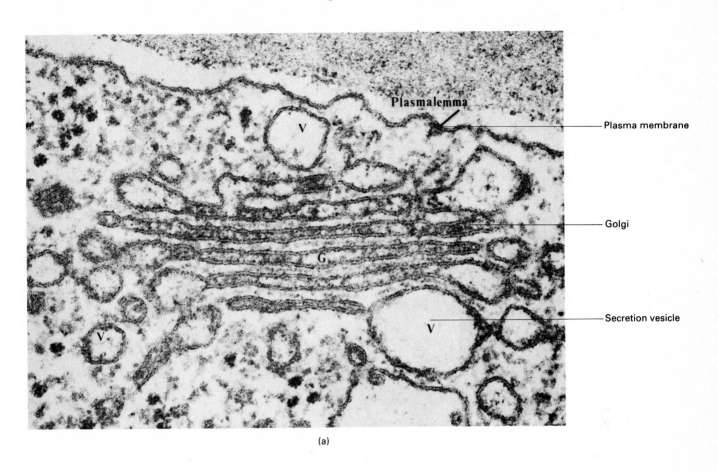

Plasmalemma

Plasma membrane

Golgi

V

G

V

V

Secretion vesicle

(a)

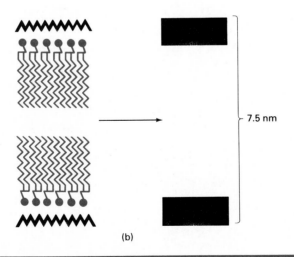

7.5 nm

(b)

FIGURE 5-2
The "unit" membrane. (a) Electron micrograph of a section through part of a root cell from the plant *Potamogeton natans*, showing the typical dark–light–dark trilaminated staining pattern of various cell membranes, including the plasma membrane. Such images provided the basis for the "unit" membrane model proposed by J. D. Robertson.

×151,000. (Photograph courtesy of M. C. Ledbetter.) (b) Schematic drawing of Robertson's membrane model, showing proteins (black) in extended conformation at each surface of the lipid bilayer (color). The interior of the membrane is modified during preparations for electron microscopy and thus appears relatively unstained in cell sections.

FIGURE 5-3
Proteins are distributed in and on the basic framework of a relatively fluid lipid bilayer of the membrane, as proposed in the fluid mosaic model by S. J. Singer and G. L. Nicolson. Peripheral proteins bind to each surface of the bilayer, whereas integral proteins extend partly or completely through the bilayer and protrude from one or both surfaces, respectively. The model applies to all membranes of the cell.

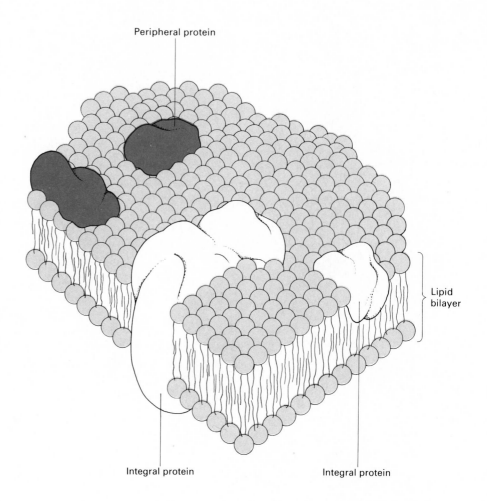

Peripheral protein

Lipid bilayer

Integral protein

Integral protein

lipid bilayer, but they rarely "flip-flop" from one surface to the other surface across the bilayer.

The distinction between peripheral and integral membrane proteins is based on operational criteria. Proteins that are easily removed from membranes by mild treatments, such as extraction by salt solutions, are presumed to be loosely bound to the bilayer surfaces as peripheral molecules. Proteins that can be removed only after disruption of the membrane by organic solvents or detergents are presumed to be integral molecules, held tenaciously by hydrophobic and other interactions with each other and with lipids in the bilayer. In fact, we know little about the specific nature of the molecular interactions that hold peripheral and integral proteins in association with the bilayer. We do, however, have a good idea about the general nature of molecular interactions in membrane structure.

Singer and Nicolson proposed that the predominant forces responsible for membrane structure are *hydrophilic* and *hydrophobic* interactions. The membrane can exist in the stable state of minimum free-energy expenditure if both these kinds of molecular interactions are maximized. This would be the case in the aqueous environment inside and outside the cell if nonpolar uncharged fatty acid chains of the phospholipids and nonpolar amino acid residues of the proteins were kept from contact with water to the greatest possible extent, at the same time that polar

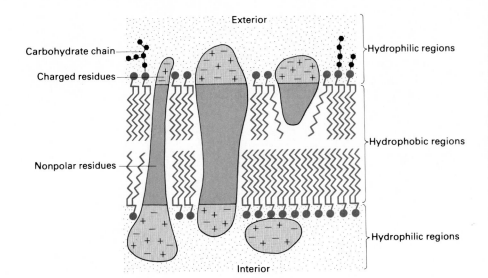

Carbohydrate chain

Charged residues

Nonpolar residues

Exterior

Hydrophilic regions

Hydrophobic regions

Hydrophilic regions

Interior

FIGURE 5-4
In the fluid mosaic membrane, hydrophilic interactions involve the charged residues of amphipathic membrane proteins, polar heads of amphipathic phospholipids, and the aqueous phases on each side of the membrane. Hydrophobic interactions occur between nonpolar residues of proteins and nonpolar hydrocarbon chains of the phospholipid bilayer. The membrane exists in the most stable energetic state because both kinds of interactions are maximized in the aqueous environments inside and outside the cell.

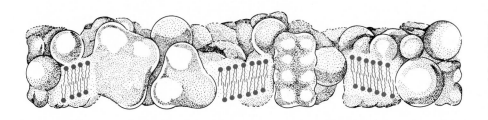

FIGURE 5-5
Model of a mosaic membrane in which interacting proteins (shown as globular components) provide the basic framework and patches of phospholipid bilayer are dispersed among the proteins. Such a membrane would display protein–protein interactions far more than protein–lipid or lipid–lipid interactions, and it would be less fluid a structure than the Singer–Nicolson membrane. (Adapted from Sjöstrand, F., and L. Barajas, 1970, *J. Ultrastruct. Res.* **32**:293.)

charged (ionic) or neutral groups of membrane proteins, lipids, and carbohydrates were in contact with water (Fig. 5.4). Because membrane lipids and many membrane proteins are *amphipathic*, and thus contain hydrophilic and hydrophobic regions in the same molecule, the Singer–Nicolson model adheres to the thermodynamic requirements for membrane structure, whereas the earlier protein "sandwich" models do not. The Danielli–Davson and Robertson models of membrane structure stipulated that the proteins were external layers and that the lipids were entirely contained within the interior of the membrane. These arrangements would be thermodynamically unstable because the polar heads of the lipids would be excluded from water by the covering proteins, and the nonpolar residues of membrane proteins would be exposed to water and not be sequestered in the hydrophobic interior of the membrane. In addition, we know that protein conformation is a critical aspect of protein function, so we would not expect every protein in a membrane to be either globular or extended in conformation.

Some controversy exists concerning the molecular basis for the cementing framework of the membrane. Singer and Nicolson proposed that the lipid bilayer was the basic framework for membrane construction and that proteins were incorporated into this framework as a mosaic of molecules. Such a membrane would exhibit lipid–lipid, lipid–protein, and protein–protein interactions to varying degrees, and it would best account for lateral mobility of lipids and proteins within the plane of the membrane. Other investigators have proposed a cementing framework of interacting proteins as the basis for membrane structure, with patches of lipid dispersed here and there among the proteins (Fig. 5.5). This

TABLE 5-1
Composition of Mammalian Membrane Preparations*

Component	Myelin	Erythrocyte Plasma Membrane	Liver Plasma Membrane	Heart Mitochondria
Proteins	22	60	60	76
Total lipids	78	40	40	24
Phospholipids	33	24	26	22
Glycolipids	22	trace	0	trace
Cholesterol	17	9	13	1
Other lipids	6	7	1	1

* Values taken from various sources, expressed in percentage by weight.

kind of membrane would display predominantly protein–protein interactions in its activity as well as its construction, and there would be greater restraint on mobility. The difference between these two viewpoints can be further illustrated, using the analogy of lipids as water and proteins as ice, in the following way. The Singer–Nicolson membrane would be analogous to an ocean (lipids) in which icebergs (proteins) were located in different places and in different concentrations in the ocean. The other model would be analogous to an ice field (proteins) with puddles of water (lipids) located in pockets of different size scattered around the ice field.

Little direct evidence is available in support of the protein framework model of the fluid mosaic membrane. One argument that has been used in favor of the protein–protein framework, and against the lipid bilayer model, is that the mitochondrial inner membrane consists of about 75% protein by weight (Table 5.1). In view of this fact, protein–protein interactions are considered the most likely to predominate in these membranes. There would appear to be little room for lipids in the mitochondrial inner membrane. On the other hand, about 40% of the mitochondrial membrane proteins are easily extracted by gentle treatments, which means that far less than 75% of the membrane mass consists of integral proteins. Furthermore, a lipid molecule is considerably smaller than a protein, and there are always more lipid molecules than protein molecules in a membrane. In a membrane that is 50% protein by mass, there are approximately 50 lipid molecules for every protein molecule.

5.2
Membrane Lipids

The most abundant lipids in cellular membranes are *phospholipids*, which are amphipathic molecules that consist of two hydrocarbon chains and a polar head group (see Section 2.9). The major phospholipids in the eukaryotic plasma membrane are phosphatidylcholine, phosphatidylethanolamine, phosphatidylinositol, and phosphatidylserine (Fig. 5.6). These and other lipids are not distributed randomly in the lipid bilayer of the membrane. For example, in the plasma membrane of the human

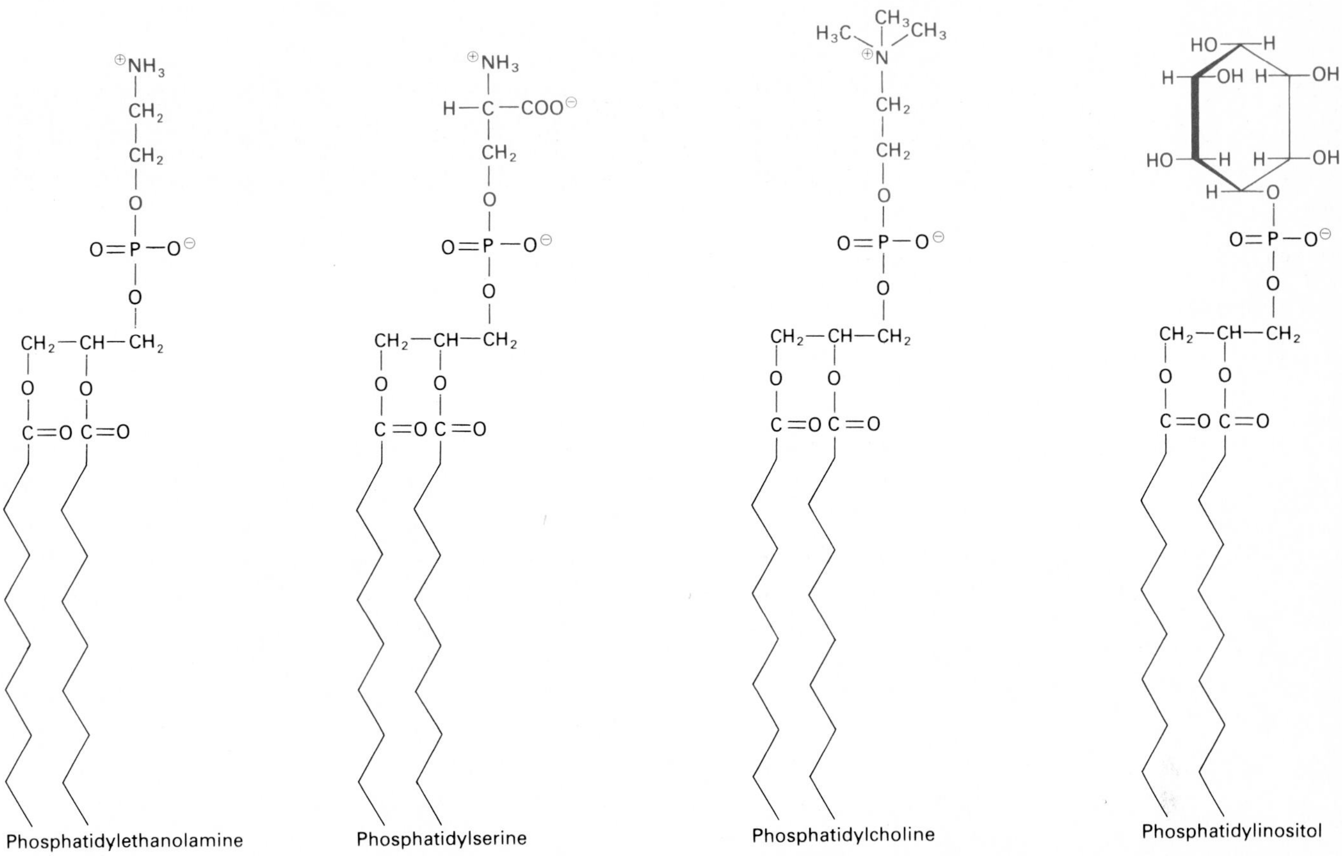

Phosphatidylethanolamine   Phosphatidylserine   Phosphatidylcholine   Phosphatidylinositol

FIGURE 5-6
The four major kinds of membrane phospholipids all display the characteristic features of a polar head and two fatty acid chains bonded through ester links (—O—) to the three carbons derived from glycerol. Each kind of phospholipid is distinguished by the component (color) bonded to the phosphate residue of the head region. The name of the compound indicates whether this head component is ethanolamine, serine, choline, or inositol.

erythrocyte (red blood cell), molecules with choline head groups (phosphatidylcholine, sphingomyelin) occur mainly in the lipid layer facing the extracellular surface, whereas phospholipids terminating in aminated head groups are highly concentrated in the layer facing the cytoplasmic interior of the cell. Distributions such as these contribute to the *asymmetry* of the lipid bilayer. In addition, the hydrocarbon chains of membrane phospholipids differ in the two layers of the membrane. Differences in carbohydrate residues and proteins make the two halves of the plasma membrane even more distinct. These and other aspects of membrane asymmetry will be discussed in a later section.

Another kind of amphipathic lipid in the plasma membrane of many organisms is the group of *glycolipids*. Glycolipids resemble phospholipids and sphingolipids in construction, but they are distinguished by the occurrence of one or more sugar residues as the polar head group (Fig. 5.7). One of the simplest glycolipids is *galactocerebroside*, which has only one galactose residue as its head group. This compound has a sphingosine residue in place of one fatty acid chain, so that this compound and similar glycolipids formed from sphingosine are sometimes called glycosphingolipids. Galactocerebroside is particularly abundant in myelin, the multilayered sheath of membranes that surrounds and insulates the nerve fiber, and it may constitute about 40% of the outer layer of the myelin sheath.

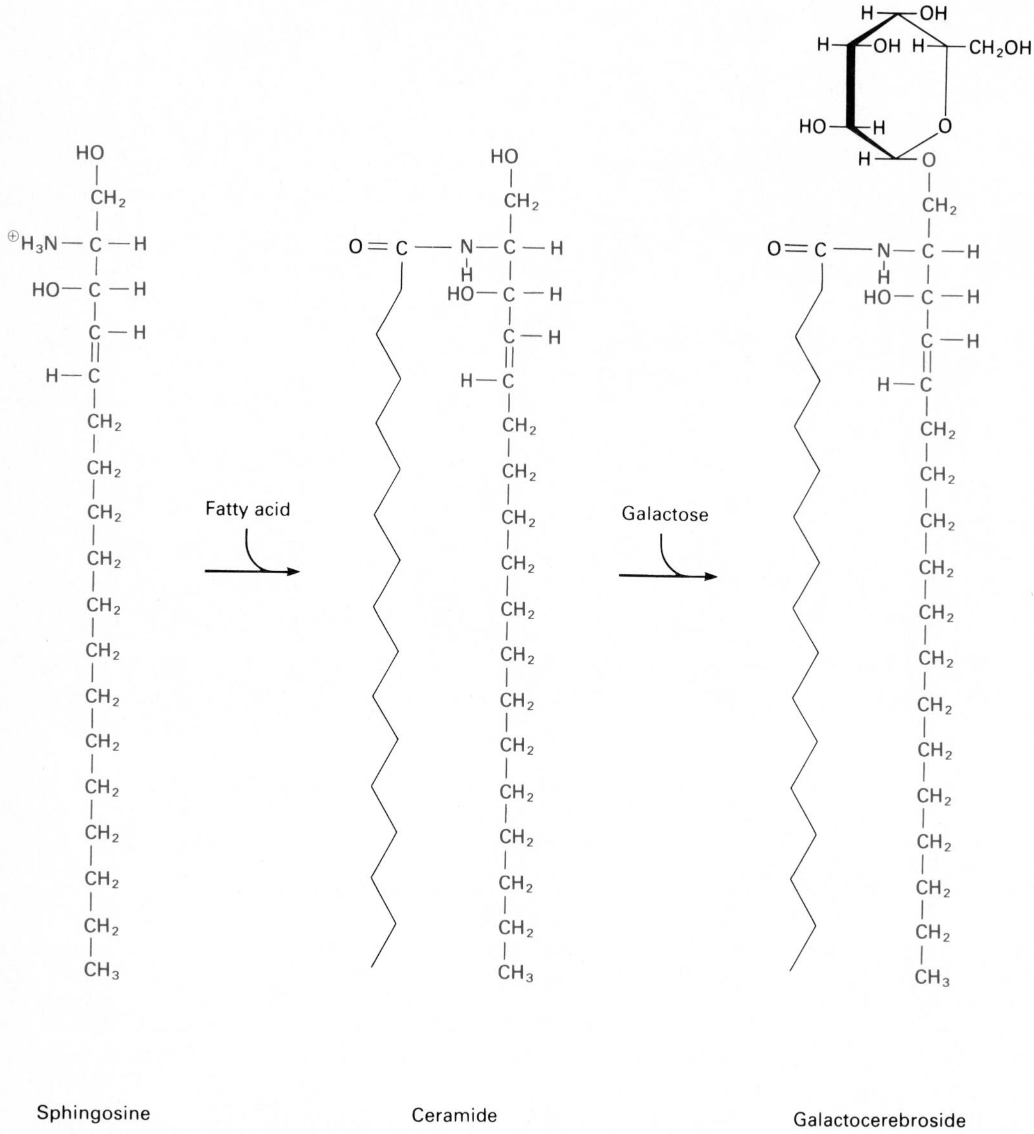

FIGURE 5-7

The synthesis of galactocerebroside, an amphipathic glycolipid in myelin membranes, proceeds through reactions in which sphingosine combines with a fatty acid to form ceramide, and a single galactose residue is added to ceramide. Such a glycolipid is sometimes referred to as a glycosphingolipid because of the sphingosine tail. Myelin membranes are arranged in layers to form the myelin sheath, which insulates the nerve fiber.

The most diversified and complex glycolipids are the *gangliosides*, which contain one or more sialic acid (*N*-acetlneuraminic acid) residues as well as sugar in the polar head of the molecule (Fig. 5.8). Gangliosides are especially characteristic of the plasma membrane of neurons, but they also occur in smaller quantities in many animal cell types. Children who suffer from the lethal inherited Tay-Sachs disease are unable to process the ganglioside G_{M2} to make G_{M3}, because the enzyme hexosaminidase A is missing. In the absence of this enzyme, huge amounts of the ganglioside G_{M2} accumulate in nerve and brain cells, leading to degeneration of the central nervous system and death by the age of 2 to 6 years. The normal function of the enzyme is to catalyze the reaction that cleaves G_{M2} to produce G_{M3} + *N*-acetylgalactosamine.

In the plasma membrane and certain other membranes of animal cells, a third kind of lipid, *cholesterol*, is present in substantial amounts (Table 5.2). The cholesterol molecule consists of three distinct regions:

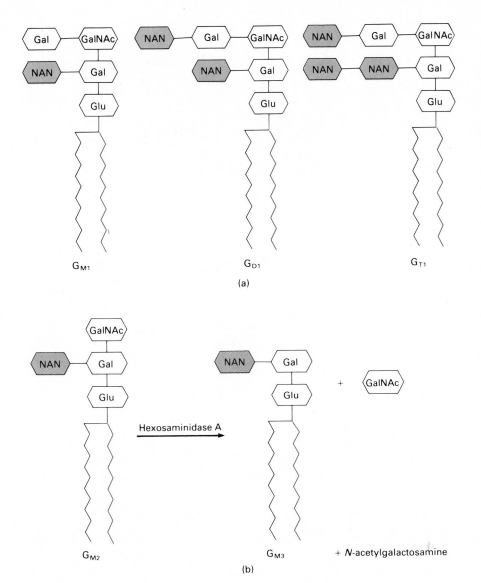

(a)

(b)

FIGURE 5-8
Gangliosides. (a) The molecules are glycolipids whose polar head contains one or more residues of sialic acid, or *N*-acetylneuraminic acid (NAN), and a variable number of sugar residues such as galactose (Gal), glucose (Glu), and *N*-acetylgalactosamine (GalNAc). A sphingosine chain (color) and a fatty acid chain constitute the hydrophobic region of the amphipathic molecule. The G$_1$ gangliosides carry the same four sugar residues but differ in the number of NAN residues, as indicated in the subscript (M, mono-; D, di-; T, tri-). (b) The ganglioside G$_{M2}$ has only three sugars and one NAN residue. In normal cells the enzyme hexosaminidase A cleaves G$_{M2}$ to produce G$_{M3}$ and free *N*-acetylgalactosamine (GalNAc). The reaction does not occur in children with Tay-Sachs disease, and unprocessed G$_{M2}$ accumulates in nerve and brain cells, leading to deterioration of the central nervous system and to death by the age of 2 to 6 years.

the polar head represented by a hydroxyl group, the nonpolar platelike steroid ring structure, and a nonpolar hydrocarbon tail (Fig. 5.9). Cholesterol molecules are oriented in the bilayer in a way that contributes to membrane fluidity. The steroid rings interact with those regions of the phospholipid and glycolipid hydrocarbon chains nearest the polar head groups, leaving the remainder of the chains relatively flexible. In this way the hydrocarbon chains remain apart and thus do not crystalize into a rigid aggregate within the membrane. In addition to modifying membrane fluidity, cholesterol is also believed to contribute to the mechanical stability of the animal cell plasma membrane. This function is apparent from studies of mutant cells in culture, which are unable to synthesize cholesterol. The cells will burst unless cholesterol is added to the culture medium.

Eukaryotic membranes are quite variable in lipid composition, and any particular membrane usually consists of a number of different lipid molecules. Bacterial cells, on the other hand, are often mainly composed of a single kind of phospholipid. For example, the plasma membrane of

TABLE 5-2
Lipid Compositions of Various Mammalian Cell Membranes

Lipid	PERCENTAGE BY WEIGHT OF TOTAL LIPID				
	Myelin	Plasma Membrane (erythrocyte)	Plasma Membrane (liver)	Endoplasmic Reticulum	Mitochondria
Phosphatidylcholine	10	17	24	40	39
Phosphatidylethanolamine	15	18	7	17	35
Phosphatidylserine	9	7	4	5	2
Sphingomyelin	8	18	19	5	0
Glycolipids	28	3	7	<1	<1
Cholesterol	22	23	17	6	3
Others	8	13	22	27	21

FIGURE 5-9
Cholesterol. (a) Structural formula showing the polar OH terminus and the hydrophobic region composed of a planar ring structure and hydrocarbon chain. (b) Cholesterol is oriented in the lipid bilayer such that interactions occur with the uppermost portions of phospholipids, leaving the remainder of the phospholipid chains relatively flexible and therefore allowing greater fluidity in such a region of the membrane.

Polar headgroup [OH

Planar ring structure

CH₃

CH₃ CH₃
CH
CH₂
CH₂
CH₂
CH
H₃C   CH₃

Nonpolar hydrocarbon tail group

(a)

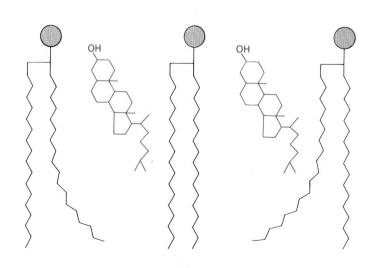

(b)

E. coli contains 70% by weight of phosphatidylethanolamine, the only phospholipid present. The basic organization of the lipid bilayer, however, is the same in all kinds of cells regardless of the specific lipid content.

5.3
Membrane Proteins

Many of the specific functions of cellular membranes are carried out by their constituent proteins, and, accordingly, the kinds and amounts of proteins in a membrane reflect its functions. Energy-transducing membranes of mitochondria and chloroplasts are about 75% protein by weight, and the bulk of these proteins are enzymes and other molecules associated with energy transduction. At the other extreme, myelin membranes are approximately 25% protein by weight, which coincides with the primary insulating function of the myelin sheath around a nerve fiber and the greater importance of lipids in performing this function. About 50% of the mass of a typical plasma membrane in eukaryotes is protein. With new methods now available, more than 50 different proteins have been resolved in a single membrane (Fig. 5.10). The

FIGURE 5-10
Two-dimensional gel display of Coomassie-blue-stained proteins of the entire membranous envelope of *E. coli* cells. Migration of proteins in the vertical plane led to separation of molecules of different molecular weights, and migration in the horizontal plane led to further separation according to the pH affinities of these molecules. (Photograph courtesy of S. Palmer and A. St. John.)

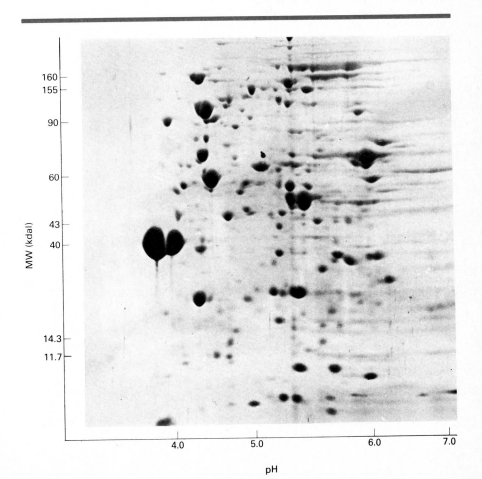

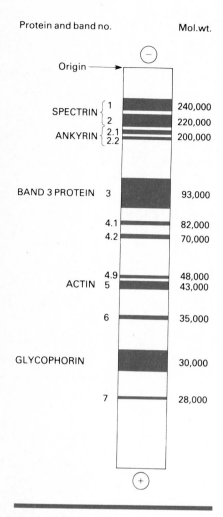

Protein and band no.   Mol.wt.

Origin

SPECTRIN { 1   240,000
           2   220,000
ANKYRIN { 2.1   200,000
          2.2

BAND 3 PROTEIN   3   93,000

          4.1   82,000
          4.2   70,000

          4.9   48,000
ACTIN   5   43,000

          6   35,000

GLYCOPHORIN   30,000

          7   28,000

FIGURE 5-11
Gel pattern of some of the major proteins separated by gel electrophoresis from preparations of erythrocyte plasma membrane. Only a few of the proteins have been identified and named; others are referred to by their band number (position) in the gel column. Molecular weights of the proteins are shown at the right of the gel.

resolving power of *two-dimensional gel* techniques enables us to recognize more than 1000 different molecules in a single preparation. Identifying the different kinds of molecules, however, is a far more difficult matter that requires a variety of other techniques.

The plasma membrane of the human erythrocyte has been better characterized than any other surface membrane. Because it is the only membrane in red blood cells, and because large quantities of relatively uncontaminated cells can easily be obtained and processed, the plasma membrane of these cells has been studied more extensively than others. About 10 to 15 prominent proteins of the erythrocyte plasma membrane can be detected by gel electrophoresis. Two of these proteins, **glycophorin** and **band 3 protein**, have been particularly well characterized (Fig. 5.11). Both compounds have covalently bonded carbohydrate residues and are thus *glycoproteins*. In addition, they are transmembrane proteins; they completely traverse the lipid bilayer and protrude from both surfaces of the membrane.

Glycophorin is 131 amino acids long, and all of its sugar residues are located on the extracellular face of the plasma membrane (Fig. 5.12). The molecule extends through the lipid bilayer as a single α helix, but most of the mass of the molecule is on the external surface of the membrane. About 35 amino acid residues at the carboxy terminus of the molecule are located on the internal surface of the membrane, facing the cytoplasmic interior of the cell. Glycophorin is unique to red blood cells, but its specific function remains unknown.

Band 3 protein, so named because of its position relative to other proteins in a gel, is believed to play a role in CO_2 disposal as the red blood cells move through the lungs from the body tissues. In effect, band 3 protein is a transport protein that mediates the movement of polar molecules across the nonpolar lipid bilayer of the plasma membrane. Although its amino acid sequence and its exact disposition in the membrane are uncertain, band 3 protein is believed to differ from glycophorin in its orientation in the bilayer. Band 3 protein probably crosses the bilayer more than once, rather than as a single α helix, because most of the mass of the molecule is in the lipid bilayer (Fig. 5.13). Furthermore, the amino terminal portion of the band 3 protein appears to consist of a relatively large hydrophilic region inside the cell, which serves to anchor a number of soluble enzymes involved in glycolysis close to the inner membrane surface.

Far more specific information is available for an unusual transport protein called **bacteriorhodopsin**, which is located in specialized regions of the "purple membrane" of the salt-loving bacterium *Halobacterium halobium*. Bacteriorhodopsin functions as a light-activated proton pump in the bacterial membrane, whereby H^+ is transferred from the inside to the outside of the cell. The molecule contains a light-absorbing prosthetic group, or *chromophore*, which is covalently bonded to a side-chain of the protein. When the chromophore is activated by a photon of light, the excited chromophore causes a conformational change in the protein. This conformational change leads to H^+ transfer to the outside of the cell, thus establishing a voltage gradient across the membrane. This energy-rich gradient drives the energy-requiring synthesis of **ATP**.

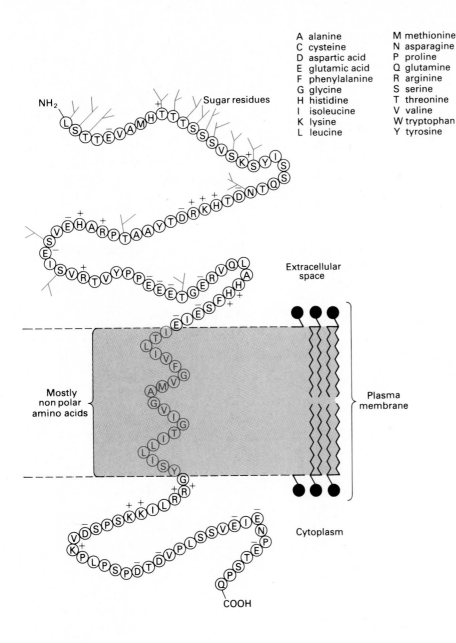

A	alanine	M	methionine
C	cysteine	N	asparagine
D	aspartic acid	P	proline
E	glutamic acid	Q	glutamine
F	phenylalanine	R	arginine
G	glycine	S	serine
H	histidine	T	threonine
I	isoleucine	V	valine
K	lysine	W	tryptophan
L	leucine	Y	tyrosine

FIGURE 5-12

Glycophorin is a glycoprotein component of the erythrocyte plasma membrane, and its 131-amino-acid sequence has been determined, along with its orientation in the plasma membrane. Most of the transmembrane molecule, including its bound oligosaccharide side-chains, occurs on the exoplasmic face of the membrane. A short region of mainly nonpolar amino acids in an α-helix conformation is threaded through the bilayer, and the remainder of the molecule protrudes from the cytoplasmic face of the membrane. The amino-terminal portion outside and the carboxy-terminal portion inside the cell include predominantly charged and uncharged polar amino acids, unlike the highly nonpolar region embedded within the lipid bilayer itself.

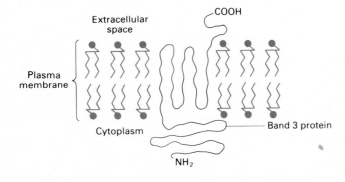

FIGURE 5-13

The transmembrane band 3 protein molecule (black) is believed to have more than one α-helix region threaded through the lipid bilayer (color), perhaps in successive loops as shown here, because most of the protein mass is contained within the bilayer. A short carboxy-terminal component occurs at the exoplasmic face of the membrane, and a relatively long hydrophilic sequence with the amino terminus is exposed at the cytoplasmic face of the membrane. This hydrophilic region anchors a number of glycolytic enzymes to the inner surface of the plasma membrane.

FIGURE 5-14
Bacteriorhodopsin is folded into seven closely packed α-helix regions that pass through the "purple" membrane of *Halobacterium halobium* at approximately right angles to the plane of the membrane. The top and bottom of the molecule are in contact with aqueous environments, and the remainder of the molecule is in contact with the hydrophobic interior of the membrane. The balsawood model shown here was derived from physical and microscopical analyses of the protein, which resembles a two-dimensional crystal and thus lends itself especially well to such methods of determining molecular configuration. (From Henderson, R., and P. N. T. Unwin, 1975, *Nature* **257**:28–32, Fig. 5. Copyright © by Macmillan Journals Limited.)

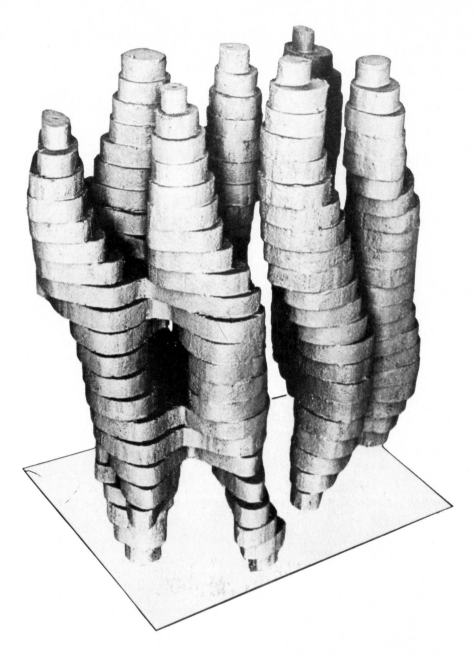

The bacteriorhodopsin molecule resembles a two-dimensional crystal, which made it possible to determine its precise disposition in the membrane. Electron microscopy and physical analyses revealed the polypeptide chain to be folded into seven closely packed α helices that pass at approximately right angles through the lipid bilayer (Fig. 5.14). Although the physical properties of bacteriorhodopsin permit relatively detailed analysis, it is uncertain whether the particular characteristics of this molecule can be extended to gain a general understanding of transport protein action.

5.4
Membrane Asymmetry

Cellular membranes are decidedly asymmetrical. The two layers of lipids are different in composition, different proteins are found on the outer and inner faces of a membrane, and the sugar residues of glyco-proteins and glycolipids are found on only one surface of a membrane. These differences can be determined to a certain extent by chemical analysis, but more dramatic evidence has been obtained using electron microscopy of materials prepared by special techniques. One of the most important of these techniques is **freeze-fracturing**, by which membranes are cleaved or fractured to reveal the surface topography of the hydrophobic interior and the two exposed faces of the membrane.

In the freeze-fracture procedure, cells are frozen in ice at $-196°C$, the temperature of liquid nitrogen, and the frozen specimen is then fractured with a cold knife. The fracture plane passes through the hydrophobic interior of any membrane and splits the lipid bilayer into two monolayers, thus revealing two fracture faces. The two *newly formed* fracture faces are called the **protoplasmic fracture face** (PF face), which is the exposed surface of the lipid layer nearest the protoplasm (cytoplasm), and the **exoplasmic fracture face** (EF face), which is the exposed surface of the lipid monolayer farthest from the cytoplasm (Fig. 5.15). The existing original membrane surfaces are the **P face** (facing the protoplasm) and the **E face** (the opposite or exoplasmic face). The membrane faces may first be *etched* as the ice sublimes, revealing membrane particles in greater contrast, or the freshly fractured membranes may be shadowed with platinum and carbon to obtain replicas of the surface. The platinum replicas of etched or nonetched membrane surfaces are then observed and photographed with the electron microscope once the underlying organic material is removed by digestion. Every membrane that has been studied by freeze-fracture electron microscopy has had a greater density of particles on one surface than on the complementary surface (P face versus E face, PF face versus

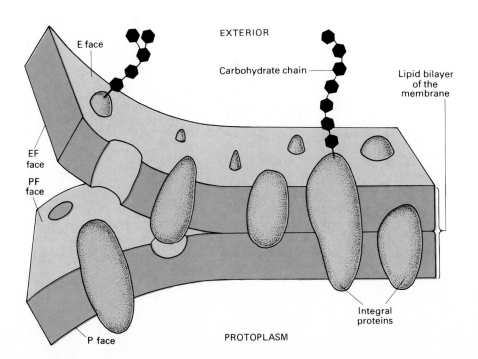

FIGURE 5-15
When frozen specimens are fractured with a cold knife, the membrane is split open between the two layers of phospholipids (its weakest plane). The surface features of the fracture faces that are produced reveal the locations of proteins by protruding particles or by depressions left vacant when proteins pull free of one lipid layer and remain in the opposite layer. The newly formed exoplasmic fracture face (EF face) is farther from the protoplasm (cytoplasm) than is its complementary protoplasmic fracture face (PF face). The original membrane surfaces are the exoplasmic or exterior face (E face) and the protoplasmic face (P face). The definition of membrane proteins can be enhanced by etching the surface to remove more of the lipid thickness from the preparation.

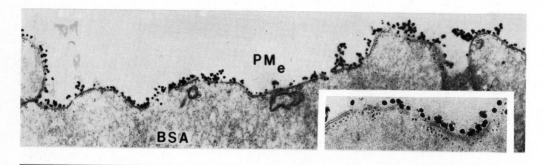

FIGURE 5-16
Localization of glycolipids to the
exoplasmic half of the plasma
membrane (PMe) of the soil ameba
Acanthamoeba castellani is shown in
electron micrographs of frozen sections
viewed on edge. Electron-dense
ferritin–concanavalin A conjugates are
distributed over the exoplasmic face of
the plasma membrane (×30,000; inset
×75,000), but are absent from the
protoplasmic face of the membrane.
The Con A component of the conjugate binds to glucose and mannose
residues, and the ferritin component provides electron density and
appropriate particle size (5.5 nm) to
visualize the binding sites. Because
glycoproteins are absent from this
membrane, the results unambiguously
show that glycolipids are restricted
to the outer layer of lipids in the
membrane bilayer. The membrane
covers a gel of bovine serum albumin
(BSA). (Photographs courtesy of P.
Pinto da Silva, from Barbosa, M. L. F.,
and P. Pinto da Silva, 1983, *Cell*
33:959–966, Fig. 2C. Copyright ©
by M.I.T. Press.)

EF face). All or most of these particles are transmembrane proteins that
have been pulled free of one monolayer and remained in the complementary monolayer after fracturing. Only those proteins with sufficient bulk are large enough to cast a shadow, so smaller molecules or
broken molecules are not revealed in the platinum–carbon shadowed
replicas. Because protein-free artificial lipid bilayers appear smooth
after being fractured, the particles seen in fractured biological membranes are most likely to be entirely or primarily proteins.

Specific labeling can be combined with freeze-fracture preparation
in order to determine the distribution of glycolipids and other membrane molecules that cannot be observed in conventional freeze-
fracture replicas. The sugar residues of glycosylated lipids and proteins
(glycolipids and glycoproteins) will bind to certain plant proteins called
lectins. Certain lectins bind certain sugars and not others; for example,
the lectin *concanavalin A* binds only to α-D-glucose and α-D-mannose
residues in oligosaccharide chains of membrane molecules. In order for
us to visualize glycosylated molecules in the electron microscope, the
lectins or other binding agents (all collectively referred to as **ligands**)
are coupled to the iron-containing protein *ferritin* before the ligands are
presented to the biological preparation. Ferritin is electron-dense and
can easily be seen in electron micrographs. Each ferritin–ligand conjugate can be recognized as an electron-dense spot of a particular size; for
example, ferritin-concanavalin A conjugates are about 5.5 nm in diameter. Although the ferritin label can easily be seen in surface views of
freeze-fractured membrane replicas, the label is particularly evident in
thin sections of freeze-fractured membranes viewed on edge (Fig. 5.16).
In a recent study of glycolipid distribution in the plasma membrane of
the soil ameba *Acanthamoeba castellani*, all the ferritin-concanavalin A
conjugates were confined to the exoplasmic, or outer, surface of the
membrane. The results could be readily interpreted because glycoproteins are absent in this plasma membrane, so all the localizations
involved only the membrane glycolipids.

5.5
Molecular Mobility Within the Membrane

Physical studies of membrane lipids clearly show that lipids move
laterally and rapidly within their own monolayer but that they rarely
"flip-flop" across the membrane from one monolayer to another. The
fluid state of the lipid bilayer depends primarily on the kinds and

relative amounts of the different hydrocarbon chains of phospholipids and glycolipids in the membrane. The membrane is more fluid in regions that contain lipids with shorter hydrocarbon chains and lipids with unsaturated hydrocarbon chains. In addition, lipid mobility is greater in regions of the membrane that have a lower concentration of transmembrane proteins.

The lipid bilayer is in a more fluid state when the hydrocarbon chains are not tightly packed. Hydrocarbons of shorter length interact with each other less often, and unsaturated hydrocarbons are more loosely packed than saturated chains because of the bends or kinks produced at double-bond sites (Fig. 5.17). Cholesterol molecules interact with phospholipids and glycolipids at the portion of the hydrocarbon chain nearest the polar head, thus leaving the remainder of the hydrocarbon in a relatively flexible state (see Fig. 5.9). These features of membrane lipids have been determined in various ways, including studies of artificial lipid bilayers subjected to different temperatures. An artificial bilayer made from one kind of phospholipid changes from a liquid state to a rigid gel state at a particular freezing point. This change of state is called a *phase transition*, and the temperature at which it occurs is lower if the hydrocarbon chains are short or unsaturated. In other words, the bilayer is less likely to assume a rigid, less fluid state when the lipid hydrocarbons are short or have double bonds.

A clear demonstration of protein mobility within the plane of the plasma membrane was provided in 1970 by L. David Frye and Michael Edidin, using mouse cells and human cells grown in culture. Each kind of cell has different membrane proteins, and each set of proteins elicits the formation of its own specific matching *antibodies* in an animal that has been challenged with foreign proteins (*antigens*) to induce an immune response. Specific anti-mouse and anti-human antibody preparations (antisera) were thus obtained, and the two preparations were tagged with different dyes in order to distinguish them and to visualize the antibodies by microscopy. The mouse antibodies were coupled with

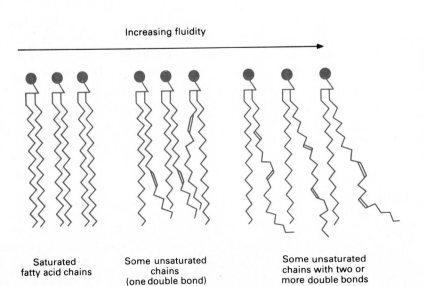

Increasing fluidity

Saturated
fatty acid chains

Some unsaturated
chains
(one double bond)

Some unsaturated
chains with two or
more double bonds

FIGURE 5-17
Regions of the membrane are more loosely packed when phospholipids or glycolipids with unsaturated hydrocarbon chains are present than when the lipid chains are fully saturated. Enhanced fluidity is a consequence of kinks or bends formed at double bonds in the hydrocarbon chains, which allow greater lateral mobility of these and associated molecules within their own monolayers.

FIGURE 5-18
Membrane proteins of mouse cells (color) and of human cells (gray) can be identified by the fluorescent antibody with which they have been labeled. Movement of membrane proteins can be followed in the surface membrane of the somatic cell hybrid formed by fusion between the original two parental cell types. L. D. Frye and M. Edidin showed by this experiment that proteins move laterally and rapidly within the plane of the surface membrane.

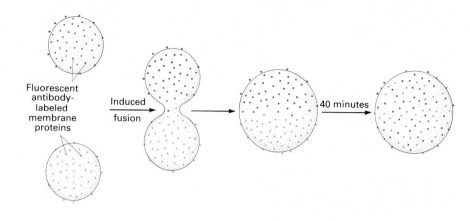

FIGURE 5-19
The addition of lectins (color) to cells leads to clustering of membrane glycoproteins and/or glycolipids and thus provides evidence of molecule mobility within the plane of the membrane. Polyvalent lectins cross-link membrane molecules by binding to sugar residues in oligosaccharide chains of neighboring molecules.

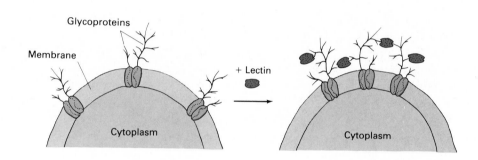

fluorescin, a green fluorescent dye, and the human antibodies were coupled with rhodamine, a red fluorescent dye.

When labeled mouse cells and labeled human cells were induced to fuse to produce somatic cell hybrids, each half of the cell hybrid was marked only with its original antibodies bound to its membrane proteins (Fig. 5.18). After 40 minutes, however, the two sets of labeled antibodies were intermixed and uniformly distributed over the entire surface of the cell hybrid. These results demonstrated in a most elegant way that the plasma membrane proteins had moved laterally within the plane of the membrane, because each fluorescent antibody marker was bound to its matching protein by specific antigen–antibody coupling. As the antibodies moved, so must the proteins to which they were bound.

The mobility of membrane proteins within the plane of the lipid bilayer can be demonstrated by the use of lectins coupled with ferritin as an electron-dense marker for the ligand. Under suitable conditions, bound lectin–ferritin conjugates that are distributed uniformly at the membrane surface are redistributed into clusters (Fig. 5.19). Because the lectins have two or more binding sites for specific sugars in the exposed carbohydrate chains of glycoproteins and glycolipids, the polyvalent ligands can cross-link membrane molecules that have the appropriate sugar residues. If the ligands are monovalent (one binding site) or if the membrane is chemically fixed and its molecules are thus immobilized, clustering will not take place.

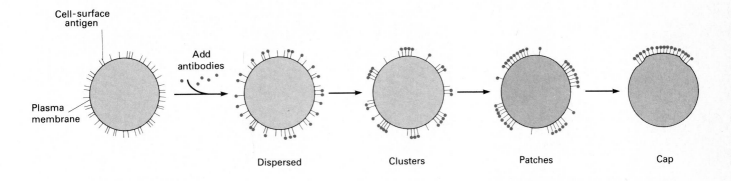

Cell-surface antigen

Add antibodies

Plasma membrane

Dispersed   Clusters   Patches   Cap

FIGURE 5-20
When divalent antibodies are added to lymphocytes, the ligands bind to surface antigenic proteins and may cross-link these proteins to different degrees, depending on the nature and concentration of the ligand. Movement of proteins within the plane of the membrane accounts for the redistribution of cross-linked molecules into clusters, patches, or a cap at the cell surface.

Similar studies using antibodies as ligands, tagged with ferritin or with a fluorescent dye, have also shown that plasma membrane proteins are redistributed into clusters, patches, and caps after a challenge with normal divalent antibodies (Fig. 5.20). Clustering does not take place if the antibody molecules have first been digested to monovalent fragments, which have only one antigen-combining site instead of two. The fluorescent or ferritin label remains uniformly distributed over the cell surface in this case, which indicates that the antibody has been bound to the membrane proteins but that cross-linking has not occurred. In studies using various ligands, therefore, the proteins can be cross-linked into large aggregates through divalent or polyvalent binding, and the proteins must thus be free to move within the plane of the membrane. The lateral mobility of membrane proteins provides unequivocal proof that the lipid bilayer of the membrane is fluid.

The redistribution of membrane proteins provides a degree of flexibility in membrane activities. Although particular proteins may be inserted in particular places in the membrane during its construction, many of these proteins can be relocated and interact more effectively with substances in the changing environments outside and inside the cell. For example, some kinds of lymphocytes (particular white blood cells of the immune system) interact through their surface proteins with invading antigens from a foreign source and undergo *capping* as the result of cross-linking between the cellular and foreign proteins. The "cap" may then be drawn into the cell and there be digested by intracellular enzymes, thus removing the foreign substances from the body's circulation and minimizing or preventing adverse consequences to health.

5.6
Restraints on Membrane Protein Mobility

One of the goals of membrane biology is to determine the relationships between membrane proteins and between these proteins and cytoplasmic components. Considerable progress toward this goal has been made with human erythrocytes, which have been studied for many years by a variety of methods and approaches.

When erythroid plasma membrane preparations are treated with solutions of low ionic strength to release loosely bound proteins, the most abundant of these proteins is **spectrin**. Electron microscopy, binding assays with particular ligands, and physical and biochemical studies have shown spectrin to be a long fibrous molecule composed of two nonidentical but similar polypeptide chains called α-spectrin and β-spectrin. Spectrin heterodimers are arranged head to head as tetramers $(\alpha, \beta)_2$ on the cytoplasmic face of the plasma membrane. The tetramers are organized into a meshwork through links with short filaments of the protein *actin* and with at least one other protein. In addition, spectrin interacts with the transmembrane *band 3 protein* indirectly through a peripheral protein called *ankyrin* (Fig. 5.21). The lateral mobility of band 3 proteins within the plane of the membrane is thus restrained by their attachment to spectrin fibers, via ankyrin. Other transmembrane proteins of the erythrocyte plasma membrane probably are similarly restrained through tethering to spectrin via spectrin-binding proteins such as ankyrin.

The spectrin-based meshwork at the cytoplasmic face of the plasma membrane is believed to help maintain the biconcave shape of the erythrocyte, even while these cells are deformed as they squeeze through narrow capillaries in the circulatory system of the body. The proteins in the plasma membrane and the underlying flexible meshwork of spectrin fibers form a continuum that is held in place through binding interactions that allow deformability without a change in cell shape or the spatial organization of transmembrane proteins. Flexible spectrin fibers may be involved in similar interactions in nonerythroid cells such as muscle, which also undergo deformation during episodes of contraction.

FIGURE 5-21

Fibrous cytoskeletal proteins (spectrin, actin) interact with peripheral membrane proteins (ankyrin, band 4.1 protein) and with the transmembrane band 3 protein to form a flexible meshwork at the cytoplasmic face of the erythrocyte plasma membrane. Spectrin tetramers (gray), formed from spectrin dimers joined head to head, bind to short actin filaments (red) and to peripheral band 4.1 proteins (black) to produce a flexible cytoskeletal network that allows some deformation of the cells as they squeeze through narrow capillaries of the circulatory system. Similar tethering to spectrin, via ankyrin (pale color), restrains the lateral mobility of band 3 protein (dark color) within the plane of the membrane. (By permission, from Lux, S. E., 1979, *Nature* **281**:427, Fig. 1. Copyright © 1979 by Macmillan Journals Limited.)

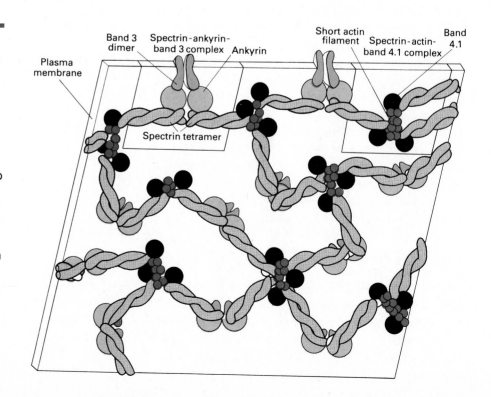

The erythroid spectrin system thus provides a model for studies of other cell types. Heterodimers of nonerythroid spectrin contain the common denominator of one α-spectrin polypeptide and a second spectrin polypeptide that is slightly different from the erythroid β-chain and is thus designated by a Greek-letter prefix other than β. Ankyrin has been found in a variety of nonerythroid cell types, and actin is a ubiquitous protein in eukaryotic cells.

Spectrin and perhaps ankyrin, along with the short actin filaments, could be viewed either as components of an underlying *cytoskeletal* network of fibers and binding proteins or as peripheral proteins of the cytoplasmic face of the plasma membrane in erythrocytes. The spectrin–actin meshwork is an unusual cytoskeleton because microtubules and intermediate filaments are not present, and the actin filaments are very short. The more typical cytoskeleton in eukaryotic cells consists of microtubules, actin microfilaments, and intermediate filaments, as well as a variety of proteins that bind to these long fibers. Furthermore, the typical cytoskeleton traverses the cytoplasm and is not confined to the plasma membrane surface alone. In more typical situations, actin filaments may control protein mobility within the membrane through binding with these proteins, very much as spectrin controls protein mobility in erythrocytes. We know very little at present about the nature of the interactions between actin filaments and protein mobility, but the erythrocyte system provides us with a model for the analysis of nucleated cells (mature mammalian erythrocytes have lost their nucleus). Actin filaments are flexible fibers, and they are believed to be among the elements governing membrane protein mobility in many kinds of cells.

Large aggregates of interacting proteins in cell membranes may have limited mobility because the molecules exist in fixed relationships with one another. We know this to be the case in the purple membrane of *Halobacterium*, where the bacteriorhodopsin molecules have little or no lateral mobility within the membrane as a result of their assembly into large two-dimensional crystals. In other situations, proteins assemble into specialized regions that join two adjacent plasma membranes, such as *cell junctions*, and their relative lateral mobility is restrained by their fixed relationships in the junctional area. We will discuss junctions in the next chapter.

In addition to restraints imposed by the aggregation of integral proteins to form complexes, the interactions of integral proteins with peripheral proteins of the membrane, and the interaction of integral proteins with components of the cell cytoskeleton, limitations on the mobility of membrane proteins can be imposed through lipid-mediated effects (Fig. 5.22). Integral membrane proteins are found in areas of the lipid bilayer that are relatively fluid, whereas little protein is present in more solid lipid domains.

Integral membrane protein mobility is impeded or enhanced through interactions with proteins and lipids within the membrane and with proteins or binding agents at the exoplasmic and cytoplasmic faces of the membrane. The control over membrane protein mobility leads to the formation of membrane domains with different properties and accounts for the dynamic nature of the interface between the exterior and interior of the cell.

(a) Aggregation of proteins or lipids   MOBILITY RESTRAINT MECHANISMS

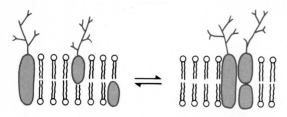
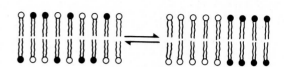

Aggregation of integral proteins   Aggregation of lipids

(b) Domain formation

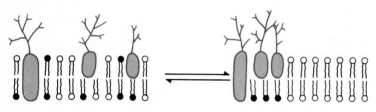
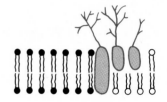

Random arrangement of lipids   Proteins sequestered   Proteins excluded

(c) Interaction of peripheral components with integral proteins

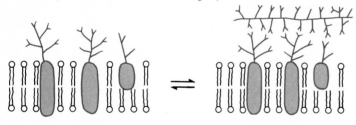

Proteins uncoupled   Proteins coupled

(d) Interaction with cytoskeletal components

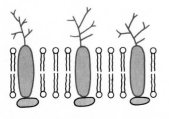
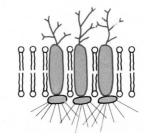
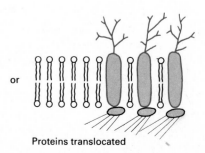

Proteins uncoupled   Proteins immobilized   Proteins translocated

◄ **FIGURE 5-22**
Mobility restraint mechanisms.
(a) Associations between integral proteins or between specific phospholipids of the membrane may limit lateral movements of these molecules when they form interacting groups. (b) Integral proteins may be less mobile when restricted to domains of specific lipid compositions, when either sequestered within such lipid domains or excluded from them because of physical or physicochemical properties. (c) Protein mobility is restrained when peripheral components, such as oligosaccharides, cross-link and thereby couple the molecules together. (d) Proteins may be immobilized upon interaction with membrane-associated proteins (black) bound to cytoskeletal fibers, such as actin filaments, or their mobility may be directed within the membrane by such interacting structures and lead to translocation of proteins from one region to another. (With permission, from Nicolson, G. L., 1976, *Biochim. Biophys. Acta* **457**:57–108, Fig. 2.)

Transport of Molecules Across Membranes

Substances move *selectively* through membranes in the living cell. If the cell is killed or its plasma membrane is irreparably damaged, molecules move freely across the membrane and equilibrium may be attained. Because equilibrium is rarely reached in living systems, the living membrane must serve as a dynamic, regulatory barrier to the entry and exit of molecules and particles. Substances cross the membrane barrier by three general routes: (1) *passive transport*, by free diffusion or by facilitated diffusion, along a concentration gradient from higher to lower concentration of the substance; (2) *active transport*, in which energy is expended as a substance moves against its concentration gradient, going from its lower to its higher concentration; and (3) enclosure of substances in membranous vesicles so that they may enter a cell by the process of *endocytosis* or be expelled from the cell by *exocytosis*, with an expenditure of energy in each process.

5.7
Passive Transport

The rate at which a molecule diffuses across an artificial, protein-free lipid bilayer depends largely on the size of the molecule and on its relative solubility in oil. The more soluble it is in oil—that is, the more hydrophobic or nonpolar it is—and the smaller its size, the more rapidly a molecule diffuses across a lipid bilayer. Small hydrophobic molecules diffuse most rapidly across a bilayer, closely followed by small uncharged polar molecules such as urea or glycerol (Fig. 5.23). Larger uncharged polar molecules, such as glucose and various amino acids, make a slow passage across the bilayer. Charged molecules, which are usually highly hydrated, find the lipid bilayer highly impermeable, no matter how small the anion or cation may be. The artificial bilayer is about 10^9 times less permeable to small ions such as Na^+ and Cl^- than to water molecules. Water molecules diffuse rapidly across the bilayer despite their relative insolubility in oil; they are exceptional in this respect. The dipolar nature of water molecules, as well as their small size

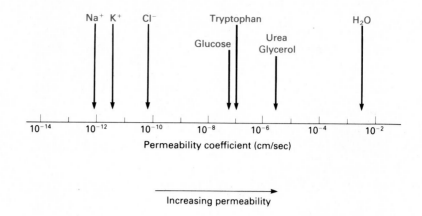

Increasing permeability

FIGURE 5-23
Molecules diffuse across a membrane in relation to their size and relative solubility in oil. Small hydrophobic or nonpolar molecules, such as urea and glycerol, move more rapidly through the membrane than glucose, various amino acids, and other uncharged, larger, polar molecules. Charged ions, such as Cl^-, K^+, and Na^+, find the membrane bilayer highly impermeable. Water molecules are exceptional in their ability to diffuse across the membrane very rapidly despite their insolubility in oil. The rate of diffusion of a substance through an artificial lipid membrane is shown by its permeability coefficient in measurements of centimeters per second.

and lack of net electrical charge, undoubtedly contribute to their rapid movement across the regions of lipid polar head groups in the bilayer.

Water and nonpolar molecules diffuse rapidly across cell membranes, just as they readily permeate artificial bilayers. Many cell metabolites also move rapidly through cell membranes, in contrast to their slow diffusion through lipid bilayers. Specific membrane proteins, called **transport proteins**, allow solutes to move across membranes by the process of **passive transport** down the concentration gradient of the solute. Some of the transport proteins, called **channel proteins**, are believed to form aqueous channels that traverse the membrane and permit solutes of appropriate size and charge to move across the bilayer by simple *free diffusion*. Other transport proteins, called **carriers**, bind a specific molecule and transfer it across the bilayer by the process of *facilitated diffusion*. Carrier proteins are highly specific and a particular carrier will transport only one type of chemical compound, such as ions or sugars, or even only a certain molecule. For example, the encoded carrier β-galactoside permease in *E. coli* is required to help lactose and other β-galactosides across the plasma membrane. Mutants that are defective in synthesizing the permease are unable to utilize β-galactosides in the culture medium because they lack the specific transport protein to bind these sugars and carry them into the cells.

Uncharged solute molecules move toward their region of lower concentration along a concentration gradient, which is the only determinant of their direction of transport. Charged solutes, however, move by passive transport toward their lower concentration along an **electro-chemical gradient**. Such a gradient consists of both the concentration gradient of the solute and the total electrical gradient across the membrane (the membrane potential). The voltage gradient across a plasma membrane is such that the outer or exoplasmic side of the membrane is positive and the inner cytoplasmic side is negative. This membrane potential thus impedes the entry into the cell of negatively charged solutes but facilitates the entry of positively charged ions and molecules.

All the known transport proteins are transmembrane molecules or are parts of larger complexes that completely traverse the bilayer. Channel proteins do not interact directly with small, charged solutes, which move freely through the aqueous passageway formed by charged,

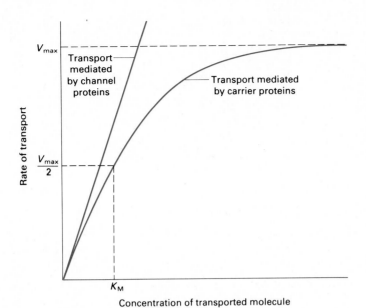

Rate of transport

V_{max}

Transport mediated by channel proteins

Transport mediated by carrier proteins

$\dfrac{V_{max}}{2}$

K_M

Concentration of transported molecule

FIGURE 5-24
The kinetics of transport across the membrane show that the rate of transport mediated by channel proteins is always proportional to the concentration of the transported solute, whereas the rate of transport mediated by carrier proteins varies according to the amount of bound solute and reaches a maximum (V_{max}) when the carrier protein is saturated with solute molecules. The binding constant of the solute for the carrier protein (K_M) is presumed to be equal to one-half the maximal transport rate ($V_{max}/2$). The kinetics of carrier-mediated transport resemble enzyme kinetics in these respects.

hydrophilic regions of the membrane protein in the lipid bilayer. Carrier proteins, on the other hand, specifically bind a solute molecule and transfer it across the lipid bilayer. Each type of carrier has a specific binding site for the solute, which can be blocked by competitive inhibitors that compete for the same binding site. In addition, solute binding can be blocked by noncompetitive inhibitors that bind elsewhere to the carrier and alter the conformation of the transport protein. Carrier proteins behave like enzymes in their interactions with inhibitors and in the kinetics of the solute diffusion that they mediate. Although the rate of diffusion of solutes mediated by channel proteins is always proportional to the solute concentration, the rate of diffusion of solutes mediated by carrier proteins varies according to the amount of bound solute (Fig. 5.24). Despite these and other similarities, carrier proteins are not enzymes, because carriers do not covalently modify the bound solute and they may alter the equilibrium point of the process. An enzyme changes only the rate at which equilibrium is reached, not the point of equilibrium itself.

The bound solute is probably delivered across the membrane through a molecular mechanism that involves a reversible conformational change in the carrier protein (Fig. 5.25). It is highly unlikely that the carrier flip-flops across the membrane during transport, because transmembrane proteins studied by physical methods have been found to cross from one side of the bilayer to the other only at infrequent intervals. Furthermore, a number of transport proteins (including band 3 protein in the erythrocyte plasma membrane) appear to be held in restraint through tethering to peripheral or cytoskeletal proteins. These transport proteins have limited lateral mobility within the bilayer as well as limited ability to tumble across the bilayer.

Certain transport proteins or protein complexes open only in response to a particular stimulus and are otherwise closed passageways. Such transiently open passageways are called **gated pores** or gated channels. Gated pores may open in response to a ligand binding to a

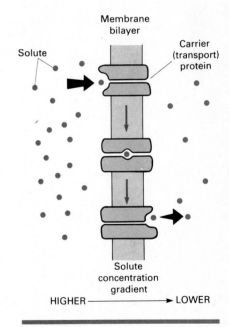

Membrane bilayer

Solute

Carrier (transport) protein

Solute concentration gradient

HIGHER ⟶ LOWER

FIGURE 5-25
Delivery of bound solute across the membrane involves progressive conformational change in the carrier (transport) protein, shown here as a transmembrane molecule composed of two subunits. Transport by facilitated diffusion occurs along a gradient from higher to lower solute concentration. Upon delivery of its bound solute, the carrier protein assumes its original conformation and is prepared for another transport event.

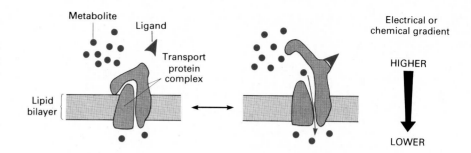

FIGURE 5-26
Transport of metabolites and other solutes may involve transport proteins that act as gated pores and open only in response to some stimulus but are otherwise closed. Upon binding to a ligand, for example, one component of the transport protein complex undergoes a conformational change and thereby exposes the passageway through which solute molecules may cross the membrane in the direction of their lower electrical potential or chemical concentration. Gated pores may open in response to agents or stimuli such as changes in ion concentration or in membrane potential, as well as to ligands.

cell-surface receptor, to changes in the extracellular or intracellular concentration of specific ions, or to changes in the membrane potential, among other stimuli (Fig. 5.26). Gated pores usually close rapidly and spontaneously, often within milliseconds of having opened. The speed with which gated pores open and close is particularly important in sequentially dependent processes in which the substance pouring in through one gated-pore system induces another gated-pore system to open. The rapidity of closing of the first gated pore modulates the action of the second gated-pore system, which may cause yet other stimulus-specific gated pores to open during a sequence of events. Gated pores, therefore, open in response to a particular agent or stimulus and close spontaneously even if the original stimulus is still operating.

Passive transport of ions down their electrochemical gradients may be mediated by **ionophores**, which are small hydrophobic molecules that dissolve in lipids. Ionophores increase the permeability of a membrane to ions by covering the charge of the transported ion so that it can move through the hydrophobic interior of the lipid bilayer. There are two kinds of ionophores: *mobile ion carriers* and *channel forming carriers* (Fig. 5.27).

The ring-shaped polymer *valinomycin* is an example of a mobile ion carrier. The exterior of the ring is hydrophobic by virtue of its valine side-chains, and the interior of the ring is lined by six negatively charged oxygen atoms that allow a single K^+ to fit within. Valinomycin picks up a K^+ on one side of the membrane, diffuses across the lipid bilayer down the K^+ electrochemical gradient, and releases K^+ on the other side of the membrane. The carrier shuttles K^+ in both directions across a membrane, which means that net transport to one side of the membrane or the other depends on the K^+ concentration gradient and the membrane potential.

Gramicidin A is a linear polypeptide composed of 15 amino acids, all of which have hydrophobic side-chains. Two such molecules are believed to associate side by side in a bilayer and thus to create a transmembrane channel that guides monovalent cations down their electrochemical gradients. This channel-forming ionophore is an unstable dimer, which has an average open time of about one second. Although a gramicidin A channel is constantly forming and dissociating, it can transport about a thousand times more cations per second in an open channel than can a single mobile ion carrier in the same time.

The two classes of ionophores can be distinguished experimentally by their response to temperatures below the freezing point of the membrane or artificial bilayer. Transport is maintained normally by

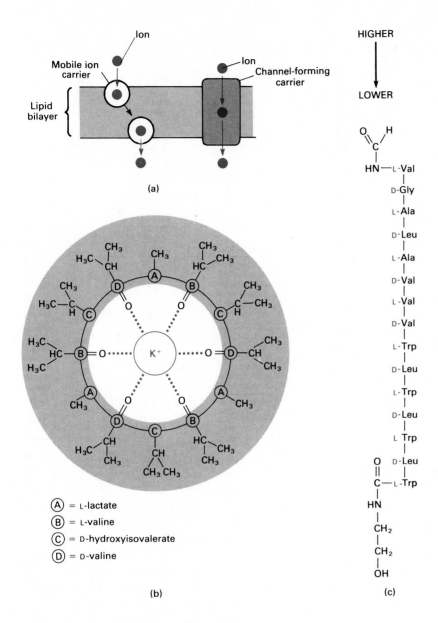

(a)

(b)

(A) = L-lactate
(B) = L-valine
(C) = D-hydroxyisovalerate
(D) = D-valine

(c)

FIGURE 5-27
Mediation by ionophores of ion passive transport. (a) Ionophores are small hydrophobic molecules of two general types: mobile ion carriers, which directly carry a bound ion across the membrane, and channel-forming carriers, which provide a channel through the membrane for passage of ions down their electrochemical gradients. (b) Valinomycin, a mobile ion carrier, is a ring-shaped polymer with a hydrophobic exterior and six negatively charged oxygens within the ring that just fit one K^+ in the center of the structure. K^+ is transported in either direction across the membrane, but always toward the lower end of its electrochemical gradient. (c) Gramicidin A consists of 15 D- and L-amino acids, all of which have hydrophobic side-chains. In an unstable dimer form, a transmembrane channel is created between the two associated polypeptide chains, which guides monovalent cations down their electrochemical gradients to the opposite side of the membrane.

channel-forming carriers in gel-phase (frozen) bilayers, but transport by mobile ion carriers stops when the temperature of a membrane drops below freezing. Mobile carriers can no longer diffuse across a frozen bilayer, thus halting their transport function. Channel-forming carriers, on the other hand, can remain open and functional in a frozen membrane or lipid bilayer because the proteins themselves do not undergo diffusion.

5.8
Active Transport

The movement of ions and metabolites against their electrochemical gradients by the process of **active transport** requires an expenditure of

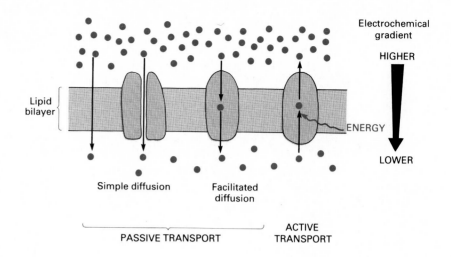

FIGURE 5-28
Passive transport, whether by simple or facilitated diffusion, can occur spontaneously as molecules and ions move down their electrochemical gradients. Active transport, however, is an energy-requiring "uphill" process. Transport proteins (color) are involved in helping hydrophilic substances across the hydrophobic lipid bilayer of the membrane.

energy. Metabolic energy drives active transport, whereas passive transport can occur spontaneously as molecules move in a thermodynamically favorable downhill direction along their gradients (Fig. 5.28). The two transport processes are similar in some ways, including the need for transport proteins that specifically bind to ions or metabolites and help to transfer these substances across the lipid barrier of the membrane.

One major source of metabolic energy to drive active transport is ATP, which is hydrolyzed by transmembrane ATPases that catalyze the release of free energy as ATP is dephosphorylated to ADP. These membrane-bound enzymes function as *pumps*, which supply the energy for translocating substances across the membrane in the direction of their higher concentration or against the electrical gradient across the membrane. The **Na$^+$—K$^+$ ATPase** in the plasma membrane of virtually all animal cells actively pumps Na$^+$ out of the cell against an electrochemical gradient and pumps K$^+$ into the cell against the K$^+$ concentration gradient. This **Na$^+$—K$^+$ pump** generates and maintains the membrane potential, or voltage gradient across the membrane, which in turn is responsible for driving the active transport of sugars and amino acids into the cell. The pump is *electrogenic*: It helps generate an electrical potential across the membrane.

Na$^+$–K$^+$ ATPase has been purified and found to consist of a large catalytic component and a smaller associated glycoprotein whose function is unknown. The principal evidence showing that the Na$^+$–K$^+$ pump is identical to the Na$^+$–K$^+$ ATPase came from studies using isolated red blood cell *ghosts*, which are the plasma membrane–cytoskeleton remainders of cells whose cytoplasmic contents have been removed by lysis. These red blood cell ghosts can be manipulated to vary the concentrations of ATP, ions, and drugs on either side of the resealed boundary. In these studies it was found that the hydrolysis of ATP is tightly coupled to the transport of Na$^+$ and K$^+$; neither occurs without the other. In addition, the coupled processes can only occur when ATP and Na$^+$ are inside the ghosts and K$^+$ is outside. The binding sites must therefore be distributed such that K$^+$ binds to the

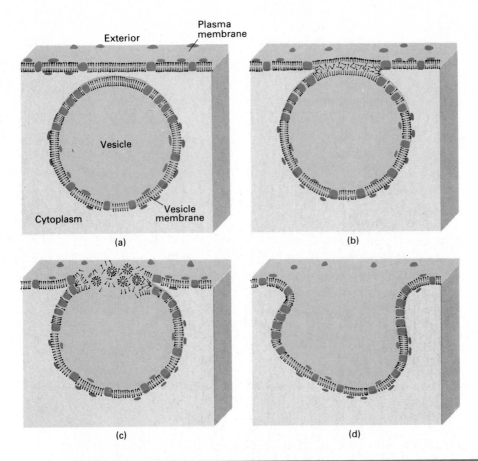

FIGURE 5-33
Possible molecular events of
membrane fusion during exocytosis.
(a) The secretion vesicle membrane
is located beneath the plasma
membrane, and (b) lipids in each
membrane move aside as the two
membranes touch. Lipid movement
may result from enzymatically altered
fluidity in the lipid bilayers. (c) The
contents of the secretion vesicle are
discharged, and (d) the remaining
vesicle membrane and the plasma
membrane fuse when their lipids
interact. Membrane proteins are shown
in color in all four illustrations.

FIGURE 5-34
Scanning electron micrograph of
phagocytic polymorphonuclear
leucocytes engulfing yeast cells.
(Photograph courtesy of D. F. Bainton.)

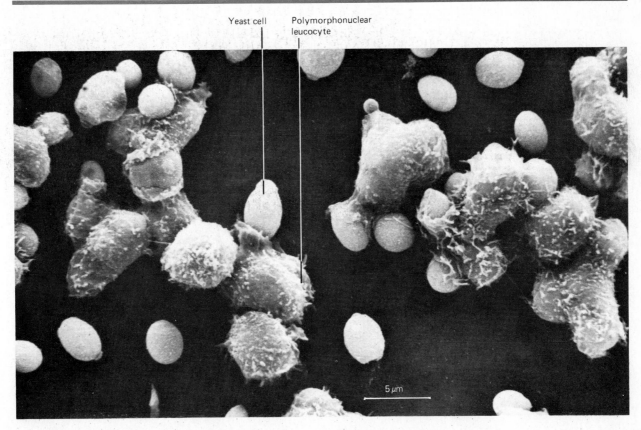

5.10
Receptor-Mediated Endocytosis

In the process of **receptor-mediated endocytosis**, specific macromolecules bind to specific cell-surface receptors in regions of the plasma membrane called **coated pits**, and the macromolecules and receptors are internalized when coated pits invaginate and pinch off from the membrane as **coated vesicles** (Fig. 5.35). The process serves as a mechanism for selectively concentrating particular macromolecules, which allows the cell to take in large amounts of these molecules in a minimum of extracellular fluid. For this reason alone, substances enter the cell by receptor-mediated endocytosis at much greater rates than by ordinary endocytosis, which is mediated by smooth, uncoated vesicles derived from uncoated regions of the plasma membrane. It is often difficult to distinguish between endocytotic coated vesicles and smooth vesicles, because coated vesicles shed their coats within seconds after being formed. In addition, endocytotic vesicles formed by either pathway soon fuse with other intracellular membranous structures and thus lose morphological identity.

FIGURE 5-35
Electron micrographs of coated vesicle formation from coated pits during receptor-mediated endocytosis of LDL particles in a hen oocyte. Invagination of the plasma membrane at the site of a coated pit progresses until a coated vesicle is pinched off in the cytoplasm. LDL particles are bound to receptors in the coated pit and coated vesicle, and the clathrin coating of the cytoplasmic face of a coated pit becomes the external surface of the clathrin-coated vesicle. (From Perry, M. M., and A. B. Gilbert, 1979, *J. Cell Sci.* **39**:257–272.)

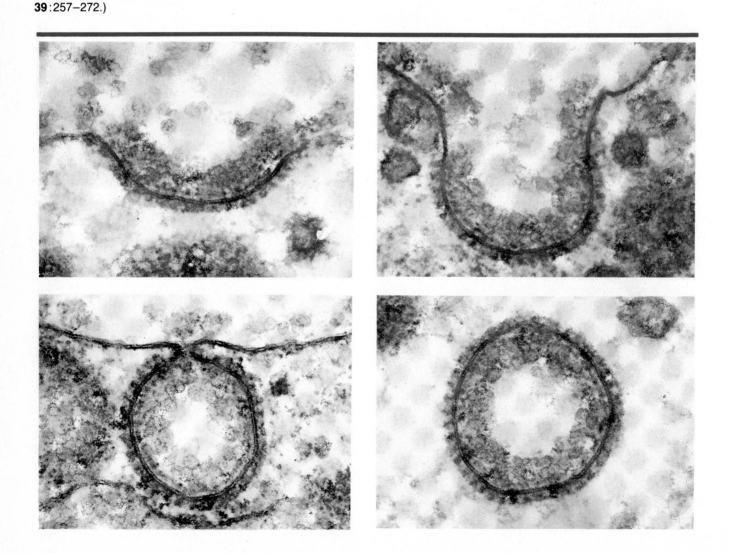

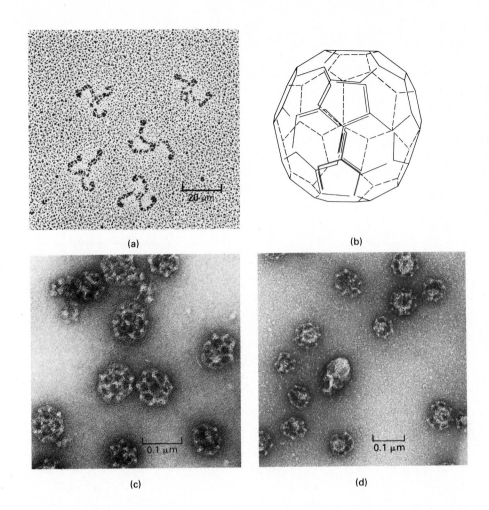

(a)

(b)

(c)

(d)

FIGURE 5-36
Structure of the clathrin coat of a coated vesicle. (a) Electron micrograph and schematic drawing of a three-legged, or triskelion, assembly unit, consisting of three clathrin molecules and three smaller polypeptides. (b) Schematic drawing of the arrangement of triskelions in a polyhedral network on the exterior surface of a coated vesicle. The network is made up of 8 hexagons and 12 pentagons; 2 triskelions are shown in color. (c) Electron micrograph of isolated clathrin baskets, or cages, formed *in vitro* from purified clathrin isolated from calf brain. (d) Electron micrograph of clathrin-coated vesicles isolated from calf brain. (Photographs courtesy of T. Kirchhausen, from Harrison, S. C., and T. Kirchhausen, 1983, *Cell* **33**:650, Figs. 2 and 3. Copyright © by M.I.T. Press.)

Several major proteins have been found in membranes of isolated coated vesicles. The best characterized of these proteins is **clathrin**, a large fibrous molecule that binds with a smaller protein to form the basic assembly unit of the characteristic polyhedral coat on the surface of coated vesicles. The assembly unit is a *triskelion*, or three-legged complex, consisting of three of the clathrin and three of the smaller polypeptides. The triskelions are arranged as a basket of pentagons and hexagons, forming a polyhedral network (Fig. 5.36).

Animal cells take in cholesterol by receptor-mediated endocytosis and use the lipid in membrane synthesis. Cholesterol is transported in the blood in the form of spherical complexes called **low-density lipoproteins (LDL)** or LDL particles. Each LDL particle contains a core of about 1500 esterified cholesterol molecules bounded by a lipid bilayer containing a single kind of protein, which binds specifically to LDL receptor proteins in the plasma membrane. The cell makes LDL receptor proteins and inserts them into its plasma membrane whenever it requires cholesterol for membrane synthesis. The receptor proteins associate spontaneously with coated pits, but some receptors may be induced to move to coated pits after binding LDL. The LDL particles and the LDL receptors to which they are bound then are taken into the cell in coated endocytotic vesicles. Once internalized, the vesicles shed their coats and fuse with small vesicles to form endosomes, which fuse with primary lysosomes. Within the lysosome the cholesterol esters are hydrolyzed to free cholesterol, which is thus made available for synthesis of new membrane. The LDL receptor proteins recycle; they return to the plasma membrane, become inserted in coated pits, and are ready to bind LDL particles in another endocytotic episode (Fig. 5.37).

Individuals who have high levels of blood cholesterol because of the inherited or acquired disorder of *hypercholesterolemia* tend to develop atherosclerotic plaques of cholesterol in their blood vessels, and they are prone to develop coronary heart disease as a result. Those who are homozygous for the defective gene may develop coronary atherosclerosis before the age of 20, and heterozygous individuals (about 1 in 500 people) usually develop symptoms by the age of 40 or 50. Whether the disorder is inherited or is acquired because of external factors, the abnormality is due to missing or defective LDL receptor proteins (Fig. 5.38). LDL particles are poorly internalized whether the receptors are absent or exist in an altered form that permits binding but not endocytosis.

Receptor-mediated endocytosis is a means of entry for a variety of substances, including hormones, iron-carrying transferrin, enzymes, and some viruses and toxins. The hormone insulin binds to receptor proteins at the cell surface, and both the hormone and the receptor molecules are internalized in coated vesicles. In this case the receptors are degraded in lysosomes, thereby decreasing the concentration of receptors available for further endocytotic entry of the hormone. The rapid turnover of

FIGURE 5-37
Receptor-mediated endocytosis of LDL particles. LDL receptor proteins in the plasma membrane bind LDL particles (color) at coated pits, and the whole system is endocytosed as a coated vesicle. After shedding its clathrin coat, the vesicle fuses with a small vesicle to form an endosome, within which LDL particles dissociate from their receptors and are separated into different vesicles by an undetermined mechanism. Receptors are recycled to the plasma membrane, but the LDL-containing vesicles fuse with primary lysosomes. Upon the development of secondary lysosomes, enzymatic hydrolysis releases free cholesterol molecules from the LDL particle complex, and the lipids can then be used for membrane synthesis in the cell.

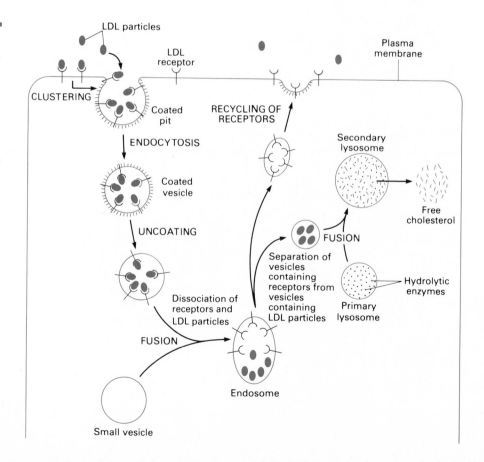

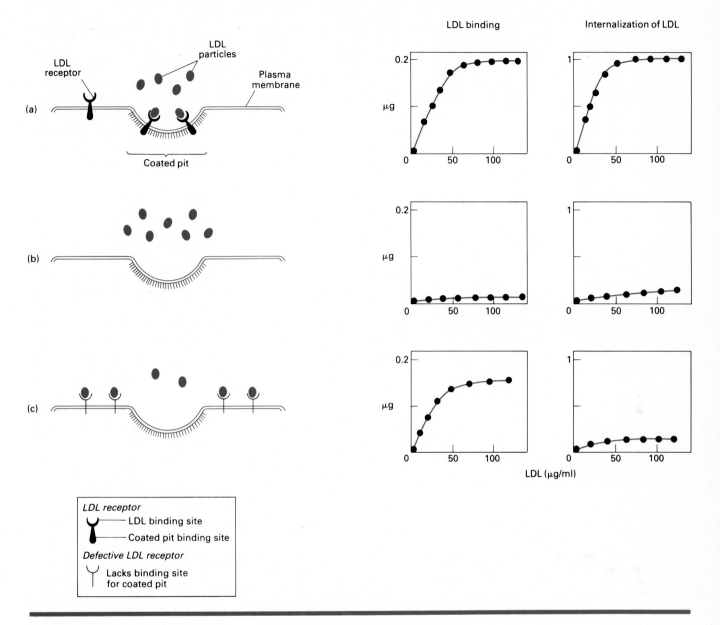

FIGURE 5-38
Genetic defects of receptor-mediated endocytosis of LDL. (a) In normal individuals, LDL particles bind to their receptors and the LDL-receptor complexes are internalized, as shown by the results of separate assays. (b) In individuals with an inherited deficiency of LDL receptors, LDL is very poorly bound and very poorly internalized. (c) Individuals carrying a mutant gene for defective LDL receptors show reasonably good LDL binding but very poor internalization of LDL. These results indicate that transmembrane LDL receptors have two separate domains—one domain that binds LDL and another domain that is required for receptors to bind at the coated pit in order for LDL to be internalized by endocytosis after it has been bound to its receptor. (From Brown, M. S., and J. L. Goldstein, 1979, *Proc. Nat. Acad. Sci. U.S.* **76**: 3330–3337.)

receptor-bound hormones ensures a rapid response in the body to changes in circulating hormone concentration.

The major carrier of iron in the blood serum of vertebrates is *transferrin*, which is a folded polypeptide that can bind two atoms of ferric iron. Circulating transferrin ferries iron to many kinds of cells and binds at the cell surface to a specific transferrin receptor in coated pits (Fig. 5.39). Studies of hemoglobin-synthesizing reticulocytes have provided much of the information that we have on the transferrin receptor and transferrin uptake. Active reticulocytes have about 300,000 transferrin receptors and can incorporate more than a million atoms of iron per minute. The events occur rapidly in cells studied in culture medium, because transferrin binding, internalization, iron release, and return to the medium of the iron-depleted transferrin and its receptor take place within 15 to 30 seconds. The iron released from transferrin is picked up and bound by ferritin in the cytosol, and the unloaded transferrin and its receptors are exocytosed at the cell surface and are available for reutilization in the same or other cells.

The transferrin receptor is a dimer made of two 90,000-molecular-weight polypeptides held together by disulfide bridges. It is a transmembrane glycoprotein with oligosaccharide chains exposed on the exoplasmic face of the membrane and its transferrin-binding sites are located in the portion of the protein that protrudes at the same membrane surface (Fig. 5.40). From binding assays and other tests it was found that one transferrin molecule binds to each subunit of the receptor. Interestingly, transferrin binds efficiently to receptors of many different species and cell types, indicating that the gene encoding the receptor polypeptide has been largely conserved during vertebrate evolution and that the protein has undergone little significant change over hundreds of millions of years. From genetic studies using somatic

FIGURE 5-39
Electron micrograph of guinea pig erythrocyte, showing electron-dense transferrin in coated pits (at arrows) at the cell surface. After transferrin binds to its receptors in coated pits and is taken into the cytosol by endocytosis, iron atoms are released from transferrin and are picked up and bound to ferritin protein. Erythrocytes obtain iron atoms for hemoglobin synthesis by this series of events. Both unloaded transferrin and its receptors are recycled back to the cell surface for reutilization in the same or other cells. (Photograph courtesy of D. W. Fawcett.)

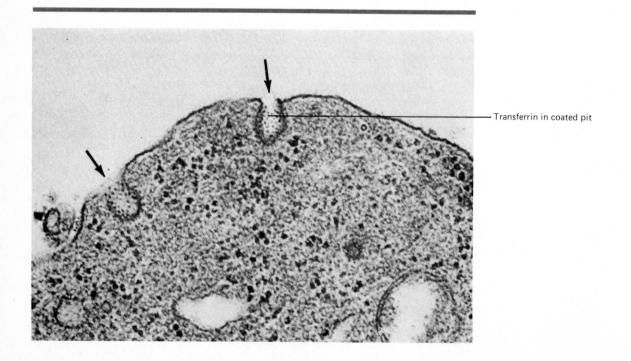

Transferrin in coated pit

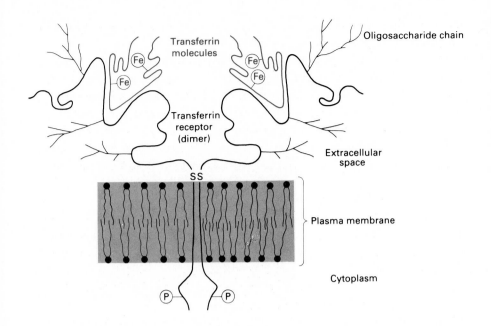

FIGURE 5-40
The transferrin receptor (black) is a dimer composed of two transmembrane glycopeptide chains, the bulk of which protrude from the exoplasmic surface of the plasma membrane. Each chain of the dimer binds a transferrin molecule (color) to which two iron atoms are bound. A short region of the receptor at the cytoplasmic face of the membrane contains one phosphorylated (P) serine residue in each polypeptide chain.

cell hybrids, the gene for transferrin and the gene for the transferrin receptor polypeptide have been located on chromosome 3 in the human genome.

Receptor-mediated endocytosis and other processes that transfer molecules across membranes are vitally important in metabolism, as indicated above. In addition, we know that these same processes are essential to the orderly events and phenomena that underlie growth, development, and reproduction of the organism. In the next chapter we will discuss other features of the cell surface and see once again that the plasma membrane is a dynamic structure that contributes to the order that distinguishes living systems from their surroundings. In later chapters we will consider special features of internal membranes, the synthesis of new membranes and recycling of existing membranes, and the sorting of molecules into specific cellular organelles.

Summary

We understand membrane structure to be a fluid mosaic in which a lipid bilayer serves as a fluid medium supporting protein components. The lipids include various kinds of phospholipids, cholesterol, and (in some tissues) glycolipids. A variety of membrane proteins and glycoproteins are associated with the bilayer. Peripheral proteins are readily extracted from the membrane surfaces whereas integral proteins are firmly fixed in the bilayer and may even span it. The association between lipid and protein is stabilized by hydrophobic and hydrophilic interactions. The two lipid layers usually differ in both protein and lipid composition, so the membrane is asymmetric. Unless otherwise restricted, both components are free to diffuse in their particular lipid layer. Mobility of membrane proteins may be restricted, however, by linkage to cytoskeletal proteins, interaction with other proteins in the membrane, or exclusion from lipid domains whose composition confers reduced fluidity.

This molecular organization allows membranes to function as selectively permeable barriers between compartments within the cell and between the cell and its environment. Molecules cross a membrane only if they can dissolve in the lipid component (hydrophobic molecules and small, uncharged polar molecules) or if there are specific membrane proteins that serve as channels or carriers facilitating their diffusion (large polar molecules and all charged molecules). Channel proteins do not interact directly with the molecule being transported, but carriers bind specifically and undergo conformational changes that effect the transport. Certain drugs can act as ionophores, promoting the permeability of membranes in which they are dissolved. All these types of passive transport allow net movement of solutes from regions of high electrochemical potential (high concentration and charge) to regions of low.

In active transport, cells use transport proteins to concentrate a substance against its electrochemical gradient, and the necessary energy is usually provided by ATP. The gradients and membrane potential developed by the action of such pumps represent stored potential energy that can be used in turn for cotransport. In this kind of active transport, two molecules move simultaneously, the energy required for pumping one molecule against its electrochemical gradient is provided by the discharging of the gradient of the other. That gradient is in turn restored by ATP-linked transport.

By the processes of endocytosis and exocytosis, materials can enter and leave cells without crossing membranes. In these processes, membrane-bound vesicles form from the plasma membrane or fuse to it. The vesicle contents are thus brought into an appropriate position for their further function. Endocytosis may provide nutrients or serve as a protective measure. Both exocytosis and endocytosis require energy, and calcium is implicated in the movements and membrane fusions involved. Receptor-mediated endocytosis is stimulated by the specific binding of extracellular molecules to membrane receptor proteins located in specialized clathrin-lined pits on the cell surface. Invagination of this membrane region allows the bound molecules to enter in a concentrated form with a minimum of extracellular fluid. This is the favored route for uptake of cholesterol, hormones, enzymes, viruses, and toxins.

Readings and References

Anderson, R. A., and R. E. Lovrien. 1984. Glycophorin is linked by band 4.1 protein to the human erythrocyte membrane skeleton. *Nature* **307**:655.

Anderson, R. G. W., J. L. Goldstein, and M. S. Brown. 1977. A mutation that impairs the ability of lipoprotein receptors to localize in coated pits on the surface of human fibroblasts. *Nature* **270**:695.

Barbosa, M. L. F., and P. Pinto da Silva. 1983. Restriction of glycolipids to the outer half of a plasma membrane: Concanavalin A labeling of membrane halves in *Acanthamoeba castellanii*. *Cell* **33**:959.

Birchmeier, W. 1984. Cytoskeleton structure and function. *Trends Biochem. Sci.* **9**:192.

Branton, D., C. M. Cohen, and J. Tyler. 1981. Interaction of cytoskeletal proteins on the human erythrocyte membrane. *Cell* **24**:24.

Bretscher, M. S. 1973. Membrane structure: Some general principles. *Science* **181**:622.

Bretscher, M. S. 1983. Distribution of receptors for transferrin and low-density lipoprotein on the surface of giant HeLa cells. *Proc. Natl. Acad. Sci. U. S.* **80**:454.

Brown, M. S., and J. L. Goldstein. November 1984. How LDL receptors influence cholesterol and atherosclerosis. *Sci. Amer.* **251**:58.

Buisseret, P. D. August 1982. Allergy. *Sci. Amer.* **247**:86.

Capaldi, R. A. March 1974. A dynamic model of cell membranes. *Sci. Amer.* **230**:26.

Capaldi, R. A. 1982. Structure of intrinsic membrane proteins. *Trends Biochem. Sci.* **7**:292.

Danielli, J. F., and H. Davson. 1935. A contribution to the theory of permeability of thin films. *J. Cell Physiol.* **5**:495.

Dautry-Varsat, A., A. Ciechanover, and H. F. Lodish. 1983. pH and the recycling of transferrin during receptor-mediated endocytosis. *Proc. Natl. Acad. Sci. U. S.* **80**:2258.

Dautry-Varsat, A., and H. F. Lodish. May 1984. How receptors bring proteins and particles into cells. *Sci. Amer.* **250**:52.

Frye, C. D., and M. Edidin. 1970. The rapid intermixing of cell surface antigens after formation of mouse–human heterokaryons. *J. Cell Sci.* **7**:319.

Geuze, H. J., *et al.* 1983. Intracellular site of asialoglycoprotein receptor–ligand uncoupling: Double-label immunoelectron microscopy during receptor-mediated endocytosis. *Cell* **32**:277.

Goldstein, J. L., R. G. W. Anderson, and M. S. Brown. 1979. Coated pits, coated vesicles, and receptor-mediated endocytosis. *Nature* **279**:679.

Harrison, S. C., and T. Kirchhausen. 1983. Clathrin, cages, and coated vesicles. *Cell* **33**:650.

Henderson, R., and P. N. T. Unwin. 1975. Three-dimensional model of purple membrane obtained by electron microscopy. *Nature* **257**:28.

Heuser, J. 1980. Three-dimensional visualization of coated vesicle formation in fibroblasts. *J. Cell Biol.* **84**:560.

Keynes, R. D. March 1979. Ion channels in the nerve-cell membrane. *Sci. Amer.* **240**:126.

Lazarides, E., and W. J. Nelson. 1982. Expression of spectrin in nonerythroid cells. *Cell* **31**:505.

Lodish, H. F., and J. E. Rothman. January 1979. The assembly of cell membranes. *Sci. Amer.* **240**:48.

Lux, S. E. 1979. Dissecting the red cell membrane skeleton. *Nature* **281**:426.

Mueller, S. C., and D. Branton. 1984. Identification of coated vesicles in *Saccharomyces cerevisiae*. *J. Cell Biol.* **98**:341.

Nicolson, G. L. 1976. Transmembrane control of the receptors on normal and tumor cells. I. Cytoplasmic influence over cell surface components. *Biochim. Biophys. Acta* **457**:57.

Pastan, I. H., and M. C. Willingham. 1981. Journey to the center of the cell: Role of the receptosome. *Science* **214**:504.

Pearse, B. M. F., and R. A. Crowther. 1982. Packing of clathrin into coats. *Cold Spring Harbor Sympos. Quant. Biol.* **46**:703.

Quinn, P. J. 1976. *The Molecular Biology of Cell Membranes.* Baltimore: University Park Press.

Ralston, G. B. 1978. The structure of spectrin and the shape of the red blood cell. *Trends Biochem. Sci.* **3**:195.

Rettenmier, C. W., *et al.* 1985. Transmembrane orientation of glycoproteins encoded by the v-*fms* oncogene. *Cell* **40**:971.

Robertson, J. D. 1981. Membrane structure. *J. Cell Biol.* **91**:189s.

Rothman, J. E., and J. Lenard. 1977. Membrane asymmetry. *Science* **195**:743.

Schwartz, J. H. April 1980. The transport of substances in nerve cells. *Sci. Amer.* **242**:152.

Sharon, N. June 1977. Lectins. *Sci. Amer.* **236**:108.

Sharon, N. 1984. Glycoproteins. *Trends Biochem. Sci.* **9**:198.

Shotten, D. 1980. Quick-freezing—the new frontier. *Nature* **283**:12.

Singer, S. J., and G. L. Nicolson. 1972. The fluid mosaic model of the structure of cell membranes. *Science* **175**:720.

Skulachev, V. P. 1984. Membrane bioenergetics. *Trends Biochem. Sci.* **9**:182.

Smith, R. L., and E. Oldfield. 1984. Dynamic structure of membranes by deuterium NMR. *Science* **225**:280.

Steinman, R. M., I. S. Mellman, W. A. Muller, and Z. A. Cohn. 1983. Endocytosis and the recycling of plasma membrane. *J. Cell Biol.* **96**:1.

Sundqvist, K.-G., and A. Ehrnst. 1976. Cytoskeletal control of surface membrane mobility. *Nature* **264**:226.

Sweadner, K. J., and S. M. Goldin. 1980. Active transport of sodium and potassium ions: Mechanism, function and regulation. *New Engl. J. Med.* **302**:777.

Ungewickell, E., and D. Branton. 1981. Assembly units of clathrin coats. *Nature* **289**:420.

Ungewickell, E., and D. Branton. 1982. Triskelions: The building blocks of clathrin coats. *Trends Biochem. Sci.* **7**:358.

Ungewickell, E., E. R. Unanue, and D. Branton. 1982. Functional and structural studies on clathrin triskelions and baskets. *Cold Spring Harbor Sympos. Quant. Biol.* **46**:723.

Unwin, N., and R. Henderson. February 1984. The structure of proteins in biological membranes. *Sci. Amer.* **250**:78.

Unwin, P. N. T., and P. D. Ennis. 1984. Two configurations of a channel-forming membrane protein. *Nature* **307**:609.

Weissmann, G., and R. Claiborne, eds. 1975. *Cell Membranes.* New York: Hospital Practice.

Wickner, W. 1980. Assembly of proteins into membranes. *Science* **210**:861.

CHAPTER 6

The Cell Surface

Cells make contact and interact with each other and with their external surroundings through their cell surfaces. The **cell surface** consists of the exoplasmic layer of the plasma membrane and any external coats covering this membrane. Cells can recognize each other, receive external stimuli and respond, and adhere in assemblies to form *tissues* and in combinations of tissues to form *organs* (Fig. 6.1). These capacities depend in part on the macromolecules that make up the exoplasmic half of the plasma membrane and on the highly organized network of macromolecules called the *extracellular matrix*. This network of extracellular molecules consists of secreted fibrous proteins and polysaccharides that provide anchorage in body tissues and provide support and protection to unicellular as well as multicellular organisms. In addition, localized specializations of the cell surface, called *junctions*, provide animal cells with the ability to bind securely to each other and to open or seal intercellular channels for communication and transport.

Cell Junctions

Cell junctions are easily visualized by thin-section or freeze-fracture electron microscopy, but they are usually too small to be seen at the low level of magnification and resolution of the light microscope. From electron micrographs it is evident that junctions are regions of interacting plasma membranes of adjacent cells. The cytoplasm underlying

FIGURE 6-1
Scanning electron micrograph of some of the tissues making up the brain (an organ) in a shark. The ependymal wall (ep) tissue covers ventricles filled with cerebrospinal fluid; nerve axons (arrowhead) and their ciliated terminal end bulbs (starred) are parts of nervous tissue; blood vessels (bv), made of wall and blood tissues, are part of the circulatory system of the brain. ×2000. (Photograph courtesy of M. F. MacDonnell.)

these regions and the intercellular space between interacting regions of membranes are also distinguishable from cytoplasm and spaces in nonjunctional areas of adjacent cells. Cell junctions are usually grouped into three functional categories: (1) **adhering junctions**, which mechanically hold cells together in tissues; (2) **impermeable junctions**, which bind cells together and also seal them in a way that prevents molecules from passing through the space between the sealed adjacent cells, and (3) **communicating junctions**, which allow ions and small molecules to move freely from one interacting cell to its joined neighbor cell and through the intercellular space. *Desmosomes* are the main type of adhering junction, *tight junctions* are the main type of impermeable junction, and *gap junctions* function in communication between cells in a wide variety of tissues in animals.

6.1
Desmosomes

Desmosomes enable groups of cells to function as structural units. They are widely distributed in tissues but are most abundant in tissues that are subject to severe mechanical stress, such as cardiac muscle or skin epithelium. Three different forms of desmosomes are usually recognized in animal epithelium: spot desmosomes, hemidesmosomes, and belt desmosomes.

Spot desmosomes are isolated points of contact that act like spot welds or rivets to hold adjacent cells together. A disc of dense fibrous material, called a *plaque*, occurs just under the plasma membrane in both cells, and *keratin filaments* (a kind of intermediate filament, also called tonofilaments) are inserted directly into each plaque. The keratin filaments anchored in the plaque extend across the interior of the cell, forming a structural cytoplasmic framework. Separating the two plasma membranes in the spot desmosome is an intercellular space about 30 nm wide that is filled with moderately dense filamentous material. The entire buttonlike complex of intercellular space, plasma membranes, plaques, and inserted keratin filaments is about 200–300 nm in diameter, which puts it just within the range of visibility by light microscopy (Fig. 6.2).

Living cells held together by spot desmosomes can be separated without damage after a brief period of digestion with a dilute trypsin solution; only the intercellular filamentous material is affected. This method is routinely used to separate cells in young embryos or in tissue culture. The filamentous material is probably glycoprotein in nature, however, because the trypsin-sensitive material is stained with ruthenium red, a reagent known to interact with carbohydrate groups. When prolonged digestion with proteases is carried out on desmosomes, all the component parts are destroyed. These results indicate that the plaques, as well as the intercellular filaments, keratin filaments, and membranes, are all constructed in whole or in part from proteins. Because keratin filament networks inside adjacent cells are connected indirectly through intercellular filaments and other parts of spot desmosomes, a continuous network of fibers is present across the entire epithelial sheet of cells. Such a fibrous framework provides the tissue

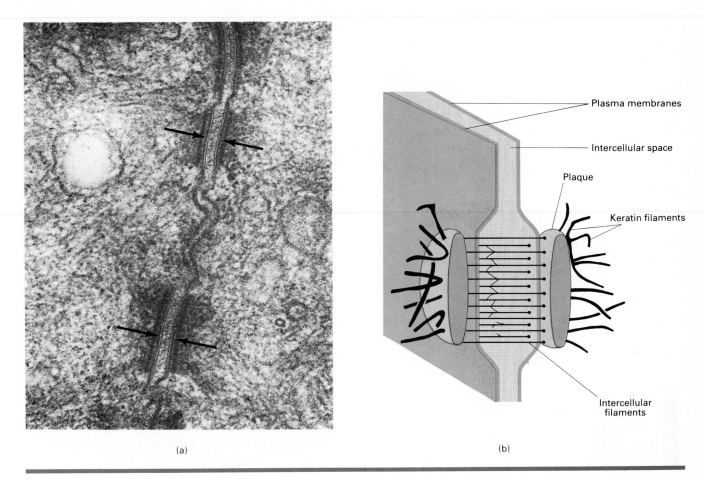

(a)

Plasma membranes

Intercellular space

Plaque

Keratin filaments

Intercellular
filaments

(b)

FIGURE 6-2
Spot desmosomes. (a) Electron micrograph of a section of rat intestinal epithelium showing two spot desmosomes shared by adjacent cells. Filaments attached to a plaque at the cytoplasmic face of each plasma membrane extend into the cytoplasm of each cell, and the 30-nm-wide intercellular space of the junctional region is filled with dense filamentous material. ×156,000. (Photograph courtesy of N. B. Gilula, from Gilula, N. B., 1974, *Cell Communications* [ed. R. P. Cox], John Wiley & Sons, N.Y., pp. 1–29, Fig. 12.) (b) Schematic drawing showing the components of a spot desmosome and their organization into an adhesion site, which enables cells to function together as a structural unit in a tissue.

with considerable mechanical stability and protects it against shear or lateral stress.

Hemidesmosomes, or half-desmosomes, resemble spot desmosomes except that they join the cell surface to a substratum rather than joining cells together (Fig. 6.3). Hemidesmosomes anchor the basal surface of epithelial cells to the *basal lamina*, which is a specialized extracellular matrix composed of epithelial cell secretions. Hemidesmosomes also develop on the inside surface of the plasma membrane in cells grown in tissue culture, and they help bind the cells to the culture vessel in which they are grown.

Belt desmosomes (also called *adherens junctions* or *zonulae adherens*) lack dense plaques and 10-nm-wide tonofilaments. Instead, thinner actin filaments are anchored in the cytoplasm just under the plasma membranes of adjacent cells, and the bundles of filaments form a continuous band or belt around each of the interacting cells in the tissue (Fig. 6.4). Epithelial belt desmosomes are usually located near the apex of the cell, and they often occur just basal to tight junctions, which are closest to the cell's apex. Between apposing halves of a belt desmosome the intercellular space is filled with fine filamentous material—presumably glycoproteins—which probably holds the interacting membranes together. The occurrence in each cell of bundles of contractile actin filaments running along the belt provides a structural basis for cellular

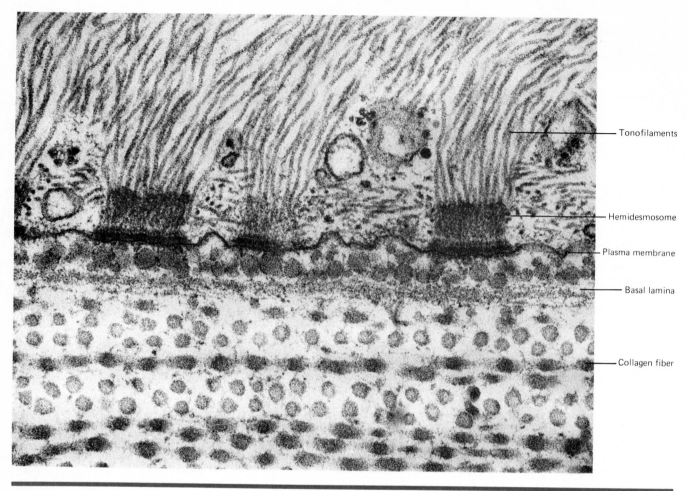

— Tonofilaments

— Hemidesmosome

— Plasma membrane

— Basal lamina

— Collagen fiber

FIGURE 6-3
Electron micrograph of the basal portion of a larval epidermal cell from the newt *Taricha torosa*. Hemidesmosomes line the intracellular face of the plasma membrane and serve as adhering junctions between the cell (above) and the extracellular matrix (below). Tonofilaments (intermediate filaments) radiate from each desomosomal plaque into the cell interior. The basal lamina and collagen fibers are evident in the extracellular matrix. (Photograph courtesy of D. E. Kelly, from Kelly, D. E., 1966, *J. Cell Biol.* **28**:51, Fig. 11. Copyright © by Rockefeller University Press.)

FIGURE 6-4
Belt desmosomes are adhering junctions that form a continuous band or belt just inside the plasma membrane of each interacting cell in the tissue. In the cutaway portion of epithelium shown here, the actin filaments that make up a belt desmosome occur just basal to tight junctions, and they interact to a limited degree with the core of microfilaments extending from each microvillus at the absorptive apex of each cell. Unlike other kinds of desmosomes, the simply constructed belt desmosome contains neither plaques nor intermediate filaments.

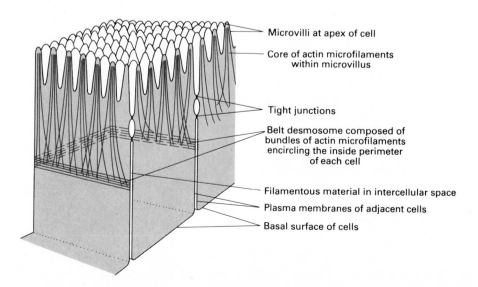

— Microvilli at apex of cell

— Core of actin microfilaments within microvillus

— Tight junctions

— Belt desmosome composed of bundles of actin microfilaments encircling the inside perimeter of each cell

— Filamentous material in intercellular space

— Plasma membranes of adjacent cells

— Basal surface of cells

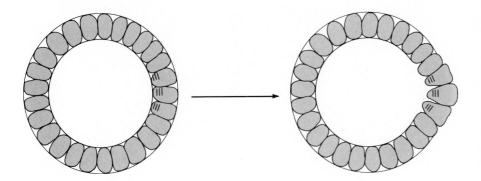

FIGURE 6-5
Changed oviduct shape in the developing bird embryo is due to narrowing of individual cells at their inner end, causing these cells to form a bulge in the oviduct wall. Actin filaments (color) located at the inner end of each cell in a bulge are the contractile components responsible for a change in shape of each cell and for the change in shape of the region occupied by these cells.

movement and change in shape during morphogenesis. For example, the sheet of cells that forms the wall of the bird oviduct develops a number of knoblike bulges during embryogenesis. On the inner side of such a bulge, some of the cells are narrowed at one end, which accounts for the curvature and rounded shape of the bulge. Bundles of actin filaments are present across the inner ends of the cells just before the bulges form and afterward. The filaments are the only observable structures in the cells that are oriented in a way that could produce cell narrowing and consequent bulge development, and actin filaments are known to function in contractility (Fig. 6.5). If actin filaments are disrupted by drug treatment, the bulges do not develop. Once the drug is washed out, normal development proceeds and bulges appear in the wall of the embryonic oviduct.

6.2
Tight Junctions

Tight junctions seal adjacent cells together and occlude the passage of intercellular fluids because there is no intercellular space between interacting membranes in the junctional area. The two plasma membranes, each 7.5 nm wide, account for the width of about 15 nm that is characteristic of tight junctions observed in thin-section electron microscopy (Fig. 6.6). In freeze-fracture electron micrographs the PF face of tight junctions shows meshed ridges, and the complementary EF face of the fractured bilayer has a meshwork of grooves that match the ridges. The ridges consist of rows of transmembrane particles that form *sealing strands*, which hold the interacting membranes together and create a permeability barrier to the passage of solutes between cells across the epithelial sheet. More impermeable junctions have more sealing strands per unit area, and "leaky" junctions have relatively fewer sealing strands. In the epithelium that lines the lumen (inner cavity) of the small intestine, tight junctions prevent the contents of the gut from spilling back into the tissue. At the same time, nutrients in the gut are transferred across the cell sheet into the extracellular fluid on the other side, and from there they are absorbed into the blood (Fig. 6.7). Tight junctions contribute significantly to both these vital functions of the intestinal epithelium. They seal adjacent cells together to form a

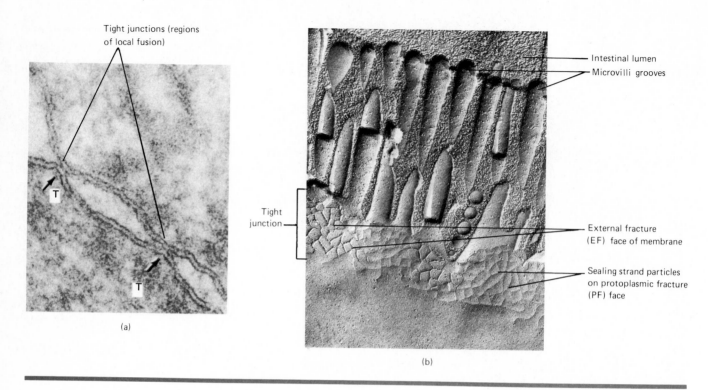

Tight junctions (regions of local fusion)

T

T

(a)

Intestinal lumen

Microvilli grooves

Tight junction

External fracture (EF) face of membrane

Sealing strand particles on protoplasmic fracture (PF) face

(b)

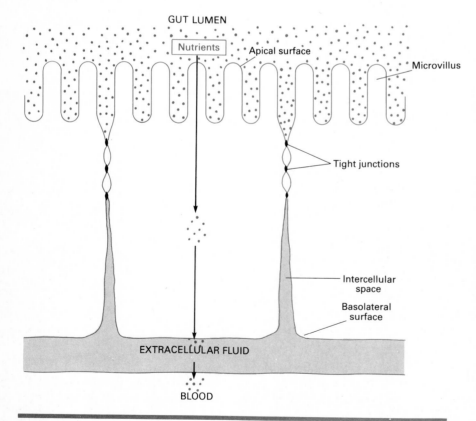

GUT LUMEN

Nutrients

Apical surface

Microvillus

Tight junctions

Intercellular space

Basolateral surface

EXTRACELLULAR FLUID

BLOOD

FIGURE 6-6
Electron micrographs of tight junctions in rat intestinal epithelium. (a) Thin section showing two tight-junction regions of membrane fusion. The width of the tight junction just equals the combined width of the two interacting adjacent plasma membranes, which indicates the absence of an intercellular space in this occluded region. (×247,500) (b) Freeze-fracture replica showing the meshwork of ridges composed of sealing strand particles in the protoplasmic fracture (PF) face and complementary grooves in the external fracture (EF) face of the plasma membrane. The matching ridges and grooves indicated fused membrane components just under the microvilli at the cell apex bordering the intestinal lumen. The sealing strands hold together the two interacting plasma membranes and occlude the intercellular space, thus preventing spillback of gut contents into the epithelial tissue. ×47,000. (Photographs courtesy of N. B. Gilula; (a) from Gilula, N. B., 1974, *Cell Communications* [ed. R. P. Cox], John Wiley & Sons, N.Y., pp. 1–29, (b) from Friend, D. S., and N. B. Gilula, 1972, *J. Cell Biol.* **52**:758.)

FIGURE 6-7
Schematic drawing of a portion of intestinal epithelium. Spillback from the gut lumen into the cell sheet is prevented by the occluding tight junctions, but nutrients from the gut lumen are absorbed into the cells and are transferred across the tissue into the extracellular fluid—and from there to the bloodstream for circulation to other parts of the body.

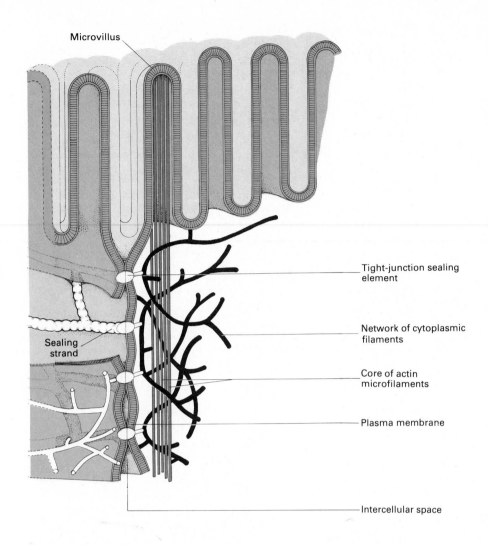

Microvillus

Tight-junction sealing element

Network of cytoplasmic filaments

Sealing strand

Core of actin microfilaments

Plasma membrane

Intercellular space

FIGURE 6-8
Three-dimensional representation of adjacent epithelial cells held together at a tight junction by sealing strands, each of which consists of two rows of closely spaced particles (one row is contributed by each cell) that terminate in a tight-junction sealing element. The network arrangement of sealing strands provides the junction with considerable flexibility as well as resistance to stress. The junction is structurally reinforced by fine filaments (at the cytoplasmic surfaces of adjacent membranes) connected to the sealing strands. The shape and flexibility of each microvillus are due largely to the reinforcing core of actin microfilaments that pass through the network of junctional filaments in the cytoplasm. (From "Junctions Between Living Cells," by L. A. Staehelin and B. E. Hull. Copyright © 1978 by Scientific American, Inc. All rights reserved.)

continuous sheet that is impenetrable to the smallest molecules, and they prevent transport proteins in the apical and basolateral surfaces of the plasma membrane from moving through the lipid bilayer away from their respective locations. The gut contents remain confined in the intestinal lumen, and the directional pumping of nutrients continues from the apical end to the basal end of the cells.

The network of sealing strands provides considerable flexibility and, at the same time, permits the epithelium to resist mechanical stress. The tight and regular network lends resistance to changes in shape of the tissue, just as a tight and orderly weave makes a fabric more resistant to stretching and changes in shape. Tight junctions are structurally reinforced by networks of fine cytoplasmic filaments connected to the sealing strands (Fig. 6.8).

Tight junctions are found only in vertebrate animals, where they occur in epithelia lining many of the internal body cavities. They are also present in other areas where mixing of fluids is prevented, as in brain capillaries where a barrier is maintained against complete mixing of blood and extracellular fluids, and in the lining of the urinary bladder where a difference in ionic concentration is maintained between the bladder and extracellular fluids.

FIGURE 6-9
Electron micrographs of gap junctions.
(a) Thin section of a gap junction region
between adjacent hamster fibroblast
cells. The two closely apposed plasma
membranes are separated by a narrow
space, or gap, about 2–4 nm wide.
(×210,000) (b) Freeze-fracture
replica of a gap junction between
mouse liver cells. The junction is
characterized by closely spaced
homogeneous membrane particles
on the protoplasmic fracture (PF)
face and by complementary pits or
depressions on the external fracture
(EF) face of the plasma membrane.
The plaquelike junctional region is
very different from nonjunctional
portions of the membrane, which
have randomly distributed particles
of various sizes. ×108,000. (Photographs courtesy of N. B. Gilula, from
Gilula, N. B., 1974, *Cell Communications* [ed. R. P. Cox], John Wiley
& Sons, N.Y., pp. 1–29.)

6.3
Gap Junctions

Gap junctions are widely distributed in tissues of all animals and are the most common type of cell junction known. Small water-soluble molecules and ions pass directly from one cell to another through a narrow channel formed from protein molecules in the two apposed membranes. Cells are thus coupled metabolically and electrically through these communicating junctions.

When viewed by thin-section electron microscopy, gap junctions appear to be localized regions consisting of two closely apposed plasma membranes that are separated by a gap or space about 2–4 nm wide (Fig. 6.9). In freeze-fracture replicas, small plaques consisting of a regular lattice of homogeneous particles are present on the PF face of the split bilayer, and matching pits or depressions occur in the complementary EF face of the fractured gap junction. The shape and organization of these particles are especially evident in thin sections cut

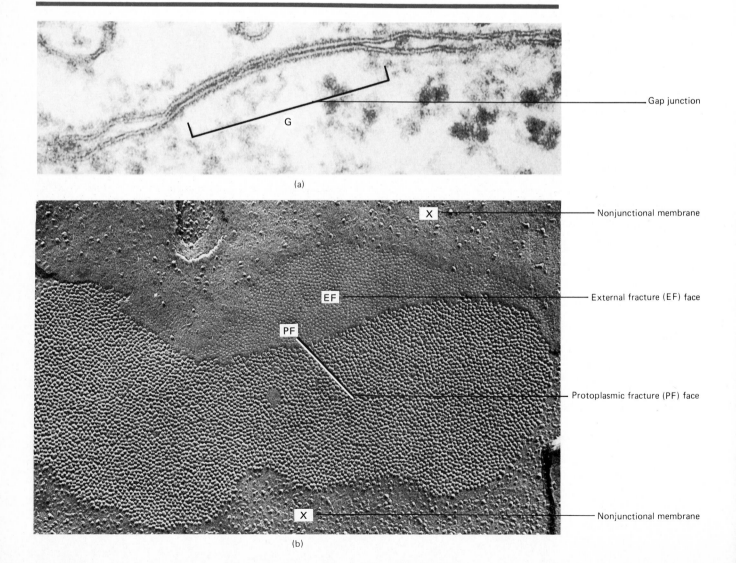

(a)

(b)

Gap junction

Nonjunctional membrane

External fracture (EF) face

Protoplasmic fracture (PF) face

Nonjunctional membrane

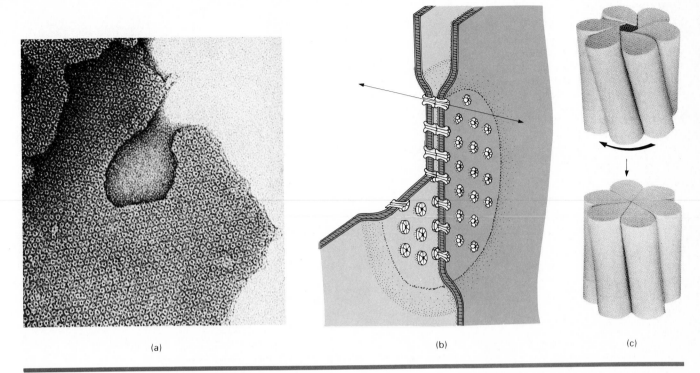

(a)   (b)   (c)

FIGURE 6-10
Organization of the gap junction.
(a) Electron micrograph of a negatively stained gap junction from
rat liver cells, cut parallel to the
plane of the plasma membrane. An
electron-dense spot is visible in the
center of each polygonal particle
(connexon) in the lattice of a gap
junction plaque. The stain accumulates in sites that lack biological
material, such as a hole, whereas
biological materials remain unstained.
(×240,000) (b) Three-dimensional
representation of a gap junction,
showing connexons to be physically
continuous across the membranes of
adjacent cells and thereby to provide
intercellular channels for molecular
exchange. (c) Model of connexon
construction and action, showing its six
connexin subunits and a possible
means by which the central channel
may open and close. Sliding of the
subunits in one direction opens the
channel, and sliding in the opposite
direction closes the channel. (Photograph in (a) courtesy of N. B. Gilula;
(b) from "Junctions Between Living
Cells," by L. A. Staehelin and B. E. Hull,
copyright © 1978 by Scientific
American, Inc., all rights reserved; (c)
from Unwin, P. N. T. and G. Zampighi,
1980, *Nature* **283**:545.)

parallel to the junction and *negatively stained* with salts of heavy metals such as lanthanum or tungsten. The stain accumulates in spaces, which then appear dark or opaque, but it does not bind to biological materials, which remain unstained or are only lightly stained. From such preparations and from x-ray diffraction studies, it is evident that each particle is composed of six subunits arranged side by side in a circular array around a small central pore (Fig. 6.10). The subunits are made of a protein called *connexin*, and the structure consisting of six subunits is termed a **connexon**.

Connexons serve as channels in gap junctions shared by adjacent cells. Using fluorescent molecules of different molecular weights, it was found that substances smaller than 1000–1500 daltons could easily pass through connexons, whereas larger molecules could not (Fig. 6.11). Ions, sugars, amino acids, nucleotides, hormones, vitamins, and other vital metabolites and regulatory substances are thereby shared by coupled cells. Macromolecules such as proteins and nucleic acids are apparently too large to penetrate a pore diameter of about 1.5 nm, and these substances are not shared by interacting cells. Both large and small molecules tagged with fluorescent or isotopic markers can be detected in the intercellular space between the apposing membranes of a gap junction. Thus the intercellular space is not occluded, and communication between cells can take place through intercellular fluids as well as through connexons directly.

By the relatively simple device of injecting tagged molecules into selected cells, we can show that the molecules pass into neighboring cells only when gap junctions join the injected cells to their neighbors

FIGURE 6-11
Small metabolite molecules and ions move easily through the connexon channels of a gap junction and may thus be shared by coupled cells. Macromolecules, such as many proteins and nucleic acids, are too large to pass through the narrow connexon openings, which are about 1.5 nm wide.

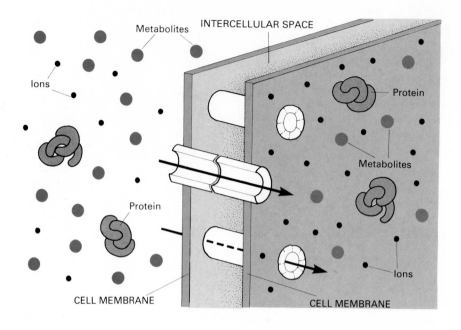

FIGURE 6-12
When molecules that are tagged with fluorescent or radioactive markers are (a) injected into one cell, the molecules (b) appear a few minutes later in an adjoining cell only if gap junctions are present between them. These experiments make it clear that passage occurs through gap junctions and not by transport across the nonjunctional membranes, because no labeled molecules are found in the extracellular spaces or surroundings outside the cells.

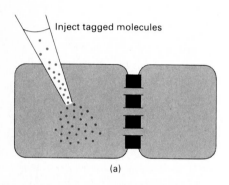
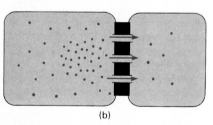

(Fig. 6.12). In the absence of gap junctions, or if the cells are dissociated and not joined, the tagged molecules do not enter uninjected cells from the injected cells. Ions move readily through gap junctions, which can be demonstrated by inserting microelectrodes into cells and recording electrical measurements. Gap junctions mediate *metabolic cooperation* between coupled cells giving and receiving metabolites, and they mediate ionic cooperation or coupling in cases involving the passage of ions between joined cells. The harmonious and coordinated activities of cells in tissues are the outcome of cell-to-cell communication via gap junctions, among other factors.

The ability of cells to form gap junctions is inherited. When cells from cultures of normal fibroblasts are mixed together with junctionless mutant fibroblasts, only the normal cells couple. A normal and a mutant cell or two mutant cells do not bind together because they fail to develop intercellular gap junctions. This result can be confirmed by electron microscopy. A simpler and less time-consuming procedure is to determine whether the normal and mutant cells can become metabolically coupled. If the normal cells can synthesize a metabolite needed for growth by the junctionless mutant or any other junctionless cell, we can predict that the mutants will be able to grow in a medium that lacks the needed metabolite only if there is metabolic cooperation via gap junctions between the normal and mutant cells. When such experiments are performed, the junctionless mutants fail to grow in minimal medium but the normal cells flourish. The inability of normal cells to "rescue" junctionless mutants indicates the failure of metabolic cooperation and, therefore, the absence of intercellular gap junctions between normal and junctionless mutant cells.

Certain kinds of cells never form gap junctions, even though many other kinds of cells in the same organism do. Lymphocytes, a type of white blood cell of the immune system, do not have gap junctions. When lymphocytes that can synthesize an essential metabolite are mixed with mutant lymphocytes that cannot make the needed molecule, metabolic cooperation is not established. The absence of metabolic coupling and the absence of gap junctions in electron micrographs of these lymphocyte cultures provide clear evidence of the inability of this cell type to develop gap junctions.

Gap junctions in competent cells can form within minutes when dissociated cells are mixed together. The speed of their formation, even in the absence of protein synthesis, indicates that these junctions self-assemble from available connexin subunits. The mechanism of assembly is not known. When cells from different vertebrate species are mixed together in culture, they often form functional intercellular gap junctions. This indicates that connexin is a highly conserved protein that has changed little during evolution. There must be a considerable degree of similarity in the connexin protein of different species if interacting cells can form the continuous aqueous channels made by joined connexons across gap junctions (see Fig. 6.10b).

Gap junctions must be important in embryonic development, because they form very early but exist transiently in many tissues as development proceeds. In the amphibian embryo, for example, cells of the developing neural tube are coupled to overlying ectoderm cells at first, but uncoupling occurs when the neural tube closes. Immature muscle cells, called myoblasts, establish gap junctions just before they fuse to form striated muscle fibers. These and other examples of communication between cells during development and differentiation provide strong circumstantial evidence for exchange of information between developing cells via gap junctions. It is very likely that communication between coupled cells provides one means by which these cells can develop coordinately and that severing the communication links permits different tissues to establish their own identities and pathways of differentiation.

6.4
Septate Junctions

Septate junctions are found only in invertebrate tissues, but their function is uncertain. They have been considered impermeable junctions, communicating junctions, and adhering junctions at various times in the past. A **septate junction** is easily identified morphologically by thin-section and by freeze-fracture electron microscopy. In thin-section views of the cut edge of the junction, regularly spaced *septa* or bars occur throughout the intercellular space, which is about 15–17 nm wide (Fig. 6.13). Parallel rows of particles that exactly correspond to the septa can be seen on the PF face of freeze-fracture replicas, and complementary rows of depressions occur on the EF face of the fractured bilayer. The septa thus appear to be composed of rows of protein particles that cross the intercellular space and connect the two apposing plasma membranes of interacting cells.

It is unlikely that septate junctions seal the intercellular space between joined cells, because negative stains readily penetrate this space and thus indicate that fluid flow is not impeded in the junctional region. There is little direct evidence, however, to indicate whether septate junctions function in adherence or in communication. Tests for meta-

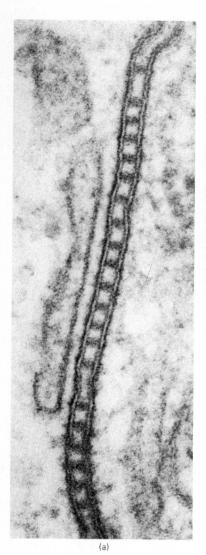

(a)

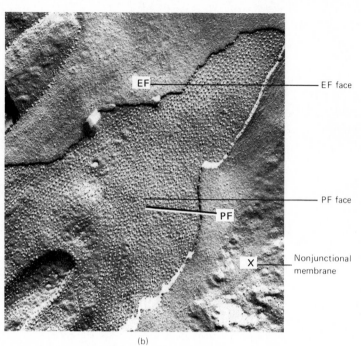

EF ———— EF face

PF face

PF

X ———— Nonjunctional membrane

(b)

FIGURE 6-13

Electron micrographs of a septate junction between epithelial cells of a mollusc. (a) Thin section showing adjacent junctional plasma membranes with regularly spaced bars, or septa, throughout the intercellular space of 15 nm–17 nm width. ×216,000. (b) Freeze-fracture replica of septate junction surfaces. The grooves in the external fracture (EF) face are com-plementary to the rows of particles in the protoplasmic fracture (PF) face, and they represent the regularly spaced septa seen in thin section. Particles are randomly dispersed in nonjunctional regions of the membranes. ×45,000. (Photographs courtesy of N. B. Gilula, from Gilula, N. B., 1974, *Cell Communications* [ed. R. P. Cox], John Wiley & Sons, N.Y., pp. 1–29.)

bolic coupling should be performed to determine whether or not septate junctions are functionally similar to gap junctions, which are usually found linking cells that are also held together by septate junctions. Some investigators doubt we can conclude that septate junctions have a communication function just because they appear together with gap junctions in invertebrate tissues. When we have evidence instead of conjecture, we will be in a better position to determine the nature and true function of septate junctions.

Extracellular Matrix

Many kinds of animal cells and virtually all prokaryotes, protists, fungi, and plants secrete proteins and polysaccharides at the cell exterior, where these molecules interact to form organized external structures collectively called the **extracellular matrix**. Secreted extracellular materials form the rigid *cell walls* in prokaryotes, certain protists, fungi, and plants. The extracellular matrix of animal cells and tissues may exist as thick, extensive deposits that provide protection, support, and elasticity to cartilage, tendons, bones, and other specialized structures. Chitinous coverings of crustaceans and insects, calcareous shells of molluscs and secretions of corals, and the silica walls of diatoms, all constitute examples of extracellular matrix. The extracellular structures in all organisms provide mechanical support, and they also influence a wide range of behaviors, functions, and activities of the cell, tissue, or organism.

6.5
Extracellular Matrix in Animal Tissues

The cells that secrete the macromolecules of the extracellular matrix are widely distributed within this matrix. The extracellular matrix and the cells contained in it, such as fibroblasts and mast cells, are often referred to as *connective tissue* (Fig. 6.14). The amount of connective tissue in organs varies considerably, as do the relative amounts of the different types of macromolecules in the matrix and their specific organization therein. Each form of extracellular matrix appears to be highly adapted to the function of the particular tissue or organ. Skin and bone consist mainly of connective tissue, whereas the brain contains very little.

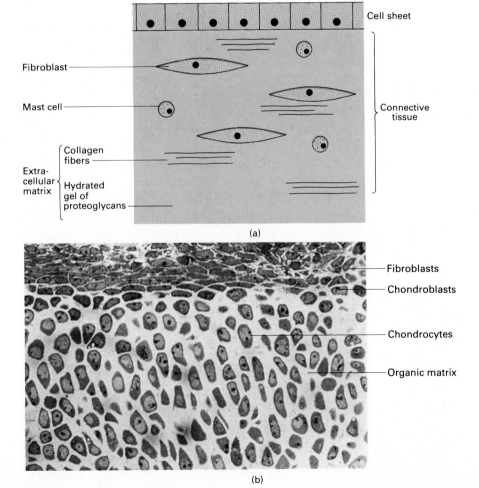

(a)

(b)

FIGURE 6-14
Connective tissue. (a) Generalized scheme showing fibroblasts, mast cells, and collagen fibers embedded in the extracellular matrix of hydrated macromolecules, all of which are parts of connective tissue underlying a sheet of cells. (b) Light micrograph of a 1–μm–thick section of cartilage from mouse embryo. Layers of fibroblasts overlay immature chondroblasts that become mature chondrocytes and secrete the extracellular matrix materials surrounding them in the mature area of the tissue. ×550. (Photograph courtesy of B. Babiarz.)

Specialized cells called osteoblasts secrete the extracellular macro-molecules in bone, and this matrix becomes hard as stone when it is calcified during development. Cartilage is formed by cells called chondroblasts, which secrete an extracellular matrix that has flexibility and cushions joints during times of activity and stress. The same fibers that characterize cartilage are also the principal component of the tendons formed by fibroblasts, but the protein fibers are organized like ropes or cables and thereby provide tendons with their great tensile strength. The cornea of the eye covers the iris and pupil but is transparent and admits light, largely as a result of the paracrystalline order of the matrix molecules.

Two of the main classes of macromolecules that make up the extracellular matrix are the *collagens*, which are a family of fibrous proteins with a three-stranded helical structure, and the *proteoglycans*, which are molecules composed of polysaccharide *glycosaminoglycans* covalently linked to a large core protein of about 250,000 molecular weight. The collagen fibers are embedded in a ground substance that is a highly hydrated, gel-like material formed by the proteoglycan mole-cules. The collagen fibers strengthen and organize the extracellular matrix, and the aqueous phase of the proteoglycan gel permits nutrients, metabolites, and regulatory substances to diffuse between the tissue cells and the bloodstream. We will discuss each class of macromolecule, and other important components of the extracellular matrix, separately in the following sections.

6.6
Collagen Chemistry and Biosynthesis

Collagens are found in all animals, and they are the most abundant proteins in vertebrates. A **collagen** molecule consists of three collagen polypeptides, called α-*chains*, that wind around each other to form a three-stranded helix. Each α-chain of the stiff, cablelike molecule is made up of about 1000 amino acid residues, fully half of which may consist of glycine, hydroxyproline, and hydroxylysine units. The sugars glucose and galactose occur in pairs, linked to hydroxylysine residues along the 300-nm length of each polypeptide (Fig. 6.15). Collagens are thus glycoproteins, but glycoproteins with a most unusual amino acid composition and molecular organization.

Seven genetically different collagen α-chains have been identified at the present time, and others may yet be found. All these kinds of α-chains are of the same general length but they differ in amino acid sequence. Although more than 300 different kinds of triple-helix col-lagens could be assembled from various combinations of these seven α-chains, only a small number of different collagens have been de-scribed. Five of these (types I, II, III, IV, and V) predominate in vertebrate animals. Types I, II, and III are the main collagens in connective tissues, and type I accounts for about 90% of the collagen in the body (Table 6.1).

Collagen I, II, and III molecules in the extracellular matrix assemble into polymers called **collagen fibrils**, which are 50–150 nm wide and many micrometers long. Collagen fibrils often assemble into

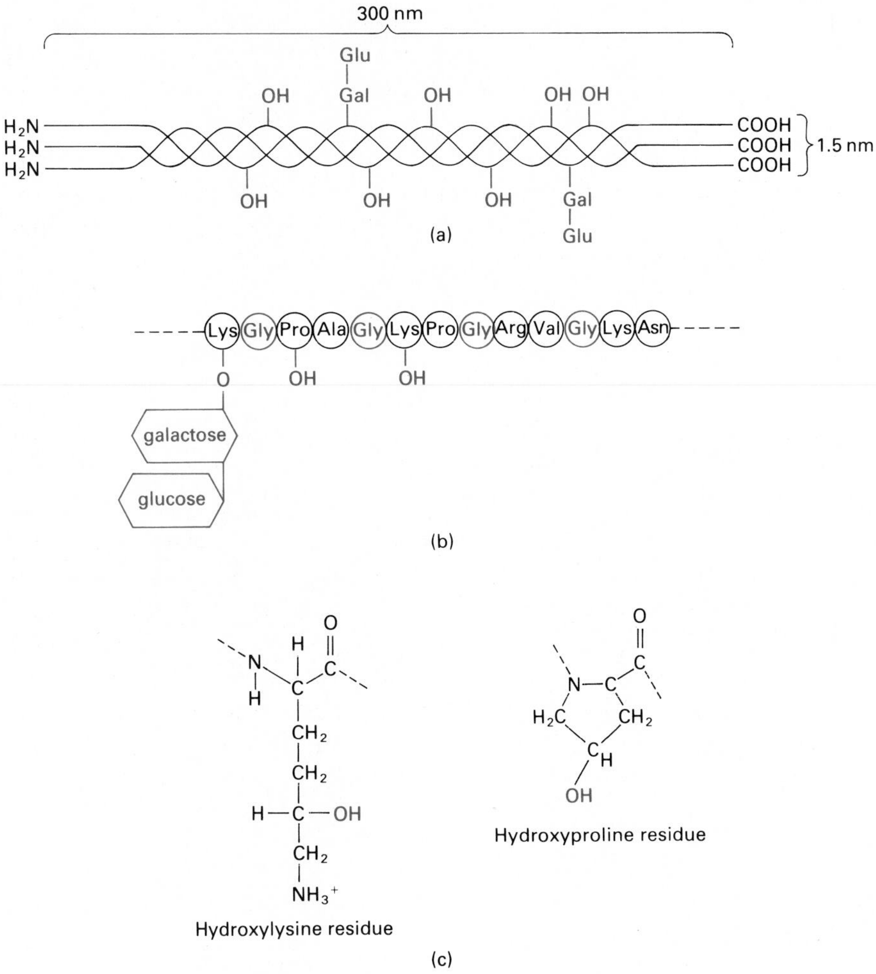

FIGURE 6-15
Collagen molecular organization. (a) A single collagen molecule consists of three α-chain polypeptides wound around each other to form a stiff, three-stranded helix about 300 nm long. (b) Each α chain is made up of approximately 1000 amino acid residues, about half of which are glycines, hydroxyprolines, and hydroxylysines. Glucose–galactose disaccharide units are linked to some of the hydroxylysines in each α chain of the glycoprotein molecule. Note that glycine residues are repeated at regular intervals in the chain. (c) Structure of hydroxylysine and hydroxyproline, two of the residues that make collagen unusual among proteins in its amino acid composition.

TABLE 6-1
Selected Characteristics of the Five Major Types of Collagen in Animal Tissues

| Type of Collagen | α-CHAINS PRESENT IN TRIPLE-HELIX COLLAGEN MOLECULES | | | | | | | Molecular Features | Distribution in Tissues |
	α-1(I)	α-1(II)	α-1(III)	α-1(IV)	α-1(V)	α-2(I)	α-2(V)		
I	2					1		low hydroxylysine low carbohydrate	skin, bones, teeth, tendons, ligaments, internal organs
II		3						high hydroxylysine high carbohydrate	cartilage, notochord, vitreous body of eye
III			3					low hydroxylysine high hydroxyproline low carbohydrate	skin, blood vessels, uterine wall, cornea of eye
IV				3				high hydroxylysine high carbohydrate	basement membranes
V					2		1	high hydroxylysine high carbohydrate	basal lamina in small amounts in many parts of the body

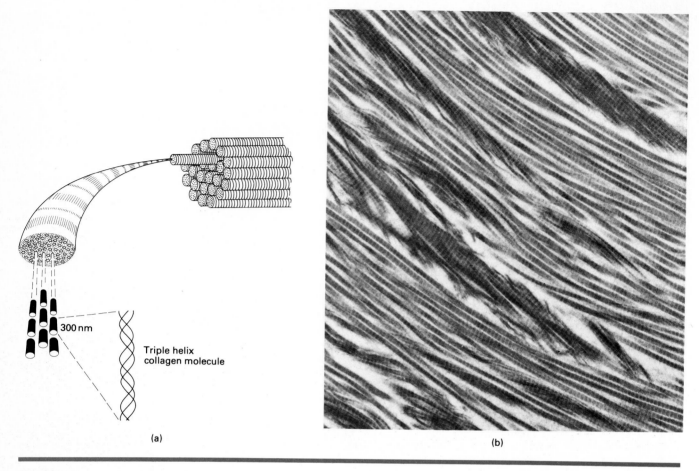

FIGURE 6-16

Structural organization of collagen fibrils and fibers in connective tissue. (a) The large collagen fiber in connective tissue is made up of individual collagen fibrils, each 50–150 nm in diameter, which are themselves aggregations of smaller microfibrils. Each microfibril, in turn, is an aggregation of triple-helix collagen molecules that all measure 300 nm in length. (b) Electron micrograph of collagen fibers in connective tissue from human skin. Note the banded appearance of the individual collagen fibrils and of the fiber aggregates. ×18,550. (Photograph courtesy of K. A. Holbrook.)

large bundles, called **collagen fibers**, which may be several micrometers in diameter and are thus easily seen by light microscopy (Fig. 6.16). The arrangement of type IV and type V collagen molecules is uncertain, but they do not form fibrils or fibers in the extracellular matrix.

Collagen polypeptide chains are synthesized at the rough endoplasmic reticulum in precursor forms called *pro-α-chains*. In the ER lumen, pro-α-chains are hydroxylated at selected proline and lysine residues, and some of the hydroxylysine residues are glycosylated by the covalent addition of paired glucose-galactose units before the processed pro-α-chains assemble to form triple-helix **procollagen**, the precursor of extracellular collagen (Fig. 6.17). Each pro-α-chain has an extra amino acid sequence, called an *extension peptide*, at both the carboxy- and amino-terminal ends of the polypeptide. Extension peptides guide the assembly of triplex procollagen molecules from individual pro-α-chains, but whether procollagen assembles in the ER lumen or elsewhere is still uncertain.

Procollagen molecules move from the ER lumen to the Golgi region and are there packaged in secretory vesicles for discharge by exocytosis into the extracellular matrix. Proteolytic enzymes called *procollagen peptidases* are also secreted from the cell. They catalyze the removal of extension peptides from procollagen, which is thus converted to collagen

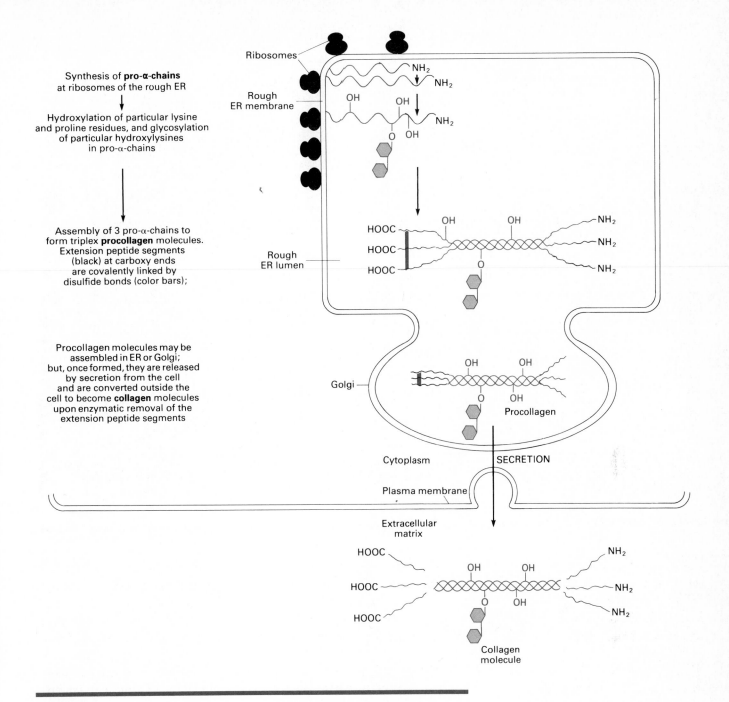

Synthesis of pro-α-chains at ribosomes of the rough ER

Hydroxylation of particular lysine and proline residues, and glycosylation of particular hydroxylysines in pro-α-chains

Assembly of 3 pro-α-chains to form triplex **procollagen** molecules. Extension peptide segments (black) at carboxy ends are covalently linked by disulfide bonds (color bars);

Procollagen molecules may be assembled in ER or Golgi; but, once formed, they are released by secretion from the cell and are converted outside the cell to become **collagen** molecules upon enzymatic removal of the extension peptide segments

Ribosomes

Rough ER membrane

Rough ER lumen

Golgi

Procollagen

Cytoplasm

SECRETION

Plasma membrane

Extracellular matrix

Collagen molecule

FIGURE 6-17

Schematic drawing showing the sequence of events in the synthesis of pro-α-chains within the ER lumen, their assembly into triple-helix procollagen molecules, and procollagen release in Golgi secretion vesicles to the extracellular matrix. Procollagen extension peptides are next removed in the formation of collagen molecules, which may then aggregate into fibrils, and these into collagen fibers.

molecules (also called *tropocollagen*) outside the cell. Types I, II, and III collagen in the extracellular matrix then polymerize to form collagen fibrils, and these may aggregate into fibers. Type IV collagen, and possibly type V collagen, retain the extension peptides after secretion, which may account for these collagens remaining unpolymerized in the basal lamina. Fortunately, none of the procollagens polymerize while still inside the cell. This is probably due to the influence of extension

FIGURE 6-18
End-to end assembly of collagen
molecules, in precisely packed rows
of polymers, produces the typical
banded appearance of collagen fibrils.
(a) Schematic drawing of collagen
molecules in a collagen fibril, showing
the head-to-tail arrangement of individual monomers in each polymeric
row and the side-by-side packing of
polymers in a fibril. A gap of 35 nm
separates 300-nm-long collagen
molecules in each row, and the tails
of molecules in adjacent rows are
displaced by a space of 67 nm. The
regularity of spacing is such that each
set of five adjacent rows produces a
repeating pattern, and the first molecule
of one set is in register with the first
molecule of the adjacent set of five.
(b) The staggered arrangement of
collagen molecules is responsible
for the banded appearance of an
individual fibril, which is particularly
evident in an electron micrograph of
a negative stained preparation. The
accumulation of stain in the gaps
between molecules is responsible
for the periodic staining pattern.
×199,500. (Photograph courtesy of
K. A. Holbrook.)

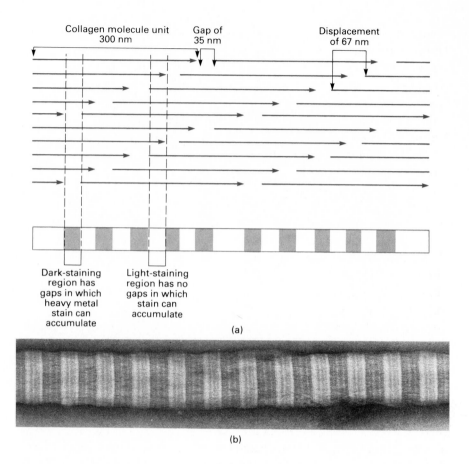

(a)

(b)

peptides in preventing the characteristic end-to-end assembly of individual molecules to form fibrils (Fig. 6.18).

The proper processing of pro-α-chains to form stable triple-helical
procollagen molecules that can be transported through the cell, and the
removal of extension peptides from procollagen in the extracellular
matrix, are essential to the normal development of connective tissues. If
proline and lysine are not hydroxylated because of an insufficiency of
oxygen or ascorbic acid (vitamin C), pro-α-chains are degraded in the
cell and a deficiency of collagen causes the skin and blood vessels to
become extremely fragile, as occurs in individuals who develop scurvy.
In other diseases the inadequacy of connective tissues may be due to
defects in cleaving extension peptides from secreted procollagen, which
is essential for the formation of collagen molecules and for the assembly
of collagen into fibrils and fibers in the extracellular matrix. At least
seven different enzymes are required to process pro-α-chains and
procollagen, so various genetic defects or dietary and environmental
deficiencies may interfere with collagen biosynthesis and polymerization
in the organism.

6.7
Glycosaminoglycans and Proteoglycans _____

Glycosaminoglycans (GAGs) are long, unbranched polysaccharide
chains composed of repeating dissacharide units one of whose two
monosaccharide residues is always the amino sugar (hexosamine)

N-acetylglucosamine or N-acetylgalactosamine (Fig. 6.19). Seven major kinds of glycosaminoglycans are found in the extracellular matrix: *hyaluronic acid, chondroitin 4-sulfate, chondroitin 6-sulfate, dermatan sulfate, keratan sulfate, heparan sulfate*, and *heparin*. These GAGs, formerly called acid mucopolysaccharides, are distinguished by their sugar residues, the number and location of sulfates in the disaccharide units, and other features (Table 6.2).

Hyaluronic acid is an atypical GAG in several ways, but particularly because it is not linked to protein in proteoglycan molecules. All the other GAGs are covalently modified in the Golgi apparatus by sulfation and other reactions. They become covalently linked to serine residues of a high-molecular-weight *core protein* to form proteoglycans before being secreted by exocytosis into the extracellular matrix. Hyaluronic acid is believed to be particularly important in aiding cell migration in tissues undergoing development or wound repair. The molecule is produced in large quantities in such tissues, the extracellular matrix is even more highly hydrated than usual because hyaluronic acid attracts water, and cell migration stops when these molecules are destroyed by the enzyme *hyaluronidase*.

Proteoglycans are highly atypical glycoproteins because they generally contain 90% to 95% carbohydrate by weight, in the form of numerous long, unbranched glycosaminoglycan chains that usually lack sialic acid (Fig. 6.20). Typical glycoproteins contain 1% to 60% carbohydrate by weight, in the form of relatively short, branched chains of sugar residues that often include a terminal sialic acid component. Polysaccharide chains of GAGs and proteoglycans are rather inflexible, so they assume a highly extended conformation and occupy a very large volume relative to molecular mass. In addition, GAGs are highly hydrophilic and have a high density of negative charges, so highly

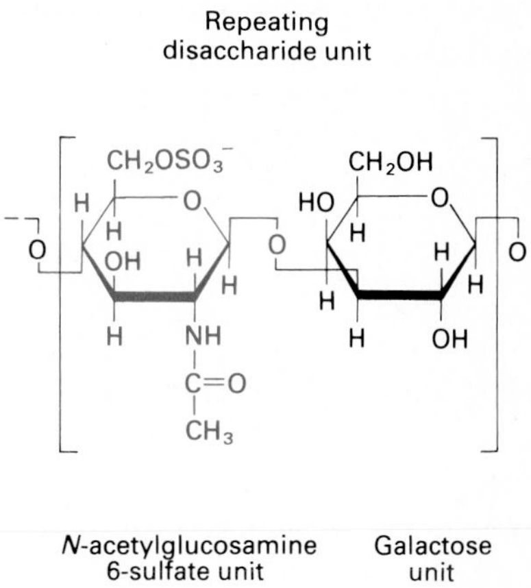

Repeating
disaccharide unit

N-acetylglucosamine   Galactose
6-sulfate unit   unit

FIGURE 6-19
The repeating disaccharide unit of keratan sulfate, a long unbranched glycosaminoglycan (GAG) molecule, consists of a monomer unit of *N*-acetylglucosamine 6-sulfate and a monomer unit of galactose. All GAG disaccharide repeats contain a hexosamine, which may or may not be sulfated.

TABLE 6-2
Characteristics of Different Types of Glycosaminoglycans (GAGs)

Type of Glycosaminoglycan	Repeating Disaccharide Unit	Other Sugar Components	Molecular Weight	Distribution in Tissues
Hyaluronic acid	D-glucuronic acid— N-acetylglucosamine	None	4,000 to 8,000,000	various connective tissues, skin, cartilage
Chondroitin 4-sulfate	D-glucuronic acid— N-acetylgalactosamine	D-galactose D-xylose	5,000 to 50,000	cartilage, bones, skin, arteries, cornea of eye
Chondroitin 6-sulfate	D-glucuronic acid— N-acetylgalactosamine	D-galactose D-xylose	5,000 to 50,000	bones, skin, arteries, cornea of eye
Dermatan sulfate	D-glucuronic acid*— N-acetylgalactosamine	D-galactose D-xylose	15,000 to 40,000	skin, heart, blood vessels
Heparan sulfate	D-glucuronic acid*— N-acetylglucosamine	D-galactose D-xylose	5,000 to 12,000	arteries, lung
Heparin	D-glucuronic acid*— N-acetylglucosamine	D-galactose D-xylose	6,000 to 25,000	skin, lung, liver
Keratan sulfate	D-galactose— N-acetylglucosamine	L-fucose D-galactosamine D-mannose sialic acid	4,000 to 19,000	cartilage, cornea of eye, intervertebral disc

* or L-iduronic acid, a product of D-glucuronic acid molecular rearrangement

FIGURE 6-20
Highly schematic illustration of a proteoglycan, showing the stiff core protein bristling with stiff chains of glycosaminoglycans (GAGs), which account for the very high carbohydrate content of these unusual glycoproteins. GAGs are highly hydrophilic and carry a high density of negative charges, which together are responsible for the highly hydrated gel nature of proteoglycans.

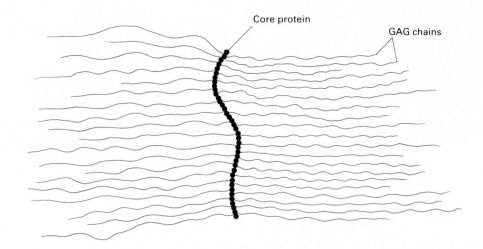

Core protein

GAG chains

hydrated gels are formed at low concentrations of carbohydrate. The osmotic pressure resulting from hydration by large amounts of water provides the GAG and proteoglycan gelled regions with considerable resistance to compression. The compressive resistance of the gel and the resistance to stretching by the embedded collagen fibrils account for the great resilience and padding properties of many connective tissues. The consistency of the extracellular matrix varies, however, from a watery gel to the hard, unyielding mass of bones and teeth. These differences in consistency depend on the relative proportions of fibers and hydrated gel and on the various kinds and combinations of minerals, fibrous elements, proteoglycans, and GAGs that are present.

We know little about the organization of GAGs and proteoglycans in the extracellular matrix, beyond their ability to bind to collagens and other macromolecular components of the matrix. The specific patterns of organization in functionally different tissues and the remarkable diversity of proteoglycans all indicate underlying complexity, but few details are available. The role of hyaluronic acid in proteoglycan aggregation has been studied for a number of years in well-preserved extracts of cartilage. In this material, monomer units of proteoglycan are attached to a chain of hyaluronic acid via a link protein (Fig. 6.21). Few or no attached GAG chains are found in the hyaluronic acid-binding region of the proteoglycan core protein, and each proteoglycan monomer is locked in place on the hyaluronic acid chain by the link protein and not by direct covalent bonding. These same aggregates may be found in tissues other than cartilage, but very different ones must occur in tissues that have little or no hyaluronic acid, such as mature cornea.

6.8
Other Structural Matrix Proteins

Collagen is not the only fiber-forming protein in the matrix that interacts with glucosaminoglycans and proteoglycans. Among the named structural proteins that contribute fibrillar components to extracellular matrix are *elastin, fibronectin, chondronectin,* and *laminin.* These four proteins interact with other matrix constituents and contribute to specific properties and functions of the extracellular matrix.

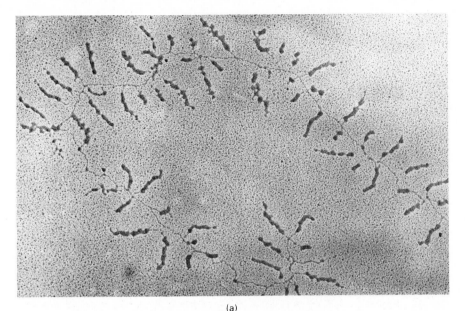

(a)

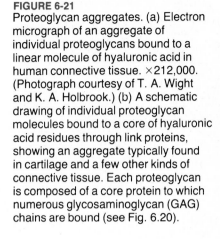

FIGURE 6-21
Proteoglycan aggregates. (a) Electron micrograph of an aggregate of individual proteoglycans bound to a linear molecule of hyaluronic acid in human connective tissue. ×212,000. (Photograph courtesy of T. A. Wight and K. A. Holbrook.) (b) A schematic drawing of individual proteoglycan molecules bound to a core of hyaluronic acid residues through link proteins, showing an aggregate typically found in cartilage and a few other kinds of connective tissue. Each proteoglycan is composed of a core protein to which numerous glycosaminoglycan (GAG) chains are bound (see Fig. 6.20).

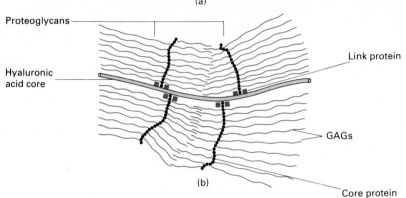

Proteoglycans

Hyaluronic acid core

Link protein

GAGs

(b)

Core protein

Elastin is rich in glycine and hydroxyproline, like collagen, but the molecule lacks hydroxylysine and neutral sugars. Little is known about elastin synthesis and processing, but the protein is synthesized in a soluble precursor form that is secreted by exocytosis. Outside the cell, elastin forms filaments and sheets of highly cross-linked fibers that are associated with microfibrils of an unnamed glycoprotein distributed on the surfaces of the elastic fibers (Fig. 6.22). The network of elastic fibers can stretch and retract without tearing the tissue, because long collagen fibers that are interwoven with the elastic fibers limit the degree of stretching.

Fibronectin is a fiber-forming glycoprotein synthesized by various types of cells. One form, called cellular fibronectin, is part of the extracellular matrix; another form, called plasma fibronectin, is found in the blood and other body fluids. Both forms of fibronectin are able to bind to fibrin and aid in blood clotting. Cellular fibronectin in the matrix is believed to aid in cell adhesion through indirect binding with intracellular actin filaments across the plasma membrane (Fig. 6.23). In studies of fibroblast cells grown in culture, fibronectin is synthesized in substantial amounts in normal cells, which adhere to the solid substratum of the culture vessel, flatten out, and stop moving and proliferating when the cells form a confluent monolayer on the substratum. Cells that

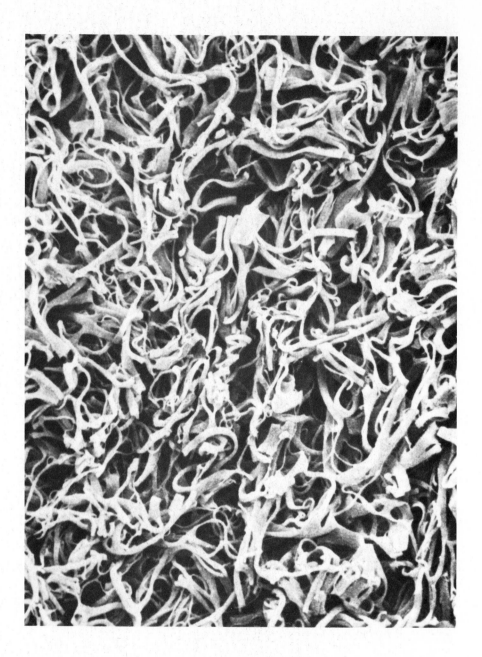

have been transformed to a state of uncontrolled migration and proliferation produce little fibronectin, and they behave very differently in culture. Transformed cells fail to adhere properly to the substratum and to assume a flattened cell shape, and they continue to multiply and move about, thereby producing disordered mounds of cells. In addition to these behavioral differences, normal fibroblasts produce thick bundles of actin filaments (stress fibers) just under and parallel to the plasma membrane, whereas transformed cells fail to develop organized stress fibers. If large amounts of fibronectin are added to transformed cells in culture, the cells adhere, flatten out, and produce stress fibers, but they continue to proliferate without restraint. These observations indicate that fibronectin promotes cell adhesion rather than cell division and growth. In fact, cells adhere to each other or to collagen and other substrates when provided with purified fibronectin. These and other

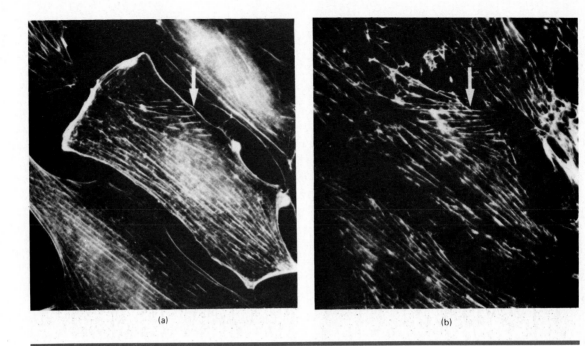

(a)   (b)

kinds of evidence underline the importance of fibronectin and the extracellular matrix in the orderly processes of cell migration and tissue development during embryogenesis and in the unrestrained cell behavior leading to tumor development and tumor spread in metastasis.

Chondronectin and **laminin** are much more restricted in distribution than other fiber-forming glycoproteins. Chondronectin is a binding agent for chondrocytes to collagen in cartilage matrix, and laminin is a binding agent for epithelial cells to collagen in the underlying basal lamina (basement membrane).

The great variety of fiber-forming proteins, proteoglycans, and GAGs in the extracellular matrix of different tissues interact with cell surfaces and with actin (and perhaps other components) inside the cell. Our study of differences in development, behavior, and function of cells and tissues must therefore include the matrix as much as the cells themselves if we are to understand multicellular organisms as complex but orderly communities of cells, tissues, and organs.

FIGURE 6-23
Double-labeled immunofluorescence micrographs of cultured rat fibroblasts. (a) Intracellular actin filaments, visualized by rhodamine-coupled anti-actin antibodies, and (b) cellular fibronectin fibers secreted into the surrounding extracellular matrix, visualized by fluorescin-coupled anti-fibronectin antibodies, are almost identically oriented parallel to the long axis of the cell. The two kinds of fibers are believed to bind to each other indirectly across the intervening plasma membrane of the cell. (Photographs courtesy of R. O. Hynes, from Hynes, R. O., and A. T. Destree, 1978, *Cell* **15**:875. Copyright © by M. I. T. Press.)

6.9
Plant Cell Walls

Virtually all plant cells are surrounded by walls composed of polysaccharide and protein secretions. The dividing cell lays down a *cell plate* that thickens into the *primary cell wall*, which is relatively flexible and thus allows cell elongation during growth. As the cell matures, a thicker, more rigid *secondary cell wall* is deposited over the existing wall.

Cellulose is the predominant fibrous component in cell walls of higher plants, occurring as *microfibrils* composed of 30–40 individual unbranched chains of glucose monomers held together by β-glycosidic bonds (see Fig. 2.10). The cell wall matrix, in which cellulose microfibrils are embedded, is a gel-like substance largely composed of two major types of polysaccharides: pectin and hemicellulose. **Pectins** are acidic, branched polymers of various monosaccharide units, particularly rich in galacturonic acid. Pectins form stable gels of variable consistency because these polysaccharides attract and trap water molecules. **Hemicellulose** resembles pectin in its branched construction, but it differs in having no net electrical charge. Hemicellulose molecules cross-link and thereby contribute to the gelation of the matrix. In addition to pectin and hemicellulose, the matrix contains *extensin*, a protein with a high content of hydroxyproline. Extensin is believed to be linked to matrix carbohydrates and to occur in the form of glycoprotein. Many mature plant cells contain *lignin*, a hard, dense substance constructed from polymers of aromatic alcohols. The density and strength of many hardwoods are due to the high lignin content of cell walls in woody tissues.

Many of the enzymes involved in the synthesis of cell wall constituents are located outside the cell membrane boundary. Enzymes involved in the initial steps of synthesis are concentrated in the Golgi apparatus, and there they catalyze the formation of precursor molecules of the matrix. These precursors are enclosed in vesicles and are secreted by exocytosis to the cell exterior, where enzymes located in the wall complete the synthesis of matrix molecules and bind them covalently to the matrix network. Cellulose fibers are synthesized by enzymes on the exoplasmic surface of the plasma membrane. They probably assemble into microfibrils there too, according to interpretations of freeze-fracture electron microscopy and other lines of evidence (Fig. 6.24).

FIGURE 6-24
Electron micrograph of the exoplasmic fracture (EF) face of a freeze-fracture preparation of the plasma membrane of the green alga *Oocystis apiculata*. Particulate cellulose-synthesizing complexes (at arrows) are associated with impressions of cellulose microfibrils left in the plasma membrane. ×60,000. (Photograph courtesy of D. Montezinos and R. M. Brown, Jr.)

FIGURE 6-25
Electron micrograph of a freeze-
fracture preparation through the cell
wall of the giant alga *Valonia*. Cellulose
microfibrils of the primary cell wall
(above) are disorganized, whereas
highly organized arrays of cellulose
microfibrils are part of the secondary
cell wall (below). ×17,500. (Photograph
courtesy of T. Itoh and R. M. Brown, Jr.)

Cellulose fibers exhibit quite different patterns of organization in
primary and secondary cell wall deposits. Cellulose microfibrils are
arranged in a flexible network in primary cell walls, whereas in
secondary walls they exhibit an ordered pattern of parallel rows,
although successive layers may be deposited at different angles and
display a cross-weave pattern (Fig. 6.25). Whether or not the orderly
pattern of cellulose microfibrils is organized by microtubules in the
underlying cytoplasm remains a controversial matter. The relationship
between cytoplasmic microtubules and wall cellulose microfibrils is
suggested by their parallel orientation. In addition, if microtubules are
disrupted by drug treatment, the deposition of cellulose sometimes (but
not always) becomes disordered even though cellulose synthesis remains
unaffected. It is impossible to decide from the available evidence,
however, whether microtubules influence cellulose deposition through
chemical or physical interactions or whether the ordered rows of
cellulose microfibrils are an outcome of cell elongation and changes in
cell shape, with which microtubules are known to be involved.

Plasmodesmata
Cell wall   Cytoplasmic bridge

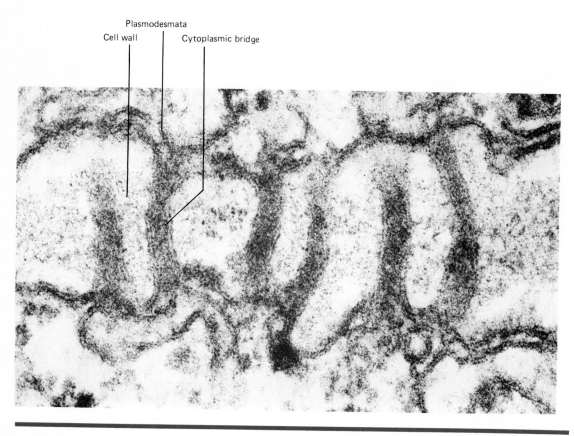

FIGURE 6-26
Electron micrograph showing cytoplasmic strands passing through
plasmodesmata openings in root cells
of the plant *Potamogeton natans.*
These continuities crossing the walls
between adjacent cells provide a
passageway for the transfer of
materials from a cell to its neighbor.
×231,000. (Photograph courtesy of
M. C. Ledbetter.)

Cells in many plant tissues are in open communication through
cytoplasmic bridges that pass from cell to cell through minute openings,
called **plasmodesmata**, in adjacent cell walls (Fig. 6.26). Rapid transfer
of ions and molecules between cells has been shown by tracing molecules
labeled with fluorescent stains or radioactive isotopes, and by measurements showing substantial electrical resistance between adjacent plant
cells. In addition to the apparently direct transfer of water and other
molecules, and of ions, in strands of cytoplasm that extend through
plasmodesmata, ions and molecules move relatively freely through the
cell wall. Molecules that move across the wall, however, encounter the
selectively permeable plasma membrane, which regulates the flow of
materials in and out of plant cells just as it does in all other kinds of cells.

Intercellular Aggregation, Recognition, and Communication

Cells in tissues and organs are held together by extracellular matrix and
cell junctions. But how do cells recognize each other in the process of
developing into multicellular assemblies? And how do cells communicate with each other, perceive signals and respond, and achieve the high
degree of coordinated activity that distinguishes one tissue or organ from
another in the body? These are fundamental and far-reaching questions
to which we have as yet only fragmentary and limited answers. In many
cases we have only models derived from studies of very simple organisms

barely at the level of multicellularity; in other cases we have made considerable progress toward understanding systems in the most complex vertebrate organisms.

6.10
Cell Recognition and Aggregation _____

In the simplest situations, specialized cells form a tissue by producing progeny cells that remain associated by the formation of cell junctions and by being sequestered in, and held by, extracellular matrix. Sheets of epithelial cells form in this way and later undergo characteristic folding and differentiation during animal development. In more complex situations, individual cells migrate to some new location and assemble with other migrant and local cells into a tissue. For example, proliferating epithelial cells of the embryonic neural tube give rise to the neurons and glial cells of the central nervous system. Immature motor neurons migrate radially outward from the lumen to the outer part of the neural tube and there begin to send out axons to connect with limb muscles. The migration of these immature nerve cells depends on guidance by a specialized class of glial cells, each of which stretches across the wall of the neural tube from the lumen to the outer surface of the tube. The migrating immature neurons evidently crawl along these glial cells during their travel outward. These glial cells provide a road for neuronal migration during development, but they disappear from most regions of the brain and spinal cord in the mature nervous system.

We know relatively little about the mechanisms or factors underlying interactions and recognition between neurons and glial cells, but general models for intercellular recognition and aggregation have been derived from studies of simple eukaryotic organisms such as slime molds and sponges. In the slime mold *Dictyostelium discoideum*, independent ameboid cells proliferate and remain unicellular until their food supply is exhausted. Starved cells stop dividing and begin to aggregate in response to *cyclic AMP* (cAMP), which is synthesized and secreted by individual cells and acts as a chemical signal for *chemotaxis* (migration in response to chemical attractants). The multicellular aggregate may form a stationary pseudoplasmodium or a motile slug that later becomes attached to a surface and stops moving. In either case, the stationary aggregate undergoes cellular differentiation to form a stalked fruiting body in which spores are produced. Under favorable conditions the spores germinate into free-living ameboid cells that start the cycle again (Fig. 6.27).

In the aggregation phase, the initial cells attract other starved amebae to join the aggregate, and new cells attract others into the aggregate through the agency of pulsating waves of newly made cyclic AMP. Each pulse of cAMP attracts surrounding cells to move toward the source of the chemical—and also induces newly added cells to secrete their own cAMP in pulses. The aggregate grows at a constant rate as swarms of ameboid cells move into the group and attract others to join them there. In addition to serving as an attractant, cAMP orients the movement of an incoming cell by binding to cell-surface receptors

FIGURE 6-27
Life cycle of the slime mold *Dictyostelium discoideum*. (a) Spores germinate into independent ameboid cells, which multiply until the food supply is exhausted. Starved cells aggregate in response to secreted cyclic AMP and form multinucleate masses called pseudoplasmodia, which may or may not proceed through a motile "slug" phase before being attached to a surface. The immobilized mass develops into a stalked fruiting body, whose spores germinate to begin a new cycle. (b) Light micrographs of selected stages photographed at 30–minute intervals during the development of a fruiting body of the slime mold *Dictyostelium discoideum*. (Photographs courtesy of J. T. Bonner, from Bonner, J. T., 1967, *The Cellular Slime Molds*, plate 6. Copyright © by Princeton University Press.)

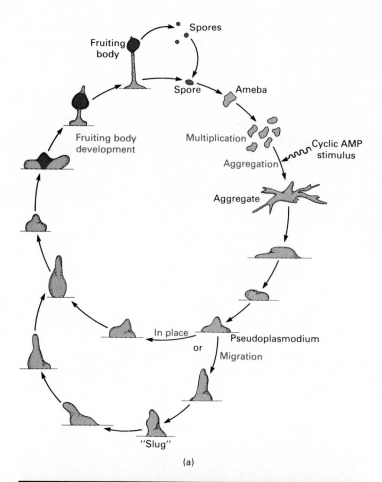

(a)

(b)

and inducing the formation there of a pseudopod, which then pulls the cell in the direction of the cAMP source (Fig. 6.28). The aggregated cells adhere tightly to each other by virtue of binding between cell-surface molecules, one or more of which are glycoproteins. These cell-surface receptors appear to be synthesized only by starved amebae. This

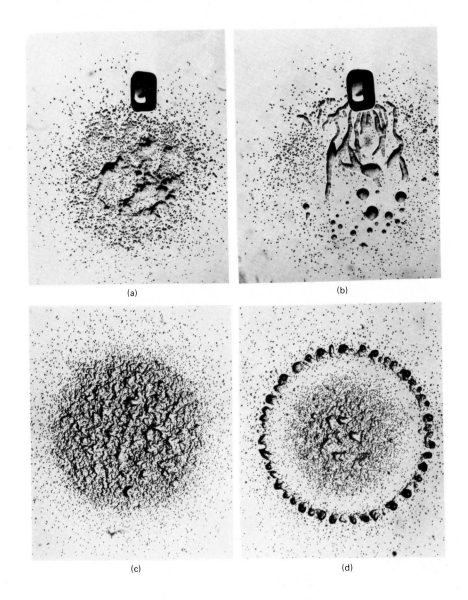

(a)

(b)

(c)

(d)

FIGURE 6-28
Formation in response to cyclic AMP of a multicellular aggregate derived from individual ameboid cells of the slime mold *Dictyostelium discoideum.*
(a) Hundreds of amebas have been placed near a small agar block containing cyclic AMP, and (b) the cells respond to the chemical attractant by streaming toward the block. (c) The cells come to occupy a circular area and later (d) fuse to initiate the multicellular phase of the organism. (Photographs courtesy of J. T. Bonner, from Konijn, T. M., *et al.*, 1968, *Amer. Naturalist* **102**:225.)

indicates that certain genes are activated in response to new conditions and subsequently contribute to new potentials and new behaviors that guide cellular aggregation.

When the stationary aggregate begins to develop into a stalked fruiting body, two kinds of cells, *stalk cells* and *spores*, differentiate according to their relative locations within the aggregate. The tip of the aggregate consists of the first cells that came together; those cells that entered later give rise to the base of the pseudoplasmodium. As development begins, cells located at the tip move down toward the base and form the stalk, and cells at the base move upward and develop into spores. The key to cellular differentiation is the relative location of cells, however, not the sequence in which cells joined together to form the pseudoplasmodium. This distinction has been shown by simple experiments in which pseudoplasmodia are chopped into pieces that include only the tip, only the base, or parts of each. Regardless of the origin of the pseudoplasmodial piece, each gives rise to a complete and functional fruiting body with stalk and spores. The direction of migration and the ultimate differentiation of cells in the fruiting body are under cAMP control, but the precise nature of this control is uncertain.

Experimental studies of tissue and organ formation in multicellular animals are often conducted with dissociated cells whose reassembly into organized structures presumably provides information on normal processes in developing organisms, which are difficult to analyze directly. This model for vertebrate developmental studies emerged from observations over many years of the reassembly of dissociated cells to form a normal sponge. Consisting of only a few kinds of cells, sponges are the simplest multicellular animals. When sponges are dissociated into single cells by gentle mechanical means, or by incubation in sea water depleted of Ca^{2+} and Mg^{2+}, the cells quickly reaggregate and are eventually reordered to form a normal sponge. Reaggregation is mediated by a huge extracellular *aggregation factor* that may be over 100 nm in diameter and exceed 20 million molecular weight. This factor is believed to be a complex of proteoglycan or glycoprotein molecules (or perhaps both), and it binds to specific glycoprotein receptors on sponge cell surfaces. The factor is species-specific and binds only to cells of the same sponge species in which it was produced. Binding to surface receptors is Ca^{2+}-independent, but cross-linking between sponge cells by factors binding to one another takes place only when Ca^{2+} is present (Fig. 6.29). These features are shown by cells that have been dissociated in sea water lacking Ca^{2+}. During dissociation the aggregation factor is released into the sea water. Cells washed free of the factor and put back

FIGURE 6-29
Schematic drawing showing that large aggregation factors bind to receptor molecules on the sponge cell surface independently of Ca^{2+}, but that cross-linking to produce aggregates of cells occurs only when Ca^{2+} is present in the surrounding medium.

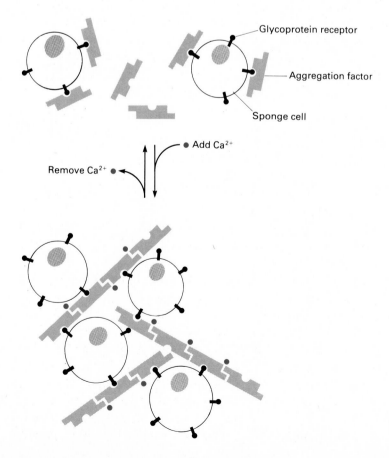

into normal sea water do not reaggregate unless the factor is added. When washed cells are put into sea water lacking Ca^{2+} and supplied with the aggregation factor, the factors bind to cells but the cells do not reaggregate. They do reaggregate if Ca^{2+} is supplied along with the factor. The mechanism by which sponge cells recognize others of their own kind (species) and bind together to form a multicellular organism thus involves binding of a large linker particle to the same receptor protein on different cells. At the molecular level, therefore, recognition involves interactions between specific extracellular secretions and specific components of the cell surface in cells of the same genetic background, mediated by environmental or external agents such as Ca^{2+}.

Dissociated cells from vertebrate embryos can easily be obtained by treatment with dilute trypsin solutions, but adult vertebrate tissues are extremely difficult to dissociate. When the dissociated cells from different embryonic tissues are mixed together, they form mixed aggregates that eventually sort themselves into groups each containing cells from an original tissue. This is true of organs and even of whole young embryos in many cases, and the arrangements of the different tissues in the organ or embryo show internal organization typical of the intact system. For example, dissociated cells from frog or salamander embryos can reaggregate such that cells sort out to form overlying ectoderm, inner endoderm, and middle mesoderm layers of cells.

In some cases we know that cell sorting and adhesion involve membrane glycoproteins and aggregation factors. In other cases aggregation factors are not involved, and cell sorting and adhesion are the outcome of binding between molecules of adjacent membranes, often involving the formation of cell junctions. Unfortunately we know very little about specific molecules in specific tissues and virtually nothing about the regulation of the orderly processes of tissue, organ, and organism morphogenesis.

6.11
Chemical Signals in Intercellular Communication

Two principal known modes of communication between cells are by the formation of gap junctions, which provide direct connections between interacting cells, and by the secretion of chemicals that signal **target cells** at a distance to undertake some particular activity inside or at the surface of the receiving (target) cells. We discussed gap junctions in Section 6.3. Here we will be concerned only with **chemical signaling** between cells.

The cell responds to molecular signals once these molecules bind to specific protein receptors on the cell surface. Target cells usually respond by initiating protein synthesis or by altering the rates of synthesis of existing proteins or their properties. Different target cells with the same receptors may respond differently to the same chemical signal. For example, the hormone thyroxine induces cells in the tail of a tadpole to break down during metamorphosis, whereas it induces particular cells in muscle and cartilage to proliferate as the animal changes to its adult form. In the metamorphosing tadpole, thyroxine in tail cells induces the release of lysosomal enzymes that dissolve the tail,

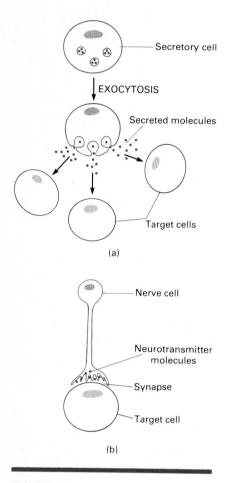

FIGURE 6-30
Chemical signals in intercellular communication. (a) When stimulated in some fashion, secretory cells exocytose their secretions, which interact with specific target cells nearby or at some distance away in the body. (b) Neurotransmitters, such as acetylcholine, are released from nerve cells and act only on adjoining target cells from which they are separated by a synapse, or intercellular gap.

and in muscle and cartilage the hormone stimulates mitosis and division of cells to which it binds in other parts of the body. Target cells are thus equipped with a specific set of receptors for each chemical signal, but different cells may respond to each signal in their own distinctive fashion. Both these properties of target cells depend on the genetic program that determines and regulates gene expression in different cells at different times in the organism.

Most cells secrete chemical signals that act only on target cells in their immediate environment, because the molecules are very rapidly taken up or destroyed. Three examples of locally acting signals are histamine, acetylcholine, and prostaglandins. *Histamine*, a derivative of the amino acid histidine, is secreted by mast cells in connective tissues in various parts of the body. When stimulated by an allergic reaction, injury, or local infection, the histamine stored in secretory granules is released by exocytosis from mast cells and acts on local blood vessels to make them dilate and thus become more permeable. Phagocytic white blood cells and serum components such as antibodies are thereby provided greater access to the site of trauma through leaky blood vessels in the immediate vicinity. *Acetylcholine* and other neurotransmitter molecules are released from nerve cells and act only on adjoining target cells with which they communicate through specialized junctions called chemical synapses (Fig. 6.30). *Prostaglandins* are a family of fatty acid derivatives secreted more or less continuously by a wide variety of cells, rather than being released from storage. They are rapidly degraded and therefore act locally to induce a variety of biological effects. Under certain conditions, cells may increase their rates of prostaglandin synthesis. For example, particular prostaglandins are produced in large amounts in the uterus before and during childbirth, and they influence the contractions of uterine smooth muscles that are required for delivery through the birth canal. These same prostaglandins are widely used to induce therapeutic abortion. Pregnant women are now advised to discontinue the use of aspirin because it apparently inhibits prostaglandin synthesis.

Hormones secreted by specialized endocrine cells travel through the bloodstream to influence target cells at distant sites in the body, rather than acting locally to influence nearby cells (Fig. 6.31). Most hormones are water soluble, as are most of the locally acting chemical signals and all known neurotransmitters, and they therefore encounter difficulty in crossing the lipid bilayer of the target cell surface. The water-soluble chemical signals are thus believed to act only if they first bind to cell-surface receptors, after which a response may be elicited. Some hormones, particularly the steroid sex hormones, are hydrophobic molecules that can easily cross the lipid bilayer of the target cell. Steroids bind to specific carrier proteins for transport through the bloodstream to their target cells. Once at the target, the steroid hormone molecules are released from their carriers, pass by simple diffusion through the membrane to the interior of the cell, and bind to specific receptors inside the cell. Whether they are hormones or other kinds of chemicals, hydrophilic and hydrophobic molecules usually signal through different sets of receptors: *cell-surface receptors* or *intracellular*

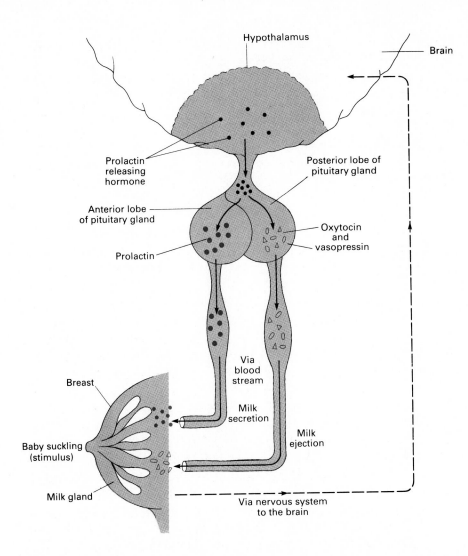

FIGURE 6-31

Milk let-down is the result of hormonal, nervous, and muscular activities that occur in response to the stimulus of the baby suckling on the nipple of the breast. Suckling generates electrical signals that travel through the nervous system from the breast to the hypothalamus at the base of the brain. Upon receipt of these electrical signals, the hypothalamus secretes prolactin-releasing hormone into the pituitary gland attached to the base of the brain. The pituitary gland then releases prolactin from the anterior lobe and oxytocin and vasopressin from the posterior lobe, and all three hormones move through the bloodstream to the breast. Oxytocin and vasopressin cause contraction of small musclelike cells around the milk glands, so the milk produced under the influence of prolactin moves out of the milk glands into a system of ducts that converge at the nipple. Suckling produces a negative pressure that brings out the milk through duct openings at the tip of the nipple.

receptors. In the next sections we will discuss particular examples of signals mediated by intracellular receptors and by cell-surface receptors and see how target cells respond at the molecular level to the communications received from nearby or distant secretory cells.

6.12
Intracellular Receptors and Steroid Hormone Action _____

Once inside the target cell, the steroid molecule binds to a specific receptor protein and causes the protein to alter its conformation, which increases the ability of the receptor to bind to DNA. The hormone–receptor complexes can pass through nuclear pores and accumulate inside the nucleus. Once the complexes are bound to DNA, specific gene activation is induced and the DNA is transcribed into messenger RNA encoding a specific protein. Subsequent synthesis of this encoded protein constitutes the ultimate effect of the steroid hormone on the target cells, whereas the initial effect of hormone action is to stimulate transcription of specific genes in the nucleus through the mediation of bound intracellular receptors. Experimental confirmation of these events is

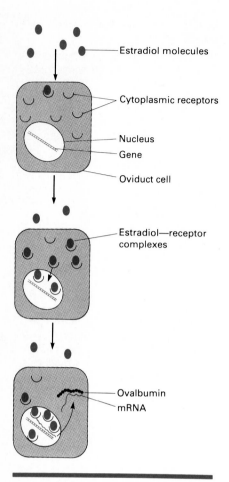

Estradiol molecules

Cytoplasmic receptors

Nucleus

Gene

Oviduct cell

Estradiol—receptor complexes

Ovalbumin mRNA

FIGURE 6-32
Molecules of estradiol, an estrogenic hormone, bind to intracellular receptors in oviduct cells. The estradiol–receptor complexes then move from the cytoplasm into the nucleus, where they bind to ovalbumin DNA. The gene is thereby induced to transcribe ovalbumin mRNA, which is translated into ovalbumin protein in the cytoplasm. Uninduced oviduct cells lack cytoplasmic receptors, do not transcribe ovalbumin DNA, and thus make no ovalbumin protein.

available in considerable detail for the effect of the steroid female sex hormone *estradiol* on hen *oviduct* targets.

When the estrogenic hormone estradiol is provided to immature chick oviduct or mature hen oviduct grown in organ culture, the egg-white protein *ovalbumin* is synthesized in oviduct cells. Uninduced oviduct does not make ovalbumin, and molecular analysis of cytoplasmic extracts and nuclear extracts of the tissues shows that receptors are not present in the cytoplasm and that the ovalbumin messenger RNA is not transcribed in the nucleus. After induction by the hormone, its receptors are present in abundance in the cytoplasm, and functional messenger RNA is transcribed and processed correctly (Fig. 6.32). Ovalbumin protein is then translated from messenger RNA that has moved out of the nucleus into the cytoplasm. Investigators using cloned ovalbumin DNA have further shown that the hormone–receptor complexes bind specifically at or near the region of the genic DNA (the promoter) at which transcription is initiated. When RNA synthesis is inhibited by the drug *actinomycin*, or when protein synthesis is inhibited by the drug *cycloheximide*, estradiol does not induce the synthesis of messenger RNA or ovalbumin, respectively. These data support the conclusion that steroid hormones induce specific gene expression at the level of messenger-RNA transcription. At the present time, however, we know very little about the influence of estradiol and other hormones on the synthesis of their specific protein receptors. We do know that a hormone leads to receptor synthesis only in its particular target cells and not in others. For example, if estradiol is given to reticulocytes in culture, these cells do not make estradiol receptors and do not transcribe ovalbumin messenger RNA, even though the ovalbumin genes are present in the nucleus, all of which is determined by molecular analyses.

The primary response of oviduct tissues to estradiol is followed by a cascade of events that produce a secondary response, which involves the activation of a number of other genes over a period of time, leading to the development of the system for egg production and other secondary sex characteristics in the female. If the initial response is absent or defective, the later events do not take place, presumably because later gene activations do not occur. This is precisely the situation in several mammalian species (including humans) for the inherited condition called *testicular feminization syndrome*. Genetically male individuals with this inherited condition have the normal XY chromosome constitution, but they make defective receptors for the steroid male sex hormone *testosterone*. Such individuals develop the secondary sex characteristics of females rather than those of males. Mutants for the *tfs* gene differentiate normal testosterone-producing testes during early embryonic development, but the target cells cannot respond to the hormone because the mutant gene encodes defective receptor protein. As the fetus develops, female secondary sex characteristics appear because there is no testosterone action to divert subsequent development from female structures to male structures. These individuals have testes (which fail to descend and remain in the abdomen), but their outward appearance throughout sexual development before and after birth is that of a female. They are sterile because the embryonic gonads differentiated into testes instead of ovaries, but their testes are nonfunctional.

6.13
Cell-Surface Receptors and Second Messengers ————————

Many hydrophilic signaling molecules enter target cells by receptor-mediated endocytosis, a process we discussed in Section 5.10. In that process the signal molecule and the plasma membrane receptor to which it binds are taken into the cell in coated vesicles. The signal-receptor complexes may then be routed to various places within the cell, and such signals may very well act directly inside the cell and not at the cell surface. The most common fate of water-soluble ligands, however, is to remain outside the cell after binding to their specific cell-surface receptors. The receptors are believed to undergo a conformational change when they bind to a ligand, and this extracellular event generates an intracellular signal that affects the activity and behavior of the target cell. The receptor-generated intracellular chemical signal is called a **second messenger**, because the extracellular ligand itself is the first messenger in the sequence of events.

Cell-surface receptors are known to generate intracellular signals in at least two major ways: (1) by activating or inactivating an enzyme bound to the plasma membrane and (2) by opening or closing gated ion pores in the plasma membrane. An important example of a membrane-bound enzyme that is activated by many different signal-receptor complexes is **adenylate cyclase**, which catalyzes the synthesis of cyclic AMP from ATP at the inner surface of the plasma membrane (Fig. 6.33). Cyclic AMP then acts as a second messenger in many kinds of cells by activating enzymes called *cyclic-AMP-dependent protein kinases*. These kinases catalyze the transfer of a phosphoryl group from ATP to a specific amino acid residue in particular proteins in the target cell. The phosphorylated proteins then participate in the regulation of cellular activities. A well-known example of such a cascade of effects involves glycogen metabolism in skeletal muscle fibers. When an animal is subjected to some form of stress its adrenal glands secrete *epinephrine*, and the circulating hormone exerts its effects on various tissues, including muscle. Epinephrine induces muscle fibers to stop new glycogen synthesis and to break down existing stored glycogen to glucose 1-phosphate. Glucose 1-phosphate is then converted to glucose 6-phosphate, which is oxidized in glycolysis to produce ATP (see

FIGURE 6-33
Adenosine triphosphate (ATP) is converted to cyclic AMP (cAMP) when the enzyme adenylate cyclase cleaves a pyrophosphate residue from the ATP precursor molecule. The remaining phosphoryl residue is cyclized through carbon 5 of the ribose component.

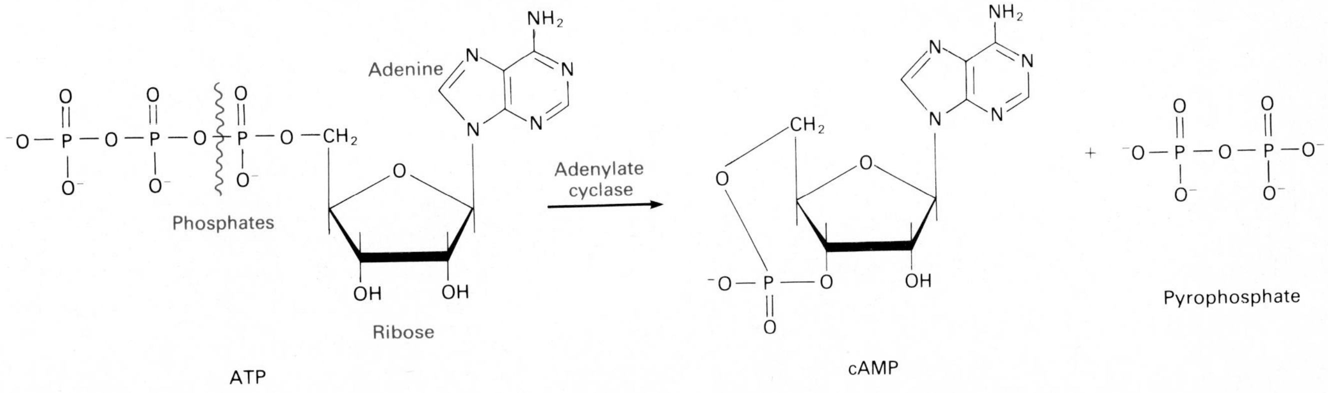

Fig. 3.20). Epinephrine thus prepares muscle fibers for sustained contraction during strenuous activity.

Epinephrine receptors are activated after the ligand is bound, but these receptors do not influence adenylate cyclase directly. Instead, the activated receptor binds to membrane-bound *G protein* (a GTPase that hydrolyzes GTP to GDP) and activates G protein by altering its conformation so that it can bind GTP. The coupled receptor and G protein, each made capable of binding after conformational changes, can then bind to adenylate cyclase at the membrane and activate the enzyme through altering its conformation. Adenylate cyclase can then bind ATP and catalyze its conversion to cyclic AMP, which is thereby increased in concentration in the cytoplasm. Cyclic AMP activates a protein kinase that phosphorylates specific amino acid residues in the enzyme *glycogen synthase*, which catalyzes the final step in glycogen synthesis from glucose monomers (Fig. 6.34).

Glycogen synthase is inactivated by phosphorylation, and glycogen synthesis is thereby shut off. Glucose residues are then removed from

FIGURE 6-34
Highly simplified schematic summary showing the influence of chemical signaling on glycogen metabolism in skeletal muscle. The binding of epinephrine to receptors at the cell surface acts indirectly via G protein to bind and thereby activate adenylate cyclase, which converts ATP to cAMP, a second messenger. Cyclic AMP activates a protein kinase, which catalyzes phosphorylation of amino acids in the enzyme glycogen synthase, thereby inactivating the synthase and shutting off glycogen synthesis. At the same time, the protein kinase activates the enzyme glycogen phosphorylase, which catalyzes the breakdown of glycogen to its constituent glucose units. In response to stress, circulating epinephrine causes muscles to stop making glycogen and to break down glycogen to glucose for subsequent ATP production in glycolysis, thus allowing sustained muscular contraction during strenuous activity. In the absence of stress, cAMP levels remain low and glycogen synthesis proceeds uninterruptedly as glucose monomers are polymerized in reactions catalyzed by glycogen synthase.

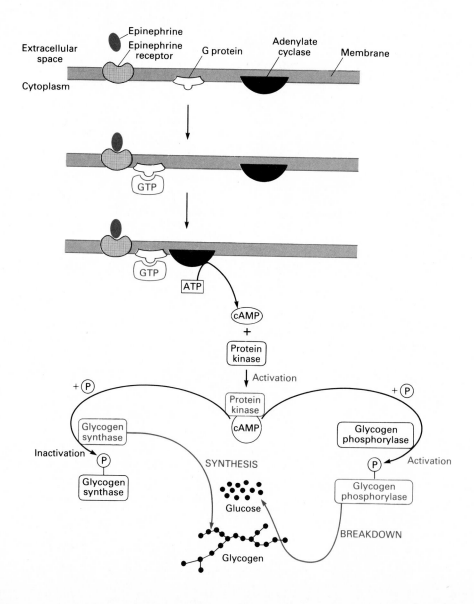

glycogen polymers by the enzyme *glycogen phosphorylase*, which is activated in reactions initiated by the same protein kinase that inactivated glycogen synthase. The amount of glucose is substantially increased in the cell, because it is released in glycogen breakdown and is not used to make new glycogen. Both of these outcomes result from an increase in the levels of cytoplasmic cyclic AMP.

The effects of cyclic AMP last only briefly, which we would expect if cells are to be able to change rapidly in response to hormones and other extracellular signals. Degradation and changes in their rates of synthesis lead to a high rate of turnover for cyclic AMP and other mediators. In the case of cyclic AMP, its formation stops when G protein hydrolyzes its bound GTP and resumes its original inactive conformation. Adenylate cyclase is then released from the altered G protein, causing the cyclase to resume *its* original inactive conformation and thus stopping cyclic AMP formation. In assays using GTP analogues that cannot be converted to GDP, the hormonal activation of adenylate cyclase is greatly increased and prolonged compared to cells provided with GTP itself. These results also give us some insight into the advantages of interposing a step between receptor activation by a ligand and the activation of adenylate cyclase at the membrane. Each activated receptor protein can physically interact with many molecules of G protein and amplify the signal in this way. Relatively few hormone molecules can thus elicit a rapid and considerable response in the target cell. Similarly, inactivation of G protein leads to a rapid shutdown in cyclic AMP formation. Through the mediation of G protein, therefore, the target cells are able to respond more quickly and specifically to changing external and internal conditions.

6.14
Ca^{2+} as a Second Messenger

Some cell-surface receptors are coupled to gated Ca^{2+} pores in the plasma membrane. After receptor activation by a bound ligand, Ca^{2+} enters the cytosol through opened gated pores and there acts as a second messenger. In some cases an extracellular signal may lead to the release of Ca^{2+} across internal membranes, such as mitochondria or the sarcoplasmic reticulum in skeletal muscle fibers. We know very little, however, about the mechanisms that lead to openings for Ca^{2+} release across internal cellular membranes. Whether channels are present in internal membranes or in the plasma membrane, they open transiently and the Ca^{2+} is rapidly pumped out or bound to intracellular molecules. The effect of Ca^{2+}, like that of cyclic AMP, is therefore subject to rapid fluctuations.

In some cases, receptor activation causes the plasma membrane to depolarize, and Ca^{2+} enters the cell through voltage-dependent gated pores that open in response to the change in membrane potential. Regardless of the conditions that open gated pores, once Ca^{2+} floods into the cytoplasm, the ions interact with Ca^{2+}-binding proteins or with phosphate. One particular Ca^{2+}-binding protein is **calmodulin**, which is present in every plant or animal cell that has been studied. Calmodulin is a single polypeptide chain containing 148 amino acid residues, and

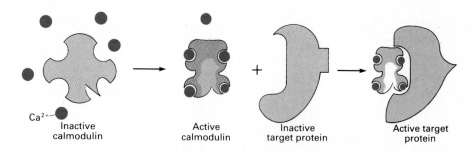

FIGURE 6-35
Calmodulin is a calcium-binding protein with four binding sites for Ca^{2+}. When activated by bound Ca^{2+}, calmodulin binds to, and thereby activates, various target proteins. Calmodulin thus mediates the intracellular response to Ca^{2+}, a second messenger in many receptor-mediated cellular activities.

it is involved in the majority of Ca^{2+}-regulated processes in eukaryotic cells. Not only is the protein ubiquitous, but it is also very similar in virtually all cells and is therefore encoded by a gene that has been highly conserved over hundreds of millions of years of evolution. The protein has four Ca^{2+}-binding sites, and its conformation is altered in different ways depending on how many of these binding sites are filled. Calmodulin is known to be a permanent subunit of certain enzymes, but the protein occurs predominantly in free form in the cell. In general, free calmodulin becomes bound to various target proteins in the cell after being allosterically activated by bound Ca^{2+} at one or more of its four binding sites. Calmodulin serves as an intracellular receptor of Ca^{2+}, and in its activated form it mediates the intracellular response to the second messenger (Fig. 6.35).

The concentration of free Ca^{2+} in the cytoplasm is much lower than the extracellular Ca^{2+} level. Because of the steep electrochemical gradient across the membrane, Ca^{2+} continues to move into the cell. When additional Ca^{2+} floods into the cell in response to extracellular signals, it is important for the cell to expel or sequester Ca^{2+} so that the steep gradient is maintained for continued Ca^{2+} influx. Ca^{2+} is effectively pumped out of the cell by membrane-bound Ca^{2+}–ATPase and other active-transport pumps, and free Ca^{2+} is also reduced in concentration by combining with phosphate to form insoluble precipitates and by binding to calmodulin and other Ca^{2+}-binding macromolecules. The target cell can thereby respond or stop responding to Ca^{2+} or the first messenger by one or more mechanisms that regulate a variety of cellular activities, many of which are interrelated.

Summary

At the cell surface the cell interacts with other cells and with the environment. These interactions are mediated by specializations of the plasma membrane and by secretions that form the extracellular matrix.

Cells can form junctions with each other for adhesion, compartmentation, and communication from cell to cell. Each function is associated with a morphologically specialized membrane junction. Desmosomes (adhering junctions) may be spots or belts of symmetric structure in the two apposing cells or hemidesmosomes wherein a cell is attached to a substratum. Intracellular keratin or actin filaments and extracellular filaments of glycoprotein stabilize them against mechanical stress. Tight junctions seal the space between adjoining cells with interacting strands of transmembrane particles so material cannot penetrate between them. In an epithelium, tight junctions prevent extracellular fluid from one compartment leaking between cells to another compartment. Gap junctions are channels from cytoplasm to cytoplasm and permit the direct passage of small metabolites and ions. This communication may be important in the coordination of cell responses to regulatory and developmental signals. Septate junctions, in invertebrates, have a characteristic appearance but their function is less well understood.

An extracellular matrix surrounds most animal cells, providing physical support while remaining permeable to nutrients and other solutes. In different tissues the matrix secreted by connective-tissue cells varies in rigidity, strength, and composition; but, in all, it consists of hydrated polysaccharide gels with embedded fibers of collagen and other proteins. The collagen fibers are assembled from procollagen monomers, rich in glycine and hydroxyproline residues. Characteristic differences among the seven kinds of polypeptides lead to a variety of recognizable collagen types. Defects in collagen synthesis, caused by by mutation or nutrient deficiency (scurvy), lead to connectiive-tissue disorders. The collagen fibers are arrayed in a hydrated gel of glycosaminoglycans and proteoglycans—carbohydrate-rich macromolecules that provide an inflexible, hydrophilic support resistant to compression or stretching. Other proteins, such as elastin, fibronectin, chondronectin, and laminin, are also found in the matrix. They facilitate specific cell adhesion, cell migration, and flexibility.

The extracellular matrix of plant cells is the cell wall. Its primary fibrous component is cellulose, a polymer of glucose. Other components include the polysaccharides pectin and hemicellulose and the glycoproteins extensin and lignin. The cell wall is produced from secreted precursors by extracellular enzymes. The primary cell wall is flexible; the later secondary cell wall is more ordered and rigid. Cytoplasmic strands may connect cells through plasmodesmata openings in the cell wall.

Cells recognize and adhere to each other and to their matrix in specific ways. The complexity of cell aggregation varies from the simple adherence of daughter cells to their parents in epithelial sheets, through specific migrations and adhesion during development, to programmed aggregation in response to chemotactic mediators as seen in *Dictyostelium*. Species-specific or tissue-specific aggregation results from membrane receptor recognition of either soluble or bound signals from the target cell.

Similar recognition processes allow cells to signal each other by secreting a chemical that diffuses to a receptor on a target cell. The recognition of the stimulus usually elicits a specific response in the target cell. This response is different in different cell types responding to the same stimulus. The stimulus may be short-lived and local in its action, as with histamine, acetylcholine, or prostaglandins. Hormones, on the other hand, can diffuse through the extracellular fluid for a considerable distance to their target cells. Hydrophobic steroid hormones must be carried by binding proteins in the extracellular fluid but readily cross the plasma membrane of their target cells, to bind to cytoplasmic receptor proteins. The bound hormone–receptor complex then enters the nucleus, associates with specific regions of chromatin, and initiates the transcription of specific genes. The activities of the new proteins determine the characteristic response of the target cell and may in turn activate additional genes in a secondary response. Particularly well understood examples of steroid hormone activity are ovulation induced by estradiol in the hen oviduct and the testicular feminization syndrome in human males who are genetically deficient in testosterone receptors.

Peptide hormones react with glycoprotein receptors in the target cell's plasma membrane. After binding, some may be internalized by receptor-mediated endocytosis and act directly. Others stimulate transient production of a second messenger, such as cyclic AMP or calcium ions. Several intermediate steps allow amplification of the original hormone signal. The second messenger binds to modulating proteins (protein kinases for cyclic AMP, calmodulin for calcium); these control the activity of specific target proteins that produce the characteristic hormone response.

Readings and References

Albersheim, P. April 1975. The walls of growing plant cells. *Sci. Amer.* **232**:80.

Aplin, J. D., and R. C. Hughes. 1982. Complex carbohydrates of the extracellular matrix. Structures, interactions, and biological roles. *Biochim. Biophys. Acta* **694**:375.

Bonner, J. T. April 1983. Chemical signals of social amoebae. *Sci. Amer.* **248**:114.

Branton, D. 1966. Fracture faces of frozen membranes. *Proc. Natl. Acad. Sci. U. S.* **55**:1048.

Caplan, A. I. October 1984. Cartilage. *Sci. Amer.* **251**:84.

Chakrabarti, B., and J. W. Park. 1982. Glycosaminoglycans: Structure and interaction. *CRC Crit. Rev. Biochem.* **8**:225.

Cheung, W. Y. June 1982. Calmodulin. *Sci. Amer.* **246**:62.

Cohen, P. 1982. The role of protein phosphorylation in neural and hormonal control of cellular activity. *Nature* **296**:613.

Cohen, S. M., G. Gorbsky, and M. S. Steinberg. 1983. Immunochemical characterization of related families of glycoproteins in desmosomes. *J. Biol. Chem.* **258**:2621.

Cox, R. P., ed. 1974. *Cell Communication*. New York: Wiley.

Curtis, A. S. G., ed. 1978. *Cell–Cell Recognition*. Cambridge, England: Cambridge University Press.

Dunant, Y., and M. Israël. April 1985. The release of acetylcholine. *Sci. Amer.* **252**:58.

Edelman, G. M. April 1984. Cell adhesion molecules: A molecular basis for animal form. *Sci. Amer.* **250**:118.

Eyre, D. R. 1980. Collagen: Molecular diversity in the body's protein scaffold. *Science* **207**:1315.

Francis, M. J. O., and D. Duksin. 1983. Heritable disorders of collagen metabolism. *Trends Biochem. Sci.* **8**:231.

Franke, W. W., *et al.* 1981. Isolation and characterization of desmosome-associated tonofilaments from rat intestinal brush border. *J. Cell Biol.* **90**:116.

Franzblau, C., and B. Faris. 1982. Elastin. In *Cell Biology of the Extracellular Matrix*, ed. E. D. Hay, p. 65. New York: Plenum.

Giddings, T. H., Jr., D. L. Brower, and L. A. Staehelin. 1980. Visualization of particle complexes in the plasma membrane of *Micrasterias denticulata* associated with the formation of cellulose fibrils in primary and secondary cell walls. *J. Cell Biol.* **84**:327.

Gilula, N. B. 1977. Gap junctions and cell communication. In *International Cell Biology 1976–1977*, eds. K. R. Porter and B. R. Brinkley, p. 61. New York: Rockefeller University Press.

Gilula, N. B., ed. 1980. *Membrane–Membrane Interactions*. New York: Raven.

Goodman, C. S., and M. J. Bastiani. December 1984. How embryonic nerve cells recognize one another. *Sci. Amer.* **251**:58.

Hawkes, S., and J. L. Wang, eds. 1982. *Extracellular Matrix*. New York: Academic Press.

Hay, E. D. 1981. Extracellular matrix. *J. Cell Biol.* **91**:205s.

Hay, E. D., ed. 1982. *Cell Biology of the Extracellular Matrix*. New York: Plenum.

Henkart, P., S. Humphreys, and T. Humphreys. 1974. Characterization of sponge aggregation factor, a unique proteoglycan complex. *Biochemistry* **12**:3045.

Hertzberg, E. L., T. S. Lawrence, and N. B. Gilula. 1981. Gap junctional communication. *Ann. Rev. Physiol.* **43**:479.

Hertzberg, E. L., D. J. Anderson, M. Friedlander, and N. B. Gilula. 1982. Comparative analysis of the major polypeptides from liver gap junctions and lens fiber junctions. *J. Cell Biol.* **92**:53.

Hirokawa, N., and J. Heuser. 1982. The inside and outside of gap junction membranes visualized by deep etching. *Cell* **30**:395.

Hoppe, J., and K. G. Wagner. 1979. Cyclic AMP-dependent protein kinase I, a unique allosteric enzyme. *Trends Biochem. Sci.* **4**:282.

Hynes, R. O. 1982. Fibronectin and its relation to cellular structure and behavior. In *Cell Biology of the Extracellular Matrix*, ed. E. D. Hay, p. 295. New York: Plenum.

Hynes, R. O, and K. M. Yamada. 1982. Fibronectins: Multifunctional modular glycoproteins. *J. Cell Biol.* **95**:369.

Kleinman, H. K., R. J. Kleve, and G. R. Martin. 1981. Role of collagenous matrices in the adhesion and growth of cells. *J. Cell Biol.* **88**:473.

Lennarz, W. J., ed. 1980. *The Biochemistry of Glycoproteins and Proteoglycans*. New York: Plenum.

Llinas, R. R. October 1982. Calcium in synaptic transmission. *Sci. Amer.* **247**:56.

Lowenstein, W. R. 1976. Permeable junctions. *Cold Spring Harbor Sympos. Quant. Biol.* **40**:49.

Majerus, P. W., *et al.* 1985. Phosphoinositide turnover provides a link in stimulus–response coupling. *Trends Biochem. Sci.* **10**:168.

Marx, J. L. 1984. A new view of receptor action. *Science* **224**:271.

Maurer, R. A. 1982. Estradiol regulates the transcription of the prolactin gene. *J. Biol. Chem.* **257**:2133.

Mayne, R. 1984. The different types of collagen and collagenous peptides. In *The Role of Extracellular Matrix in Development*, ed. R. L. Trelstad, New York: Liss.

Means, A. R., G. R. Slaughter, and J. A. Putkey. 1984. Postreceptor signal transduction by cyclic adenosine monophosphate and the Ca^{2+}–calmodulin complex. *J. Cell Biol.* **99**:226s.

Mitchell, B. 1983. Ca^{2+} and protein kinase C: Two synergistic cellular signals. *Trends Biochem. Sci.* **8**:263.

Mueller, S. C., and R. M. Brown, Jr. 1980. Evidence for an intramembrane component associated with a cellulose microfibril-synthesizing complex in higher plants. *J. Cell Biol.* **84**:315.

Mulvihill, E. R., and R. D. Palmiter. 1977. Relationship of nuclear estrogen receptor levels to induction of ovalbumin and conalbumin mRNA in chick oviduct. *J. Biol. Chem.* **252**:2060.

Murphy, T. L., G. Decker, and J. T. August. 1983. Glycoproteins of coated pits, cell junctions, and the entire cell surface revealed by monoclonal antibodies and immunoelectron microscopy. *J. Cell Biol.* **97**:533.

Nishizuka, Y. 1983. Phospholipid degradation and signal translation for protein phosphorylation. *Trends Biochem. Sci.* **8**:13.

Pastan, I. August 1972. Cyclic AMP. *Sci. Amer.* **227**:97.

Pechak, D. G., D. A. Carrino, and A. I. Caplan. 1985. Electron microscopic characterization of chick embryonic skeletal muscle proteoglycans. *J. Cell Biol.* **100**:1767.

Pinto da Silva, P., and B. Kachar. 1982. On tight-junction structure. *Cell* **28**:441.

Prockop, D. J., K. I. Kivirikko, L. Tuderman, and N. Guzman. 1979. The biosynthesis of collagen and its disorders. *New Engl. J. Med.* **301**:13, 77.

Racker, E. 1980. Fluxes of Ca^{2+} and concepts. *Fed. Proc.* **39**:2422.

Raff, M. May 1976. Cell-surface immunology. *Sci. Amer.* **234**:30.

Rauvala, H. 1983. Cell surface carbohydrates and cell adhesion. *Trends Biochem. Sci.* **8**:323.

Rodbell, M. 1980. The role of hormone receptors and GTP-regulatory proteins in membrane transduction. *Nature* **284**:17.

Rubenstein, E. March 1980. Diseases caused by impaired communication. *Sci. Amer.* **242**:102.

Sandberg, L. B., N. T. Soskel, and J. G. Leslie. 1981. Elastin structure, biosynthesis, and relation to disease states. *New Engl. J. Med.* **304**:566.

Smith, S. B., H. D. White, J. B. Siegel, and E. G. Krebs 1981. Cyclic AMP-dependent protein kinase I: Cyclic nucleotide binding, structural changes, and release of the catalytic subunits. *Proc. Natl. Acad. Sci. U. S.* **78**:1591.

Staehelin, L. A., and B. E. Hull. May 1978. Junctions between living cells. *Sci. Amer.* **238**:140.

Steinberg, M. S. 1970. Does differential adhesion govern self-assembly processes in histogenesis? Equilibrium configurations and the emergence of a hierarchy among populations of embryonic cells. *J. Exp. Zool.* **173**:395.

Strosberg, A. D. 1984. Receptors and recognition: From ligand binding to gene structure. *Trends Biochem. Sci.* **9**:166.

Timpl, R., J. Engel, and G. R. Martin. 1983. Laminin—a multifunctional protein of basement membranes. *Trends Biochem. Sci.* **8**:207.

Trelstad, R. L., ed. 1984. *The Role of Extracellular Matrix in Development*. New York: Liss.

Trelstad, R. L., and D. E. Birk. 1984. Collagen fibril assembly at the surface of polarized cells. In *The Role of Extracellular Matrix in Development*, ed. R. L. Trelstad. New York: Liss.

Unwin, P. N. T., and G. Zampighi. 1980. Structure of the junction between communicating cells. *Nature* **283**:545.

Weissmann, G., and R. Claiborne, eds. 1975. *Cell Membranes*. New York: Hospital Practice.

Wessells, N. K. October 1971. How living cells change shape. *Sci. Amer.* **225**:76.

Yamada, K. M. 1983. Cell surface interactions with extracellular materials. *Ann. Rev. Biochem.* **52**:761.

Yamada, K. M., M. Hayashi, H. Hirano, and S. K. Akiyama. 1984. Fibronectin and cell surface interactions. In *The Role of Extracellular Matrix in Development*, ed. R. L. Trelstad. New York: Liss.

Zampighi, G., J. M. Corless, and J. D. Robertson. 1980. On gap junction structure. *J. Cell Biol.* **86**:190.

PART III

Organization of the Cytoplasm

CHAPTER 7

Endoplasmic Reticulum and Golgi Apparatus

Eukaryotic cells are compartmentalized systems roughly subdivided into two major membrane-bounded compartments—the nucleus and the cytoplasm. Each of these major compartments is further subdivided into functionally distinct but highly coordinated structures. Cytoplasm consists of the relatively amorphous *cytosol* in which are suspended membranous organelles and fibrous elements. The principal membrane-bounded organelles are *mitochondria* and *chloroplasts*, which are energy-transducing systems; *lysosomes*, in which intracellular digestion takes place; *microbodies* of various types and functions, which are primarily involved in oxidative metabolism; the *Golgi apparatus* that acts as a processing and packaging station for a variety of macromolecules; and the *endoplasmic reticulum* that synthesizes new membrane proteins and lipids as well as many different proteins destined for export or for activities in the cells in which they are produced. The cytoplasmic components not bounded by membranes include *ribosomes*, which are essential for protein synthesis, and the fibrous *microtubules*, *microfilaments*, and *intermediate filaments* associated with motility. In this chapter and the next four chapters, we will discuss various cytoplasmic components. Afterward we will concentrate on the nucleus and its role as the control center of the cell.

Endoplasmic Reticulum

The **endoplasmic reticulum** (**ER**) was discovered and characterized in the 1950s, after the introduction of thin-section electron microscopic methods for cell studies. It is very difficult to see ER by light microscopy, even if cells are stained to heighten internal contrast. In electron micrographs we usually see only the cut edges of ER membranes, but three-dimensional reconstructions of these membranes reveal the ER to be a repeatedly folded sheet or sheets of membrane

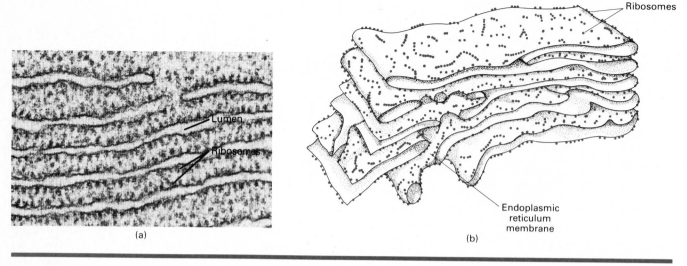

FIGURE 7-1

Endoplasmic reticulum. (a) The two-dimensional perspective of an electron micrograph shows cut edges of ribosome-studded membranes, which appear unconnected. ×85,000. (Photograph courtesy of K. R. Porter.) (b) When reconstructed in three dimensions, the endoplasmic reticulum is revealed to be a repeatedly folded sheet of membrane with ribosomes (color) distributed on only one of the two surfaces.

rather than numerous unconnected elements (Fig. 7.1). The amount of ER varies in different kinds of cells and at different times in development. Animal cells generally display more ER than protists, algae, fungi, or higher plants, and more ER is present in cells engaged in active protein synthesis than in less active cells of the same or a different type. In some cells, such as maturing mammalian reticulocytes, the ER may disappear entirely during development.

7.1
Rough ER and Smooth ER

The endoplasmic reticulum is differentiated into regions of **rough ER (RER)**, which is studded with ribosomes on its outer surfaces, and **smooth ER (SER)**, which lacks attached ribosomes (Fig. 7.2). These two regions of ER membranes are functionally distinct, because RER is involved in protein synthesis and SER is not. Membrane disposition and abundance also distinguish RER and SER in many kinds of cells. Most of the RER membranes are arranged in stacks of flattened sacs when seen in cross section, whereas SER membranes are usually organized into a network of tubular elements. RER membranes are usually more abundant than SER, particularly in cells actively engaged in protein synthesis, but SER may predominate in cells that specialize in lipid metabolism.

Two kinds of spaces or channels are created by the repeatedly folded ER membrane in both RER and SER regions: (1) the ER lumen, which is an internal channel between the facing *inner* surfaces of the folded membrane sheet, and (2) the external cytosolic channel, which bathes the facing *outer* surfaces of the folded sheet. In thin sections of RER, it is easy to recognize these two kinds of spaces; facing ribosome-studded outer membrane surfaces enclose cytosolic channels, whereas facing ribosomeless inner surfaces of the folded sheet define the ER lumen (Fig. 7.3). In such cross-sectional views of ER it is apparent that ER lumenal spaces and cytosolic spaces *alternate* with one another. In fact, this arrangement provides one line of evidence in support of the

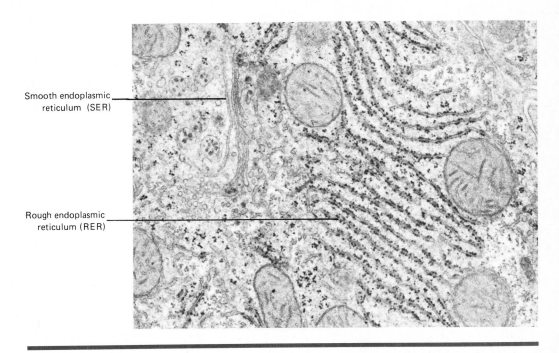

Smooth endoplasmic
reticulum (SER)

Rough endoplasmic
reticulum (RER)

FIGURE 7-2
Electron micrograph of rat liver cell
showing smooth ER without ribosomes
and rough ER with numerous attached
ribosomes, as well as a number of
mitochondrial profiles in the cytosol.
×36,000. (Photograph courtesy of
H. H. Mollenhauer.)

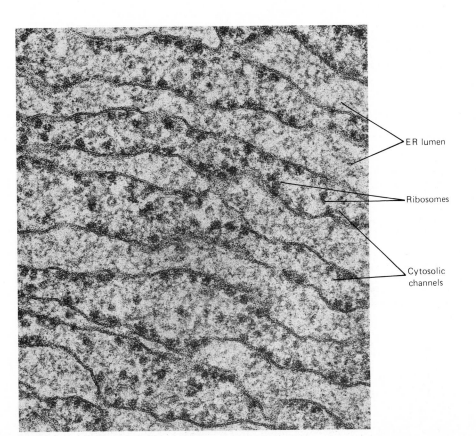

ER lumen

Ribosomes

Cytosolic
channels

FIGURE 7-3
Electron micrograph of rat liver cell
showing the two kinds of channels, or
lumen, created by the folding of a sheet
of rough ER membrane. The cytosolic
channels are formed by facing folds of
the ribosome-studded outer surface of
the membrane, and the ER lumen are
the alternating channels formed by
facing folds of the ribosomeless internal surface of the membrane sheet.
×100,000. (Photograph courtesy of
K. R. Porter.)

interpretation that ER is a flat membrane sheet that is repeatedly folded back.

When cells are disrupted and the cell-free *brei* or *homogenate* is centrifuged, the ER fraction is recovered in the form of many small vesicles called **microsomes**. These vesicles were named by Albert Claude, who pioneered studies of cells by the use of cell fractionation methods and by the application of biochemical assays to the isolated cell fractions. Although we know that microsomes are artifacts created during the preparation and centrifugation of cells and tissues and that they do not exist in the intact cell, the term *microsome* remains in use as a convenient reference for ER. Microsomes derived from rough ER are studded with ribosomes on their outside surface, which is thus equivalent to the outer surface of rough ER bathed in cytosol *in vivo* (Fig. 7.4). The interior of the microsome is equivalent to the ER lumen, both structurally and biochemically.

Smooth microsomes are about the same size as rough microsomes (about 100 nm diameter), but their origin is more difficult to determine. Smooth membranous vesicles may represent fragments of sealed membrane from smooth ER, Golgi apparatus, plasma membrane, and other structures disrupted by homogenization of cells and tissues. In hepatocytes, the principal cell type in liver, the smooth ER is so abundant that virtually all the smooth vesicles in hepatocyte homogenates are smooth microsomes. Hepatocytes thus provide a suitable system to analyze smooth microsomes, whereas most other cells give rise to populations of

FIGURE 7-4

Electron micrograph through part of a yeast cell disrupted during preparation for centrifugation. The ribosome-studded vesicles (at arrows) in the cytosol resemble microsomes recovered from cell-free homogenates after centrifugation, but they are the result of cell damage and are rarely observed in undamaged cells. × 43,300. (From Szabo, A., and C.J. Avers, 1969, *Ann. N.Y. Acad. Sci.* **168** : 302–312, Fig. 2.)

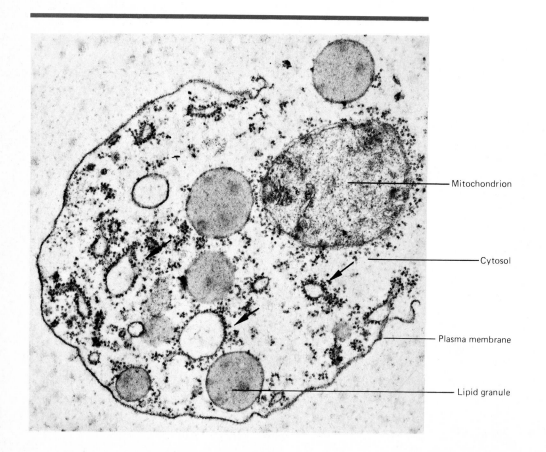

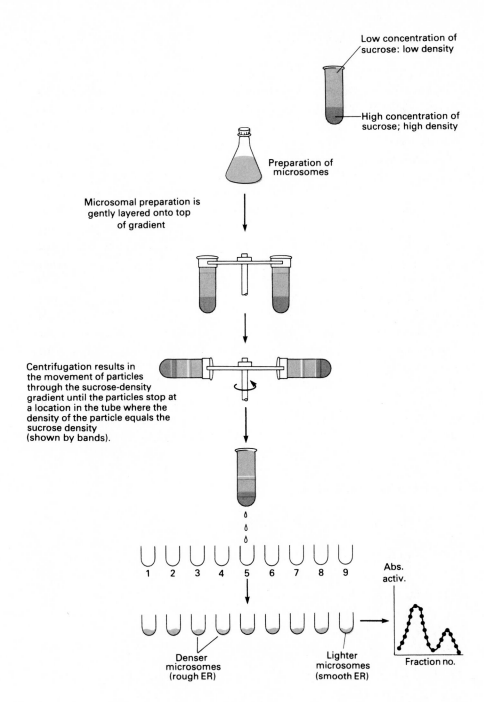

Low concentration of sucrose: low density

High concentration of sucrose; high density

Preparation of microsomes

Microsomal preparation is gently layered onto top of gradient

Centrifugation results in the movement of particles through the sucrose-density gradient until the particles stop at a location in the tube where the density of the particle equals the sucrose density (shown by bands).

1 2 3 4 5 6 7 8 9

Abs. activ.

Denser microsomes (rough ER)

Lighter microsomes (smooth ER)

Fraction no.

FIGURE 7-5
A mixture of microsomes derived from rough ER and smooth ER of disrupted cells can be separated by centrifugation to equilibrium in sucrose-density gradients. Denser microsomes (from ribosome-containing rough ER) equilibrate in a denser region of the gradient, and the ribosomeless smooth ER vesicles come to rest in a lighter region of the sucrose gradient. The separated fractions can be studied individually in assays conducted *in vitro*.

ambiguous smooth vesicles of limited experimental value. It is possible, of course, to separate rough and smooth vesicles by centrifuging the mixture to equilibrium in a sucrose density gradient. As a consequence of their ribosomal load, rough microsomes are more dense than smooth microsomes, and they therefore equilibrate in the denser region of the gradient where the sucrose concentration is higher. Smooth microsomes come to rest in a less dense region of the sucrose gradient (Fig. 7.5).

Purified rough microsomes are structurally and functionally equivalent to RER, so they can be studied under controlled conditions *in vitro*. When radioactively labeled amino acids are presented to a preparation of microsomes, the amino acids are incorporated into polypeptides. These and other studies show that microsomes behave *in vitro* as miniature protein-synthesizing units. An important observation made in these studies was that the new polypeptides, recognized by their radioactivity, accumulated in the interior of the microsomal vesicles. But were these polypeptides made on attached ribosomes at the surface of the microsomes and then transported into the microsomal cavity, or were the polypeptides initiated at surface ribosomes and lengthened *inside* the microsome until the completed molecules were released in the interior?

In 1966 David Sabatini provided experimental evidence showing that polypeptides were translocated across the microsomal membrane *during* chain synthesis at the attached ribosomes and not after synthesis was completed. He allowed polypeptide synthesis to begin and then added the drug *puromycin* to the active microsomes. Puromycin causes the growing polypeptide chain to be released prematurely from the ribosomes, so that unfinished molecules accumulate inside or outside the microsomes depending on where chain synthesis occurs. Unfinished polypeptide chains were found inside the microsomes, which showed that growing chains moved vectorially (from the cytosol to the lumen) across the membrane into the microsomal cavity (Fig. 7.6). Because the microsomal interior is equivalent to the ER lumen, these data provided evidence for a mechanism that effects the transfer of proteins across ER membranes during translation of the genetic message. This mechanism is referred to as **vectorial discharge** of nascent polypeptides, and the phenomenon is referred to as **cotranslational transfer** of nascent polypeptides because transfer occurs at the same time that translation is in progress. After translation has been completed, the finished poly-peptides are usually transported within the ER lumen to their particular destinations in the cell.

Many polypeptides are synthesized on free cytosolic ribosomes and never enter the ER lumen. Other polypeptides are made at the RER but are integrated there into ER membrane structure, and these proteins do not move away. How can we account for these different specificities of protein synthesis? Why are some proteins made at ribosomes attached to the RER and others in the cytosol? How are some proteins retained as components of ER membranes and others discharged into the ER lumen

FIGURE 7-6
Diagram illustrating the results of experiments showing that polypeptides are transferred across the membrane into the microsomal cavity (equivalent to ER lumen) during their translation at the ribosome. Puromycin causes premature release of growing polypeptides, and the fact that these released nascent chains were found inside the microsome indicated that they had been lengthening within the cavity. The amino terminus is the first portion of the polypeptide chain to be synthesized.

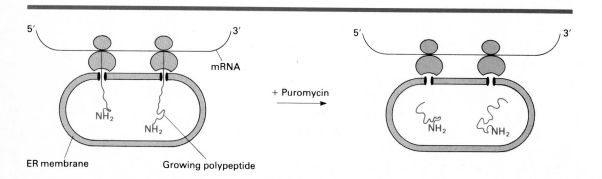

for transport to other sites? At first glance it might seem that cytosolic ribosomes and ER-bound ribosomes are different populations of particles, thus explaining the different sites of protein synthesis. This possibility was ruled out by two kinds of evidence: (1) Free ribosomes and bound ribosomes have identical RNA and protein constituents and identical physical properties. (2) The same small subunits bind to large subunits of free ribosomes and of bound ribosomes during the normal cyclic events of protein synthesis, which indicates that the large subunits of free and bound ribosomes are the same, as are their small subunits.

The available evidence supports the current view that some free ribosomes are directed to the ER membranes because of a special property of the polypeptide chain they happen to be translating. As first suggested by Sabatini and Günter Blobel and later formalized in the *signal hypothesis* proposed by Blobel and Bernhard Dobberstein in 1975, the ribosomes that attach to the ER must be engaged in translating a polypeptide that includes a sequence of amino acids acting as a signal to direct free ribosomes to the cytosolic surface of the ER membrane, where binding occurs. Ribosomes in the process of translating a polypeptide that lacks such a signal sequence remain free in the cytosol and there complete the process of polypeptide translation from the genetic message. The signal hypothesis explains the cotranslational transfer of nascent polypeptides by vectorial discharge in prokaryotes as well as in eukaryotic cells, with certain shades of difference. For example, vectorial discharge occurs from the cell interior to the outside spaces across the plasma membrane in prokaryotes.

7.2
The Signal Hypothesis

The basic premise of the **signal hypothesis** is that information determining the association of particular ribosomes with the ER membrane is contained in the amino-terminal segment of the nascent polypeptide chain and that this amino acid sequence acts as a signal that determines the ribosome–membrane interaction and in some way assists in the cotranslational transfer of the polypeptide across the microsomal membrane. The great majority of polypeptides made at bound ribosomes are secretory proteins that move through the ER lumen to the Golgi apparatus and from there are expelled by exocytosis to the exterior. By direct analysis of amino acid sequences or by sequence analysis of DNA or of the region of messenger RNA encoding the amino terminus, every secretory protein analyzed to date has been found to have a *hydrophobic* amino acid sequence, called the **signal peptide** sequence, of 18 to 30 residues near the amino terminus of the chain. Nonsecretory proteins lack this signal peptide sequence, as predicted by the hypothesis. Direct evidence for the role of the signal peptide in cotranslational transfer of the nascent chain across the membrane has come from studies of *E. coli* mutant strains. In these strains a defect exists in the signal peptide, and the growing polypeptide is not transferred across the membrane but remains instead within the cytoplasm. The genetic defect may cause the substitution of a charged amino acid for an uncharged or hydrophobic

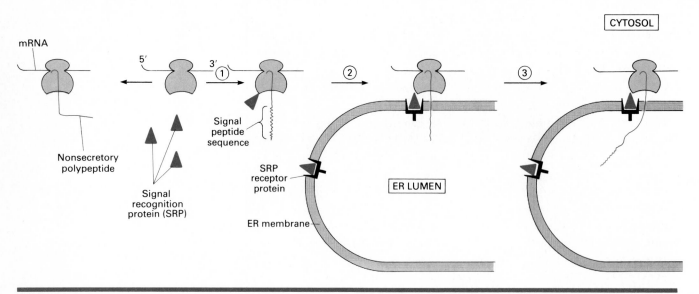

FIGURE 7-7
Ribosome–membrane interactions in secretory protein synthesis. Only ribosomes engaged in synthesizing a secretory protein, which has a signal peptide sequence at its newly formed amino terminus, bind signal recognition particles (SRP, color). Such ribosomes then bind to the ER membrane through an interaction between the SRP on the ribosome and the SRP receptor protein in the ER membrane. Translation stops between the time SRP binds to a ribosome and the time the active SRP–ribosome complex binds to a membrane receptor. Once this complex is bound to a receptor at the membrane, polypeptide synthesis resumes and the chain elongates inside the ER lumen. Nonsecretory polypeptides are synthesized in the cytosol.

one, or it may cause small deletions within the hydrophobic portion of the signal peptide. The exact number and composition of amino acids in the signal peptide of prokaryotic and eukaryotic secretory proteins does vary, but the common feature in all cases is hydrophobicity.

A number of important features of the ribosome–membrane interaction have been discovered within the last few years. Blobel and his associates have isolated and purified a particle that mediates the binding of a ribosome to the ER membrane if the ribosome is engaged in translating a secretory protein. This **signal recognition particle (SRP)** consists of six polypeptide subunits plus a small RNA molecule whose sedimentation value is 7S. The SRP binds to a ribosome after the signal peptide sequence has been translated, presumably by some mechanism involving an interaction between the SRP and the signal peptide, and the ribosome then binds to the ER membrane through an embedded **SRP-receptor** protein (also called "docking" protein) that recognizes SRP on the ribosome (Fig. 7.7). From the time that SRP binds to the ribosome until the time that the SRP–ribosome complex binds to SRP-receptor in the ER membrane, translation is halted. Translation resumes only after the SRP–ribosome complex is bound to SRP-receptors in the membrane. The SRP thus stops translation upon binding to the ribosome and aids in the transfer of the ribosome to the membrane. In experimental systems in which the ER membrane is absent, translation is arrested once SRP binds to ribosomes engaged in translation, and no further progress occurs. When ER membrane is added to the system, translation of the secretory protein resumes once the SRP–ribosome complex binds to SRP-receptors embedded within the added membrane. Protein synthesis and transport proceed continuously after SRP–ribosome complexes bind to membrane receptors. The exact mechanism of binding between SRP and the ribosome is uncertain, but the discovery of 7S RNA as a component of SRP raises the possibility of an interaction involving 7S RNA and ribosomal or messenger RNA. Before the discovery of this small RNA constituent, the most likely interaction was considered to be one involving recognition between SRP protein and ribosomal protein. Although this may still prove to be the case, other possibilities can now be tested.

Once the SRP–ribosome complex binds to ER membrane receptors, the interaction is stabilized by additional binding interactions between the ribosomal large subunit and at least two integral membrane proteins called **ribophorin I** and **ribophorin II**. Ribophorins are found only in rough microsomal membranes, and they are absent from smooth microsomal membranes as well as from the prokaryotic plasma membrane. The association between ribosomes and ribophorins is maintained even when most of the other proteins are removed from rough membranes, and the amount of ribophorin in these membranes is correlated with the amount of bound ribosomes. The tenacity of binding is even more evident in membranes whose ribosomes have been induced to aggregate by treatment with neutral detergents. In such treated membranes the ribosomes redistribute to invaginated areas of the membrane, and the ribophorins redistribute together with the ribosomes to the same pockets. It is uncertain at present whether ribophorins function in any other aspects of the cotranslational transfer processes, but their role in stabilizing the binding of ribosomes to ER membranes is well established.

The signal peptide determines the insertion of the nascent polypeptide into the ER membrane, but it apparently serves no other function. This interpretation is based on the observation in virtually every case that the signal peptide is cleaved from the growing chain shortly after it has passed through the membrane and entered the lumen. The excision of the signal peptide is catalyzed by an enzyme called a **signal peptidase**, which is believed to be associated with the lumenal surface of the ER membrane in eukaryotes and with the periplasmic space at the outer surface of the plasma membrane in prokaryotes (Fig. 7.8). The transient nature of the signal peptide sequence is apparent from various kinds of evidence. For example, when a *brief pulse* of labeled amino acids is provided to actively synthesizing microsomes, labeled signal peptides accumulate inside the microsomal cavity. These labeled fragments can be isolated without special treatment, which indicates that they are unattached and have not been broken off longer chains by experimental manipulation. When the nascent polypeptides are collected after puromycin treatment or mechanical disruption, they are found to be unlabeled and to lack the signal sequence, if their translation has progressed to a sufficient degree beyond the signal sequence at the amino terminus.

The signal peptide is required for the insertion of the nascent polypeptide and for threading it through the thickness of the membrane into the lumenal space, after which the signal can be dispensed with. It is not essential for the signal peptide to be removed in order for translation to continue, however, because at least one secretory protein, chicken ovalbumin, retains its hydrophobic amino terminus in the finished polypeptide. The reason for, or advantage of, this exception is unknown.

FIGURE 7-8

The signal hypothesis. Ribosomes engaged in secretory protein synthesis become membrane-bound because of the signal peptide sequence at the amino terminus of the growing polypeptide, and cotranslational secretion ensues. The signal peptide sequence is usually cleaved early in translation by a signal peptidase at the membrane, and the growing polypeptide chain is vectorially discharged through the membrane into the lumen or periplasmic space. (a) In eukaryotic cells, the ribosomes bind to ER membrane via signal recognition particle (SRP) interactions, and the polypeptide chain elongates in the ER lumen. Initial binding of ribosomes requires SRP and SRP receptor interactions, but continued tenacious binding requires ribophorins situated in the membrane. (b) In prokaryotic cells, secretory proteins are vectorially discharged into the periplasmic space (between the plasma membrane and cell wall) during cotranslational secretion at ribosomes that bind to the membrane through nascent polypeptide chains rather than by direct attachment to membrane receptors. Nonsecretory proteins, on the other hand, are translated at free ribosomes (not attached to membrane) in the cytosol and remain in the cytosol on completion of their synthesis. (*a* From Blobel, G., 1977, In *International Cell Biology 1976–1977*, p. 318, B. R. Brinkley and K. R. Porter, eds., New York: Rockefeller University Press. *b* From Davis, B. D., and P. C. Tai, 1980, *Nature* **283**:433.)

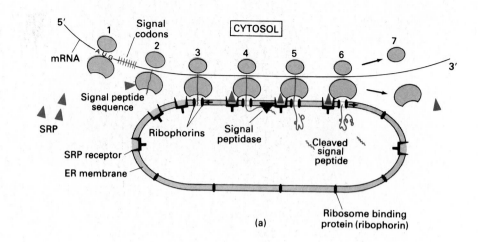

(a)

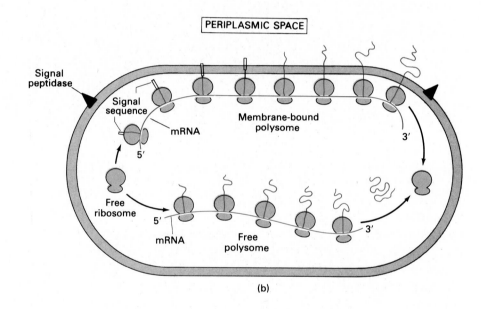

(b)

7.3
Glycosylation of Proteins in the ER

Most of the proteins made in the ER for secretion or for transport to other destinations within the cell are glycoproteins, whereas soluble proteins made in the cytosol are not glycosylated. The oligosaccharide that is linked to proteins in the ER lumen is mainly a species composed of *N*-acetylglucosamine, mannose, and glucose, and this oligosaccharide is always linked to the amino group on a side chain of an asparagine residue of the protein (Fig. 7.9). These **N-linked oligosaccharides** are added to proteins only in the ER, according to autoradiographic and other forms of information. For example, if slices of tissue are briefly exposed to [³H]mannose and then prepared for autoradiography, the label is found only in the ER lumen. Glycoproteins often have **O-linked oligosaccharides** that link covalently to OH groups on the side chain of serine, threonine, or tyrosine residues in the protein component. Glycosylation involving O-linked oligosaccharides takes place exclu-

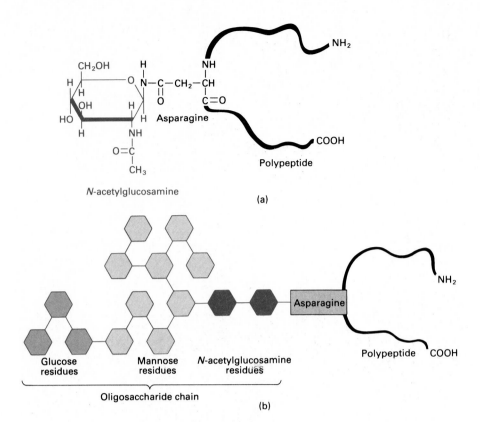

(a)

(b)

FIGURE 7-9
N-glycosylated proteins. (a) The first sugar of an oligosaccharide is linked to the amino group of an asparagine side-chain projecting from the polypeptide. (b) The predominant oligosaccharide of *N*-glycosylated proteins produced in the rough ER consists of glucose, mannose, and *N*-acetylglucosamine residues in the numbers and organization shown. Many of these sugar units are removed later during protein processing in the Golgi apparatus.

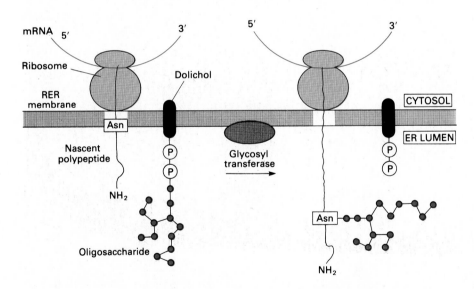

FIGURE 7-10
N-glycosylation of proteins in the rough ER. The oligosaccharide is synthesized sugar by sugar on the membrane-bound lipid molecule dolichol, to which the first sugar residue joins by a pyrophosphate link. Almost as soon as a receptive asparagine residue in the growing polypeptide is threaded through the membrane, a completed oligosaccharide chain is transferred from the lipid donor and is covalently bonded to the amino acid in a reaction catalyzed by the membrane-bound enzyme glycosyl transferase. After the finished protein has been released into the ER lumen, it travels to the Golgi apparatus, where the oligosaccharide is extensively processed to remove all but the two *N*-acetylglucosamine and three of the nine mannose residues (see Fig. 7–9).

sively or primarily in the Golgi apparatus, whereas glycosylation in the ER lumen involves *N*-linked carbohydrates.

N-glycosylation takes place at the lumenal surface of the ER membrane in a one-step reaction catalyzed by a membrane-bound enzyme called *glycosyl transferase*. The oligosaccharide is synthesized and processed on the lumenal side of the ER membrane through the mediation of **dolichol**, a membrane lipid, and the entire preformed carbohydrate is transferred to an asparagine residue in the nascent polypeptide almost as soon as the amino acid residue emerges from the membrane surface (Fig. 7.10). When translation and glycosylation are complete, the glycoprotein is transported through the ER lumen to the Golgi apparatus, where the oligosaccharide component is trimmed and processed.

Glycosylation of the polypeptide within the ER lumen is an advantageous feature of glycoprotein synthesis in the RER. If the oligosaccharides were to be linked to the polypeptide before or during its transfer to the ER lumen, the glycosylated segments of the chain would encounter great difficulty in moving through the membrane by the vectorial discharge mechanism. The linking of polypeptide and oligosaccharide is feasible only if the two components are made in separate processes and are joined together afterward. Glycosylation is important in glycoprotein function and in the directing of macromolecules to their different destinations within the cell. We will discuss macromolecular traffic and "sorting out" in Section 7.5.

7.4
Cotranslational Insertion of Integral Membrane Proteins

The nature of the amino acid sequence in an integral protein and its orientation with respect to the phospholipid bilayer provide important clues to the mechanism of insertion of transmembrane proteins in the ER. Many transmembrane proteins have their carboxy-terminal end exposed on the cytosolic side of the membrane and their amino-terminal end exposed on the opposite side, which is the lumenal space in the ER and the extracellular space for the plasma membrane. (The plasma membrane is ultimately derived from the ER membrane, and the two membranes can be studied as equivalent systems with respect to their integral protein components.) This disposition of transmembrane proteins leads to the postulate that their orientation results from cotranslational insertion of the polypeptides into the membrane by a process involving *interrupted vectorial discharge* (Fig. 7.11). If this were the case, we would expect the nascent transmembrane polypeptides to have amino-terminal cotranslational transfer signals like those in secretory pro-

FIGURE 7-11
Cotranslational insertion of integral membrane proteins is accomplished through a vectorial discharge process that is interrupted by one or more halt transfer signals in the amino acid sequence of the growing polypeptide. (a) A ribosome engaged in synthesis of an integral membrane protein binds to the membrane through conventional interactions involving the signal peptide (also called a cotranslational insertion signal), SRP, and SRP receptors, and the polypeptide chain lengthens during vectorial discharge across the membrane. (b) A halt transfer signal in the growing polypeptide chain interrupts vectorial discharge and anchors the chain in the membrane. (c) The remainder of the polypeptide is completed in the cytosol, so that the transmembrane molecule has one terminus on each side of the membrane and an embedded halt transfer signal sequence in the membrane. Such a sequence is usually highly hydrophobic, and it is followed by a charged sequence that cannot penetrate the membrane.

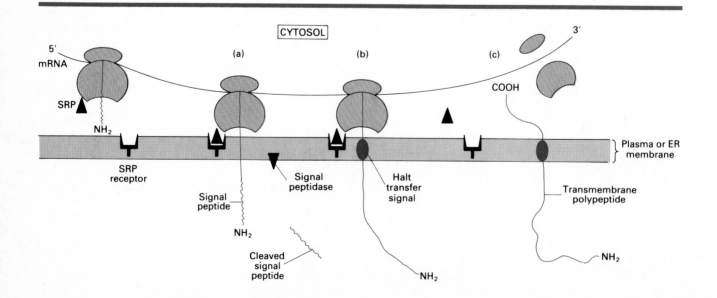

teins—and also to have *halt transfer* signals that cause an interruption of the vectorial discharge across the membrane and lead to retention of the protein in the phospholipid bilayer. A halt transfer signal would be represented by a membrane-embedded hydrophobic segment followed by charged amino acid residues nearer to the carboxy-terminal end of the molecule. After the hydrophobic segment had entered the phospholipid bilayer, the following charged residues would not be able to enter the bilayer because of their unfavorable interactions with membrane lipids. Translation would thus be completed at the cytosolic surface of the membrane, leaving the carboxy-terminal end of the polypeptide exposed on that face of the membrane. The location of the halt transfer signal with respect to the carboxy-terminal end of the molecule would determine the proportion of protein length that remains in the cytoplasm upon completion of translation. If the halt transfer signal were near the carboxy terminus, there would be only a short segment of the polypeptide remaining at the cytosolic surface, whereas a halt transfer signal farther away from that terminus would cause a larger segment of the transmembrane protein to remain there (Fig. 7.12).

Examination of the amino acid sequences or of the encoded DNA or RNA that specify these sequences in a number of transmembrane proteins has shown in each case that there is a hydrophobic region of some 20 to 30 amino acids just before a carboxy-terminal segment composed of highly charged amino acid residues. Although the exact disposition of most of these proteins in the membrane is unknown, other than their transmembrane nature, the data are consistent with the postulated halt transfer signal. In the case of the erythrocyte plasma membrane protein *glycophorin*, however, we know exactly how its 131 amino acids are arranged with respect to the membrane (see Fig. 5.12). The bulk of this molecule is exposed at the extracellular face of the membrane, but there is a transmembrane segment of 23 hydrophobic amino acid residues followed by a highly charged segment of 36 amino acids at the carboxy-terminal end, which is exposed on the cytosolic side of the plasma membrane. Presumably, translation proceeded after the nascent chain had threaded its way through the membrane, but the last 36 amino acid residues to be translated could not penetrate the lipid barrier and thus remained at the cytosolic surface of the membrane. It happens that all the transmembrane proteins analyzed thus far have

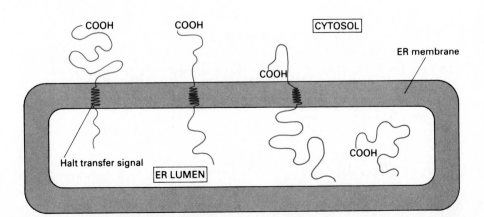

FIGURE 7-12
The location of a halt transfer signal in the polypeptide sequence determines the proportion of the molecule threaded through the membrane and the proportion that remains behind at the cytosolic face of the membrane. In the absence of a halt transfer signal, the entire protein is secreted across the membrane into the lumen.

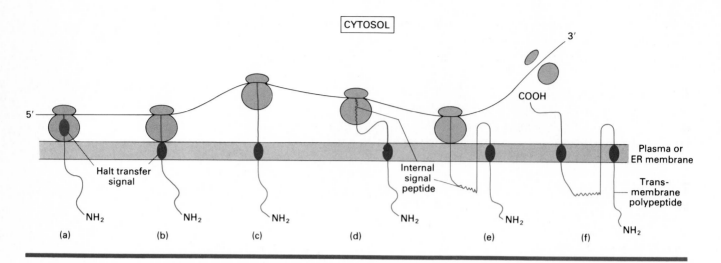

FIGURE 7-13
Schematic summary of events that could explain how a transmembrane polypeptide becomes disposed in the membrane such that more than one region of the molecule is embedded in the lipid bilayer. (a) Vectorial discharge takes place across the membrane until (b) it is interrupted by a halt transfer signal that becomes embedded in the membrane. (c) Translation continues, but the ribosome is displaced slightly and remains displaced until (d) an internal signal peptide sequence is translated and (e) serves to bring the ribosome back to the membrane in a different location from the site it occupied earlier, creating a polypeptide loop. (f) As each halt transfer signal appears during translation, another anchor in the membrane is provided. The finished chain may cross the membrane more than once, depending on the number of halt transfer signals in the polypeptide sequence.

their putative halt transfer signals very close to the carboxy terminus of the molecule, but there is no theoretical need for this to be true in every case. We would therefore predict that some transmembrane proteins would have a halt transfer signal farther from the carboxy-terminal end and that proportionately more of the polypeptide chain in such molecules would be exposed on the cytosolic side of the membrane (see Fig. 7.12).

In fact, it is entirely possible that a transmembrane polypeptide could have two or more halt transfer signals in the interior of the chain, which could lead to multiple crossings of the membrane during translation. In a speculative model explaining such a disposition for a transmembrane polypeptide, David Sabatini and associates have suggested that a polypeptide may have more than one halt transfer signal and one or more *internal* cotranslational transfer signals (Fig. 7.13). According to this scheme, the nascent chain is threaded through the membrane via the mediation of a conventional amino-terminal cotranslational transfer signal peptide, until the first halt transfer signal is reached. Translation would proceed on the cytosolic side of the membrane until an internal signal peptide was reached. If the ribosome is displaced from the membrane even slightly, the segment of the growing chain could loop out between the previous halt transfer signal and the first internal signal peptide. Translation would continue afterward, with the new segment being threaded through the membrane via its mediating signal peptide. Depending on how many halt transfer and cotranslational transfer signals happen to be present in a polypeptide, looping would occur to various degrees and would cause the transmembrane polypeptide to cross the membrane more than once before its translation was completed. Similar speculations have been made to explain the presence of the amino-terminal end of a polypeptide in the cytoplasm and of the carboxy terminus in the lumen or at the extracellular face of the plasma membrane, which we know to be the case for erythrocyte band 3 protein and a number of others (see Fig. 5.13).

It is clear that descriptive information about the amino acid sequence and the disposition in the membrane of integral proteins has led to some fruitful insights into ways by which such proteins are retained in the membrane. These data alone, however, do not provide us with information on the *mechanisms* leading to protein insertion and disposition in the membrane. The Sabatini model and other models are open to experimental verification, however, and we can expect future studies to bring us closer to an understanding of macromolecular interaction mechanisms that underlie the cotranslational insertion of integral proteins in the membrane, as well as the vectorial discharge of secretory proteins through the same membrane.

7.5
Intracellular Sorting of Protein Traffic from the ER

Proteins and other macromolecules that are made in the ER either remain in ER membranes as components of the fluid mosaic membrane or are transported through the ER lumen to various destinations within the cell. Soluble proteins are enclosed in small **transport vesicles** that bleb from the smooth membranes in the transitional region between rough and smooth ER (Fig. 7.14). When such vesicles fuse with a specific target membrane, the ER-synthesized vesicle membrane becomes part of the target membrane (either of the plasma membrane or of

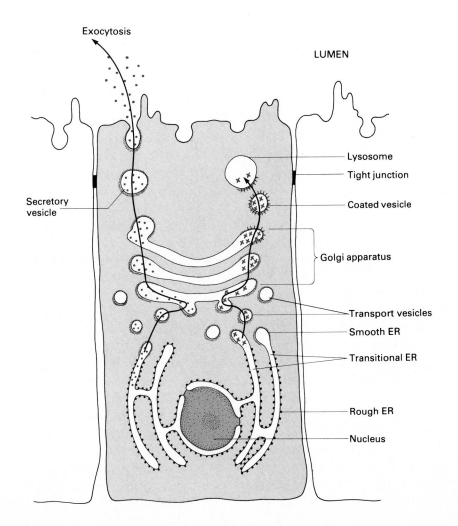

FIGURE 7-14
Glycoproteins made in the rough ER are enclosed in transport vesicles derived from smooth ER elements. These vesicles deliver their contents to the Golgi apparatus, where sorting takes place. Glycoproteins destined for the secretory pathway (colored dots) are packaged in uncoated secretory vesicles that fuse with their target (plasma membrane) and release their contents by exocytosis. Nonsecretory glycoproteins (colored x's) are packaged in coated regions of the Golgi apparatus, and such coated vesicles fuse with internal targets, such as lysosomes. Particular molecular features of the glycoproteins themselves determine the pathways taken during protein sorting in the Golgi apparatus. Membrane originally derived from smooth ER (color) also moves from place to place in the cell as a consequence of fusion events.

an organelle membrane), and the contents of the vesicle are delivered to the interior of the organelle or to the extracellular side of the plasma membrane. The flow of membrane traffic from ER to vesicles, organelles, and the plasma membrane is part of *membrane recycling*, a topic we will discuss later in this chapter.

Apart from the separate questions of membrane traffic and recycling, how do different proteins get sorted out so that some are transferred to the Golgi apparatus, lysosomes, secretory granules, or other organelles, whereas others are discharged by exocytosis at the cell surface? The principal molecules that are vectorially discharged into the ER lumen are secretory proteins, so a simple model for a sorting-out mechanism would involve structural features of secretory molecules that would determine their complete passage through the secretory apparatus and their discharge at the cell surface. Nonsecretory proteins would then be expected to have additional structural features that diverted them from the secretory pathway to other intracellular destinations. Virtually all the proteins synthesized by the RER are glycoproteins, but they vary in the kinds and amounts of carbohydrate residues linked to their polypeptide chains. It was suggested, therefore, that the presence and nature of these carbohydrate residues might contain the information for sorting out secretory proteins, lysosomal enzymes, and transmembrane proteins—the three major classes of glycoproteins made in the ER.

Unfortunately, the available evidence now indicates that glycosylation is not a requirement for secretion or for the transfer of integral membrane proteins to the plasma membrane. For example, cells treated with the drug *tunicamycin*, an inhibitor of *N*-linked glycosylation of polypeptides, may continue to produce and secrete proteins or make nonglycosylated proteins that are properly incorporated into membranes. The sorting out of lysosomal enzymes from secretory proteins, however, seems to depend on the addition of mannose 6-phosphate sugar residues to the oligosaccharide core of precursor forms of the lysosomal enzymes. This information had first been inferred by Elizabeth Neufeld and colleagues from studies of human fibroblasts grown in culture. Normal fibroblasts make lysosomal enzymes and incorporate them into lysosomes, whereas genetically deficient fibroblasts from patients with mucolipidosis II secrete lysosomal hydrolases into the culture medium instead of incorporating them into lysosomes. Lysosomal enzymes contained mannose 6-phosphate residues, but the enzymes secreted by the genetically deficient fibroblasts lacked this phosphorylated sugar. In addition, it has been found that the enzymes lacking the mannose 6-phosphate residues are secreted in a precursor form. Because newly synthesized lysosomal enzymes in normal cells are converted from the precursor form to the mature enzyme by posttranslational processing, it seems possible that the addition of mannose 6-phosphate residues to the oligosaccharide core is necessary to divert the lysosomal enzymes from the secretory pathway and direct them toward the lysosomes instead. These interpretations are consistent with the model in which additional signals are required to divert vectorially discharged glycoproteins from the secretory pathway to other destinations within the cell. We need far more evidence, however, before this general model or any other can be accepted.

In normal cells, lysosomal enzyme precursors are modified by the addition of mannose 6-phosphate residues to the oligosaccharide core of the polypeptides, but how are these precursors directed specifically to the lysosomes once diverted from the secretory pathway to the cell exterior? Recent evidence from *in vitro* studies of various cell types and from analyses of highly purified fractions from these cells has indicated that *clathrin-coated vesicles* are specific intermediaries in the transfer of lysosomal enzyme precursors from the ER or Golgi apparatus to lysosomes. These coated vesicles are similar or identical to coated vesicles involved in receptor-mediated endocytosis (see Section 5.10), but they are formed at ER or Golgi membranes rather than at the plasma membrane (Fig. 7.15). Highly purified clathrin-coated vesicles isolated from various mammalian tissues have been shown to contain receptors for mannose 6-phosphate, and these membrane-embedded receptors face toward the *inside* of the coated vesicles. Lysosomal enzyme precursors in the ER or Golgi apparatus could therefore bind to membrane domains that contain these receptors, and when such portions of the membrane are coated with clathrin and pinched off from ER or Golgi, the coated vesicle and its contents would be diverted toward structures involved in lysosome formation rather than toward the cell surface for secretory discharge. We will discuss this topic further in Chapter 8 when we consider lysosome formation and function.

7.6
Protein Transfer from the Cytosol to Mitochondria and Chloroplasts

Mitochondria and chloroplasts are unique cytoplasmic organelles in that they can synthesize a few of their own proteins from encoded information in their own DNA genomes. Most of the organelle proteins, however, are made in the cytosol on free ribosomes and are then delivered to the intended organelle. These cytosol-synthesized proteins include integral and peripheral proteins of the inner and outer membranes, enzymes that catalyze energy-transducing reactions of respiration and photosynthesis, and at least 50 different proteins of the organelle ribosomes (Fig. 7.16). All these proteins must not only be directed to a particular kind of organelle but they must also be distributed in each organelle in appropriate orientation in the inner and outer membranes and in the correct spaces within the organelle (matrix or intermembrane space). On the basis of our understanding of protein transport from the ER to other parts of the cell, we would expect both the proteins and the target membranes to contain structural features that would serve as signals to determine specific interactions between the transported proteins and the target membranes and to stabilize these macromolecular interactions afterward. Only the broad outlines of protein import and intraorganelle distribution will be given here, because a more detailed discussion appears in Chapter 9.

Import of a polypeptide into mitochondria and chloroplasts apparently involves the following steps: (1) synthesis of a precursor

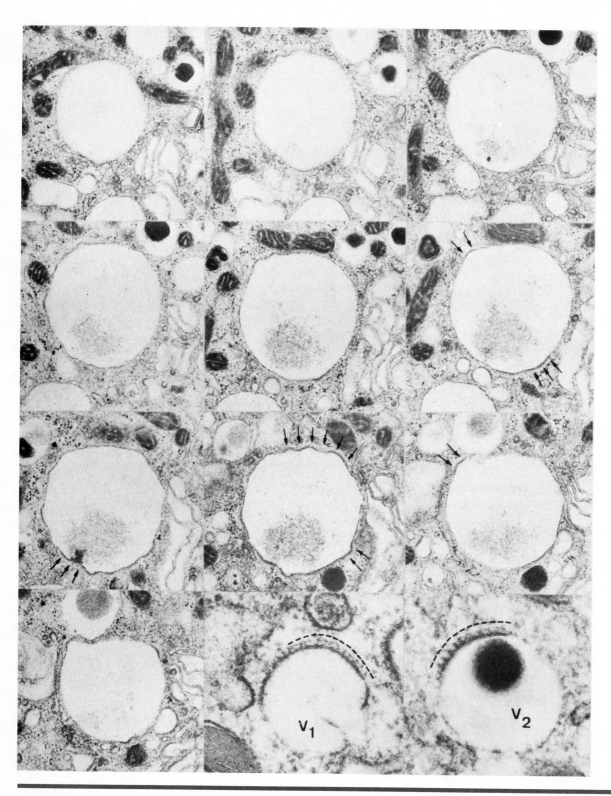

FIGURE 7-15
Electron micrographs of insulin-producing secretory vesicles in B-cells from isolated islets of Langerhans of rat pancreas. The first ten photographs are a series of successive sections through a vesicle in the Golgi apparatus of cells treated with monensin, an ionophore that arrests transit of polypeptides into Golgi vesicles. The arrows point to clathrin-coated segments of the vesicle membrane. × 22,000. The last two photographs (lower right) are from stained monensin-treated cells, showing clathrin-coated segments (dashed lines) on two vesicles (V₁ and V₂) at a higher magnification. Vesicle V₂ contains a densely-stained core of secretory materials. ×69,000 and × 81,000. (Photographs courtesy of L. Orci, from Orci, L., *et al.*, 1984, *Cell* **39** : 39, Fig. 4. Copyright © by M. I. T. Press.)

polypeptide in the cytosol, (2) binding of this precursor to a receptor on the organelle surface, (3) translocation into or across the organelle membranes, and (4) processing of the precursor to the mature form of the polypeptide. Most of the data for these interpretations have come from *in vitro* studies using isolated mitochondria or chloroplasts, and the organelle proteins have been analyzed in isolated fractions of outer membrane, inner membrane, intermembrane space, and matrix. In some studies, particularly with yeast, *in vivo* analysis has been carried out with mutant strains as well as normal cells.

Although the four steps we have listed are characteristic in general, there are important variations depending on the final destination of the proteins in the organelle. Proteins destined for the inner membrane or the matrix are usually synthesized as precursors that have an amino-terminal extension sequence which is absent from the mature poly-peptide (Fig. 7.17). Details concerning this amino-terminal sequence are currently available for a few polypeptides, but for many others we know only that the precursor is a larger molecule than the mature form. An ATPase subunit of the inner membrane–matrix compartment in *Neurospora crassa* mitochondria has a highly hydrophobic amino-terminal extension sequence of 66 amino acids, which is cleaved during or after the polypeptide enters the organelle. Similarly, the amino-terminal extension of 44 amino acids is cleaved from the precursor of a polypeptide subunit of the chloroplast enzyme ribulose 1,5-bisphosphate carboxylase during or immediately after its incorporation in the organelle matrix. These hydrophobic segments are removed in each case by matrix peptidases that catalyze the proteolytic cleavage reaction. In some cases, however, the precursor and the mature polypeptide have the same molecular weights but appear to have different conformations. The common feature in all these instances of inner membrane–matrix proteins may very well be concerned with the final conformation of the mature molecule, whether it is achieved by cleaving an amino-terminal sequence or by another means, such as binding between the precursor and some other component. In fact, we know that the precursor of cytochrome *c* enters the mitochondrion and is there altered in its conformation by binding a heme group during maturation of the molecule. No proteolytic cleavage is involved. Because the net result in these situations is a conformational change leading to the mature polypeptide, the mature configuration of the molecule could serve as the signal for subsequent distribution of the polypeptide to its ultimate location in the organelle.

Precursor polypeptides can bind to the cytoplasmic face of the outer organelle membrane. Binding is inhibited by briefly treating the outer surfaces with dilute trypsin solution, which could destroy or modify surface protein receptors. Binding may also be inhibited by removing the amino-terminal segment of precursor polypeptides, which may indicate that these segments are signals for interaction with the putative membrane receptors. These speculations can be tested by isolating the putative receptors and demonstrating specificity in their binding with precursor polypeptides. With new methods developed by Gottfried Schatz and others for isolating separate fractions representing each of the membranes and spaces of the mitochondrion, it should be possible to

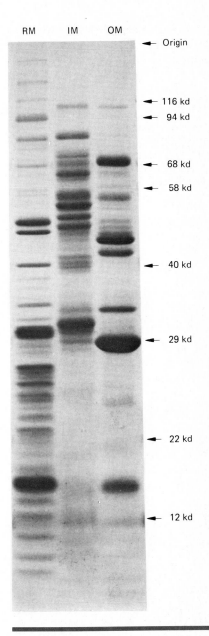

FIGURE 7-16
Polypeptide composition of isolated fractions from yeast cells of rough membranes (RM) of the cytosolic endoplasmic reticulum, and the inner membrane (IM) and outer membrane (OM) of mitochondria. After electrophoresis the gel was stained with Coomassie blue. Each fraction contains a set of unique proteins in addition to others present in two, or all three, of these subcellular membranes. The mobilities of molecular-weight standards (in kilodaltons, kd) are given at the right side of the figure. (Photograph courtesy of G. Schatz, from Riezman, H., *et al.*, 1983, *EMBO J.* **2**:1105, Fig. 3. Copyright © by IRL Press Limited.)

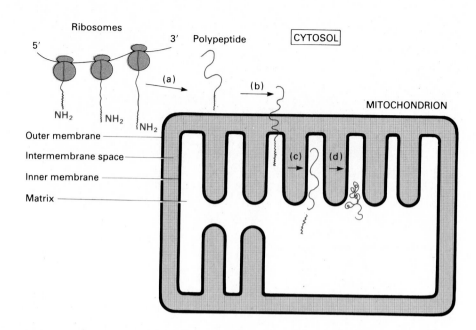

FIGURE 7-17
Mitochondrial import of a matrix protein synthesized in the cytosol. (a) Matrix polypeptides are synthesized at cytosolic ribosomes in a precursor form that contains an amino-terminal hydrophobic sequence (jagged line), which directs the finished molecule to the mitochondrial membrane. (b) The precursor molecule passes through the membranes to the organelle interior, where (c) the hydrophobic terminus is cleaved by a peptidase, and (d) the mature functional protein is available for matrix activities.

purify protein import receptors, precursors, and proteases and to reconstitute the import process from these components. Such studies will be essential for the understanding of how proteins move across biological membranes and are distributed to their ultimate locations in mitochondria and chloroplasts.

The Golgi Apparatus

The **Golgi apparatus** is a collection of smooth membranes that serves as a way station in the cell for processing and packaging secretions and other macromolecular products synthesized in the ER and transported from the ER through lumenal channels. The existence of a distinctive set of intracellular structures corresponding to the Golgi apparatus was first reported in 1898 by the Italian cytologist Camillo Golgi. By the use of a particular silver stain, he was able to see platelike and threadlike elements near the nucleus in nerve cells. Unfortunately, the staining method was difficult to use in other tissues, and his results were not readily repeatable. These problems led many investigators to question the existence of the elusive structures, and the controversy continued until the development of electron microscopy in the 1950s. Not only is the Golgi apparatus now recognized as a ubiquitous compartment in eukaryotic cells, but we also know a great deal about the organization of the membranes and the biochemical processes of the system.

7.7
Ultrastructural Organization of Golgi Membranes

The Golgi apparatus is composed of smooth membranes that are generally considered to be differentiated regions of the smooth endoplasmic reticulum. In its usual distinctive form the Golgi apparatus consists of stacks of **cisternae**, which are flattened sacs filled with fluid and

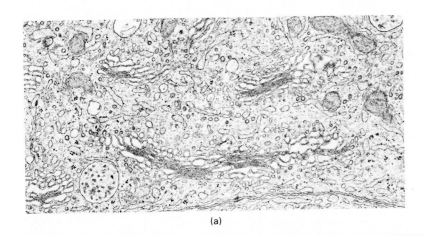

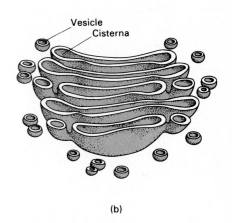

(a)

(b)

dissolved or suspended substances (Fig. 7.18). The cisternal stacks are often associated with a peripheral system of tubules and an assortment of coated and uncoated vesicles of varying sizes. The peripheral tubules often form a network of elements that extend outward for a distance of several micrometers from the central platelike cisternae, with which they are continuous. The perforated (fenestrated) cisternal membranes and their tubular outgrowths are particularly evident in negatively stained electron micrographs of isolated cell-free fractions obtained by centrifugation (Fig. 7.19).

The cisternae are usually organized into stacks called **dictyosomes**. A dictyosome often consists of 5 to 8 cisternae piled one on top of another

FIGURE 7-18
The Golgi apparatus. (a) Electron micrograph of a section through rat testis cell showing a typical two-dimensional view of parallel cisternae, or flattened membranous sacs, and numerous vesicles of the Golgi apparatus. ×12,600. (Photograph courtesy of H. H. Mollenhauer.)
(b) A three-dimensional representation of one stack of cisternae and associated vesicles.

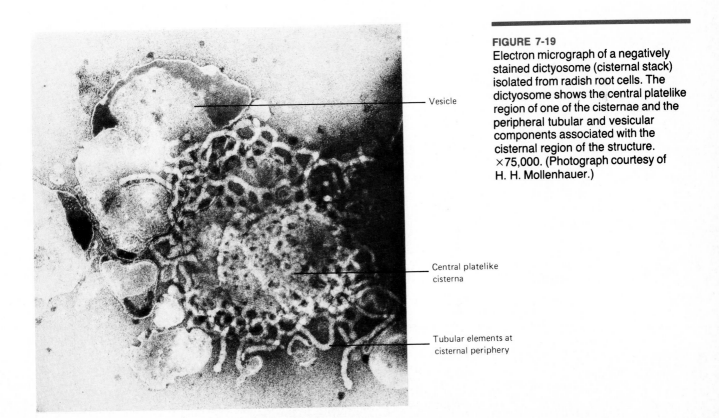

Vesicle

Central platelike cisterna

Tubular elements at cisternal periphery

FIGURE 7-19
Electron micrograph of a negatively stained dictyosome (cisternal stack) isolated from radish root cells. The dictyosome shows the central platelike region of one of the cisternae and the peripheral tubular and vesicular components associated with the cisternal region of the structure. ×75,000. (Photograph courtesy of H. H. Mollenhauer.)

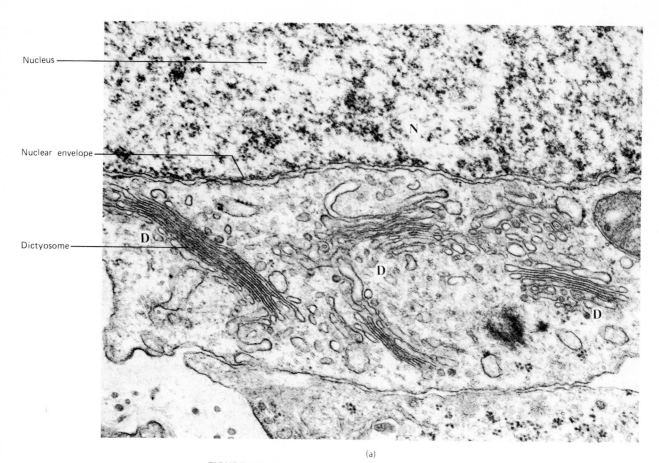

(a)

FIGURE 7-20 ▲ ▶

Electron micrographs showing the different patterns of dictyosome distribution in sections through animal and plant cells. (a) A portion of the Golgi apparatus in a rat testis cell showing dictyosomes clustered near the nucleus. ×50,000.

(b) Dictyosomes of the Golgi apparatus in root cap cells of maize (*Zea mays*) are widely distributed throughout the cytosol, unlike the confined distribution typical of vertebrate animal cells. ×19,500. (Photographs courtesy of H. H. Mollenhauer.)

like plates, but 30 is not an unusual number of cisternae for a dictyosome in invertebrate animals and some other organisms. A single Golgi apparatus may be composed of one or more dictyosomes.

Some controversy exists over the interpretation of observed similarities and differences in the form and organization of the Golgi apparatus, because the distribution of Golgi membranes and dictyosomes varies in cells of different types, species, and metabolic states. A single region of Golgi membranes is generally displayed near the nucleus in mammalian cells, which gives the appearance of there being a single, compact Golgi apparatus (Fig. 7.20). Electron micrographs of cell thin sections from protists, fungi, invertebrates, and higher plants, however, generally reveal a dispersion of well-separated individual dictyosomes rather than a concentration in one cellular region. Cells from many of these organisms may contain from 1 to 25,000 dictyosomes, although even a single dictyosome may not be present in certain kinds of cells or at

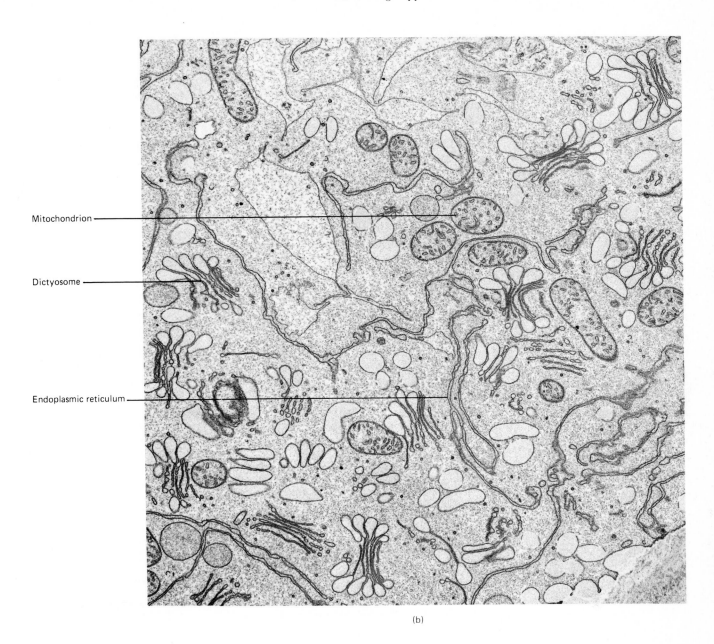

Mitochondrion

Dictyosome

Endoplasmic reticulum

(b)

particular stages of development. In certain fungi and some other kinds of cells only a single cisterna may be present or a system of vesicle-producing tubules, either of which can function as a Golgi apparatus. Although we cannot be entirely certain in every case, a comparison of negatively stained isolated Golgi from cell-free fractions of plants and of animals shows the systems to be similarly organized, despite the compaction or dispersion of dictyosomes seen in cross-sectional views of the cells.

Dictyosomes of the Golgi apparatus are structurally and biochemically polarized. Two distinct faces can be observed: a *cis* **face**, or **forming face**; and a *trans* **face**, or **maturing face**. The forming face in a dictyosome is closely associated with rough ER, usually with a smooth transitional region of these membranes. In secretory cells in particular, the maturing face is oriented toward the plasma membrane and away from the nucleus. In favorable preparations the two faces can be

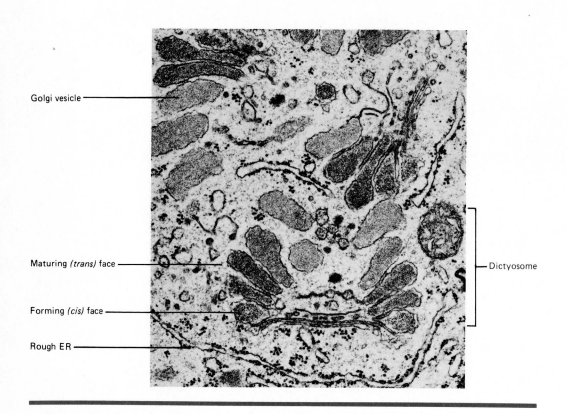

Golgi vesicle

Maturing *(trans)* face

Forming *(cis)* face

Rough ER

Dictyosome

FIGURE 7-21
Electron micrograph of a section through part of a root cap cell of maize, showing the polarized aspect of a dictyosome actively engaged in processing secretions. The forming (cis) face of the dictyosome is associated with smaller vesicles, whereas the maturing (trans) face has larger vesicles associated with it. The dense contents are secretions synthesized at the rough ER and subsequently packaged in Golgi-derived vesicles. A region of rough ER is usually found adjacent to the forming (cis) face of a dictyosome. ×35,000. (Photograph courtesy of H. H. Mollenhauer.)

further distinguished by the relative size of the attached or associated vesicles at the cisternal periphery. Vesicles are usually smaller and attached to cisternae at the forming face, and they are larger and often appear to be detached from cisternae at the maturing face (Fig. 7.21). The cisternal membranes of the forming face are thinner and resemble ER membranes, whereas cisternal membranes at the maturing face are thicker and more like the plasma membrane in this regard—and also in showing a more distinct three-layered staining pattern when fixed in osmium reagents. The polarity gradient thus seems to be from a more ER-like morphology at the forming face to a more plasmalemma-like morphology at the maturing face of a dictyosome. Biochemical polarity, from the forming face to the maturing face, is evident from studies of the pathway and time course of enzymatically catalyzed reactions in the Golgi apparatus. Molecular reactions begin in ER-like elements at the forming face and proceed through the cisternal stack to the maturing face, where vesicles pinch off and then proceed to the cell apex for exocytosis or to some destination within the cell.

7.8
Functions of the Golgi Apparatus

For some years it was believed that chemical syntheses did not take place in the Golgi regions but that compounds produced elsewhere in the cell were merely packaged during their passage through the Golgi apparatus. After being wrapped in a membrane, the enzymes or other organic molecules were then thought to be discharged through the plasma membrane or be sent elsewhere in the cell.

With the development of autoradiographic methods, the sequence of protein synthesis and packaging and the participation of the Golgi apparatus in these processes could be studied. Lucien Caro and George Palade reported on experiments designed to follow the migration of radioactively labeled amino acids injected into pancreatic cells of the guinea pig. After 3 minutes of exposure to radioactive amino acids, cells were collected and prepared for electron microscope autoradiography. These cells contained radioactivity only in the rough ER regions, indicating that amino acids had become incorporated into proteins in these areas. Any unincorporated labeled amino acid would have been washed out during the standard procedures, leaving insoluble polypeptides that could be distinguished by the presence of silver grains in the emulsion over these sites.

The 3-minute labeling, or "pulse," was also followed by a "chase" period begun by injecting unlabeled amino acids. The duration of the "chase" was varied in the experiment so that the sequence of events following protein synthesis could be studied and the fate of the original labeled amino acids introduced during the original "pulse" could be traced (Fig. 7.22). Because unlabeled amino acids were provided, syntheses would continue but only the original products manufactured in the first 3 minutes would contain the radioactive label. After a 3-minute pulse and 17-minute chase, the labeled amino acids were found to be distributed over rough ER near the Golgi region and over cisternae and secretion vesicles of the Golgi complex itself. If the chase period was 117 minutes in duration, the labeled amino acids were found exclusively in the **zymogen granules** near the apex of the cell, and in some of the discharged contents in the extracellular space. Zymogen granules contain pancreatic enzyme precursors that are distributed to the small intestine, where digestive activities occur.

FIGURE 7-22
Schematic illustrations showing the time course of radioactive label distribution in autoradiographs of guinea pig pancreatic cells after three different chase times following an initial 3-minute pulse of labeled amino acids. The labeled amino acids (color) first appear in proteins in the rough ER and pass through the Golgi apparatus before their release from the cell by exocytosis of zymogen granule packages. These data indicate that amino acids are incorporated into zymogens (precursors of digestive enzymes) in the rough ER, packaged in the Golgi apparatus, and secreted at the pancreatic cell apex during exocytosis.

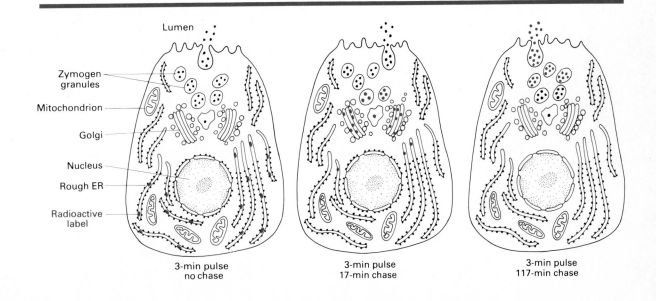

3-min pulse
no chase

3-min pulse
17-min chase

3-min pulse
117-min chase

From these data and other observations made in experiments with various intervals of chase time, the sequence of events could be reconstructed as follows:

1. Proteins are synthesized along ribosomes of the rough ER.

2. The newly synthesized proteins move from the ER to the Golgi apparatus.

3. These proteins are enclosed within a membrane while in the Golgi region, and they can then be considered contents of the zymogen granules.

4. The newly formed zymogen granules move to the apex of the cell and discharge their contents into the lumen bordering the pancreatic cell.

These experiments provided evidence that proteins were packaged at the Golgi sites, but they did not provide direct evidence concerning the origin of the membrane of the newly formed zymogen granules. It can be inferred that the membranes are derived from Golgi components, however; no other reasonable site of origin was involved in the sequence of events traced during the autoradiographic studies.

A more informative series of experiments was reported by Marian Neutra and Charles Leblond for mucus granule formation in goblet cells of rat intestine. Microscopical studies by the Spanish histologist S. Ramón y Cajal in 1914 had provided early evidence of possible Golgi involvement in mucus droplet formation in intestinal goblet cells. He observed that mucus droplets were present in the Golgi region of these cells and suggested that the Golgi apparatus might be involved in production of these secretion droplets. The mucus produced in goblet cells is released to the intestinal lumen and covers the cells as a lining that provides resistance to foreign materials, such as bacteria. It is also protective in other ways.

As background for the Neutra–Leblond experiments, we need to describe the structure of goblet cells. Goblet cells are squeezed between other cells of the intestinal lining and are thus long and narrow in form (Fig. 7.23). In goblet cells the Golgi region is cup-shaped and includes closely packed dictyosomes. Each dictyosome is made up of eight to ten cisternae, with the forming face near the nucleus and the maturing face of each stack directed toward the apex of the cell, pointing toward the intestinal lumen. The cisternae at the forming face appear empty and greatly flattened whereas those at the maturing face appear swollen due to the presence of mucus-filled globules. The globules detach from the topmost cisterna and migrate up to the cell membrane where the contents are discharged from the cell into the lumen.

The experimental design utilized by Neutra and Leblond was similar to the one described for pancreatic cells. Labeled amino acids were injected into the bloodstream of rats, and the time course of migration of these labeled amino acids was followed autoradiographically. Labeled amino acids were first seen at the rough ER, then in the Golgi cisternae, and finally in the mucus droplet secretions that were ultimately discharged at the cell apex. These events were similar to migrations noted for labeled amino acids in the pancreas. But Neutra

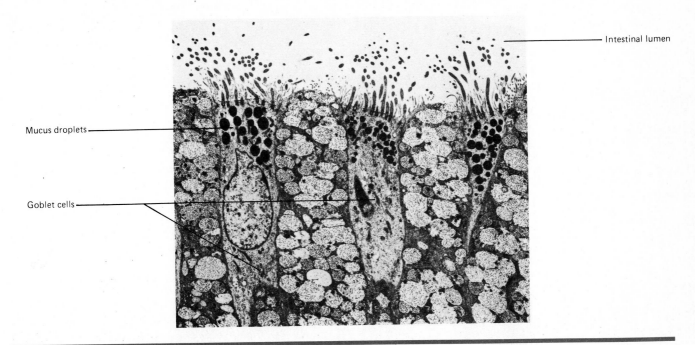

FIGURE 7-23
Photograph of a region of quail
intestinal epithelium showing goblet
cells squeezed between columnar cells
of the tissue lining the intestinal lumen.
Mucus secretion is associated only with
the goblet cells of this tissue. ×3,000.
(From Sandoz, D., et al., 1976, *J. Cell
Biol.* **71**:460, Fig. 6.)

and Leblond went further in order to answer important questions raised by the preliminary observations. One major question was whether proteins pass through the Golgi apparatus only to be packaged or are processed *before* being packaged within a membrane. Mucus is a typical secretory protein in that it is a glycoprotein. Experiments were designed to find out whether sugar was linked to protein to form the mucus glycoprotein within the Golgi apparatus or elsewhere in the cell. These experiments were conducted, therefore, to determine whether the Golgi apparatus biochemically processed the glycoprotein or merely packaged it.

The experimental procedure involved the injection into rats of radioactively labeled glucose, because it was known that glucose is incorporated into the mucus glycoprotein molecule. Within 15 minutes after injection of tritiated glucose, all the radioactivity was concentrated in Golgi cisternae and vesicles; after 20 minutes radioactivity began to appear in mucus globules; after 4 hours the labeled mucus molecules were discharged into the intestinal lumen (Fig. 7.24). These experiments

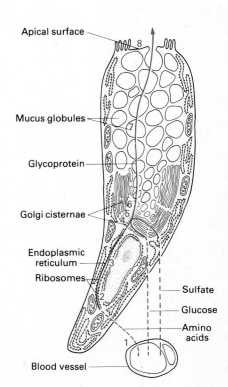

FIGURE 7-24 ▶
Summary diagram showing the flow of precursor and finished glycoprotein molecules in the intestine, as deduced from time-course autoradiographic data obtained in different experiments. Radioactively labeled amino acids, glucose, or sulfated molecules pass from the bloodstream to the goblet cells of the intestinal epithelium. In these cells, proteins are made in the rough ER and pass to the Golgi apparatus, where they are glycosylated and also sulfated. The finished mucus glycoprotein molecules are packaged in Golgi-derived membrane, and the mucus globules move to the cell apex where secretion occurs. (From "The Golgi Apparatus" by M. Neutra and C. P. Leblond. Copyright © 1969 by Scientific American, Inc. All rights reserved.)

FIGURE 7-25
Electron micrograph of a section through a maize epidermal cell in the process of new cell wall formation during cell division. The dense vesicles in the region of the developing cell wall are derived from dictyosomes of the Golgi apparatus, which is readily evident from their identical appearance in both regions of the cell and from our understanding of Golgi functions in packaging cell wall pectins and other glycoproteins. × 14,000. (Photograph courtesy of H. H. Mollenhauer.)

also revealed that a stack of 8 to 10 cisternae was converted to mucus globules in about 40 minutes and that a new stack of cisternae had formed as replacements during this time. These studies demonstrated that proteins synthesized in the rough ER pass on to the Golgi apparatus, where glycosylation and packaging take place before the finished molecules are expelled from the cell.

We now know that many types of molecules pass through the Golgi apparatus before heading for some intracellular or extracellular destination. In addition to secreted glycoproteins and proteoglycans, the other kinds of molecules that are also processed and packaged in the Golgi apparatus include plasma membrane glycoproteins, glycolipids, lysosomal enzymes, and pectins and other constituents of plant cell walls (Fig. 7.25). During their sojourn in the Golgi apparatus, macro-

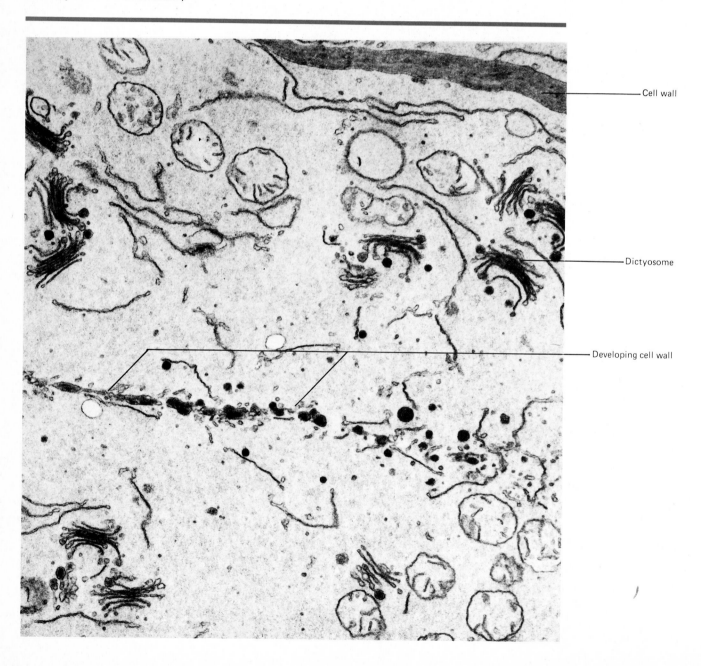

Cell wall

Dictyosome

Developing cell wall

molecules are covalently modified by alterations in their N-linked oligosaccharides, by glycosylation of some tyrosine, serine, and threonine residues in the formation of O-linked carbohydrate chains of many polypeptides, by sulfate addition, by fatty acid addition, and by specific proteolytic cleavages. Some of the biochemical steps involved in these modifications are known, and some of the enzymes that catalyze these reactions have been purified and identified.

7.9
Carbohydrate Processing in the Golgi Apparatus

One of the important biochemical activities of the Golgi apparatus involves the modification of N-linked oligosaccharides that were covalently added to polypeptide chains in the rough ER (see Section 7.3). Mature glycoproteins may contain one or both types of the two major classes of N-linked oligosaccharides: the complex oligosaccharides and the high-mannose oligosaccharides. Both these classes of carbohydrates contain mannose and N-acetylglucosamine residues in the *core region* bonded to asparagine, but they differ in their *terminal region*, which is linked to the core residues of mannose (Fig. 7.26).

1. **High-mannose oligosaccharides** contain only mannose residues in the terminal region, sometimes in considerable numbers. All the mannose residues and the core sugars are added to the precursor glycoprotein in the rough ER, not in the Golgi.

2. **Complex oligosaccharides** have a terminal region composed of a variable number of N-acetylglucosamine, galactose, and sialic acid (N-neuraminic acid, or NAN) residues. These sugars often occur as trisaccharide units, and there may also be an occasional fucose residue linked to the core N-acetylglucosamine that is bonded to asparagine in the polypeptide chain. All the sugars of the terminal region and the occasional fucose are added to the precursor glycoprotein in the Golgi. The core sugars, however, are covalently added to the polypeptide chain in the rough ER, like the core of high-mannose oligosaccharides (see Fig. 7.9).

Glycoprotein processing in the Golgi apparatus involves a considerable amount of trimming as well as the addition of sugar residues to the N-linked oligosaccharide chains. Mannose residues may be trimmed from the core and terminal regions of the high-mannose oligosaccharides by specific *mannosidases*, and in complex oligosaccharides the terminal sugar residues are linked in sequence and covalently bonded to core mannose residues by specific *glycosyl transferase* enzymes. All these enzymes are present in the Golgi, as shown by enzyme activity assays carried out with isolated fractions of Golgi vesicles. Autoradiographic studies have provided information on the location of particular reactions in which sugar residues are added to polypeptide or glycoprotein molecules. For example, cells briefly incubated with [³H]mannose show silver grains only in the ER, whereas [³H]galactose and [³H]sialic acid residues occur in electron microscope autoradiographs only in the Golgi. As might be expected from their occurrence in both the core and

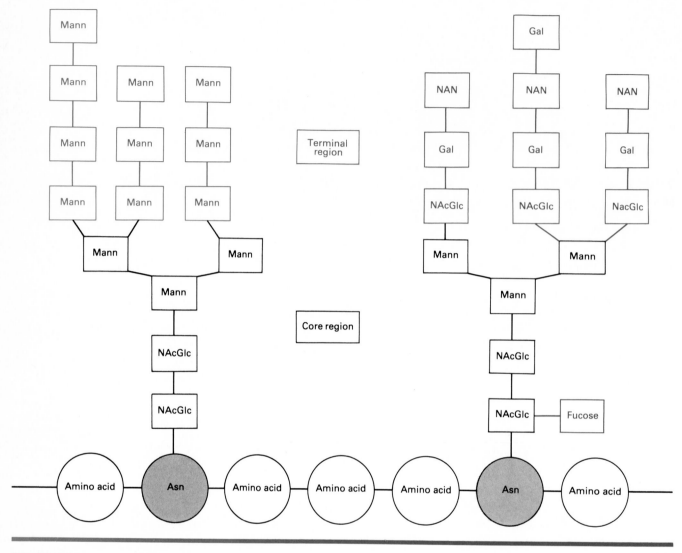

FIGURE 7-26
High-mannose oligosaccharides and complex oligosaccharides are the two major classes of *N*-linked carbohydrates covalently bonded to asparagine residues of glycoproteins. The core region (color) is the same in both types of branched-chain oligosaccharides, but they differ in their terminal region residues. The entire high-mannose oligosaccharide is linked to asparagine in the rough ER, whereas only the core region of complex oligosaccharides is added in the rough ER. The remainder of the complex oligosaccharide (terminal region plus fucose units) is added by glycosylation reactions in the Golgi apparatus.

terminal regions of complex oligosaccharides, a brief incubation with [³H]*N*-acetylglucosamine results in the simultaneous labeling of both the ER and the Golgi compartments of the cells.

Recent studies by James Rothman, his co-workers, and others have provided exciting new information about biochemical compartmentation of a stack of Golgi cisternae. By the analysis of Golgi cisternae recovered after centrifugation and by specific labeling of enzymes in the Golgi of intact cells, the *cis*, central, and *trans* cisternae of a Golgi stack were shown to harbor different sets of enzymes for the processing of oligosaccharide chains in *N*-glycosylated glycoproteins transported from the ER to the Golgi. The *cis* cisternae carry out mannose phosphorylation, the central cisternae have enzymes that transfer *N*-acetylglucosamine to the oligosaccharide, and the *trans* cisternae have enzymes responsible for transferring sialic acid, or NAN, and galactose units to the sugar chain. The three cisternal regions of a Golgi stack are thus biochemically specialized for carrying out particular steps in the oligosaccharide-processing pathway. The sequence of reactions proceeds from the *cis* face to the *trans* face, in parallel with the sequence of cisternae in a stack. This correspondence of biochemistry and structural organization may be advantageous. In addition, the compartmentation may be related to the sorting of glycoproteins for delivery to the secretory pathway, to the plasma membrane for incorporation there, and to the lysosomes. The pace of research is very rapid, and we can expect more important information and insights in the next year or two.

7.10
Membrane Recycling via the Secretory Pathway

Until recently it was generally believed that the flow of membranes as well as that of secretions was unidirectional, proceeding as follows: ER → transitional membranes and vesicles → Golgi cisternae from the forming (cis) to the maturing (trans) face of a stack → secretion granules → plasma membrane. Once the secretion granule had fused with the plasma membrane and the contents had been expelled by exocytosis, the granule membrane was presumed to be incorporated into the plasma membrane, thus adding to its area. Because the plasma membrane remains relatively constant in area, compensating endocytosis events were held to be responsible for removing bits of plasma membrane just as exocytosis events had added to the cell surface. The endocytosed plasma membrane was then considered to be directed to lysosomes and to be degraded there by lysosomal digestive enzymes. According to this scenario, new membrane was synthesized at the ER and added to the Golgi apparatus as the cisternae were used up in making secretion granules (Fig. 7.27). We now have persuasive evidence, however, that membrane recycling takes place and that it involves a number of different transport routes within the cell. In this section we will concentrate on membrane traffic in secretory cells. In the next chapter we will examine alternative pathways of membrane recycling and traffic. By **membrane recycling** we refer specifically to the retrieval and re-use of existing membrane domains that retain their original specificity during recycling.

A good deal of the confusion and misinterpretation in the earlier studies was due to two factors: (1) We assumed that by following the route taken by secretory proteins we also were following the route taken by the membrane wrapper, and that the synthesis, processing, and distribution of contents and membranes could be analyzed from the contents alone. (2) Very few unambiguous markers were available to investigate the manufacture and fate of the membranes separately from the contents of secretory granules. Since the late 1970s, new information has been presented by Marilyn Farquhar, Volker Herzog, and others, which clearly shows that many kinds of secretory cells experience considerable membrane traffic, a large portion of which appears to be associated with the recycling of the membrane wrappers used in packaging secretory proteins (Fig. 7.28). A major innovation in these studies was the use of relatively inert electron-dense tracers that served as unambiguous membrane markers for electron microscope autoradiographic and morphological analyses.

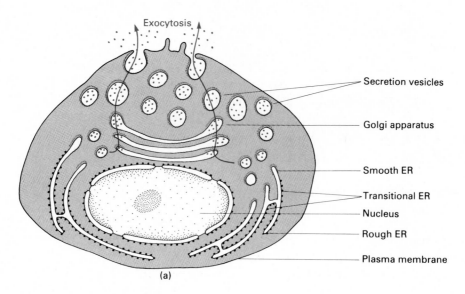

(a)

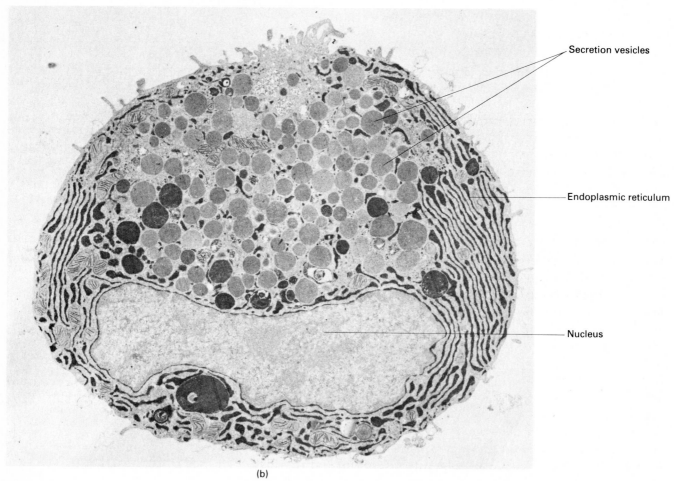

(b)

◀ **FIGURE 7-27**

Formation and fate of membranes and secretions in the secretory pathway. (a) Schematic drawing showing the secretory pathway of glycoproteins made in the rough ER and released by exocytosis from membranous vesicles formed in the Golgi apparatus. On the basis of tracing the flow of secretions, it was earlier presumed that an accompanying unidirectional flow of membrane (color) occurred between the ER and the plasma membrane. Such a unidirectional pathway of membrane flow, however, was not demonstrated directly. (b) Electron micrograph of a secretory cell from rat lacrimal gland. ×7,400. (Photograph courtesy of V. Herzog, from Herzog, V., et al., 1976, *J. Cell Biol.* **70**:692, Fig. 10.)

Two of the electron-dense tracers used by Farquhar and Herzog since 1977 are *dextrans*, which are inert polysaccharides, and *cationized ferritin*, which binds avidly to membranes because of its net positive charge and which is electron-dense by virtue of its iron content. When either of these tracers was used *in vivo* or *in vitro* to study secretory cells from endocrine and exocrine glands and from immunoglobulin-producing lymph nodes or myeloma cell cultures, the results were fairly similar. The tracers were initially distributed over the plasma membrane, were then taken into the cell by endocytosis, and later appeared principally or entirely over Golgi cisternae and their associated secretory vesicles (Fig. 7.29). Membrane thus appears to be continually recovered from the cell surface of secretory cells and funneled to the Golgi apparatus, primarily to the trans-most cisternae where active packaging occurs and to the maturing vesicles and granules destined for export by exocytosis. We know from all the earlier studies that, during active secretion, membrane traffic occurs in the direction of the plasma membrane from the Golgi apparatus, so it seems clear that membrane added to the plasmalemma during exocytosis is retrieved after endocytosis by the Golgi apparatus, where it is reutilized in new cycles of secretory granule formation.

According to the earlier prevailing view of unidirectional membrane flow, membrane from the ER moved to the Golgi at the cis face and emerged from it on the opposite side, or the trans face. The cisternae were thus believed to be progressively displaced one by one, with new membranes being provided at the cis face as existing membranes were used up in packaging secretions on the trans face of a Golgi stack. The current view of bidirectional membrane flow between the plasma membrane and the Golgi does not dispute the synthesis of new Golgi membranes from ER precursors. We know this must occur because the ER is the ultimate source of newly synthesized proteins and lipids that become incorporated into new ER, Golgi, and plasma membrane domains. Membrane recycling provides the cell with reusable materials, which may even be the major source of secretory granule and Golgi membrane components in actively secreting systems. Because the dextran, cationized ferritin, and other membrane markers are concentrated over the trans-most Golgi cisternae and well-developed secretion vesicles and granules, and *not* on the cis face of the cisternal stack, it would appear that membrane recycling does not involve cisternal replacement from the cis face to the trans face of a stack. Cycling

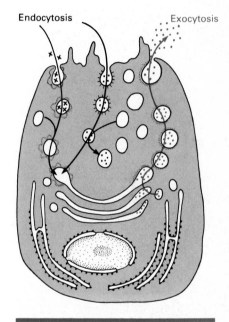

FIGURE 7-28

As deduced directly from studies of labeled membrane, membrane recycling is now known to occur in secretory cells. Recycling involves the intake of plasma membrane segments by endocytoses, their incorporation into cisternal membranes and associated vesicles of the Golgi apparatus, and their return to the plasma membrane in the secretory pathway. The flow and recycling of cell membrane are an outcome of fusion events within the cell and at the cell surface during endocytosis and exocytosis.

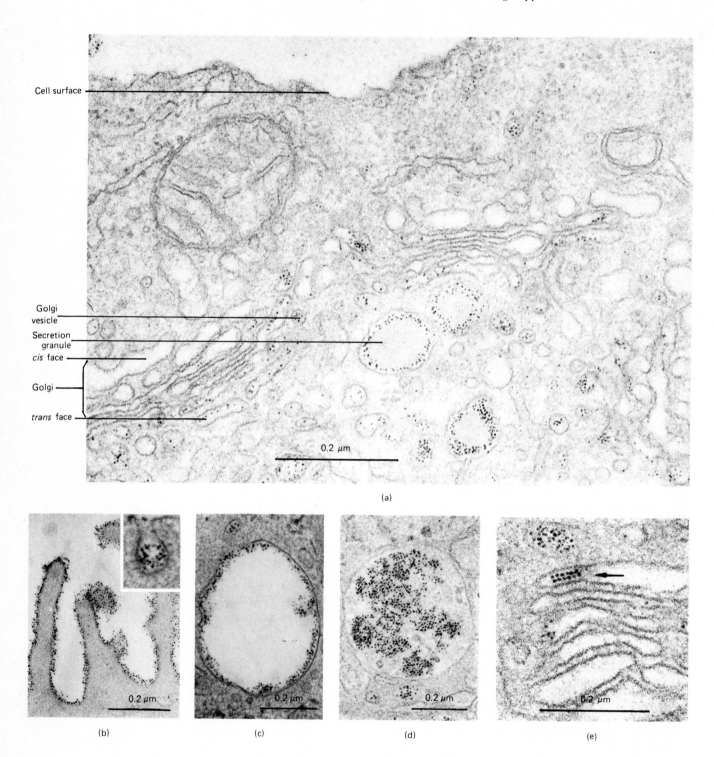

(a)

Cell surface

Golgi
vesicle

Secretion
granule

cis face

Golgi

trans face

0.2 μm

(b)   (c)   (d)   (e)

0.2 μm   0.2 μm   0.2 μm   0.2 μm

involves the maturing portions of the Golgi stack, and its interactions with the plasma membrane via endocytotic and exocytotic vesicles, at least in active secretory cells. The relative proportion of new membrane synthesis and recycled membrane usage must vary among different kinds of cells and their different physiological states.

Not all the membrane moving from the Golgi apparatus to the plasma membrane is recycled. Some of this membrane is permanently

◄ **FIGURE 7-29**

Electron micrographs of subcellular structures involved in membrane recycling in secretory cells studied with cationized ferritin (CF) as a membrane marker. Cationized ferritin is visible as dark particles in all the photographs. (a) After 60 minutes of incubation with CF, the membrane marker is found in Golgi cisternae and vesicles of growth hormone-secreting cells and in secretion granules containing the hormone (dense central material). Membrane carried into the cell by endocytosis is returned to the cell surface by exocytosis of the secretory granules, to a greater or lesser degree in different kinds of cells. In a timed study of CF intake and distribution in thyroglobulin-secreting thyroid follicle cells, (b) CF quickly binds to the entire apical surface of the cell and collects in coated pits (inset) at the microvillar bases. Within 5 minutes, (c) CF is found in endosomes, and increasingly in (d) lysosomes, where CF detaches from the membrane. After 30 minutes of incubation, (e) CF is also found in stacked Golgi cisternae, preferentially in the trans-most Golgi elements. (Photograph *a* courtesy of M. G. Farquhar, from Farquhar, M. G., 1978, *J. Cell Biol.* **77**: R35, © by Rockefeller University Press; photographs *b–e* by courtesy of V. Herzog, from Herzog, V., 1981, *Trends Biochem. Sci.* **6**: 319.)

installed in plasma membrane domains after being shuttled there in Golgi transport vesicles. Some Golgi membrane that was added to the plasmalemma during exocytosis is returned by endocytosis and is directed to lysosomes, where it is digested and the soluble materials are returned to the cell to enter precursor pools for new rounds of synthesis. We will discuss these alternative pathways of membrane traffic in the next chapter, along with the importance of this traffic in sorting proteins into different subcellular compartments.

Summary

Eukaryotic cells are rich in intracellular membranes arranged in sheets, tubules, and vesicles. Certain membranous regions acquire characteristic structural and functional properties despite regular communication or even continuity with other membranes. New methods permit separation of the various membranes and study of their properties.

The rough endoplasmic reticulum (ER) membrane sheet is folded back on itself repeatedly, creating two kinds of channels in the cytoplasm: the cytosolic channels formed by facing regions of the folded ribosome-studded membrane surface, and the lumenal channels formed by facing regions of the folded ribosomeless ER surface. The two kinds of channels alternate, suggesting the entire rough ER is a single folded membrane sheet. Smooth endoplasmic reticulum lacks attached ribosomes and appears more tubular in conformation than the rough ER. Studies of microsomes, the vesicles that form from disrupted ER during cell homogenization, reveal that the two types of ER differ in their biochemical properties, though *in vivo* the two compartments are probably continuous.

The rough ER is the site of synthesis of proteins that function in the noncytosolic regions of the cytoplasm. Such proteins are primarily secretions, transmembrane components, and constituents of lysosomes. Ribosomes synthesizing such proteins become bound to the rough ER after an *N*-terminal sequence of 18 to 30 hydrophobic amino acids has been translated from the mRNA. This amino acid sequence constitutes a signal peptide that allows the ribosome to become associated with a signal recognition particle that in turn binds the ribosome to a receptor in the rough ER (docking protein). Translation is suspended during this process, but it resumes once the binding is completed. Two integral membrane proteins, ribophorin I and ribophorin II further stabilize ribosome binding to the membrane. The hydrophobic signal peptide sequence carries the growing polypeptide across the ER membrane into the ER lumen by the processes of cotranslational transport and vectorial discharge. In the lumen peptidases remove the signal peptide. Certain asparagine residues on the growing polypeptide become glycosylated with an oligosaccharide composed of *N*-acetylglucosamine, mannose, and glucose.

Formation of this *N*-linked oligosaccharide is the first in a series of glycosylations and modifications that determine the ultimate fate of the polypeptide.

Membrane proteins frequently are oriented with their N-terminus exposed to the extracellular space (corresponding to the lumenal space) and their C-terminus exposed to the cytoplasm, suggesting that their vectorial discharge was interrupted. Indeed, near their C-terminus is found a sequence of 20 to 30 hydorphobic amino acid residues followed by charged residues. This hydrophobic sequence halts transfer and remains in the membrane. The charged amino acids of the C-terminus do not penetrate the membrane.

Once a soluble protein enters the lumen of the rough ER, it may be transported to other compartments by passage along lumenal channels and by enclosure in vesicles that bud from one membrane and fuse with another. The major pathway is taken by secretory proteins; alternative patterns of glycosylation may determine alternative pathways and fates for other proteins. Secretory proteins are enclosed in vesicles that arise from the Golgi apparatus. Lysosomal enzymes are found in clathrin-coated transport vesicles with receptors for mannose-6-phosphate, one of the characteristic components of their oligosaccharide.

Proteins destined for the mitochondria and chloroplasts are translated on free ribosomes in the cytoplasm and are not glycosylated. They are recognized by receptors on the surface of their target organelle and are then translocated and processed to their mature functional form.

The Golgi apparatus consists of a specialized array of membrane-bounded cisternae arranged in stacks and surrounded by an interconnected network of tubules and coated and uncoated vesicles. Golgi show biochemical and structural polarization with a forming face (associated with the rough ER) on one and a maturing face (toward the plasma membrane and resembling it in structure) on the other. Golgi enzymes are localized in the different layers of membranes. Golgi function has been revealed by pulse–chase autoradiographic studies. Newly synthesized secretory proteins pass through the Golgi en route to secretory granules and the extracellular space. Their N-linked oligosaccharides are modified and trimmed to become high-mannose or complex oligosaccharides, and O-linked oligosaccharides are built up on serine, threonine, and tyrosine residues.

The membrane forming the secretory granules circulates from the Golgi apparatus to the plasma membrane and is reinternalized by endocytosis and returned to the Golgi. New membranes may also be produced in the smooth ER.

Readings and References

Anderson, R. G. W., J. R. Falck, J. L. Goldstein, and M. S. Brown. 1984. Visualization of acidic organelles in intact cells by electron microscopy. *Proc. Natl. Acad. Sci. U. S.* **81**:4838.

Anderson, R. G. W., and R. K. Pathak. 1985. Vesicles and cisternae in the *trans* Golgi apparatus of human fibroblasts are acidic compartments. *Cell* **40**:635.

Balch, W. E., W. G. Dunphy, W. A. Braell, and J. E. Rothman. 1984. Reconstitution of the transport of protein between successive compartments of the Golgi measured by the coupled incorporation of N-acetylglucosamine. *Cell* **39**:405.

Balch, W. E., B. S. Glick, and J. E. Rothman. 1984. Sequential intermediates in the pathway of intercompartmental transport in a cell-free system. *Cell* **39**:525.

Bergman, J. E., K. T. Tokuyasu, and S. J. Singer. 1981. Passage of an integral membrane protein, the vesicular stomatitis virus glycoprotein, through the Golgi apparatus en route to the plasma membrane. *Proc. Natl. Acad. Sci. U. S.* **78**:1746.

Blake, C. C. F., and L. N. Johnson. 1984. Protein structure. *Trends Biochem. Sci.* **9**:147.

Blobel, G. 1982. Regulation of intracellular membrane traffic. *Harvey Lect.* **76**:125.

Blobel, G., and B. Dobberstein. 1975. Transfer of proteins across membranes. I. *J. Cell Biol.* **67**:835.

Braell, W. A., W. E. Balch, D. C. Dobbertin, and J. E. Rothman. 1984. The glycoprotein that is transported between successive compartments of the Golgi in a cell-free system resides in stacks of cisternae. *Cell* **39**:511.

Braell, W. A., D. M. Schlossman, S. L. Schmid, and J. E. Rothman. 1984. Dissociation of clathrin coats coupled to hydrolysis of ATP: Role of an uncoating ATPase. *J. Cell Biol.* **99**:735.

Brown, M. S., R. G. W. Anderson, and J. L. Goldstein. 1983. Recycling receptors: The round-trip itinerary of migrant membrane proteins. *Cell* **32**:663.

Brown, R. M., Jr., and J. H. M. Willison. 1977. Golgi apparatus and plasma membrane involvement in secretion and cell surface deposition, with special emphasis on cellulose biogenesis. In *International Cell Biology 1976–1977*, eds. B. R. Brinkley and K. R. Porter, p. 267. New York: Rockefeller University Press.

Campbell, C. H., R. E. Fine, J. Squicciarini, and L. H. Rome. 1983. Coated vesicles from rat liver and calf brain contain cryptic mannose 6-phosphate receptors. *J. Biol. Chem.* **258**:2628.

Chua, N.-H., and G. W. Schmidt. 1979. Transport of proteins into mitochondria and chloroplasts. *J. Cell. Biol.* **81**:461.

Claude, A. 1940. Particulate components of normal and tumor cells. *Science* **91**:77.

Claude, A. 1975. The coming of age of the cell. *Science* **189**:433 (Noble lecture).

Colman A. 1982. Cells that secrete foreign proteins. *Trends Biochem. Sci.* **7**:435.

Davis, B. D., and P.-C. Tai. 1980. The mechanism of protein secretion across membranes. *Nature* **283**:433.

Dautry-Varsat, A., and H. F. Lodish. May 1984. How receptors bring proteins and particles into cells. *Sci. Amer.* **250**:52.

de Duve, C. 1975. Exploring cells with a centrifuge. *Science* **189**:186 (Nobel lecture).

Elbein, A. D. 1981. The tunicamycins—useful tools for studies on glycoproteins. *Trends Biochem. Sci.* **6**:219.

Emr, S. D., M. N. Hall, and T. J. Silhavy. 1980. A mechanism of protein localization: The signal hypothesis and bacteria. *J. Cell Biol.* **86**:701.

Engelman, D. M., and T. A. Steitz. 1981. The spontaneous insertion of proteins into and across membranes: The helical hairpin hypothesis. *Cell* **23**:411.

Evered, D., ed. 1982. *Membrane Recycling.* Ciba Found. Sympos. 92. London: Pitman.

Farquhar, M. G., and G. E. Palade. 1981. The Golgi apparatus (complex)—(1954–1981)—from artifact to center stage. *J. Cell Biol.* **91**:77s.

Feizi, T., and R. A. Childs. 1985. Carbohydrate structures of glycoproteins and glycolipids as differentiation antigens, tumour-associated antigens, and components of receptor systems. *Trends Biochem. Sci.* **10**:24.

Fulton, A. B. 1982. How crowded is the cytoplasm? *Cell* **30**:345.

Gibson, R., S. Kornfeld, and S. Schlesinger. 1980. A role for oligosaccharides in glycoprotein synthesis. *Trends Biochem. Sci.* **5**:290.

Gilmore, R., P. Walter, and G. Blobel. 1982. Protein translocation across the endoplasmic reticulum. II. Isolation and characterization of the signal recognition particle receptor. *J. Cell Biol.* **95**:470.

Gonatas, N. K., *et al.* 1984. Endosomes and Golgi vesicles in adsorptive and fluid phase endocytosis. *J. Cell Biol.* **99**:1379.

Griffiths, G., P. Quinn, and G. Warren. 1983. Dissection of the Golgi complex. I. *J. Cell Biol.* **96**:835.

Herzog, V. 1981. Pathways of endocytosis in secretory cells. *Trends Biochem. Sci.* **6**:319.

Herzog, V., and H. Reggio. 1980. Pathways of endocytosis from luminal plasma membrane in rat exocrine pancreas. *Europ. J. Cell Biol.* **21**:141.

Hubbard, S. C., and R. J. Ivatt. 1981. Synthesis and processing of asparagine-linked oligosaccharides. *Ann. Rev. Biochem.* **50**:555.

Jamieson, J. D., and G. E. Palade. 1967. Intracellular transport of secretory proteins in the pancreatic exocrine cell. II. Transport of condensing vacuoles and zymogen granules. *J. Cell Biol.* **34**:597.

Kreibach, G., B. L. Ulrich, and D. D. Sabatini. 1978. Proteins of rough microsomal membranes related to ribosome binding. I. Identification of ribophorins I and II, membrane proteins characteristic of rough microsomes. *J. Cell Biol.* **77**:464.

Lawson, D., *et al.* 1977. Molecular events during membrane fusion. A study of exocytosis in rat peritoneal mast cells. *J. Cell Biol.* **72**:242.

Leader, D. P. 1979. Protein synthesis on membrane-bound ribosomes. *Trends Biochem. Sci.* **4**:205.

Leblond, C. P., and G. Bennett. 1977. Role of the Golgi apparatus in terminal glycosylation. In *International Cell Biology 1976–1977*, eds. B. R. Brinkley and K. R. Porter, p. 326. New York: Rockefeller University Press.

Ledger, P. W., and M. L. Tanzer. 1984. Monensin—a perturbant of cellular physiology. *Trends Biochem. Sci.* **9**:313.

Lipsky, N. G., and R. E. Pagano. 1985. Intracellular translocation of fluorescent sphingolipids in cultured fibroblasts: Endogenously synthesized sphingomyelin and glucocerebroside analogues pass through the Golgi apparatus en route to the plasma membrane. *J. Cell Biol.* **100**:27.

Meyer, D. I. 1982. The signal hypothesis—a working model. *Trends Biochem. Sci.* **7**:320.

Meyer, D. I., E. Knause, and B. Dobberstein. 1982. Secretory protein translocation across membranes—the role of the "docking protein." *Nature* **297**:647.

Mollenhauer, H. H., and D. J. Morré. 1978. Structural differences contrast higher plant and animal Golgi apparatus. *J. Cell Sci.* **32**:357.

Mollenhauer, H. H., and D. J. Morré. 1980. The Golgi apparatus. In *The Biochemistry of Plants*, vol. 1, ed. N. E. Tolbert. New York: Academic Press.

Moog, F. November 1981. The lining of the small intestine. *Sci. Amer.* **245**:154.

Morré, D. J. 1981. Exocytosis: Flow routes and kinetics as related to membrane recycling. In *International Cell Biology 1980–1981*, ed. H. G. Schweiger, p. 622. New York: Springer-Verlag.

Müller, M., *et al.* 1982. A bacterial secretory protein requires signal recognition particle for translocation across mammalian endoplasmic reticulum. *J. Biol. Chem.* **257**:11860.

Neutra, M., and C. P. Leblond. February 1969. The Golgi apparatus. *Sci. Amer.* **220**:100.

Olden, K., *et al.* 1985. Function of glycoprotein glycans. *Trends Biochem. Sci.* **10**:78.

Orci, L., *et al.* 1984. A clathrin-coated, Golgi-related compartment of the insulin-secreting cell accumulates proinsulin in the presence of monensin. *Cell* **39**:39.

Palade, G. E. 1975. Intracellular aspects of protein synthesis. *Science* **189**:347 (Nobel lecture).

Pastan, I., and M. C. Willingham. 1983. Receptor-mediated endocytosis: Coated pits, receptosomes, and the Golgi. *Trends Biochem. Sci.* **8**:250.

Pearse, B. 1980. Coated vesicles. *Trends Biochem. Sci.* **5**:131.

Pesonen, M., R. Bravo, and K. Simons. 1984. Transcytosis of the G protein of vesicular stomatitis virus after implantation into the apical membrane of Madin-Darby canine kidney cells. II. Involvement of the Golgi complex. *J. Cell Biol.* **99**:803.

Pesonen, M., and K. Simons. 1984. Transcytosis of the G protein of vesicular stomatitis virus after implantation into the apical membrane of Madin-Darby canine kidney cells. I. Involvement of endosomes and lysosomes. *J. Cell Biol.* **99**:796.

Porter, K. R., and J. B. Tucker. March 1981. The ground substance of the living cell. *Sci. Amer.* **244**:56.

Quinn, P., G. Griffiths, and G. Warren. 1983. Dissection of the Golgi complex. II. Density separation of specific Golgi functions in virally infected cells treated with monensin. *J. Cell Biol.* **96**:851.

Redman, C., and D. D. Sabatini. 1966. Vectorial discharge of peptides released by puromycin from attached ribosomes. *Proc. Natl. Acad. Sci. U. S.* **56**:608.

Robbins, A. R., *et al.* 1984. A single mutation in Chinese hamster ovary cells impairs both Golgi and endosomal functions. *J. Cell Biol.* **99**:1296.

Robinson, D. G., and U. Kristen. 1982. Membrane flow via the Golgi apparatus of higher plants. *Internat. Rev. Cytol.* **77**:89.

Robinson, M. 1984. Membrane traffic and the problem of protein secretion. *Nature* **307**:594.

Rothman, J. E. 1981. The Golgi apparatus: Two organelles in tandem. *Science* **213**:1212.

Rothman, J. E., and J. Lenard. 1984. Membrane traffic in animal cells. *Trends Biochem. Sci.* **9**:176.

Rothman, J. E., and H. F. Lodish. 1977. Synchronised transmembrane insertion and glycosylation of a nascent membrane protein. *Nature* **269**:775.

Rothman, J. E., R. L. Miller, and L. J. Urbani. 1984. Intercompartmental transport in the Golgi apparatus is a dissociative process: Facile transfer of membrane protein between two Golgi populations. *J. Cell Biol.* **99**:260.

Sabatini, D. D., G. Kreibich, T. Morimoto, and M. Adesnik. 1982. Mechanisms for the incorporation of proteins in membranes and organelles. *J. Cell Biol.* **92**:1.

Satir, B. October 1975. The final steps in secretion. *Sci. Amer.* **233**:28.

Schatz, G. 1985. Reconstituting membrane flow. *Trends Biochem. Sci.* **10**:95.

Schatz, G., and R. A. Butow. 1983. How are proteins imported into mitochondria? *Cell* **32**:316.

Schmidt, M. F. G. 1982. Acylation of proteins—a new type of modification of membrane glycoproteins. *Trends Biochem. Sci.* **7**:322.

Sharon, N. 1984. Glycoproteins. *Trends Biochem. Sci.* **9**:198.

Siekevitz, P., and P. C. Zamecnik. 1981. Ribosomes and protein synthesis. *J. Cell Biol.* **91**:53s.

Steinman, R. M., I. S. Mellman, W. A. Muller, and Z. A. Cohn. 1983. Endocytosis and the recycling of plasma membrane. *J. Cell Biol.* **96**:1.

Strous, G. J. A. M., *et al.* 1983. Vesicular stomatitis virus glycoprotein, albumin, and transferrin are transported to the cell surface via the same Golgi vesicles. *J. Cell Biol.* **97**:1815.

Tartakoff, A. M. 1982. Simplifying the complex Golgi. *Trends Biochem. Sci.* **7**:174.

Tartakoff, A. M., and P. Vassalli. 1983. Lectin-binding sites as markers of Golgi subcompartments: Proximal-to-distal maturation of oligosaccharides. *J. Cell Biol.* **97**:1243.

Tilney, L. G., J. G. Clain, and M. S. Tilney. 1979. Membrane events in the acrosomal reaction of *Limulus* sperm. *J. Cell Biol.* **81**:229.

Unwin, P. N. T. 1977. Three-dimensional model of membrane-bound ribosomes obtained by electron microscopy. *Nature* **269**:118.

Walter, P., and G. Blobel. 1981. Translocation of proteins across the endoplasmic reticulum. III. Signal recognition protein (SRP) causes signal sequence-dependent and site-specific arrest of chain elongation that is released by microsomal membranes. *J. Cell Biol.* **91**:557.

Walter, P., and G. Blobel. 1982. Signal recognition particle contains a 7S RNA essential for protein translocation across the endoplasmic reticulum. *Nature* **299**:691.

Weigel, P. H., and J. A. Oka. 1984. Recycling of the hepatic asialoglycoprotein receptor in isolated rat hepatocytes. *J. Biol. Chem.* **259**:1150.

Wickner, W. 1980. Assembly of proteins into membranes. *Science* **210**:861.

CHAPTER 8

Lysosomes and Microbodies

Lysosomes and microbodies are cytoplasmic organelles bounded by a single limiting membrane, like the endoplasmic reticulum and Golgi compartments of the eukaryotic cell—and unlike mitochondria, chloroplasts, and the nucleus, all three of which are surrounded by two membranes of different specificities. All the double-membrane organelles have some degree of autonomy and can specify at least some of their own macromolecules. Most important, new nuclei, mitochondria, and chloroplasts can arise only from pre-existing structures like themselves. A cell that has lost its nucleus, mitochondria, or chloroplasts cannot make replacements and will continue without the lost components for the remainder of its lifetime. Single-membrane organelles, by contrast, are derived from other membranes or from newly synthesized precursors that assemble into lysosomes, microbodies, Golgi, or ER. Single-membrane organelles have no autonomy.

In addition to these differences in organelle autonomy, lysosomes and microbodies are packages of proteins made from encoded genetic instructions that are translated at ribosomal sites of synthesis. In this sense they resemble secretion granules, which are also packages of gene products. All these packages of gene products, be they lysosomes, microbodies, or secretion granules, carry out unique and specific activities that are nonoverlapping. We must therefore address the questions of protein sorting into functionally different packages, as well as the questions of organelle formation and function.

Lysosomes

Unlike other organelles, lysosomes were first detected by biochemical evidence and not by microscopic observations. Christian de Duve and colleagues accidentally obtained evidence of the existence of a cytoplasmic structure during their studies with rat liver homogenates of the subcellular distribution of enzymes involved in carbohydrate metabolism.

They had included an assay for *acid phosphatase* activity to serve as a control because this enzyme was known to have no role in carbohydrate metabolism. In 1949 de Duve reported that acid phosphatase activity was higher in tissues that had been isolated in distilled water than in tissues isolated in an osmotically balanced sucrose solution. Enzyme activity was also higher in aged preparations than in freshly isolated materials, and in the aged preparations the acid phosphatase activity was in a soluble fraction unassociated with sedimented particles. These characteristics led de Duve to search for a cytoplasmic particle showing acid phosphatase activity, in which the enzyme was enclosed within a membrane that was sensitive to damage or which could be disrupted and thus release its enzymatic contents. Between 1949, when this preliminary evidence was obtained, and 1955, when the lysosome was first observed by microscopy, a few other digestive enzymes were shown to be associated with acid phosphatase in the same membranous container. The combined methods of biochemistry and electron microscopy continue to shed light on the nature of the lysosome and its participation in cellular activities.

8.1
General Nature of Lysosomes

The **lysosome** is an organelle whose contents of digestive enzymes are surrounded by a single limiting membrane. All the digestive enzymes catalyze hydrolytic reactions and all have an optimum pH of 5.0 for activity; they are all **acid hydrolases**. About 50 different acid hydrolases have been localized in populations of lysosomes, including lipases, proteases, peptidases, nucleases, phosphatases, glycosidases, and sulfatases (Fig. 8.1). Taken together, these enzymes provide cells with the ability to digest all the biologically significant groups of macromolecules. The general hydrolysis reaction catalyzed by acid hydrolases is

$$R_1\text{—}R_2 + H_2O \longrightarrow R_1\text{—}H + R_2\text{—}OH$$

In 1955 Alex Novikoff produced electron micrographs of lysosomes from centrifugate fractions prepared in de Duve's laboratory. The organelles were a heterogeneous collection of large and small vesicles, some with inclusions and others with only an electron-dense granular matrix. The lysosomal identification of such a heterogeneous assemblage was later confirmed in cell-free fractions and in tissues by light and electron microscope **cytochemistry**, by which a precipitated end product of acid phosphatase or another acid hydrolase activity can be visualized within the boundaries of the organelles. One of the earliest cytochemical tests for acid phosphatase activity involved the use of an organic phosphate substrate for enzymatic action and lead hydroxide as a marker of the end product of the reaction. When lysosomal acid phosphatase cleaves the phosphate residue from the substrate, the freed phosphate combines with lead ions of the hydroxide and forms insoluble lead phosphate. The lead precipitate is black in color and is easily visualized within the lysosomes by light or electron microscopy (Fig. 8.2). Control preparations that either lack the substrate or have an

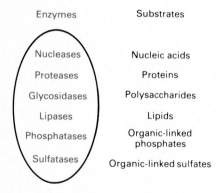

Enzymes	Substrates
Nucleases	Nucleic acids
Proteases	Proteins
Glycosidases	Polysaccharides
Lipases	Lipids
Phosphatases	Organic-linked phosphates
Sulfatases	Organic-linked sulfates

The intact lysosomal membrane is impermeable to enzymes and substrates

FIGURE 8-1
Summary of the general groups of acid hydrolases in lysosomes and the kinds of substrates they digest under appropriate cellular conditions.

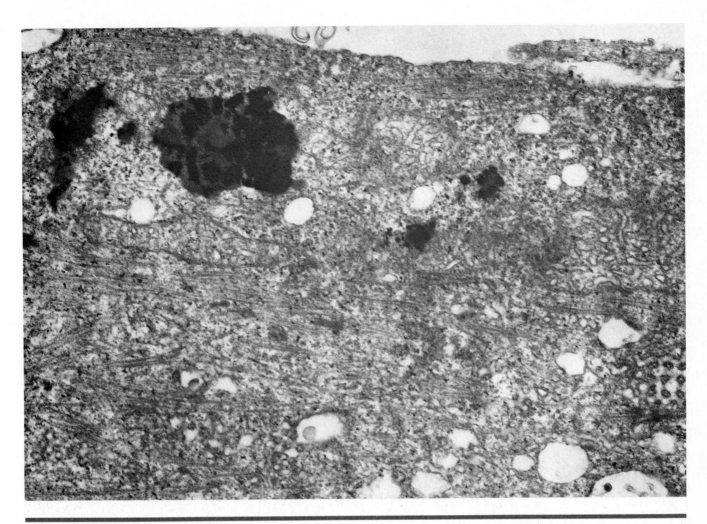

added enzyme inhibitor show no black deposits in the cells. Cytochemistry offers an important approach to the analysis of many kinds of tissues, particularly those that are difficult to analyze biochemically because of low yield or extensive contamination by other membranous elements in centrifugate fractions.

With few exceptions lysosomes occur in virtually all animal cells, as well as in many protists and fungi and a variety of plant cells. Lysosomes range in size from 0.05 μm in diameter to large vesicles that measure several micrometers in diameter. Most of the observed variability in lysosomal size and morphology is due to developmental changes associated with their past or present digestive activities.

8.2

Intracellular Digestion

Newly formed or otherwise virgin lysosomes that have not encountered substrates in the cell are characterized by the presence of latent enzymes. All such lysosomes that have not experienced episodes of digestion are called **primary lysosomes**. Once the primary lysosome has absorbed a substrate or fused with a vesicle containing substrates, its membrane undergoes a change and its enzymes are activated so that the

FIGURE 8-2
Electron micrograph of part of a cultured chick embryonic skeletal muscel cell (myoblast) after a cytochemical assay for acid phosphatase activity. The dense lead precipitate produced by the enzymatically catalyzed reaction is evident in a large lysosome, or digestive vacuole, but is absent from mitochondria and other components of the cell. ×32,000. (Photograph courtesy of J. W. C. Bird, from Bird, J. W. C., *et al.*, 1981, *J. Histochem. Cytochem.* **29**:431, Fig. 2C.)

substrate is digested. Such experienced lysosomes are called **secondary lysosomes**, and they may engage in repeated episodes of digestion after their initial encounter with some organic substrate.

Secondary lysosomes are generally larger than primary lysosomes and they may attain considerable size in some cases, as well as internalized membranes on occasion. Secondary lysosomes are a heterogeneous lot, primarily due to the nature of the substances they have previously encountered, those that they are currently engaged in digesting, and their stage of development during digestion episodes. Among this assortment of secondary lysosomal forms we can include *digestive vacuoles*, which are particularly large structures; *autophagic vacuoles*, in which some part of the cell itself is being digested or has been partially digested; *multivesicular bodies*, in which membranous vesicles are retained after they have been taken into the lysosome; and *residual bodies*, in which the undigested remnants of various substances persist in the organelle for the remainder of its lifetime (Fig. 8.3). All these diverse forms of secondary lysosomes contain active acid hydrolases that can be visualized by cytochemical tests. It was from such cytochemical analysis that we gradually learned the sequences of developmental changes in lysosomes as they carried out their intracellular digestive functions. Lysosomal morphology and contents vary in relation to differences in the stages of digestive activity and the kinds of substances under attack in different organelles in cellular populations. Because lysosomes may be found in any or all of their varied activities and morphology in a tissue, it is understandable that there was initial controversy and confusion about lysosome structure and identification.

FIGURE 8-3
Summary schematic drawing showing the heterogeneous nature of secondary lysosomes in the cell. Primary lysosomes containing latent hydrolases (color) fuse with incoming endocytotic vesicles to form secondary lysosomes. The latent enzymes are activated, and they may digest the substrates completely or only partially. Digestion products may be used in the same cell or be released by exocytosis for use elsewhere in the system. Autophagic vacuoles, multivesicular bodies, residual bodies, and digestive vacuoles are secondary lysosomes with different contents and often are of different sizes.

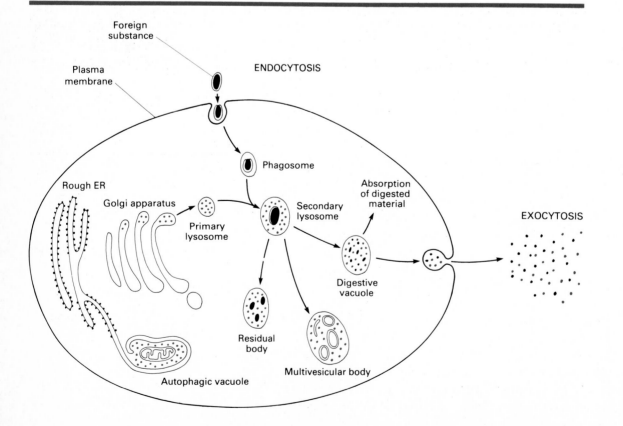

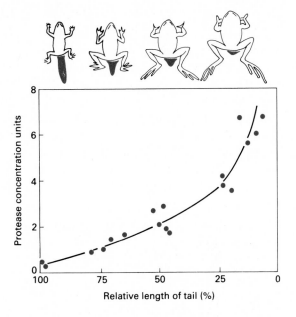

FIGURE 8-4
During metamorphosis of the tadpole to the adult frog, the tail disappears as its constituent cells are digested and the products are absorbed in the developing animal. Tail cell dissolution is caused by lysosomal digestive enzymes, as shown by the corresponding increase in protease activity during metamorphosis.

The processes of intracellular digestion are generally held in control within the lysosome because of the protecting membrane boundary of the organelle. In some cases during normal development or because of some pathological condition, the lysosomal membrane may be damaged or dissolved so that lysosomal enzymes move into the cytoplasm. Self-dissolution occurs, often leading to the death of the cell. In each mammalian ovarian cycle in which fertilization does not occur, lysosomal enzymes enter the cytoplasm and cause the cells of the corpus luteum to degenerate. A new corpus luteum forms after the next ovulation and it will also degenerate in the absence of fertilization. These episodes are normal events of the reproductive cycle in female mammals. In lower animals (such as amphibians) that undergo metamorphosis from an immature to an adult form, lysosomal enzymes are largely responsible for the dissolution of larval tissues as the animal progresses toward adulthood. One particular study reported by Rudolf Weber showed that the activity of lysosomal proteases increased in the tail cells just before tadpole metamorphosis began and continued to increase as the tail cells dissolved and were absorbed in the developing frog (Fig. 8.4).

An interesting example of a specialized lysosome is the **acrosome** that covers the head of an animal spermatozoan. The acrosome is derived from the Golgi apparatus in spermatocytes through the coalescence of a collection of Golgi vesicles. The origin of the acrosome from the Golgi and the acrosomal contents of acid hydrolases, such as *hyaluronidase*, suggest that the acrosome is a giant specialized lysosome uniquely associated with the spermatozoan in many animals (Fig. 8.5). Within seconds after a sperm has attached itself to the outer coat of the egg, the acrosomal and plasma membranes of the sperm fuse together, creating perforations through which the acrosomal contents are dispersed into the surrounding medium. The outer coat of the egg and the follicular cells adhering to it are then digested rather quickly, which allows the sperm to reach and contact the plasma membrane of the egg cell. This process takes about 30 minutes in some mammals. As the sperm and egg

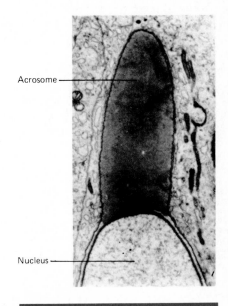

Acrosome

Nucleus

FIGURE 8-5
Electron micrograph of a section through a guinea pig spermatozoan, showing the acrosomal cap filled with dense material, which consists largely of hyaluronidase and other acid hydrolases. Its enzymatic contents and its origin from the Golgi apparatus suggest that the acrosome is a specialized lysosome covering the nucleus in the head of the animal spermatozoan. (Photograph courtesy of D. W. Fawcett.)

plasma membranes fuse, the sperm nucleus becomes surrounded by the egg cytoplasm. Fertilization proceeds as the sperm and egg nuclei approach each other in the cytoplasm, until they fuse to become the new nucleus of the zygote that initiates the next generation.

The egg undergoes a number of almost instantaneous reactions in response to sperm penetration. One of these reactions is disruption of the egg's *cortical granules*, which themselves have enzymatic and staining properties common to lysosomes. After the contents of the cortical granules have been dispersed into the egg cytoplasm, the outer layers of the egg are broken down and a new ("fertilization") membrane is formed. This fertilization membrane is resistant to enzymatic degradation. Cleavages are initiated soon afterward, and the zygote goes on to develop into the multicellular embryo.

In addition to all of the events just described, the specific fusion of a sperm and egg must involve factors that permit the gametes to recognize each other and to initiate joint interactions. Each sex cell is the exclusive target of the other, so that a fusion involves only an egg and a sperm and not two sperm or two eggs. Cell–cell recognition must involve cell surface receptors, and the specificity of membrane fusion almost certainly depends on these receptors and other properties of the cell surfaces of gametes.

Lysosomes are not simply garbage dumps in which unwanted materials are degraded and expelled from the cell, or which dissolve unwanted cells and barriers to fertilization. A number of recent studies have made it increasingly clear that lysosomal digestion plays a role in the regulation of cellular growth and nutrition, as well as in development. The principal source of cholesterol in cells is the lysosome, which hydrolyzes esterified cholesterol in low-density lipoprotein (LDL) particles that have been taken into the cell by receptor-mediated endocytosis (see Section 5.10). Coated vesicles carry LDL particles into the cell and the particles ultimately fuse with lysosomes, whose digestive enzymes then convert cholesterol esters to free cholesterol. Upon being released from the lysosome, free cholesterol is available for the synthesis of new membranes in various parts of the cell. The concentration of a number of hormones is controlled in part by the digestive activity in lysosomes. For example, when insulin binds to cell-surface receptors and the insulin–receptor complexes are internalized in coated vesicles, both the insulin and its receptor molecules are degraded in lysosomes with which the coated vesicles have fused. In this way the hormonal concentration in the extracellular fluid and the insulin receptors on the cell surface are subjected to *down regulation*, by which the cell can respond to changing internal and external conditions that influence sugar metabolism. Lysosomes replenish the pools of metabolites in the cytosol when they digest a variety of macromolecules to sugars, amino acids, nucleotides, and other products that can be reutilized in the synthesis of new macromolecules, once these breakdown products have passed through the lysosomal membrane. Lysosomes, then, are sites of intracellular digestion. Through their digestive activities the organelles interact with other parts of the cell and with a diversity of cellular processes in growth and metabolism.

8.3
Lysosome Formation

The prevailing view today is that new primary lysosomes bud from the individual cisternae of the Golgi apparatus, very much like secretory granules. In cytochemical tests, regions within the cisternae and dilations at the borders of cisternae (as well as unattached vesicles in the vicinity) have been found to contain acid phosphatase. Many of the small vesicles, about 50 nm in diameter, that are associated with the trans-most cisternae of the Golgi stacks appear to be coated. In fact, in the few available favorable sections in which these small vesicles appear to be budding from the Golgi cisternae, the vesicles always appear to be coated (Fig. 8.6). The coating is made of the same clathrin triskelions that characterize coated vesicles which pinch off from the plasma membrane and carry ligands into the cell by receptor-mediated endocytosis (see Fig. 5.37). In view of the small size of the coated and uncoated vesicles and the variety of transport vesicles in the Golgi region, it is extremely difficult to make many specific identifications. However, the generally accepted scheme is that primary lysosomes are derived from coated vesicles that pinch off from the Golgi cisternae and that the clathrin coat is removed after the membranous vesicle has separated from the Golgi apparatus.

The major emphasis in recent studies of lysosome formation is concerned with the packaging of lysosomal hydrolases within the organelle. The problem is part of the general phenomenon of protein sorting, by which different gene products are directed into different membranous packages. By what means are acid hydrolases directed to be packaged in lysosomes at the same Golgi apparatus that also packages secretion granules with quite different contents? The information needed to answer this question has come from studies in several laboratories, but particularly those of Elizabeth Neufeld, William Sly, and Stuart Kornfeld.

With the exception of cathepsin B1, all the lysosomal enzymes are glycoproteins whose sugar residues are mannose, galactose, glucose, and

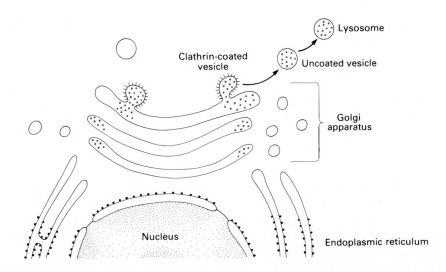

FIGURE 8-6
Schematic drawing showing the prevailing view that primary lysosomes are formed from clathrin-coated vesicles that bud off the trans-most cisternae of the Golgi apparatus. After separation from the Golgi apparatus, the vesicles are uncoated and begin their cellular existence as primary lysosomes.

fucose. Although little is known of the amino acid sequences of lysosomal enzymes, it is most likely that the *N*-linked oligosaccharide chains are added to the protein chain in the rough ER, just like similar glycoproteins with various functions. These molecules should be equipped with signal peptides to facilitate their vectorial discharge into the RER lumen, but confirming evidence for this expectation has thus far been obtained for only one of the acid hydrolases. The precursor glycoproteins are processed along the way or after they have reached the Golgi apparatus from the rough ER sites of synthesis and discharge. From kinetic studies that showed a relatively slow pace of processing of the enzyme precursors, Neufeld suggested that proteolytic cleavages and much of the trimming of sugar residues may be delayed until the enzymes have been lodged in the lysosomes. Perhaps some of these steps are involved in activating lysosomal enzymes through changes that convert the precursors to mature forms of the catalysts. These studies are important, but they do not address the primary question of protein sorting into lysosomes in the Golgi apparatus. Vital evidence in this regard was provided by studies conducted by Sly and Kornfeld.

A unique feature of lysosomal enzymes is the occurrence in their oligosaccharide chains of *phosphorylated mannose* residues. The presence of phosphomannosyls led to a search for specific receptors that recognize these sugars and serve to divert them to membrane domains that will bud off as primary lysosomes from the Golgi apparatus. Glycoproteins that lack phosphomannosyls would be sorted to other Golgi membrane domains marked with other receptors, and the lysosomal enzyme precursors would thereby be separated into their own membranous packages at the Golgi apparatus. Specific receptors for phosphomannosyl residues were identified by Sly and others, and these residues were present in internal cellular membranes for the most part, although a low concentration of the same receptors was also associated with plasma membrane fractions. It thus appeared that acid hydrolases were sorted out as a consequence of the binding of their oligosaccharides, via phosphomannosyls, to specific receptors in Golgi or ER membranes. Strong supporting evidence for these conclusions was provided by Kornfeld's studies of the biochemical pathway involved in mannose phosphorylation—in normal cells and in cultures from patients with inclusion-cell (I-cell) disease (also called mucolipidosis II). In normal cells the acid hydrolases have phosphomannosyl residues and these enzymes occur predominantly in the lysosomes. I-cell cultures, by contrast, secrete most of their lysosomal enzyme precursors into the medium and package little or none in lysosomes. The precursors lack phosphomannosyl residues. These results indicate that enzyme precursors take the secretory pathway rather than being directed at the Golgi into lysosomes because they lack the residues to bind to receptors on those membrane domains destined to bud off as primary lysosomes. In other studies Kornfeld found that I-cells lack the *N*-acetylglucosaminylphosphotransferase that catalyzes the first step in phosphorylating mannose (Fig. 8.7).

Protein sorting into lysosomes at the Golgi thus appears to involve specific biochemical modifications which provide precursor molecules with the capacity to bind to membrane receptors in certain membrane

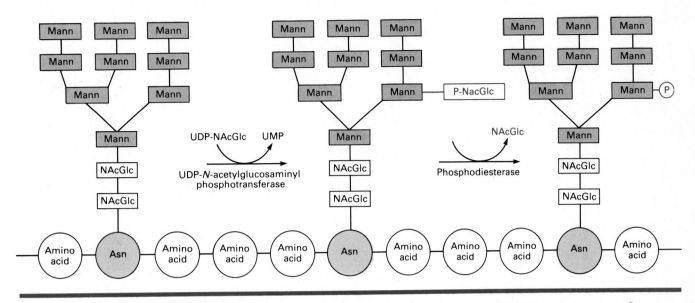

domains that later bud off as primary lysosomes. Protein sorting must be coordinated with other processes that are involved in determining the specificity of different membrane domains. Specific receptors impose uniqueness to different parts of a membrane or to different membranes, but we don't know by what means the different receptors are directed to membranes. In addition to the challenging problems of analyzing the mechanisms of protein sorting into the interior of different functional compartments, we must also address the equally challenging problems of how integral and peripheral membrane proteins are directed to functionally distinctive organelle boundaries.

8.4
Protein Traffic to the Lysosomes

By endocytosis solids and dissolved substances are taken into the cell in a membrane wrapper budded from the plasma membrane. The usual fate of endocytosed vesicles is to fuse with primary or secondary lysosomes, in which the solid or fluid-phase materials are then digested. When fusion occurs with a lysosome, it is usually only the contents and not the membrane of the vesicle that enter the lysosome. On occasion, however, the entire vesicle may be taken into the lysosome, which we believe accounts for the internal membranes seen in multivesicular bodies.

The first evidence showing that incoming materials were directed to the lysosomes was reported in 1964 by Werner Straus. He added the protein *horseradish peroxidase* (an enzyme) to cells and stained the cells afterward with benzidine to locate the peroxidase, and with a naphthol dye to visualize acid phosphatase in lysosomes. The peroxidase protein reacts with benzidine to produce a blue color, and the naphthol dye reacts with acid phosphatase to produce a red color. Straus examined the cells at different times after administering the horseradish peroxidase. Shortly after the peroxidase was added he found blue-stained vesicles in the peripheral cytoplasm and a population of red-stained

FIGURE 8-7
In high-mannose *N*-linked oligosaccharide chains of lysosomal enzyme precursors, phosphorylation of mannose residues occurs in a two-step reaction sequence. In the first catalyzed reaction, a phosphorylated *N*-acetylglucosaminyl residue bonded to a mannose unit as uridine diphospho-*N*-acetylglucosamine (UDP-NAcGlc) is converted to uridine monophosphate (UMP). In the second catalyzed reaction, *N*-acetylglucosamine is released as the sugar unit is converted to a phosphomannosyl residue in the oligosaccharide chain. Mannose phosphorylation is a crucial feature in sorting hydrolase precursors from the Golgi apparatus into lysosomes—rather than sorting the proteins into secretion vesicles for exocytosis, as occurs in patients with I-cell disease.

FIGURE 8-8
Schematic summary of interpretations of time-course experiments in which blue-stained peroxidase protein and red-stained lysosomes were observed by microscopy. The peroxidase (1) entered the cell by endocytosis and was wrapped in membranous vesicles (phagosomes) derived from the plasma membrane, (2) traveled in these vesicles from the peripheral cytoplasm to the perinuclear region, where lysosomes were located, and (3) fused with primary lysosomes to form secondary lysosomes.

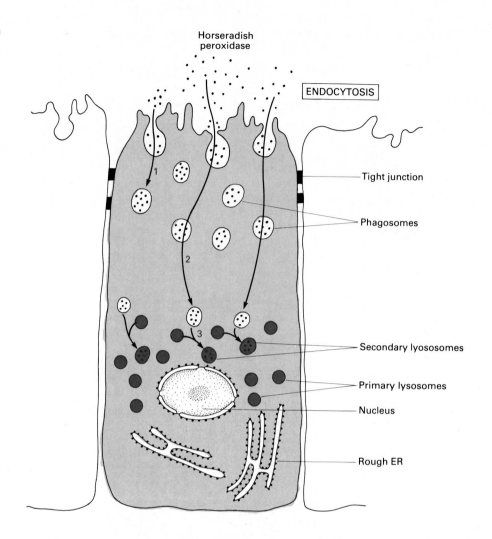

vesicles in the space near the nucleus (perinuclear space). Some time later the blue vesicles were present in the perinuclear space, as were the red vesicles. Still later Straus found purple vesicles in the perinuclear space, which indicated that the blue- and red-stained materials had been fused together and were both present in the same vesicles (Fig. 8.8). Because acid phosphatase identifies lysosomes, the results were interpreted as showing that incoming endocytosed peroxidase had been directed in a vesicular container to the lysosomes, where fusion occurred. Straus called the transport vesicle a *phagosome* and suggested that this structure was one part of the whole system of membranous vesicles and vacuoles that were involved in the uptake and processing of endocytosed material.

Although the evidence is still fragmentary, many investigators consider the phagosome, which is now called by the more general name **endosome**, to be an intermediary vesicle and not to be the primary endocytotic vesicle pinched off from the plasma membrane. Whether both coated and smooth vesicles bud off from the plasma membrane, or only coated vesicles, these primary endocytotic vesicles are taken into the peripheral cytoplasm. Shortly afterward the primary endocytotic vesicles fuse with endosomes, and the endosomes transport the endocytosed substances to the lysosomes. In special situations endosomes may function as storage vacuoles, which we know to be the case for yolk proteins in oocytes. But the endosome is not simply a transport or storage vehicle. In addition to those functions, endosomes sort out the endocytotic vesicle membrane and bound receptors from the contents. The endosomal ligand contents are delivered to the lysosome, and most of the endosomal membrane and bound receptors is recycled to the cell surface where it may be assimilated into the plasma membrane by exocytosis (Fig. 8.9). Membrane recycling from lysosomes as well as from endosomes is believed to take place via exocytosis, although to a lesser degree. Apart from kinetic studies of the recycling of membrane receptors, which have indicated influx and efflux of membrane flow in the cell, we know that membrane recycling must occur in order to explain the constant surface area of the plasma membrane—despite the fact that up to 200% of the plasma membrane area is internalized per hour in many animal cells.

Endosomes possess no distinctive morphological features, so microscopic analysis is conducted by taking advantage of the endosome's

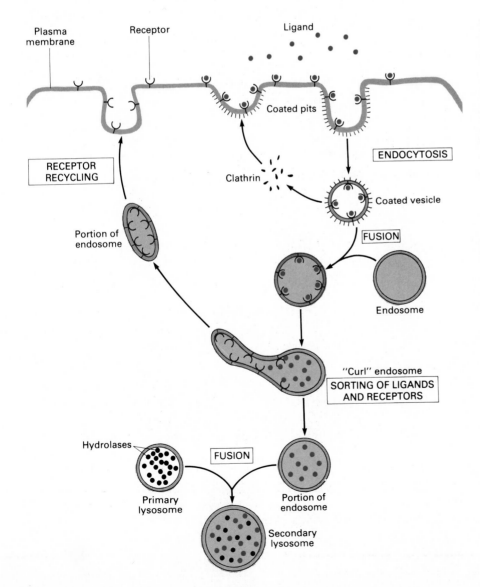

FIGURE 8-9
Schematic summary of the current view of protein sorting and membrane traffic in the cell. Ligands bind to receptors in coated (or uncoated) pits and enter the cell in coated (or uncoated) vesicles that soon fuse with endosomes present in the cytoplasm. Ligands and their receptors are sorted into different membrane domains of the fusion product, whose shape has been altered to a "curl" endosome. The portion of the curl endosome containing ligands fuses with a primary lysosome to form a secondary lysosome, whereas the portion of the curl endosome bearing receptors is recycled to the plasma membrane in exocytotic events. Endosomes thus serve as systems for the sorting of ligands and receptors and as transport vehicles to deliver ligands to the lysosomes and to deliver receptors and membrane to the cell surface.

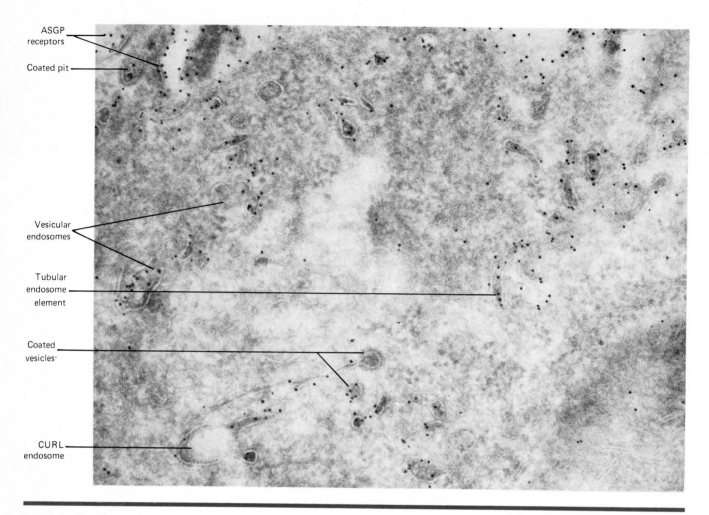

ASGP
receptors

Coated pit

Vesicular
endosomes

Tubular
endosome
element

Coated
vesicles·

CURL
endosome

FIGURE 8-10
Electron micrograph of a rat liver cell
with a variety of vesicular and tubular
elements in the peripheral cytoplasm
near the plasma membrane.
Asialoglycoprotein (ASGP) receptors
were labeled with anti-ASGP receptor
antibodies and were made visible by
complexing with 8-nm gold particles.
Receptors are evident in a coated pit of
the plasma membrane (at upper left)
and in a system of thin anastomosing
tubules that are continuous with coated
vesicles. A curl endosome is evident at
the lower left, and consists of a large
receptor-poor vesicular portion
continuous with receptor-rich tubular
elements. The curl endosome is the
compartment where receptor and
ligand uncouple. ×75,000. (Photograph
courtesy of H. J. Geuze, from Geuze,
H. J., et al., 1983, Cell **32**:277, Fig. 4.
Copyright by M. I. T. Press.)

ability to take in substances that can be suitably labeled. For example,
endosomes may be recognized by the presence of endocytosed horseradish peroxidase that has been stained blue with benzidine, or by
endocytosed ligands coupled with ferritin, colloidal gold, or a fluorescent
marker for visibility. Even though these same endocytosed ligands may
also be present in lysosomes that have acquired the materials by fusions
with endosomes, the two kinds of organelles can be distinguished by the
use of the acid phosphatase cytochemical test. Developmental changes
in endosomes can be studied in cells that have been incubated with
marked ligands at 16° to 20°C. Under these conditions ligands continue
to be endocytosed and transferred to endosomes, but ligand transfer to
lysosomes is blocked, and endosomes accumulate in the incubated cells.
In these cells a population of small endosomes (0.3 to 1.0 μm in
diameter) is found in the peripheral cytoplasm near the plasma membrane; these are new or early endosomes. A heterogeneous population of
spherical vesicles of somewhat larger size, or of tubular aggregates, often
accumulates in the perinuclear space near the Golgi and lysosomes of
the cell. This heterogeneous collection consists of endosomes that have
progressed and undergone some internal changes during their transit
from the peripheral cytoplasm to the cell interior (Fig. 8.10).

8.5
Sorting Out of Receptors in Membrane Recycling _____

It is very likely that membrane recycling mainly involves endosomes and that lysosomes are involved to a much lower degree. Endosomes more than lysosomes are implicated in membrane recycling for several reasons: (1) Plasma membrane proteins and receptors have a relatively long half-life of about 40 hours, which indicates that they are not often exposed to lysosomal enzymes during recycling. (2) The recycling time for certain receptors is very rapid (less than 5 minutes), which contrasts with the relatively slow delivery of substances into lysosomes (20 minutes or more). (3) At 16° to 20°C, receptor-mediated uptake and receptor recycling continue to occur, whereas traffic of endocytosed material to the lysosomes is inhibited. (4) In the case of transferrin–receptor complexes, we know that internalization into endosomes takes place after receptor-mediated endocytosis in coated vesicles and that, after unloading its iron, the transferrin molecules as well as the receptors are returned to the extracellular space without passing through lysosomes. Although most of the known ligands and their receptors are taken into lysosomes, studies of the transferrin–receptor complexes and a few others have made it clear that a direct pathway exists between endosomes and plasma membrane.

Two particular questions can be asked concerning the role of endosomes in protein sorting out: (1) How are ligands and receptors dissociated so that the ligands are transferred to lysosomes, whereas the receptors are recycled back to the cell surface? (2) By what mechanism are the receptors transferred back to the cell surface for reutilization? We have enough evidence to provide at least partial answers to these two questions.

A critical factor known to be usually responsible for dissociation of ligands and receptors is low pH, and we also know that the affinity of many ligands for binding to their receptors is dramatically reduced when the pH is lowered to 5 to 6. Furthermore, agents that raise the pH in endosomes or lysosomes inhibit receptor-mediated endocytosis by preventing the dissociation of ligand–receptor complexes and, accordingly, reducing the supply of receptors for re-use by the cell. From these and other considerations it seems most probable that endosomes provide an acid bath for endocytosed ligand–receptor complexes and thereby encourage their dissociation, at least in those cases in which ligands are known to be discharged from their receptors at pH 5 to 6 (Fig. 8.11).

The low pH in endosomes accounts for a number of other modifications that influence the behavior of internalized proteins and their subsequent passage in the cell. The acid-sensitive regions of the transferrin molecule are at its iron-binding sites and not at its receptor-binding sites. When internalized, the iron-carrying transferrin unloads its iron but remains associated with its receptor. After the iron has been released, both transferrin and its receptor are returned to the cell surface for release and reutilization. The release of iron takes place in the acid interior of the endosome, according to evidence obtained by Jos van Renswoude and his colleagues in their studies of isolated endosome-rich and lysosome-rich centrifugate fractions. The same situation has been

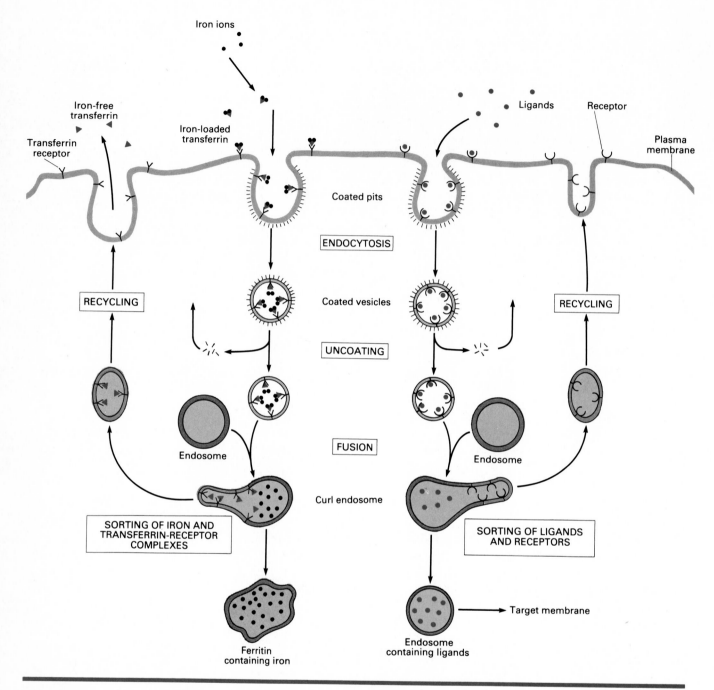

FIGURE 8-11

After receptor-mediated endocytosis in coated pits, protein sorting and receptor recycling processes take place in the acid interior (color) of endosomes. In the case of iron-loaded transferrin and transferrin receptors, the iron is released from transferrin in the acid bath of the curl endosome, and the intact transferrin–receptor conjugates are recycled to the plasma membrane. The iron is picked up by ferritin protein for use in hemoglobin synthesis in erythrocytes. In most cases, however, receptors are sorted from their ligands and each of these components is directed to a particular target membrane of the cell (receptors to the plasma membrane and ligands elsewhere).

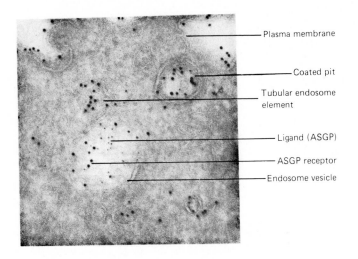

Plasma membrane

Coated pit

Tubular endosome element

Ligand (ASGP)

ASGP receptor

Endosome vesicle

FIGURE 8-12

Electron micrograph of an endosome in the peripheral cytoplasm of a rat liver cell double-labeled with anti-ASGP (asialoglycoprotein ligand) antibodies and anti-ASGP receptor antibodies, and made visible by complexing with 5-nm and 8-nm gold particules, respectively. The smaller ligand particles and the larger receptor particles are both present in the vesicle interior and in a coated pit at the cell surface. However, only receptor is present in the tubular endosome elements. ×75,000. (Photograph courtesy of H. J. Geuze, from Geuze, H. J., et al., 1983, *Cell* **32**:277, Fig. 5B. Copyright by M. I. T. Press.)

shown to characterize a few other ligand–receptor complexes that recycle together back to the cell surface.

Invasive agents such as bacterial toxins and enveloped viruses may enter the cell via an endocytotic pathway. In the case of diphtheria toxin, the low pH of the endosome causes a change in the substance such that the toxin can be inserted into the lipid bilayer of the organelle membrane, thus facilitating the passage of the toxic subunit into the cytosol. In the case of many of the enveloped animal viruses, a conformational change is induced in the viral spike glycoprotein after the viruses have encountered the low pH of the endosome interior. The change in the viral envelope glycoprotein leads to the fusion of the viral membrane envelope and the endosomal membrane. After fusion has occurred, the viral nucleic acid passes through the endosomal membrane into the cytosol, where it influences cellular activities.

Hans Geuze, Harvey Lodish, and their co-workers provided electron microscopical evidence in 1983 that ligands and their receptors were dissociated in the endosome and subsequently sorted into different regions of the organelle. These investigators labeled clathrin, asialoglycoprotein (ASGP) ligand, and ASGP receptor molecules with distinguishable antibody markers that could be visualized by electron microscopy. After administering the labeled substances to rats and allowing time for passage of these molecules to the liver, they prepared hepatic parenchymal cells for electron microscopy and then examined them. Geuze and his co-workers found small endocytosed coated vesicles near the plasma membrane. All three labeled markers were in these vesicles, with clathrin forming the coat and ASGP ligands and receptors associated with the membrane. Endosomes in the peripheral cytoplasm had no clathrin, but the ASGP ligands and receptors were present in the organelle interior, not at its membrane (Fig. 8.12). Other structures in the perinuclear space, which presumably were endosomes in a transitional stage of activity, contained ASGP ligands in a spherical portion of the structures and ASGP receptors in tubular projections at the periphery of the same structures. The ASGP ligands were digested in lysosomes, whereas the receptors were probably recycled back to the cell

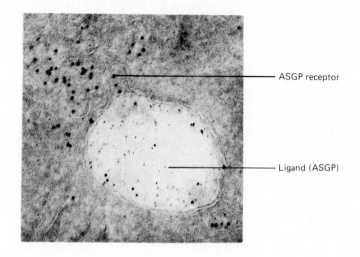

FIGURE 8-13
Electron micrograph of a curl endosome in the cytoplasm of a rat liver cell double-labeled with anti-ASGP antibodies and anti-ASGP receptor antibodies, and made visible by complexing with 5-nm and 8-nm gold particles, respectively. Dissociation of ASGP ligand and receptor has occurred, with free ligand (smaller particles) in the vesicular portion of the organelle, and free receptor (larger particles) in the connected tubular portion of the endosome structure. See also Figs. 8.10 and 8.12. ×75,000. (Photograph courtesy of H. J. Geuze, from Geuze, H. J., *et al.*, 1983, *Cell* **32**:277, Fig. 5D. Copyright by M. I. T. Press.)

surface in tubular transport vesicles (Fig. 8.13). The data are indeed provocative: It would appear that ligands and their receptors are sorted into different parts of the transitional endosomes once dissociation has occurred in the acid interior. Ligands collect in the spherical portion of the endosome, and receptors are somehow directed into the tubular projections. After the tubular components pinch off, they are probably directed back to the cell surface where the receptors are released and become available for re-use in membrane recycling. Denuded of its tubular projections, the remaining spherical vesicle carries its ligand load to the lysosomes and releases the molecules there. The ligands are then digested in the lysosomes, but the vesicle membrane may be either recycled or taken into the lysosomes and digested. A great deal remains to be learned about these processes of uptake, transfer, and sorting of endosomal passenger molecules and about the endosomal membrane domains in functionally different regions of the transitional structures, though a promising start has already been made. In addition, we have yet to discover the mode of endosome formation and the nature of the processes by which endosomes mediate the transport of molecules between the cell surface and the cell interior.

8.6
Lysosomes and Disease

Except for protozoa and mammalian white blood cells, very few kinds of cells regularly engulf materials by phagocytosis; many cell types do so on occasion. White blood cells, or leucocytes, constitute an important element of the body's defenses against infection and disease. Lysosomes develop quite extensively in leucocytes, and these intracellular digestive structures appear to be stored against some future contingency. When a leucocyte engulfs bacteria or some other foreign material, the lysosomes rapidly fuse with the material and digest it. Some kinds of white blood cells die shortly afterward, having expended their stores of lysosomes. Phagocytes in tissues such as liver, lung, and spleen also contain large lysosomes that are important in the digestion of foreign materials.

Some kinds of bacteria, such as the tuberculosis bacterium, and nonliving materials, such as silica particles or asbestos fibers, are not destroyed by lysosomal enzymes. Tuberculosis bacteria have a thick, waxy coat that makes them immune to attack by lysosomal hydrolases. These organisms thus survive leucocyte and other phagocyte incursions and may then be able to initiate infections in the organism.

Studies by Anthony Allison and by other investigators have provided important insights into the relationship of lysosomes to disease processes and other aspects of cellular development. When silicon dioxide particles (such as sand or glass) are inhaled into the lungs, they are taken up by phagocytes in the tissues. These cells die, releasing the silica, which can then be ingested by other phagocytes with the same lethal result. Repeated phagocytic deaths ultimately stimulate fibroblasts to deposit nodules of collagen fibers that decrease lung elasticity and thus impair lung function.

In experiments using tissue culture procedures, Allison showed that ingestion of nontoxic particles such as diamond dust resulted in accumulation of the material in secondary lysosomes, which persisted for a long time and did not damage the cells. Secondary lysosome formation also occurred when silica was phagocytized by the cells in culture, but these lysosomes ruptured rapidly and the released hydrolases caused cell death. When red blood cells are suspended with different kinds of particles of various sizes and shapes, the cells lyse only when silica is present and not in the presence of any nontoxic substances, even if the nontoxic particles are identical to silicon dioxide in size and shape. Apparently the reactivity of silica is caused by the formation of silicic acid on the particle surface and subsequent hydrogen bonding between hydroxyl groups of the acid and receptor molecules of the lysosomal membrane. Membrane disruption can be circumvented if some kinds of protective materials, which react with the silicic acid hydroxyl groups and prevent their attachment to membrane molecules, are added to the system along with silica.

Chemical reactions between silica particles and the lysosomal membrane lead to lysosomal membrane damage and eventual disruption of the organelle. Some factor that is released from the dead phagocytic cells apparently causes the formation of fibrous nodules of connective tissue, because a culture of fibroblasts produces these fibers after material has been added from a culture of phagocytes that had previously been exposed to silica particles. The development of fibrous tissues in the lungs of people who have been exposed to silica particles is one symptom of silicosis, a debilitating and often lethal disease. Silicosis is similar in many ways to asbestosis, a disease associated with the inhalation of asbestos fibers and particles, and to black lung disease, which is associated with the inhalation of coal dust (inorganic carbon).

Recent medical genetics studies have provided molecular and cytological information about certain kinds of "lysosomal storage" diseases, in which some kind of macromolecule remains incompletely processed and accumulates in the body, ultimately leading to the development of a pathological condition. Many of these inherited disorders affect the central nervous system, leading to its deterioration and to premature death.

One well-studied example of a metabolic defect that leads to accumulations of fatty materials in neurons and some other cells is *Tay-Sachs disease*, a condition inherited as an autosomal recessive trait. The disease occurs predominantly among eastern European Jews (Ashkenazim), but some 5–10% of babies with this trait come from Mediterranean Jewish (Sephardim) or from non-Jewish families. Afflicted children begin to show symptoms by the age of 6 to 8 months and they deteriorate rapidly afterward. Death invariably occurs when the child is 2 to 6 years old.

Victims of Tay-Sachs disease do not make the lysosomal hydrolase hexosaminidase A, which is needed to cleave terminal *N*-acetyl-galactosamine residues from the carbohydrate side-chains of the glyco-lipid called ganglioside M2 (G_{M2}) (see Fig. 5.8). The ganglioside is synthesized at normal rates but is degraded very slowly, so the molecules accumulate in lysosomes and the cells develop abnormally. The same pattern of slow degradation due to missing or defective lysosomal hydrolases is characteristic of more than 20 known lysosomal storage diseases, all of which are genetic in origin. Any kind of organic macromolecule may be the source of the particular problem, so that carbohydrates, proteins, or lipids may be improperly processed because a particular hydrolase is missing or defective. In the case of glycogen storage disease type II, which was the first of these diseases to be

FIGURE 8-14
Electron micrograph of a section of liver biopsy from a patient with Hurler disease. The inherited condition is characterized by the lack of a lysosomal hydrolase, which leads to particular bone deformities due to defective processing of proteoglycans of the extracellular matrix. The huge bloated lysosomes are filled with unprocessed proteoglycan molecules. ×7200. (Photograph courtesy of F. Van Hoof.)

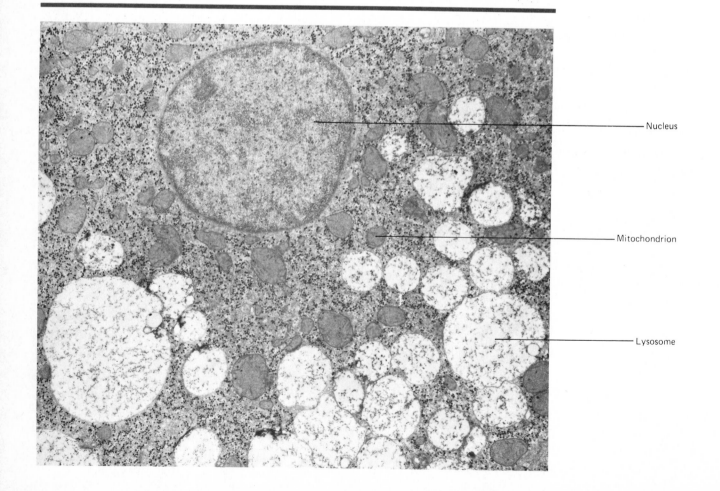

Nucleus

Mitochondrion

Lysosome

described, lysosomal α-glycosidase is missing and large glycogen-filled lysosomes occur in the liver. Many storage diseases involve the accumulation of unprocessed proteoglycans (mucopolysaccharides), which fill the huge, bloated lysosomes in the liver and other organs of individuals afflicted with Hurler disease or Hunter disease, among others (Fig. 8.14).

In some of the lysosomal storage diseases, the enzyme appears to be missing because it is not synthesized or it is synthesized in insufficient amounts. In other cases, as in inclusion-cell (I-cell) disease, the hydrolase precursors are secreted from the cell instead of being directed to the lysosomes because of the deficiency of N-acetylglucosaminyl-phosphotransferase, which catalyzes the first step in phosphorylating mannose residues (see Fig. 8.7). In still other cases it seems likely that the inherited defect involves membrane receptors to which the hydrolases must bind in order to be included in prelysosomal vesicles at the Golgi membranes (Fig. 8.15).

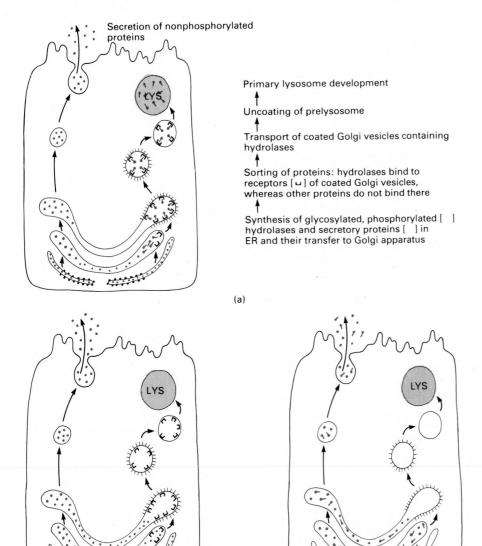

Secretion of nonphosphorylated proteins

Primary lysosome development

↑

Uncoating of prelysosome

↑

Transport of coated Golgi vesicles containing hydrolases

↑

Sorting of proteins: hydrolases bind to receptors [⊔] of coated Golgi vesicles, whereas other proteins do not bind there

Synthesis of glycosylated, phosphorylated [ ] hydrolases and secretory proteins [ ] in ER and their transfer to Golgi apparatus

(a)

(b)   (c)

FIGURE 8-15
Pathway for sorting of acid hydrolases in normal and defective cells. (a) In normal cells, phosphorylated hydrolases are transferred from the rough ER to specific membrane domains in the Golgi apparatus, which are characterized by an external clathrin coat and by receptors bound to the internal surface of the membrane. The Golgi vesicles are uncoated to become prelysosomes, and these mature into functional primary lysosomes. Nonphosphorylated proteins are sorted to uncoated, nonreceptor Golgi membrane domains and thereby enter the secretory pathway. (b) Nonphosphorylated hydrolases enter the secretory pathway rather than the lysosomal pathway because they cannot bind to membrane receptors in coated Golgi regions. (c) Phosphorylated hydrolases enter the secretory pathway if receptors are defective or lacking in coated membrane domains of the Golgi apparatus. The situations shown in parts (b) and (c) are due to inherited defects that involve processing and sorting of lysosomal hydrolases or their precursor forms.

Microbodies

In 1954 Johannes Rhodin described small ovoid organelles, about 0.5 μm in diameter, in mouse kidney tissue. The organelles had a granular matrix bounded by a single membrane, and because of their nondescript nature, Rhodin gave them the vague name **microbodies**. Microbodies were soon found in rat liver cells, and for about ten years, studies continued to focus on mammalian liver and kidney tissues, using biochemical and biophysical analyses as well as electron microscopy. We now know that microbodies are ubiquitous eukaryotic organelles, which occur in all the different kingdoms of nucleated organisms. They are absent in prokaryotes.

One of the amazing features of microbodies is the remarkably varied repertory of enzymes in different species and tissues and in the same kinds of cells in different developmental or physiological states. This degree of variety is totally unknown for any other kind of organelle. In the past 20 years about 40 different enzymes have been localized in microbodies, although never in the same organelle or even in the same tissue. The bewildering diversity of microbody reactions has created some difficulties in developing a uniform nomenclature, let alone a uniform concept of microbody functions and contributions to cellular activities. There is even some doubt about whether all organelles with the same nondescript size and appearance should be called microbodies if they have exceptional metabolic activities or lack specific enzymes that characterize virtually all other organelles of the same physical description. Of course, it is this incredible diversity that makes the microbody an interesting system to study by all available means.

8.7
Microbody Morphology and Metabolism

Typical microbodies are about 0.5 μm in diameter, but they range in size from 0.2 to 1.7 μm. Microbodies may be spherical, ovoid, or dumbbell-shaped, and they may or may not be intimately associated with tubular components of the endoplasmic reticulum, though they are always near ER membranes. Microbodies in many kinds of tissues have a homogenous granular matrix, whereas in some tissues there is a distinct crystalline or fibrous core of dense material in every microbody (Fig. 8.16). Considerable effort was devoted to identifying the nature of the core material in animal microbodies, and it was found to consist of crystallized *urate oxidase*, an enzyme that catalyzes uric acid oxidation during purine degradation. Interest in these inclusions declined by the late 1960s, but it later enjoyed a minor revival when plant microbodies were discovered to have a variety of inclusions, some of which contained urate oxidase. The significance of these microbody inclusions still remains to be determined, but they no longer hold much interest.

Microbodies are often found in clusters rather than dispersed throughout the cell. Three-dimensional reconstructions from serially sectioned cells examined by electron microscopy, however, suggest that a

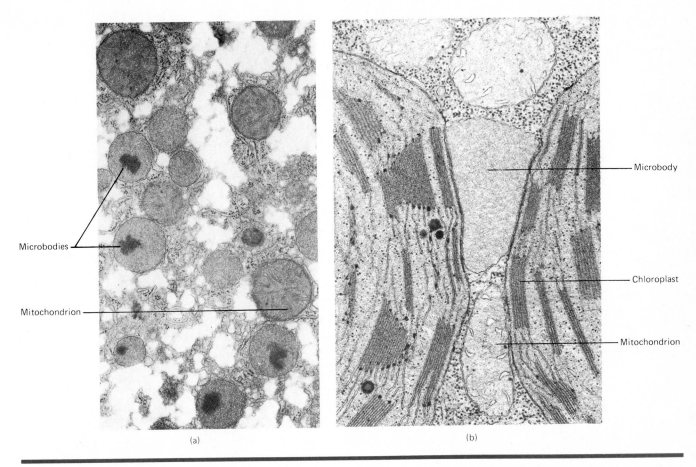

(a)   (b)

FIGURE 8-16

Electron micrographs of microbodies. (a) Section of rat liver cell showing the core inclusion typical of microbodies in this tissue; the inclusion consists of crystallized urate oxidase. ×20,250. (Photograph courtesy of M. Federman.) (b) Core inclusions are not characteristic of microbodies in leaf mesophyll cells, although fine fibrils of some unknown substance are often present in the organelle. Note the single limiting membrane of the microbody and the double-membrane envelopes of the chloroplast and mitochondria in this tobacco leaf cell. × 50,000. (Photograph courtesy of E. H. Newcomb and S. E. Frederick.)

single microbody may actually be a relatively large, irregularly shaped organelle rather than an individual in a cluster of small bodies. What appears to be a cluster of separate organelles in one section may actually be a cross-sectional view of some knobby parts of a single microbody (Fig. 8.17).

A major breakthrough in the characterization of microbodies came from the biochemical and biophysical studies of centrifugate fractions that were under way in Christian de Duve's laboratory. During studies of lysosomes and their unique acid hydrolase contents in rat liver, de Duve and co-workers found that urate oxidase activity was localized in a particle that could be separated from lysosomes and other organelles by equilibrium density gradient centrifugation. In the standard fractionation procedures it was difficult to separate lysosomes from the particles with urate oxidase activity, but they were assumed to be different organelles because urate oxidase remained in the particles after certain treatments that damaged lysosomal membranes and caused hydrolases to be redistributed into cytosolic fractions. Reasonably good separation of intact lysosomes and intact particles containing urate oxidase was later achieved by perfusing a mild detergent into rats about two days before they were sacrificed for study. The detergent accumulated in lysosomes and greatly reduced their density, so that lysosomes and the new particles were cleanly separated in different regions of the density

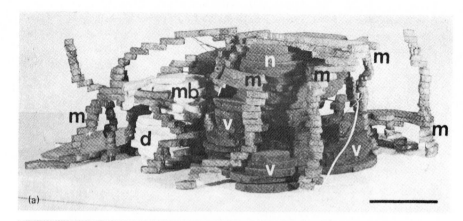

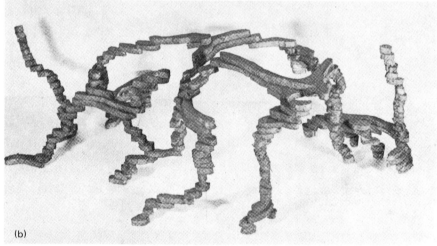

FIGURE 8-17

Three-dimensional models of subcellular structures reconstructed from electron micrographs of a series of 21 consecutive sections through part of the unicellular green alga *Chlorella fusca*. (a) A single mitochondrion (m), a single microbody (mb), a Golgi dictyosome (d), and the nucleus (n) are shown here; chloroplasts, endoplasmic reticulum, and other structures have been omitted for greater clarity. (b) The mitochondrion from (a) is shown here in isolation, for greater clarity. Each piece of the model corresponds to one membrane-bounded profile seen in each consecutive cell section of the electron micrograph series. (From Atkinson, A. W., Jr., P. C. L. John, and B. E. S. Gunning, 1974, *Protoplasma* **81**:77, Figs. 17 and 18. Copyright by Springer-Verlag.)

gradient. Lysosomes settled at equilibrium in regions of lower density; the new particles settled in regions of higher density (Fig. 8.18).

Once the new particles were well isolated, it was possible to determine their morphology and to search for other enzyme activities in the same organelles that contained urate oxidase, which de Duve and other workers proceeded to do. From his studies de Duve showed that the new particles with urate oxidase activity were morphologically identifiable as microbodies and that catalase and a number of other enzymes were present along with urate oxidase in the same microbodies. As more information was provided in several laboratories, it appeared that microbodies were enzymatically variable but that each species and tissue that was analyzed had a common metabolic feature—namely, one or more *oxidases* that reduced O_2 to H_2O_2 as they oxidized a particular substrate, and **catalase** that thereupon reduced H_2O_2 to H_2O (Fig. 8.19). In view of the central feature involving *peroxide production and disposal*, in 1965 de Duve proposed the name **peroxisome** for any microbodylike organelle with peroxide-producing oxidase(s) and peroxide-destroying catalase. As new and diverse kinds of microbodylike organelles were discovered, the term *peroxisome* was reserved for certain of these organelles; new terms were proposed for others, as we will see later.

Another important development in the methodology for microbody studies was the introduction of a cytochemical test for catalase

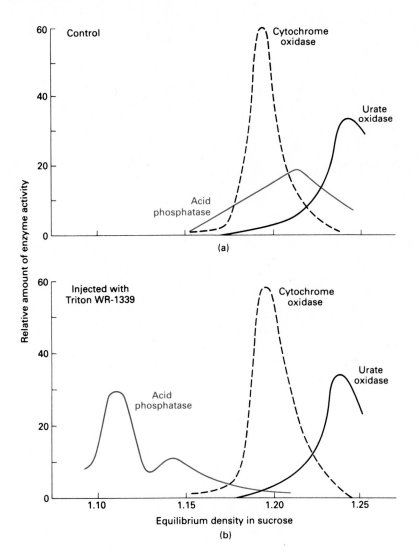

FIGURE 8-18
Separation of organelle fractions from rat liver by centrifugation of cell-free homogenates in sucrose density gradients. (a) In preparations from rats that have not been injected with detergent, the lysosome fraction (indicated by acid phosphatase activity) overlaps the mitochondrial fraction (cytochrome oxidase activity marker) and the microbody fraction (urate oxidase activity marker). (b) Rats perfused with the detergent Triton WR-1339 two days before sacrifice yielded well-separated fractions of all three kinds of organelles. The detergent accumulated in lysosomes and thereby reduced their density, so that the lysosome fraction settled in a much lighter region of the gradient than either mitochondria or microbodies.

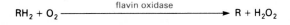

FIGURE 8-19
Production and disposal of hydrogen peroxide in microbodies. (a) In the first of the two general reactions, hydrogen peroxide is produced as the reduction product of oxygen when any one of a number of substrates is oxidized by a flavin-containing oxidase. In the second reaction, hydrogen peroxide is converted by catalase to water and oxygen. (b) A common flavin oxidase in microbodies is glycolate oxidase, which oxidizes glycolate to glyoxylate and reduces oxygen to hydrogen peroxide. Catalase disposal of the peroxide occurs in the second reaction of the sequence.

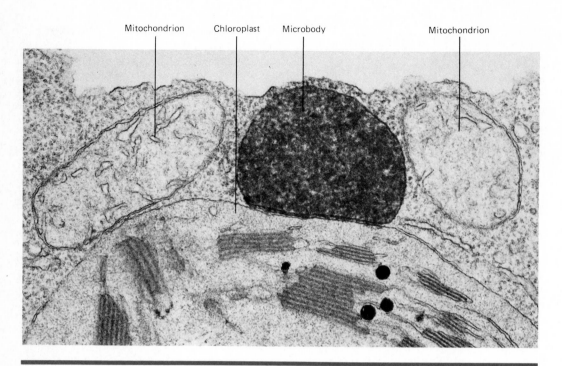

Mitochondrion   Chloroplast   Microbody   Mitochondrion

FIGURE 8-20
Electron micrograph of part of a tobacco leaf mesophyll cell after the diaminobenzidene (DAB) cytochemical test for catalase activity. The dense product (hence, the enzyme itself) is uniquely localized in the microbody. ×31,000. (Photograph courtesy of E. H. Newcomb, from Frederick, S. E., *et al.*, 1975, *Protoplasma* **84**: 1–29, Fig. 5.)

localization in cells and tissues observed by light or electron microscopy. In 1968 Alex Novikoff and Sidney Goldfischer introduced a modified *diaminobenzidine* (DAB) staining test that produced an opaque deposit in catalase-active sites (Fig. 8.20). The mechanism of DAB action is still unclear, but the test is unambiguous, particularly when comparisons are made with cell and tissue sections that have been incubated with the catalase inhibitor aminotriazole as a control. The cytochemical test is invaluable for the many kinds of cells and tissues that cannot be analyzed by biochemical methods because of extensive damage to microbodies during preparations for centrifugation or because of contamination by various other subcellular components. The microscopic localization of catalase within microbodylike organelles is widely accepted as evidence of the occurrence and identification of these structures in eukaryotic organisms. Detailed analyses of the enzymes that may be present in microbodies, however, are absolutely dependent on the isolation by centrifugation of a reasonably good microbody-rich fraction and on subsequent assays of enzyme activities on aliquots of this fraction. Once a centrifugate fraction has been found to have catalase activity, it can be presumed to be enriched in microbodies, and a search may be initiated for additional enzymes. Microbodies would not be confused with lysosomal fractions, marked by acid phosphatase activity; with mitochondrial fractions, marked by cytochrome oxidase activity; or with other subcellular fractions that possess unique markers by which they can be identified (Fig. 8.21).

8.8
Peroxisomes and Glyoxysomes

When systems other than mammalian liver and kidney were studied, beginning in the late 1960s, peroxisomes were found in algae, fungi,

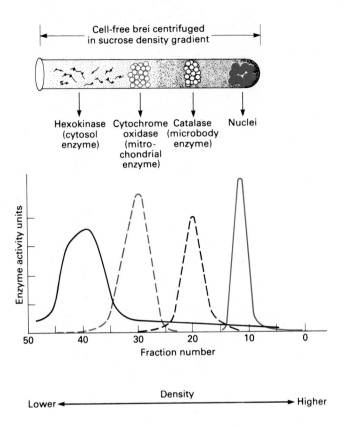

FIGURE 8-21
Different subcellular fractions separated by centrifugation in sucrose density gradients can be identified by some unique feature of each component. Once an enzyme or particular macromolecule is located uniquely or predominantly in one part of the cell (such as cytochrome oxidase only in mitochondria or DNA in nuclei), assays can be carried out to characterize various other features of each unequivocally identified cellular compartment.

protists, and cells of higher plants and a variety of animal tissues. The organelles could be identified by the DAB cytochemical test for catalase activity and by enzyme activity assays of centrifugate fractions in many species. In each case the analysis of isolated peroxisomes revealed the occurrence of catalase and one or more peroxide-producing oxidases. These oxidases all possessed a flavin cofactor bonded to the protein portion of the enzyme and thus were examples of a *flavin oxidase* that produced peroxide, which was then destroyed by catalase. Different flavin oxidases were identified according to the particular organic substrate on which they acted. For example, urate oxidase oxidized uric acid, and glycolate oxidase oxidized glycolic acid (glycolate). In fact, although many kinds of cells lacked urate oxidase (including mammalian kidney cells such as those studied in 1954 by Rhodin), virtually all the cells studied seemed to exhibit glycolate oxidase activity. The peroxisome concept proposed by de Duve thus served as a fruitful basis for an expanded set of studies and of searches for the organelle.

By 1968, however, many other enzymes were found in peroxisomes in addition to the basic flavin-oxidase–catalase system. In particular, all or some of the enzymes of the glyoxylate cycle were found in peroxisomes in plant seedlings, protozoa, and fungi. The **glyoxylate cycle** is a variation of the Krebs cycle in mitochondrial respiration, and three of the five glyoxylate cycle enzymes catalyze the same reactions as their three equivalents in the Krebs cycle. *Aconitase* converts citrate to isocitrate, *malate dehydrogenase* oxidizes malate to oxaloacetate, and *citrate synthase* catalyzes the condensation of acetyl coenzyme A (CoA) with oxaloacetate to form citrate. The two unique enzymes of the glyoxylate cycle are **isocitrate lyase**, which splits 6-carbon isocitrate to 4-carbon succinate and 2-carbon glyoxylate, and **malate synthase**, which catalyzes the condensation of glyoxylate with acetyl CoA to form malate (Fig. 8.22; see also Fig. 9.10). The great interest in the glyoxylate cycle (first discovered by Hans Kornberg and Sir Hans Krebs in bacteria that could use acetate as their only source of carbon and energy for growth) was the knowledge that the cycle functioned primarily in the pathway of **gluconeogenesis**, in which fats are converted to carbohydrates.

Harry Beevers initiated a search for glyoxylate cycle enzymes in castor bean microbodies, because the stored fats in castor bean seeds were known to be converted to carbohydrates during seed germination and to sustain the growing seedling until its leaves expanded and it began to photosynthesize. Beevers and co-workers found all five enzymes of the glyoxylate cycle in the same microbody fraction that contained glycolate oxidase and catalase. Because the glyoxylate cycle in gluconeogenesis was of greater functional importance than peroxide disposal in these organelles, Beevers called them **glyoxysomes** rather than peroxisomes.

Beevers and co-workers continued to analyze relatively pure preparations of glyoxysomes that could be cleanly separated from mitochon-

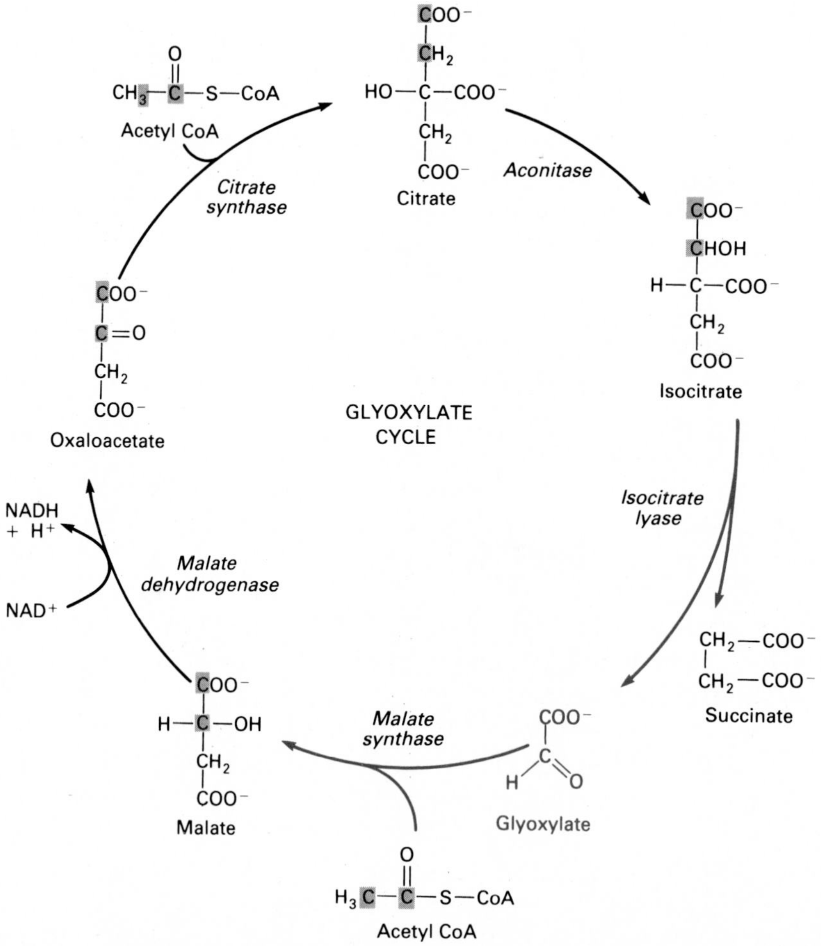

FIGURE 8-22
Three of the five reactions of the glyoxylate cycle are catalyzed by isozymes of the same enzymes that are active in the mitochondrial Krebs cycle, but two of the five enzymes are unique to the glyoxylate cycle (malate synthase and isocitrate lyase). Carbons from acetyl CoA (color) in the first condensation reaction end up in glyoxylate, and carbons from acetyl CoA (color) of the second condensation reaction regenerate the four-carbon compounds that initiate a new cycle.

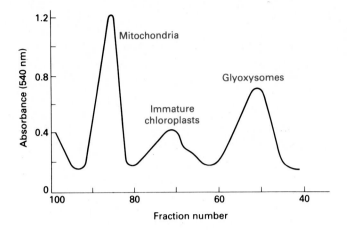

FIGURE 8-23
Sucrose density gradient centrifugation of castor bean endosperm tissue yields glyoxysomes that are well separated from mitochondria and immature chloroplasts, without special pretreatments of the cells. The relatively pure fraction of glyoxysomes can be studied by a variety of *in vitro* assays to determine the enzymatic repertory of these organelles in fatty seeds and seedlings.

dria and proplastids (immature chloroplasts) by centrifugation in sucrose density gradients (Fig. 8.23). The glyoxysomes were morphologically identical to microbodies of other species, but they proved quite unusual in their enzymatic contents. The glyoxylate cycle requires an input of acetyl CoA units, so Beevers looked for enzymes of the fatty acid β-oxidation cycle in which fatty acids are rendered to two-carbon acetyl CoA products (Fig. 8.24). These enzymes are located in mitochondria in other kinds of cells, but the entire β-oxidation cycle is in glyoxysomes in fatty seeds and germinating seedlings. Stored fats are hydrolyzed to fatty acids in the cytosol of all cells, but the fatty acids enter the glyoxysomes instead of mitochondria in fatty seeds and seedlings. The acetyl CoA is thus funneled directly into the glyoxylate cycle in glyoxysomes, where the products and intermediates of the cycle can be utilized for growth rather than oxidized in a mitochondrial respiratory pathway. Through glyoxysomal activities in conjunction with cytosolic and mitochondrial metabolism, stored fats are quantitatively converted to sugars and considerable energy is released for seedling growth (Fig. 8.25). In these gluconeogenic sequences, therefore, growing seedlings receive energy and the carbon they need to synthesize all the molecules and structures of the developing plant. Glyoxysomes have been found in germinating fatty seeds from various plants, including peanut, cucumber, and watermelon, as well as castor bean. The organelle activities first become evident shortly after seed germination begins and they reach a peak of activity within a few days. The organelle activities decline shortly afterward and, by the tenth or eleventh day, no trace remains of glyoxysomes or their unique enzymatic activities. The microbody population that is present in the leaves of older seedlings and mature plants is totally different in its enzymatic repertory, as we shall soon see.

Although all five enzymes of the glyoxylate cycle have been found only in germinating fatty seeds and seedlings, the microbodies of many protists, fungi, and cells of lower plants and animals contain the two unique enzymes of the cycle, malate synthase and isocitrate lyase. In these cases the two enzymes participate in a *glyoxylate bypass* sequence by which metabolites can be synthesized from acetyl CoA and distributed into biosynthetic or energy-yielding pathways in other parts of the cell.

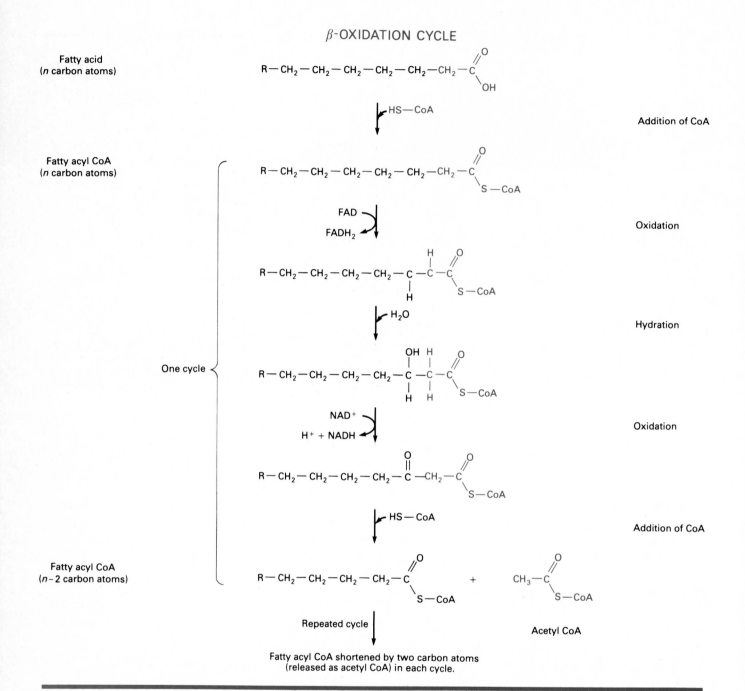

FIGURE 8-24

In the fatty acid β-oxidation cycle, a hydrocarbon chain undergoes a series of changes in reactions that lead to the removal of two carbon residues (color) at the carboxy terminus of the molecule and their release as acetyl CoA (color). The shortened hydrocarbon undergoes repeated cycles, in each of which two carbons are removed and processed to acetyl CoA, until the entire fatty acid has been converted to acetyl CoA products. The β-oxidation cycle typically occurs in mitochondria, but in fatty seeds and seedlings the cycle operates in glyoxysomes instead. The acetyl CoA products are utilized directly in glyoxylate cycle reactions in glyoxysomal metabolism.

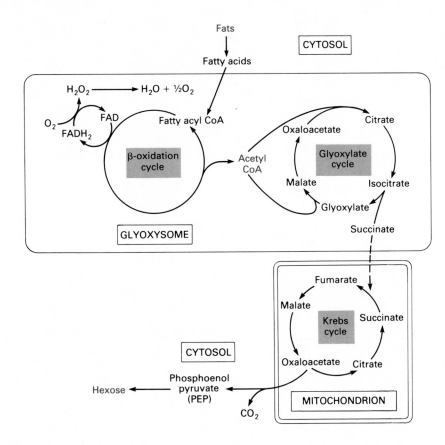

FIGURE 8-25
Interactions among compartmented metabolic pathways in castor bean endosperm cells. Fats are digested to to fatty acids that then enter the glyoxysome and undergo β-oxidation to acetyl CoA units. These units in turn are shunted to the glyoxylate cycle within the same organelles. Succinate produced during glyoxylate cycle reactions is transferred to the mitochondrion, where it is converted to oxaloacetate during Krebs cycle oxidations. Oxaloacetate leaves the mitochondrion and is converted in the cytosol to sugars in a reverse glycolysis sequence. This pattern of gluconeogenic conversion of fats to sugars is a major feature of glyoxysome metabolism during castor bean seedling germination and growth. Note that reactions associated with the β-oxidation cycle lead to the production of H_2O_2, which is then disposed of by catalase activity. These latter reactions are typical of virtually all microbodies.

Malate and succinate are the products of the glyoxlate bypass reactions, and both molecules provide an entry into biosynthetic pathways as well as the energy-yielding pathway of mitochondrial respiration (Fig. 8.26). The bypass is particularly important for cells in limiting growth conditions, such as those in which energy-poor acetate, methanol, or similar substances are the only nutrients available. With marginally useful nutrients, cells do not obtain an adequate supply of intermediates to sustain growth and the vital energy-yielding activities of mitochondrial respiration. By replenishing the supply of malate and succinate for the Krebs cycle, microbodies perform an **anaplerotic function**; that is, they supply or replenish essential substances for respiration and for certain gluconeogenic sequences whereby carbohydrates can be pro-

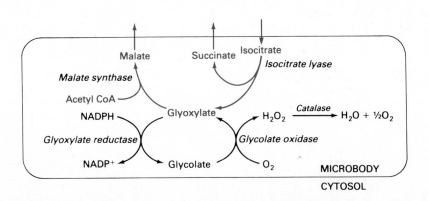

FIGURE 8-26
Reactions of the glyoxylate bypass (color) in yeast microbodies serve as an anaplerotic pathway to replenish malate and succinate for cell metabolism. Other reactions involving glyoxylate also occur in these organelles, including the expected microbody flavin (glycolate)-oxidase–catalase reaction sequence.

FIGURE 8-27

A general summary of some glu-coneogenic sequences leading to carbohydrate production. Amino acids may serve as precursors by media-tion of pyruvate or by Krebs cycle intermediates to form oxaloacetate. Or, pyruvate may be formed from lactic acid and other compounds and then be carboxylated to form oxaloacetate. Other pathways exist, such as conver-sion of fats to sugars through acetyl CoA formation and subsequent re-actions in the glyoxylate cycle or the Krebs cycle.

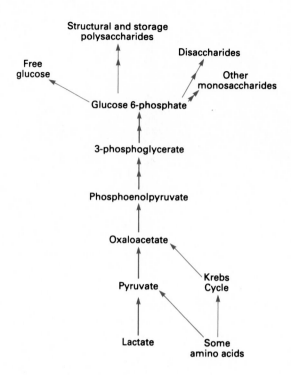

duced (Fig. 8.27). Whether microbodies with both the flavin-oxidase–catalase sequence and the glyoxylate cycle or bypass sequence should be called peroxisomes or glyoxysomes remains a controversial matter more than fifteen years after the new term was introduced by Beevers.

8.9
Leaf Peroxisomes, Hydrogenosomes, and Glycosomes _____

The variety of microbodies has no comparison among eukaryotic or-ganelles. In leaves of higher plants the microbodies are morphologically identical to those in other organisms, and a conventional flavin-oxidase–catalase sequence indicates that the microbodies are peroxisomes. Glyoxylate cycle and bypass enzymes are absent, as they are in vertebrate animal cells, so there is no confusion about the nomenclature. However, leaf peroxisomes have unique enzymes that are intimately related to reaction sequences and functions in neighboring chloroplasts and to mitochondria in the same cells. In fact, the close association of all three kinds of organelles is evident in electron micrographs as well as in their biochemical interactions (see Fig. 8.16b). Hydrogenosomes and glycosomes are microbodylike organelles in certain parasitic protozoa, and they have enzymes found in no other microbodies. However, because these organelles lack the basic flavin-oxidase–catalase se-quence, some doubt exists about their true identification despite their microbodylike morphology.

Under conditions such as low CO_2 levels, green leaf cells begin to consume oxygen and release carbon dioxide in the process of **photo-respiration**. Unlike photosynthesis, in which chemical energy is con-verted from light energy and used to reduce CO_2 in the manufacture of high-energy carbohydrates, photorespiration is an energy-wasting process. In photorespiration, energy is diverted from the photosynthetic pathway to the production of glycolate in the chloroplast, where it serves no useful function. Some of the glycolate is transferred to peroxisomes, where a series of coordinated reactions involving mitochondria and chloroplasts allows the cell to recover useful carbohydrate intermediates for continued growth despite the absence of meaningful photosynthetic activity.

The following picture has emerged from the biochemical studies of N. Edward Tolbert and co-workers and the electron microscopic information provided by Eldon Newcomb and his associates. Glycolate is transferred from photorespiring chloroplasts to peroxisomes, where it is oxidized to glyoxylate and the glyoxylate is converted to the amino acid glycine by the catalytic action of a *transaminase* enzyme. These glycines and others in the cytosol are transferred to mitochondria, where two glycines are transformed oxidatively to the amino acid serine and CO_2. Serine moves from mitochondria into peroxisomes, where it is eventually converted to glyceric acid (glycerate). After glycerate is phosphorylated to phosphoglycerate, it can be channeled into pathways by which phosphorylated sugars are made in the chloroplasts or in the cytosol (Fig. 8.28). In this way plants whose photosynthetic activities are minimal or inhibited can still produce metabolites and derive energy for growth. Leaf peroxisomes also contain enzymes that catalyze reactions that produce other essential amino acids as well as oxaloacetate and other intermediates in gluconeogenesis and in Krebs cycle activities. Green leaf cells thus offer a stunning example of intracellular coordination among different organelles, which provides the capacity for cellular recovery from harmful circumstances.

Hydrogenosomes are microbodylike in morphology but not in their enzymatic activities. These organelles are found in trichomonatids, which are parasitic flagellated protozoa that inhabit and infect

FIGURE 8-28
Coordination among compartments in the leaf cell. Glycolate, which is manufactured in excess in chloroplasts of photorespiring leaves, is transferred to the microbody where it is processed to the amino acid glycine. Some glycine is converted to the amino acid serine within the mitochondrion, and some serine, in turn, is transferred back into the microbody. Various metabolic intermediates are produced in different enzyme-catalyzed reactions within the microbody, but glycerate may be phosphorylated and enter the chloroplast as 3-phosphoglycerate. In this form, it is one of the critical intermediates of the photosynthetic dark reactions, through which sugars are manufactured. The circuitous metabolic route "salvages" some of the "waste" glycolate formed during photorespiration and allows some sugar production, despite low-efficiency photosynthesis under those conditions. Note that during the conversion of glycolate to glyoxylate in the microbody there is H_2O_2 production (by flavin oxidase activity) and H_2O_2 disposal (by catalase) in typical microbody reactions. Reactions are shown by solid arrows, and transfers across the membrane by dashed arrows.

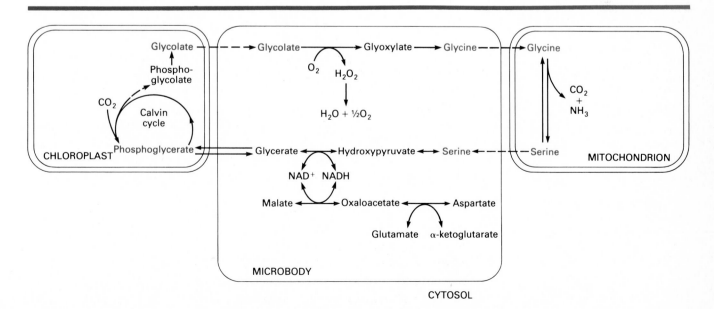

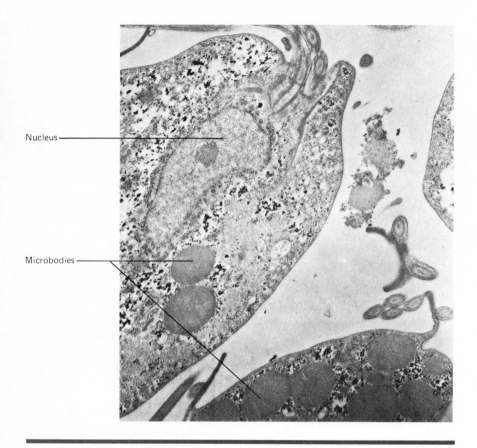

Nucleus —

Microbodies —

FIGURE 8-29
Electron micrograph of the trichomonatid *Pentatrichomonas*. The cells
contain hydrogenosomes, which
resemble microbodies morphologically
but differ in their enzymatic activities. Respiratory reactions, including
coupled ATP synthesis, take place in
hydrogenosomes in these organisms,
which have no mitochondria. ×25,000.
(Photograph courtesy of C. F. T.
Mattern and B. M. Honigberg.)

the mammalian urogenital tract (Fig. 8.29). The protozoa have no
mitochondria, but they can respire actively in the presence of O_2 by
oxidizing pyruvate to acetate and CO_2. The transfer of electrons from
acetate is toward O_2 and the processes are coupled to ATP synthesis just
as they are in conventional mitochondria, except that they occur in the
microbodylike organelles in these parasites. Under anaerobic conditions, electrons are transferred to protons (H^+) instead and hydrogen
gas (H_2) is formed. Whether the trichomonatids are under aerobic or
anaerobic conditions, therefore, their microbodylike organelles perform
totally different functions when compared with other organisms. In
addition, the flavin-oxidase–catalase pathway is active in the cytosol
and not in the hydrogenosomes. Is the hydrogenosome a unique
organelle because of its unique metabolism, or is it a microbody because
of its morphology? A controversy exists because some investigators
consider the hydrogenosome to be a unique and different organelle,
whereas others call it a microbody.

The situation is somewhat similar for glycosomes. **Glycosomes**
were discovered by Fred Opperdoes to be microbodylike in morphology
but unique in their biochemical reactions and enzymes. Glycosomes are
present in trypanosomes, which are flagellated protozoan blood parasites that are responsible for various human diseases, including African
sleeping sickness, Chagas’ disease of Latin America, and leishmaniasis
diseases in various parts of the world. A major function of the glycosome
involves the breakdown of glucose to smaller carbon compounds via a
large portion of the chain of reactions in glycolysis—a process known to

occur only in the cytosol of other organisms (see Fig. 3.20). Under aerobic conditions, glycosomes collaborate with mitochondria in supplying the energy needs of the cells in which they are found. Glycosomal metabolism can furnish *all* the energy needs of the cells, however, if the mitochondrial pathway is blocked. Glycosomes are thus quite different from the great majority of microbody types in eukaryotes. Is the glycosome a unique organelle or only another variant functional form of the ubiquitous microbody? As with hydrogenosomes, the answer is a matter of controversy.

The glycolytic enzymes in trypanosomal glycosomes are physico-chemically different from their equivalents in the cytosol of host cells. Different properties have been found to characterize functionally equivalent enzymes in general, whether they occur in different compartments of the same cells or in different compartments in different kinds of cells. In the case of trypanosomes and their hosts, however, this fact has provided a basis for the search to find drugs that will selectively inhibit glycosomal enzymes in the trypanosome without affecting the equivalent cytosolic enzymes in the host cells. In view of the serious nature of trypanosomal infections that cause profoundly debilitating effects in millions of people all over the world, a number of laboratories are now engaged in a search for appropriate drug therapies.

8.10
An Overview of Microbody Formation and Functions

The manner and location of microbody formation are either unclear or controversial. According to many electron microscopic studies, microbodies appear to bud from the ER, particularly smooth ER, and often to retain connections with ER elements. The difficulties in accepting the interpretations based on microscopy lie mainly in the uncertainties of obtaining an accurate three-dimensional image from random sections that show two-dimensional views of selected areas within one or a few cells. What little evidence is available from biochemical studies casts even more doubt on the formation of microbodies as buds from smooth ER membranes. In 1978 Günter Blobel reported that the peroxisomal enzymes urate oxidase and catalase were synthesized on free cytosolic ribosomes and not on ER-bound ribosomes. He administered radioactively labeled amino acids and later used specific antibody preparations to *immunoprecipitate* urate oxidase and catalase from ribosomes. The labeled enzyme proteins were recovered only from free ribosomes and not from bound ribosomes of the rough ER, which indicated that the proteins had been synthesized only on free cytosolic ribosomes. Similarly, when labeled peroxisomal proteins are added to isolated peroxisomes, the proteins are later recovered *inside* these organelles. All these studies indicate that peroxisomal enzymes are made in the cytosol and are later transported into membranous envelopes, rather than the whole functional organelle being formed at the ER. Neither the mode of presumed transport of the enzymes nor the manner and site of formation of the peroxisomal membranes are known at the present time. The situation may be analogous to the transport of cytosolically synthesized proteins into existing mitochondria and their subsequent incorporation

TABLE 8-1
Enzyme Activities in Microbodies (Peroxisomes, Glyoxysomes) of Various Cells and Species*

Enzyme	Rat Liver	Rat Kidney	Frog Liver	Frog Kidney	Tetra-hymena	*Saccharomyces cerevisiae*	Spinach Leaves	Castor Bean Endosperm
Allantoinase	−	−	+	−	+	−	−	+
Aminotransferases (various)	+	−					+	+
Carnitine acyl transferases	+	−					−	+
Catalase	+	+	+	+	+	+	+	+
Fatty acid β-oxidation cycle	+	−			+	+	+	+
Glycolate oxidase	+	+			+	+	+	+
Glyoxylate cycle:								
Isocitrate lyase	−	−	−	−	+	+	−	+
Malate synthase	−	−	−	−	+	+	−	+
Aconitase	−	−	−	−	−	−	−	+
Citrate synthase	−	−	−	−	−	−	−	+
Malate dehydrogenase	−	−	−	−	−	−	+	+
Monoglyceride lipase								+
Urate oxidase	+	−	+	+	−	−	−	+

* Enzyme present, +; enzyme absent, −; enzyme not tested, left blank

within the membranous boundaries. These speculations must be tested before any part of the proposal can be accepted.

By whatever means microbodies and microbodylike organelles may be formed, the structures house an astonishing number of different subsets of the forty or more enzymes known to occur in all the microbody populations studied thus far (Table 8.1). Some of these enzymes promote functions that occur in many cells and organs, whereas other enzymes are uncommon and catalyze unique functions. The common functions include the following:

1. All peroxisomes and glyoxysomes have a flavin-oxidase–catalase pathway by which potentially harmful hydrogen peroxide is converted to harmless water. *Peroxide disposal* is thus a widespread microbody function. These enzymes are absent from trichomonatid and trypanosome microbodylike structures, but perhaps these are not microbodies at all but some other kind of package containing specific encoded proteins.

2. Fatty seed glyoxysomes harbor the largest number of enzymes known for any microbody type, and these enzymes catalyze reactions that underlie the function of *gluconeogenesis* by which stored fats are converted to carbohydrates for growth and development of young seedlings.

3. The microbodies of many protists, fungi, and other lower organisms have the glyoxylate bypass enzymes malate synthase and isocitrate lyase, which catalyze anaplerotic reactions that serve to *replenish metabolites* under limiting conditions for growth. Leaf peroxisomes have many unique and many commonly occurring microbody enzymes, which catalyze reactions in which some of the end products are four-carbon intermediates that can be used for biosynthesis in other parts of the cell. Thus, despite their lack of

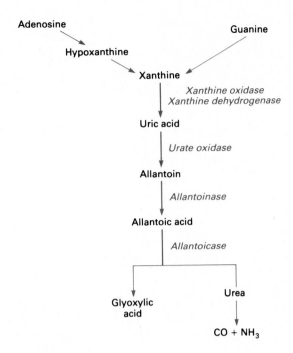

FIGURE 8-30
Sequence of purine degradation. Different portions of the pathway occur in different species and cell types, and many of these enzymes have been localized in microbodies.

glyoxylate cycle or bypass enzymes, the leaf peroxisomes also perform an anaplerotic function under the limiting conditions that induce photorespiration in green plants.

4. Microbodies with urate oxidase activity participate in at least one of the steps in the degradation of the purine bases adenine and guanine. In many species, including frogs, chickens, certain protozoa, and fatty seeds of plants like castor bean, additional enzymes of the *purine degradation* pathway have been located in microbodies (Fig. 8.30).

In addition to these functions in organelles that are recognized to be microbodies by all investigators, we could add the unique functions of hydrogenosomes and glycosomes in the energy-yielding reactions of electron transfer to O_2 or H^+ (in hydrogenosomes) and in the glycolytic breakdown of glucose (in glycosomes). The microbody, by whatever name it is called, is a truly remarkable eukaryotic organelle.

Summary

Among the various membrane-bounded cytoplasmic organelles associated with characteristic enzymes, the lysosomes are the best understood and characterized. Cell fractionation and cytochemical studies reveal them to be a population of vesicles ranging in size from 0.5 to several micrometers in diameter. They are identified by their content of acid hydrolases, whose substrates are virtually all biological macromolecules. The smallest vesicles are primary lysosomes, and arise from the Golgi. Fusion with an endocytotic vesicle that contains a digestible substrate activates the primary lysosome to become a secondary lysosome. It now functions as a digestive vacuole, hydrolyzing the contents of the endocytotic vesicle (and the contents of any subsequent vesicles with which it fuses) and releasing monomeric metabolites that diffuse across its membrane to the cytoplasm. Cholesterol esters are hydrolyzed in lysosomes, and receptor-bound insulin is degraded by this mechanism. A lysosome may also engulf another vesicle in its entirety to form a multivesicular body; it may even surround components of the cytoplasm, as in autophagic vacuoles. Lysosomes with materials that are resistant to digestion become residual bodies that persist for the life of the cell.

If the membrane surrounding the lysosome is disrupted, either by accident or as part of the physiological process, the cell is killed. Several normal reproductive processes involve cell death via disruption of the lysosomal membrane, including dissolution of the corpus luteum, breakdown of the cells surrounding an egg by the action of the sperm acrosome prior to fertilization, and metamorphosis in amphibians. Disruption of lysosomal membrane and cell death accompany ingestion of silicates, asbestos, and coal dust. The repeated cycle of particle release from lysed cells and re-uptake by other phagocytes leads to fibrosis. Other diseases result from genetic deficiencies of one or another of the lysosomal enzymes, giving rise to deposits of undigested materials that disrupt cell function.

Primary lysosomes probably bud from the *trans* face of the Golgi apparatus, their enzymes having been concentrated in an area of membrane with receptors for mannose-6-phosphate. Endocytotic vesicles originate as clathrin–coated vesicles at the plasma membrane, but shed their coat upon fusion with endosomes in the periplasmic cytoplasm. The acid pH of the endosome allows dissociation of ligands from membrane receptors, permitting these two components to be separated by selective budding into different vesicles destined either for return to the plasma membrane or for transport to lysosomes.

Another group of organelles, the microbodies, also contain specialized enzymes. Microbodies are considerably more diverse than lysosomes, however, and are more difficult to study. Usually found associated with the tubular smooth ER in animal cells, they contain flavin-linked oxidases and catalase, an enzyme that degrades the peroxide by-product of such oxidations. Microbodies can be classified according to the particular array of enzymes they contain. Peroxisomes, found in all eukaryotes, have a flavin oxidase–catalase system, permitting the oxidation of substrates like urate or glycolate without harm to the cell from the peroxide by-product. Glyoxysomes, in fatty plant seedlings, have in addition the enzymes of the glyoxylate cycle, a pathway that facilitates gluconeogenesis of carbohydrates from the fats stored in the seed. In protists, fungi, and lower plants and animals, a portion of the glyoxylate cycle is found in microbodies as a glyoxylate bypass, allowing noncarbohydrate metabolites to be directed toward generation of either energy or carbohydrates. In plant leaves, the interaction of peroxisomes with physically associated mitochondria and chloroplasts reduces damaging effects of photorespiration under conditions where carbon dioxide is limiting. Hydrogenosomes in trichomonatids generate ATP from the oxidation of pyruvate under aerobic conditions (as in mitochondria), but under anaerobic conditions, electrons are transferred to H^+ to generate H_2. Glycosomes in trypanosomes supply mitochondria with glycolytic intermediates under aerobic conditions; under anaerobic conditions glycosomes supply energy to the cell by processes similar to cytoplasmic glycolysis. Microbodies may originate from the smooth ER, but the enzymes appear to be synthesized on cytoplasmic ribosomes and subsequently taken up by vesicles.

Readings and References

Allison, A. C. May 1967. Lysosomes and disease. *Sci. Amer.* **217**:62.

Atkinson, A. W., Jr., P. C. L. John, and B. E. S. Gunning. 1974. The growth and division of the single mitochondrion and other organelles during the cell cycle of *Chlorella*, studied by quantitative stereology and three-dimensional reconstruction. *Protoplasma* **81**:77.

Bainton, D. F. 1981. The discovery of lysosomes. *J. Cell Biol.* **91**:66s.

Beevers, H. 1969. Glyoxysomes of castor bean endosperm and their relation to gluconeogenesis. *Ann. N. Y. Acad. Sci.* **168**:313.

Beevers, H. 1979. Microbodies in higher plants. *Ann. Rev. Plant Physiol.* **30**:159.

Blobel, G. 1982. Regulation of intracellular protein traffic. *Cold Spring Harbor Sympos. Quant. Biol.* **46**:7.

Brady, R. O. August 1973. Hereditary fat-metabolism diseases. *Sci. Amer.* **229**:88.

Braell, W. A., D. M. Schlossman, S. L. Schmid, and J. E. Rothman. 1984. Dissociation of clathrin coats coupled to hydrolysis of ATP: Role of an uncoating ATPase. *J. Cell Biol.* **99**:735.

Breidenbach, R. W., A. Kahn, and H. Beevers. 1968. Characterization of glyoxysomes from castor bean endosperm. *Plant Physiol.* **43**:705.

Brown, M. S., R. G. W. Anderson, and J. L. Goldstein. 1983. Recycling receptors: The round-trip itinerary of migrant membrane proteins. *Cell* **32**:663.

Callahan, J. W., and J. A. Lowden, eds. 1981. *Lysosomes and Lysosomal Storage Diseases.* New York: Raven.

Campbell, C. H., R. E. Fine, J. Squicciarini, and L. H. Rome. 1983. Coated vesicles from rat liver and calf brain contain cryptic mannose 6-phosphate receptors. *J. Biol. Chem.* **258**:2628.

de Duve, C. 1975. Exploring cells with a centrifuge. *Science* **189**:186 (Nobel lecture).

de Duve, C. May 1983. Microbodies in the living cell. *Sci. Amer.* **248**:74.

Erickson, A. H., and G. Blobel. 1979. Early events in the biosynthesis of the lysosomal enzyme cathepsin D. *J. Biol. Chem.* **254**:11771.

Erickson, A. H., G. E. Conner, and G. Blobel. 1981. Biosynthesis of a lysosomal enzyme. *J. Biol. Chem.* **256**:11224.

Evered, D., ed. 1982. *Membrane Recycling.* Ciba Found. Sympos. 92. London: Pitman.

Frederick, S. E., P. J. Gruber, and E. H. Newcomb. 1975. Plant microbodies. *Protoplasma* **84**:1.

Frederick, S. E., and E. H. Newcomb. 1969. Cytochemical localization of catalase in leaf microbodies (peroxisomes). *J. Cell Biol.* **43**:343.

Gabel, C. A., D. E. Goldberg, and S. Kornfeld. 1983. Identification and characterization of cell deficient in the mannose 6-phosphate receptor: Evidence for an alternate pathway for lysosomal enzyme targeting. *Proc. Natl. Acad. Sci. U. S.* **80**:775.

Gabel, C. A., and S. Kornfeld. 1984. Targeting of β-glucuronidase to lysosomes in mannose 6-phosphate receptor-deficient MOPC 315 cells. *J. Cell Biol.* **99**:296.

Geisow, M. J., P. D. Hart, and M. R. Young. 1981. Temporal changes of lysosome and phagosome pH during phagolysosome formation in macrophages: Studies by fluorescence spectroscopy. *J. Cell Biol.* **89**:645.

Geuze, H. J., *et al.* 1983. Intracellular site of asialoglycosprotein receptor–ligand uncoupling: Double-label immunoelectron microscopy during receptor-mediated endocytosis. *Cell* **32**:277.

Geuze, H. J., *et al.* 1984. Intercellular receptor sorting during endocytosis: Comparative immunoelectron microscopy of multiple receptors in rat liver. *Cell* **37**:195.

Gibson, R., S. Kornfeld, and S. Schlesinger. 1980. A role for oligosaccharides in glycoprotein synthesis. *Trends Biochem. Sci.* **5**:290.

Goldman, B. M., and G. Blobel. 1978. Biogenesis of peroxisomes: Intracellular site of synthesis of catalase and uricase. *Proc. Natl. Acad. Sci. U. S.* **75**:5066.

Gonzalez-Noriega, A., J. H. Grubb, V. Fallad, and W. S. Sly. 1980. Chloroquine inhibits lysosomal enzyme pinocytosis and enhances lysosomal enzyme secretion by impairing receptor recycling. *J. Cell Biol.* **85**:839.

Hasilik, A. 1980. Biosynthesis of lysosomal enzymes. *Trends Biochem. Sci.* **5**:237.

Helenius, A., I. Mellman, D. Wall, and A. Hubbard. 1983. Endosomes. *Trends Biochem. Sci.* **8**:245.

Herman, B., and D. F. Albertini. 1983. Ligand-induced rapid redistribution of lysosomes is temporally distinct from endosome translocation. *Nature* **304**:738.

Hopkins, C. R. 1983. The importance of the endosome in intracellular traffic. *Nature* **304**:684.

Kindl, H., and P. B. Lazarow, eds. 1982. Peroxisomes and glyoxysomes. *Ann. N. Y. Acad. Sci.* **386**.

Kolodny, E. H. 1976. Lysosomal storage diseases. *New Engl. J. Med.* **294**:1217.

Kornberg, H. L. 1966. The role and control of the glyoxylate cycle in *Escherichia coli*. *Biochem. J.* **99**:1.

Kornfeld, S. 1982. In *Membrane Recycling*, ed. D. Evered. *Ciba Found. Sympos.* **92**:138.

Lennarz, W. J., ed. 1980. *The Biochemistry of Glycoproteins and Proteoglycans*. New York: Plenum.

Lindmark, D. G., and M. Müller. 1973. Hydrogenosomes, a cytoplasmic organelle of the anaerobic flagellate *Tritrichomonas foetus*, and its role in pyruvate metabolism. *J. Biol. Chem.* **243**:5385.

Lord, J. M., and L. M. Roberts. 1980. Formation of glyoxysomes. *Trends Biochem. Sci.* **5**:271.

Marsh, M., *et al.* 1982. Are lysosomes a site of enveloped-virus penetration? *Cold Spring Harbor Sympos. Quant. Biol.* **46**:835.

Müller, M. 1980. The hydrogenosome. *Sympos. Soc. Gen. Microbiol.* **30**:127.

Neufeld, E. F., and V. A. McKusick. 1983. Disorders of lysosomal enzyme synthesis and localization: I-cell disease and pseudo-Hurler polydystrophy. In *The Metabolic Basis of Inherited Disease*, ed. J. B. Stanbury *et al.* New York: McGraw-Hill.

Novikoff, A. B., and S. Goldfischer. 1969. Visualization of peroxisomes (microbodies) and mitochondria with diaminobenzidene. *J. Histochem. Cytochem.* **17**:675.

Opperdoes, F. R., and P. Borst. 1977. Localization of nine glycolytic enzymes in a microbody-like organelle in *Trypanosoma brucei*: The glycosome. *FEBS Letters* **80**:360.

Pesonen, M., and K. Simons. 1984. Transcytosis of the G protein of vesicular stomatitis virus after implantation into the apical membrane of Madin-Darby canine kidney cells. I. Involvement of endosomes and lysosomes. *J. Cell Biol.* **99**:796.

Reitman, M. L., and S. Kornfeld. 1981. Lysosomal enzyme targeting: N-acetylglucosaminylphosphotransferase selectively phosphorylates native lysosomal enzymes. *J. Biol. Chem.* **256**:11977.

Reitman, M. L., A. Varki, and S. Kornfeld. 1981. Fibroblasts from patients with I-cell disease and pseudo-Hurler polydystrophy are deficient in uridine 5′-diphosphate-N–acetylglucosamine: glycoprotein N-acetylglucosaminylphosphotransferase activity. *J. Clin. Invest.* **67**:1574.

Robbins, A. R., *et al.* 1984. A single mutation in Chinese hamster ovary cells impairs both Golgi and endosomal functions. *J. Cell Biol.* **99**:1296.

Rothman, J. E., E. Fries, W. G. Dunphy, and L. J. Urbani. 1982. The Golgi apparatus, coated vesicles, and the sorting problem. *Cold Spring Harbor Sympos. Quant. Biol.* **46**:797.

Rothman, J. E., and J. Lenard. 1984. Membrane traffic in animal cells. *Trends Biochem. Sci.* **9**:176.

Simons, K., H. Garoff, and A. Helenius. February 1982. How an animal virus gets into and out of its host cell. *Sci. Amer.* **246**:58.

Sly, W. S., and H. D. Fischer. 1982. The phosphorylation recognition system for intracellular and intercellular transport of lysosomal enzymes. *J. Cell. Biochem.* **18**:67.

Steinman, R. M., I. S. Mellman, W. A. Muller, and Z. A. Cohn. 1983. Endocytosis and the recycling of plasma membrane. *J. Cell Biol.* **96**:1.

Storrie, B., *et al.* 1984. Evidence for both prelysosomal and lysosomal intermediates in endocytic pathways. *J. Cell Biol.* **98**:108.

Straus, W. 1967. Lysosomes, phagosomes, and related particles. In *Enzyme Cytology*, ed. D. B. Roodyn, p. 239. New York: Academic Press.

Tolbert, N. E. 1981. Metabolic pathways in peroxisomes and glyoxysomes. *Ann. Rev. Biochem.* **50**:133.

Tolbert, N. E., and E. Essner. 1981. Microbodies: Peroxisomes and glyoxysomes. *J. Cell Biol.* **91**:271s.

Tougard, C., D. Louvard, R. Picart, and A. Tixier-Vidal. 1985. Antibodies against a lysosomal membrane antigen recognize a prelysosomal compartment involved in the endocytic pathway in cultured prolactin cells. *J. Cell Biol.* **100**:786.

van Renswoude, J., K. R. Bridges, J. B. Harford, and R. D. Klausner. 1982. Receptor-mediated endocytosis of transferrin and the uptake of Fe in K562 cells: Identification of a nonlysosomal acidic compartment. *Proc. Natl. Acad. Sci. U. S.* **79**:6186.

Waheed, A., A. Hasilik, and K. von Figura. 1981. Processing of the phosphorylated recognition marker in lysosomal enzymes. *J. Biol. Chem.* **256**:5717.

Waheed, A., R. Pohlmann, A. Hasilik, and K. von Figura. 1981. Subcellular localization of two enzymes involved in the synthesis of phosphorylated recognition markers in lysosomal enzymes. *J. Biol. Chem.* **256**:4150.

Wall, D. A., and A. L. Hubbard. 1981. Galactose-specific recognition system of mammalian liver: Receptor distribution on the hepatocyte cell surface. *J. Cell Biol.* **90**:687.

White, J., K. Matlin, and A. Helenius. 1981. Cell fusion by Semliki Forest, influenza, and vesicular stomatitis viruses. *J. Cell Biol.* **89**:674.

CHAPTER 9

Mitochondria

The mitochondrion has been called the "powerhouse of the cell" because its metabolic activities provide the energy required to sustain aerobic eukaryotic life. Virtually the same energy-yielding reactions occur in aerobic prokaryotes as well, but the enzymes are situated in the plasma membrane and cytoplasm rather than in a specialized organelle as in eukaryotic cells.

All organisms must have energy and building blocks for growth, reproduction, repair, and maintenance of their viability. Carbohydrates are the principal fuels in most life forms, and the primary mechanism for processing fuel molecules and extracting free energy is provided by the reactions of aerobic respiration. Even photosynthetic species that make their own sugars must process these sugars to derive energy and metabolites for all their activities.

In addition to our interest in understanding the profoundly important events of aerobic respiration in mitochondria, we have focused our attention on mitochondria as model systems to investigate other basic phenomena. Among these phenomena are membrane organization in relation to membrane functions, coordination and communication between mitochondrial compartments and between mitochondria and other parts of the cell, and, most recently, the nature and organization of the mitochondrial genome and associated genetic components and processes.

Mitochondrial Structure and Form

Mitochondria were first described in 1886 by Robert Altmann as tiny rods and granules within the cytoplasm. Altmann used conventional preparations for light microscopy and was able to discern stained particles against an unstained background. Today we can also study mitochondria in living cells, either by phase-contrast microscopy of unstained material or by the use of a *vital dye* that accumulates inside

FIGURE 9-1
Light micrograph of a rat fibroblast stained with rhodamine 123. The unstained nucleus in the center of this triangular-shaped cell is surrounded by brightly stained mitochondria of various shapes and sizes. ×650. (Photograph courtesy of L. B. Chen.)

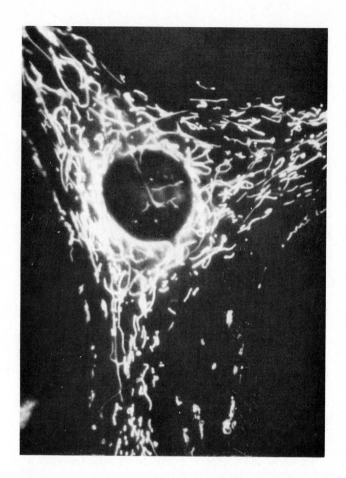

mitochondria, rendering them visible and doing no harm to the cells. A particularly effective vital dye is the fluorescent reagent called rhodamine 123. Mitochondria are clearly visible as fluorescent snakelike structures against an unstained dark background when viewed by fluorescence light microscopy (Fig. 9.1). Whether unstained or vitally stained, mitochondria in many kinds of living cells move rapidly from place to place and undergo dramatic changes in size and shape. Apart from these observations, little else can be seen with the light microscope, and we learn nothing about the internal structure or organization of mitochondria at such levels of resolution. A new and more appropriate dimension of observation became available with the development of improved methods for electron microscopy in the early 1950s. Mitochondrial ultrastructure was an early focus of electron microscopic studies, and such studies continue to the present day to provide new insights into the relationship between organelle structure and function.

9.1
Mitochondrial Ultrastructure

The usual mitochondrial images seen in electron micrographs of cell thin sections are spheroid, ovoid, or elongated tubular outlines of structures bounded by two separate membranes (Fig. 9.2). The **outer mitochondrial membrane** is smooth and unfolded, but the **inner mitochondrial membrane** is infolded at numerous sites so that the infolds invade the

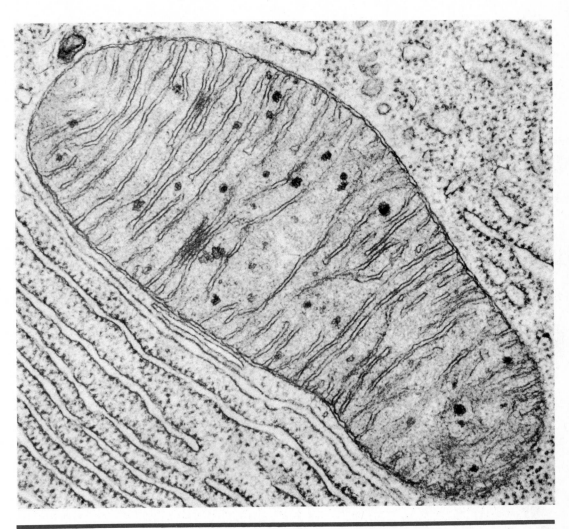

FIGURE 9-2
Electron micrograph of a section
through a mitochondrion in bat pancreas showing the infolded cristae
of the inner membrane, the unique
identifying ultrastructural feature of
the eukaryotic organelle. ×70,000.
(Photograph courtesy of K. R. Porter.)

interior of the mitochondrion. These infoldings, called **cristae**, are a
unique identifying feature for mitochondria in electron micrographs.
Cristae provide a substantial increase in the amount of inner membrane
than can be accommodated within the organelle boundary. With such
an increase in membrane surface area, the inner mitochondrial membrane can house many more of the respiratory enzymes that are part of
its fluid mosaic construction and can thereby provide greater metabolic
efficiency in the relatively small, confined space of the organelle. Albert
Lehninger has calculated that the surface area of mitochondrial cristae
in rat liver cells is ten times greater than the surface area of the plasma
membrane in these cells. Rat liver mitochondria are not particularly well
endowed with cristae, so even greater differentials in surface area are
characteristic of muscle and other more metabolically active cell types.

The two mitochondrial membranes enclose and define two separate
mitochondrial spaces, or compartments: the narrow **intermembrane
space** and the much larger internal **matrix** space. Many kinds of
molecules can penetrate the outer membrane, including proteins as large
as 10,000 molecular weight, but relatively few molecules can cross the
highly impermeable inner membrane and enter the matrix space. The

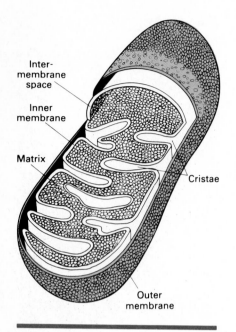

FIGURE 9-3

Three-dimensional reconstruction
of the mitochondrion as a small,
rod-shaped structure based on interpretations of random sections of
mitochondrial profiles seen in electron
micrographs. The matrix and intermembrane space are quite different
in their molecular contents and
activities, as are the outer and inner
membranes of the organelle.

two compartments, therefore, are quite different in their chemical
contents and in their enzymatic repertories as well. The matrix is far
more diverse and specialized in its activities than the intermembrane
space and, together with the inner membrane, provides the bulk of the
metabolic workings that characterize mitochondrial respiration and
other reaction pathways. Also situated within the matrix compartment
is the mitochondrial genetic apparatus, consisting of multiple copies of
the DNA genome, distinctive ribosomes, and the enzymes that catalyze
transcription and translation of mitochondrial genes.

9.2
Mitochondrial Shape and Numbers

The mitochondrion has conventionally been viewed as a rod-shaped
structure about the size of a bacterial cell. This three-dimensional image
is based on interpretations and measurements of mitochondria in static
photographs taken at the light microscopic and electron microscopic
levels of magnification (Fig. 9.3). From these same data, it has been
estimated that cells contain numerous mitochondria, ranging up to
hundreds of thousands per cell, although a few exceptional species were
found to contain one or a few organelles per cell. These interpretations
were supported by electron micrographs of isolated mitochondria collected after centrifugation (Fig. 9.4).

Quite a different mitochondrial form is evident from observations of
living cells, which reveal rapid and dramatic changes in organelle shape

FIGURE 9-4

Electron micrographs of yeast mitochondrial profiles in (a) a section of
the whole cell closely resemble (b)
isolated mitochondria in fractions
obtained by centrifugation of cell-free
homogenates. (a) × 16,250; (b)
× 18,600. (Photographs by H. -P.
Hoffmann.)

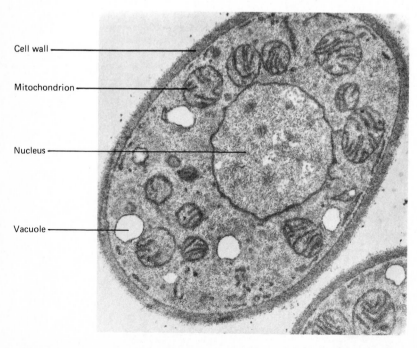

(a)

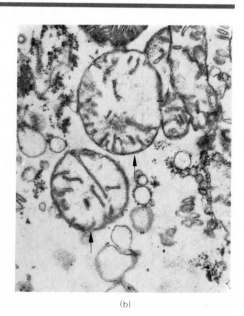

(b)

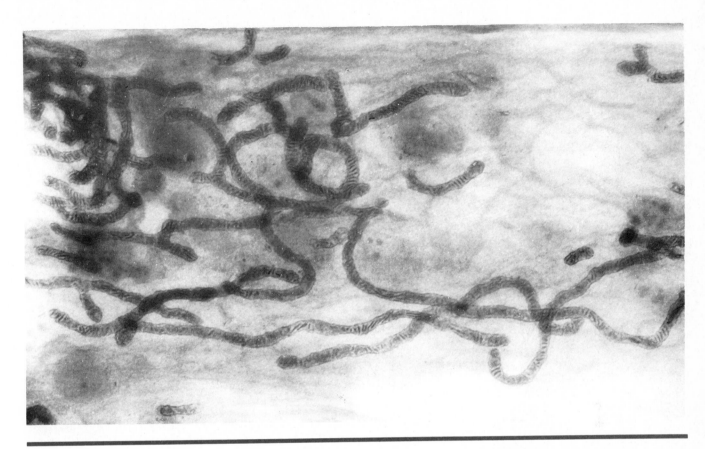

FIGURE 9-5
High-voltage electron micrograph of a
4-μm-thick section of snail mucous
gland showing long, sinuous
mitochondrial profiles. ×18,000.
(Photograph courtesy of Nina and
Pierre Favard.)

but a predominance of long snakelike or filamentous mitochondria. Similar structures can be seen in photographs taken with the high-voltage electron microscope, which has a electron beam of high enough intensity to allow observations of relatively thick sections, in contrast with the ultrathin sections needed for the standard lower voltages of conventional transmission electron microscopes (Fig. 9.5). Even larger and more complex mitochondrial forms have been described in various species that have been analyzed by three-dimensional reconstructions of the two-dimensional images obtained from a series of photographs taken of a consecutive group of serial sections through an entire cell or a large portion of a cell. When each successive image in the series is superimposed on the previous image, the mitochondrion emerges in reconstruction as a large structure with long tubular branches, forming a reticulum or network (Fig. 9.6). Similar large, branching mitochondria have been described in mammalian cells as well as in algae, fungi, and insects, all based on three-dimensional reconstructions of serial thin sections through all or most of a cell.

Whichever model of the mitochondrion proves to be nearest to the shape of the organelle in living cells will have important implications for our understanding of organelle interactions with one another and with the surrounding cytosol. Even more important, an accurate picture of mitochondrial size and form will influence our conceptions of mitochondrial biogenesis, genetic interplay, and the origin of the organelles in eukaryotic evolution. As long as we think of the mitochondrion as a bacterial equivalent, we will continue to think in terms of mitochondrial

FIGURE 9-6
Three-dimensional model of a giant, branched mitochondrion from yeast. The model was reconstructed from photographs of a complete series of thin sections cut consecutively through one budding cell. The bulk of the mitochondrion was in the mother-cell portion, and a small connected mitochondrial region was in the small bud growing from the mother cell. (From Hoffmann, H. -P., and C. J. Avers, 1973, *Science* **181**: 749–751.)

biogenesis by a fissionlike division process and lean more toward the hypothesis that mitochondria are modern descendants of an ancient bacterial ancestor. Whether or not these widely held beliefs are actually true, however, remains to be determined by objective analysis rather than by intuitive interpretations of fragmentary and subjective data.

Aerobic Respiration

The building blocks and energy for cellular growth and reproduction are derived from *fuel* molecules. Insoluble fats, proteins, and polysaccharides, or their breakdown products of fatty acids, amino acids, and sugars, must be dismantled in metabolism and made available to the cell so that energy can be extracted. By whatever pathways these molecules are provided to the cell, the common end product of fuel breakdown is the activated form of two-carbon acetate called **acetyl CoA** (acetyl coenzyme A). In aerobic conditions acetyl CoA enters the pathway of the *Krebs cycle* and is fully oxidized to CO_2 in the second stage of fuel processing. The electrons obtained in the oxidation of acetyl CoA are then channeled, in the third stage of processing, to a respiratory chain of enzymes that transport these electrons to O_2, the final electron acceptor in **aerobic respiration**. As electrons are moved along the respiratory chain of transport enzymes, many of which are *cytochromes*, coupled reactions take place at three different sites and ATP is synthesized (Fig. 9.7). The ATP made in aerobic respiration is a major

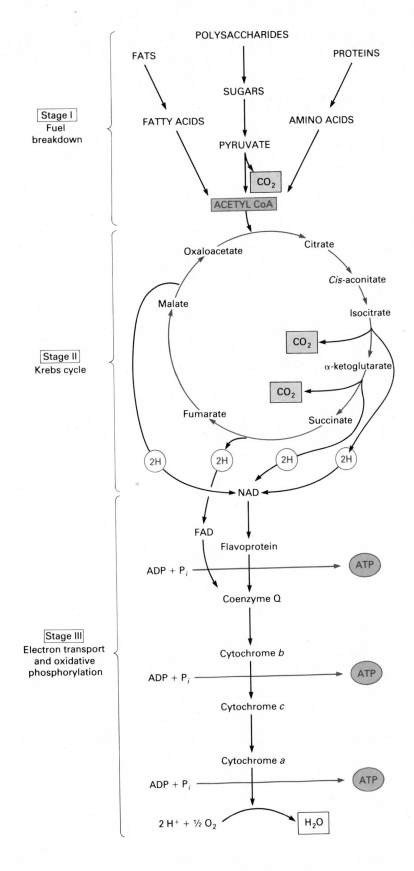

POLYSACCHARIDES

FATS

PROTEINS

SUGARS

Stage I
Fuel
breakdown

FATTY ACIDS

AMINO ACIDS

PYRUVATE

CO_2

ACETYL CoA

Oxaloacetate

Citrate

Cis-aconitate

Malate

Isocitrate

CO_2

Stage II
Krebs cycle

α-ketoglutarate

CO_2

Fumarate

Succinate

2H 2H 2H 2H

NAD

FAD

Stage III
Electron transport
and oxidative
phosphorylation

Flavoprotein

ADP + P_i → ATP

Coenzyme Q

Cytochrome *b*

ADP + P_i → ATP

Cytochrome *c*

Cytochrome *a*

ADP + P_i → ATP

$2 H^+ + ½ O_2$ → H_2O

FIGURE 9-7
Three stages of fuel breakdown and processing. In stage I, insoluble fats, polysaccharides, and proteins are digested to simpler, soluble products in various pathways. In stage II, soluble intermediates of fuel breakdown are channeled into the Krebs cycle, via acetyl CoA, and are oxidized completely to CO_2. Fuel energy is transferred temporarily to the electron carriers NAD (nicotinamide adenine dinucleotide) and FAD (flavin adenine dinucleotide). In stage III, electrons from reduced NAD and FAD are transported to molecular oxygen through a chain of electron carriers that includes a number of cytochromes. For each pair of electrons transported to oxygen, ATP is synthesized in reactions coupled to three different steps in the transport sequence. Stage I reactions occur whether or not oxygen is present, but stages II and III involve oxygen-dependent processes.

source of free energy for the great majority of cellular activities in which biosynthesis, movement, and other phenomena are involved. The processes of aerobic respiration in the last two stages of fuel processing take place in mitochondria in eukaryotes, and in the cytosol and plasma membrane of prokaryotic life. The initial stage of fuel breakdown—from insoluble foods to fatty acids, amino acids, and pyruvate—occurs primarily or entirely in the cytosol of all cellular life.

9.3
Fermentation

When oxygen is limiting or absent, virtually all cells are capable of extracting energy from glucose and other fuels by **fermentation**, in which the final electron acceptor is some product of the fermentation sequence itself. In aerobic respiration, by contrast, molecular oxygen is the final electron acceptor of fuel processing. Because it is virtually certain that life on the primeval Earth originated and evolved for billions of years in an *anaerobic* environment, primeval life must have obtained its energy mainly by fermentations. These ancient capacities have been retained to the present day in almost all organisms, including mammals.

Although fuels are completely oxidized to CO_2 in aerobic respiration and a maximum amount of free energy is extracted and stored in ATP, relatively little energy is obtained by fermentation of an equivalent amount of fuel. The end products of fermentations still retain a high level of energy that ordinarily is unavailable for use by the cell.

Glucose and other hexose sugars are the most common substrates for fermentation reactions. The two major fermentation processes for glucose oxidation are *lactate fermentation* (anaerobic glycolysis), in which

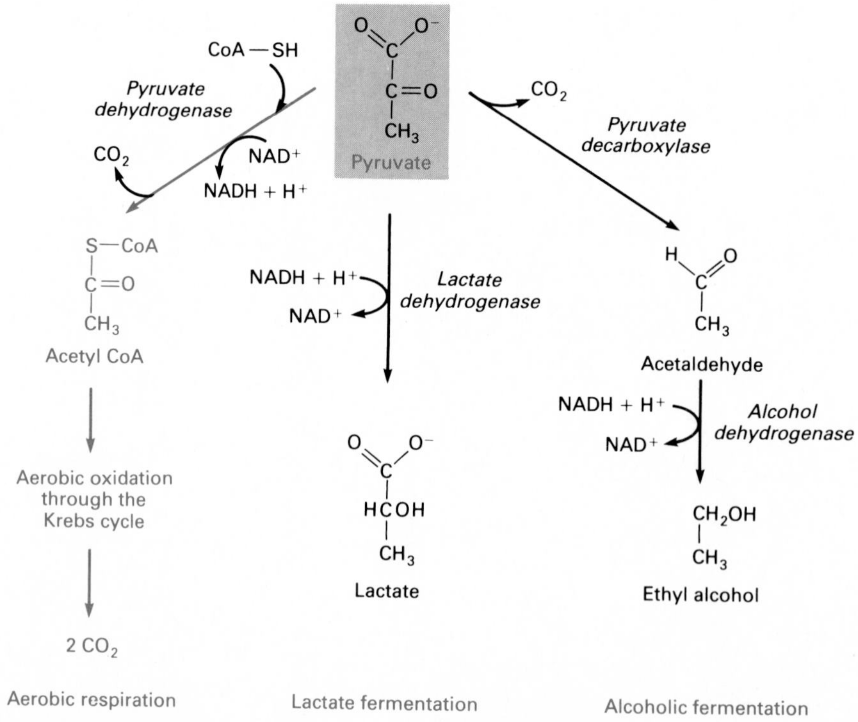

FIGURE 9-8
Pyruvate produced from glucose in glycolysis is oxidized completely to CO_2 under aerobic conditions in the cell, but it is processed only to lactate or to ethyl alcohol in anaerobic fermentation processes.

lactate is the sole end product, and *alcoholic fermentation*, which yields ethanol and CO_2. The breakdown of glucose to pyruvate occurs by *glycolysis* whether or not molecular oxygen is present (see Fig. 3.20). If oxygen is present, pyruvate is processed by aerobic respiration to its fully oxidized form of CO_2 and much energy is released for ATP synthesis, as described above. Under anaerobic conditions, however, pyruvate may be reduced to lactate in a reaction catalyzed by lactate dehydrogenase, or it may be processed in a two-step reaction sequence to yield ethyl alcohol and CO_2 (Fig. 9.8). Far less ATP is made in fermentations, because lactate or alcohol retains much of the original glucose free energy. The vast amounts of energy obtained from fuel processing in aerobic organisms made the evolution of large and complex life forms possible. Life today would consist entirely of micro-scopic organisms if fermentations were the only processes for energy extraction from fuels; these processes are quite inefficient for the needs of higher organisms.

9.4
The Krebs Cycle

Glycolysis takes place in the cytosol as glucose is oxidized to pyruvate. When oxygen is present, pyruvate preferentially enters the mito-chondrion from the cytosol instead of continuing there to be processed to lactate or ethanol. Once in the mitochondrion, pyruvate is converted to **acetyl CoA** and in this energized form, the molecule is fully oxidized to CO_2 by reactions of the *Krebs cycle*, which is the *final common pathway* in virtually all aerobic cells for the complete oxidation of fat, protein, or carbohydrate fuels. The Krebs cycle, named for its discoverer, Sir Hans Krebs, is sometimes referred to as the citric acid cycle (named for its initial product) or the tricarboxylic acid cycle in reference to such acid intermediates early in the cycle of reactions.

The acetate formed from pyruvate can be processed only if it occurs at an activated, or high-energy, level. The acetate is energized by the addition of coenzyme A, and in its activated form of acetyl CoA the intermediate can proceed toward complete oxidation to CO_2 in the Krebs cycle. Coenzyme A is an energy carrier that resembles ATP and NAD in construction (Fig. 9.9). Each of these energy carriers serves in a different capacity as an intermediary in energy metabolism. Coenzyme A engages in organic group transfer by binding its sulfhydryl group (—SH) to the organic residue it carries into reactions; NAD is an electron carrier; and ATP engages in phosphoryl group transfer (see Chapter 3).

The Krebs cycle proceeds vigorously under aerobic conditions because pyruvate continues to be channeled into the mitochondria in eukaryotes. The Krebs cycle itself, however, does not use O_2 directly as a reactant, and neither ADP nor ATP is an immediate participant or product in the reactions. The formation of acetyl CoA is not a part of the Krebs cycle, but its formation is essential to provide entry for acetate into the Krebs cycle for oxidation. A major function of the Krebs cycle is the oxidation of acetate to two CO_2 and the transfer of four pairs of its electrons to the carriers NAD and FAD (see Fig. 9.7). In each turn of the cycle, one molecule of acetate (as acetyl CoA) enters the cycle by

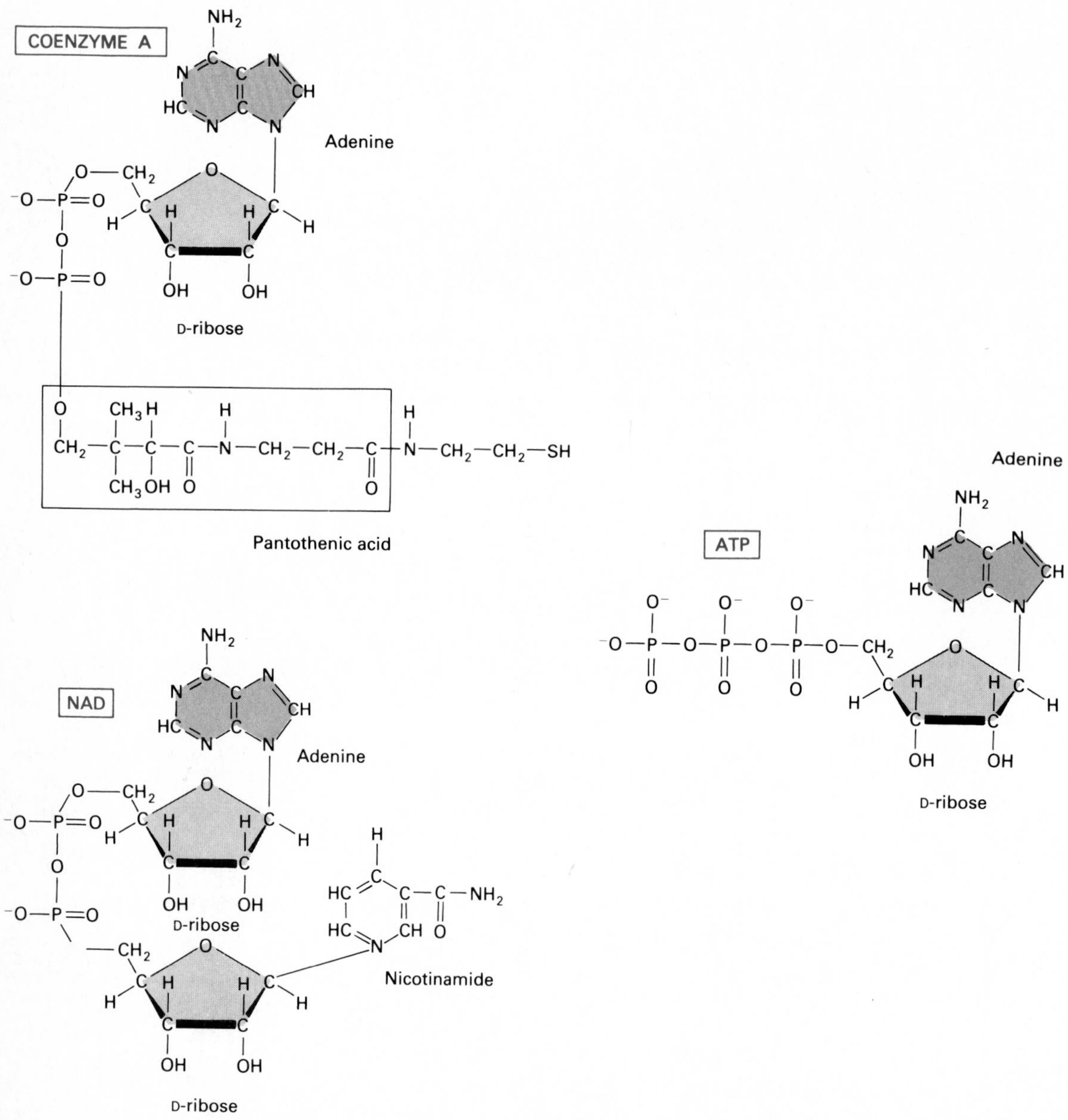

FIGURE 9-9
The three major energy-transferring molecules of cellular metabolism share many structural features related to their similar function in the cell.

condensing with one molecule of oxaloacetate to form citrate. Citrate is ultimately oxidized to succinate, a four-carbon compound, and two of the six carbons in citrate are released as CO_2. Succinate proceeds to be oxidized to oxaloacetate, and the cycle is ready for another turn as oxaloacetate is thus regenerated (Fig. 9.10). Because oxaloacetate is regenerated in each turn of the cycle, one molecule of oxaloacetate can bring about the oxidation of an infinite number of acetate molecules. Four of the Krebs cycle reactions are oxidations, and two of these reactions are more specifically referred to as *oxidative decarboxylations* because carboxyl groups (—COO^-) are released as CO_2.

Condensation of oxaloacetate and acetyl CoA to form citrate is the rate-setting step of the cycle. The reaction is catalyzed by *citrate synthase*,

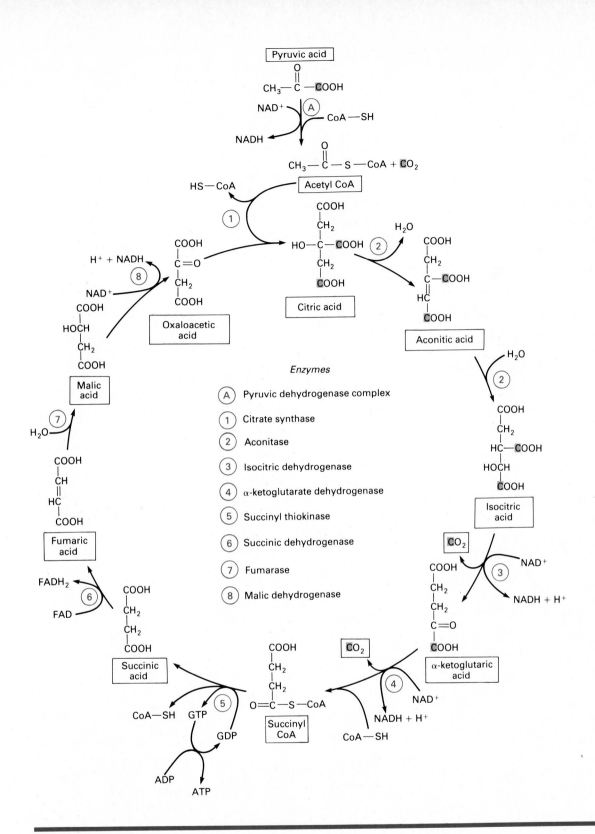

FIGURE 9-10

The Krebs cycle. Pyruvic acid is processed to acetyl CoA inside the mitochondrion, and the activated acetate enters the Krebs cycle by condensation with oxaloacetic acid to form the six-carbon compound citric acid. The acetate carbons (color box) are released in CO_2 during reactions leading to succinyl CoA, a four-carbon intermediate. In the remaining reactions oxaloacetic acid is regenerated, and it combines with another acetyl CoA in a new cycle. One oxaloacetate can thus aid the oxidation of an infinite number of acetates in successive turns of the Krebs cycle. During the cycle, a total of four pairs of electrons from each acetate are ultimately transferred to NAD and FAD. ATP is not produced directly in the Krebs cycle, but it may be formed indirectly from the GTP product of the cycle. The enzymes that catalyze the pictured reactions are listed in the center of the illustration.

which is therefore a regulatory enzyme of the pathway. After a series of enzymatically catalyzed steps, the six-carbon citrate has been processed to five-carbon and then to four-carbon intermediates. The loss of a carbon is represented in each instance by release of CO_2 in oxidative decarboxylation reactions. In addition, two NAD^+ have been reduced to NADH. The first of the four-carbon intermediates combines with coenzyme A to produce succinyl CoA. When succinyl CoA is hydrolyzed to succinate, there is enough free-energy difference to drive phosphorylation of guanosine diphosphate (GDP) to form guanosine triphosphate (GTP). GTP participates directly as an energy carrier in some reactions, and it can also be enzymatically converted to ATP:

$$GTP + ADP \leftrightarrows GDP + ATP$$

Succinate is oxidized to fumarate by the flavoprotein enzyme *succinic dehydrogenase*. The electron carrier FAD is covalently bound as a coenzyme to the protein portion of the enzyme, and FAD is reduced to $FADH_2$ in a reduction coupled to the oxidation of succinate. Fumarate is hydrated to form malate, and malate is oxidized to oxaloacetate in an oxidation–reduction catalyzed by NAD-linked *malate dehydrogenase*. NAD^+ accepts a pair of electrons (one of which is part of a hydrogen atom) and is reduced to NADH in a coupled reaction during which malate is oxidized. You probably have noticed that each enzyme catalyzing an oxidation during which NAD or FAD is reduced is a **dehydrogenase**. Dehydrogenases generally have a NAD or FAD group bound as a coenzyme to the protein portion of the whole enzyme.

During one turn of the Krebs cycle, four pairs of hydrogen atoms are removed from substrate intermediates; three pairs are accepted by NAD^+ and one pair by FAD. Two turns of the cycle are required to process two acetates from one molecule of glucose, so a total of six NADH and two $FADH_2$ are produced per glucose oxidized in the cycle. Each acetate, of course, is fully oxidized to two CO_2 molecules. The overall reaction summarizing *two* turns of the Krebs cycle is

2 acetate + 6 NAD^+ + 2 FAD + 2 GDP + 2 P_i

$\downarrow$ [9.1]

6 NADH + 6 H^+ + 2 $FADH_2$ + 4 CO_2 + 2 GTP + 2 H_2O*

In addition to the total of six NADH, two $FADH_2$, and two GTP formed during glucose processing in the Krebs cycle reactions, four NADH were produced in earlier steps along with two ATP. During glycolysis, two NADH and two ATP were formed:

glucose + 2 ADP + 2 P_i + 2 NAD^+

$\downarrow$ [9.2]

2 pyruvate + 2 ATP + 2 NADH + 2 H^+

Each pyruvate that is converted to acetyl CoA also yields one NADH.

---

* In phosphorylation of GDP or ADP, H_2O is produced along with GTP or ATP, as follows:

$GDP + P_i \rightleftarrows GTP + H_2O$, or $ADP + P_i \rightleftarrows ATP + H_2O$

Because two pyruvates per glucose are involved, we can add the reaction

$$2 \text{ pyruvate} + 2 \text{ NAD}^+ + 2 \text{ coenzyme A}$$

$$\downarrow \qquad\qquad\qquad [9.3]$$

$$2 \text{ acetyl CoA} + 2 \text{ NADH} + 2 \text{ H}^+ + 2 \text{ CO}_2$$

Taking reactions [9.1], [9.2], and [9.3] together, we can summarize the oxidation of glucose by glycolysis to pyruvate, from pyruvate to acetyl CoA, and through the Krebs cycle, as follows:

$$\text{glucose} + 2 \text{ ADP} + 2 \text{ GDP} + 4 \text{ P}_i + 10 \text{ NAD}^+ + 2 \text{ FAD}$$

$$\downarrow \qquad\qquad\qquad [9.4]$$

$$6 \text{ CO}_2 + 2 \text{ ATP} + 2 \text{ GTP} + 4 \text{ H}_2\text{O} + 10 \text{ NADH} + 10 \text{ H}^+ + 2 \text{ FADH}_2$$

Production of ATP, GTP, NADH, and $FADH_2$ is the significant energy-conserving achievement of glucose oxidation to CO_2. Some of the free-energy difference between glucose and CO_2 has been conserved in ATP and GTP, but most of the free-energy difference resides in electron-carrying NADH and $FADH_2$. Transfer of energy from the reduced electron carriers to processes leading to ATP synthesis constitutes the major theme of the next aerobic respiratory pathway, electron transport from NADH and $FADH_2$ toward O_2. This pathway represents stage III of catabolic processing of fuels (see Fig. 9.7).

9.5
Electron Transport Toward Oxygen

Electrons are transported from NADH and $FADH_2$ along a chain of *electron carriers*, most of which are integral membrane proteins. The transfer of electrons from one carrier to another takes place in oxidation–reduction reactions. The carriers, therefore, are examples of *redox couples*, which exist in the oxidized or reduced states upon donating or accepting electrons, respectively. The main components of these redox couples involved in electron transport are **flavin mononucleotide (FMN)**, **coenzyme Q (CoQ)**, and **heme** (Fig. 9.11).

NADH produced in coupled substrate oxidations is itself oxidized by *NADH dehydrogenase*, a *flavoprotein* enzyme that has a tightly bound FMN prosthetic group. Electrons are transferred from the $FMNH_2$ component of the dehydrogenase to CoQ, a lipid-soluble quinone derivative. CoQ is sometimes called *ubiquinone* because of its ubiquitous occurrence in cells. In mammals, the most common form of CoQ is designated CoQ_{10} because it has ten isoprene units in its construction. Once CoQ has accepted electrons from NADH via the agency of $FMNH_2$ of the flavoprotein, the electrons are passed along to other members of the **electron transport chain**. Electrons from $FADH_2$ have too low a transfer potential to enter the chain at the same point as NADH, but they can be accepted directly by CoQ at a lower energy level.

Between CoQ and O_2 is a chain of electron-carrying **cytochromes**, each of which has a heme prosthetic group. Heme is a porphyrin derivative complexed with an iron atom that alternates between the

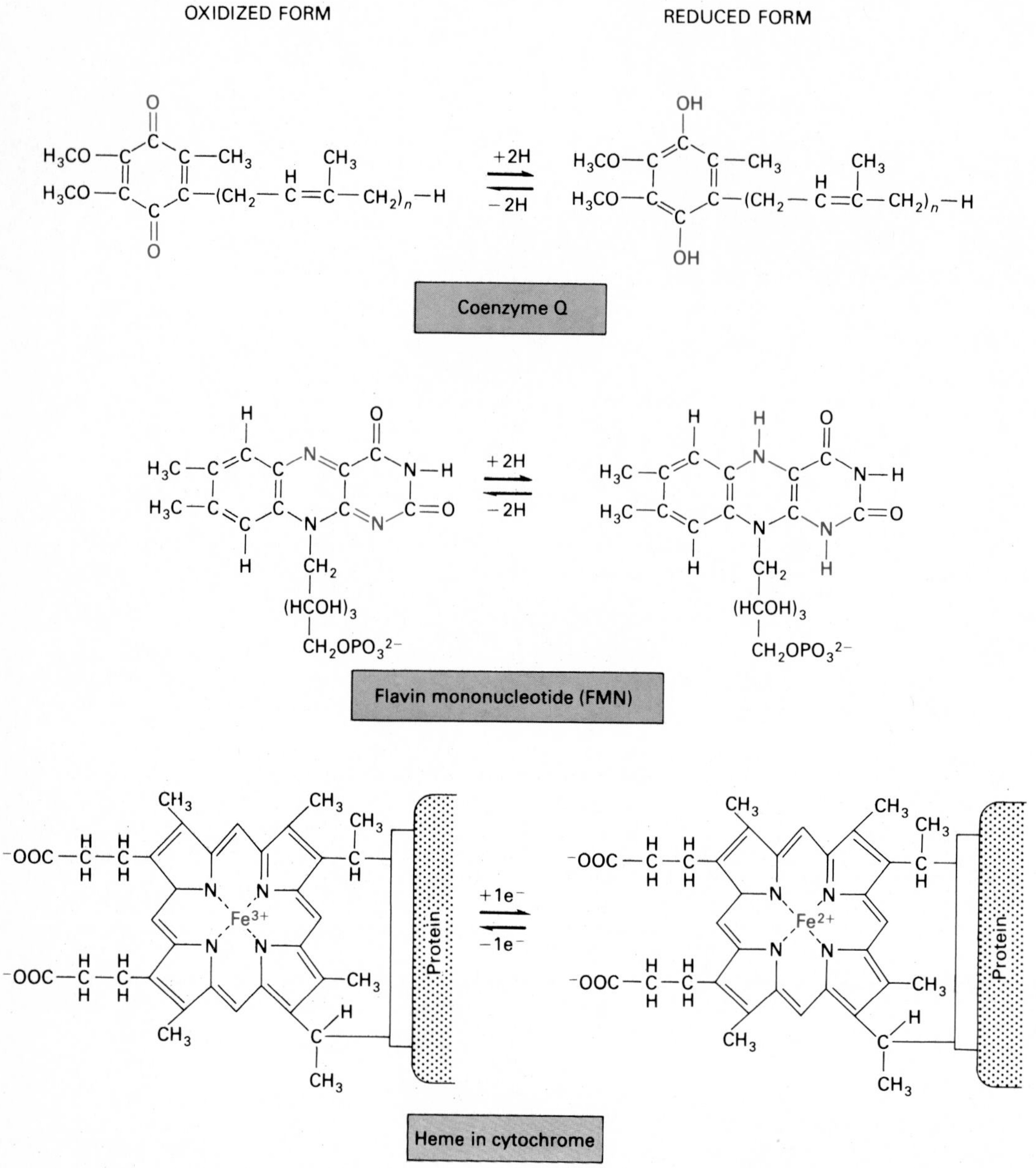

OXIDIZED FORM   REDUCED FORM

Coenzyme Q

Flavin mononucleotide (FMN)

Heme in cytochrome

FIGURE 9-11

Redox couples involved in electron transfer. The oxidized and reduced states of coenzyme Q, flavin mononucleotide (FMN), and the heme component of cytochromes are shown with the redox changes emphasized (color). Oxidation–reductions of coenzyme Q and FMN involve the transfer of two electrons (in H) at a time, whereas the change in state of a heme involves the transfer of one electron at a time, to and from the coordinated iron atom.

reduced ferrous (Fe^{2+}) state and the oxidized ferric (Fe^{3+}) state (see Fig. 9.11). Unlike NADH, flavins, and CoQ, which transfer two electrons at a time, the heme group accepts or transfers only one electron at a time. Reduced CoQ must therefore transfer its two high-potential electrons to two molecules of cytochrome b, the next member of the chain of electron carriers (Fig. 9.12). At the terminus of the electron transport chain, molecular oxygen accepts electrons from cytochrome a_3 and is thereby reduced. In this reduced state, previously unreactive O_2 is activated to a high enough energy level for it to combine with protons and be reduced to water, another end product of aerobic respiration. Sufficient free-energy differences exist at three different sites in the chain of reactions so that ATP synthesis can be subsidized in reactions coupled to electron transport.

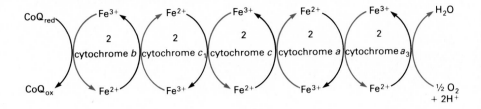

David Keilin discovered the central role of the cytochromes in respiration during the 1920s. He recognized three general classes of cytochromes, called a, b, and c, which differ slightly in their spectral absorption and other properties (Fig. 9.13). We now know that five specific cytochromes (cytochromes b, c_1, c, a, and a_3) are members of the aerobic respiratory electron transport chain and that the sequence of electron transfer reflects the order in which they are listed.

Cytochromes $a + a_3$ make up the enzyme **cytochrome oxidase**, which is the terminal member of the electron transport chain. Only cytochrome oxidase can interact with molecular oxygen and be reoxidized by transferring electrons to O_2. In particular, the cytochrome a_3 component of the enzyme transfers electrons directly to molecular oxygen and is thereby reoxidized to its Fe^{3+} state as oxygen is reduced.

The sequence of electron transfers from one carrier to another and finally to oxygen must be in the thermodynamically expected direction of free-energy decline, or from higher to lower reducing (energy) potential. Because the free-energy difference, $\Delta G°$, is correlated with the reducing potential, E_0, we would expect a greater decrease in free energy between the first reactant and oxygen than between subsequent reactants and oxygen. From many such measurements in assays of free-

FIGURE 9-12
The transfer of two electrons from reduced coenzyme Q requires two cytochrome b acceptor molecules because the heme of a cytochrome accepts only one electron at a time as its oxidized ferric ion (Fe^{3+}) is reduced to a ferrous ion (Fe^{2+}). The pathway of electron transport along the chain of cytochromes involves a valency change in the iron atom in each case, until the electrons are accepted by molecular oxygen at the terminus of the pathway.

FIGURE 9-13
The absorption spectra of the three classes of cytochromes in their oxidized (dashed lines) and reduced (solid color lines) states reveal slight but consistent differences. In each case the reduced cytochrome absorption spectrum exhibits peaks of absorption, called the α, β, and γ bands. By definition, the α band absorbs at the highest wavelength, the γ band at the lowest wavelength, and the β band at an intermediate wavelength. The precise locations of the three absorption peaks vary by a few nanometers in the spectrum of individual cytochromes in each of the three classes, and cytochromes c are further distinguished by a fourth (δ) absorption band at a wavelength of about 315 nm.

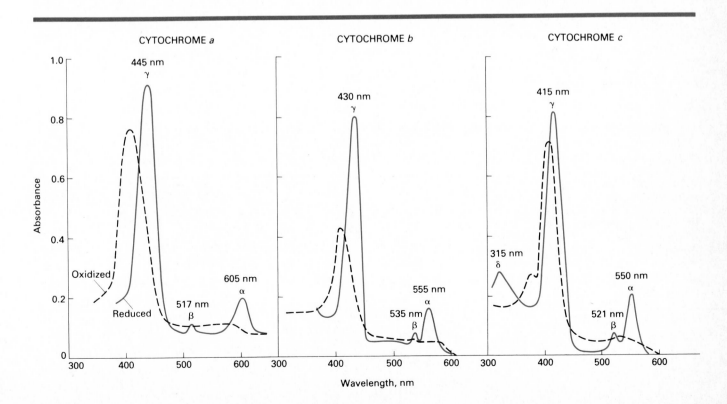

TABLE 9-1
Decline in Free Energy During Electron Flow Down the Respiratory Chain

Electron carrier (red/ox)	E_0 (volt)	$\Delta G°$ (kcal/mole)
$NADH/NAD^+ + H^+$	−0.32	−52.6
Flavoprotein red/ox	−0.12	−43.4
CoQ red/ox	+0.10	−33.2
2 cytochrome b red/ox	+0.05	−35.6
2 cytochrome c_1 red/ox	+0.22	−27.8
2 cytochrome c red/ox	+0.25	−26.2
2 cytochrome a–a_3 red /ox	+0.28	−25.0
Water/oxygen	+0.82	0

energy release or reducing potential as electrons are transferred to oxygen by individual reactants, it is clear that NAD is the first reactant in the sequence and that cytochrome oxidase is the last member of the sequence (Table 9.1).

An independent and supporting line of evidence for the postulated electron transfer sequence has been obtained from studies of selective inhibition of the different steps in the pathway. When we add a particular inhibitor to the test system, we expect all the components on the oxygen side of the inhibited step to remain oxidized because they cannot receive electrons from carriers on the NAD side of the blocked step. In the same vein, all the components preceding the inhibited step remain reduced because they cannot transfer electrons to carriers past the inhibited point. For example, when the antibiotic *antimycin A* is added to a suspension of active mitochondria, the pyridine nucleotides, flavoprotein, and cytochrome b all remain reduced, whereas cytochromes c and a are fully oxidized. These results indicate that cytochromes c and a are on the oxygen side of the block and therefore occur later in the sequence than the reduced substances. When cyanide is provided as an inhibitor of active mitochondrial respiration, all the carriers remain reduced. Because cyanide is known to be a specific inhibitor of cytochrome a_3, the results of the inhibition assay clearly show that cytochrome a_3 is the terminal member of the electron transport chain; none of the carriers become oxidized while the poison is present. These and other kinds of experimental tests have made it possible to locate many of the respiratory chain components in relation to one another in the sequence. Other electron carriers in the respiratory chain, such as iron–sulfur (FeS) complexes and copper in metalloproteins, have not all been positioned precisely in the sequence nor have they been as fully characterized as the cytochromes.

When preparations of purified inner mitochondrial membrane are rendered soluble by the relatively mild anionic detergents *cholate* and *deoxycholate*, both of which are bile acids, four major **respiratory enzyme complexes** can be recovered in separate fractions. Each enzyme complex retains high activity and can be studied under controlled conditions that are exceedingly difficult to achieve with intact membranes. The simplified diagram in Fig. 9.14 shows the sequence of

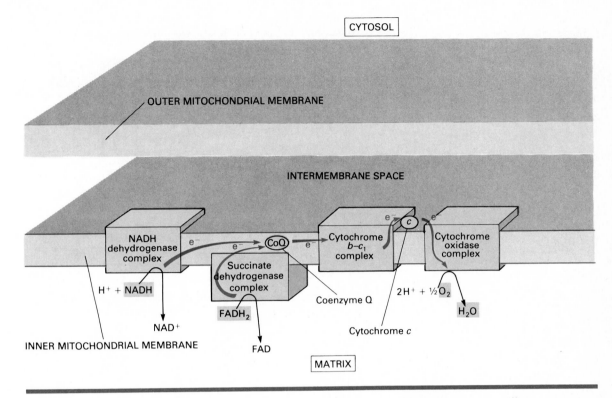

FIGURE 9-14
Schematic summary of the sequence of electron transfers from reduced NAD and FAD to molecular oxygen via the activities of the four complexes of respiratory enzymes (color) situated in the inner mitochondrial membrane. Electrons are passed to coenzyme Q (CoQ) from NADH via the NADH dehydrogenase complex and from FADH₂ via the succinate dehydrogenase complex. Reduced CoQ gives up its electrons to the cytochrome b–c₁ complex, and the electrons are then transferred via cytochrome c to the cytochrome oxidase complex, and finally from this complex to oxygen, which is thereby reduced to water. Each of the respiratory complexes consists of a number of electron carriers in addition to the one for which the complex is named, but these details are not shown here.

electron transfers from reduced NAD and FAD to molecular oxygen, via the activities of the four respiratory enzyme complexes. Electrons from NADH are accepted by the **NADH dehydrogenase complex**, which gives up its electrons to CoQ, which also receives electrons from FADH$_2$, the reduced coenzyme of succinate dehydrogenase in the **succinate dehydrogenase complex**. Electrons are passed from reduced CoQ to the **cytochrome b–c_1 complex** and from there to cytochrome c. Cytochrome c gives its electrons to the **cytochrome oxidase complex**, which passes them on to molecular oxygen, and water is formed when reduced oxygen combines with protons.

Each respiratory enzyme complex includes other electron carriers in addition to the major dehydrogenase or cytochrome proteins (Table 9.2). In some cases the sequence of electron transfer within an enzyme complex can be established on the basis of the reactions that can be carried out by fractions separated from the whole complex. For the NADH dehydrogenase complex, for example, three fractions have been resolved: (1) a soluble NADH dehydrogenase, (2) a crude particulate fraction with redox centers FeS 3 and FeS 4, and (3) a soluble nonheme iron protein with center FeS 2. On the basis of the redox reactions of these three fractions, the postulated sequence of electron transfer from NADH to CoQ is

$$NADH \rightarrow \overbrace{FMN \rightarrow FeS\ 1}^{\substack{NADH \\ dehydrogenase}} \rightarrow \overbrace{FeS\ 4 \rightarrow FeS\ 3}^{\substack{Crude\ particulate \\ fraction}} \rightarrow \overbrace{FeS\ 2}^{\substack{Nonheme\ iron \\ protein}} \rightarrow CoQ$$

Some difference of opinion exists concerning the amounts of the electron transfer complexes and their ratios in the inner membrane of

TABLE 9-2
**Components of the Four Respiratory Complexes in the
Mitochondrial Inner Membrane**

Complex	Components
I, NADH dehydrogenase complex	NAD FMN Iron sulfur (FeS) centers Coenzyme Q_{10} Phospholipids
II, Succinate dehydrogenase complex	FAD Iron sulfur (FeS) centers Cytochrome b_{558} Phospholipids
III, Cytochrome b–c_1 complex	Cytochrome b Cytochrome c_1 Nonheme iron protein Coenzyme Q_{10} Phospholipids
IV, Cytochrome oxidase complex	Cytochrome a Cytochrome a_3 Copper Phospholipids

the mitochondrion. A large part of the difficulty in obtaining quantitative date is the elaborate nature of the procedures used in such analyses and the inaccuracy that results from the need to apply a variety of correction factors for overlaps in absorption spectra of cytochrome components and for contamination by other flavoproteins with prosthetic groups that are the same as the ones in respiratory complex flavoproteins. The importance of accurate determinations of the stoichiometry of electron transfer carriers is related to the manner in which the carriers are organized in the membrane and to the interactions made possible by their organization. If the complexes occurred in approximately equal amounts, we would expect them to be formally organized into relatively fixed assemblies that interact appropriately because of their physical juxtaposition. If the enzyme complexes were present in different amounts, however, they would be more likely to interact by random collisions as they moved more freely within the plane of the membrane. Unfortunately, we cannot distinguish between the two possible modes of organization on the basis of quantitative data, because the values derived from different studies differ considerably. Each proposed organization enjoys its own experimental and quantitative supporting data. We do know that CoQ and cytochrome c are present in the membrane in considerable excess over the other carriers and that these two small molecules have diffusion coefficients indicating that they move at least ten times faster than the respiratory enzyme complexes within the membrane. Whether the complexes move independently of one another or are organized into larger aggregate assemblies, we have calculations showing that electron transfers can take place at an appropriate rate along the respiratory chain primarily as a consequence of the high mobility of the intermediary carriers. It is, after all, CoQ and cytochrome c that accept electrons from one enzyme complex and pass on the electrons to the next enzyme complex of the respiratory chain (see

Fig. 9.14). Each of the two patterns of organization of the respiratory enzyme complexes thus remains a viable option, and we need additional data to determine the precise geometry and means of interaction that characterize the respiratory chain of carriers within the inner membrane of the mitochondrion.

9.6
ATP Synthesis During Respiratory Electron Transport

During the passage of a pair of electrons from NADH to oxygen along a gradient of declining free-energy levels, a large enough change in free energy occurs (at least 9–10 kcal/mole) at three different sites to sponsor ATP synthesis from ADP and P_i. The measured redox potentials and their corresponding free-energy changes drop in large enough steps as electrons are transferred within the NADH dehydrogenase complex, from NADH to CoQ; within the cytochrome b–c_1 complex, from CoQ to cytochrome c; and within the cytochrome oxidase complex, from cytochrome c to molecular oxygen (Fig. 9.15). The passage of a pair of electrons to oxygen from $FADH_2$ of the succinate dehydrogenase complex exhibits only two large drops in redox potential and, therefore, sponsors only two ATP synthesis events. In this case there is insufficient free-energy difference to sponsor ATP synthesis as electrons pass from $FADH_2$ to CoQ, because the redox potential of $FADH_2$ is only slightly higher than the redox potential for CoQ (about 0 mV). The drops in redox potential are the same, however, for electron transfers from CoQ to oxygen through the cytochrome b–c_1 complex and the cytochrome oxidase complex, whether CoQ has accepted a pair of electrons from NADH or from $FADH_2$.

The synthesis of ATP during respiratory electron transport is called **oxidative phosphorylation** to distinguish it from ATP synthesis during substrate phosphorylations in metabolic pathways such as glycolysis. Oxidative phosphorylation is the single most important

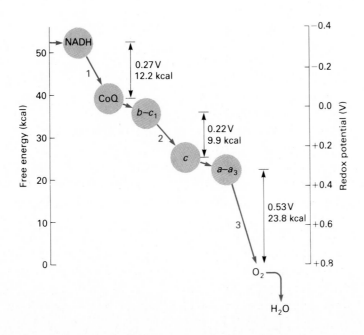

FIGURE 9-15
The decline in kilocalories (kcal) of free energy and its corresponding measurement of redox potential (volts) are shown for each of the major steps in the transport of a pair of electrons from NADH to oxygen. At three of these five steps (colored numbers), there is a large enough free-energy difference to sponsor ATP synthesis (at least 9–10 kcal/mole).

FIGURE 9-16
The efficiency of oxidative phosphorylation during electron transport is determined from the P/O ratio, which represents mole equivalents of phosphate utilized in ATP synthesis per oxygen atom consumed (reduced) in electron transport. The P/O ratio is calculated by polarographic measurement of the decline in oxygen concentration in the medium upon the addition of substrate (source of electrons) followed by one or more pulses of measured amounts of ADP. A P/O ratio of 3 indicates that the maximum of 3 molecules of ATP are synthesized for each pair of electrons transferred from the substrate to oxygen.

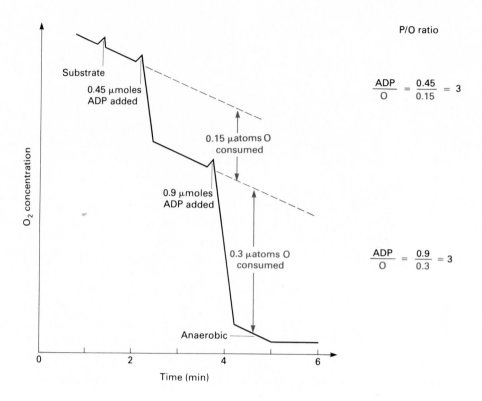

function of the mitochondrion, and it is the process by which aerobic organisms obtain the preponderance of their energy for a myriad of activities. A customary means of expressing the efficiency of oxidative phosphorylation is the **P/O ratio**, or mole equivalents of P_i esterified per atom of oxygen consumed (reduced). The P/O values are readily determined by a radiochemical assay of the incorporation of $^{32}P_i$ or by the polarographic measurement of oxygen concentration in the assay medium to which different substrates can be added during the course of an experiment (Fig. 9.16). When electrons pass to oxygen from substrates that reduce NAD, or from NADH itself, the P/O ratio is 3.0 or nearly 3.0, but when electrons pass from succinate or reduced FAD to oxygen, the P/O ratio is only 2.0 (Table 9.3). These ratios indicate that 3 molecules of ATP are synthesized for every pair of electrons transferred from NADH to oxygen but that only 2 ATP per pair of electrons passed from FADH$_2$ of succinate dehydrogenase to oxygen (Fig. 9.17). Using reaction [9.4] (Section 9.3), we find that the 10 NADH per glucose lead to 30 ATP (3 ATP per NADH × 10 = 30 ATP), and the 2 FADH$_2$ per glucose allow the synthesis of 4 ATP (2 ATP per FADH$_2$ × 2 = 4 ATP). When we add the 2 ATP from glycolysis and the 2 ATP (from GTP) from the Krebs cycle reactions, a total of 38 ATP is conserved for each glucose fully oxidized in the cell to CO_2 and H_2O.

TABLE 9-3
P/O Ratios of Oxidations in the Krebs Cycle

Reaction	P/O
Pyruvate → acetyl CoA	3
Isocitrate → α-ketoglutarate	3
α-ketoglutarate → succinate	4*
Succinate → fumarate	2
Malate → oxaloacetate	3

* One of these is a substrate-level phosphorylation.

$$C_6H_{12}O_6 + 6\ O_2 + 38\ ADP + 38\ P_i$$

$$\downarrow \qquad \Delta G° = -420\ \text{kcal/mole}$$

$$6\ CO_2 + 44\ H_2O + 38\ ATP$$
$$(6 + 38)$$

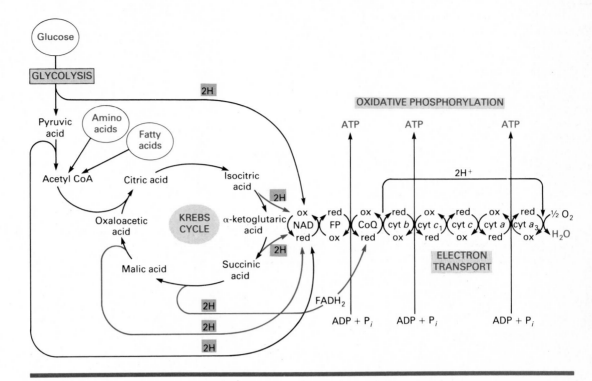

FIGURE 9-17
Summary of the reaction systems by which glucose is oxidized to CO_2 and H_2O and by which the released fuel energy is conserved in ATP synthesized in oxidative phosphorylation reactions coupled to electron transport toward oxygen. Electrons derived from NADH produced in glycolysis and in the processing of pyruvate to acetyl CoA (black arrows), plus electrons from the NADH and $FADH_2$ produced in the Krebs cycle (red arrows), are transported toward oxygen along the respiratory chain of electron carriers. ATP is synthesized at three different sites in the transport of electrons from NADH—but at only two of these sites for electrons from $FADH_2$ to oxygen.

When glucose is oxidized to CO_2 and H_2O in air under standard *in vitro* conditions, the free-energy difference between glucose and its end products is -686 kcal/mole, all of which is dissipated as heat.

$$C_6H_{12}O_6 + 6\ O_2 \rightarrow 6\ CO_2 + 6\ H_2O;\quad \Delta G^\circ = -686\ \text{kcal/mole}$$

Because the living cell conserves about 7 kcal of free energy per mole of ATP synthesized:

$$ADP + P_i \rightarrow ATP + H_2O;\quad \Delta G^\circ = 7\ \text{kcal/mole}$$

266 kcal/mole are conserved (38 ATP $\times$ 7 kcal = 266 kcal), and only 420 of the 686 kcal are released as heat in a typical aerobic cell during the complete oxidation of one mole of glucose. The efficiency of energy conservation in the cell is $266/686 \times 100 = 39\%$, which is quite high compared with a typical combustion e gine, which may extract only 10% to 20% of the available energy o do work and dissipate the remainder as heat.

9.7
Chemiosmotic Coupling of Oxidative Phosphorylation and Electron Transport

In the late 1940s and early 1950s, a sufficient body of evidence was available to show that oxidative phosphorylation was *coupled* to respiratory electron transport, rather than being an entirely independent process. We can readily demonstrate that the two processes are related to one another by adding an *uncoupling agent*, such as 2,4-dinitrophenol, to an actively respiring mitochondrial preparation. In the presence of dinitrophenol, ATP synthesis stops and electron transport continues, but at a higher rate. All the energy is released as heat in these preparations. When dinitrophenol is removed from the preparation, ATP synthesis resumes and respiration, as measured by oxygen uptake or another suitable method, is reduced to its earlier rate. Data such as these clearly show that oxidative phosphorylation can be halted independently of any inhibition of electron transport, but that *control* over the rate of electron transport is determined in part by coupled oxidative phosphorylation. The effect of dinitrophenol is specific for oxidative phosphorylation because substrate-level phosphorylations, such as those in glycolysis, remain unchanged in the presence of the uncoupling agent.

The most widely accepted mechanism for coupling oxidative phosphorylation and electron transport is stated in the **chemiosmotic hypothesis**, which was first proposed in 1961 by Peter Mitchell on purely theoretical rather than experimental grounds. In essence Mitchell proposed that, as high-energy electrons pass down the respiratory chain, the energy released is used to pump protons across the inner mitochondrial membrane, from the matrix to the intermembrane space. An **electrochemical proton gradient** is thus formed across the inner membrane, and the energy stored in this gradient is used to drive ATP synthesis by the enzyme **ATP synthetase**. Mitchell listed four basic postulates of the mechanism, each of which corresponded to structural and functional features of the membrane and each of which was open to experimental verification. In terms of the mitochondrion, the postulates were as follows:

1. The inner mitochondrial membrane is impermeable to H^+ and OH^- in particular and to other ionic species in general.

2. The components of the electron transport chain are so situated in the membrane that, as electrons are transferred from one carrier to another, protons are directionally translocated out of the matrix space and into the intermembrane space, across the membrane.

3. The ATP synthetase complex can harness the energy of the electrochemical proton gradient to subsidize the synthesis of ATP, or the complex can act in reverse as an ATP hydrolase and use the energy of ATP hydrolysis to pump protons out of the matrix when the electrochemical gradient is insufficient for ATP synthesis.

4. The membrane contains H^+-linked or OH^--linked carrier systems that help metabolites across the membrane and thus to enter or leave the matrix space.

The movement of protons during electron transport generates a *pH gradient* and an *electrical gradient* across the membrane. The pH gradient results from the difference in H^+ concentration between the mitochondrial matrix, where it is low, and the rest of the cell, where it is higher (about pH 7). The electrical gradient results from the outflow of positive ions making the outside positive while the interior space is negatively charged. The total protonic potential difference, or **protonmotive force**

(Δp), is composed of both the electrical ($\Delta \psi$) and the chemical activity (ΔpH) components, according to the equation

$$\Delta p = \Delta \psi - Z\Delta pH$$

where $Z = 2.303RT/F$, and R, T, and F are the gas constant, absolute temperature, and Faraday constant, respectively. The units of Z are volts, and the value of Z is 0.059 at 25°C, or 59 millivolts (mV). The typical protonmotive force in respiring mitochondria is more than 200 mV, of which about 150 mV is the electrical component and the pH gradient differential is about -1 pH unit.

To account for the three phosphorylation sites along the chain of electron transport from NADH to oxygen, Mitchell proposed a linearly arranged series of redox circuits within the inner membrane. Each circuit contains a proton-carrying sequence and an electron-carrying sequence, which results in the translocation outward of two protons for every two electrons transported from one carrier to another *within* the circuit (Fig. 9.18). The electrons are ultimately transferred to oxygen by the cytochrome oxidase complex, and the outflow of protons creates an electrochemical gradient across the membrane. If the protonmotive force of the electrochemical gradient is sufficiently high, the membrane-bound ATP synthetase can use the energy to translocate protons back across the membrane and into the matrix space. In so doing, the enzyme catalyzes the synthesis of ATP as the electrochemical gradient is discharged. The ATP synthetase is reversible, however, and it remains poised in favor of ATP synthesis as long as a sufficiently large protonmotive force is generated by electron transfers. In the absence of electron transfer, the ATP synthetase acts reversibly as an ATP hydrolase. In its role as an ATP synthetase, the enzyme catalyzes the synthesis of one ATP for each pair of protons pumped across the membrane during electron transport, using the protonmotive force of the electrochemical gradient. Three ATP are thus synthesized for the three pairs of protons that are translocated as one pair of electrons makes its way from carrier to carrier and finally to oxygen (Fig. 9.19).

The electrochemical gradient is maintained across the membrane by the continued transfer of electrons and associated proton translocation, even as portions of the gradient are discharged during ATP synthesis. A number of other processes also depend on the electrochemical gradient, however, and these processes essentially compete with ATP synthetase for available protonmotive force. Among the most important of the alternative processes are those that require energy for active transport of ions and metabolites across the membrane and into the mitochondrial matrix, where the Krebs cycle, β-oxidation of fatty acids, and other metabolic pathways occur. In addition, ATP synthesis at the membrane must be provided with supplies of ADP and phosphate from the cytosol, and ATP must be transported into the cytosol where energy is utilized for biosynthesis and other energy-requiring activities. Carrier proteins situated within the membrane help molecules and ions across, often in association with an active ion pump (see Fig. 5.30). In the case of ATP, for each ADP moved into the mitochondrial matrix, one ATP molecule moves out of the matrix along its declining gradient, whereas phosphate

FIGURE 9-18
Schematic summary of Mitchell's
proposed organization in the mitochondrial inner membrane of the
series of proton-carrying and electron-
carrying circuits. Protons (H^+) are
translocated outward (black arrows)
as the electrons pass via carriers
from NADH to oxygen (red arrows).
The outflow of protons creates an
electrochemical proton gradient
across the inner membrane. If the
protonmotive energy of this gradient is
high enough, membrane-bound ATP
synthetase (color) can use the energy
to translocate protons back across the
membrane into the matrix and proceed
to catalyze the energy-requiring
synthesis of ATP.

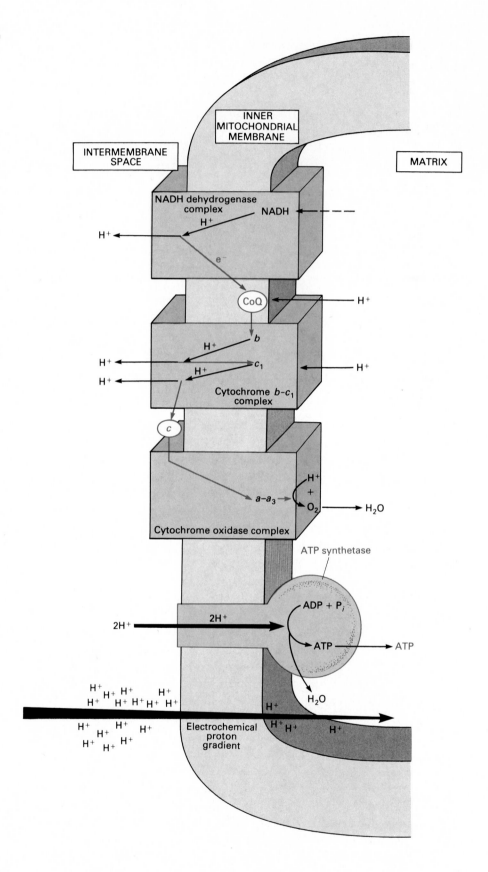

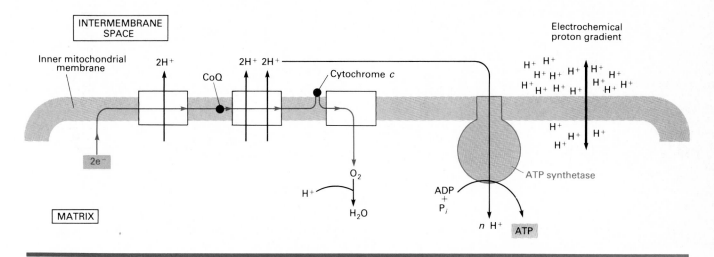

FIGURE 9-19
Schematic illustration of the coupled processes of electron transport and oxidative phosphorylation. Using the protonmotive force of the electrochemical proton gradient generated by the pumping of protons across the mitochondrial inner membrane, ATP synthetase (color) catalyzes the synthesis of one ATP molecule for each pair of protons pumped out. In this way, three molecules of ATP are made for the three pairs of protons pumped out as one pair of electrons is transported (red arrows) through the respiratory carrier chain to oxygen.

moves in via another system that is coupled to the inward flow of H^+ down its electrochemical gradient. Like phosphate, pyruvate is carried into the matrix from the cytosol via a coupled inflow of H^+ through the mediation of a common carrier protein in the inner mitochondrial membrane (Fig. 9.20).

Ca^{2+} is actively transported out of the cytosol and into the mitochondrial matrix via a transport protein in the inner membrane, using the protonmotive force of the electrochemical gradient. The concentration of free Ca^{2+} is thereby kept at levels of 10^{-7} M or less, which is important for many biological functions that are regulated by

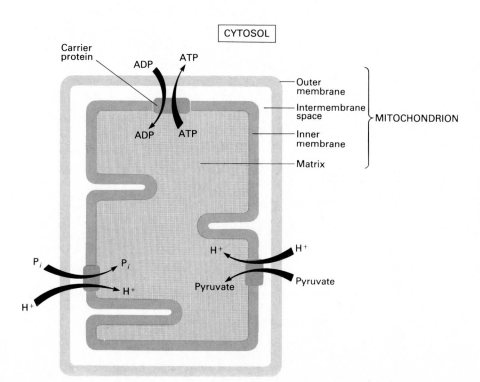

FIGURE 9-20
Compounds required for mitochondrial reactions, such as ADP and P_i for ATP synthesis and pyruvate for oxidation in aerobic respiration, cross the relatively impermeable mitochondrial inner membrane with the help of carrier proteins (color) situated in this membrane. For each molecule of ADP that enters, one molecule of ATP exits the mitochondrion and moves into the cytosol for use in various metabolic pathways. Phosphate and pyruvate move from the cytosol into the mito-chondrion via the coupled inflow of H^+, but different carrier proteins are involved in these events. Many other metabolites and ions also cross the inner membrane with the help of particular carrier proteins.

signals embodied in small changes in Ca^{2+} concentration in the cytosol. A relatively small amount of energy is probably required for the active transport of Ca^{2+}, because much of it is removed from solution by precipitation as calcium phosphate within the matrix. Because of calcium phosphate formation, little free Ca^{2+} remains within the mitochondrial matrix and relatively little energy is therefore utilized for ion movement against such a shallow incline, compared with a steeper gradient. It is clear, however, that competing energy-requiring processes do exist, because the addition of large amounts of Ca^{2+} to respiring mitochondria leads to the halt of ATP synthesis in the preparation. The removal or dissipation of the high ion concentration leads to the resumption of ATP synthesis.

We mentioned earlier in this section that dinitrophenol uncouples oxidative phosphorylation from electron transport, leading to a cessation of ATP synthesis and an enhanced rate of electron transport (as shown by increased oxygen uptake in uncoupled systems). The explanation for the uncoupling effect is that the protons pumped out of the mitochondrion are captured by the uncoupling agent and thus cannot be taken back into the matrix through the proton channel of the ATPase protein. The protonmotive force of the membrane gradient is dissipated, and ATP synthetase activity stops. Cessation of ATP synthesis in turn is believed to allow electron transport to proceed at an unrestrained rate subject only to the supply of substrates from the cytosol. Such **respiratory control** is believed to function via direct inhibitory influence of the proton gradient on the rate of electron transport down the respiratory carrier chain. When the proton gradient collapses in uncoupled mitochondria, electron transport is enhanced, and when the electrochemical proton gradient is reinstituted, the rate of electron transport again comes under the inhibitory control of the gradient.

Mitochondrial electron transport is naturally uncoupled from oxidative phosphorylation in brown fat cells, and all of the energy of substrate oxidation is released as heat. In these specialized cells, the inner mitochondrial membrane contains a particular transport protein that helps protons move down their electrochemical gradient rather than being pumped out of the matrix. As a result of uncoupling electron transport, the brown fat cells produce heat rather than ATP as they rapidly oxidize their stored fat reserves. Brown fat tissues are characteristic of hibernating animals, which are aided in their reawakening by the heat produced during relatively unrestrained electron transport in large mitochondria of the fat cells.

All the basic postulates of the chemiosmotic mechanism are now supported by experimental evidence. Indeed, even though Mitchell's proposal in 1961 was met with considerable skepticism, he and others were able to swing the balance of favor to the chemiosmotic mechanism by the mid-1970s, on the basis of strong experimental confirmation of the hypothetical premises. In 1978 Mitchell received a Nobel prize in chemistry for his incisive and powerful contributions to our understanding of membrane-based energy transfer systems. The broad sweep of the picture is established, but some details of the mechanism remain to be clarified.

9.8
ATP Synthetase in Chemiosmotic Coupling Membranes _____

A transmembrane protein with ATPase properties (ATP synthetase and/or ATP hydrolase) is known to be present in chemiosmotic coupling membranes in chloroplasts and bacteria, as well as in mitochondria. The mitochondrial enzyme is composed of nine polypeptide chains, of which four hydrophobic chains are embedded in the membrane bilayer and the remaining five subunits are bound together in a spherical head portion that juts out from the matrix-facing surface of the inner membrane (Fig. 9.21). The spherical head of the lollipop-shaped enzyme is called the F_1 factor, and the embedded stalk portion is the F_o factor (it is sensitive to the respiratory inhibitor *oligomycin*, whereas the F_1 factor is resistant). The whole enzyme is often designated the **F_oF_1ATPase**.

In the 1960s, Ephraim Racker showed that submitochondrial particles obtained by the sonication of isolated mitochondria could carry out coupled electron transport and oxidative phosphorylation only if the spherical heads of the ATPase were present. Submitochondrial particles stripped of F_1 factor could carry out electron transport but not oxidative phosphorylation. When the F_1 heads were added back to the stripped submitochondrial particles, oxidative phosphorylation was restored and was again coupled to electron transport (Fig. 9.22). Relatively little is known about the functions of the individual polypeptides, but one of the five head chains is believed to contain the catalytic center of the enzyme,

FIGURE 9-21
The F_oF_1ATPase that catalyzes mitochondrial ATP synthesis and/or ATP hydrolysis is a transmembrane protein. Its stalklike F_o portion is embedded in the membrane, and its knoblike F_1 head portion juts out from the matrix-facing surface of the chemiosmotic coupling inner membrane. (a) Electron micrograph of a negatively stained crista of isolated mitochondria from adult bee tissue. The ATPase molecules line only the matrix-facing surface of the membrane. ×264,500. (Photograph courtesy of B. Chance.) (b) Drawing of a portion of the mitochondrion showing the orientation of the F_o and F_1 portions of the ATPase in the inner mitochondrial membrane.

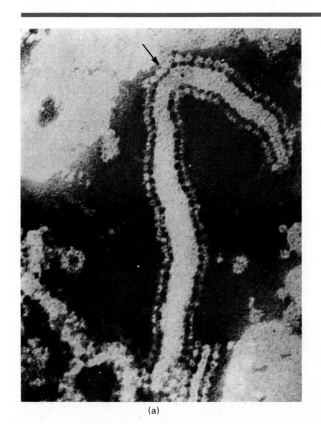

(a)

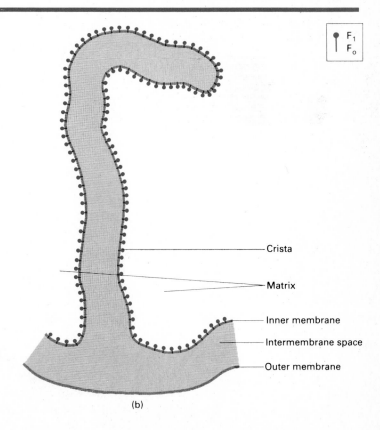

F_1
F_o

Crista

Matrix

Inner membrane

Intermembrane space

Outer membrane

(b)

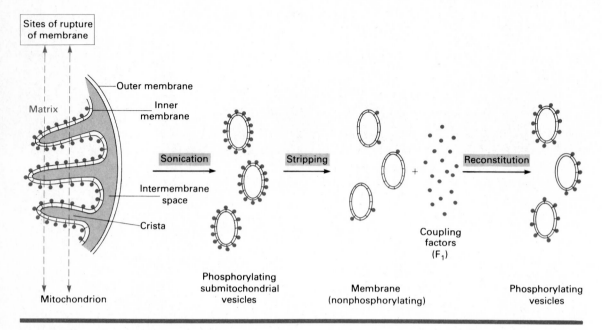

FIGURE 9-22
Diagrammatic summary of Racker's reconstitution experiments that showed that oxidative phosphorylation was a function of the F_1 heads (color), or coupling factors, and not of the stripped mitochondrial inner membrane. Submitochondrial vesicles derived by sonication from mitochondrial cristae could carry out oxidative phosphorylation only when the knoblike F_1 components were present, either in the original vesicles or in vesicles reconstituted from stripped membrane plus coupling factors.

and the other F_1 and F_o components are believed to have structural or regulatory functions. The enzyme can use the energy of the electrochemical gradient to drive the synthesis of ATP by harnessing the flow of protons back into the mitochondrial matrix, through a transmembrane proton channel in the embedded F_o portion of the protein. Under conditions that are energetically more favorable for ATP hydrolysis, the ATPase can use the energy of ATP hydrolysis to pump protons across the membrane in the opposite direction, from the matrix to the outside space. Therefore the ATPase is a reversible system that can convert protonmotive energy to chemical bond energy in ATP or the chemical bond energy of ATP to protonmotive force in an electrochemical proton gradient (Fig. 9.23).

The ATP synthetase of photosynthetic membranes in chloroplasts works in conjunction with an electron transport chain embedded in these same membranes. As electrons are transferred from one electron carrier to the next in a linear series, protons are pumped across the membrane. The protonmotive force generated by the electrochemical proton gradient is used by ATP synthetase to drive ATP synthesis in a strictly light-dependent process called *photophosphorylation*. In chloroplasts, the electron source is water, rather than oxidized substrates, and the electron carriers are cytochromes and quinones that resemble but are not identical to the electron carriers in the mitochondrial respiratory chain. In chloroplasts as in mitochondria, an uncoupling agent causes ATP synthesis to stop while electron transport continues. In the dark, both electron transport and photophosphorylation come to a halt, because electrons are no longer provided from water to the photosynthetic pigments for relay to the electron transport chain. We will discuss these systems in the next chapter.

Virtually all bacteria have an ATP synthetase in the plasma membrane, as well as an electron transport chain. The ATP synthetase is very much like the enzyme in mitochondria and chloroplasts, and the

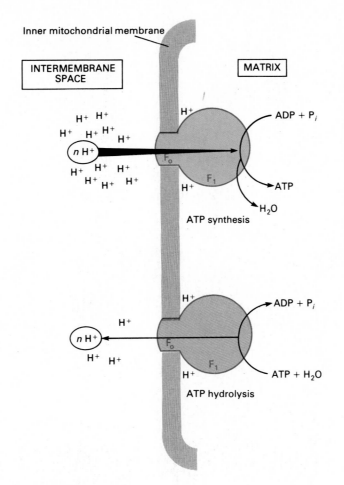

Inner mitochondrial membrane

INTERMEMBRANE
SPACE

MATRIX

ATP synthesis

ATP hydrolysis

FIGURE 9-23
The mitochondrial F_oF_1ATPase (color) may act reversibly as a synthetase or as a hydrolase, depending on the particular prevailing conditions. An inward flow of protons drives ATP synthesis, thereby converting proton-motive energy to chemical bond energy, whereas protons pumped out of the matrix during ATP hydrolysis convert chemical energy to proton-motive energy in an electrochemical proton gradient. The catalytic center is believed to reside in one of the polypeptide subunits of the spherical F_1 head of the enzyme.

electron transport chain generally includes carriers similar to those in eukaryotic organelles. The final electron acceptor is oxygen in aerobic bacteria, but anaerobes utilize various alternative acceptors such as nitrates, nitrites, sulfates, sulfites, and simple organic compounds such as carbonates. Some strict anaerobes may derive their energy from glycolysis alone, without the subsequent oxidations to CO_2 and H_2O via the Krebs cycle and electron transport. In anerobic bacteria that lack an electron transport chain, the ATPase acts as an ATP hydrolase and generates protonmotive force by establishing an electrochemical proton gradient across the membrane, using the energy of ATP hydrolysis. In bacteria that possess an electron transport chain, the enzyme utilizes the protonmotive force of the electrochemical proton gradient generated by electron transport to synthesize ATP, just as occurs in mitochondria and chloroplasts.

In bacterial cells, many of the amino acids and sugars enter via an active transport system that relies on the protonmotive force of an electrochemical proton gradient. Nutrients and metabolites are transported across the plasma membrane against their concentration gradients, often through coupled entry with H^+ by means of specific carrier proteins within the membrane, subsidized by the protonmotive force of the electrochemical gradient established across the membrane. The gradient is established by the respiratory proton pump under aerobic conditions, or by ATP hydrolysis and other means in anaerobic systems

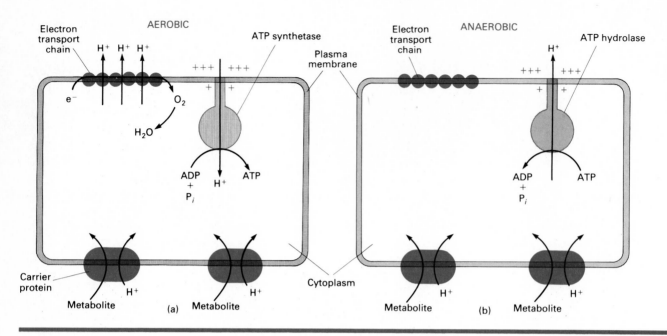

FIGURE 9-24
Many metabolites enter bacterial cells by an active transport system that relies on the protonmotive force of an electrochemical proton gradient. (a) Under aerobic conditions, the gradient develops as the result of coupled electron transport and oxidative phosphorylation in aerobic respiration, and its protonmotive force subsidizes the active transport of metabolites into the cell. Carrier proteins that facilitate the active transport of metabolites also aid in the coupled passive transport of H^+. (b) Under anaerobic conditions, the electrochemical proton gradient is established by ATP hydrolysis or other means, and the active transport of metabolites is thus sustained even when the respiratory proton pump is not active.

(Fig. 9.24). The proton pumps of the bacterial plasma membrane closely resemble the proton pumps of mitochondrial and chloroplast membranes. In all these cases (at least under aerobic conditions), protons pumped out across the membrane by the respiratory chain generate an electrochemical proton gradient whose protonmotive force is used for ATP synthesis and the inward flow of many metabolites. By contrast, animal cells have Na^+ pumps in the plasma membrane that extrude Na^+ against its concentration gradient, using the energy of ATP hydrolysis by ATPase components of the pump. The Na^+ gradient thus generated is responsible for the inward flow of metabolites to the cytosol from the exterior space, in active-transport episodes coupled to the entry of Na^+ along its concentration gradient, aided by specific carrier proteins in the membrane (see Fig. 5.30). The ATPase of the Na^+ pump acts primarily as an ATP hydrolase, whereas the ATPase of the respiratory chain acts primarily as an ATP synthetase and only occasionally as an ATP hydrolase.

Mitochondrial Compartmentation

The mitochondrion has a total of four compartments or locations where enzymes can be situated: the outer membrane, inner membrane, matrix, and intermembrane space. Purified mitochondria can be subfractionated to separate all four of these compartments, and each can then be studied in relatively pure form. The outer membrane can be disaggregated with digitonin, a plant steroid with surface-active properties, and the four subfractions can then be collected by differential centrifugation (Fig. 9.25). By the use of the digitonin method or some other method, each of the four compartments has been analyzed and shown to have its own unique enzyme repertory and biochemical activities (Table 9.4).

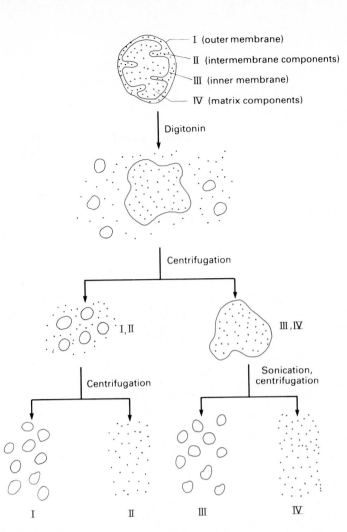

I (outer membrane)
II (intermembrane components)
III (inner membrane)
IV (matrix components)

Digitonin

Centrifugation

I, II

III, IV

Centrifugation

Sonication, centrifugation

I

II

III

IV

FIGURE 9-25
After digitonin treatment to break up the outer membrane, the four compartments (I–IV) of mitochondria can be separated by successive differential centrifugations. The first centrifugation produces a sediment of particles containing the heavier III and IV components (color) and a fluid supernatant phase in which the lighter I and II components are suspended. Recentrifugation of the I, II mixture separates a sediment of outer membranes (I) from the suspension of intermembrane components (II). After sonication and the resuspension of the III,IV fraction, centrifugation produces a sediment of heavier inner membrane vesicles (III) and a fluid supernatant phase in which the lighter matrix materials (IV) remain suspended. The four submitochondrial fractions can then be assayed to determine their particular characteristics.

TABLE 9-4
Enzyme Distribution in the Four Mitochondrial Compartments

Outer Membrane	Inner Membrane	Intermembrane Space	Matrix
Cytochrome b_5	δ-aminolevulinic acid synthase	Adenylate kinase	Aconitase
Fatty acid elongation enzymes	Choline dehydrogenase	Cytochrome c peroxidase (yeast)	Amino acid activating enzymes
Glycerolphosphate acyl transferase	Coenzyme QH_2–cytochrome c reductase	Nucleoside diphosphokinase	Aspartate aminotransferase
Kinurine hydroxylase	Cytochrome b	Nucleoside monophospho-kinase	Carbamyl phosphate synthase
Lysophosphatidyl acyl transferase	Cytochrome c_1	Sulfite oxidase	Citrate synthase
Monoamine oxidase	Cytochrome oxidase		Enol hydrase
NADH–cytochrome c reductase	Fatty acyl carnitine transferase		Fatty acyl-CoA synthase
Nucleoside diphosphokinase	Ferrochetalase		Fatty acyl-CoA dehydrogenase
Phosphatidate phosphatase	Glycerol 3-phosphate dehydrogenase		Fumarase
Phospholipase A	β-hydroxybutyrate dehydrogenase		Glutamate dehydrogenase
	NADH dehydrogenase		β-hydroxyacyl-CoA dehydrogenase
	Nicotinamide nucleotide transhydrogenase		Isocitrate dehydrogenase
	Oligomycin-sensitive ATPase		β-ketoacyl-CoA thiolase
	Succinate dehydrogenase		α-ketoglutarate dehydrogenase
			Malate dehydrogenase
			Ornithine carbamyl transferase
			Pyruvate carboxylase
			Pyruvate dehydrogenase
			DNA polymerase
			RNA polymerase

The spatial distributions of enzymes not only indicate that each membrane and internal space performs different functions, but also that all the compartments must communicate with each other in order to carry out the complex and coordinated processes of the organelle and to allow interactions between compartments and between mitochondria and the cytosol around them. The movement of substrates, end products, energy-carrier molecules, ions, and other components is largely dependent on the nature of the membranes that define the two internal spaces and separate the mitochondrion from its cytosolic surroundings.

9.9
Communication by Carriers

The outer mitochondrial membrane is relatively permeable to large molecules, up to 10,000 molecular weight, and it contains a fair number of enzymes. Because these enzymes do not constitute any integrated metabolic pathway, we have no clear idea of the function of the outer membrane other than its obvious ability to synthesize some phospholipids. It is clear, however, that the outer membrane poses no particular permeability barrier to the entry and exit of metabolically important molecules. The inner membrane, on the other hand, is highly impermeable to ions and to molecules larger than 100 to 150 molecular weight. Because the two mitochondrial membranes have such different permeability properties, the matrix and intermembrane space assume and maintain very different metabolic capacities, and each space faces different problems in receiving and disposing of ions and molecules and in energy transfers.

As we have discussed earlier in this chapter and in Chapter 5, transport across the inner membrane occurs in conjunction with specific carrier proteins embedded in the membrane and with the electrochemical ion gradients generated by the action of ion pumps. Pyruvate from sugar oxidations and amino acids from protein hydrolysis are taken across the inner membrane by carrier proteins that also sponsor the coupled transport of H^+ or Na^+ into the matrix. Once these are processed to acetyl CoA, further oxidations take place in Krebs cycle reactions and the NADH and $FADH_2$ produced in the matrix transfer their electrons to respiratory enzyme complexes situated within the inner membrane (see Fig. 9.20). Fatty acids derived from hydrolyzed fats in the cytosol are taken across the inner membrane with the help of enzymes in the membrane. Once inside the matrix, the fatty acids are processed to acetyl CoA by the β-oxidation enzymes in the mitochondrial matrix (see Fig. 8.24). The acetyl CoA in turn is fed into the Krebs cycle, and its electrons are passed from reduced NAD and FAD to the respiratory enzyme chain in the inner membrane.

Because most of the ATP utilized in the cytosol is generated in the mitochondrial matrix of the aerobic eukaryotic cell, an ADP/ATP exchange system is essential to move ADP into the mitochondrion and ATP out. The **ADP/ATP translocator**, or carrier, protein is regulated by the electrochemical proton gradient in mitochondria, such that ADP uptake and ATP release are highly favored over other exchanges and occur almost exclusively in normal, coupled mitochondria. The

ADP/ATP translocator of the mitochondrial membrane is the most abundant protein in mitochondria, and it differs in its exchange and regulatory properties from other ADP/ATP carriers in other eukaryotic cell membranes and in the bacterial plasma membrane. Through its properties ushering ADP into and ATP out of the mitochondrion, the ADP/ATP translocator serves as a vital link between metabolic compartments in eukaryotic cells.

9.10
Communication by Shuttles _____

The inner mitochondrial membrane is impermeable to oxidized and reduced NAD (and NADP), which leads to separate pools of NADH in the mitochondrion and the cytosol. The single most active system for regenerating NAD$^+$ from NADH is the electron transport chain in the inner mitochondrial membrane. The system effectively regenerates NAD$^+$ for continued cycles of reduction during substrate oxidations within the mitochondrion, but it cannot act directly to regenerate NAD$^+$ in the cytosol because the active electron-transferring centers of the respiratory enzyme complexes are oriented toward the matrix-facing surface of the membrane and not outward toward the cytosol. It is essential, however, for NAD$^+$ to be regenerated in the cytosol if continued substrate oxidations are to take place in that compartment of the cell. Little NAD is present, and that small amount must serve as electron acceptor for a number of important oxidation reactions that would otherwise be shut down. The problem of getting electrons from cytosolic NADH across the mitochondrial membrane to the respiratory electron transport chain, is solved by **shuttle** systems that provide an indirect route for electron transfer across the membrane. Electrons from NADH are taken across the membrane by a reduced metabolite, which transfers these electrons to the respiratory chain and is thereby reoxidized. The reoxidized metabolite returns to the cytosol for another reduction episode and another load of electrons from NADH. About seven different shuttle systems have been proposed, with varying amounts of experimental support for each of these. The principle of a shuttle can be illustrated by the *glycerol phosphate shuttle*, which has received more attention than the others.

NAD is the coenzyme of cytosolic glycerol phosphate dehydrogenase, whereas FAD is the coenzyme of the mitochondrial glycerol phosphate dehydrogenase. In the cytosol, the glycolytic metabolite dihydroxyacetone phosphate is reduced to glycerol 3-phosphate upon receiving electrons from NADH, the reduced coenzyme of the dehydrogenase, and NADH is oxidized to NAD$^+$. Glycerol 3-phosphate moves from the cytosol into the mitochondrion where it is reoxidized to dihydroxyacetone phosphate in a coupled oxidation–reduction catalyzed by the mitochondrial glycerol phosphate dehydrogenase (Fig. 9.26). Having unloaded the electrons it received from cytosolic NADH, the reoxidized metabolite moves back into the cytosol and is available once again for reduction by NADH and for another trip across the membrane into the mitochondrial matrix. The electrons released from the reduced metabolite are accepted by the respiratory electron transport chain of

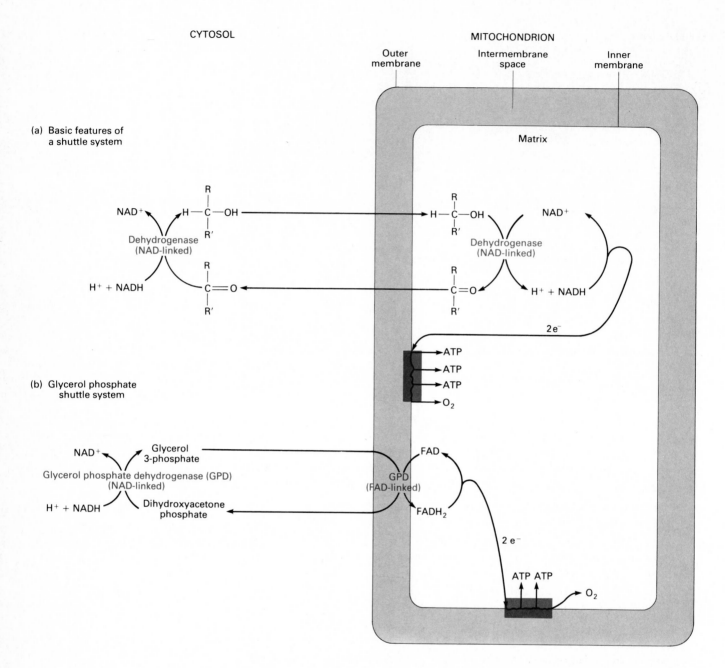

(a) Basic features of a shuttle system

(b) Glycerol phosphate shuttle system

the inner mitochondrial membrane, and they are passed from the carrier chain down to oxygen. The reducing power of cytosolic NADH can thus be utilized for mitochondrial ATP synthesis or for redox reactions in the cytosol in pathways there that require NADH reducing equivalents. The shuttle permits NADH to be utilized by the cell on both sides of the membrane barrier, but its major significance is the reoxidation of cytosolic NAD for ongoing cytosolic reactions such as ethanol oxidation in the liver and sugar or lactate oxidations in tissues that depend on these substrates for aerobic respiratory reactions.

The shuttle system operates *vectorially*, the flow of reducing equivalents being from the cytosol to the mitochondrion, even though it might seem equally probable for the flow also to occur in the opposite direction because both the oxidized and the reduced forms of the shuttle system can move freely across the mitochondrial membrane. In fact, in many

◄ **FIGURE 9-26**

Shuttle systems channel electrons indirectly from cytosolic NADH to the mitochondrial respiratory chain, thereby regenerating the cytosolic NAD^+ needed for continued substrate oxidations in the cytosol. (a) The basic features of a shuttle system involve the transfer of electrons from NADH to a metabolite in coupled oxidation–reduction reactions catalyzed by a NAD-linked dehydrogenase. The reduced metabolite crosses the mitochondrial membranes and unloads these electrons in another coupled oxidation–reduction catalyzed by a mitochondrial dehydrogenase, which is often but not always NAD-linked. The reoxidized metabolite returns to the cytosol, and the reduced mitochondrial NAD transfers the electrons to the aerobic respiratory chain (color) in the inner membrane. (b) The glycerol phosphate shuttle differs in some features from the basic system, but it carries out the same basic functions in the indirect routing of electrons from cytosolic NADH to the mitochondrial respiratory chain. The reduced metabolite, glycerol 3-phosphate, carries electrons into the mitochondrial intermembrane space, where a FAD-linked glycerol phosphate dehydrogenase on the outer surface of the inner membrane catalyzes the reduction of FAD to $FADH_2$ and the coupled reoxidation of glycerol 3-phosphate to dihydroxyacetone phosphate. The oxidized metabolite returns to the cytosol for another oxidation–reduction reaction. Because the pair of electrons has been accepted by a FAD prosthetic group, only two ATP molecules are made in this particular case.

cells the $NADH/NAD^+$ ratio is higher within the mitochondrion than in the cytosol, so the pressure is for an outward flow of reducing equivalents from the mitochondrion rather than the inward flow known to occur. The driving force provided to the shuttle system in order to sustain the inward flow is derived from a strongly exothermic reaction coupled to one step of the shuttling system. The overall cycle thus becomes essentially irreversible in favor of an inward flow, and electrons are transferred unidirectionally from the cytosol to the mitochondrion. In the glycerol phosphate shuttle, the oxidation of the mitochondrial glycerol phosphate dehydrogenase is strongly exothermic and is not influenced by the relatively high reducing level of intramitochondrial NAD. The energy input to the shuttle system from the dehydrogenase oxidation reaction causes the system to operate irreversibly.

The regulation of compartmented metabolism under different environmental conditions depends in large measure on the management of pathways that compete for $NADH/NAD^+$ and ADP/ATP. In aerobic conditions there is competition for cytosolic NADH between lactate dehydrogenase of the fermentative pathway and a shuttle that transports electrons from NADH into the mitochondrial respiratory chain. The lactate dehydrogenase has a lower affinity for NADH, so it cannot compete with the shuttle system. As a result, pyruvate is drawn into the mitochondria rather than being reduced to lactate by lactate dehydrogenase in the cytosol. When oxygen is present, pyruvate is channeled into mitochondrial pathways, whereas pyruvate remains in the cytosol and is reduced to lactate when oxygen is absent and the fermentative pathway prevails (Fig. 9.27).

The competition for ADP between the fermentative and respiratory pathways also depends on the existence of aerobic versus anaerobic conditions. When oxygen is present, ADP is channeled preferentially into mitochondria and is phosphorylated there even if relatively low

FIGURE 9-27

The regulation of compartmented mitochondrial metabolism depends a great deal on the management of pathways that compete for $NAD^+/NADH$ and for ATP/ADP. Under aerobic conditions, NADH electrons and metabolites (pyruvate, amino acids, fatty acids) enter the mitochondrion and participate in aerobic respiration through the mediation of acetyl CoA. Similarly, when oxygen is present, ADP preferentially enters the mitochondrion and is utilized in ATP synthesis by oxidative phosphorylation. Under anaerobic conditions, the competing fermentative pathway is favored, and various components (including metabolites, NADH, and ADP) remain in the cytosol and are processed in various reaction pathways.

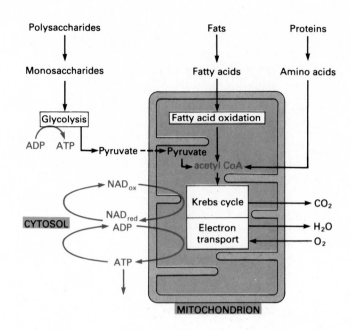

concentrations of ADP exist. This is due to the high affinity of the respiratory components for ADP, compared with the lower affinity of fermentative enzymes for ADP. Under aerobic conditions, therefore, the respiratory pathway prevails over the fermentative pathway. If oxygen is not present, however, ADP is utilized in fermentation because it no longer enters mitochondria preferentially.

In addition to competitive interactions involving $NADH/NAD^+$ and ADP/ATP, many other factors contribute to the orderly ebb and flow of metabolism in the various cellular compartments. Among these factors are membrane permeability, carrier and shuttle communication systems, and the regulatory controls of various pacemaker enzymes. Through all these and other devices, the cell is able to utilize raw materials and produce the substances and energy required for efficient and orderly activities that underlie growth, reproduction, and repair in living systems.

Mitochondrial Biogenesis

New mitochondria are produced by growth and division of pre-existing mitochondria rather than being formed from other cellular membranes or by *de novo* synthesis from molecular components in the cytosol, as are ER, Golgi, lysosomes, and other structures. The only other cellular compartments known to be produced only from pre-existing structures of their own kind are chloroplasts and nuclei.

In order for new mitochondria to be formed, proteins and lipids must be assembled from cytosolic locations, and specific polypeptides, DNA, and RNA must be synthesized within the mitochondrion itself from encoded instructions in mitochondrial genes. In recent years we have learned a great deal about the mitochondrial genetic system and its contributions to mitochondrial biogenesis. Because of this new information, it is necessary to reexamine the widely held belief that mitochondria evolved from ancient prokaryotic ancestry, as symbiotic partners of indigenous eukaryotic cellular compartments. In addition, mitochondrial genetic processes per se have proved extremely useful as model systems for studies of genetic mechanisms and systems that characterize the nucleocytoplasmic components of the cell.

9.11
Growth and Division of Pre-existing Mitochondria

The strongest experimental evidence for the growth-and-division mechanism was provided in the 1960s by David Luck. By the use of a choline-requiring mutant of *Neurospora crassa*, Luck was able to follow the incorporation into mitochondrial membranes of isotopically labeled choline, a precursor of membrane phospholipids. In one set of experiments, cultures of the choline-requiring mutant were grown in media with a particular concentration of choline that led to the formation of mitochondria with a characteristic sedimentation density. In low concentrations of choline, mitochondria were *dense*, whereas newly formed mitochondria were *light* if the cells grew in high-choline media. Dense and light mitochondria could be distinguished by their sedimentation patterns after centrifugation in sucrose-density gradients. The incorporated choline itself could be identified in mitochondrial membranes by the use of the heavy isotope ^{15}N as a choline marker, thus allowing verification that new membranes were present in the preparations.

The cultures were first grown in low-choline media to allow the development of an initial population of dense mitochondria. Afterward, the cultures were shifted to high-choline media to allow the formation of light mitochondria. The distribution of dense and light mitochondria in the mixture extracted from cells at the end of the experiment provided the basis for determining which of the three possible modes of mitochondrial biogenesis was correct. The rationale was as follows:

1. If mitochondria formed *de novo*, the cells would have two distinct populations of mitochondria: the original dense population and a newly formed light population. The original population would be unchanged, but the new population would be formed in high-choline media and would therefore be of light density. No mitochondria of intermediate densities would be present, because the new population would form independently of the original dense mitochondria, which would still be present in all the cells (Fig. 9.28).

2. If mitochondria formed from nonmitochondrial membranes, the original dense population would be unchanged because the mitochondria would make no contribution to the new population. Because new mitochondria would be made from original dense cellular membranes and from light cellular membranes made in high-choline media, the new mitochondrial population would be expected to have an intermediate density. Two distinct populations of mitochondria would be found, but the population of new mitochondria would be light, according to the *de novo* hypothesis, but

FIGURE 9-28
Schematic summaries of the mitochondrial biogenesis experiments
conducted by David Luck. (a) In
preliminary experiments it was
established that mitochondria of
different densities were produced in
cells grown in media containing choline
(colored dots). Dense mitochondria
were produced in low-choline media,
and light mitochondria in high-choline
media. These organelle populations
could be distinguished by their equilibrium position in sucrose density
gradients after centrifugation. (b) The
density transfer experiment was
predicted to produce any one of
three mutually exclusive patterns of
mitochondrial populations, each of
which would provide support for
one of the three possible modes of
mitochondrial biogenesis. The results
actually observed supported the
formation of new mitochondria by a
process of growth and division of
pre-existing mitochondria, rather
than by *de novo* formation or from
nonmitochondrial membrane
precursors.

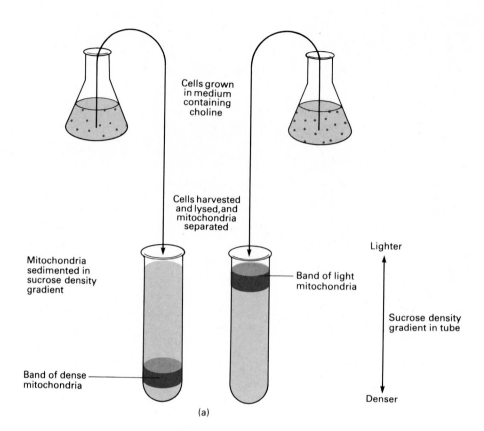

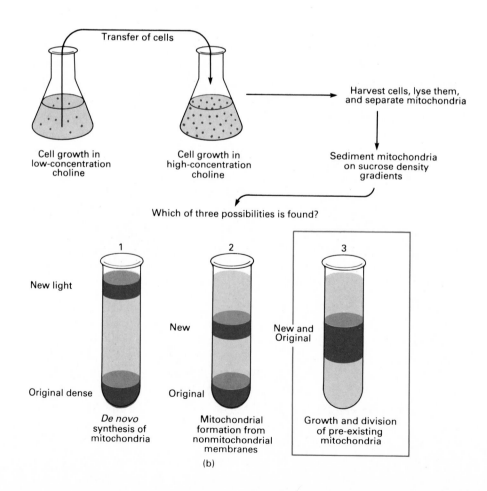

FIGURE 9-29
Three-dimensional reconstruction of a single, giant mitochondrion from a yeast cell with a large bud. The mitochondrion is continuous in the mother cell (at the right) and the bud (at the left). The model was reconstructed from electron micrographs of a complete series of consecutive sections through the entire budding complex.

of intermediate density if made from nonmitochondrial membranes of the cell.

3. If new mitochondria formed by the growth and division of pre-existing mitochondria, the original dense population would gradually disappear and *all* the mitochondria would be of intermediate density, because new light membrane and original dense membrane would be incorporated together into progeny organelles.

The data obtained were supportive of the growth-and-division mechanism; all the mitochondria at the end of the experiment were of intermediate densities and none of the original dense mitochondria remained. Growth and division were observed directly in another study with yeast cells, providing additional support for the mechanism. In yeast, mitochondrial changes were analyzed by three-dimensional reconstructions from electron micrographs taken of sets of complete consecutive serial sections through entire budding cells (Fig. 9.29). During the budding that precedes division of the cell, the single mitochondrion enlarges until it is about twice the size of the original mitochondrion in the mother cell. When the wall is completed between the bud and mother cell, the enlarged mitochondrion is cut in two by the new cell wall so that each cell has a whole mitochondrion of about the size of the original in the mother cell. The separation into two mitochondria is a passive event that is apparently due entirely to the formation of the cell wall across the middle of the organelle, rather than to an active division process such as occurs when a bacterial cell divides in two.

9.12
Import of Proteins Synthesized in the Cytosol

Except for the few polypeptides made within the mitochondrion from encoded instructions in mitochondrial genes, the great majority of proteins must be imported by the mitochondrion from their sites of synthesis in the cytosol. Imported proteins include components of the mitochondrial ribosomes; DNA and RNA polymerases; all or most of the enzymes of the outer membrane, intermembrane space, and matrix; most of the polypeptide chains of the ATP synthetase and cytochromes of the inner membrane; and a variety of membrane carrier and structural proteins. A substantial body of experimental evidence has been collected in recent years by Gottfried Schatz and others concerning the processes that lead to protein penetration into and through the mitochondrial membranes. Very little is known, however, about the means by which these proteins reach their proper intramitochondrial locations.

In general, import of a polypeptide into the mitochondrial spaces and inner membrane involves the following steps: synthesis of a precursor polypeptide on free cytosolic ribosomes, binding of the precursor to receptors on the outer surface of the mitochondrion, and translocation into or across the mitochondrial membranes. Some significant variations do exist, however, depending on the final destination of the imported polypeptide within the organelle.

Proteins destined for the inner membrane or the matrix usually have an amino-terminal hydrophobic *signal sequence*, which facilitates passage across the lipid bilayer (see Section 7.2). The signal sequence is cleaved by protease action during maturation of the precursor molecule within the mitochondrion (Fig. 9.30). Studies with precursors synthesized *in vitro* have shown that the molecules can bind to the outer face of the mitochondrion, because either mild trypsin digestion of the mitochondrial surface or removal of the amino-terminal signal sequence prevents penetration and entry of the precursor into mitochondria. By the use of radioactively labeled *in vitro*-synthesized precursors, it has been shown that the labeled polypeptides reach their correct intramitochondrial location in preparations of isolated mitochondria analyzed after subfractionation into the four organelle compartments. The process of protein translocation into mitochondria usually requires an electrochemical gradient across the membrane. Virtually nothing is known, however, about how the accurate localizations are accomplished.

Polypeptides that are destined for the intermembrane space are processed either in a two-step sequence that requires an electrochemical potential across the inner membrane or in a simpler sequence that occurs whether or not the inner membrane is energized. In the case of cytochrome c_1, which is located on the outer face of the inner membrane, the precursor is translocated across both membranes and is cleaved to an intermediate form. The intermediate combines with heme in a second step and is converted to the mature form in the intermembrane space. With cytochrome c, however, a heme-free apoprotein, rather than a larger precursor molecule, enters the mitochondrion and is converted to the mature form upon the addition of heme. Proteolytic cleavage is not required to process cytochrome c, nor is there a need for an energized

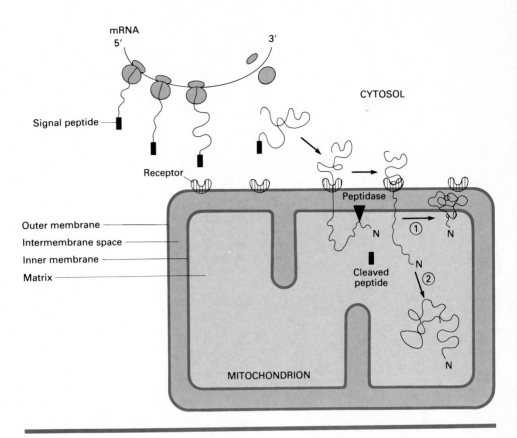

FIGURE 9-30
Import into mitochondria of poly-peptides synthesized at cytosolic ribosomes. Precursor polypeptides released from the ribosome and destined for the mitochondrial matrix or inner membrane contain a hydrophobic signal peptide sequence at their amino terminus; the signal peptide binds the polypeptide to a receptor on the mitochondrial surface. As the polypeptide is translocated into or across the mitochondrial inner membrane, the signal peptide is cleaved by peptidase action and the polypeptide assumes its mature form. Translocation of polypeptides destined for (1) the inner membrane, or (2) the matrix, requires the energy of a transmembrane electrochemical gradient. We know little or nothing, however, about the means by which the protein is guided to its correct location in the organelle.

membrane as there is for the translocation of cytochrome c_1 into the organelle.

Polypeptides incorporated into the outer mitochondrial membrane require neither an energized membrane nor binding to mitochondrial outer-surface receptors, and proteolytic processing is not involved. In fact, *in vitro*-synthesized outer membrane proteins even enter vesicles that consist only of outer mitochondrial membrane.

Traffic of proteins proceeds only from the cytosol into mitochondria and not in the reverse direction. Any polypeptides made within the organelles stay there, along with any DNA or RNA synthesized by mitochondria. Because the mitochondrial genetic system uniquely specifies certain of its essential nucleic acid and protein constituents, functional organelles are produced from pre-existing ones only if both the mitochondrial and the nucleocytoplasmic system provide wild-type products of mitochondrial and nuclear genes. In the next sections we will examine the important features of the mitochondrial genetic system and the interactions between mitochondrial and nucleocytoplasmic genetic systems in the generation of the organelles on which aerobic life depends for its major energy supply.

9.13
The Mitochondrial Genetic System

Mitochondria possess a DNA genome encoded for about 35 to 40 genes. By the use of polymerases and other enzymes imported from the cytosol,

TABLE 9-5
Size of Circular Mitochondrial DNA Molecules in Various Organisms

Organism	Contour Length (μm)
Animals	
Invertebrates	4.5–5.9
Vertebrates	4.7–5.9
Plants	
Flowering plants	30–500
Fungi	
Aspergillus	10
Kluyveromyces	11
Neurospora	19
Podospora	31
Saccharomyces	26
Saprolegnia	14
Slime molds (*Physarum*)	19
Protists	
Chlamydomonas	4.6
Protozoa	
Ciliates (*Paramecium, Tetrahymena*)	14–15*
Amebas (*Acanthameba, Plasmodium*)	9–13
Trypanosomes	0.2–0.8 (minicircles)**
	6–11 (maxicircles)**

* Linear, not circular.
** Minicircles and maxicircles occur together in a DNA meshwork, which is called kinetoplast DNA.

mitochondrial DNA (**mtDNA**) *replicates* and serves as the template for *transcription* of all the mRNAs, rRNAs, and tRNAs required to *translate* the relatively few polypeptides specified in the organelle genome. The genome itself consists of a single duplex DNA molecule that is circular in almost every species but differs in length in the four kingdoms of eukaryotic organisms (Table 9.5).

The first convincing evidence of mtDNA was obtained in 1963, and the existence of mitochondrial ribosomes was reported in 1970 (Fig. 9.31). In addition to electron microscopy, biochemical and biophysical methods were widely used to analyze and describe the organelle genetic components. When purified whole-cell DNA is centrifuged in CsCl density gradients, mtDNA settles at equilibrium in a different region of the gradient from nuclear DNA, and the two DNAs can easily be resolved and identified. In 1966, Piotr Slonimski and colleagues analyzed mtDNA from wild-type and respiration-deficient strains of yeast and showed for the first time that mtDNA had a genetic function. Wild-type, or *grande*, yeast carries out aerobic respiration and makes ATP from energy released in the oxidation of glucose and other substrates. Respiration deficient, or *petite*, yeast can derive energy only from fermentations and not from aerobic respiration. The petite phenotype is due to an inherited change in the mitochondrion and not to a defect in a nuclear gene, as shown by the non-Mendelian inheritance pattern of respiration deficiency in progeny of crosses between grande and petite strains. When whole-cell DNAs from grande and petite strains are

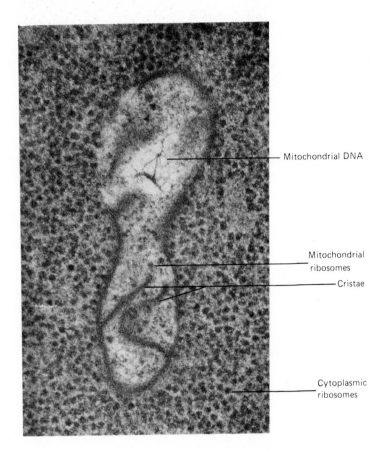

Mitochondrial DNA

Mitochondrial ribosomes

Cristae

Cytoplasmic ribosomes

FIGURE 9-31
Electron micrograph of a section through a mitochondrion from yeast, showing a region containing DNA fibrils. The relatively few mitochondrial ribosomes are virtually identical to the cytoplasmic ribosomes present in great abundance around the organelle. × 132,600. (Photograph by H. -P. Hoffmann.)

compared after equilibrium density gradient centrifugation in CsCl, the nuclear DNAs of the two strains are identical but their mtDNAs are different (Fig. 9.32). The change in mtDNAs is paralleled by a change in mitochondrial ultrastructure and respiratory ability, indicating that the alteration in mtDNA is probably responsible for the alteration in organelle structure and function. These correlations were amply verified and extended by subsequent genetic analysis and, most recently, by molecular evidence from DNA sequencing of mitochondrial genomes and from RNA and polypeptide products of mitochondrial gene action.

Petite mutants were of limited use in defining the details of the mitochondrial genetic contribution to organelle formation and development, because the petite genome has deletions of a variable proportion of its genes. By 1970, however, new classes of yeast mitochondrial mutants were discovered in which point mutations had occurred. These mutations were later shown to be due to base substitutions in mitochondrial genes encoding specific polypeptides, or mutations in mitochondrial genes that specified rRNAs or tRNAs. Sequence analysis of mtDNAs from yeast, mammalian species, and several other organisms revealed the organization of mitochondrial genes in the circular genomes and the organization of the genes themselves. The complete sequence of 16,569 base pairs in the human mitochondrial genome was published in 1981 by a group of 14 investigators in England. Human mtDNA includes genes for the 2 rRNAs, for 22 tRNAs, and for 13 polypeptides (Fig. 9.33). Only 5 of the polypeptides have been identified: 3 of the 7

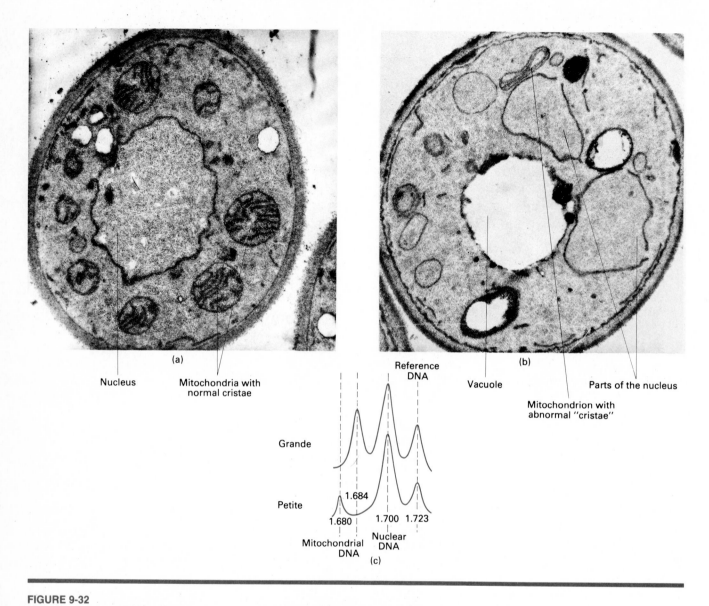

FIGURE 9-32
Ultrastructural and DNA differences
between mitochondria in normal
grande and in respiration-deficient
petite strains of yeast. (a) Electron
micrograph of a section through a
grande yeast cell, showing mitochondrial profiles with typical cristae.
×28,000. (b) Electron micrograph of
a section through a petite yeast cell,
showing mitochondria with abnormal
inner membrane organization. (The
nucleus appears in two parts due
to the plane of sectioning through
the irregularly shaped structure.)
×38,000. (c) Densitometer tracings
of whole-cell DNA from grande and
petite yeast after centrifugation to
equilibrium in CsCl density gradients.
The different densities of grande
(1.684 g/cc) and petite (1.680 g/cc)
mitochondrial DNAs reflect differences
in the base composition of the
DNAs from each source.
(Photographs from Federman, M.,
and C. J. Avers, 1967, *J. Bacteriol.* **94**:1236.)

subunits of cytochrome oxidase, 1 of the 9 subunits of the ATP
synthetase, and cytochrome b of the b–c_1 enzyme complex. The remaining 8 of the 13 genes for polypeptides have been temporarily designated
as *unassigned reading frames* (URF), because their sequences specify amino
acids but the nature of the polypeptide product is undetermined.

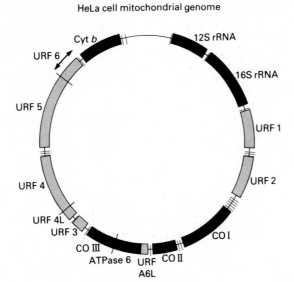

HeLa cell mitochondrial genome

Interestingly, the same 8 URFs have been found in other mammalian
mitochondrial genomes (this is believed to indicate that the polypeptides
have a significant function because they have been conserved during 180
million years of mammalian evolution). The DNA sequences and
organization of genes in other mammalian mitochondrial genomes are
essentially the same as in the human mitochondrial genome.

Although the yeast mitochondrial genome has not been sequenced
yet in its entirety, sufficient data are available for us to note the
differences and similarities when compared with mitochondrial genomes
of other fungi and with mammalian species. Virtually the same number
and kinds of genes are present in yeast and human mtDNAs, except that
the yeast genome includes a gene for ATP synthetase subunit 9 as well
as for subunit 6. The most striking differences, however, concern the
arrangement of genes in the circle, the amount of noncoding DNA in the
genomes, and the organization of several of the genes themselves.

The yeast mitochondrial genome is almost five times longer than the
human mitochondrial genome, and, unlike human mtDNA, there is a
considerable amount of noncoding, "spacer" DNA between genes. The
two rRNA genes are clustered together in human mtDNA, as are the
genes for cytochrome oxidase and ATPase subunits, whereas these same
genes are widely scattered around the yeast genome (Fig. 9.34). In
contrast with these gene distributions, tRNA genes are scattered around
the human genome but are grouped predominantly in one region of the
yeast genome. The distribution of tRNA genes has an important bearing
on the processing of the RNA transcript of mtDNA. By far the most
unexpected difference, however, is the organization of the genes encoded
for cytochrome *b* and cytochrome oxidase subunit 1 (CO I). These are
split genes in yeast, with exon–intron organization, but with an uninterrupted sequence of contiguous codons in the human gene equivalents.
These two genes, which specify very similar polypeptides of identical
functions in the two species, are organized in yeast like eukaryotic
nuclear genes, but they resemble typical uninterrupted prokaryotic
genes in the human mitochondrial genome (see Section 4.6). The basis

FIGURE 9-34

Organization of the mitochondrial genome in yeast. In addition to 2 rRNA genes and 25 tRNA genes (colored ticks), genes encoded for 7 known polypeptides are distributed within the 76,000 base pairs (76 kilobase pairs, or 76 kbp) of the circular mitochondrial DNA molecule. Each of the three largest polypeptide subunits of the respiratory enzyme cytochrome oxidase is specified by a gene (CO I, CO II, CO III); polypeptide subunits 6 and 9 of the respiratory ATPase are both encoded by a gene; cytochrome *b* is encoded by a mitochondrial gene; and *var 1* specifies a ribosomal protein of the organelle ribosomes. Three of these 34 known genes are organized into introns and exons—namely, CO I (A1–A8), Cyt *b* (B1–B6), and 21S rRNA. Noncoding DNA is present in considerable amounts in spacer regions between genes. (Reprinted by permission from Borst, P., and L. A. Grivell, 1981, *Nature* **290**: 443–444, Fig. 1. Copyright © 1981 by Macmillan Journals Limited.)

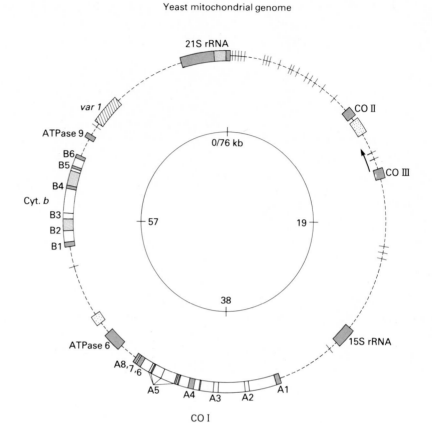

Yeast mitochondrial genome

for the difference in gene organization is unknown at the present time, as is the significance of the difference. We do know, however, that the mRNA transcripts of the yeast and human genes are processed in entirely different ways and in accordance with their organizational distinction.

Inspection of the gene map of the yeast mitochondrial genome clearly shows why petite deletion mutants are respiratory deficient, regardless of where the deletions may occur or how much DNA is missing. Deletions virtually anywhere in the genome remove all or part of genes that specify essential polypeptides of the respiratory system, leading to missing or defective enzymes or to the removal of one or more of the rRNA and tRNA components required for mitochondrial protein synthesis. Even if the genes for polypeptides were not deleted, mitochondrial ribosomes would not be assembled in the absence of one or both rRNAs, and protein synthesis would be impossible. Similarly, if one or more tRNA genes were missing, functional polypeptides would not be synthesized because one or more of the essential amino acids would have no carrier tRNA to take them to the ribosomes for protein synthesis during translation.

The importance of the mitochondrial genome for organelle biogenesis is obvious from the foregoing discussion. The contribution of the nucleocytoplasmic system to mitochondrial biogenesis is equally important, but far greater. In certain petite strains, there is no mtDNA at all but mitochondria are present nevertheless. In such *neutral* petites, as in petites that retain at least some mtDNA, mitochondria are characterized by outer and inner membranes that define the intermembrane and matrix spaces. The inner mitochondrial membrane is abnormal, however. It has either an unfolded contour or bizarre infoldings; there are no cristae (see Fig. 9.32). All the enzymes and structural proteins encoded by nuclear genes are made normally in the cytosol, and certain of these proteins find their way into pre-existing mitochondria. Because many cytosolic polypeptides can be taken into mitochondria only if an adequate electrochemical potential exists across the inner membrane, not all the cytosolic products can be imported into respiration-deficient mitochondrial structures. One of the proteins usually found in abundance in petite mitochondria is cytochrome c, a nuclear gene product that does not require an electrochemical gradient for entry and localization in the intermembrane space (see Section 9.11).

9.14
Protein Synthesis in Mitochondria

Evidence in support of an independent protein-synthesizing system in mitochondria was provided first by Anthony Linnane and colleagues in 1966, when they showed that specific drugs could selectively shut off protein synthesis in mitochondria or the cytosol. In the presence of *cycloheximide*, cytosolic protein synthesis is inhibited but mitochondrial protein synthesis proceeds as usual; *chloramphenicol, erythromycin*, and certain other antibiotics inhibit activities in mitochondria and have little or no effect on the cytosolic system. These initial data were expanded by studies of the proteins themselves, all showing that mitochondria and cytosol made different sets of polypeptide products. Among the more specific and informative studies were those in which the synthesis of particular polypeptides was correlated with the contribution made by the genomes in the nucleus and mitochondrion. Grande and petite strains of yeast were utilized to great advantage in such studies.

Grande yeast makes functional cytochrome oxidase, a protein composed of seven identifiable polypeptide subunits. Petites synthesize only four of these polypeptides, and their enzyme is therefore nonfunctional in respiration. When grande yeast was incubated with chloramphenicol or erythromycin, the cells made only the four polypeptides that petites could also synthesize. In the presence of cycloheximide, grande yeast made only those three polypeptide subunits that petites could not synthesize (Fig. 9.35). From these data it was clear that the four polypeptides made in petites and in chloramphenicol- or erythromycin-drugged grande yeast were products of nuclear genes and were synthesized in the cytosol. Petites have a functional nuclear genome and cytosolic protein-synthesis apparatus but defective mitochondrial systems, and their four enzyme subunits are made from the same genes in the same cytoplasm as are the grande polypeptides. Grandes failed to make these four components only when their cytosolic protein-synthesizing system was inhibited by cycloheximide. On the other hand, grandes failed to make the same three polypeptides for which petites were deficient only when their mitochondrial protein-synthesizing system was inhibited by chloramphenicol or erythromycin. Petites failed to make these polypeptides because both their mitochondrial genes and

FIGURE 9-35
Experimental studies of cytochrome oxidase synthesis and activity in grande yeast revealed that functional enzyme was not made in drugged cells. In the presence of cycloheximide, cytosolic synthesis of nuclear-encoded polypeptides is shut off and only mitochondrial protein synthesis occurs. Subunits I–III must therefore be made in mitochondria from information encoded in mitochondrial genes. In the presence of chloramphenicol or erythromycin, mitochondrial synthesis is shut off and only cytosolic protein synthesis occurs. Subunits IV–VII must therefore be made at cytosolic ribosomes from information encoded in nuclear genes. The synthesis of functional cytochrome oxidase in yeast thus requires genetic information and activity of both the nucleocytoplasmic system and the mitochondrial system.

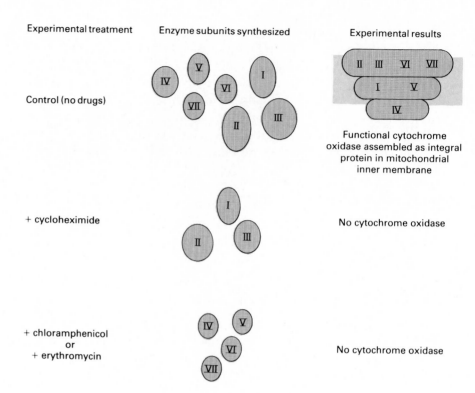

protein-synthesizing systems were defective. These three polypeptides must therefore be encoded in mitochondrial genes and be synthesized in the mitochondria themselves. All these interpretations have been amply confirmed by subsequent studies of base sequences in mtDNA and amino acid sequences in the polypeptide products of these mitochondrial genes.

A considerable amount of information has been obtained since mitochondrial ribosomes were first characterized in 1970. The ribosomes of the mitochondrial protein-synthesizing system are composed of two subunits of unequal size, just like their counterparts in the cytosol, and in most organisms each subunit consists of a set of distinctive

TABLE 9-6
Sedimentation Coefficients (S) of Monomers, Subunits, and rRNAs of Mitochondrial Ribosomes from Different Organisms

Organism	Ribosome Monomer	Small Subunit	Large Subunit	rRNA from	
				Small Subunit	Large Subunit
Animals	55–60S	30–35S	40–45S	12–13S	16–17S
Flowering plants	78S	44S	60S	18S	26S, 5S
Fungi	80S	40S	52S	14–17S	21–24S
Protists					
Euglena	71S	32S	50S	16S	23S
Tetrahymena	80S	55S	55S	14S + 21S*	

* There is no way to determine which rRNA is present in the two 55S subunits. It is possible that both rRNAs are present in each 55S subunit, which might therefore be the actual ribosome monomer.

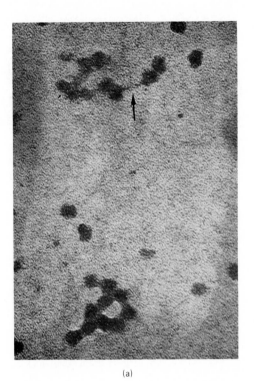

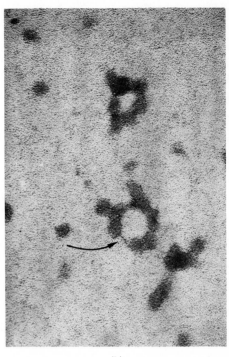

(a)   (b)

FIGURE 9-36
Electron micrographs of ribosome
groups, or polysomes, from purified
yeast mitochondria collected after
centrifugation in sucrose gradients.
The presumptive mRNA strand is
shown at the arrow. ×227,000. (From
Cooper, C. S., and C. J. Avers, 1974, in
The Biogenesis of Mitochondria, p. 289,
A. M. Kroon and C. Saccone, eds.
New York: Academic Press.)

proteins complexed with one rRNA molecule (Table 9.6). The ribosome monomers, subunits, and rRNAs are generally identified according to their sedimentation characteristics, or S value. Translation of encoded genetic information into polypeptides takes place when mRNA binds to ribosomes, and tRNAs bring amino acids to the mRNA–ribosome aggregates, just as occurs in the cytoplasm for nuclear mRNAs and cytosolic ribosomes (Fig. 9.36).

In 1980 the astonishing and unexpected discovery was made that certain of the codons of the genetic code specified different instructions in mitochondrial translation from those that they specified in nucleo-cytoplasmic translation systems. From molecular analyses of base sequences in DNA and RNA and of amino acid sequences in polypeptides specified by mitochondrial genes in yeast, *Neurospora*, mammalian species, and a growing list of organisms, it was found that the Stop codon UGA specified the amino acid tryptophan in mitochondria (Table 9.7). In other instances, a particular codon might specify a different amino acid in mitochondria of one species but not of another. For example, the codon family CUU, CUC, CUA, CUG specifies the amino acid threonine in yeast mitochondria, but these same codons specify the amino acid leucine in mitochondrial genes of other species, as well as in nuclear genes. The significance of these few variations in codon meaning is uncertain. We do know, however, that differences in *usage* of the codon dictionary in mitochondria are related to the presence of a smaller set of tRNAs specified by mitochondrial genes than tRNAs specified by nuclear genes. The properties of mitochondrial tRNAs and nuclear tRNAs in translation will be discussed in detail later.

TABLE 9-7
Differences between Codon Meanings in the "Standard" Genetic Code and Mitochondrial Genetic Codes

	CODON MEANINGS IN			
Codon	Standard genetic code	Mitochondrial genetic code of Mammals	Neurospora	Yeast
AGA AGG	Arg	STOP (?)	Arg	Arg
AUA	Ile	Met	Ile	Ile
CUU CUC CUA CUG	Leu	Leu	Leu	Thr
UGA	STOP	Trp	Trp	Trp

9.15
Evolutionary Origins of Mitochondria

The existence of a genetic system in mitochondria has provoked a number of speculative theories concerning the evolutionary origin of the organelles. We have comparative information on which to judge the various proposals, rather than direct observational or experimental evidence. The absence of living or fossil intermediary forms also weakens each formal hypothesis of mitochondrial origin.

The **endosymbiont theory** revived by Lynn Margulis in 1967 is an idea that has attracted many enthusiastic proponents. Margulis proposed that the ancestral cell type was anaerobic, prokaryotic, and capable of ingesting solids through the activities of its mobile cell surface. Such a cell is postulated to have engulfed respiring prokaryotic cells, not unlike modern *Bdellovibrio* or *Paracoccus* species, leading to a mutually beneficial (symbiotic) relationship between the host and its internalized *endo*symbionts (Fig. 9.37). The host provided the endosymbionts with nutrients and protection, and the endosymbionts provided energy-efficient aerobic respiration to the anaerobic host. In an anaerobic world undergoing an atmospheric transition to aerobic conditions, the host derived great benefit from its internal partners. The mtDNA and the mitochondrial translation system are thus viewed as the result of retention of at least part of the original endosymbiont genetic system over the past 1 to 1.5 billion years of evolution. Other endosymbiotic episodes are postulated to have occurred later, during eukaryotic evolution, giving rise to modern chloroplasts from blue-green and prochlorophyte algal lineages and to flagella from a spirochetelike prokaryotic species.

Particular observed similarities between prokaryotes and mitochondria (or chloroplasts) serve as the major support for the endosymbiosis theory. For example:

1. Both the bacterial and mitochondrial genomes consist of a single, naked, circular duplex DNA molecule, whereas eukaryotic genomes consist of two or more linear DNA molecules associated with

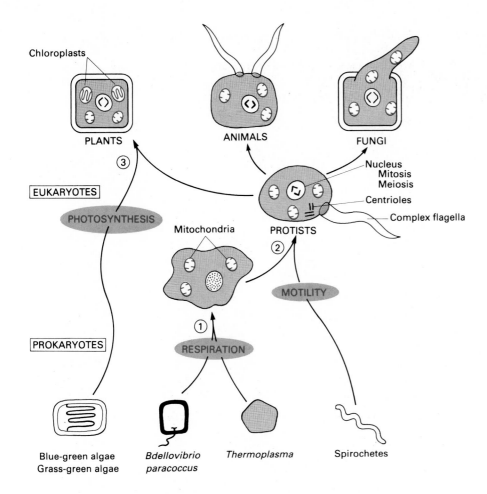

Chloroplasts

PLANTS   ANIMALS   FUNGI

③

EUKARYOTES

PHOTOSYNTHESIS

Mitochondria

Nucleus
Mitosis
Meiosis

Centrioles

Complex flagella

PROTISTS

②

MOTILITY

①

PROKARYOTES

RESPIRATION

Blue-green algae   *Bdellovibrio*   *Thermoplasma*   Spirochetes
Grass-green algae   *paracoccus*

FIGURE 9-37
Schematic summary of the endo-symbiont theory of organelle origin in eukaryotes, as proposed by Lynn Margulis. Ancient free-living prokaryotic organisms similar to particular modern bacteria and prokaryotic algae were engulfed in independent episodes by host cells at various times in evolution, and these engulfed organisms assumed a symbiotic relationship with the host. The endosymbionts ultimately evolved into organelles (mitochondria, flagella, chloroplasts) that were completely dependent on the host but provided the host with the advantageous properties of respiration, motility, and photosynthesis.

proteins in chromosomes. Bacterial and mitochondrial genomes are not separated by a membrane from the cytoplasmic surroundings, whereas eukaryotic chromosomes are contained within a membrane-bounded nucleus.

2. Bacterial and mitochondrial ribosomes are affected similarly by various drugs, such as chloramphenicol and erythromycin, whereas eukaryotic protein synthesis is insensitive to these drugs but sensitive to other compounds that have no effect on bacterial or mitochondrial protein synthesis.

3. Specific enzymes of aerobic respiration (and photosynthesis) are found in the organelle membranes and matrix, and their counterparts occur in bacterial plasma membrane and cytosol. Eukaryotic cells, however, have only their organelles to carry out these processes for the benefit of the whole cell or organism.

Endosymbiosis is a widespread phenomenon that often involves a symbiotic bacterial or blue-green algal species within a eukaryotic host. We know of no prokaryotes, however, that act as hosts for other prokaryotes in a symbiotic association, nor do we know of any prokary-otes with the capacity to ingest solids or other cellular organisms. Even if such endosymbioses had occurred in the ancient past, hundreds of genes now encoded in the nucleus of organelle traits must have moved from the

TABLE 9-8
Comparison of Selected Features of the Genomes in Human Mitochondria, Yeast Mitochondria, *E. coli* (Prokaryote), and *Drosophila melanogaster* (Eukaryote).

Feature	Human Mitochondria	Yeast Mitochondria	E. coli (Prokaryote)	D. melanogaster (Eukaryote)
genomic DNA	1 duplex; circular	1 duplex; circular	1 duplex; circular	4 duplexes; linear
contour length	5.5 μm	25–26 μm	1300 μm	>50,000 μm
number of kilobase pairs	16.57	75–78	~4,000	~150,000
intergenic spacer regions	absent	present	absent	present
genes				
polypeptide-specifying genes	5 known + 8 URFs	7 known + URFs	3000–4000	5,000–10,000
tRNA genes	22	25	32 + multiple copies	32 + multiple copies
rRNA genes*	2; adjacent	2; far apart	3 (5–10 copies of each)	2 (hundreds of copies)
noncoding leader and trailer segments	absent	present	present	present
stop codons	absent in some genes	present	present	present
exon–intron organization	absent	present in some genes	absent	present
transcription	within mitochondria	within mitochondria	within nucleoid	within nucleus
number of promoters	1	5 or more	numerous	numerous
pre-mRNA	absent	present	absent	present
mRNA	transcribed directly	processed from pre-mRNA	transcribed directly	processed from pre-mRNA
poly(A) tail	posttranscriptional	absent	absent	posttranscriptional
translation	within mitochondria	within mitochondria	within cytoplasm	within cytoplasm
ribosomes	55–60S	80S	70S	80S
codon usage	UGA = Trp	UGA = Trp	UGA = Stop	UGA = Stop
	AUA = Met	AUA = Ile	AUA = Ile	AUA = Ile
	AG_G^A = not used	$AG_G^{A\ =\ Arg}$ = not used?	AG_G^A = Arg	AG_G^A = Arg
	CUN = Leu	CUN = Thr	CUN = Leu	CUN = Leu

*Human mitochondrial rRNA genes = 12S and 16S; yeast mitochondrial rRNA genes = 15S and 21S; *E. coli* rRNA genes = 16S, 23S, and 5S; *D. melanogaster* rRNA genes = 38S (processed to 18S and 28S rRNAs) and 5S.
(Reproduced with permission from Avers, C. J., 1984, *Genetics*, 2nd ed., Boston: Willard Grant Press.)

original endosymbiont genome into the nucleus. We do have evidence from recent studies that gene transfer between mitochondria and nucleus can occur, which has put to rest some of the nagging questions about genomic modifications during evolution. On the other hand, other lines of molecular and genetic information have raised new doubts about the endosymbiont ancestry of the mitochondrion. As shown in Table 9.8, certain features of mitochondrial genomes differ significantly from one species to another and from both prokaryotic and eukaryotic systems. To explain these differences we would have to invoke either different endosymbiotic mitochondrial lineages for different kingdoms of eukaryotes or different pathways of evolutionary divergence following the initial endosymbiotic episode(s).

The major alternatives to endosymbiosis involve evolutionary changes by which some existing parts of the ancestral cell have evolved to become separate membranous compartments bathed in eukaryotic cytoplasm. Different views have been presented on the exact nature of the prokaryotic ancestor of eukaryotes and on the events culminating in the cellular organization of modern eukaryotes. Most of these proposals

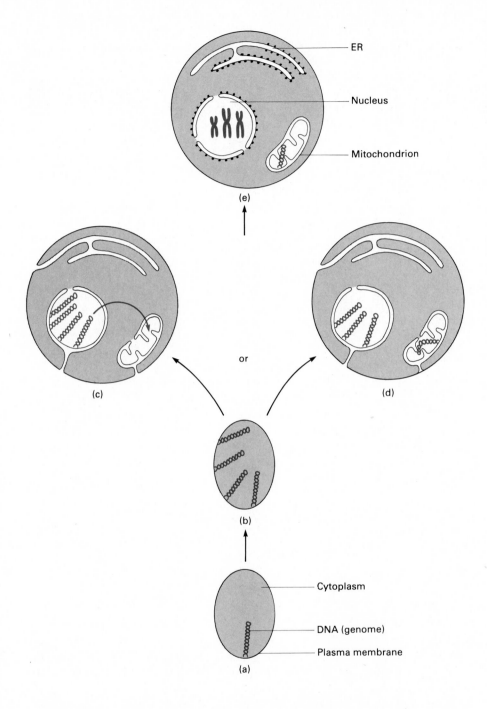

ER

Nucleus

Mitochondrion

(e)

(c)   or   (d)

(b)

Cytoplasm

DNA (genome)

Plasma membrane

(a)

FIGURE 9-38
Evolutionary origin of mitochondria and other membranous systems according to the concept of internalized membrane differentiation. Prokaryotic cell with (a) one genome molecule is assumed to have undergone genome duplications and thereby (b) to give rise to cells with multiple copies of the genome. Plasma membrane internalization and subsequent differentiation to become nuclear, ER, mitochondrial, and other systems in eukaryotic cells may have been accompanied by (c) later transfer to mitochondria of some DNA originally enclosed in the nuclear envelope, or (d) some of the cellular DNA may have been sequestered within the mitochondrial envelope, but the bulk of the DNA was partitioned into a nucleus. In either case (c or d), according to the evolutionary scenario, (e) modern eukaryotic cells have numerous internal membrane systems, and a small portion of the genetic system now resides in mitochondria, which are surrounded by the preponderant nucleocytoplasmic genetic system.

state that the cellular DNA separated into different portions that were subsequently enclosed within their own membrane systems, thereby leading to the nucleus, mitochondria, and chloroplasts (Fig. 9.38). According to other scenarios, a plasmid or plasmidlike DNA molecule carrying genes for organelle structure and function was enclosed within membranes making up the mitochondrial or chloroplast boundaries.

All these possibilities (and others) have remained speculative because of insufficient data. The evolutionary origin of mitochondria will probably evade us as long as we remain ignorant of selection factors and other factors that must have influenced organelle evolution for well over a billion years.

Summary

Mitochondria are found in all eukaryotic cells. They form complex branching tubular networks that appear to be individual ovoid structures in thin sections or cell homogenates. The mitochondrion is divided into four compartments: a readily permeable outer membrane, a convoluted, highly impermeable inner membrane, an aqueous intermembrane space, and an aqueous internal matrix. Characteristic enzyme activities are associated with each of these compartments, promoting the function of mitochondria as semiautonomous organelles of aerobic respiration.

Aerobic respiration is the process whereby acetyl coenzyme A, derived from the catabolism of fats, proteins, and polysaccharides, becomes completely oxidized to CO_2. Reduced coenzymes (NADH, $FADH_2$, $FMNH_2$) generated in the process are reoxidized by the mitochondrial electron transport system, which is in turn coupled to synthesis of ATP, allowing recovery of a substantial amount of fuel energy. The final electron acceptor is oxygen. In the absence of oxygen, the reduced coenzymes generated in glycolysis are reoxidized by lactate fermentation or alcoholic fermentation in the cytosol. Under aerobic conditions, however, the glycolytic end product, pyruvate, enters the mitochondrial matrix, where it is converted into acetyl coenzyme A, an energized 2-carbon intermediate that is also the product of oxidation of fatty acids and certain amino acids. Acetyl coenzyme A now condenses with the 4-carbon compound oxaloacetate to generate the 6-carbon citrate, which is progressively oxidized and decarboxylated to the 4-carbon succinate with the remaining two carbons released as CO_2. The succinate, in turn, is reoxidized to oxaloacetate, ready to condense with another acetyl coenzyme A. The enzymes catalyzing this series of reactions, known as the Krebs cycle, are all found in the mitochondrial matrix except for succinate dehydrogenase, which is bound to the inner membrane. Because the pathway is cyclic, only catalytic amounts of the intermediates are needed to maintain Krebs cycle activity. Some energy is recovered directly in the form of GTP. Most of the energy is still latent, however, in the form of the reduced coenzymes NADH and $FADH_2$. The net yield from one glucose molecule dismantled to this point by glycolysis and aerobic respiration is 6 CO_2, 2 ATP, 2 GTP, 10 NADH, and 2 $FADH_2$.

The energy represented by reduced coenzymes may now be recovered through the processes of electron transport and oxidative phosphorylation. In the inner mitochondrial membrane are a series of integral membrane proteins, each with the ability to be oxidized or reduced because of prosthetic groups such as flavins, quinones, or iron atoms. These proteins are physically arranged in order of decreasing free energy of oxidation such that reduction of one readily promotes reduction of the next, which may in turn be reoxidized by the third, and so on. This electron transport chain receives reducing equivalents from the reduced coenzymes and passes them from one to the next to the final electron acceptor, molecular oxygen, reducing it to water. Three of the four major respiratory enzyme complexes within the electron transport chain catalyze a sufficiently large drop in free energy to promote synthesis of an ATP molecule; an electron pair derived from NAD-linked reactions can thus produce 3 ATP molecules; an electron pair from FAD-linked processes can produce only 2 ATP molecules, because they enter the chain at a lower energy than that of the first complex. At maximum efficiency, this process allows conservation as ATP of up to 39% of the free energy of oxidation of glucose.

The mechanism by which electron transport is coupled to ATP synthesis is best understood by the chemiosmotic coupling hypothesis of Mitchell. In this model, the passage of electrons along the oxidation–reduction chain within the inner membrane causes the movement of protons from the matrix across the inner membrane into the intermembrane space, creating an electrochemical proton gradient. The energy stored in this gradient is used to synthesize ATP when protons move back into the matrix through specialized membrane channels associated with the enzyme ATP synthetase ($F_oF_1ATPase$). If the gradient is strong enough, the potential energy it represents can power ATP synthesis. In the absence of a gradient, the enzyme acts as an ATP hydrolase—it hydrolyzes ATP and pumps protons out of the matrix. Key predictions of the chemiosmotic coupling hypothesis have been tested experimentally.

A portion of the proton gradient is needed to facilitate movement of other molecules across the impermeable inner membrane, including ions (phosphate, calcium), amino acids, and intermediates of fatty acid metabolism and the Krebs cycle. Other substances cross the inner membrane by means of carriers (ADP/ATP translocator) or shuttles, such as the glycerol phosphate shuttle, which interconverts cytoplasmic and mitochondrial NADH.

Coupling of proton pumping to ATP synthesis is characteristic not just of mitochondria, but also of chloroplasts and the plasma membrane of bacteria. In chloroplasts the gradient results from light-dependent electron transport. In bacteria, even under anaerobic conditions, ATP synthesis may be coupled to oxidation and may use nontraditional agents (nitrates, sulfates) as the final electron acceptors. ATP from glycolysis may also generate a proton gradient used for cotransport of essential nutrients.

New mitochondria arise by growth and division of pre-existing mitochondria. Most of their proteins are produced on cytoplasmic ribosomes in a precursor form that is imported into the mitochondrion by binding to mitochondrial membrane receptors and maturing at their final location. Some proteins are encoded in mtDNA and produced via the mitochondrial ribosomes. The 35 to 40 genes in the single, circular mitochondrial DNA molecule encode subunits of cytochromes and ATP synthetase, as well as the rRNA and tRNA needed to synthesize them. Mutations in mitochondrial genes, detected by the characteristic non-Mendelian inheritance pattern, result in respiration-deficient mitochondria. Mitochondrial ribosomes are sensitive to protein synthesis inhibitors that do not act on cytosolic protein synthesis. The genetic code in mitochondria differs from the "universal" code in certain ways, and it is not the same in all mitochondria. These and other properties have led to speculation about the evolutionary origin of mitochondria.

One popular proposal is the endosymbiont theory, whereby an ancestral anaerobic cell is thought to have engulfed a respiring prokaryote, which evolved into a mitochondrion. An alternative theory proposes that an ancestral cell type compartmentalized both its cytoplasm and a portion of its genome, which then evolved into mitochondria and other subcellular structures.

Readings and References

Anderson, S., *et al.* 1981. Sequence and organization of the human mitochondrial genome. *Nature* **290**:457.

Atkinson, A. W., Jr., P. C. L. John, and B. E. S. Gunning. 1974. The growth and division of the single mitochondrion and other organelles during the cell cycle of *Chlorella*, studied by quantitative stereology and three-dimensional reconstruction. *Protoplasma* **81**:77.

Attardi, G. 1981. Organization and expression of the mammalian mitochondrial genome: A lesson in economy. *Trends Biochem. Sci.* **6**:86, 100.

Bernardi, G. 1979. The petite mutation in yeast. *Trends Biochem. Sci.* **4**:197.

Bibb, M. J., *et al.* 1981. Sequence and gene organization of mouse mitochondrial DNA. *Cell* **26**:167.

Bonitz, S. G., *et al.* 1980. Codon recognition rules in yeast mitochondria. *Proc. Natl. Acad. Sci. U. S.* **77**:3167.

Borst, P. 1981. The biogenesis of mitochondria in yeast and other primitive eukaryotes. In *International Cell Biology 1980–1981*, ed. H. G. Schweiger, p. 239. New York: Springer-Verlag.

Borst, P., and L. A. Grivell. 1978. The mitochondrial genome of yeast. *Cell* **15**:705.

Borst, P., and L. A. Grivell. 1981. Small is beautiful—portrait of a mitochondrial genome. *Nature* **290**:443.

Chance, B., and D. F. Parsons. 1963. Cytochrome function in relation to inner membrane structure of mitochondria. *Science* **142**:1176.

Chua, N.-H., and G. W. Schmidt. 1979. Transport of proteins into mitochondria and chloroplasts. *J. Cell Biol.* **81**:461.

Dawson, A. G. 1979. Oxidation of cytosolic NADH formed during aerobic metabolism in mammalian cells. *Trends Biochem. Sci.* **4**:171.

Dickerson, R. E. March 1980. Cytochrome *c* and the evolution of energy metabolism. *Sci. Amer.* **242**:136.

Doolittle, W. F. 1980. Revolutionary concepts in evolutionary cell biology. *Trends Biochem. Sci.* **5**:146.

Douglas, M., and M. Takeda. 1985. Nuclear genes encoding mitochondrial DNA. In *Genetic Maps 1984*, vol. 3, ed.

Ernster, L., and G. Schatz. 1981. Mitochondria: A historical review. *J. Cell Biol.* **91**:227s.

Gasser, S. M., *et al.* 1982. Imported mitochondrial proteins, cytochrome b_2 and cytochrome c_1, are processed in two steps. *Proc. Natl. Acad. Sci. U. S.* **79**:267.

Gibson, F., G. B. Cox, and J. A. Downie. 1979. Biochemical genetics of oxidative phosphorylation. *Trends Biochem. Sci.* **4**:260.

Gillham, N. W. 1978. *Organelle Heredity*. New York: Raven.

Grivell, L. A. March 1983. Mitochondrial DNA. *Sci. Amer.* **248**:78.

Grivell, L. A. 1984. Restriction and genetic maps of yeast mitochondrial DNA. In *Genetic Maps 1984*, vol. 3, ed. S. J. O'Brien, p. 234. Cold Spring Harbor, N. Y.: Cold Spring Harbor Laboratory.

Hackenbrock, C. R. 1966. Ultrastructural bases for metabolically linked mechanical activity in mitochondria. I. Reversible ultrastructural changes with change in metabolic steady state in isolated rat liver mitochondria. *J. Cell Biol.* **30**:269.

Hackenbrock, C. R. 1981. Lateral diffusion and electron transfer in the mitochondrial inner membrane. *Trends Biochem. Sci.* **6**:151.

Harold, F. M. 1978. The 1978 Nobel prize in chemistry. *Science* **202**:1174.

Heckman, J. E., *et al.* 1980. Novel features in the genetic code and codon reading patterns in *Neurospora crassa* mitochondria based on sequences of six mitochondrial tRNAs. *Proc. Natl. Acad. Sci. U. S.* **77**:3159.

Hinkle, P. C., and R. E. McCarty. March 1978. How cells make ATP. *Sci. Amer.* **238**:104.

Hoffmann, H.-P., and C. J. Avers. 1973. Mitochondrion of yeast: Ultrastructural evidence for one giant, branched organelle per cell. *Science* **181**:749.

Hollenberg, C. P., P. Borst, and E. F. J. Van Bruggen. 1970. Mitochondrial DNA. V. A 25-μ closed circular duplex DNA molecule in wild-type yeast mitochondria. Structure and genetic complexity. *Biochim. Biophys. Acta* **209**:1.

Johnson, L. V., M. L. Walsh, and L. B. Chen. 1980. Localization of mitochondria in living cells with rhodamine 123. *Proc. Natl. Acad. Sci. U. S.* **77**:990.

Klingenberg, M. 1979. The ADP, ATP shuttle of the mitochondrion. *Trends Biochem. Sci.* **4**:249.

Lamb, A. J., G. D. Clark-Walker, and A. W. Linnane. 1968. The biogenesis of mitochondria. The differentiation of mitochondrial and cytoplasmic protein synthesizing systems *in vitro* by antibiotics. *Biochim. Biophys. Acta* **161**:415.

Lee, C. P., G. Schatz, and G. Dallner, eds. 1981. *Mitochondria and Microsomes*. Reading, Mass.: Addison-Wesley.

Lehninger, A. L. 1971. *Bioenergetics*. 2nd ed. Menlo Park, Calif.: Benjamin-Cummings.

Lehninger, A. L. 1982. *Principles of Biochemistry*. New York: Worth.

Luck, D. J. L. 1965. Formation of mitochondria in *Neurospora crassa*. A study based on mitochondrial density changes. *J. Cell Biol.* **24**:461.

Margulis, L. 1981. *Symbiosis in Cell Evolution*. San Francisco: Freeman.

Mason, T. L., and G. Schatz. 1973. Cytochrome oxidase of baker's yeast. II. Site of translation of the protein components. *J. Biol. Chem.* **248**:1355.

Mitchell, P. 1961. Coupling of phosphorylation to electron and hydrogen transfer by a chemi-osmotic type of mechanism. *Nature* **191**:144.

Mitchell, P. 1979. Keilin's respiratory chain concept and its chemiosmotic consequences. *Science* **206**:1148 (Nobel lecture).

Moore, A. L., and P. R. Rich. 1980. The bioenergetics of plant mitochondria. *Trends Biochem. Sci.* **5**:284.

Mounolou, J. C., H. Jakob, and P. P. Slonimski. 1966. Mitochondrial DNA from yeast "petite" mutants: Specific changes of buoyant density corresponding to different cytoplasmic mutations. *Biochem. Biophys. Res. Commun.* **24**:218.

Nass, M. M. K., and S. Nass. 1963. Intramitochondrial fibers with DNA characteristics. I. Fixation and electron staining reactions. *J. Cell Biol.* **19**:595.

Nass, M. M. K., and S. Nass. 1963. Intramitochondrial fibers with DNA characteristics. II. Enzymatic and other hydrolytic treatments. *J. Cell Biol.* **19**:613.

Nicholls, D. 1981. Some recent advances in mitochondrial calcium transport. *Trends Biochem. Sci.* **6**:36.

Nicholls, D. G., and E. Rial. 1984. Brown fat mitochondria. *Trends Biochem. Sci.* **9**:489.

Racker, E. February 1968. The membrane of the mitochondrion. *Sci. Amer.* **218**:32.

Racker, E. 1976. Structure and function of ATP-driven ion pumps. *Trends Biochem. Sci.* **1**:244.

Racker, E. 1980. From Pasteur to Mitchell: A hundred years of bioenergetics. *Fed. Proc.* **39**:210.

Sanger, F. 1981. Determination of nucleotide sequences in DNA. *Science* **214**:1205 (Nobel lecture).

Schatz, G., and R. A. Butow. 1983. How are proteins imported into mitochondria? *Cell* **32**:316.

Schwartz, R. M., and M. O. Dayhoff. 1978. Origins of prokaryotes, eukaryotes, mitochondria, and chloroplasts. *Science* **199**:395.

Senior, A. E. 1983. Secondary and tertiary structure of membrane proteins involved in proton translocation. *Biochim. Biophys. Acta* **726**:81.

Slonimski, P. P., P. Borst, and G. Attardi. 1982. *Mitochondrial Genes*. Cold Spring Harbor, N. Y.: Cold Spring Harbor Laboratory.

Srere, P. A. 1982. The structure of the mitochondrial inner membrane-matrix compartment. *Trends Biochem. Sci.* **7**:375.

Stryer, L. 1981. *Biochemistry*. 2nd ed. San Francisco: Freeman.

Swanson, R. F., and I. B. Dawid. 1970. The mitochondrial ribosome of *Xenopus laevis*. *Proc. Natl. Acad. Sci. U. S.* **66**:117.

Teintze, M., M. Slaughter, H. Weiss, and W. Neupert. 1982. Biogenesis of mitochondrial ubiquinol:cytochrome *c* reductase (cytochrome bc_1 complex). Precursor proteins and their transfer into mitochondria. *J. Biol. Chem.* **257**:10364.

Tzagoloff, A. 1982. *Mitochondria*. New York: Plenum.

Uzzell, T., and C. Spolsky. 1974. Mitochondria and plastids as endosymbionts: A revival of special creation? *Amer. Sci.* **62**:334.

Vignais, P. V., and G. J. M. Lauquin. 1979. Mitochondrial adenine nucleotide transport and its role in the economy of the cell. *Trends Biochem. Sci.* **4**:90.

Whittaker, P. A., and S. M. Danks. 1979. *Mitochondria: Structure, Function, Assembly*. New York: Longman.

Yaffee, M., and G. Schatz. 1984. The future of mitochondrial research. *Trends Biochem. Sci.* **9**:179.

Zubay, G. 1983. *Biochemistry*. Reading, Mass.: Addison-Wesley.

CHAPTER 10

Chloroplasts

All life on Earth depends either directly or indirectly on photosynthetic organisms for its food and energy needs. Photosynthetic species convert energy from solar radiation to chemical energy in organic molecules and are thus the beginning of the food chain. In addition to providing the ultimate source of foods for all life, photosynthetic species replenish atmospheric oxygen and maintain its concentration at about 21%. Although the primeval atmosphere of the Earth was anaerobic, the appearance and multiplication of blue-green algae and of eukaryotic photosynthetic organisms caused a profound change from anaerobic to aerobic conditions because of the oxygen released as a byproduct of their light-harvesting processes. Life forms became predominantly aerobic about 1 billion years ago, and they have been the predominant forms ever since. Modern anaerobic or partially anaerobic organisms constitute a very small fraction of total life on the planet today. As long as the sun shines and photosynthetic species persist, we can be assured of a constant supply of organic foods and atmospheric oxygen.

The centers of photosynthetic reactions are chloroplasts in eukaryotic species and noncompartmented membranous and cytosolic components in the blue-green algae and certain bacterial groups. We will pay particular attention to chloroplasts in this chapter, but we will discuss pertinent features of prokaryotic systems as well. Some of these comparisons have an important bearing on current views of the evolutionary origins of chloroplasts and of their genetic apparatus.

Structure and Chemistry of Photosynthetic Systems

Chloroplasts in all cells are readily visible even at the low magnification and resolution of light microscopy. Chloroplasts were an early focus of study by seventeenth-century microscopists, including Nehemiah Grew and Antonie van Leeuwenhoek, and by physiologists for more than two hundred years. In the eighteenth and nineteenth centuries, experimental

FIGURE 10-1
Chloroplasts in land plants and many algae are typically discoid in shape, but they often occur in unusual forms in algae. The chloroplast is cup-shaped in *Chlamydomonas*, is band-shaped in *Ulothrix*, and has a spiral form in *Spirogyra*.

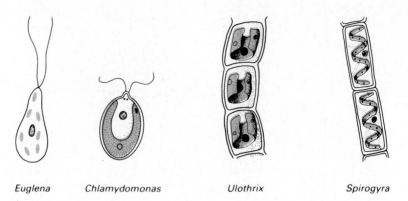

Euglena   *Chlamydomonas*   *Ulothrix*   *Spirogyra*

studies established the relationship between the absorption of light by chlorophyll in chloroplasts and the production of molecular oxygen, as well as the conversion of carbon dioxide to stored starch.

Chloroplasts of land plants (mosses and other bryophytes, ferns, and seed-bearing plants) are usually discoid or lens-shaped and may number fifty or more per cell, whereas chloroplast shape and number are quite variable among the algae and green protists. Many of the algae have only one chloroplast per cell, which is often of unusual form. For example, *Spirogyra* species have one or two ribbonlike, helical chloroplasts; *Ulothrix* has one bracelet-shaped chloroplast; and *Chlamydomonas* has one cup-shaped chloroplast in the cell (Fig. 10.1). The average chloroplast is about 1 to 10 μm long, but some algal plastids are much larger. Chloroplasts are not present in prokaryotic photosynthesizing species.

10.1
Chloroplast Structure

Each chloroplast is set apart from its cytoplasmic surroundings by two membranous envelopes separated by a narrow intermembrane space. In the interior of the organelle is a third set of membranes bathed in an amorphous matrix, or **stroma** (Fig. 10.2). These internal membranes are present as flattened sacs, called **thylakoids**, which may be arranged in stacks like neat piles of coins, or they may be single or multiple elongated components that traverse the stroma and connect individual coin-shaped thylakoids in the stacks. A stack of coin-shaped thylakoids is called a **granum** (pl., **grana**) and its individual elements are **grana thylakoids**. The elongated connecting elements are **stroma thylakoids**. The internal channels of stroma thylakoids are continuous with the spaces in the individual grana thylakoids with which they are connected, but the spaces of stacked thylakoids in a granum are separated by the membrane that surrounds each space (Fig. 10.3).

Variations exist in thylakoid arrangements in different cell types and groups of organisms. Grana or granalike stacks of coin-shaped thylakoids are fairly typical of many of the green algae and all of the land plants, though certain differentiated cells in flowering plants have chloroplasts with long, single stroma thylakoids rather than grana. In certain groups the thylakoid pattern is invariant; for example, thylakoids occur singly in the red algae, in pairs in diverse protists such as di-

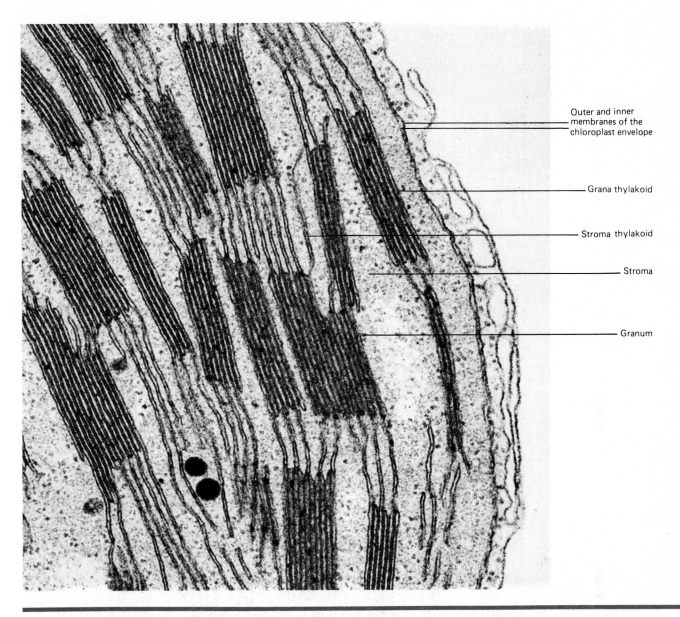

Outer and inner
membranes of the
chloroplast envelope

Grana thylakoid

Stroma thylakoid

Stroma

Granum

FIGURE 10-2
Electron micrograph of a section
through part of a chloroplast from a
leaf mesophyll cell of timothy grass
(*Phleum pratense*). The double-
membrane envelope of the organelle encloses an amorphous matrix,
called stroma, within which is found
a system of grana thylakoids organized into stacks, called grana, and
stroma thylakoids that are continuous
with the grana. × 80,000. (Photography by W. P. Wergin, courtesy
of E. H. Newcomb.)

atoms, dinoflagellates, and euglenoids, and in threes in the brown algae
(Fig. 10.4).

The stroma appears to be a relatively unstructured granular ground
substance, within which are found numerous enzymes, chloroplast DNA
and ribosomes of the organelle genetic system, and the photosynthetic
thylakoids (Fig. 10.5).

Chloroplasts, like mitochondria, are compartmented systems. The
two outer membranes appear to have different permeability properties,
such that the outermost of the two is more permeable to ions and large
molecules than is the innermost envelope. We know little about the
intermembrane space between these two membranes. The stroma is a
conspicuous compartment in which many of the so-called dark reactions
of photosynthesis take place—that is, light-independent reactions—
and all of the genetic processes of DNA replication, transcription, and
translation. Thylakoids can be considered to include two distinct
compartmented components: the *thylakoid membranes* and the *thylakoid*

FIGURE 10-3
Organization of the grana in chloroplasts. (a) Drawing showing the individual grana thylakoids to be flattened membranous sacs, interconnected by one or more stroma thylakoid sacs. Grana thylakoids are stacked like coins in the granum, with each thylakoid space separated by its surrounding thylakoid membrane (color). (b) Electron micrograph showing the densely staining region between adjacent thylakoids in grana. ×135,000. (Photograph courtesy of M. C. Ledbetter.)

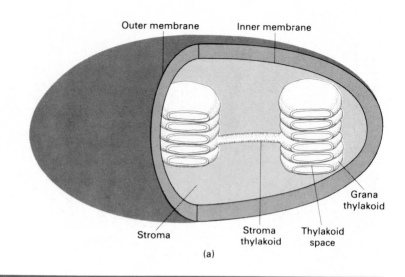

(a)

FIGURE 10-4
Electron micrograph of a section through a zoosporangial mother cell from the brown alga *Nereocystis*. The huge chloroplast is surrounded by a thin band of cytoplasm just inside the cell wall. The chloroplast itself contains thylakoids consistently grouped in threes (detail shown in insert) and bathed in stroma. A region of DNA is visible at one end of the chloroplast. ×48,000; insert, ×114,000. (Photograph courtesy of T. Bisalputra and D. C. Walker.)

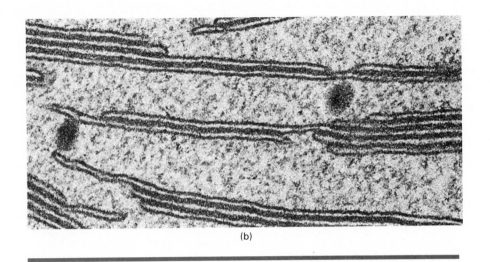

(b)

FIGURE 10-5
Electron micrograph of part of a chloroplast from *Euglena gracilis*, showing groups of ribosomes attached to DNA fibrils in the stroma regions between thylakoids. Such aggregates of DNA and ribosomes direct protein synthesis within the organelle. ×148,200. (Photograph by H. P. Hoffmann.)

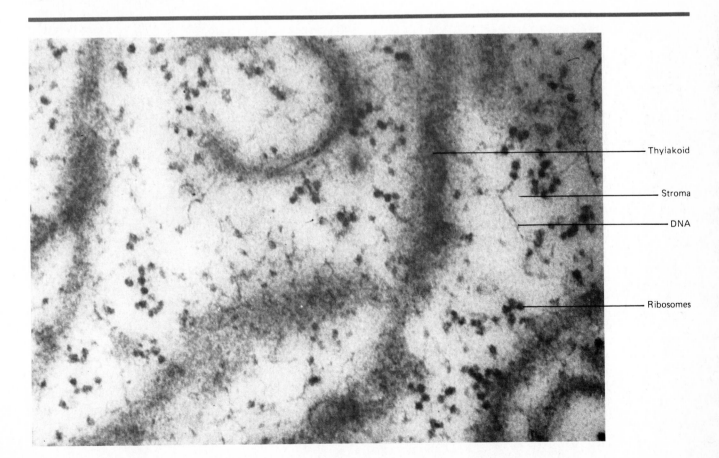

spaces. The processes of light harvesting and the conversion of light energy to chemical energy, in the forms of ATP and NADPH, take place in the thylakoid compartments. Thylakoid membranes contain the photosynthetic pigments, a light-driven ATP synthetase that can pump protons from the thylakoid spaces into the stroma, and an electron transport system capable of pumping protons into the thylakoid spaces and thereby establishing an electrochemical proton gradient across the thylakoid membrane. Thylakoid membranes are thus chemiosmotic coupling devices by which the energy of electron transport drives ATP synthesis in the light, a process known as photophosphorylation. We will discuss all these processes in detail in this chapter.

10.2
Thylakoids in Prokaryotes

Among the prokaryotes capable of photosynthesis are all of the *blue-green algae* (also called cyanophytes or cyanobacteria), grass-green *prochlorophytes*, and several groups of true bacteria of which the most important are the *purple bacteria* and the *green bacteria*. The blue-green algae and prochlorophytes are aerobic and regularly release oxygen as a byproduct of their light-harvesting activities. Both the purple and the

FIGURE 10-6
Electron micrograph of a section through the blue-green alga *Synechococcus lividus*, showing the concentrically folded thylakoids with numerous pigment granules (phycobilisomes) attached to the cytoplasm-facing surfaces of the elongated membranous sacs. The thylakoid spaces appear empty, but they are actually filled with enzymes and other molecules in aqueous suspension. ×62,400. (Photograph courtesy of E. Gantt, from Edwards, M. E., and E. Gantt, 1971, *J. Cell Biol.* **50**:896–900, Fig. 1.)

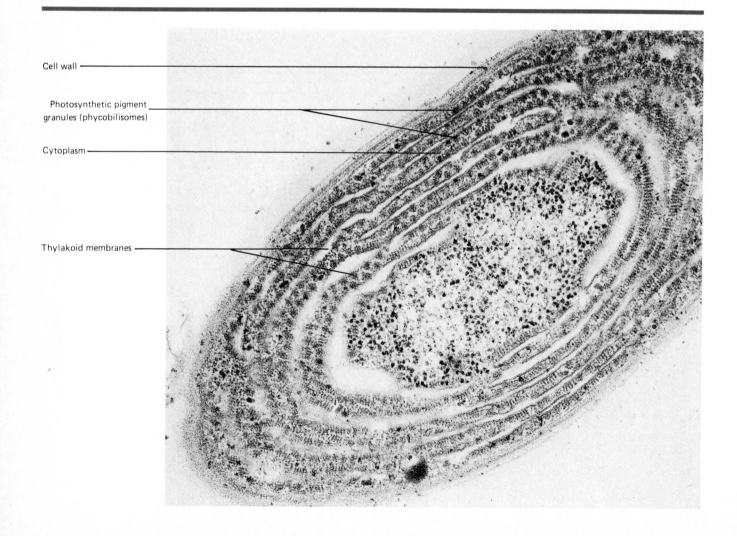

Cell wall

Photosynthetic pigment granules (phycobilisomes)

Cytoplasm

Thylakoid membranes

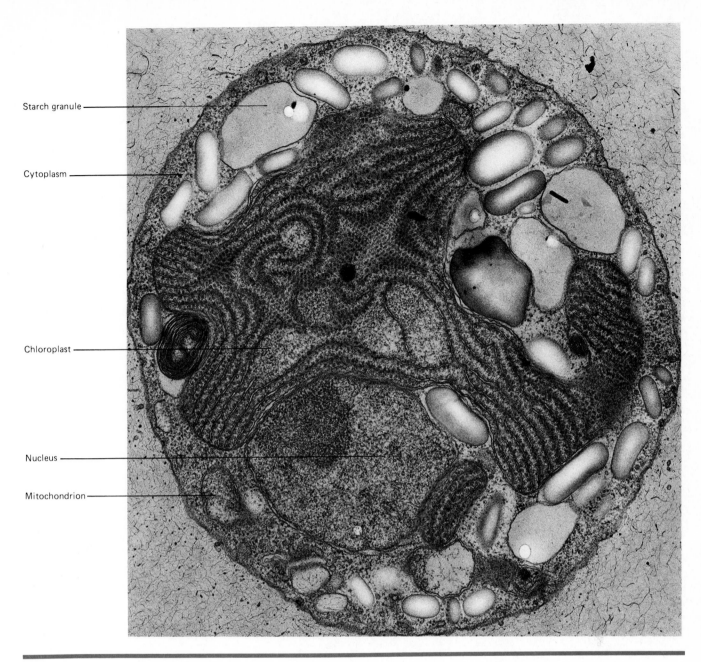

Starch granule —————————

Cytoplasm —————————

Chloroplast —————————

Nucleus —————————

Mitochondrion —————————

FIGURE 10-7
Electron micrograph of a section through the unicellular red alga *Porphyridium cruentum*. The chloroplast with its thylakoids decorated with granular phycobilisomes is strikingly similar in appearance to a blue-green algal cell (see Fig. 10.6). Red algae, however, are eukaryotes, as is apparent from the presence of a nucleus and mitochondria. In the cytoplasm are many starch granules, which are the stored food products of photosynthetic reactions that take place within the chloroplast. ×27,500. (Photograph courtesy of E. Gantt, from Gantt, E., and S. F. Conti, 1965, *J. Cell Biol.* **26**:365–381, Fig. 7.)

green bacteria, however, exist anaerobically or at least carry out photosynthesis under anaerobic conditions even if they also manage aerobic metabolic activities. Purple and green bacteria never release oxygen; in fact, oxygen is poisonous to the strictly anaerobic green bacteria and for those purple bacterial that live anaerobically. These variations reflect chemical rather than structural differences in their photosynthetic systems.

In the blue-green algae and prochlorophytes, thylakoids are distributed within the cytosol as single elements spaced fairly regularly within the volume of the cell (Fig. 10.6). Though they are rarely observed in electron micrographs, we believe that thylakoids are attached at one or more points to the plasma membrane, from which they are considered to be derived during development. The organization in blue-green algae of thylakoids, DNA, and ribosomes within the cytoplasm produces an uncanny resemblance between these cells and the chloroplasts of red algae and a few other primitive photosynthetic eukaryotes (Fig. 10.7).

The similarities in structural organization between prokaryotic algae and chloroplasts, and their similarities in photosynthetic chemistry, have had a strong bearing on the widely accepted theory that eukaryotic chloroplasts evolved from endosymbiotic prokaryotic algal ancestors. We will discuss this interesting topic at the end of the chapter, after we have considered the nature of the chloroplast genetic system.

In all purple bacteria, thylakoids develop as deeply infolded regions of the plasma membrane, with which they are continuous at all times. Three general patterns of thylakoid organization have been described. The most common pattern is that of numerous small vesicles or elongated tubules, about 40 to 50 nm wide, all of which arise by invaginations of the plasma membrane to which they remain attached (Fig. 10.8). This pattern is found in most of the purple sulfur bacteria, including *Chromatium*, and in some of the nonsulfur purple bacteria, such as *Rhodopseudomonas*. A second pattern is one in which long, branched tubular thylakoids about 45 nm in diameter are disposed in parallel arrays within the cytoplasm. The third major pattern occurs in *Rhodospirillum* and certain other purple bacteria that reproduce by budding. In these cells the thylakoids are organized into stacks of discoid components superficially similar to chloroplast grana. The thylakoid membranes in this case are connected with the plasma membrane at only one or two places, rather than being continuous at many places as in the first two patterns described. The significance of these differences is unknown, as is the basis for the variations in thylakoid organization in the purple bacteria.

Green bacteria, such as *Chlorobium*, differ from all other photosynthesizing prokaryotes in that their photosynthetic pigments are contained in special *chlorobium vesicles*. These vesicles are bounded by an unusually thin membrane 2 to 3 nm thick. The structures are completely separated from the plasmalemma, although they are distributed in a region underneath and parallel to the cell boundary. These cigar-shaped vesicles are about 50 nm wide and 120 to 150 nm long. Differentiation of chlorobium vesicles may be the equivalent of compartmentation in eukaryotes, except that the very thin membrane is quite different from typical cellular membranes.

FIGURE 10-8
Electron micrograph through the cell of the nonsulfur purple bacterium *Rhodopseudomonas spheroides*, showing the nucleoid and numerous electron-transparent membranous photosynthetic vesicles in the cytoplasm. The vesicles are invaginations of the plasma membrane, but this feature is best observed by viewing three-dimensional reconstructions of the cell or by tracing a series of consecutive sections through the cell. ×89,000. (Photograph courtesy of G. Cohen-Bazire.)

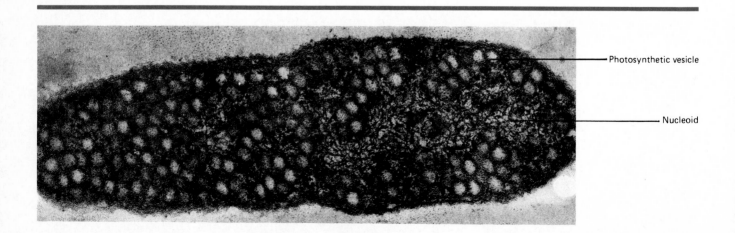

Photosynthetic vesicle

Nucleoid

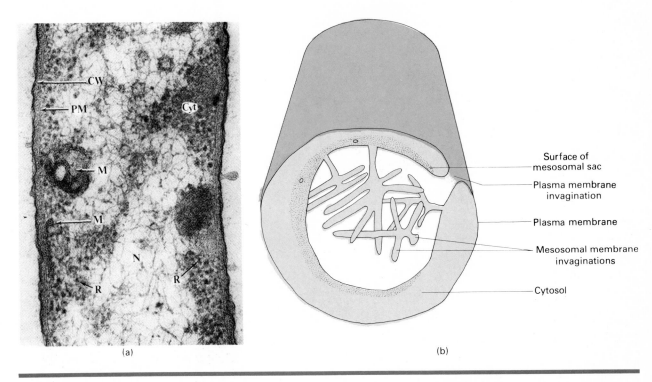

(a)   (b)

FIGURE 10-9
Mesosomes. (a) Electron micrograph
through part of the bacterium *Pseudomonas aeruginosa*, showing the
cell wall (CW), plasma membrane
(PM), nucleoid (N), cytoplasm (Cyt),
ribosomes (R), and two mesosomes
(M) at the plasma membrane. (b)
Schematic drawing of the mesosome
showing it to be a sac with multiply
branched tubular invaginations. The
mesosomal sac itself is an invaginated
region of the plasma membrane.
(Photograph by H.-P. Hoffmann.)

Infolded regions of plasma membrane are common features of green bacteria and some other groups. These infolds are called **mesosomes** (Fig. 10.9). It has been suggested that they function in respiration because they contain a high concentration of electron transport enzymes. Mesosomes may also be involved in cell division because they are usually found where the new wall is forming. They apparently have no role in photosynthesis because neligble amounts of photosynthetic pigments have been found in isolated mesosomes.

10.3
Photosynthetic Pigments

The three classes of photosynthetic pigments are **chlorophylls**, **carotenoids**, and **phycobilins**. All photosynthetic cells contain one or more kinds of chlorophyll and carotenoid, but phycobilins are found only in red algae and blue-green algae. The chlorophylls and carotenoids are integral components of thylakoid membranes in all photosynthetic species except for the green bacteria, whose pigments are localized in special chlorobium vesicles. Phycobilins, however, are loosely associated with the external face of thylakoids and are easily separated from all other photosensitive pigments. Phycobilins are concentrated in granules called **phycobilisomes**, and the numerous granules are an especially prominent feature in electron micrographs of red algal chloroplasts and blue-green algal cells (see Fig. 10.6 and Fig. 10.7).

Photosynthetic pigments are thus concentrated and localized in some fashion in all photosynthetic cells and are not randomly dispersed in either the stroma or cytosol. Taken in some combination, these pigments provide the cell with the capacity to absorb solar energy across

FIGURE 10-10
Absorption spectra of a standard
concentration of five photosynthetic
pigments extracted in ether (a–c) or
aqueous solution (d–e). (a) Bacteriochlorophyll from photosynthetic
bacteria shows absorption peaks in the
ultraviolet and infrared regions outside
the visible spectrum. (b) Chlorophyll *a*,
the major photosynthetic pigment in
chloroplasts and prokaryotic algae, and
(c) chlorophyll *b*, another chloroplast
pigment, absorb light principally in the
short and long wavelengths of the
visible spectrum. (d) Phycoerythrin and
(e) phycocyanin are found only in the
blue-green algae and the red algae.
The green color of plants is due largely
to transmission of the green wavelengths and absorption of other parts
of the visible spectrum by chlorophylls
a and *b* (red lines). Similarly, phycoerythrin appears red because the longer,
red wavelengths are transmitted, and
phycocyanin appears blue-green
because the shorter wavelengths are
transmitted.

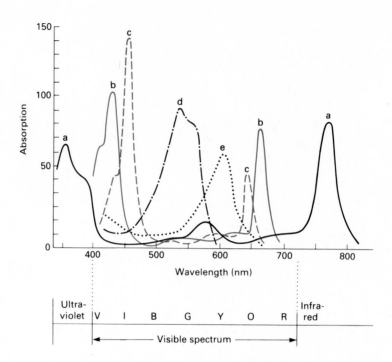

all of the visible spectrum, in wavelengths from 400 to 700 nm—and in
some cases into the far-red and infrared ranges as well (Fig. 10.10).

Comparisons of absorption spectra and action spectra for different
photosynthetic pigments reveal that chlorophylls are the major light-
capturing pigments. An *absorption spectrum* of a substance is a plot of the
degree of absorbance of different wavelengths of a spectrum by the
substance, and an *action spectrum* of a substance is a plot of the relative
efficiency of different wavelengths of light in support of some activity of
the substance, such as oxygen evolution. Because the absorption and
action spectra for chlorophylls show the same patterns of maximum
utilization in the blue and red wavelengths, chlorophylls must play a
major role in harvesting light energy (absorption) for photosynthesis
(activity) (Fig. 10.11). Comparisons of absorption and action spectra for
whole chloroplasts or cells and for individual pigments have thus
established the range and effectiveness of light-capturing capacities in
different photosynthetic systems. We see chlorophylls in a test tube or a
landscape as green substances, because the pigments transmit green
wavelengths but absorb others in the visible spectrum.

Chlorophylls are lipid-soluble and easily extracted and purified of
contaminating proteins. The pigment is constructed of a **porphyrin** ring
whose central nitrogen atom coordinates with a Mg^{2+} ion. A long
phytol side-chain is added to the porphyrin component during chlorophyll biosynthesis (Fig. 10.12). Different kinds of chlorophylls have
different substitutions in the porphyrin ring. The porphyrin part of the
chlorophyll molecule is very similar to porphyrin prosthetic groups of
hemoglobins and cytochromes, but these latter compounds have a
central iron atom rather than magnesium (see Fig. 9.11).

Higher plants, photosynthetic protists, and algae (including prokaryotic algae), all contain chlorophyll *a*. Eukaryotes contain a second
chlorophyll, which varies according to the species group. The second
chlorophyll may be *b* (higher plants and most green algae), *c* (diatoms,

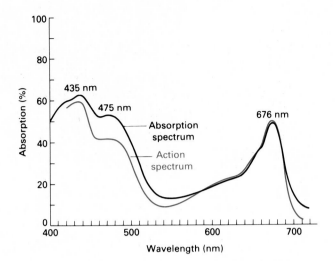

FIGURE 10-11
A comparison of the degree of light absorption (absorption spectrum) and of the relative efficiency of photosynthetic activity (action spectrum) in *Chlorella* cells shows enough similarity to permit the conclusion that chlorophylls *a* and *b* in the alga chloroplasts are the major pigments that harvest light energy for photosynthesis. Some differences are evident between the absorption spectra of whole cells and of pigment extracts (see Fig. 10.10). These differences are due to the absorption of light by proteins and light-capturing carotenoids in cells.

Chlorophyll *a*

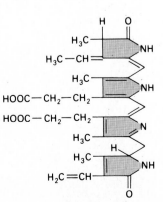

β-Carotene

Phycoerythrobilin

FIGURE 10-12
Structural formulas for representatives of the three major groups of photosynthetic pigments in plants and prokaryotic algae show the common feature of numerous conjugated double bonds. Chlorophylls have a porphyrin ring coordinated with a central Mg ion, and a long phytol hydrocarbon chain. Carotenoids, such as β-carotene, and phycobilins, such as the red pigment phycoerythrobilin, have more open-chain double bonds than occur in chlorophylls. Phycobilins, however, are conjugated with proteins (not shown) to form phycobiliproteins, which are found in phycobilisome particles attached to the outer surfaces of thylakoids in blue-green and red algae.

TABLE 10-1
Distribution of Chlorophylls and Other Photosynthetic Pigments

	CHLOROPHYLL				BACTERIOCHLOROPHYLL					
Organism	a	b	c	d	a	b	c	d	Carotenoids	Phycobiliproteins
Eukaryotes										
Mosses, ferns, seed plants	+	+	−	−					+	−
Green algae	+	+	−	−					+	−
Euglenoids	+	+	−	−					+	−
Diatoms	+	−	+	−					+	−
Dinoflagellates	+	−	+	−					+	−
Brown algae	+	−	+	−					+	−
Red algae	+	−	−	+					+	+
Prokaryotes										
Blue−green algae	+	−	−	−					+	+
Prochlorophytes	+	+	−	−					+	−
Sulfur purple bacteria					+ or	+	−	−	+	−
Nonsulfur purple bacteria					+ or	+	−	−	+	−
Green bacteria					+	−	+ or	+	+	−

dinoflagellates, and brown algae), or *d* (red algae). Interestingly, prochlorophytes also contain chlorophyll *b*, whereas cyanophytes do not. Bacteria, which do not evolve molecular oxygen, have no chlorophyll *a*. Instead, they contain one or more of the four known **bacteriochlorophylls** (Table 10.1). All the chlorophylls absorb and hold the energy of visible light efficiently because of their numerous conjugated double bonds.

The orange, red, and yellow carotenoids and the red or blue phycobilins also absorb light energy, but they do so less efficiently than the chlorophylls. Carotenoids absorb maximally in the violet to green range (400–500 nm), and phycobilins show maximal absorption in the green to orange part of the visible spectrum (550–630 nm). As with the chlorophylls, we see particular carotenoid and phycobilin colors due to their transmission of particular spectral wavelengths.

Various carotenoids have different long-chain hydrocarbon regions with many conjugated double bonds and unique chain termini. Color in carrots and tomatoes is due to **β-carotene**, a commonly occurring carotenoid pigment (see Fig. 10.12). These fatty substances are accessory pigments that can transfer absorbed light energy to chlorophyll *a* or its equivalent, although with low efficiency. Carotenoids also protect chlorophyll in plants and algae from degradative effects induced by molecular oxygen in the light.

Phycobilins are accessory pigments that are conjugated with proteins of a specific nature, whereas neither chlorophylls nor carotenoids have a protein component. The protein–pigment conjugate is called a *phycobiliprotein*, whereas the pigment alone is called a phycobilin. The red pigment–protein conjugate is *phycoerythrin*, and its blue analog is *phycocyanin*. These substances are present together in phycobilisomes of both the red and the blue-green algae, but the particular predominating pigment leads to a redder or a bluer cellular color.

Phycobilins are open-chain porphyrin-type compounds, whereas chlorophylls have a ring porphyrin component (see Fig. 10.12). Like carotenoids, phycobilins transfer their absorbed light energy to chlorophyll a, the primary photosynthetic pigment in all plants and algae. In general, energy is transferred more efficiently to chlorophyll a by phycobilins than by carotenoids.

10.4
General Features of Photosynthesis

In all photosynthesizing cells, the energy of solar radiation is absorbed by light-sensitive pigments, transferred to electron acceptors, and conserved as chemical energy for subsidizing cellular work. Except in the photosynthetic bacteria, water serves as the donor of electrons to reduce carbon dioxide or other electron-accepting substrates. As a result, water is oxidized to oxygen. In the overall view, therefore, nonbacterial photosynthesis is a process in which light energy is used to reduce ("fix") CO_2 into organic compounds, with H_2O as the electron donor for this reduction.

$$n\,H_2O + n\,CO_2 \xrightarrow[\text{chlorophyll}]{\text{light}} [CH_2O]_n + n\,O_2$$

As first proposed by C. B. van Niel, bacterial and plant photosynthesis could be viewed as essentially similar processes if the reaction reflected a more general hydrogen donor than water. For example, the hydrogen donor could be H_2S or some organic compound, such as the lactic acid used by nonsulfur purple bacteria.

$$2\,H_2D + CO_2 \xrightarrow[\text{chlorophyll}]{\text{light}} [CH_2O] + H_2O + 2\,D$$

According to this formulation, various hydrogen donors (H_2D) may be involved. H_2D could be H_2O, H_2S, or another hydrogen donor, depending on the species. The donor would be oxidized to D as its hydrogens were transferred for carbon dioxide reduction.

As van Niel noted, the molecular oxygen evolved during aerobic photosynthesis must originate from H_2O and not from CO_2 molecules. Later studies showed this was indeed the case. When the heavy ^{18}O isotope of ordinary ^{16}O was used, the evolved molecular oxygen contained oxygen atoms originally present in H_2O, but none from CO_2.

$$n\,H_2{}^{18}O + n\,C^{16}O_2 \xrightarrow[\text{chlorophyll}]{\text{light}} [CH_2O]_n + n\,{}^{18}O_2$$

In the reciprocal experiment, the results were

$$n\,H_2{}^{16}O + n\,C^{18}O_2 \xrightarrow[\text{chlorophyll}]{\text{light}} [CH_2O]_n + n\,{}^{16}O_2$$

Furthermore, it is known that CO_2 is the major acceptor of hydrogens and electrons from a donor, but not the only one. Most plants can use nitrate or even H^+, and some nitrogen-fixing plants can use molecular nitrogen as an electron acceptor during photosynthesis. Because various electron donors and acceptors may be used by different species, the more general photosynthetic reaction for any organism is

$$H_2D + A \xrightarrow[\text{chlorophyll}]{\text{light}} H_2A + D$$

in which H_2D is the donor and A the acceptor of hydrogens and electrons.

Regardless of the specific electron donor or acceptor, the light-induced flow of electrons is toward the system of greater electronegative potential—that is, *against* the usual gradient of potentials of acceptor–donor systems. In contrast to respiration processes that flow "downhill" from an electronegative (energy-rich) state to an electropositive (energy-poor) state, the force of light energy absorbed by chlorophyll in photosynthesis causes an "uphill" flow of electrons and energy (see Table 3.1).

It may be noted here that water is a very weak reductant. Water has a strongly positive standard electrode potential of +0.8 V and, therefore, a very high affinity for electrons. It has very little tendency, theoretically, to lose electrons and form O_2. Photosynthesis is the only metabolic process known to use H_2O as an electron donor.

10.5
Photoexcitation

We can see only that small portion of the electromagnetic radiation spectrum that falls between wavelengths of 400 and 700 nm; this is the "visible" spectrum to us. These energetic wavelengths reach us from the sun or artificial light sources in discrete packets call **photons**. The only difference between visible light and other electromagnetic radiations (x-rays, radio waves, ultraviolet light, and others) is in the frequency of vibrations of the radiation source. The energy of a photon is called a **quantum**, and the amount of energy in one quantum for a particular photon is given by the equation

$$E = h\nu \qquad \text{[10.1]}$$

where h is Planck's constant (1.585×10^{-34} cal·sec) and ν is vibrations (cycles)/sec. In 1900 Max Planck developed an equation by which the energy in one quantum is related to the wavelength of the particular photon:

$$E = \frac{hc}{\lambda} \qquad \text{[10.2]}$$

where h is Planck's constant, c is the speed of light (3×10^{10} cm/sec), and λ is the wavelength of emitted radiation. When an atom or molecule absorbs a photon of light, it is absorbing a quantum of energy. Photon energy is inversely proportional to wavelength, so photons of the shorter wavelengths have the higher energy content. This relationship is implied in equation [10.2].

The energy equivalent is most usefully expressed in some form that permits comparisons and relationships with numbers of molecules. One way to express photon energy equivalents is in calories or kilocalories per *einstein*. An einstein can be considered as one "mole" of light, or 6.023×10^{23} quanta, expressed in calories. Because the number of molecules in a mole is given by Avogadro's number (6.023×10^{23}), it is necessary to multiply the energy per molecule by this number to give the energy associated with one mole. Thus 1 mole of pigment containing 6.023×10^{23} molecules and absorbing 1 einstein of light at 600 nm will absorb the energy equivalent of 47.67 kcal. Or, 1 einstein of photons at

TABLE 10-2
Energy Equivalent of the Einstein at Different Wavelengths

Wavelength (nm)	Spectrum color	Kcal per einstein
400	Violet	71.5
500	Blue	57.2
600	Yellow	47.7
675	Red	42.3
700	Near-red	40.9

600 nm wavelength has an energy equivalent of 47.67 kcal. The simplified equation is

$$N_{Av}E = \frac{N_{Av}hc}{\lambda} \text{ (expressed in kcal/einstein)} \qquad [10.3]$$

where N_{Av} is 6.023×10^{23}, or Avogadro's number, h is Planck's constant in cal·sec, c is the speed of light in cm/sec, and λ is the wavelength in centimeters. Values for other wavelengths are given in Table 10.2. Another expression used quite often is the *quantum yield* of photosynthesis, or amount of molecular oxygen evolved per einstein of light.

An atom or molecule may gain energy by **excitation**, an event that converts the substance to a higher-energy state. When electrons occupy orbitals of lowest accessible energy level around the nucleus of an atom, the atom is in its *ground state*. When a sufficient packet of energy is absorbed by the atom so that an electron moves from one orbital to another of higher accessible energy level, the atom enters an *excited state*. In its higher-energy excited state, the atom can transfer excitation energy to a different atom or molecule that has a lower energy level. The energy transfer proceeds "downhill" because the excited atom is temporarily at a higher energy level than the atom receiving the energy.

When photons of particular wavelengths (energy content) succeed in exciting an atom in a molecule, events occur very rapidly. It takes 10^{-15} sec or less for excitation to occur, and the excited state only lasts about 10^{-9} to 10^{-8} sec. Excited atoms are thus extremely unstable. This brief period is sufficient time, however, to allow some or most of the light energy to be trapped chemically. Upon the atom's return to its ground state, the trapped energy may be dissipated as heat, emitted as radiation (called fluorescence), or converted to chemical energy, depending on the lifetime of the excited state of each atom or molecule involved. The significant energy of photoexcitation in biological systems is the proportion of the total that is converted to chemical energy. Absorption is even more efficient in photosynthetic cells because different pigments receive photons of different wavelengths, making more of the absorbed light energy available in the cell.

10.6

Separability of Light and Dark Reactions

Beginning early in this century, evidence began to accumulate pointing toward two separate sets of reactions for photosynthesis, one set strictly dependent on light and another set that was independent of light. In 1937 Robert Hill provided the first experimental demonstration that a separate light reaction was localized in chloroplasts. When isolated chloroplasts or whole green cells were illuminated in the presence of artificial hydrogen acceptors such as reducible dyes, molecular oxygen was evolved and the dyes were reduced simultaneously. Water was the exclusive hydrogen donor in this system and, most important, CO_2 was not required for the reaction. If CO_2 was reduced, its reduction products did not accumulate. These results provided support for the existence of separate light and dark reaction systems, because oxygen evolution could take place whether or not CO_2 was reduced. The **Hill reaction** follows the general sequence

$$2 \, H_2O + 2 \, A \xrightarrow[\text{chlorophyll}]{\text{light}} 2 \, AH_2 + O_2$$

where A is the hydrogen acceptor (oxidized dye) and AH_2 is its reduced form.

In 1950 Severo Ochoa and Roman Vishniac showed that the electron carrier $NADP^+$ (nicotinamide adenine dinucleotide phosphate, oxidized form) could act as the hydrogen acceptor in the Hill reaction. This observation was important for two reasons: (1) NADPH was already known to be an electron donor in cellular biosynthesis, and (2) it supported the prediction that an end product of the light reaction was a reducing agent that could act in reducing CO_2 during subsequent dark reactions.

Another important discovery that clearly showed that there were separate light and dark reactions was made in 1954 by Daniel Arnon. He showed that illuminated spinach chloroplasts could make ATP by phosphorylating ADP. In this light-requiring process of photophosphorylation, CO_2 was neither required nor consumed.

The view thus gradually developed that $NADP^+$ reduction and ADP phosphorylation in the initial light reactions produced NADPH and ATP. These substances were then used in dark-reaction pathways to reduce carbon dioxide and other electron acceptors. The product of CO_2 reduction in chloroplasts is sugar, often stored as starch.

During the 1950s it was also shown that oxygen evolution and photophosphorylation reactions are localized within chloroplast grana, in the same thylakoid membranes that contain chlorophylls and accessory pigments. The dark reactions, on the other hand, take place in the stroma compartment of the chloroplast.

The Light Reactions of Photosynthesis

We have known for almost thirty years that nonbacterial photosynthesis requires the interaction of two different collections of light-sensitive pigments that cooperate to evolve oxygen, synthesize ATP, and reduce $NADP^+$ in the light. The discovery of cytochromes in chloroplasts led to the suggestion that the two systems of pigments and their associated proteins were linked together in series by a chain of electron carriers, thereby explaining the basis for the cooperative action of light-harvesting pigments. We have learned a great deal about the molecular components of these two *photosystems* and their electron transport link, and about the coupled process of ATP synthesis. Most recently, data from combined studies of freeze-fractured membranes and the biochemistry of membrane components have led to a better understanding of the functional architecture of the thylakoid membrane in which light energy is converted to chemical energy.

10.7
Photosystems I and II

Light energy is absorbed by chlorophylls, carotenoids, and phycobilins in eukaryotic chloroplasts and prokaryotic algae, and by one or more bacteriochlorophylls in photosynthetic bacteria. These pigments are tightly bound in thylakoid membranes by special proteins, except for phycobiliproteins in phycobilisomes bound to the outer membrane surface. Whereas phycobiliproteins are aggregated into particles that are clearly visible in thin sections of cells, chlorophylls and their associated proteins are clustered in particles that can be seen only after membranes have been prepared by freeze-etch and freeze-fracture methods that split open the lipid bilayer or etch out lipids and reveal the embedded particles (Fig. 10.13). These particulate aggregates of photosensitive pigments and associated proteins are of two kinds, referred to as photosystem I and photosystem II. **Photosystem I** (PS I) is responsible for NADP$^+$ reduction, and **photosystem II** (PS II) accepts electrons from water and is thus associated with the evolution of molecular oxygen. The electron transport link between the two photosystems is involved in the coupled synthesis of ATP during electron flow from PS II to PS I (Fig. 10.14).

Beginning in the 1950s, Robert Emerson and others obtained evidence indicating that photosensitive pigments cooperated in collecting and delivering radiant energy to a center for conversion to chemical

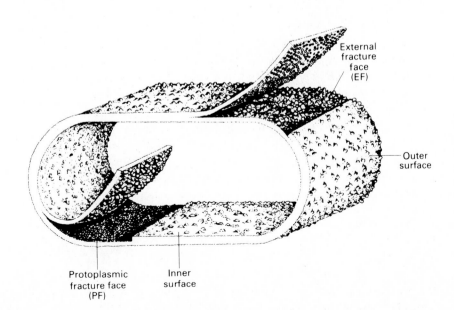

External
fracture
face
(EF)

Outer
surface

Protoplasmic
fracture face
(PF)

Inner
surface

FIGURE 10-13
Drawing of a chloroplast thylakoid after freeze-fracturing and subsequent etching to reveal particle displays of the original outer and inner surfaces of the thylakoid membrane and particle displays in split membrane of the fracture face nearest the protoplasm (PF face) and its complementary EF face closest to the thylakoid interior. (From Garber, M. P., and P. L. Steponkus, 1974, *J. Cell Biol.* **63**:28, Fig. 5.)

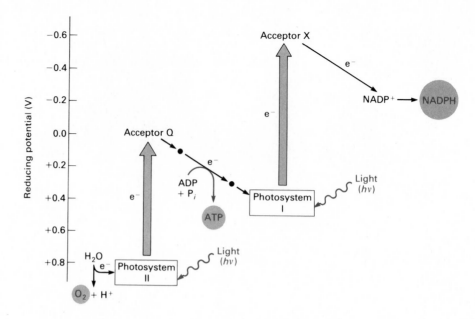

energy. They showed that, for approximately every 3000 chlorophyll molecules present, 1 molecule of oxygen was produced by the absorption of 8 quanta of light energy. These and other data led to the central postulate that chlorophylls and other pigments exist in *light-harvesting complexes* that transfer excitation energy to a special **reaction center** chlorophyll *a*, along a declining energy gradient. Reaction center chlorophyll *a* molecules are thus energized, and, in a reaction mediated by associated proteins, the excited electron in the reaction center is transferred to a closely associated electron acceptor. The ionized chlorophyll *a* is left with a positively charged electron hole that has a high affinity for electrons, and the hole is quickly filled by an electron from an electron donor closely associated with the reaction center chlorophyll. Reaction center chlorophyll *a* and its associated electron acceptor and electron donor molecules are thus the core of the photosystem and the site of the conversion of light energy to chemical energy. The light-harvesting complexes of pigments serve as *antennae* for collecting and delivering excitation energy to the reaction center, which acts as a trap for this energy and as an *electron lead* from excited pigments to chemical electron acceptors (Fig. 10.15).

Reaction center chlorophyll *a* molecules are structurally similar in their magnesium–porphyrin makeup to other chlorophyll *a* molecules, but they behave differently because of their special molecular environment. Reaction center chlorophyll *a* absorbs maximally at higher wavelengths, and it is therefore at a lower energy level than other chlorophylls. The reaction center chlorophyll *a* of PS I is known as **P700**; it is a pigment whose maximum absorption is at 700 nm. The equivalent in PS II is **P680**, a chlorophyll *a* with maximum absorption at 680 nm.

10.8
Electron Flow in Chloroplasts

In nonbacterial photosynthesis the ultimate electron donor is water and the ultimate electron acceptor is $NADP^+$. During electron flow from

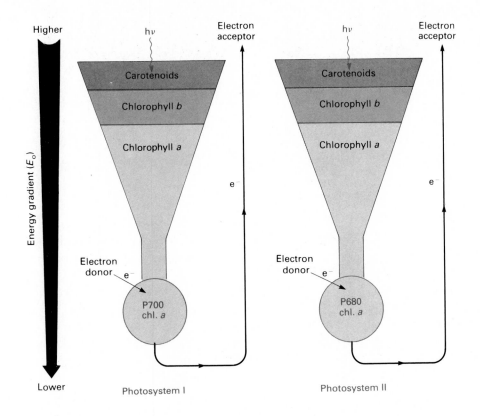

FIGURE 10-15
The light-harvesting complexes of chloroplast pigments in photosystems I and II collect and deliver excitation energy to special reaction center chlorophyll *a* molecules in the thermodynamically favorable direction along a declining energy gradient. The excited electron is transferred from P700, the reaction center chlorophyll *a* of photosystem I, and from P680, the reaction center chlorophyll *a* of photosystem II, to their associated electron acceptors. The electron hole left in ionized reaction center chlorophyll *a* is filled by an electron from an associated electron donor in each photosystem. The site of conversion of light energy to chemical energy is reaction center chlorophyll *a* and its closely associated electron donor and electron acceptor molecules. The light-harvesting complexes of pigments serve as antennae for collecting and delivering energy to reaction center chlorophyll *a*, which acts as an energy trap and as an electron lead from excited pigments to chemical electron acceptors.

water to $NADP^+$ in the pathway of linked PS I and PS II reactions, some of the free-energy difference of electron transport steps is conserved in ATP synthesis. Both NADPH and ATP from the light reactions serve as reservoirs of chemical energy that subsidize the reduction of CO_2 to high-energy sugars in the dark reactions of photosynthesis. The pathway of transport of energized electrons proceeds from water to PS II (so named because it was described after PS I), from PS II via the electron transport chain to PS I, and from PS I to $NADP^+$.

In the light, water molecules are "split" (*photolysis*) by a Mn^{2+}–containing enzyme to yield electrons, protons, and molecular oxygen. Four electrons are removed from each water molecule, using four quanta of light energy in the reaction: $H_2O \rightarrow 4\,H^+ + 4\,e^- + \frac{1}{2}\,O_2$. The electrons from water are passed along to reaction center chlorophyll *a* of PS II, thereby filling the electron holes created when energized reaction center chlorophyll was ionized. Electrons with a reducing potential of only +0.8 V in ground-state chlorophyll are boosted to 0.0 V when the chlorophyll is excited by light and by excitation energy received from light-harvesting complexes of pigments and their associated proteins (see Fig. 10.14). At the higher accessible energy level, energized electrons from P680 can be accepted by some chemical acceptor whose reducing potential is compatible with the thermodynamic requirements of the transfer. Although its precise identity is uncertain, the acceptor is believed to be a quinone and is therefore referred to as acceptor Q.

Acceptor Q then transfers electrons to a chain of electron carriers not unlike those in the mitochondrial electron transport chain, proceeding along a conventional gradient of declining energy. All the electron carriers contain metal ions that undergo oxidation–reductions. The detailed molecular structure and the exact sequence of the carriers are somewhat uncertain, but we have enough information to reconstruct the probable sequence of events during the transport of energized electrons from acceptor Q to P700 of PS I, and from there to NADP$^+$ in the so-called **Z-scheme** for the light reactions of photosynthesis (Fig. 10.16). Acceptor Q passes electrons to **plastoquinone** (which resembles mitochondrial ubiquinone), which in turn passes electrons to the **cytochrome b_6–f complex** (which resembles mitochondrial cytochrome b–c_1), and finally to **plastocyanin**, which is a small copper-containing protein. Electrons from plastocyanin are accepted by reaction center P700 of PS I. During electron transport along the carrier chain, there is sufficient free-energy difference to subsidize the synthesis of a little more than one ATP molecule per pair of electrons transferred from acceptor Q to plastocyanin. The cytochrome b_6–f complex pumps protons from the stroma into the thylakoid space across the thylakoid membrane, thereby generating an energy-rich electrochemical proton gradient that is utilized in ATP synthesis. We will discuss this topic more fully in the next section.

At approximately +0.4 V, ionized P700 chlorophyll accepts electrons from the last member of the electron transport link that joins the two photosystems together in series. Upon being raised from the ground state to an excited state by absorbing two quanta of light energy and excitation energy from excited pigments of the light-harvesting complexes, energized electrons in P700 can be accepted by an iron–sulfur protein called **ferredoxin** at the relatively high reducing potential of −0.6 V. Reaction center chlorophyll is restored to its ground state when its electron hole is filled by electrons from the carrier chain.

FIGURE 10-16

The Z-scheme for the light reactions of photosynthesis indicates the pathway of electrons from donor molecules of water to NADP$^+$, via the activities of two photosystems linked in series by a chain of electron carriers. Electrons from "split" water molecules are boosted from the low energy level of +0.8 V to 0.0 V by light-activated photosystem II pigments and can then be accepted by compound Q. Electrons are delivered by a carrier chain to ground-state photosystem I pigments at +0.4 V and are boosted to −0.6 V by light-activated PS I, for acceptance by ferredoxin. The electrons are ultimately accepted from ferredoxin by NADP$^+$, which is reduced to NADPH in reactions catalyzed by ferredoxin–NADP reductase. Some of the free-energy difference of electron transport between the linked photosystems is used in coupled ATP synthesis reactions of noncyclic photophosphorylation. NADPH and ATP made in the light are used in subsequent reactions by which CO$_2$ is reduced to carbohydrates.

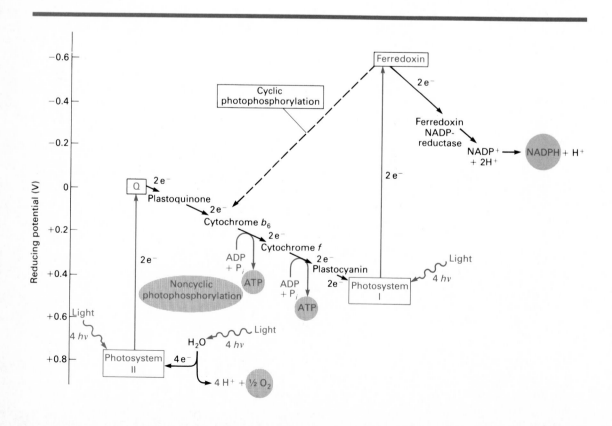

The voltage difference between water at $+0.8$ V and ferredoxin at -0.6 V is the greatest in the sequence, and it is the magnitude of this difference that accounts for the two-photosystem sequence. No single system can energize an electron by 1.4 V ($+0.8$ to -0.6 V), the amount required for water to provide the electrons that reduce $NADP^+$. Reduced ferredoxin transfers its electron to $NADP^+$ to form NADPH in a reaction catalyzed by the enzyme *ferredoxin–NADP reductase*. Ferredoxin is a one-electron carrier so that two ferredoxins must react to form one NADPH in the required two-electron process of reducing $NADP^+$. There is a sufficient voltage drop between the acceptor compound and $NADP^+$ to allow formation of NADPH in the thermodynamically expected downhill direction.

10.9
Photophosphorylation

Suspensions of isolated chloroplasts or of bacterial photosynthesizing particles can synthesize ATP in the light by the phosphorylation of ADP. The process is strictly light-dependent, and it may take place in the absence of oxygen production or of CO_2 reduction to carbohydrates. In chloroplasts and blue-green algae, photophosphorylation is coupled to electron transport along the chain of carriers that links the two photosystems (see Fig. 10.16). In particular, the process is **noncyclic photophosphorylation** because new electrons from water are required for each phosphorylation sequence. Electrons that have been transferred to P700 of photosystem I are incorporated into NADPH and are not recycled. Both ATP and NADPH are used to reduce CO_2 to carbohydrates in the subsequent dark reactions of photosynthesis.

The fact that noncyclic photophosphorylation is coupled to electron transport is shown by the ability of uncoupling agents to stop ATP synthesis in illuminated chloroplast suspensions. Studies with the herbicide dichlorophenyldimethylurea (DCMU) provide additional insight into the coupling phenomenon. In the presence of DCMU, both ATP synthesis and electron transport to $NADP^+$ stop. When an appropriate reducing agent is added as a source of electrons in a DCMU-inhibited preparation, $NADP^+$ is reduced but ATP synthesis remains blocked. This occurs because electron flow is reestablished to $NADP^+$ through PS I, whereas the transport link between PS II and PS I remains blocked by DCMU and, therefore, noncyclic photophosphorylation remains blocked (Fig. 10.17). These results demonstrate that NADP reduction is a PS I function, whereas noncyclic photophosphorylation depends on a functional electron transport link between PS II and PS I.

ATP synthesis can also occur in chloroplasts by the light-dependent process of **cyclic photophosphorylation**, which involves the transfer of high-energy electrons from ferredoxin back to the electron transport chain rather than to $NADP^+$. The passage of these recycled electrons through the electron transport chain to PS I provides the free-energy difference to drive ATP synthesis (see Fig. 10.16). The two photophosphorylation processes differ in several ways. In the noncyclic process, electrons from water reduce $NADP^+$ through the mediation of both photosystems, and O_2, ATP, and NADPH are produced. In cyclic

FIGURE 10-17

Results of experiments with the herbicide dichlorophenyldimethylurea (DCMU). (a) When DCMU is added to a suspension of chloroplasts in the light, both ATP synthesis and $NADP^+$ reduction stop. (b) When an appropriate electron donor is added to the DCMU-inhibited system, electron flow is reestablished for $NADP^+$ reduction but ATP synthesis remains inhibited. These results show that $NADP^+$ reduction is a photosystem I function, because reduction can occur in the absence of a functional electron carrier chain if a donor is provided. Photophosphorylation, however, is coupled to the flow of electrons down the carrier chain that links together photosystem II and photosystem I.

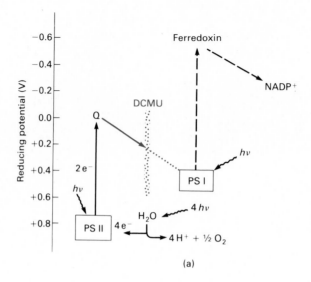

(a)

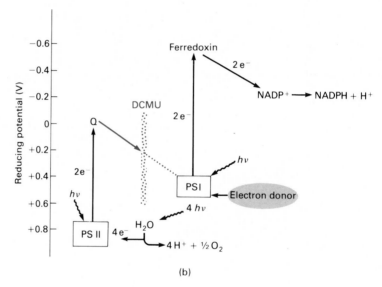

(b)

photophosphorylation, on the other hand, only PS I is involved and only ATP is produced.

The balance between cyclic and noncyclic electron flow depends on whether ferredoxin transfers electrons to $NADP^+$ or back to the cytochrome b_6–f complex of the electron transport chain. The cyclic process will be favored at the low concentrations of $NADP^+$ caused by accumulation of NADPH, and more ATP will thereby be synthesized and available for the dark reactions of photosynthesis. Because considerably more ATP than NADPH is required for CO_2 reduction, as we will discuss in a later section, their ability to make ATP alone *or* together with NADPH gives green cells an advantage.

Cyclic photophosphorylation also occurs in bacterial species, but we are unsure about its association with electron flow in photosynthesis. We know that certain uncoupling agents do not inhibit cyclic photophosphorylation in bacteria and that cyclic electron flow is unrelated to NADPH formation. Regardless of its association with photosynthesis, however, cyclic photophosphorylation provides a vital source of ATP for bacterial metabolism.

10.10
Chemiosmotic Coupling of Electron Flow and Photophosphorylation _____

The thylakoid membrane in chloroplasts, like the inner membrane of the mitochondrion, is a chemiosmotic coupling device that provides the protonmotive force that drives ATP synthesis. As electrons pass down the carrier chain that links PS II to PS I, protons are pumped across the membrane out of the chloroplast stroma and into the thylakoid space (Fig. 10.18). The electrochemical proton gradient thus generated represents a protonmotive force of about 200 mV across the thylakoid

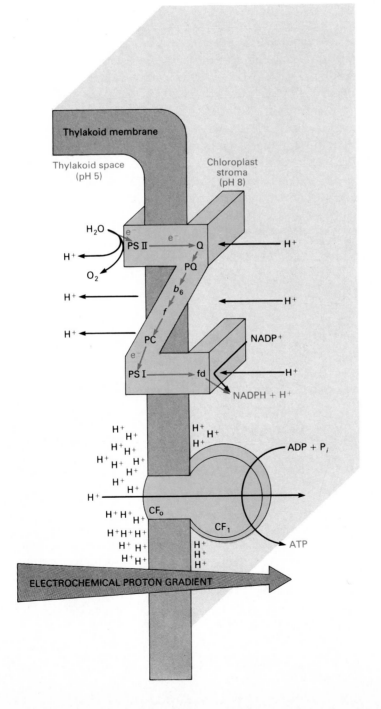

FIGURE 10-18
The thylakoid membrane is a chemiosmotic coupling device that provides the protonmotive force required for ATP synthesis by photophosphorylation. Protons are pumped across the membrane, from the stroma into the thylakoid space, as electrons pass down the carrier chain from photosystem II to photosystem I. The backflow of protons through the chloroplast ATPase (CF_oF_1ATPase) leads to a discharge of the electrochemical proton gradient, which provides the energy for ATP synthesis in the stroma. NADPH is also formed in the stroma as electrons pass from ferredoxin (fd) to $NADP^+$.

membrane. In contrast to mitochondria, in which the electrical component is primarily responsible for the protonmotive force, the pH gradient in chloroplasts is the major component of the protonmotive force. The pH difference between the chloroplast stroma (about pH 8) and the thylakoid space (about pH 5) creates a gradient of about 3 pH units, whereas only 1 pH unit of difference is typical of the mitochondrial gradient between the matrix (about pH 8) and the cell cytosol (about pH 7). In both mitochondria and chloroplasts, however, the knoblike F_1 catalytic end of the ATP synthetase juts out of the membrane and is exposed to the stroma or matrix at pH 8. The backflow of protons through the proton channel in the embedded F_o portion of the enzyme leads to discharge of the electrochemical proton gradient, and the energy harnessed from the discharge is used to drive ATP synthesis in the stroma (Fig. 10.19).

Among the earliest lines of evidence in support of Mitchell's chemiosmotic coupling mechanism was a set of experiments reported by André Jagendorf in 1967, which showed that chloroplasts could synthesize ATP in the light in response to an artificially generated pH gradient. A suspension of isolated chloroplast grana were first placed in a medium of pH 4 and were then transferred to a medium of pH 8, thereby creating a temporary pH gradient across the thylakoid membranes. Because the H^+ concentration was higher inside the thylakoid space (pH 4) than in the medium now outside the thylakoids (pH 8), the effect was equivalent to pumping protons into thylakoid spaces and generating an electrochemical proton gradient across the thylakoid membranes. Upon the addition of ADP and P_i immediately after the

FIGURE 10-19
The inner membrane of mitochondria and the thylakoid membrane of chloroplasts are similar in that they both couple electron transport to ATP synthesis via an electrochemical proton gradient. In mitochondria the electrical component of the gradient is primarily responsible for the protonmotive force, whereas in chloroplasts the pH difference (three units) along the gradient is the major component of the protonmotive force. The knoblike F_1 catalytic end of the ATPase is exposed to the higher pH (pH 8) in the internal compartment of mitochondrial matrix and in the external compartment of chloroplast stroma.

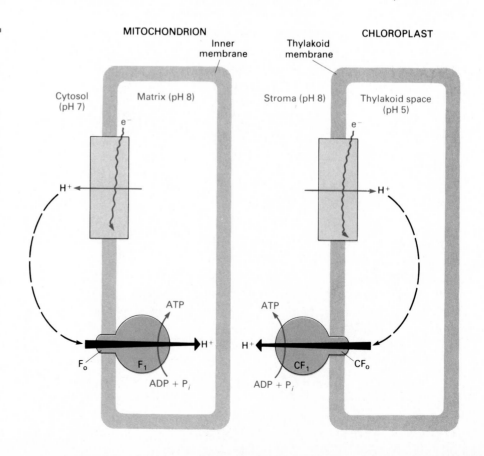

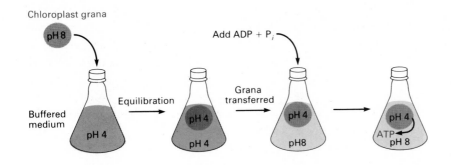

FIGURE 10-20
Schematic summary of experiments by
A. Jagendorf. Isolated chloroplast
grana previously surrounded in the
intact chloroplast by stroma at pH 8
were transferred to an acid medium
(pH 4) and allowed to equilibrate there.
The grana were then transferred to a
medium of pH 8, and ADP and P$_i$ were
added shortly afterward. ATP was
synthesized in this system at the
expense of the temporary proton (pH)
gradient generated across the thylakoid
membrane.

transfer, ATP was synthesized in the medium (Fig. 10.20). The amounts of ATP made were physiologically significant, which indicated that the artificial system was fully equivalent to the natural chloroplast system in the living cell exposed to light.

10.11
Molecular Organization of Thylakoid Membranes

All the components required for the light reactions of photosynthesis are present in chloroplast thylakoid membranes of plants and green algae. The proposed geometry of molecular organization has been derived from studies of freeze-fractured preparations viewed by electron microscopy and from chemical analysis of membrane subfractions isolated by centrifugation after digitonin treatment to render the phospholipid bilayer soluble.

Freeze-fractured thylakoid membranes can be resolved into four different fracture faces, which represent the outer stroma-facing half of stacked (PF_s) and unstacked (PF_u) membranes and the stacked (EF_s) and unstacked (EF_u) half of the bilayer facing the thylakoid interior space (Fig. 10.21). From electron micrographs it is possible to determine the size of particles, their relative numbers per unit area, their inter-mixture in any fracture face, and whether or not they are integral or peripheral components of the membranes. The morphological information gained from electron microscopy is of limited value by itself, but the nature of the particles has been determined by chemical and functional analysis of digitonin-treated membrane subfractions from wild-type and mutant plants.

The larger (>140 Å) particles of the EF_s face are PS II molecules with a full complement of light-harvesting complexes (LHC) of chlorophyll a/b pigments and proteins that transfer excitation energy to the PS II reaction-center chlorophyll. The PS II particles are smaller if only a partial LHC complement is bound, and they are only about 80 Å in diameter if none of the LHC aggregate is associated with the core particle. The PS II particles thus consist of an 80-Å core plus different amounts of noncovalently bound assemblies of pigments and proteins that have an accessory role in harvesting light energy. The smaller (80 Å) particles that predominate in the PF face of stacked and unstacked regions are PS I reaction-center cores. If LHC aggregates are associated with the core, then the PS I particles measure about 115 Å in diameter. Both the PS I and PS II particles span the lipid bilayer of stacked and unstacked regions, but they differ in their principal location

FIGURE 10-21
Freeze-fractured thylakoid membrane can be resolved (a) in electron micrographs into four different fracture faces that are distinguished by displays of particles of different sizes and in different numbers per unit area. × 85,000. (b) Diagram showing the origin and relative locations of the four different membrane faces. The inner half of the bilayer facing the thylakoid space is the face farthest from the protoplasm and is thus the external fracture (EF) face, whereas the outer stroma-facing half of the bilayer is nearest the protoplasm and is thus the protoplasmic fracture (PF) face. Each of these portions of the lipid bilayer can be further resolved to distinguish faces from stacked (EF$_s$ and PF$_s$) and unstacked (EF$_u$ and PF$_u$) regions of the thylakoid membranes. (From Staehelin, L. A., D. P. Carter, and A. McDonnel, 1980, in *Membrane-Membrane Interactions*, ed. N. B. Gilula, p. 179, New York: Raven Press.)

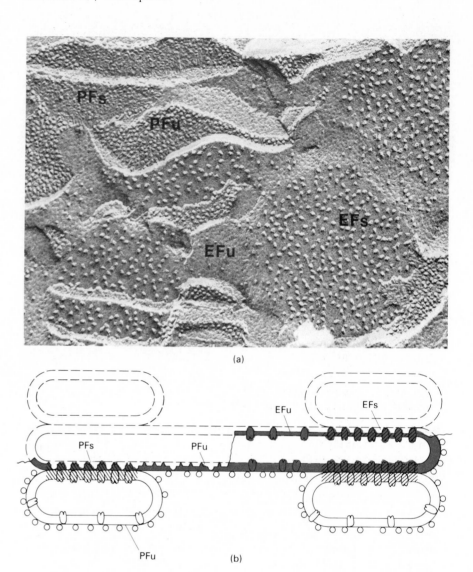

(a)

(b)

and in their proportions. The larger PS II particles occur mainly in stacked regions of thylakoid membranes, whereas PS I particles predominate in unstacked regions. In addition, PS I particles are about 3 times more numerous (about $1500/\mu m^2$) than the PS II particles (about $500/\mu m^2$). In contrast to the integral PS I and PS II particles, the chloroplast–ATPase knobs of the photophosphorylating enzyme project from the stroma-facing PF fracture face in unstacked regions and are not present in stacked regions of thylakoid membranes. The principal enzyme of the dark reactions, *ribulose 1,5-bisphosphate carboxylase*, is loosely associated with the stroma-facing surface of the thylakoids as well as within the stroma itself. The model of thylakoid molecular organization based on all these studies is shown in Fig. 10.22.

The predominance of PS II particles in stacked membranes and their sparse distribution in unstacked membranes would suggest that all or part of the PS II complex plays some role in the adhesion of membranes in stacked thylakoids. We know from studies of mutants defective in particular photosystem components, and from *in vivo* and *in vitro* studies of the effects of stacking and unstacking thylakoids, that the

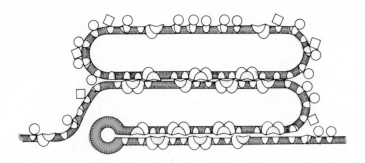

△ PS II (80 Å EF particles)

△ PS II + full complement of Chl a/b LHC (> 140 Å EF$_s$ particles)

△ PS II + partial complement of Chl a/b LHC (< 140 Å EF$_s$ and EF$_u$ particles)

△ PS I, cytochrome complexes, "free" Chl a/b LHC (?) (80 Å PF$_s$ and PF$_u$ particles)

△ PS I + LHC (?) (115 Å PF$_u$ particles)

○ Coupling facator (CF$_1$)

□ Ribulose 1,5-bisphosphate carboxylase

FIGURE 10-22
Model of the molecular organization of chloroplast thylakoid membranes, based on electron microscopy, chemistry, and functional studies. Small photosystem II (PS II) particles may have 0, 1, or 2 complements of light-harvesting complexes (LHC) and thus may exist in three different sizes. Particles representing photosystem I (PS I) may or may not have an associated complement of light-harvesting complex (LHC). The PS II and PS I systems span the thylakoid membrane, but PS II particles predominate in stacked membrane regions. The more numerous PS I particles are found mainly in unstacked membrane regions. The chloroplast F$_1$ (CF$_1$) coupling factor of the ATPase projects from unstacked membrane regions into the stroma. The enzyme ribulose 1,5-bisphosphate carboxylase, which fixes CO$_2$ in the dark reactions, is loosely associated with the stroma-facing surface of thylakoid membranes, as well as in other areas of the chloroplast stroma. (From Staehelin, L. A., D. P. Carter, and A. McDonnel, 1980, in *Membrane-Membrane Interactions*, ed. N.B. Gilula, p. 179, New York: Raven Press.)

integration of light-reaction activities depends on stacking and that stacking in turn depends on an appropriate distribution of intramembrane particles. These observations implicate one or more of the particulate components as *adhesion* molecules between thylakoids, (see Fig. 10.22) and indicate that the photosystems must be in proper juxtaposition within the membranes to permit their coordinated activities in electron transport between water and NADP$^+$ (Fig. 10.23).

By the manipulation of ionic concentrations in the medium, thylakoids of isolated grana can be experimentally unstacked in low-salt media and restacked by the addition of divalent or monovalent cations. Consideration of the effects of either kind of cation alone and of both in combination, made it appear that the positive ionic charge served to neutralize exposed, negatively charged groups on the membrane surfaces, which allowed attractive hydrophobic interactions between membranes to become dominant. When experimentally stacked and unstacked membranes are freeze-fractured and examined by light microscopy, unstacked membranes are found to have a randomly intermixed population of PS I and PS II particles instead of the specifically arranged particles we described earlier for EF and PF fracture faces (see Fig. 10.21 and Fig. 10.22). The typical nonrandom display of large and small particles in reestablished when restacking takes place.

According to studies based on the selective removal of molecules from the particles by mild trypsin treatment, the chlorophyll *a/b* light-harvesting complexes of the PS II large particles seem to be involved in membrane adhesion leading to stacking. In particular, additional evidence has been obtained to show that the selective removal of a 1000-dalton polypeptide segment from the chlorophyll *a/b* LHC of PS II abolishes Mg^{2+}-mediated membrane stacking. Although additional lines of evidence are required to confirm these interpretations, it appears that membrane adhesion and thylakoid stacking are brought

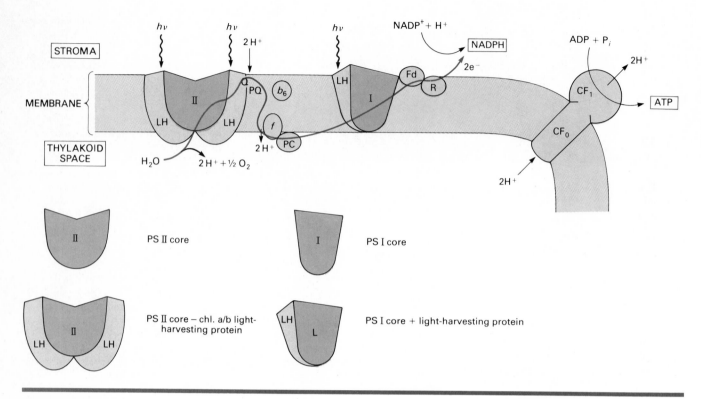

FIGURE 10-23
The arrangement in the thylakoid membrane of photosystems I and II and their associated light-harvesting complexes (LHC) allows coordinated activities in capturing light energy and in directing the flow of electrons from water molecules to NADP$^+$. Electrons are transferred from water to PS II, then to the chain of electron carriers for transport to PS I, and from PS I to ferredoxin (fd), which passes the electrons to NADP$^+$ via ferredoxin-NADP reductase (R) action. The electrochemical proton gradient across the membrane drives ATP synthesis, which is catalyzed by the transmembrane chloroplast ATPase (CF$_o$F$_1$ATPase). (From Bogorad, L., 1981, *J. Cell Biol.* **91**:256s–270s, Fig. 3.)

about by hydrophobic interactions between individual chlorophyll a/b LHC particles situated in thylakoid membranes that have been cationically stabilized. The precise distribution of these particles in stacked membranes must therefore maximize the hydrophobic interactions between particles and thereby encourage stacking. If the negative surface charges of the membranes have not been neutralized by an appropriate concentration of Mg^{2+} and other cations, however, hydrophobic reactions cannot become dominant and unstacking will occur. The consequent redistribution of intramembrane particles interrupts the communication and coordination of the photosystems and their electron transport components and interferes with the orderly flow of electrons required to convert light energy to chemical energy. In the event that ATP and NADPH are inadequate, CO_2 cannot be reduced to carbohydrates in the dark reactions of photosynthesis. The pathways for carbohydrate synthesis will be the subject of the next three sections of this chapter.

The Dark Reactions of Photosynthesis

The major pathway by which simple carbohydrates are made from atmospheric CO_2 is called the *Calvin cycle* or the *C_3 cycle*, in recognition of its discoverer and of the nature of the first detectable product of CO_2 fixation to accumulate in chloroplasts. About 15 years later, another pathway of CO_2 fixation was shown to exist as an accessory to the C_3 cycle in certain species of flowering plants; the second pathway is called the *Hatch–Slack cycle*, for its discoverers, or the *C_4 cycle*, in recognition of the first detectable accumulation product of CO_2 reduction. We will discuss important features of each of the two cycles and then explore the phenomenon of *photorespiration* in relation to these cycles and to compartmented metabolism involving chloroplasts and other organelles in eukaryotic cells.

10.12
CO$_2$ Fixation by the C$_3$ Cycle in Chloroplasts _____

In the early 1950s Melvin Calvin and Andrew Benson and their associates showed that glucose or other hexoses were not the initial products of CO_2 fixation in chloroplasts. By the use of newly available radioisotopes, Calvin and co-workers provided $^{14}CO_2$ to photosynthetic systems and collected chloroplasts after only seconds of exposure. The newly synthesized molecules were identified by their radioactivity after separation by paper chromatography, and they were found to be the triose compound *3-phosphoglycerate*. Only later, after longer incubation in $^{14}CO_2$, were labeled glucose and starch found to have been synthesized. On the basis of these and other studies, most of the **C$_3$ cycle** was postulated in more or less the form we accept today. The enzymes of the cycle were later identified by Ephraim Racker and Bernard Horecker.

In the initial step of the reduction pathway, CO_2 from the air condenses with the five-carbon sugar **ribulose 1,5-bisphosphate (RuBP)** to form a transient six-carbon compound. The reaction is catalyzed by the important and abundant enzyme *ribulose 1,5-bisphosphate carboxylase*, or **RuBP carboxylase**, which is found in the chloroplast stroma loosely associated with the surface of thylakoid membranes. The transient C$_6$ compound is rapidly hydrolyzed to two molecules of 3-phosphoglycerate, the three-carbon sugar that Calvin identified as the first detectable product of CO_2 fixation (Fig. 10.24). This triose sugar is then phosphorylated at the expense of ATP to form an activated molecule that is capable of accepting hydrogens and electrons from NADPH. The high-energy product of this reaction is the triose sugar **3-phosphoglyceraldehyde**. Hexose sugars and more complex molecules are then formed in subsequent reactions.

Radioactive labeling studies showed that all six carbons of glucose became labeled during the dark reactions but that only one CO_2 was processed in each interaction with RuBP. To account for the continuous CO_2 fixation that leads to all six carbons of the hexose becoming labeled, Calvin and Benson proposed a cyclic pathway that would involve the regeneration of RuBP for each CO_2 fixed in photosynthesis. By continuous regeneration of RuBP, continuous CO_2 fixation can occur. The regeneration sequence is rather complex, involving at least 12 different enzymes that catalyze steps leading to intermediates with various numbers of carbon atoms in the molecules (Fig. 10.25). The Calvin cycle, or C$_3$ cycle, involves CO_2 fixation and the regeneration of RuBP at each turn. It would require six turns of the Calvin cycle to fix six CO_2 into each hexose molecule made.

During RuBP regeneration in the C$_3$ cycle, **fructose 6-phosphate** is formed as one of the intermediates. Diversion of this sugar into other biosynthetic pathways leads eventually to glucose formation, and to the

FIGURE 10-24

The Calvin cycle, or the C_3 cycle, of CO_2 reduction to carbohydrates in the dark reactions of photosynthesis. The first detectable product of the cycle is the C_3 compound 3-phosphoglycerate, produced from half-molecules of a transient C_6 intermediate formed when ribulose 1,5-bisphosphate (RuBP) fixes CO_2 from the air. Upon the addition of ATP, 1,3-diphosphoglycerate is produced and this molecule can accept hydrogens and electrons from NADPH to form 3-phosphoglyceraldehyde. Various reactions occur in the processing of 3-phosphoglyceraldehyde, including the formation of ribulose 5-monophosphate, which is phosphorylated by ATP to regenerate RuBP, and that of fructose 6-phosphate, which enters a major pathway leading to the synthesis of carbohydrates. Enzymes that catalyze the C_3 cycle of reactions are shown in the center of the illustration.

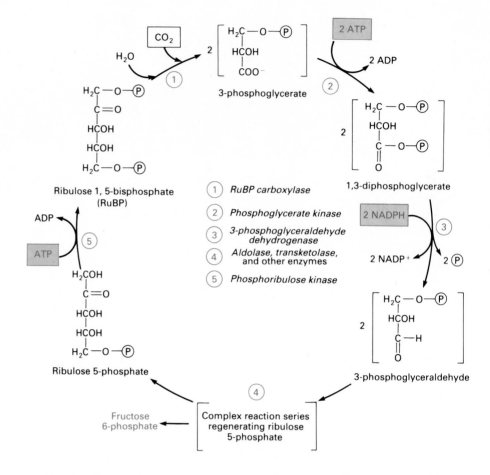

FIGURE 10-25

A complex set of reactions processes the 3-phosphoglyceraldehyde (3-PGAL) product of the C_3 cycle to produce a variety of intermediates. Important intermediates include the C_6 sugar fructose 6-phosphate (●), from which glucose and other carbohydrates are formed, and ribulose 5-monophosphate (Ru5P), from which RuBP is regenerated.

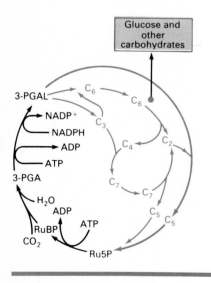

synthesis of disaccharide and polysaccharide products such as sucrose and starch, respectively. Many of the biosynthetic reactions that produce carbohydrates and various other organic molecules in green plants are exactly the same as in other organisms. The unique feature of the photosynthetic dark reactions is the reduction of CO_2 to a triose sugar through the mediation of RuBP. The triose sugar itself then enters into general biosynthetic pathways.

Each mole of hexose made from CO_2 and H_2O in the classic equation for green plant photosynthesis requires an input of 686 kcal. We know this to be true because this is the amount of energy that is released in the reverse reaction when a mole of glucose is burned in air to CO_2 and H_2O ($\Delta G° = -686$ kcal/mole). We may state that, for nonbacterial photosynthesis, the summary reaction is

$$6\, CO_2 + 12\, H_2O \xrightarrow[\text{chlorophyll}]{\text{light}} C_6H_{12}O_6 + 6\, O_2 + 6\, H_2O;\ \Delta G° = 686\ \text{kcal/mole}$$

(Note: Because all the released O_2 is derived from H_2O, 12 H_2O must be assimilated for each glucose formed in photosynthesis, to balance the equation.)

To determine the relative efficiency of photosynthetic dark reactions, we must consider the events taking place *in each turn* of the Calvin cycle:

$$2\, H^+ + CO_2 + 2\, NADPH + 3\, ATP$$
$$\downarrow$$
$$[CH_2O] + 2\, NADP^+ + 3\, ADP + 3\, P_i + H_2O$$

It takes six turns of the cycle to form one molecule of glucose, so a total of 12 NADPH (6×2 NADPH) and 18 ATP (6×3 ATP) are used to make one glucose molecule. Using the standard free-energy change for ATP hydrolysis as -7 kcal/mole, and for NADPH oxidation as -52 kcal/mole, we find that the total free-energy input to make each mole of glucose is 750 kcal [(12 NADPH $\times$ 52) + (18 ATP $\times$ 7)]. The overall efficiency of the dark reactions would then be $686/750 \times 100 = 90\%$. This is an incredibly high efficiency level, one that is rarely achieved in biological systems.

In summary, light energy is absorbed by photosensitive pigments and transduced (converted) to chemical energy in NADPH and ATP. During the light reactions, water is oxidized to molecular oxygen, which is released into the air as a by-product. The reduction of carbon dioxide is independent of light and takes place at the expense of NADPH and ATP made in the light. The initial product of the dark reactions is a triose sugar that is processed to fructose 6-phosphate. Fructose 6-phosphate then enters into biosynthetic pathways that lead to glucose and to other molecules required in growth, reproduction, and maintenance of the organism.

10.13
CO$_2$ Fixation by the C$_4$ Cycle in Chloroplasts

In 1966, M. D. Hatch and C. R. Slack reported that the earliest detectable product of $^{14}CO_2$ fixation in sugar cane was a mixture of C_4 acids and that labeled 3-phosphoglycerate appeared sometime later, but before hexoses became labeled. These results indicated the existence of an alternative or accessory pathway for CO_2 fixation in sugar cane, compared with systems studied by Calvin and others. To explain their results, Hatch and Slack postulated the pathway we now refer to as the **C$_4$ cycle**, in which the earliest detectable products of CO_2 fixation in the dark reactions are an equilibrium mixture of the four-carbon dicarboxylic acids oxaloacetate, malate, and aspartate.

The proposed pathway begins with fixation of CO_2 by phosphoenolpyruvate (PEP) to yield oxaloacetate in a carboxylation reaction catalyzed by the enzyme phosphoenolpyruvate carboxylase (**PEP carboxylase**). Oxaloacetate is reduced to malate and aspartate, thus explaining the high levels of the three C_4 acids in the equilibrium mixture found earliest in the ^{14}C-labeling studies. Because neither malate nor aspartate can continue in reactions leading to carbohydrate synthesis, some intervening steps were required before hexoses could be made from C_4 products. Hatch and Slack proposed that the C_4 acids were degraded enzymatically to yield free CO_2 and pyruvate, a three-carbon intermediate. Pyruvate is phosphorylated at the expense of ATP to form PEP, and the C_4 cycle can undergo another turn. The cycle is repeated for each CO_2 molecule that enters the leaf and is reduced there (Fig. 10.26).

The CO_2 released during the C_4 cycle is then picked up by RuBP carboxylase in the conventional C_3 cycle. CO_2 is fixed in the same way as in any other plant, as we discussed in the previous section. Basically, plants with the C_4 pathway have an *additional* sequence for CO_2 fixation

FIGURE 10-26
The C$_4$ cycle is an accessory to the C$_3$ cycle, and it serves as a means by which CO$_2$ from the air is delivered indirectly to RuBP for processing in the conventional C$_3$ cycle of the dark reactions. The C$_4$ compounds oxaloacetate, malate, and aspartate are the first detectable products of the C$_4$ cycle, whereas the C$_3$ compound 3-phosphoglycerate is the first detectable product of CO$_2$ fixation if only the C$_3$ cycle is present in the plant. The efficient enzyme PEP carboxylase catalyzes CO$_2$ fixation in the C$_4$ cycle.

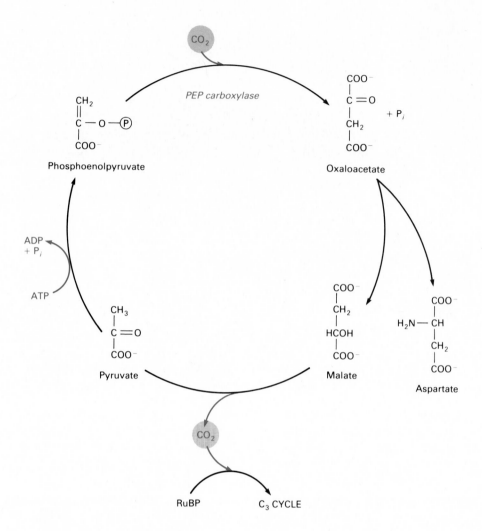

that is coordinated with RuBP carboxylase in the usual C$_3$ cycle, because the original CO$_2$ taken in and fixed by PEP carboxylase is later handed over to RuBP carboxylase (Fig. 10.27). The hundreds of diverse plant species now known to exhibit the C$_4$ cycle, rather than the C$_3$ cycle alone, share two particular characteristics: (1) anatomically similar leaf organization and (2) the ability to thrive in air with CO$_2$ levels so low that C$_3$ plants stop photosynthesizing and may even be killed.

C$_4$ plants manage well in air that contains as little as 5 parts per million (ppm) of CO$_2$, whereas C$_3$ plants stop photosynthesizing in air with 50 ppm or less. The usual CO$_2$ concentration in our atmosphere is about 300 ppm, or 0.03%. Gas exchanges between leaves and outside air take place mainly through pores in specialized cellular complexes, called *stomates*, in the leaf epidermis. No exchanges occur through the thick, waxy parts of the remainder of the epidermal tissue. Stomates open and close, and gas exchanges take place when the stomates are open or at least partially open.

In regions of high light intensity, high temperatures, and little water, leaf stomates are almost closed. In this way leaf tissues lose the least amount of water by diffusion toward the drier air outside. When stomatal pores are almost closed, however, very little CO$_2$ enters the leaf. In C$_4$ plants, PEP carboxylase efficiently sweeps up what little CO$_2$

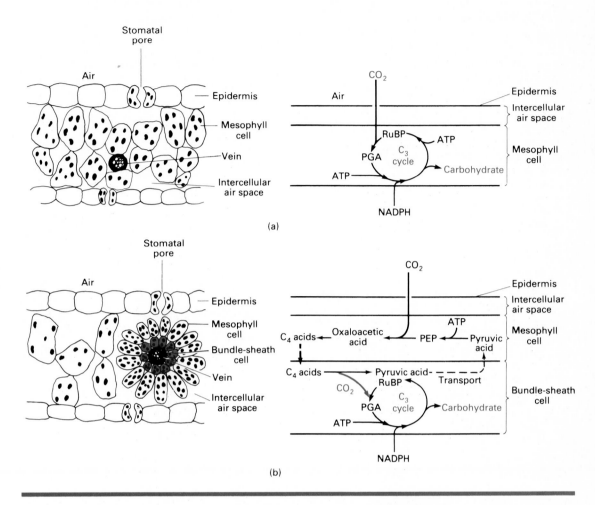

FIGURE 10-27
Comparison of the leaf anatomy and CO_2 reduction pathways in C_3 and C_4 plants. (a) Leaves having only the C_3 pathway contain large mesophyll cells with chloroplasts and air spaces saturated with water vapor. CO_2 enters through stomatal pores and moves into the chloroplasts of mesophyll cells, where reduction occurs via the C_3 cycle. (b) Leaves with the accessory C_4 cycle have most of their chloroplast-containing cells arranged in two layers around a leaf vein. CO_2 enters the mesophyll cell chloroplasts first and undergoes a reaction with the 3-carbon compound phosphoenolpyruvate (PEP) to form C_4 oxaloacetic acid. Further processing of the C_4 acids occurs in the bundle-sheath chloroplasts, where C_4 acids are decarboxylated to yield free CO_2. CO_2 enters the major C_3 reduction cycle. The remaining 3-carbon pyruvate is returned to the mesophyll cells where it is phosphorylated to PEP, and the C_4 cycle is completed and ready for another CO_2 fixation event.

continues to enter the leaf even when conditions are very unfavorable. By removing CO_2 almost as fast as it enters, through carboxylation of pyruvate to form PEP, the enzyme helps to maintain a favorable *CO2 diffusion gradient* and CO_2 continues to enter the leaf even when CO_2 levels are very low and stomatal pores are barely open. In plants lacking a C_4 pathway, RuBP carboxylase catalyzes CO_2 removal from the air, but it is a much less efficient catalyst than PEP carboxylase in C_4 plants. When CO_2 in the air around the leaf drops below 50 ppm, RuBP carboxylase is not efficient enough to remove CO_2 to internal levels that would maintain a favorable diffusion gradient. CO_2 no longer enters the C_3 leaf and sugar manufacture essentially stops. Plants with a C_4 cycle can grow very well in Death Valley when noontime temperatures approach 50°C in summer. They clearly are able to photosynthesize effectively under relatively hostile conditions.

Two kinds of programs of plant improvement are currently in progress, each directed toward increasing the food supplies in hot, dry climates. One program involves cross-breeding favorable C_3 crop plants with C_4 plants, in the expectation that some progeny will incorporate suitable genes from C_4 plants into C_3 crops usually grown in hostile climates. If this approach is successful, yields of the C_3 crops might be increased, because such plants could continue to grow well even in poor seasons. A second kind of program is aimed at finding higher-yielding strains of crops that already have a C_4 cycle. Larger harvests of these staple food crops would be particularly important in developing and underdeveloped parts of the world in which agriculture is carried out in scrubby or semi-desert zones. Three high-yield C_4 crop plants already form important foundations for world agriculture; they are sugar cane, sorghum, and corn (maize). Crabgrass is an example of a successful C_4 species that thrives when we wish it would not in otherwise well-tended lawns.

10.14
Photorespiration

The process of **photorespiration** involves consumption of oxygen and release of carbon dioxide in the light; that is, it is considered a light-enhanced respiration. The process is energetically wasteful because it diverts the flow of energy from CO_2 reduction to O_2 reduction. As much as 50% of the reducing power generated in photosynthesis may be diverted in this process. Based on measurements of the amount of CO_2 released in the light, C_4 plants do not appear to carry out photorespiration, whereas C_3 plants do photorespire. The following discussion will therefore be restricted to studies of C_3 species.

The elegant studies of N. E. Tolbert and his associates have provided a large part of the current understanding about processes affiliated with leaf photorespiration. Compartmentalized reactions within chloroplasts, mitochondria, microbodies, and cytosol of leaf cells are closely coordinated to recoup some of the reducing power that is lost in photorespiration.

It was mentioned earlier that C_3 plants stop photosynthesizing when the CO_2 air level reaches about 50 parts per million. At this concentration, photorespiration takes place, resulting in the release of CO_2 in the light rather than its incorporation into carbohydrates in photosynthesis. At the same time that CO_2 concentration is low, a high concentration of O_2 is found in the leaf cells and in the surrounding air. Under these twin conditions of low CO_2 and high O_2, the enzyme RuBP carboxylase acts catalytically as an oxygenase instead of a carboxylase. Instead of catalyzing the formation of 3-phosphoglycerate exclusively (see Fig. 10.24) by its carboxylase ability, the enzyme sponsors oxygen consumption and incorporation of an oxygen atom into RuBP by virtue of its oxygenase activity. When this happens, RuBP remains a five-carbon compound and does not become converted to a six-carbon intermediate as in the C_3 cycle. As RuBP is oxygenated, therefore, it breaks down to form some 3-phosphoglycerate and the two-carbon compound **phosphoglycolate**. The 3-phosphoglycerate is fed back into the C_3 cycle where RuBP is regenerated. Phosphoglycolate formed in the chloroplast by RuBP carboxylase–oxygenase, however, undergoes a complex set of reactions that involves three other cellular compartments (Fig. 10.28).

Phosphoglycolate is converted to *glycolate* within the chloroplast, after which glycolate is transferred to microbodies. Within the microbodies, glycolate is processed in sequential reactions and is converted to

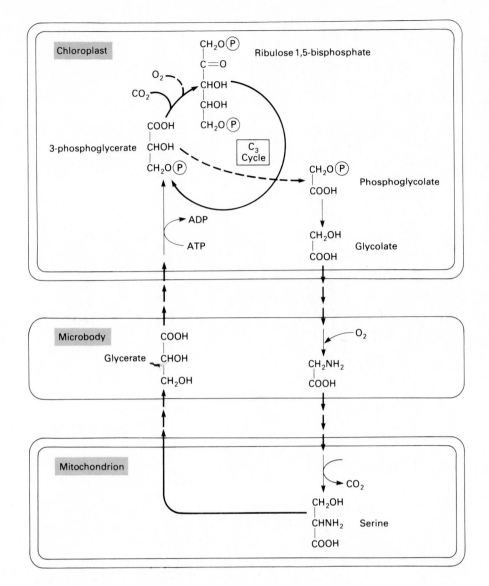

FIGURE 10-28
Chloroplasts, microbodies, and mitochondria cooperate in reactions that "rescue" phosphoglycolate produced in photorespiration and thereby provide additional 3-phosphoglycerate for C_3 cycle reactions of carbohydrate production. In addition, these reactions produce the amino acids glycine and serine, some of which contribute to 3-phosphoglycerate production in chloroplasts and some of which remain to be used in the other two organelles. These processes explain the pattern of O_2 consumption and CO_2 release in the light, which characterizes photorespiration in C_3 plants.

the amino acid *glycine*. Some of this amino acid is then transferred to mitochondria where reactions take place leading to formation of another amino acid, *serine*. Some of the serine next leaves the mitochondrion and enters the microbody where it is converted to *glycerate*. Glycerate is converted to *3-phosphoglycerate*. At this point, as occurs normally in the C_3 cycle, 3-phosphoglycerate is converted to sugar phosphates and more complex carbohydrates. The latter reactions probably occur in chloroplasts and the cytosol; enzymes of the pathway are found in both compartments.

These reactions explain the basis for the characteristic pattern of gas exchange in photorespiration. Oxygen is consumed during the step catalyzed by RuBP oxygenase activity, producing phosphoglycolate and 3-phosphoglycerate from RuBP in the chloroplast. Carbon dioxide is released from mitochondria during the conversion of glycine to serine that takes place there. Some oxygen is also taken up by microbodies in the initial step when glycolate is reduced.

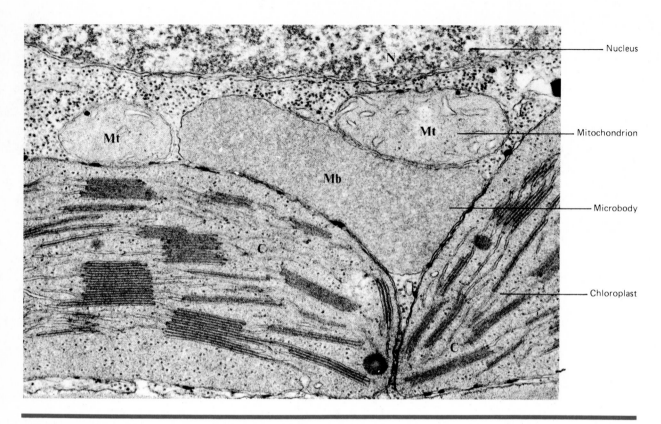

—— Nucleus

—— Mitochondrion

—— Microbody

—— Chloroplast

FIGURE 10-29
Electron micrograph of a section
through part of a tobacco leaf mesophyll cell. The microbody is wedged
against the chloroplasts and mitochondria. Free flow of metabolites
between these organelles is facilitated
by their close physical associations.
×45,000. (Photograph courtesy of
E. H. Newcomb and S. E. Frederick.)

Under unfavorable daylight conditions of high O_2 and low CO_2,
chloroplast RuBP is converted to phosphoglycolate and 3-glycero-
phosphate molecules. As phosphoglycolate is converted to glycolate
in this organelle, photorespiration reactions are triggered. If glycolate production in the light comes to a halt, photorespiration also stops.
Although there are energetically wasteful steps in the compartmented
activities described, there is continued flow of carbon from RuBP and
the Calvin cycle in chloroplasts through the glycolate pathway in
microbodies and mitochondria and back to 3-phosphoglycerate in the
chloroplast and cytosol. Some additional carbohydrate synthesis can
take place, therefore, as more of this vital three-carbon intermediate is
produced.

The photorespiration sequence is remarkably coordinated through a
circuitous route and may be aided physically, because all three kinds of
interacting organelles exist in closely apposed associations (Fig. 10.29).
Microbodies and mitochondria appear to be literally squeezed up
against chloroplasts in leaf cells. Even though photosynthetic dark
reactions take place at reduced rates, RuBP molecules continue to serve
as a link between light and dark reactions, and some carbohydrates
continue to be synthesized despite little or no CO_2 fixation. C_4 plants
are almost unaffected by low CO_2 concentration in the air, so they
maintain high rates of photosynthesis. They are therefore very efficient
in producing carbohydrates for growth in identical environments that
sharply limit or inhibit C_3 plant photosynthesis.

Chloroplast Biogenesis

Chloroplasts, like mitochondria and nuclei, arise only from pre-existing chloroplasts or from an undifferentiated primoridial plastid called a **proplastid**. Numerous studies of proplastid differentiation to mature chloroplast showed that chlorophyll synthesis and thylakoid formation are independent processes. Mutants that were defective in thylakoid development were capable of synthesizing chlorophyll, and other mutants with defects in chlorophyll synthesis were able to undergo normal thylakoid development during maturation to chloroplasts.

The chloroplast genome is typically larger than most of the known mitochondrial genomes and can therefore possess more genetic potential than mitochondria. We must be cautious, however, in equating the size of the DNA molecule with numbers of genes. After all, yeast mtDNA is five times the length of animal mtDNA, but both these DNAs encode about the same number of organelle genes. We have obtained a great deal of information about the chloroplast genome in the past few years, because DNA sequencing and other molecular approaches have been used to great advantage in probing the chloroplast genetic system.

The case for an endosymbiotic origin of chloroplasts is fairly strong, particularly because we can make detailed comparisons of proteins and nucleic acids in plastids and prokaryotes. These comparisons reveal a high level of identity or homology between plastid and prokaryotic ribosomal RNAs and other organelle macromolecules. In addition, we can study the biochemistry of modern prokaryotic algal descendants of the presumptive ancestral forms and use this information along with genetic and molecular data.

10.15
Proplastid Multiplication and Differentiation _____

Proplastids usually measure about 0.5–1.0 by 1.0–1.5 μm in size. Their two bounding membranes enclose an unstructured granular matrix or stroma in which DNA fibrils, ribosomes, and some form of starch or other carbohydrate may be present. Some tubular membrane elements or recognizable thylakoid primoridia may exist in the undeveloped proplastid (Fig. 10.30). On exposure to light, vesicular and tubular invaginations of the inner membrane pinch off and gradually become dispersed within the stroma. These membrane elements ultimately become disposed into the long, flattened stroma thylakoids, and where they are folded into multiple layers, grana thylakoid stacks may also be evident. Synthesis of photosynthetic pigments occurs simultaneously. At maturity, typical chloroplast ultrastructure and chemistry have evolved from a primordial proplastid initial. There seems to be no fusion of proplastids to produce the larger chloroplast; instead it is believed that a general growth of new membranes leads to enlargement of the mature organelle.

Proplastids increase in number by a cleavage-like process in which there is a pinching-in and a later separation of the two products. In those species where mature chloroplasts divide to produce new chloroplasts,

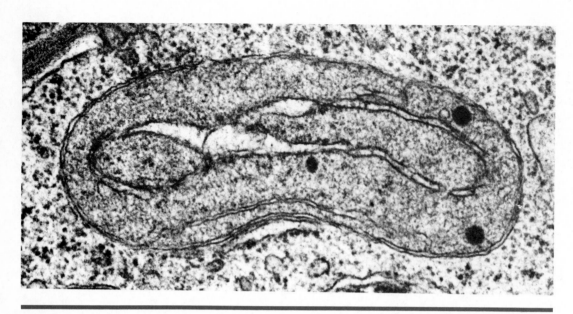

FIGURE 10-30
Electron micrograph of a proplastid from plantain (*Plantago*) showing the two membranes of the organelle envelope and a number of developing thylakoid elements in the stroma. The dense circular components are made of some unidentified substance. ×62,000. (Photograph courtesy of M. C. Ledbetter.)

there is also a type of cleavage process. Eukaryotic chloroplasts are therefore formed by some kind of constriction process involving either proplastids or mature chloroplasts, depending on the species.

When green plant cells are returned to the dark for a protracted period, chloroplasts are transformed into **etioplasts** that lack typical thylakoid structures. The aggregation of membranes in etioplasts may be somewhat disorganized or may show a latticework arrangement. In either case the membrane aggregation has been called a **prolamellar body** (Fig. 10.31). Similar membrane organization develops in plant cells that have been grown in the dark; that is, proplastids will differentiate into etioplasts in the dark or chloroplasts in the light. Upon exposure to light, etioplasts are converted or reconverted into functional green chloroplasts that have typical photosynthetic ultrastructure and chemistry.

Etioplasts contain *protochlorophyll*, a precursor of chlorophyll *a*. Protochlorophyll is localized within the prolamellar body. In the light, this precursor is reduced to chlorophyll *a*. Although it may take only 1 minute for protochlorophyll conversion to chorophyll *a* in the light, several hours elapse before detectable amounts of new chlorophyll *a* and chlorophyll *b* appear after illumination. The conversion of prolamellar-body tubules into flat sheets of thylakoids begins within minutes after etioplasts have been illuminated.

10.16
The Chloroplast Genetic System

We know from many decades of genetic analysis that hundreds of nuclear genes specify chloroplast structure and chemistry, whereas relatively few of these traits are encoded in the chloroplast genome directly. Long before we knew of chloroplast DNA, we knew that certain chloroplast traits were transmitted only through the female parent, which indicated the existence of a non-Mendelian system in addition to

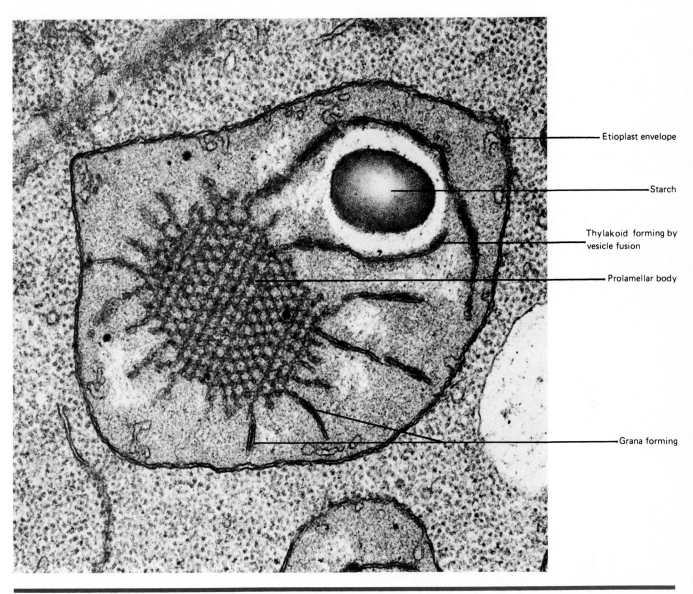

Etioplast envelope

Starch

Thylakoid forming by vesicle fusion

Prolamellar body

Grana forming

FIGURE 10-31
Electron micrograph of an etioplast in bean leaf (*Phaseolus vulgaris*) shortly after the plant was returned to the light. New thylakoids develop from the latticelike prolamellar body by fusions of small vesicles. Thylakoids stack to form grana while development proceeds. ×61,000. (Photograph courtesy of M. C. Ledbetter.)

the conventional nuclear genetic system in which traits are transmitted through both parents in sexual reproduction (Fig. 10.32). The discovery of circular **chloroplast DNA (ctDNA)** in the early 1970s provided physical evidence of the existence of a chloroplast genome, which had only been deduced from previous genetic studies with *Chlamydomonas*, corn, and a few other species.

Chloroplast duplex DNA measures 40 to 45 μm in contour length in most of the species that have been studied (Fig. 10.33), although larger circles are found in *Chlamydomonas* and a few other unicellular organisms. Many remarkable similarities have been described for chloroplast genetic systems and their equivalents in prokaryotes, and in some cases the systems are highly homologous or even identical. For example, 74% of the 1154 ribonucleotides in *E. coli* 16S rRNA occupy identical positions in corn chloroplast 16S rRNA molecules, although the maximum number of consecutive identical nucleotides is only 53. The

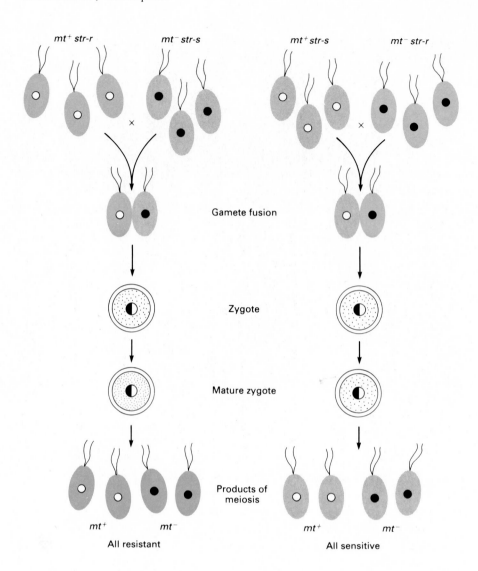

FIGURE 10-32
During sexual reproduction in *Chlamydomonas*, a unicellular green alga, the gene for streptomycin resistance (*str-r*) and streptomycin sensitivity (*str-s*) is transmitted only through the female parent (mating type +, or *mt*⁺) to all descendants (products of meiosis). The gene for female (*mt*⁺) or male (*mt*⁻) expression, however, is distributed equally by both parents to their descendants. Equal genetic contribution by both parents is characteristic of standard Mendelian inheritance of nuclear genes, whereas transmission of a trait through only one of the parents (uniparental inheritance), usually the female, indicates inheritance of some gene outside the nucleus (perhaps in the chloroplast).

ribosomal subunits from *E. coli* cytoplasm and chloroplast stroma can be interchanged, and any arrangement of hybrid ribosomes (30S + 50S subunits from either source) will guide correct polypeptide synthesis *in vitro*. In addition to these indications of close genetic relationship between chloroplasts and prokaryotes, both systems have a single circular duplex DNA molecule that houses all the genes, and the 70S ribosomes of both systems are inhibited by the same spectrum of antibiotics and are unaffected by drugs that inhibit the eukaryotic cytoplasmic system for protein synthesis.

In view of the many indications of homology between chloroplasts and prokaryotes, it was surprising to find, by base sequencing and molecular hybridization analyses, that the chloroplast genetic system has a number of eukaryotic features. Like eukaryotes but unlike prokaryotes, chloroplast genes may have one or more noncoding introns alternating with coding exon segments, and large noncoding spacer DNA segments that occupy a substantial fraction of the genome map (Fig. 10.34). In some ways, therefore, the chloroplast genetic system resembles the yeast

FIGURE 10-33
Electron micrograph of an isolated
circular duplex DNA molecule from
spinach chloroplasts, measuring 44 μm
in contour length. ×25,700. (Photograph courtesy of D. R. Wolstenholme,
from Manning, J. E., et al. 1972, *J. Cell
Biol.* **53**:594–601, Fig. 3.)

mitochondrial genetic system in having a mixture of prokaryotic and eukaryotic features. Nevertheless, chloroplasts are like prokaryotes in so many of their characteristics that we can still see a strong basis for an endosymbiotic prokaryotic ancestry for the chloroplast. We will discuss the evolutionary history of chloroplasts in the next section.

In addition to known genes for 23S, 16S, and 5S rRNAs and for anywhere from 20 to 40 tRNA genes, the chloroplast genome is large enough to code for more than 100 polypeptides. Very few of these polypeptide-specifying genes have been located or identified, but one of the best characterized of these is the gene encoded for the polypeptide of the large subunit of RuBP carboxylase (*rbcL*). The large subunit of the enzyme is an aggregate of eight identical large polypeptide chains (50,000 to 55,000 daltons) that are synthesized at chloroplast ribosomes in the stroma. The small subunit of the enzyme consists of a different set of eight identical small polypeptides (12,000 to 14,000 daltons) that are synthesized in the cytosol from mRNA transcripts of a nuclear gene. The whole enzyme assembles within the chloroplast stroma when the large subunit combines with components of the small subunit that have been transported into the chloroplast from the cytosol. This chloroplast enzyme therefore requires polypeptides made from two sets of genes in two different compartments of the cell, just like the cytochrome oxidase,

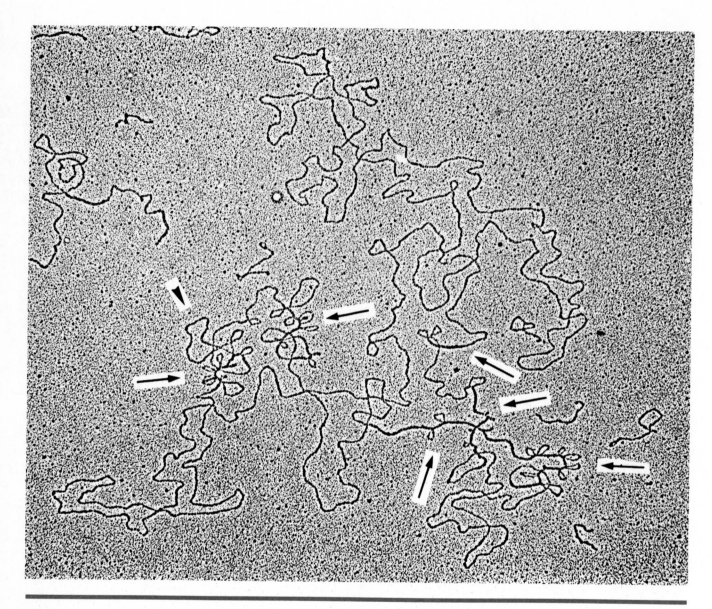

FIGURE 10-34
Electron micrograph of single–stranded circular chloroplast DNA hybridized with whole–chloroplast RNA from the protist *Euglena gracilius.* Six hybridized regions (at arrows) show intron loops in the DNA strand, which presumably were excised from pre–messenger RNA during its processing to mature mRNA in the chloroplast. The largest intron loop is 3800 bases long (at arrowhead). ×40,000. (Photograph courtesy of B. Koller, from Koller, B., and H. Delius, 1984, *Cell* **36**:613, Fig. 2. Copyright by M. I. T. Press.)

ATPase, and cytochrome $b–c_1$ of mitochondria, all of which are the result of the cooperative action of organelle plus nucleocytoplasmic systems.

The complete nucleotide sequence of the *rbcL* gene in corn ctDNA contains all the possible 61 codons for amino acids. When the DNA sequence is compared with the sequence of amino acids in the portions of the large polypeptides that have been studied, it appears that chloroplast and nuclear DNA use the same universal code for translation. The *rbcL* chloroplast gene in corn contains codons for 475 amino acids, virtually all of which are the same in the *rbcL* gene in barley, spinach, and a number of other flowering plants. Corn is a C_4 plant, so its RuBP carboxylase action is restricted to bundle sheath cells in the leaf rather than to mesophyll cells as in C_3 plants. As expected, little or no mRNA transcripts of the *rbcL* gene are found in corn mesophyll cells, whereas such transcripts are abundant in bundle sheath cells. Because the entire genome is present in the chloroplasts of both kinds of cells in the leaf, there must be some control over transcription of the organelle genome whereby the same gene is turned on in one part of the leaf but is turned off in chloroplasts in another part of the leaf. At present we have no idea of the nature of the mechanism(s) that regulate chloroplast *rbcL* gene expression.

In general, molecular studies of the chloroplast genetic system have lagged behind mitochondrial analysis, largely owing to the greater size of the chloroplast genome, limited numbers of suitable non-Mendelian mutations that affect the photosynthetic system, and less molecular information about photosynthetic components in chloroplasts than about respiratory components in mitochondria. Considering the huge strides made in the past few years through the use of nucleotide sequencing, various molecular approaches, and gene cloning to analyze chloroplasts, we may confidently anticipate an outpouring of new information in the next few years.

10.17
Evolutionary Origins of Chloroplasts

According to the endosymbiont theory proposed by Margulis (see Fig. 9.37), chloroplasts are modern descendants of an ancient oxygenic photosynthetic prokaryotic ancestry. The most probable ancestors are coccoid (nonfilamentous) blue-green algae and prochlorophytes, two known groups of prokaryotes whose photosynthetic processes involve the use of water as electron donor for $NADP^+$ reduction and that release molecular oxygen as a by-product of the light-dependent splitting of water. Presumably the ancient ancestral forms were similar to the living forms we know today.

The bulk of available evidence that supports the endosymbiotic origin of chloroplasts has come from comparative studies of the photosynthetic systems in chloroplasts and oxygenic photosynthetic prokaryotes and from comparisons of chloroplast and prokaryote genetic systems. We also know that coccoid blue-green algae are common endosymbionts in various eukaryotic hosts, where the algae perform photosynthetic functions that benefit the host organism. In addition, these algae lose their rigid cell wall after endosymbiosis, and in so doing they assume an uncanny resemblance to chloroplasts, particularly of the eukaryotic red algae (Fig. 10.35; see Fig. 10.7). The only known prochlorophyte, *Prochloron*, was discovered as a symbiont covering the external surface of the cloaca in an ascidian species, which is one of the simple nonvertebrate chordates that inhabit marine waters.

As we discussed in the previous section, chloroplast genomes and genetic processes resemble those in prokaryotes far more than those in eukaryotic nucleocytoplasmic systems. The homologies are much stronger between chloroplast and oxygenic photosynthetic prokaryote genetic systems than between chloroplast and eubacterial systems, suggesting a more direct evolutionary relationship for chloroplasts with cyanophytes (blue-green algae) and prochlorophytes than with bacteria. The strong genetic resemblances to prokaryotes and differences from eukaryotes notwithstanding, these features by themselves can be inter-

FIGURE 10-35
Electron micrograph of a section through the flagellated protozoan *Cyanophora paradoxa*. Two *cyanelles* (wall-less endosymbiotic blue-green algae) are visible in the eukaryotic host cytoplasm. (From Hall, W. T., and G. Claus, 1963, *J. Cell Biol.* **19**:551, Fig. 1. Copyright by Rockeller Univ. Press.)

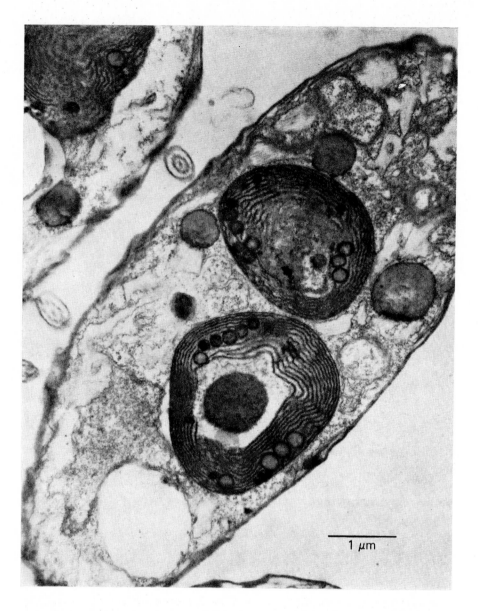

1 μm

preted to suggest either a symbiotic or a nonsymbiotic evolutionary history for chloroplasts.

If we were to accept the prokaryotic nature of the chloroplast as evidence of its prokaryotic origin, we would be choosing a history of *parallel evolution* by which endosymbiotic chloroplasts and their free-living prokaryotic relatives underwent similar evolutionary changes and thereby maintained homologous genetic systems over hundreds of millions of years. We could just as easily postulate a history of initial divergence of a nonsymbiotic chloroplast genome from the nuclear genome during eukaryote evolution, however, and invoke *convergent evolution* to explain the current similarities between chloroplasts and prokaryotic algae. In convergence, the similarities are superficial and derived by independent sets of evolutionary changes rather than by evolution in parallel of genetically related systems. According to such a nonsymbiotic scenario, the nuclear and chloroplast genomes differ now because of evolutionary divergence, whereas prokaryotic and chloroplast genomes are similar, but nonhomologous, because of evolutionary

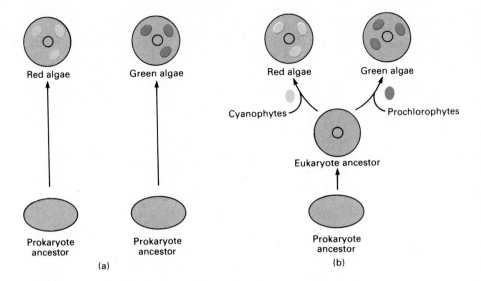

(a)

(b)

FIGURE 10-36
Origin of different chloroplasts in red algae and in green algae according to two different evolutionary scenarios. (a) Red algae and green algae may have evolved independently from different prokaryotic ancestors, which could explain the different kinds of chloroplasts in the two groups of eukaryotic algae today. The problem is that, if we accept this explanation, we are also obliged to accept the development of identical nucleocytoplasmic systems, by chance, in the evolution of the two groups of eukaryotic organisms from different ancestors. (b) A more probable scheme stipulates the evolution of a eukaryotic lineage from a single prokaryotic ancestor and the subsequent incorporation of different endosymbionts that evolved into different kinds of chloroplasts in the two algal lineages. Such a proposal more readily explains why red algae and green algae (and plants that evolved from green algae) have identical nucleocytoplasmic systems but different kinds of chloroplasts. The particular endosymbionts are believed to have been a cyanophyte in red algae and a prochlorophyte in green algal lineages.

convergence. Both the symbiotic account and the nonsymbiotic alternative are in accordance with basic evolutionary theory and with a large body of general evidence from many different lineages.

When we examine the evidence from protein and nucleic acid sequencing and from comparisons of the photosynthetic systems in chloroplasts and prokaryotic algae, however, the case for endosymbiosis is greatly strengthened. Gene and protein sequence analysis reveals strong homologies between cyanophytes and red algal chloroplasts. In addition, both systems have essentially the same phycobiliprotein pigments in phycobilisome particles, unstacked thylakoids, and no chlorophyll *b*. By contrast, chloroplasts in other eukaryotes most strongly resemble the prokaryotic prochlorophyte *Prochloron*; they lack phycobiliproteins but have chlorophyll *b*, among other features. From these and other considerations, it seems quite probable that chloroplasts arose at least twice, independently, from different prokaryotic ancestors. A prochlorophyte ancestry appears likely for chloroplasts in most of the algae and higher plants, whereas a cyanophyte ancestry is postulated for chloroplasts of the red algae. The stronger homologies between cyanophytes and red algal chloroplasts than between prochlorophytes and green-cell chloroplasts have led to the proposition that the red algal chloroplast evolved from a cyanophyte more recently and that green-cell chloroplasts arose from a prochlorophyte at an earlier time in evolution. Greater homology implies that less time has elapsed during evolution from a common ancestor, allowing fewer genetic differences to have been established.

It is considered more likely that one or both kinds of chloroplasts originated as endosymbionts in eukaryotic host cells, which explains why red algae and other eukaryotes have the same nucleocytoplasmic genetic system but different chloroplast systems. The alternative, which seems less likely, is that two different eukaryotic cell types (red algae and green algae) arose independently from two different prokaryotic lineages that both happened to evolve the same eukaryotic nucleocytoplasmic system but different chloroplast systems (Fig. 10.36).

By whatever pathways they may have arisen, the appearance of chloroplasts led to a permanent change in our world. Through their photosynthetic activities, chloroplasts oxygenated the atmosphere and provided an endless source of organic fuels for the aerobic life that now predominates on Earth.

Summary

Chloroplasts are found in all photosynthetic eukaryotes. In algae and protists chloroplasts vary somewhat in shape, but in land plants, they are characteristically discoid. Chloroplasts exhibit a highly compartmentalized ultrastructure: two outer membranes with different permeability properties enclose an aqueous stroma that contains a third set of membranes, the thylakoid membranes. These are arranged as single elongated connecting elements or as flattened stacks called grana. As in mitochondria, the various compartments of chloroplasts are functionally specialized. The stroma contains the enzymes of the photosynthetic dark reactions and the chloroplast genetic and protein synthesis apparatus. The thylakoid membranes contain the light-absorbing pigments, electron transport systems, machinery for synthesizing ATP, and proton pumps that eject protons into the thylakoid space. The thylakoid membranes are the chemiosmotic coupling devices. Photosynthetic prokaryotes lack chloroplasts, but have thylakoid membranes that form as invaginations of the plasma membrane.

A variety of photosynthetic pigments, including chlorophylls and carotenoids, are found in thylakoid membranes and constitute light-harvesting complexes absorbing energy over the entire visible spectrum. The wavelengths that are most effective in promoting photosynthesis, however, are those absorbed by chlorophyll. Its porphyrin ring with many conjugated double bonds absorbs light energy very efficiently. Carotenoids serve as accessory molecules absorbing and transferring energy to chlorophyll. Energy is transferred to a chlorophyll *a* reaction center that is the site for conversion of light energy to chemical energy.

When chlorophyll absorbs light energy, its electrons move from a low energy level (the ground state) to an excited state. The absorbed energy may be dissipated as heat or fluorescence as the electron returns to its ground state. If a suitable electron acceptor is available, however, it receives the energized electron, leaving the chlorophyll molecule ionized. This process occurs at two different stages during the light reactions of photosynthesis. In the first (PS II), the electron is transferred to a quinone and then, through an electron transport chain, to the chlorophyll of PS I. The oxidized chlorophyll of PS II is restored to its unexcited reduced state by receiving electrons from the photolysis of water. In the second stage (PS I), the chlorophyll's electron goes to ferredoxin and ultimately to $NADP^+$ to form NADPH. Thus overall, water is oxidized to molecular oxygen, and the electrons are boosted through PS II, down an electron transport chain, through PS I, and eventually to $NADP^+$. Once formed, the NADPH is used in the reactions of the stroma in which CO_2 is reduced and fixed into carbohydrates (the dark reactions of photosynthesis).

In addition to the energy conserved by the production of NADPH, additional energy is conserved in the form of ATP, synthesized in a process coupled to the electron transport chain connecting PS II and PS I. This noncyclic photophosphorylation process is obligatorily coupled to electron transport, and a proton gradient between the thylakoid space and the stroma provides the chemiosmotic potential to power a membrane-bound ATP synthetase generating ATP in the stroma. ATP can also be produced by cyclic photophosphorylation, in which reduced ferredoxin returns active electrons to one of the cytochrome complexes of the chain. The various components of thylakoid membranes can be distinguished in freeze-fracture preparations. PS I is predominantly found in unstacked membranes, whereas PS II occurs mainly in grana thylakoid membranes where it may be important in maintaining the stacking necessary for integrated activity. ATP synthetase particles are found only on the stromal side of unstacked membranes.

The dark reactions of photosynthesis are catalyzed by enzymes in the stroma and involve cyclic processes. In the C_3 cycle, found in all plants, CO_2 is coupled by RuBP carboxylase to the 5-carbon ribulose 1,5-bisphosphate (RuBP), and the resulting 6-carbon intermediate rapidly dissociates into two 3-carbon units. ATP and NADPH convert this to the high-energy 3-phosphoglyceraldehyde from which hexoses are formed. During this process ribulose 1,5-bisphosphate is regenerated to maintain cyclic operation. To fix 1 molecule of CO_2 requires 3 molecules of ATP and 2 of NADPH, derived from the light reactions. In some plants an additional adaptation permits fixation of CO_2 even when its concentration in the leaf is too low for the C_3 cycle to operate. In this C_4 cycle, PEP carboxylase catalyzes the combination of CO_2 with the 3-carbon phosphoenolpyruvate (PEP) to form a series of 4-carbon intermediates, one of which in turn transfers one carbon as CO_2 to ribulose 1,5-bisphosphate and the C_3 cycle. The addition of the extra cycle is energetically costly, but is advantageous to the plant in hot, dry environmental conditions. In the light, enhanced respiration of C_3 plants takes place at low CO_2 levels through an oxygenase activity of RuBP carboxylase and is energetically wasteful. It is not clear how plants benefit, if at all, from such photorespiration.

Chloroplasts develop from proplastids, small organelles consisting of two membranes enclosing an unstructured stroma. Proplastids lack chlorophyll. When exposed to light, the proplastid inner membrane invaginates, and additional tubular elements pinch off into the stroma where they develop into thylakoids. Independently, pigments are also synthesized. Proplastids undergo growth and division. Like mitochondria, chloroplasts have a semiautonomous genetic system. Their ribosomes more closely resemble prokaryotic ribosomes than do those of mitochondria. The genome, a circular molecule of DNA, encodes rRNA and tRNA and is large enough to encode more than 100 polypeptides. One chloroplast gene specifies the large subunit of RuBP carboxylase. Unlike mitochondria, chloroplasts use the universal genetic code, and their ribosomes have a high degree of homology with those of prokaryotes. Chloroplast structural genes may have intervening sequences, unlike genes in prokaryotes but like some genes in the mitochondria of some species. Because of the biochemical and genetic similarity of photosynthetic prokaryotes and chloroplasts, the endosymbiont theory is more widely accepted for the origin of chloroplasts than for mitochondria.

Readings and References

Akazawa, T., T. Takabe, and H. Kobayashi. 1984. Molecular evolution of ribulose 1,5-bisphosphate carboxylase/oxygenase (RuBisCO). *Trends Biochem. Sci.* **9**:380.

Anderson, J. M., and B. Andersson. 1982. The architecture of photosynthetic membranes: Lateral and transverse organization. *Trends Biochem. Sci.* **7**:288.

Armond, P. A., L. A. Staehelin, and C. J. Arntzen. 1977. Spatial relationship of photosystem I, photosystem II, and the light-harvesting complex in chloroplast membranes. *J. Cell Biol.* **73**:400.

Arnon, D. I. November 1960. The role of light in photosynthesis. *Sci. Amer.* **203**:104.

Barber, J. 1984. Has the mangano-protein of the water splitting reaction of photosynthesis been isolated? *Trends Biochem. Sci.* **9**:79.

Bassham, J. A., et al. 1954. The path of carbon in photosynthesis. *Sci. Amer.* **206**:88.

Bassham, J. A. 1971. The control of photosynthetic carbon metabolism. *Science* **172**:526.

Bassham, J. A., et al. 1954. The path of carbon in photosynthesis. XXI. The cyclic regeneration of carbon dioxide acceptor. *J. Amer. Chem. Soc.* **76**:1760.

Bedbrook. J. R., et al. 1979. Location of the single gene for the large subunit of ribulosebisphosphate carboxylase in the maize chloroplast chromosome. *J. Biol. Chem.* **254**:905.

Bennett, J. 1979. The protein that harvests sunlight. *Trends Biochem. Sci.* **4**:268.

Bisalputra, T., and A. A. Bisalputra. 1969. The ultrastructure of chloroplast of a brown alga, *Sphacelaria* sp. I. Plastid DNA configuration—the chloroplast genophore. *J. Ultrastruct. Res.* **29**:151.

Bjorkman, O., and J. Berry. October 1973. High-efficiency photosynthesis. *Sci. Amer.* **229**:80.

Bogorad, L. 1981. Chloroplasts. *J. Cell Biol.* **91**:256s.

Bolin, B. September 1970. The carbon cycle. *Sci. Amer.* **223**:124.

Branton, D., et al. 1975. Freeze-etching nomenclature. *Science* **190**:54.

Calvin, M. 1962. The path of carbon in photosynthesis. *Science* **135**:879.

Carillo, N., and R. H. Vallejos. 1983. The light-dependent modulation of photosynthetic electron transport. *Trends Biochem. Sci.* **8**:52.

Chollet, R. 1977. The biochemistry of photorespiration. *Trends Biochem. Sci.* **2**:155.

Chua, N.-H., and N. W. Gillham. 1977. The sites of synthesis of the principal thylakoid membrane polypeptides in *Chlamydomonas reinhardtii*. *J. Cell Biol.* **74**:441.

Chua, N.-H., and G. W. Schmidt. 1979. Transport of proteins into mitochondria and chloroplasts. *J. Cell Biol.* **81**:461.

Cline, K., et al. 1981. Separation and characterization of inner and outer envelope membranes of pea chloroplasts. *Proc. Natl. Acad. Sci. U. S.* **78**:3595.

Cloud, P., and A. Gibor. September 1970. The oxygen cycle. *Sci. Amer.* **223**:110.

Cohen-Bazire, G., and R. Kunisawa. 1963. The fine structure of *Rhodospirillum rubrum*. *J. Cell Biol.* **16**:401.

Cramer, W. A., W. R. Widger, R. G. Herrmann, and A. Trebst. 1985. Topography and function of thylakoid membrane proteins. *Trends Biochem. Sci.* **10**:125.

Curtis, S. E., and R. Hasselkorn. 1983. Isolation and sequence of the gene for the large subunit of ribulose-1,5-bisphosphate carboxylase from the cyanobacterium *Anabaena* 7120. *Proc. Natl. Acad. Sci. U. S.* **80**:1835.

Dickerson, R. E. March 1980. Cytochrome *c* and the evolution of energy metabolism. *Sci. Amer.* **242**:136.

Doolittle, W. F. 1980. Revolutionary concepts in evolutionary cell biology. *Trends Biochem. Sci.* **5**:146.

Douce, R., and J. Joyard. 1981. Does the plastid envelope derive from the endoplasmic reticulum? *Trends Biochem. Sci.* **6**:237.

Dron, M., M. Rahire, and J.-D. Rochaix. 1982. Sequence of the chloroplast DNA region of *Chlamydomonas reinhardii* containing the gene of the large subunit of ribulose bisphosphate carboxylase and parts of its flanking genes. *J. Mol. Biol.* **162**:775.

Ehleringer, J., and R. W. Pearcy. 1983. Variation in quantum yield for CO_2 uptake among C3 and C4 plants. *Plant Physiol.* **73**:555.

Ellis, R. J. 1979. The most abundant protein in the world. *Trends Biochem. Sci.* **4**:241.

Ellis, R. J. 1981. Chloroplast proteins: Synthesis, transport, and assembly. *Ann. Rev. Plant Physiol.* **32**:111.

Foyer, C. H., and D. O. Hall. 1980. Oxygen metabolism in the active chloroplast. *Trends Biochem. Sci.* **4**:188.

Frederick, J. F., ed. 1981. Origins and evolution of eukaryotic intracellular organelles. *Ann. N. Y. Acad. Sci.* **361.**

Gantt, E. 1981. Phycobilisomes. *Ann. Rev. Plant Physiol.* **32**:327.

Gantt, E., and S. F. Conti. 1965. The ultrastructure of *Porphyridium cruentum. J. Cell Biol.* **26**:365.

Gantt, E., and S. F. Conti. 1966. Granules associated with the chloroplast lamellae of *Porphyridium cruentum. J. Cell Biol.* **29**:423.

Gantt, E., and S. F. Conti. 1969. Ultrastructure of blue-green algae. *J. Bacteriol.* **97**:1486.

Gibbs, S. P. 1981. The chloroplasts of some algal groups may have evolved from endosymbiotic eukaryotic algae. *Ann. N. Y. Acad. Sci.* **361**:193.

Giddings, T. H., Jr., N. W. Withers, and L. A. Staehelin. 1980. Supramolecular structure of stacked and unstacked regions of the photosynthetic membranes of *Prochloron* sp., a prokaryote. *Proc. Natl. Acad. Sci. U. S.* **77**:352.

Gillham, N. W. 1978. *Organelle Heredity.* New York: Raven.

Goodenough, U. W., and R. P. Levine. 1969. Chloroplast ultrastructure in mutant strains of *Chlamydomonas reinhardi* lacking components of the photosynthetic apparatus. *Plant Physiol.* **44**:990.

Govindjee, and R. Govindjee. December 1974. The absorption of light in photosynthesis. *Sci. Amer.* **231**:68.

Gray, M. W., and W. F. Doolittle. 1982. Has the endosymbiont hypothesis been proven? *Microbiol. Rev.* **46**:1.

Gromet-Elhanan, Z. 1977. Electrochemical gradients and energy coupling in photosynthetic bacteria. *Trends Biochem. Sci.* **2**:274.

Hammes, G. G. 1983. Mechanism of ATP synthesis and coupled proton transport: Studies with purified chloroplast coupling factor. *Trends Biochem. Sci.* **8**:131.

Hatch, M. D., and C. R. Slack. 1966. Photosynthesis by sugarcane leaves: A new carboxylation reaction and the pathway of sugar formation. *Biochem. J.* **101**:103.

Heber, U., and G. H. Krause. 1980. What is the physiological role of photorespiration? *Trends Biochem. Sci.* **5**:32.

Heber, U., and D. A. Walker. 1979. The chloroplast envelope—barrier or bridge? *Trends Biochem. Sci.* **4**:252.

Hill, R. 1937. Oxygen evolved by isolated chloroplasts. *Nature* **139**:881.

Hinkle, P. C., and R. E. McCarty. March 1978. How cells make ATP. *Sci. Amer.* **238**:104.

Hoober, J. K. 1970. Sites of synthesis of chloroplast membrane polypeptides in *Chlamydomonas reinhardi* y-1. *J. Biol. Chem.* **245**:4327.

Hoober, J. K. 1984. *Chloroplasts.* New York: Plenum.

Jagendorf, A. 1967. Acid–base transitions and phosphorylation. *Fed. Proc.* **26**:1361.

Kamminga, H. 1981. van Niel and the unity of photosynthesis. *Trends Biochem. Sci.* **6**:164.

Koller, B., and H. Delius. 1984. Intervening sequences in chloroplast genomes. *Cell* **36**:613.

Miller, K. R. October 1979. The photosynthetic membrane. *Sci. Amer.* **241**:102.

Miller, K. R. 1982. Three-dimensional structure of a photosynthetic membrane. *Nature* **300**:53.

Mitchell, P. 1979. Keilin's respiratory chain concept and its chemiosmotic consequences. *Science* **206**:1148 (Nobel lecture).

Moore, P. D. 1978. When C_4 plants do best. *Nature* **272**:400.

Murata, N., and M. Miyao. 1985. Extrinsic membrane proteins in the photosynthetic oxygen-evolving complex. *Trends Biochem. Sci.* **10**:122.

Olson, J. M. 1981. Evolution of photosynthetic and respiratory prokaryotes and organelles. *Ann. N. Y. Acad. Sci.* **361**:8.

Roughan, G., and R. Slack. 1984. Glycerolipid synthesis in leaves. *Trends Biochem. Sci.* **9**:383.

Ruben, S., M. Randall, M. Kamen, and J. L. Hyde. 1963. Heavy oxygen (O^{18}) as a tracer in the study of photosynthesis. *J. Amer. Chem. Soc.* **63**:877.

Somerville, C. R., and W. L. Ogren. 1982. Genetic modification of photorespiration. *Trends Biochem. Sci.* **7**:171.

Staehelin, L. A. 1983. Control and regulation of the spatial organization of membrane components by membrane–membrane interactions. In *Modern Cell Biology,* vol 2, ed. B. Satir, p. 73. New York: Liss.

Staehelin, L. A., D. P. Carter, and A. McDonnel. 1980. Adhesion between chloroplast membranes: Experimental manipulation and incorporation of the adhesion factor into artificial membranes. In *Membrane–Membrane Interactions,* ed. N. B. Gilula, p. 179. New York: Raven.

Stumpf, P. K. 1981. Plants, fatty acids, compartments. *Trends Biochem. Sci.* **6**:173.

Thornber, J. P., and J. P. Markwell. 1981. Photosynthetic pigment–protein complexes in plant and bacterial membranes. *Trends Biochem. Sci.* **6**:122.

Van Valen, L. M. 1982. Phylogenies in molecular evolution: *Prochloron. Nature* **298**:493.

von Wettstein, D. 1981. Chloroplasts and nucleus: Concerted interplay between genomes of different cell organelles. In *International Cell Biology 1980–1981,* ed. H. G. Schweiger, p. 250. New York: Rockefeller University Press.

Westerhoff, H. V., and Z. Dancsházy. 1984. Keeping a light-driven proton pump under control. *Trends Biochem. Sci.* **9**:112.

Whitfield, P. R., and W. Bottomley. 1983. Organization and structure of chloroplast genes. *Ann. Rev. Plant Physiol.* **34**:279.

CHAPTER 11

Cytoskeletal Systems and Movement

Movement is a basic property of living systems, whether of organisms, cells, or parts of cells. Among the familiar examples of moving cells are the unicellular protists such as *Paramecium* and *Euglena*, which swim through fluid media by means of cilia or flagella. The motility organelles propel cells from one place to another in a manner very much like oars that move a boat in one specific direction or another. Amebae creep along a solid surface in essentially the same way in which some of our own blood cells move within the body. Cells in culture inch across a solid surface by yet another propulsive mechanism. Animals walk, run, jump, swim, and fly by the use of special tissues, such as muscle, and an assortment of auxiliary structures and processes that underlie directional motion.

Parts of cells also demonstrate movement. Muscle components contract, relax, and expand; chromosomes move toward the poles during nuclear division; protoplasm streams or churns in many kinds of cells. Organelles and particles are displaced or guided to different sectors in the cell, and individual molecules may move from one location to another, as we know to occur in fluid mosaic membranes. Molecules or organelles may be swept along by the streaming of cytoplasm or in a circulatory system made up of many kinds of cells and fluids.

Growth itself is a manifestation of cellular movement in that cells or groups of cells are displaced in space as the system enlarges and differentiates. During animal embryogenesis, an essential feature of development and differentiation involves specifically plotted migrations of a variety of immature cells. In effect, living systems display constant motion of one kind or another during all of their existence.

All of these movements are based on common structural and energetic themes within the cell. In particular, directional movements involve fibrous protein structures of one or more kinds and the ubiquitous energy source of ATP. The organized system of fibrous structures is referred to as the **cytoskeleton**.

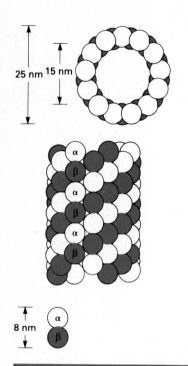

FIGURE 11-1
Microtubules are hollow, unbranched cylinders of indefinite length, whose walls are made up of 13 protofilaments lined up side by side in a circle. Each protofilament consists of a long chain of heterodimer subunits made up of α tubulin and β tubulin. The drawings show a microtubule in cross section (above) and in longitudinal section (below).

Cytoskeletal Protein Fibers

The two most prominent types of protein fibers in the cytoskeleton are **microtubules** and **microfilaments**. Microtubules are long, hollow cylinders made up of monomers of the globular protein *tubulin*, and microfilaments are polymers of the globular protein *actin*. A third class of protein fibers consists of the **intermediate filaments**, so called because their diameter of 10 nm is intermediate between the 6-nm-wide microfilaments and the 25-nm-wide microtubules. Intermediate filaments are made up of one or more of several kinds of protein monomers, differing from one another in their occurrence in particular differentiated cells. A fourth class is made up of **myosin filaments**, polymers of the protein *myosin* about 15 nm in diameter; myosin filaments are sometimes referred to as **thick filaments** because of their contrast with the thinner actin filaments. Myosin filaments are found in many kinds of cells, but they are most abundant and prominent in skeletal muscle.

Each class of cytoskeletal protein fiber has a set of accessory proteins bound to the filamentous or tubular polymer, and each class of fibers interacts with specific sets of other proteins or protein structures to produce movements and influence cell shape. The organized systems of fibers that make up the cytoskeleton of the cell are often referred to as the "bones and muscles" of the cell, in reference to their functions in determining the shape and internal organization of cells and in underlying the many expressions of movement.

11.1
Microtubules

Microtubules are hollow, unbranched cylinders. They are of indefinite length but usually measure many micrometers long. The average diameter of a microtubule is 25 nm, of which about 15 nm represents the hollow core. The cylinder wall itself can be resolved into 13 *protofilaments* arranged side by side in a circle. Each protofilament consists of a long chain of subunits, which are heterodimers (two different units) of one α-tubulin and one β-tubulin (Fig. 11.1). These two types of tubulin are chemically related and each type is encoded by a different gene or set of genes.

Tubulins can be purified from cell homogenates by subjecting the preparations to several cycles of disassembly and assembly induced by temperature shifts. In 1972 R. C. Weisenberg showed that isolated microtubules dissociated into their constituent subunits in the cold ($<18°C$) and reassembled into microtubular structures when the temperature was raised (18–$37°C$). Purified tubulin or microtubules can thus be obtained for biochemical and biological studies by successively cooling and warming the protein solutions and later clarifying the preparation by centrifugation to remove debris and large aggregates.

The use of isolated microtubules and tubulin subunits has revealed that sets of accessory **microtubule-associated proteins**, or **MAPs**, are bound to microtubules and that different sets of MAPs occur in different types of cells. Furthermore, MAPs are bound to the surface of microtubules *after* tubulin dimers have assembled into the typical hollow cylindrical fibers. These and other *in vitro* observations indicate that MAPs are not integral building blocks of the microtubule wall. Because microtubule disassembly is limited when MAPs are present but occurs readily when MAPs are removed, it seems likely that MAPs somehow stabilize microtubule polymer structure. MAPs may therefore play a critical role in regulating microtubule stability, which is an important aspect of the equilibrium between intracellular pools of tubulin subunits and tubulin polymeric structures. Microtubular stability is particularly important in cilia and flagella, which are relatively permanent structures because their microtubular construction is stabilized.

Microtubules are a ubiquitous component of eukaryotic cells, but they are not present in the great majority of prokaryotes. Until recently we believed microtubules to be absent from all prokaryotes, but we now know that they are present in a few exotic types of spirochete bacteria. The bacterial microtubules are morphologically similar to eukaryotic structures in length and width, and they consist of or contain tubulin (spirochete fibers showed cross reactions with anti-tubulin serum from eukaryotic sources). Such immunological assays provide a sensitive measure of the relatedness of proteins from different sources.

11.2
Microfilaments

Microfilaments are composed primarily of globular actin (**G actin**) molecules that are polymerized into strands of filamentous actin (**F actin**). Each microfilament consists of two strands of F actin twisted around each other in a helix conformation, giving an average diameter of 6 nm to filaments of indefinite length (Fig. 11.2). When treated with dilute salt solutions, isolated microfilament preparations yield G actin monomers, and when the monomers are exposed to higher salt concentrations they polymerize to form actin filaments. Individual actin molecules are stabilized in a globular conformation by one tightly bound Ca^{2+}, and their one bound ATP molecule is hydrolyzed when F actin polymers are formed. ATP hydrolysis increases the rate of polymerization, but it is not required because filament formation is not an energy-requiring process. The major significance of the bound ATP is related to regulation of microfilament stability and to controlled polymerization in the cell, which we will discuss later.

Although actin is the major component of the microfilament, several other proteins are also present. Some of these accessory proteins regulate the interaction between actin filaments and other protein fibers, and some act directly as binding agents. In skeletal muscle, which we will soon discuss in detail, two accessory proteins of the actin filament control the interaction between actin filaments and myosin filaments and thereby regulate muscle contraction, which involves direct binding between actin and myosin. In erythrocytes, short actin filaments bind to spectrin fibers to form the basic cytoskeletal framework that allows the red blood cell to maintain its biconcave shape even while it is deformed when it squeezes through the narrow capillaries of the bloodstream (see Fig. 5.21). In fact, actin binds to various proteins in different types of

6 nm

FIGURE 11-2
Microfilaments are composed of globular G-actin monomers in long polymer strands of filamentous F actin. Two F-actin polymer chains are wound around each other in the microfilament, which is 6 nm wide but of indefinite length.

cells and thereby contributes to cell movement phenomena as well as to the modification or maintenance of cell shape.

We know that multiple actin genes encode slightly different proteins in vertebrate cells of different tissues or stages of development. Virtually all eukaryotic species, in fact, also possess different sets of actin genes, which appear to be highly conserved during evolution because actins from different species are functionally interchangeable *in vitro*. Actins from different sources are quite similar, so studies of muscle actin can be extended to help us understand other actins from cells that are more difficult to analyze or from which only small amounts of actin can be isolated. Most of our information on the properties of actin monomers and polymers has in fact been obtained from studies of muscle actin, which can readily be obtained in large quantities.

11.3
Intermediate Filaments

Intermediate filaments have a characteristic diameter of about 10 nm, and they are the most stable of the cytoskeletal protein fibers. Studies of intermediate filaments lagged behind until recently, because they are relatively insoluble in salt solutions (the other classes of protein fibers are readily solubilized). Although we have been able to identify some of the polypeptides in a variety of intermediate filament types, we still know little about their assembly and how they are organized into the polymeric filament structure.

Each type of intermediate filament is composed of a characteristic set of subunit proteins, and any one kind of cell usually contains only one of the many different types of intermediate filament. Epithelial cells contain *tonofilaments* composed primarily of the protein keratin and are therefore referred to more often as **keratin filaments**. Keratin filaments inside the cell are anchored into spot desmosomes on their cytoplasm-facing surface. Together with an intercellular fiber of another type, which connects the two halves of a spot desmosome across the intercellular space, keratin filaments form part of a fibrous network that extends across the entire sheet of epithelium and provides the tissue its tensile strength. Keratin filaments also make a major contribution to the durable nature of outer coverings, such as the hair, nails, hooves, and skin of vertebrate animals. These filaments accumulate in the cytoplasm during the lifetime of a cell and become cross-linked to each other and to other proteins. The fibrous protein network remains as a tough protective layer after the epithelial cells die and provides the animal with a coating that reduces water and heat loss, as well as a durable protective surface. Keratins are highly diverse within a single animal—and even within a single structure or organ of an animal. The slightly different keratins are products of different families of keratin genes, all of which are related according to information from amino acid and nucleic acid analysis.

Fibroblasts contain **decamin filaments**, many types of cells contain **vimentin filaments**, muscle cells have intermediate filaments composed of the related proteins vimentin and **desmin**, glial cells of the central nervous system possess intermediate filaments **(glial filaments)**

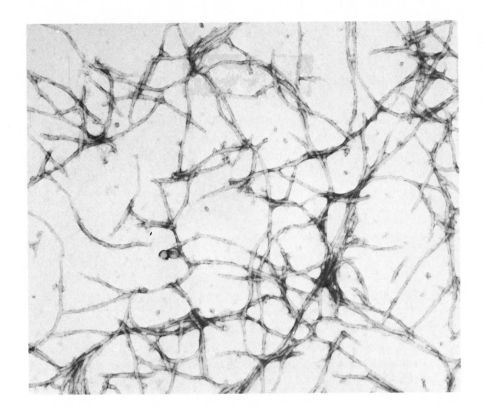

FIGURE 11-3
Electron micrograph of negatively stained intermediate filaments reconstituted from purified vimentin. Notice their uniform diameter (10 nm) and lack of significant curvature. ×100,000. (Photograph courtesy of N. Geisler.)

composed of vimentin and a 50,000-dalton acidic protein, and **neurofilaments** in vertebrate neurons consist of three different polypeptides referred to as a neurofilament triplet. Within each of these and other types of intermediate filaments, we believe the individual polypeptides to be fibrous rather than globular in conformation and to be associated together in a cablelike structure not unlike that of a collagen molecule. When seen by electron microscopy in negatively stained preparations, intermediate filaments are visible as displays of straight or slightly curving fibers (Fig. 11.3). The remarkable durability and tensile strength of fibrous intermediate filaments must be due in part to the particular fibrous nature of individual polypeptides and their mode of organization into fibrous polymers. The aggregates of filaments and their binding to other proteins and cell structures serve as the basis for the same durability and tensile strength imparted to tissues and to individual cells subjected to mechanical stresses, such as smooth muscle or skin. In fact, we have no evidence for a pool of protein monomers nor for a dynamic interplay between monomeric and polymeric forms of intermediate filaments. These features, plus the extraordinary difficulty of degrading intermediate filaments *in vitro*, all lead us to believe that the formation of the fibers is an irreversible process in the living cell. Although the available evidence is quite limited, it is possible that the only way intermediate filaments may be depolymerized in the cell is by enzymatic degradation. A number of proteolytic enzymes have been found to degrade one or another type of intermediate filament, and because the reaction is specific, it is possible that fiber disassembly occurs by controlled degradation *in vivo*. We know nothing at present, however, of the cellular conditions that might sponsor depolymerization.

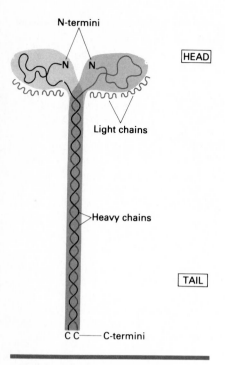

FIGURE 11-4
Schematic diagram of a myosin molecule showing the rodlike tail formed from two intertwined heavy polypeptide chains, whose N-termini exist in a globular conformation in each of the two heads. One pair of small light chains is associated with each globular head of the protein molecule.

11.4
Myosin Filaments

Myosin molecules can be extracted from virtually every kind of animal cell and from many other kinds of eukaryotic cells as well. Different forms of myosin are known to exist, but the best characterized of these forms is myosin from skeletal muscle. We will discuss myosin in some detail in the sections on muscle contraction, but some general features of the molecule and its filamentous polymer should be mentioned in this preliminary survey of cytoskeletal fibers.

Myosin is soluble in high salt solutions, and the molecules can be extracted from skeletal muscle and other sources rather easily. The individual molecule is about 500,000 molecular weight, and it consists of 6 polypeptide subunits. Two heavy chains of about 200,000 daltons each are coiled around each other to form the long rodlike tail, and each chain terminates in a globular head portion of the molecule (Fig. 11.4). The conformational difference between the two parts of the molecule is due to the existence of long α-helix regions in the heavy chains coiled around each other in the tail, but each chain has a less ordered region at its N-terminus and thus assumes a globular conformation in each head. Two pairs of light polypeptide chains, of about 20,000 daltons and 16,000 daltons each, are associated with the heads of the molecule; one chain of each pair is present on each head.

Myosin filaments of skeletal muscle, or thick filaments about 15 nm in diameter, form spontaneously at physiological salt concentrations. Individual molecules associate by their tails, beginning with oppositely oriented molecules and ending with a filament in which a central bare zone separates the two halves of a filament whose myosin heads project leftward and rightward on each side of the bare zone (Fig. 11.5). Each myosin filament in skeletal muscle therefore has two separately and oppositely oriented sets of heads and tails of its individual myosin molecules in the polymer.

The globular head of the myosin molecule is the site of binding to actin filaments and the site of ATPase catalytic activity in ATP hydrolysis leading to fiber movement and, in skeletal muscle, to contraction of the tissue. The chemical energy for the mechanical work

FIGURE 11-5
Myosin thick filaments (15 nm wide) form spontaneously by the association of individual myosin molecules. Oppositely oriented molecules associate at their tails, which creates a central bare zone devoid of heads and produces a thick filament whose myosin heads project in opposite directions on each side of the bare zone.

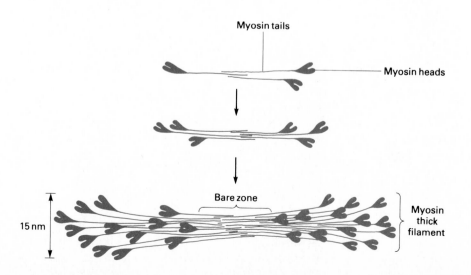

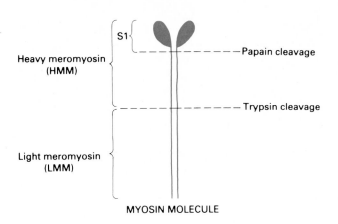

MYOSIN MOLECULE

FIGURE 11-6
When digested with trypsin, the myosin molecule is cleaved into heavy meromyosin (HMM) and lower-molecular-weight light meromyosin (LMM) fragments. Digestion with the enzyme papain cleaves the myosin heads (S1 fragments) either from heavy meromyosin or from whole myosin molecules. From functional studies of digest fragments it is clear that the S1 fragments, or myosin heads, contain all of the ATPase activity and actin-binding properties of myosin.

of contraction comes from the free-energy difference attendant upon the hydrolysis of ATP to ADP and P_i. The specificity of myosin interaction with actin is localized to the heads of the myosin molecule, as shown by *in vitro* studies of fragmented preparations. When treated with the proteolytic enzyme papain, myosin heads are cleaved from the rodlike tail of the molecule (Fig. 11.6). Isolated heads retain all the ATPase and actin-binding properties of the intact molecule. Myosin heads can hydrolyze ATP *in vitro*, but the reaction is quite sluggish in the absence of actin. In the presence of actin filaments, myosin ATPase is stimulated to hydrolyze ATP at much higher rates comparable to those in contracting muscle. The rate-limiting step of the reaction is the release of ADP and P_i from myosin, not the binding of ATP or the hydrolysis reaction itself. Myosin that is bound to actin can release the products of hydrolysis very rapidly and can thus bind another molecule of ATP and undergo repeated reactions in quick succession. In the absence of actin, ADP and P_i remain tightly bound to myosin ATPase, which prevents further binding of ATP and its hydrolysis by the enzyme.

Each G actin monomer of a microfilament can bind one globular myosin head. When isolated myosin heads form complexes with actin filaments, the filaments become decorated with heads in a display that gives the appearance of arrowheads when seen by electron microscopy (Fig. 11.7). Each myosin head projects from the actin filament, and the

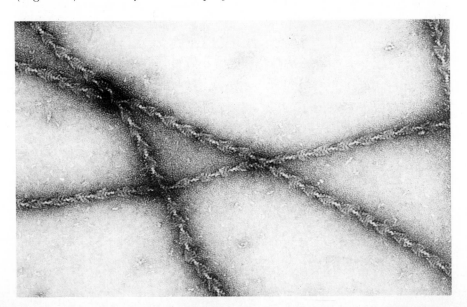

FIGURE 11-7
Electron micrograph of negatively stained actin filaments decorated with myosin-head fragments (sub-fragment-1, or S1 fragments). The bound myosin-head fragments are tilted in one direction, which gives the appearance of arrowheads and indicates the structural polarity of each actin filament. ×200,000. (Photograph courtesy of R. W. Craig.)

helical arrangement of the grouped heads on the two intertwined strands of the filament leads to the distinctive pattern of decoration. The fact that all the arrowhead displays on a single filament point in the same direction shows that the microfilament possesses inherent structural *polarity*. This property of polarity plays an important role in the coherent movements of muscle fibers during episodes of contraction and relaxation, as we will discuss in the next part of the chapter.

Muscle Contraction

The mechanical work of muscle contraction is subsidized by chemical energy derived from ATP hydrolysis. The fibrous contractile apparatus of striated muscle in vertebrate and invertebrate animals is the most highly organized of all the intracellular systems for movement—and the best understood of all the known motility systems. Skeletal muscle has been studied for many years, and the relationships between the ultrastructure and chemistry of the contractile system in striated (skeletal) muscle are clear. Hence we not only have developed a relatively thorough understanding of these relationships but have also used the muscle system as a model to explore the basis for simpler expressions of motility in the other types of cells and tissues. In addition to *striated muscle*, which is firmly anchored to bones or equivalent skeletal components in animals, and on which we will concentrate in this section, other forms of muscle are also able to perform the mechanical work of contraction through the operations of contractile protein fibers. Skeletal muscle contraction produces voluntary movements, whereas *smooth muscle* engages in involuntary movements such as the regular and repeated cadences of heart pumping and the writhing but rhythmic movements of the lining of the intestine, uterus, and various other organs in the body. Walking, running, jumping, flying, and swimming all depend on the contraction and relaxation of skeletal muscle, which occur as a result of interactions between actin filaments, myosin filaments, and a number of proteins associated with these protein fibers.

11.5
Muscle Fibers

Striated muscle, also called *skeletal muscle* or *voluntary muscle*, has a distinctive appearance due to a pattern of cross-striations or bands of alternating dark and light material in its individual muscle fibers. The individual **muscle fiber** is a long, large, cylindrical cell formed during development by the fusion of many separate cells called myoblasts (Gr. *myos*, muscle). The muscle fiber is therefore multinucleate and may vary considerably in length, but it is usually about 50 μm to 200 μm in diameter. The plasma membrane, called the **sarcolemma**, surrounds an interior that is packed with numerous long, cylindrical elements called **myofibrils**, each of which is about 1 μm to 3 μm in diameter but extends the entire length of the cell (Fig. 11.8). Thinly dispersed around and between the myofibrils are typical components of any eukaryotic

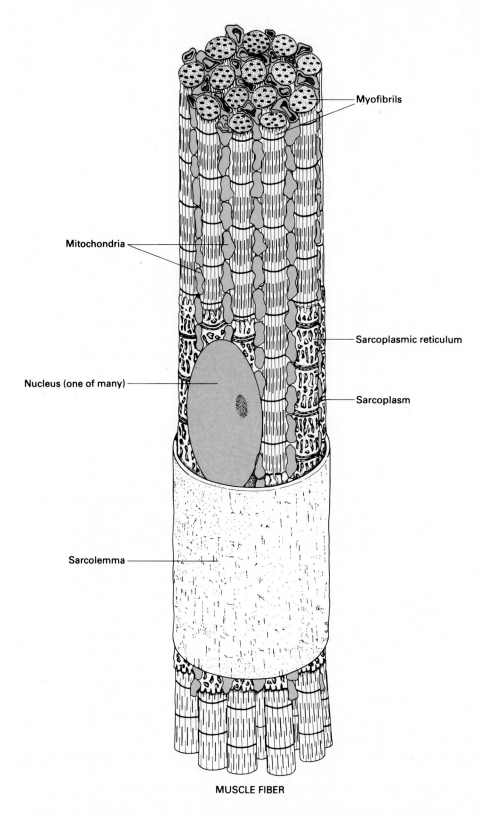

Myofibrils

Mitochondria

Nucleus (one of many)

Sarcoplasmic reticulum

Sarcoplasm

Sarcolemma

MUSCLE FIBER

FIGURE 11-8
Organization of striated muscle fiber. The individual muscle fiber is a multi-nucleated "cell" formed by fusion of many separate cells called myoblasts. The plasma membrane, or sarcolemma, surrounds numerous cylindrical myofibrils that extend the length of the muscle fiber. The remainder of the interior contains typical subcellular components, including cytoplasm (sarcoplasm), nuclei, mitochondria (color), endoplasmic reticulum (sarcoplasmic reticulum), and other structures.

cell, including cytoplasm (called *sarcoplasm*), endoplasmic reticulum (called *sarcoplasmic reticulum*), nuclei, mitochondria, and other less evident components.

In longitudinal sections of striated muscle fibers, it is quite clear that the striated effect of the whole cell is the result of striations of its

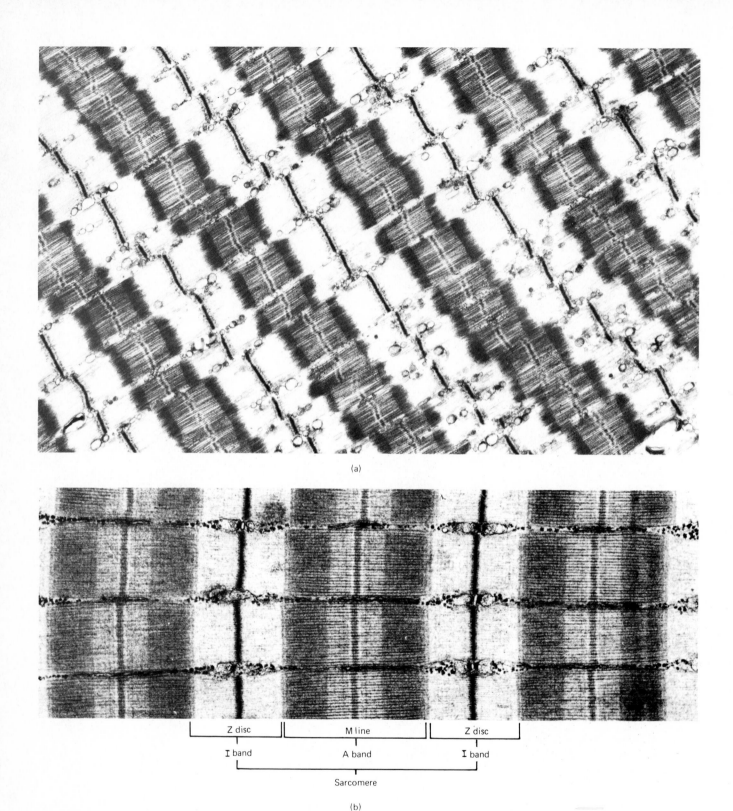

(a)

Z disc   M line   Z disc

I band   A band   I band

Sarcomere

(b)

FIGURE 11-9
Electron micrographs of longitudinal sections from rabbit striated muscle fiber. (a) A low-magnification view showing the parallel arrangement of individual myofibrils with characteristic banding, which accounts for the banded appearance of the whole muscle fiber. ×74,000. (b) A higher-magnification view of several myofibrils in parallel register. Lighter I bands alternate with denser A bands. A sarcomere extends between adjacent Z discs. Each I band is bisected by a Z disc and each A band is bisected by an M line. Myosin filaments are confined to the A band, but actin filaments extend from their Z-disc connection into the A band borders. ×120,250. (Photographs courtesy of R. W. Craig.)

individual myofibrils, which are arranged in parallel. The pattern consists of alternating dark stripes and light stripes, and each light stripe is bisected by a thin line separated by about 2.5 μm from the thin lines on either side. The region between two thin lines is a **sarcomere**, and the sarcomeres of adjacent myofibrils are aligned in register, which causes the entire muscle fiber to have a consistent striation pattern (Fig. 11.9). The dark stripes are called **A bands**, and these alternate with lighter **I bands** whose central bisecting line is called a Z line or **Z disc**. The sarcomere therefore extends between adjacent Z discs, and each sarcomere includes a centrally located A band flanked on each side by part of a light I band; any single I band is shared by two adjacent sarcomeres because a Z disc runs down the middle of each I band (Fig. 11.10).

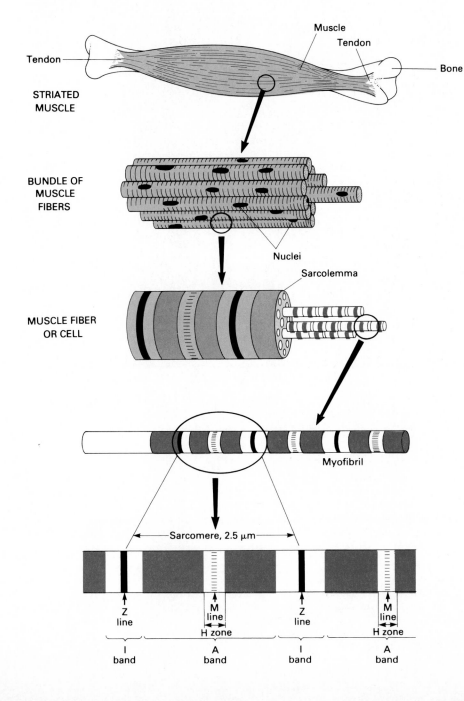

STRIATED
MUSCLE

Tendon

Muscle

Tendon

Bone

BUNDLE OF
MUSCLE
FIBERS

Nuclei

Sarcolemma

MUSCLE FIBER
OR CELL

Myofibril

Sarcomere, 2.5 μm

Z
line

M
line

H zone

Z
line

M
line

H zone

I
band

A
band

I
band

A
band

FIGURE 11-10
Striated muscle is made up of many muscle fibers, each of which is packed with myofibrils. The banded pattern of a myofibril can be resolved into alternating darker A bands and lighter I bands. The center of the A band has a lighter-staining H zone bisected by an M line. The center of the I band is bisected by a densely staining Z disc. The contractile unit of a myofibril is called a sarcomere, which extends across 2.5 μm of distance between adjacent Z discs throughout the length of each myofibril.

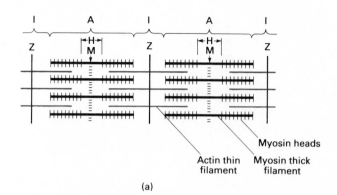

(a)

Myosin heads

Actin thin
filament

Myosin thick
filament

Longitudinal section

Cross sections

(b)

FIGURE 11-11

Organization of the myofibril in striated muscle fibers. (a) Diagram showing the regular arrangement of myosin thick filaments and actin thin filaments across a span of two sarcomeres. (b) Electron micrographs of a sarcomere from striated muscle of the freshwater killifish *Fundulus diaphanus*: (1) longitudinal section showing the dense A band of myosin filaments bordered by paler I-band regions of actin filaments, which extend from the Z disc to the edge of the H zone. A Z disc bisects each I band, and the H zone occupies the center of the A band. The H zone is a region containing only myosin filaments, and at its center is the bare zone (bz) of overlapping tails of myosin molecules. The M line that bisects the H zone consists of a protein that binds myosin filaments. (2-6) Cross-sectional views through various regions of the sarcomere, providing a third dimension of perspective: (2) thick filaments surrounded by thin filaments in a region of overlap within the A band; (3) thick filaments only, in the H zone; (4) thick filaments in the bare zone region of the A band; (5) thick filaments in the M-line region of the A band, showing each thick filament connected to six neighboring thick filaments by M protein, producing a lattice arrangement; (6) thin filaments only, in the I band. (Photographs courtesy of F. Pepe, from *Biological Macromolecules Series: Subunits in Biological Systems*, 1971, pp. 323–353, New York: Marcel Dekker.)

From electron micrographs it is evident that each sarcomere contains two sets of parallel filaments arranged in a regular manner. The thick filaments extend across the width of an A band (about 1600 nm), and the thin filaments extend all across an I band and partway into the A bands on either side, a distance of about 2000 nm. The 15-nm thick filaments are composed of myosin, and the 6-nm thin filaments are made up primarily of actin. Each actin filament is about 1000 nm long and is attached at one end to the Z disc, so that the filament extends from its attachment at the Z disc partway into the A band. When seen in cross section, the regular pattern is evident in each case but varies depending on the particular region of the sarcomere in which the cut has been made. Cross sections through an I band include only thin actin filaments, cross sections through the central part of an A band include only thick myosin filaments, and cross sections through the remainder of the A band include both thick and thin filaments (Fig. 11.11). Where both kinds of filaments occur in an A band, each myosin filament is encircled by six actin filaments in a regular array. Where only myosin filaments occur in the central region of an A band, the so-called *H zone* of the A band, the filaments also are ordered in a regular pattern. From both the longitudinal and cross-sectional views, therefore, myofibrils exhibit a highly organized and regular display of both kinds of filaments and other proteins to which they are bound. As we mentioned in Section 11.4, myosin molecules aggregate by their tails in oppositely oriented directions. The very center of each myosin filament therefore consists of a region of myosin tails only, and this region is referred to as the *bare zone* (bare of myosin heads). The *M line* that runs down the center of the bare zone consists of a protein that binds myosin filaments in a regular hexagonal lattice (see Fig. 11.11b5). No part of the sarcomere is unordered.

11.6
The Sliding Filament Model of Muscle Contraction

When striated muscle contracts, all the sarcomeres of a muscle fiber contract to the same extent. During an episode of contraction, the length of the A band remains unchanged but the I band shortens. The fact that the entire A band is unchanged makes it obvious that individual myosin filaments undergo no change in length. Actin filaments also retain their original length because the H zone, as well as the I band, is reduced in length. To account for these measured features, Hugh Huxley and Andrew Huxley and their respective groups proposed in 1954 that sarcomere contraction was the result of myosin filaments and actin filaments sliding past each other (Fig. 11.12). In addition to evidence gleaned from electron microscopy for the **sliding filament model** of muscle contraction, various other supporting evidence has been obtained. For example, x-ray diffraction studies revealed that the subunits of each kind of filament retained the same packing in both contracted and relaxed cells. The internal packing would have been altered if individual filaments contracted; subunits would be displaced in a contracted filament when compared with a relaxed filament. Once

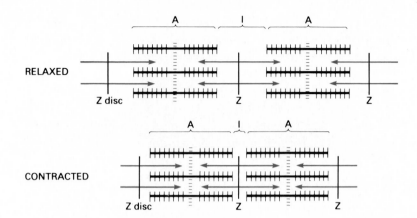

FIGURE 11-12

Diagram illustrating the sliding filament theory of striated muscle contraction. Actin filaments slide over myosin filaments and move inward toward the center of the A band, but the individual myosin and actin filaments retain their original lengths during contraction. The sarcomere is contracted as I bands are narrowed when adjacent Z discs are drawn together by virtue of their attached actin filaments moving inward toward the center of the A band. Actin filaments on each side of the Z disc have opposite polarity, so each sarcomere contracts during filament sliding.

this simple model was presented, it stimulated a variety of studies directed toward analyzing the mode of interaction between thick and thin filaments, the relationship of the energy source to filament sliding, the regulation of actin–myosin interactions in contraction, and many other aspects of muscle movement.

Myosin filaments have an opposite structural polarity on either side of the bare zone by virtue of their mode of assembly from individual myosin molecules (see Fig. 11.5). In order to explain the physical interaction between myosin filaments and actin filaments within the sarcomere, we would predict that the actin filaments attached to the Z disc borders of a sarcomere were also of opposite structural polarity. If this were the case, actin filaments would slide inward toward the center of the A band and would thus lead to the observed shortening of each I band and to a decrease in the H zone of the A band, without a change in the length of the actin filaments themselves. A simple test of this prediction is to bind heavy meromyosin or S1 head fragments to fragments of muscle containing isolated Z discs with actin filaments still attached. When such *decorated actin filaments* are examined by electron microscopy, the bound arrowhead displays are seen to point away from the Z discs and toward the center of the sarcomere (see Fig. 11.7). Actin filaments thus possess the structural polarity that corresponds to the opposite polarity of the myosin filaments in each sarcomere.

We know that only the myosin heads possess ATPase activity and the ability to bind to actin filaments, and we would therefore expect the molecular mechanism for sliding to involve specific interactions between myosin filament heads and actin filaments all around them in hexagonal lattice displays (see Fig. 11.11). From a variety of evidence collected over many years, we believe that sliding occurs by the successive attachment and detachment of myosin heads to actin filaments, which pulls the actin filaments over the myosin filaments and inward toward the center of the A band. Presumably, the myosin head binds to an actin subunit and, in so doing, releases its bound ADP and P_i from a prior hydrolysis event. When a new molecule of ATP binds to the myosin head, the head detaches from the actin filament and, when this new ATP is hydrolyzed, the head is once again prepared for another cycle of attachment and detachment. As a myosin head changes its conformation in cycles of attachment and detachment from actin, the actin filament is pulled along the myosin filament in a manner similar to the action of a ratchet device. At any one time, some myosin heads of a filament are attached and others are detached from the actin filament. But there are about 500 myosin heads per filament, so a sufficient number of heads can act and exert an adequate mechanical force in each cycle of a contraction episode.

In order to explain how a myosin molecule uses the energy of ATP hydrolysis to make and break contact and thereby pull the actin filament inward toward the center of the A band, it is necessary to consider both the change in conformation of the myosin head and the flexibility of the whole myosin molecule in a thick filament. We speculate that a myosin molecule has two "hinge" regions that correspond to the regions of trypsin and papain attack when myosin is enzymatically fragmented to light meromyosin and heavy meromyosin (trypsin "hinge") and when heavy meromyosin is fragmented to release S1 heads from the remainder of the tail (papain "hinge") (see Fig. 11.6). If such weak regions indeed correspond to hinges, a myosin molecule has enough flexibility to bridge the space of 8 nm to 10 nm and make contact with a neighboring actin filament (Fig. 11.13). We further speculate that, when a myosin head makes contact with actin (presumably by random diffusion movement), the head changes in conformation as it releases ADP and P_i in response to binding with actin. The conformationally modified myosin head pulls against the actin filament, causing sliding, and when another ATP binds to the head, it detaches from the actin filament. Once the new ATP molecule is hydrolyzed, the myosin head assumes its original conformation and is ready for another cycle of attachment and detachment to and from actin (Fig. 11.14). We believe that the two heads of a myosin molecule cycle independently of each other, because each S1 head fragment is capable of independent ATPase activity and binding to actin *in vitro*.

What is the stimulus for muscle contraction? How is contraction regulated? How do all the myofibrils of a thick muscle fiber, and all the muscle fibers of a muscle, contract at the same time in a coherent and

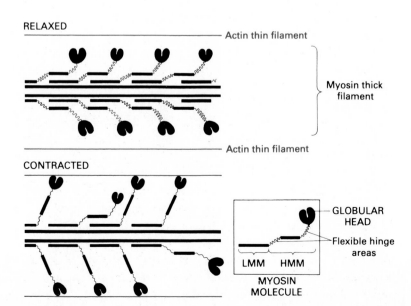

RELAXED

Actin thin filament

Myosin thick filament

Actin thin filament

CONTRACTED

GLOBULAR HEAD

Flexible hinge areas

LMM   HMM

MYOSIN MOLECULE

FIGURE 11-13
Postulated mode of myosin action in striated muscle. During contraction, myosin molecules can bridge the space between actin filaments via bends in the presumptive hinge regions corresponding to the sites of trypsin and papain sensitivity. Bending in these two sites may account for the alternating waves of attachment and detachment during episodes of contraction and relaxation, as myosin heads make and break contact with actin filaments.

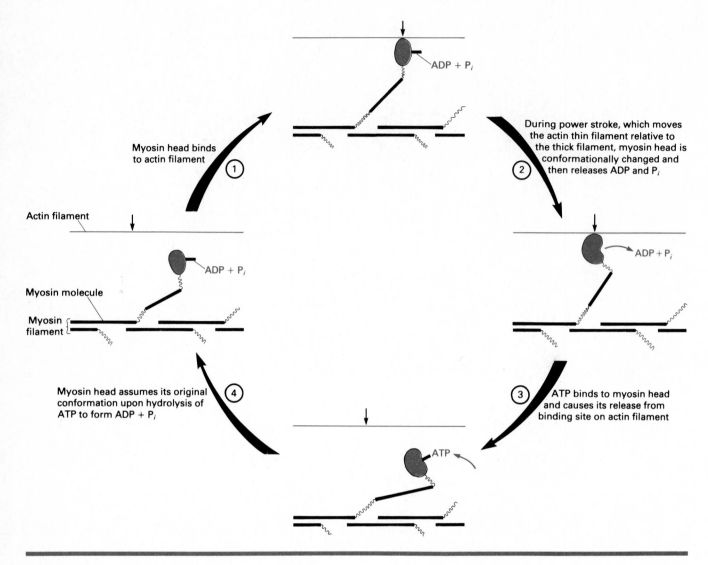

FIGURE 11-14
Cyclic attachment and detachment of myosin filaments to and from actin filaments may occur as the result of conformational changes in the myosin heads. Myosin heads carrying ADP and P$_i$ bind to actin filaments and there undergo a conformational change as ADP and P$_i$ are released in response to actin binding. The myosin heads pull against the actin filament and cause it to slide over the myosin thick filament. Upon binding ATP, the myosin head detaches from the actin filament. When the ATP is hydrolyzed, the myosin head resumes its original conformation and is ready for another cycle of attachment and detachment.

Labels within figure:
Myosin head binds to actin filament ①
During power stroke, which moves the actin thin filament relative to the thick filament, myosin head is conformationally changed and then releases ADP and P$_i$ ②
Actin filament
ADP + P$_i$
Myosin molecule
Myosin filament
ADP + P$_i$
Myosin head assumes its original conformation upon hydrolysis of ATP to form ADP + P$_i$ ④
③ ATP binds to myosin head and causes its release from binding site on actin filament
ATP

orderly fashion? These and other fundamental questions have been answered in whole or in part by many studies conducted over the past twenty years. This fascinating story is still unfolding, but we have a clear understanding of many of the processes and phenomena that are involved. We will discuss these topics next.

11.7
Coupled Excitation and Contraction

It is plausible to expect contraction to be initiated when the ATP supply is high and for contraction to terminate upon depletion of ATP in the muscle. This cannot be the case, however, because the levels of ATP are relatively high in resting muscle as well as in contracting muscle. Rather than arising in response to changes in the ATP reserves, the stimulus that triggers contraction is produced only when an electrical impulse from an excited nerve to the muscle depends on special properties of the muscle cell membranes—particularly of the sarcolemma and the sarcoplasmic reticulum.

The electrical excitation from the nerve is received by the muscle and spreads quickly over the sarcolemma of individual muscle fibers. The higher electrical charge outside than inside the sarcolemma boundary creates a difference in potential across the membrane. As the sarcolemma suddenly becomes permeable to cations such as Na^+, K^+, and Ca^{2+}, the transmembrane potential is discharged in the phenomenon of **depolarization**, which is caused by the flow of cations across the membrane. The electrical impulse not only spreads rapidly but is also communicated almost instantly to all the muscle fibers and their myofibril contents, which undergo essentially simultaneous contraction in the muscle. This rapid and instantaneous communication of the electrical excitation to all the myofibrils of a muscle is due to the existence of a series of *transverse tubular infolds*, or the **T system**, of the sarcolemma. Because of the T system of tubular infolds, the sarcolemma makes contact with the sarcoplasmic reticulum throughout the interior of each muscle fiber in the excited tissue (Fig. 11.15). The electrical

FIGURE 11-15
Three-dimensional view of part of a muscle fiber showing the T system of transverse tubular invaginations of the sarcolemma. Through the T system of invaginations, the sarcolemma makes contact with the sarcoplasmic reticulum throughout the thickness of the muscle fiber. In this way an incoming electrical charge is transmitted rapidly from the sarcolemma to the sarcoplasmic reticulum in each muscle fiber of a striated muscle. (From "The Sarcoplasmic Reticulum" by K. R. Porter and C. Franzini-Armstrong. Copyright © 1965 by Scientific American, Inc. All rights reserved.)

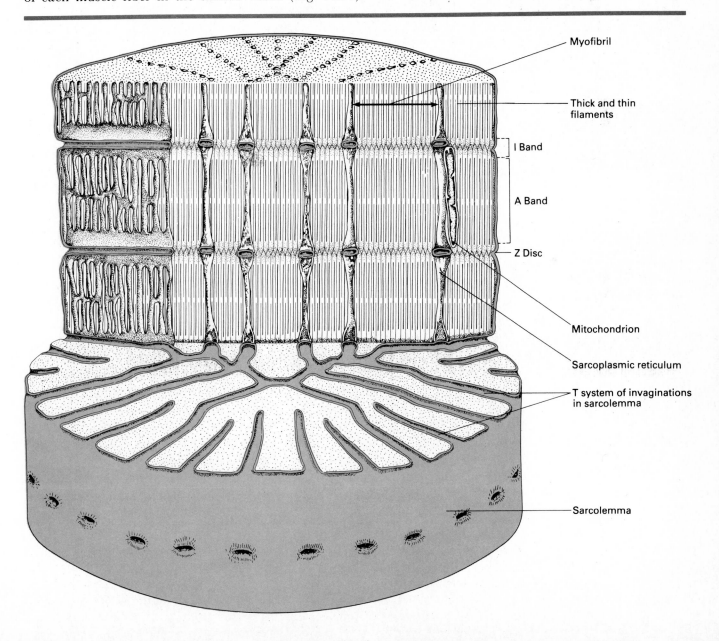

charge is thus transmitted from the sarcolemma to the reticulum membranes, causing these membranes to become more permeable to cations and resulting in an outflow of stored Ca^{2+} from the lumen of the sarcoplasmic reticulum into the surrounding sarcoplasm. The sudden increase in concentration of free Ca^{2+} in the sarcoplasm bathing the myofibrils triggers their contraction.

Once in the sarcoplasm, Ca^{2+} activates myosin ATPase and thus initiates the interaction between myosin filaments and actin filaments that leads to contraction. It has been estimated that a concentration of 10^{-6} M to 10^{-5} M free Ca^{2+} is adequate to activate myosin ATPase and initiate contraction. Such a concentration exists in the sarcoplasm of excited muscle as a consequence of Ca^{2+} outflow from the sarcoplasmic reticulum to the sarcoplasm, whereas the concentration of free Ca^{2+} is believed to be only 10^{-7} M in the sarcoplasm of resting muscle. At the end of an episode of contraction, Ca^{2+} is pumped back into the lumen of the reticulum by a transmembrane "relaxing factor" that uses the free energy of ATP hydrolysis to move ions by an active transport process, against the Ca^{2+} concentration gradient. Upon receipt of the next electrical impulse, Ca^{2+} is again released from storage in the sarcoplasmic reticulum lumen and enters the sarcoplasm to trigger another cycle of contraction.

Muscle contraction is clearly dependent on an adequate supply of free Ca^{2+} to activate myosin ATPase, as we have just discussed. When myosin is incubated with *pure* actin filaments artificially reconstituted only from actin monomers, however, myosin ATPase is activated even in the absence of Ca^{2+}. The Ca^{2+}-dependence of myofibril contraction is evident only in intact myofibrils or when actin filaments in their native state are mixed with myosin. These observations indicate that the *regulation* of muscle contraction triggered by Ca^{2+} depends on one or more components that are present, along with actin, in the native thin filaments. These regulatory components are *troponin* and *tropomyosin*, which are accessory proteins bound to actin filaments.

Before we proceed to discuss regulation of the Ca^{2+} effect, it is appropriate to consider the observation mentioned at the beginning of this section that ATP levels remain high in resting muscle despite the use of ATP in subsidizing the work of contraction. How can this be explained? Quite simply, we would predict that some other energy reserve exists and that it serves to replenish the ATP supply in striated muscle. This prediction seems in order because we can poison glycolysis and respiration, but muscle contraction continues to occur even when ATP synthesis is inhibited in this way. We know that there is relatively little ATP in muscle, and, because the ATP level remains more or less the same even when its synthesis is inhibited, some high-energy reserve must be present and must replenish ATP in the cells.

In vertebrate striated muscle and other tissues, **phosphocreatine** occurs in nearly five times the amount of ATP. The enzyme *creatine kinase* catalyzes the transfer of a phosphoryl residue from phosphocreatine to ADP to form creatine and ATP.

$$\text{phosphocreatine + ADP} \overset{\text{creatine kinase}}{\rightleftharpoons} \text{creatine + ATP}$$

Under conditions known to exist in the sarcoplasm, the reaction for ATP formation is favored over the reverse reaction, so the ATP levels remain constant in the cells. The concentration of ATP diminishes in poisoned muscle, leading eventually to a cessation of contraction, only when the phosphocreatine supply is exhausted. In normal cells the concentration of ATP is maintained at a relatively constant level by various feedback controls that regulate the rate of glycolysis and respiration and thus the rate of ATP synthesis in these pathways, as well as controls over phosphocreatine reactions and other means by which ADP is phosphorylated to form ATP.

11.8
Troponin and Tropomyosin: Regulatory Proteins

Cycles of muscle contraction and relaxation are regulated by the sarcoplasmic concentration of free calcium ions, under sarcoplasmic reticulum control. The *responsiveness* to Ca^{2+}, however, involves the participation of two accessory proteins bound to actin filaments: **troponin** and **tropomyosin**. Troponin is a protein composed of three polypeptides designated as *troponins T, I,* and *C*. Troponin T has a binding site for the stiff, rod-shaped tropomyosin molecule, and it is believed to be responsible for the precise positioning of the troponin–tropomyosin complex along an actin filament (Fig. 11.16). The addition of troponin I to a troponin-T–tropomyosin complex does not sponsor an interaction between myosin filaments and actin filaments, even in the presence of Ca^{2+}. When troponin C is added to complete the complex, thick and thin filaments interact in response to free Ca^{2+}. The relief of the inhibition of contraction on adding troponin C is due to the ability of each troponin C unit to bind up to four Ca^{2+} ions. Once Ca^{2+} is bound, troponin C is believed to undergo a conformational change and actually to "push" tropomyosin away from its original position and closer inward toward the groove between the two actin chains in a thin filament. In relaxed muscle, tropomyosin physically blocks the actin sites that make contact with myosin heads. In contracting muscle, Ca^{2+}-loaded troponin C causes tropomyosin to shift position and thereby expose the actin binding sites that interact with myosin ATPase and lead to filament sliding and muscle contraction.

Troponin behaves like a calcium-dependent switch for muscle contraction. By virtue of the calcium-binding properties of its C subunit, troponin detects the flood of Ca^{2+} into the sarcoplasm, which is the signal for muscle contraction. The contraction is triggered when troponin removes the steric block of contact between actin monomers and myosin ATPase by causing a slight relocation of the hindering tropomyosin molecules bound to the actin filament. Upon contact between thick and thin filaments, ATP is hydrolyzed and sliding leads to contraction.

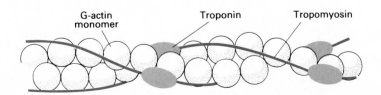

FIGURE 11-16
Actin filaments in vertebrate striated muscle are composed of two helically wound F-actin polymers, each made up of globular G-actin monomers. The regulatory proteins troponin and tropomyosin are precisely positioned along the actin filament.

When Ca^{2+} levels decrease as ions return to storage in the reticulum lumen, tropomyosin can shift back to its original hindering position because unloaded troponin assumes its original noninterfering conformation. Troponin and tropomyosin are bound together in a coordinated complex on the actin filament, so the two proteins act coordinately in regulating muscle contraction in response to Ca^{2+} levels in the sarcoplasm.

Vertebrates and all invertebrate animals except molluscs have an actin-linked regulatory system involving troponin and tropomyosin. The only system in molluscs (but a second system in all other invertebrates) is a control that involves myosin, and neither troponin nor tropomyosin is required. In fact, troponin is absent from mollusc muscle altogether and its tropomyosin has no regulatory role in muscle contraction. No vertebrate is known to possess any other system than the actin-linked system that we have discussed in this section.

In molluscs (clams, scallops, and others) and in other invertebrates, Ca^{2+} triggers muscle contraction via direct interaction with myosin filaments. The Ca^{2+}-stimulated myosin then interacts with actin filaments and contraction occurs. The distinction between vertebrate and molluscan filaments is apparent from their Ca^{2+}-binding properties. Vertebrate actin filaments will bind Ca^{2+}, whereas molluscan actin filaments will not bind Ca^{2+}; conversely, vertebrate myosin filaments will not bind Ca^{2+}, but molluscan myosin will. Molluscan myosin includes a light-chain component that itself does not bind Ca^{2+} but that does regulate Ca^{2+} binding by myosin filaments.

The actin-linked and myosin-linked control systems of muscle contraction share a number of features, such as their dependence on appropriate Ca^{2+} levels to stimulate myosin ATPase activity. The two control systems differ mainly in whether troponin is present and in whether the calcium effect is regulated at the actin filaments or at the myosin filaments in myofibrils.

Now that we have examined the detailed features of muscle contraction, we can proceed to other systems of cellular movement and see what insights we can gain from the model system of striated muscle. Muscle contraction depends entirely on filaments; microtubules are not involved in the process. We will next discuss systems at the other extreme, in which only microtubules appear to underlie movement. Afterward we can deal with movements that require both filaments and microtubules.

Ciliary Movement

Cilia and **flagella** are small hairlike surface structures that extend from many kinds of cells in all the kingdoms of eukaryotic organisms. They are noticeably absent only from seed-bearing plants of the highest evolutionary rankings: the higher gymnosperms (such as conifers) and all the flowering plants. We are especially familiar with the coordinated ciliary beating that propels paramecia through a fluid and with the whiplike undulations of flagella that allow sperm to swim and serve as

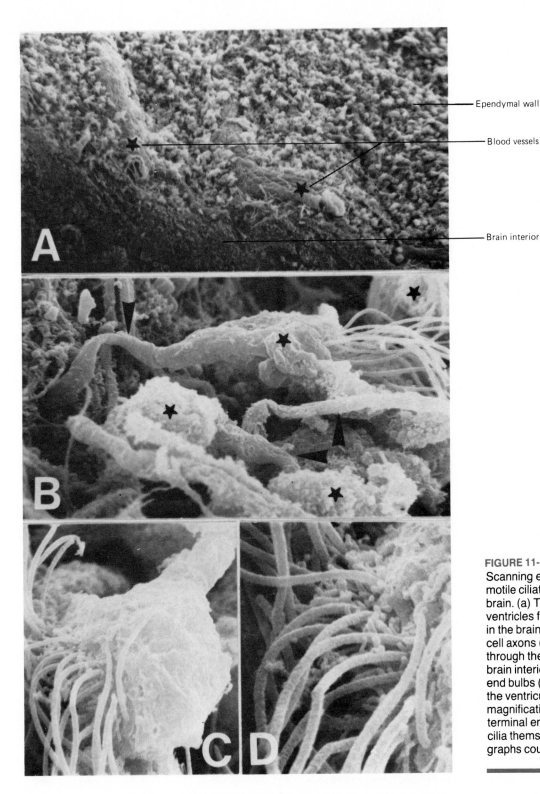

Ependymal wall

Blood vessels

Brain interior

FIGURE 11-17
Scanning electron micrographs of non-motile ciliated neural elements in shark brain. (a) The ependymal wall covers ventricles filled with cerebrospinal fluid in the brain interior. ×150. (b) Nerve cell axons (at arrowheads) emerge through the ependymal wall from the brain interior and the ciliated terminal end bulbs (starred) of these cells lie on the ventricular surface. ×3600. Higher magnification views of (c) a ciliated terminal end bulb, ×5000, and of (d) cilia themselves. ×10,000. (Photographs courtesy of M. F. MacDonnell.)

motility organs for a variety of other cell types (Fig. 11.17). In addition to their function in moving cells through fluids, cilia may sweep materials past the cell surface even in nonmotile cells. Paramecium sweeps food particles toward its gullet by ciliary action, in the same way that ciliary movements help to sweep mucus and various particles across the epithelial cells lining the respiratory tract or gently nudge the ovum along in its slow journey through the fallopian tube, or oviduct. Ciliary and flagellar movements are based on a microtubular system of protein fibers subsidized by ATP, which functions in many ways like the contractile system of striated muscle filaments.

11.9
Ciliary Ultrastructure and Chemistry

The distinction between cilia and flagella is somewhat arbitrary in that both types of motility appendages have identical ultrastructure and composition. Flagella are whiplike structures that measure over 150 μm in some cases; cilia are generally shorter and measure 5 μm to 10 μm on the average. Cilia are found in relatively large numbers on the cell surface; flagella are usually few in number, but they may occur in thousands in certain protozoa, some plant sperm, and a few other cell types. Each cilium or flagellum is produced as an outgrowth of an underlying *centriole* positioned just under the cell surface. This was first shown in 1960 by Ian Gibbons and A. V. Grimstone in a careful and detailed ultrastructural study of flagellated protozoa that live in the gut of termites.

Gibbons and Grimstone traced the nine triplets of microtubules in the embedded centriole to a transition zone just under the cell surface and found that one microtubule from each triplet terminated in the transition zone but that the remaining two microtubules continued on into the shaft of the flagellum as nine doublets (Fig. 11.18). At the same transition zone in which the microtubule triplets emerged as doublets, a new pair of single microtubules appeared in the center of the flagellar shaft. The nine encircling microtubule doublets and the central pair of singlet microtubules make up the so-called 9 + 2 pattern of fiber organization that is typical of most eukaryotic cilia and flagella. Some variations in this pattern have been described, particularly in sperm tails of animal species. Male gametes of a parasitic protozoan species have a 3 + 0 pattern, which is the simplest motile flagellum yet described. The fibrous core of the cilium is referred to as the **axoneme**; it consists of the principal microtubule fibers and accessory proteins that are bound to microtubules. The fibrous axoneme is surrounded in intact cells by the cell membrane, which bulges outward and covers the ciliary shaft (Fig. 11.19).

FIGURE 11-18 ▶

Microtubular organization of centriole and flagellum. (a) Schematic drawings of cross-sectional views at 10 different sites along the length of a centriole (basal body) and flagellum. The patterns of microtubules observed in each of the four regions indicate that a central pair of singlet microtubules extends the length of the flagellum proper, to the very tip of the structure. The microtubule doublets of the flagellum proper continue into the transitional region and centriole, but each doublet is joined by a third microtubule in the centriole and produces nine sets of microtubule triplets there. (b) Electron micrograph of a cross section through three centrioles in the protozoan *Hypotrichomonas acosta*; each centriole has a "cartwheel" interior. ×49,400. (c) Electron micrograph of a cross section through two flagella of the protozoan *Pentatrichomonas*, showing the typical 9 + 2 microtubular pattern. ×56,000. (Photographs courtesy of C. F. T. Mattern and B. M. Honigberg.)

From electron microscopy and chemical analysis of isolated axonemes and their component proteins, the system of accessory structures
and of the doublet and singlet microtubules has been described and their
functions in ciliary movement have been proposed. The major protein of
all the microtubules is **tubulin**, which assembles as heterodimers into
long protofilaments that form the wall of the cylindrical structures (see
Fig. 11.1). Each singlet microtubule and the *A subfiber* of each doublet

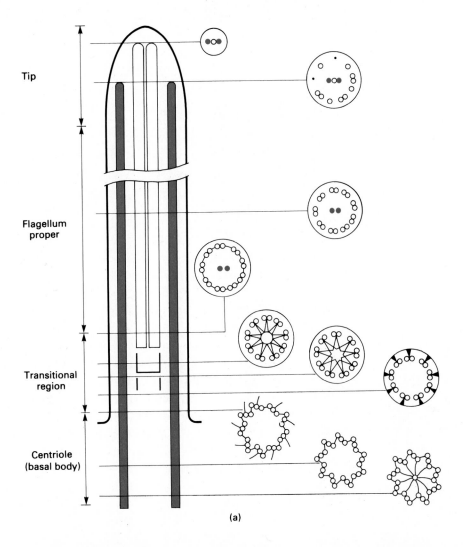

(a)

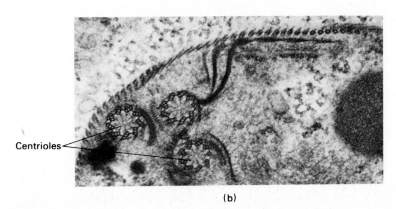

(b)

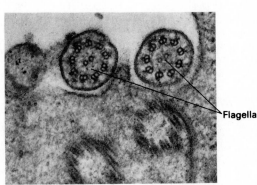

(c)

FIGURE 11-19
Electron micrograph of a centriole and part of the attached cilium in *Paramecium*. The cell membrane is continuous around the cell periphery and bulges out in covering the protruding fibrous axoneme of the cilium. (Photograph courtesy of R. V. Dippell.)

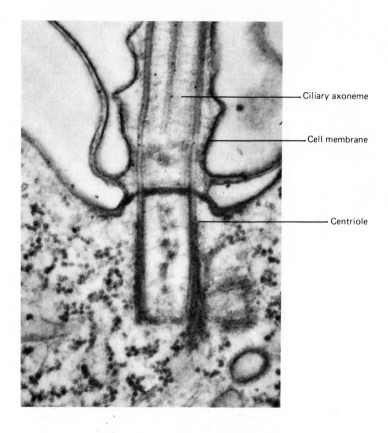

— Ciliary axoneme

— Cell membrane

— Centriole

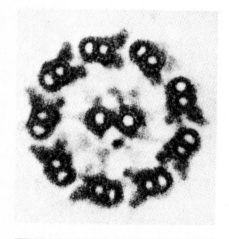

FIGURE 11-20
Electron micrograph of a cross section through a ciliary axoneme showing 9 microtubule doublets encircling 2 singlet microtubules. The A subfibers of each doublet and the 2 singlets are composed of 13 protofilaments in parallel register, producing a circular outline. The B subfiber of each doublet, however, has only 10 protofilaments and appears in outline as an indented circle nestled snugly against its companion A subfiber. ×165,000.

are composed of the usual 13 parallel protofilaments. The *B subfiber* of each doublet, however, is composed of 10 protofilaments that form an indented cylinder that fits snugly against the A subfiber (Fig. 11.20). Projecting all along the length of each A subfiber of the nine doublets are pairs of arms made of the protein **dynein**, which is a Mg^{2+}-dependent ATPase. The nature of the dynein arms was clearly shown in preparations of isolated microtubule doublets from which dynein was first removed and later restored. When dynein was extracted from tubule doublets, the arms disappeared; when dynein was added back to the stripped doublets, the arms reappeared. Isolated dynein or dynein attached to microtubule doublets possesses ATPase activity, which hydrolyzes ATP and thereby provides energy for the mechanical work of ciliary movement. The distribution of dynein arms along microtubule doublets closely resembles the distribution of pairs of myosin heads along myosin filaments in striated muscle (Fig. 11.21). This resemblance of organization and the ATPase activity of both kinds of paired projections have been important features in extending the model of filament sliding in muscle contraction to the model of microtubule sliding in ciliary movement, which we will discuss shortly.

Adjacent microtubule doublets are held together by flexible links made of the protein **nexin**. A **radial spoke** projects inward from its attachment to the A subfiber of each doublet and terminates in a *knob* close to the **inner sheath** around the central pair of singlet microtubules (Fig. 11.22). The inner sheath is composed of narrow protein subunits that project from the singlet microtubules and encircle them. All the links, spokes, arms, and subunits of the axoneme have their own periodicity of spacing along the length of the ciliary shaft, so that the

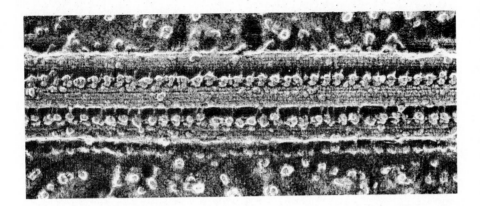

FIGURE 11-21
Freeze-fracture, deep-etch electron micrograph of part of a flagellar axoneme from *Chlamydomonas reinhardi*. Dynein arms line the A subfibers of microtubule doublets, much like the myosin heads aligned along the length of myosin thick filaments in striated muscle (see Fig. 11.5). ×145,000. (From Goodenough, U.W., and J.E. Heuser, 1982, *J. Cell Biol.* **95**:798, Fig. 12. Copyright by Rockefeller Univ. Press.)

fibrous structure is highly organized at every level of its construction and assembly. Each of these axonemal components makes a contribution to ciliary movement and to the regulation of this movement.

11.10
The Sliding Microtubule Mechanism of Ciliary Movement

Isolated cilia or flagella continue to move in a normal fashion after they have been detached from the cell by mechanical agitation or other means, but the cell itself stops moving if its cilia are stripped away. Amputated cilia continue to swim until their ATP supply is exhausted, and they may resume swimming if provided with a fresh supply of ATP. These and other observations allow us to draw at least four conclusions.

1. Cells are propelled in fluids by their cilia or flagella, which are thus the primary organs of motility in such media.

2. The ciliary axoneme serves as the contractile machinery for such locomotion in a fluid.

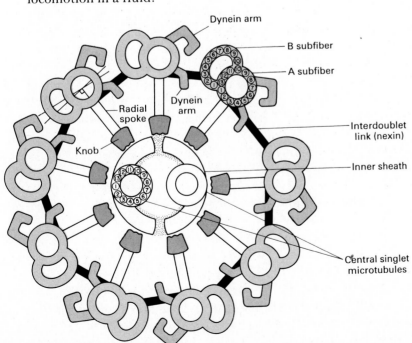

FIGURE 11-22
Diagram of a cross section through the 9 + 2 axoneme of a cilium or flagellum. The 9 doublets, which are connected by nexin links, encircle the inner sheath and the central pair of singlet microtubules. The A subfibers bear dynein arms and radial spokes, each of the latter terminating in a knob close to the inner sheath in the axoneme center. Each B subfiber is constructed from 10 protofilaments, instead of 13 protofilaments, and fits snugly against the A subfiber in each of the 9 sets of microtubule doublets.

Direction of fluids moved
over cell surface

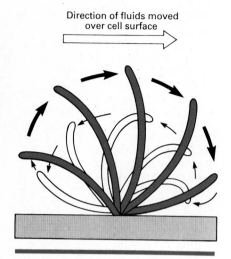

FIGURE 11-23
Ciliary bending involves a power stroke (color), by which fluid is driven over the cell surface, and a return stroke to the original position. Cycles of alternating power strokes and return strokes result in ciliary movements that propel cells through a fluid or sweep materials past stationary ciliated cells.

3. ATP hydrolysis provides the free energy for ciliary movement.

4. ATP must be provided to the cilia from within the cell rather than being made in the cilium itself, because external supplies of ATP are needed to maintain the energy supply for continued locomotion.

Several independent lines of evidence provide strong support for the **sliding microtubule mechanism** that produces the force for ciliary bending in cycles consisting of a *power stroke* by which fluid is driven over the cell surface and a *return stroke* to the original position (Fig. 11.23). Studies by Peter Satir, Fred Warner, and others have provided ultrastructural evidence showing that microtubules do not expand or contract during ciliary bending but that they are displaced within the axoneme of bent cilia. Precise measurements of electron micrographs showing cuts through different regions of bent and relaxed cilia reveal that microtubule doublets on the inner (concave) side of a bend apparently slide toward the tip of the cilium. This seems to be the case because cross-sectional views of the axoneme near the tip of the cilium show that all nine doublets terminate at the same level in resting cilia but that doublets in bent cilia are no longer seen at the tip on the outer (convex) side of the bend and appear only on the inner (concave) side (Fig. 11.24). In other studies, isolated axonemes were partially digested with trypsin to disrupt nexin links and radial spokes—but preserving intact doublets and their dynein arms. When such structures were incubated with small amounts of ATP, the loosened doublets slid against each other and resulted in greatly lengthened axonemes in the preparations. Once freed from their normal constraints, the doublets could slide a considerable distance. In the intact cilium, however, nexin links and radial spokes restrict the extent of doublet sliding, and the sliding is converted to bending. Even more striking confirmation of doublet sliding has come from electron micrographs showing longitudinal views of bent cilia, in which the radial spokes serve as markers along the length of each doublet. In such photographs it is clear that the spokes are systematically displaced along the microtubule doublets, which can be interpreted most easily as an indication that the doublets slide against each other in motile cilia (Fig. 11.25).

Microtubule sliding depends on an energy supply of ATP and on the presence of dynein arms on the doublets. When extracted axonemes are provided with ATP, and dynein arms are present on the doublets, microtubule sliding will occur. If dynein arms are removed, even in the presence of ATP, sliding stops. When the arms are restored to the doublets, sliding once again resumes and continues as long as ATP is provided. Dynein is an ATPase, so it is reasonable to expect that the force required for sliding is provided by ATP hydrolysis. Dynein arms make and break contact with adjacent doublets, in response to bound ATP and its hydrolysis products of ADP and P_i, perhaps in a manner similar to myosin heads making and breaking contact with actin filaments (see Fig. 11.14). We can see in electron micrographs that dynein arms are tilted downward and do not quite touch their neighbor doublets in resting cilia but that the arms *do* make contact in bending cilia, where the arms form cross-bridges that are at right angles to the adjacent doublets (Fig. 11.26). Similar changes in the angle at which the

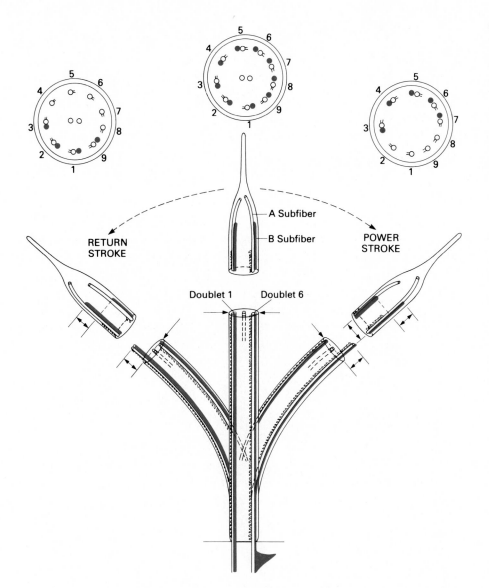

A Subfiber

B Subfiber

RETURN
STROKE

POWER
STROKE

Doublet 1   Doublet 6

FIGURE 11-24
Diagrammatic illustration of the sliding
microtubule theory of ciliary motion,
based on electron microscopic studies.
The cilium is pictured in the resting
position (center), bent in the direction of
the power stroke (right), and bent in the
direction of the return stroke (left). A
representative cross section of a cilium
in each of these positions is shown at
the top of the illustration. The behavior
of subfiber doublets 1 and 6 served as
the visible references in electron
micrographs to relate microtubule
sliding to cilium bending, because
these two recognizable doublets made
possible the identification of all the
other ciliary doublets. In the resting
position, the B subfiber (color) is visible
in all nine doublets of the cross section,
indicating that they all terminate at the
same level across the tip of the cilium.
In the bent positions, the B subfiber of
doublet 1 or of doublet 6 (as well as
others) is missing from the outer
(convex) side of the bend. Because
the microtubules are flexible, these
cross-sectional views indicate that the
microtubule doublet on the inner
(concave) side of a bend must slide
tipward. When microtubules slide past
each other, shear resistance in the
cilium converts sliding to bending.
(From Satir, P., 1968, *J. Cell Biol.*
39:77.)

dynein arms project can be elicited by providing and depleting ATP
supplies.

How is doublet sliding converted to ciliary bending? Studies of
nonmotile mutants, particularly in *Chlamydomonas* but in human beings
and other organisms as well, show that isolated axonemes with various
single defects will not move in the presence of ATP. Dyneinless mutants
are nonmotile because microtubule sliding does not occur, but mutants
that lack radial spokes or the central pair of singlet microtubules and its
surrounding inner sheath are immobile even though microtubule sliding
can take place. Although the evidence from genetic studies and from
biochemical and kinetic studies has not yet provided us with enough
information to understand the situation fully, it seems clear that cyclic
interactions between radial spokes and the inner sheath are involved in
the conversion of sliding to bending in beating cilia. Somehow, as sliding
occurs, the radial spokes attached to each A subfiber move along the
inner sheath and induce a local bend in the cilium. The wave of
movement from the base to the tip of a beating cilium reflects the
existence of some level of coordination to produce the coherent action of

FIGURE 11-25
Median longitudinal section through the basal end of a beating cilium from the freshwater mussel *Elliptio complanatus*, clearly showing eight of the many groups of radial spokes in the axoneme pictured in the electron micrograph. In a resting cilium, the similarly numbered spokes would be directly opposite each other. In the bent cilium, the sets of spokes on the inner (concave) side of the bend have been displaced tipward relative to their numbered opposites on the outer side of the bend. The amount of displacement during microtubule sliding is given by the measure Δl, which is 950 Å (95 nm) in this case. (From Warner, F. D., and P. Satir, 1974, *J. Cell Biol.* **63**:35–63, Fig. 15.)

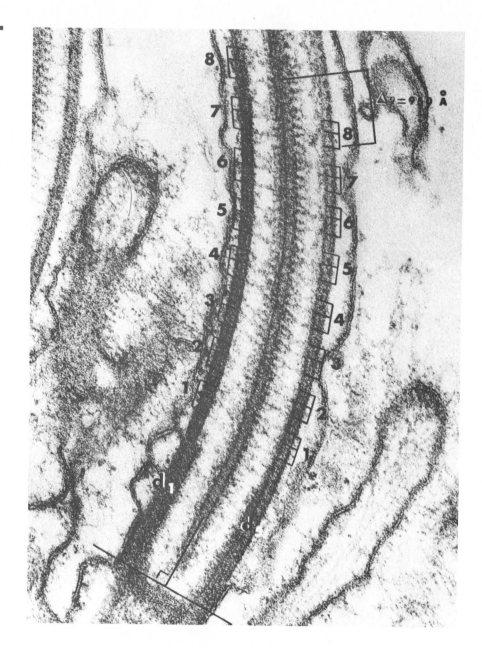

FIGURE 11-26
Freeze-fracture, deep-etch electron micrograph of a ciliary axoneme from the protozoan *Tetrahymena thermophila*. A thin stalk attached to the bulbous head of each dynein arm extends from the A subfiber of a microtubule doublet and makes contact with the B subfiber of an adjacent doublet. (From Goodenough, U. W., and J. E. Heuser, 1982, *J. Cell Biol.* **95**:798, Fig. 5. Copyright by Rockefeller Univ. Press.)

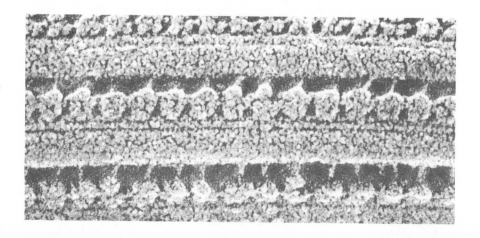

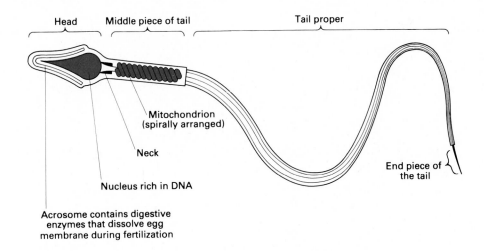

Head | **Middle piece of tail** | **Tail proper**

Mitochondrion (spirally arranged)

Neck

Nucleus rich in DNA

Acrosome contains digestive enzymes that dissolve egg membrane during fertilization

End piece of the tail

FIGURE 11-27
Movement of the flagellum (tail) of a mature human spermatozoan is powered by ATP produced in the mitochondrion wrapped around the middle piece of the tail, near the head of the sperm cell. Genetic information is contained in the nucleus of the sperm head, and the acrosome covering the head is believed to be a modified lysosome (see Fig. 8.5).

dynein arms in a progressive series of attachment–detachment cycles from one end of the cilium to the other. If all the dynein arms moved simultaneously, the axoneme would simply become tightly twisted all along its length. Microtubule doublets slide for relatively short distances because they are restrained by nexin links, but the activation of dynein arms in a progressive wave from base to tip of the axoneme must be regulated by other axonemal proteins. Proteins that sponsor the orderly cycles of dynein attachment and detachment thereby allow the orderly cycles of spoke–sheath interactions that create a progressive series of local bends. Bending is translated into a regular and effective pattern of power strokes and recovery strokes that characterize ciliary beating. Presumably, the same or a similar set of circumstances underlies the undulating movement of the longer flagellum, which also experiences a progressive wave of local bends that lead the entire organelle to whip back and forth.

From the foregoing discussion of movement in conventional 9 + 2 axonemes, we can understand why naturally occurring cilia with a 9 + 0 axoneme are nonmotile; 9 + 0 cilia lack the inner sheath (and singlet microtubules) with which radial spokes make contact, and bending does not occur even if doublets can slide. Unfortunately we know of various exceptions in which cells possess motile cilia with 9 + 0, 6 + 0, 3 + 0, and other atypical patterns. It is true that these atypical cilia move very slowly compared with 9 + 2 organelles, but they can bend and thereby propel the cell in a fluid. Many of these atypical motility structures exist as the sperm tails in insects and in male gametes of protozoan species. It remains to be seen whether these exceptions can be accommodated by the sliding microtubule mechanism or by some other mechanism still unstated.

The most probable source of ATP for ciliary movement is the mitochondrion, which is usually located very close to the subtending ciliary centrioles. ATP could easily be transferred from mitochondria to neighboring motility organelles, much as mitochondrial ATP is distributed anywhere else throughout the cell. In the case of the sperm cell in mammals and other species, a modified mitochondrion is wrapped around the middle piece of the tail, just next to the head of the sperm cell (Fig. 11.27). Sperm stop swimming when their ATP supply is exhausted or if ATP synthesis is poisoned by inhibitors of glycolysis and respiration.

FIGURE 11-28
Electron micrograph of guinea pig sperm, shown in cross section through the middle piece of the tail. Nine dense accessory fibers surround the typical 9 + 2 microtubules of this flagellum. ×55,700. (Photograph courtesy of D. W. Fawcett.)

11.11
Modified Cilia and Flagella

We have mentioned that sperm tails in a few species display some pattern other than the typical 9 + 2 axoneme. Another kind of modification in animal sperm, particularly in mammals but also found in a variety of species, is a set of nine **accessory fibers** that lie outside and around the circle of microtubule doublets (Fig. 11.28). These long fibers may be dense, massive structures. Little is known about the origin or function of accessory fibers, but they are usually found in species characterized by internal fertilization. On the basis of this correlation, it is possible that accessory fibers may aid sperm movement in the viscous environment of the female reproductive tract. Accessory fibers do

FIGURE 11-29
Diagram of part of a mammalian retinal rod cell showing the pair of centrioles associated with the modified cilium connecting the outer and inner segments of the cell. The outer segment is filled with rod sacs, which are transversely folded discs formed from folded ciliary membrane. As shown in cross section a, the centriole wall is made up of nine sets of subfiber triplets. Cross section b shows the ciliary axoneme to lack the pair of central singlet microtubules but to have the expected nine subfiber doublets.

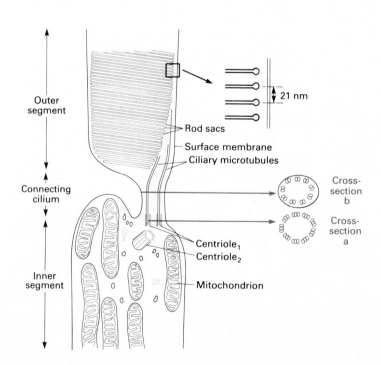

contain an ATPase and at least one contractile protein. They may thereby provide an additional system that helps sperm to overcome viscous drag as they move toward the ovum in the female.

Specialized cells that respond to environmental stimuli such as light, sound, and odor are called **sensory receptors**. A modified cilium, subtended by a centriole, is found in many but not all of these cell types (Fig. 11.29). The central pair of singlet microtubules is usually missing or is extremely short in the ciliary shaft. Both rod and cone types of visual receptor cells have a ciliary structure that connects the outer and inner segments of the cell. A ring of nine doublets encircles a hollow center where the singlet tubule pair would otherwise be located. In vertebrate visual receptors there may be up to 1000 membrane-limited disks arranged transversely in the outer segment. The disks are apparently formed from extensively folded ciliary membrane, which is derived from the cell plasma membrane just as in any cilium. The folded membrane system in visual receptors provides increased surface area for the conversion of light into electrical impulses. This represents an evolutionary advance in vertebrate eye organization.

11.12
Bacterial Flagella

The bacterial version of a flagellum is very different from the 9 + 2 eukaryotic organelle. In bacteria each flagellum is made up of 2 to 5 individual filaments that are only 4 nm to 5 nm wide but up to several μm long. The width of the flagellum (about 20 nm) depends entirely on the bundle of fibrils. Each filament in a flagellum is made up of a single kind of protein called **flagellin**. Globular monomers of flagellin aggregate end to end to form a filament, like beads on a string. No membrane encloses the flagellum, except in spirochetes, which have an unusual sheathing as well as very different internal components.

The flagellum is attached by a hook to a complex structure embedded in the bacterial cell membranes. The embedded structure consists of (1) a pair of protein discs, the innermost being rotary and the outermost being stationary, in the plasma membrane, and (2) a thick disc embedded in the outer bacterial membrane, with a rotating rod inserted through all the discs and into the hook to which the flagellum is attached (Fig. 11.30). As the innermost disc rotates, using energy obtained from the proton gradient across the plasma membrane, the connecting rod is caused to rotate and thereby to make the entire flagellum rotate. The thick disc in the outer membrane seals the opening through which the connecting rod passes to engage with the flagellar hook. The rotary disc may move in both clockwise and counterclockwise directions, and its direction of rotation switches very often every minute. When the flagella are rotated clockwise, they all move as far apart from one another as possible and lead to a disoriented bouncing movement. As the disc switches to counterclockwise rotation, all the flagella group together in a bundle and propel the cell uniformly in the same direction. When bacteria swim in a fluid, therefore, they switch every few seconds from moving in a straight line to chaotic tumbling in different directions and then again to movement in one direction.

FIGURE 11-30
Organization of the rotary apparatus associated with bacterial flagella. (a) Electron micrograph of a negatively stained preparation of lysed cells of the bacterium *Rhodospirillum molischianum*, showing a long flagellum attached by a thicker hook to the embedded rotary apparatus (bracketed). ×160,800. (b) Diagram of the flagellar rotary apparatus and its organization in relation to the cell membranes. A rotating connecting rod is inserted through all the discs and into the hook to which the flagellum is attached. As the innermost disc (dark color) rotates, the connecting rod is caused to rotate and thereby to lead to rotation of the flagellum. (Photograph courtesy of G. Cohen-Bazire, from Cohen-Bazire, G., and J. London, 1967, *J. Bacteriol.* **94**: 458–465, Fig. 3.)

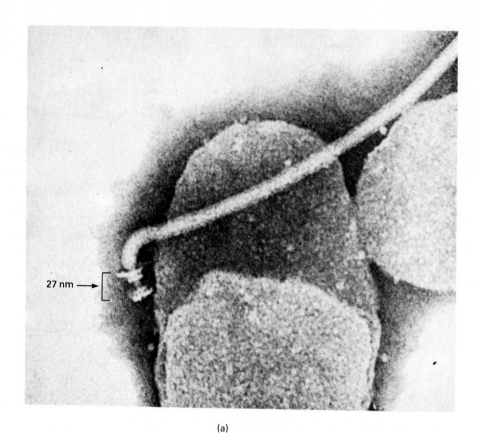

(a)

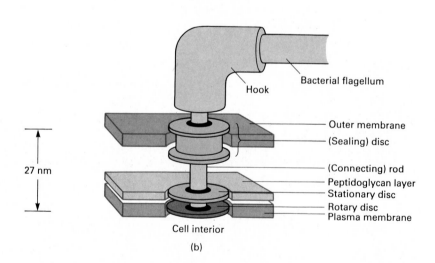

(b)

Purified flagellin can be obtained from flagella, which break off readily when cells are mechanically agitated. As the pH of the medium is varied, globular monomers of flagellin protein aggregate and disaggregate in what appears to be spontaneous assembly and disassembly, respectively. Bacterial filament monomers therefore resemble monomers of eukaryotic filaments and microtubules in their ability to form long-chain polymers under appropriate conditions. Unlike myosin filaments and doublet microtubules, but like actin filaments, bacterial flagellar fibers have no ATPase activity. The energy for flagellar movement in bacteria comes from the protonmotive force of the transmembrane gradient, produced by active proton pumping systems embedded in the plasma membrane.

Anaphase Movement of Chromosomes

Although we will discuss chromosomes and related structures in nuclear division processes in later chapters, it should be instructive to see how protein fibers underlie chromosome movement to the poles during anaphase of mitosis and meiosis. In both of these division processes, a **spindle** composed of microtubules called **spindle fibers** assembles early in the division, guides chromosome alignment and distribution to the poles, and disassembles at the conclusion of the nuclear division sequence. In contrast to the relatively permanent myofibrils of muscle and microtubules of cilia, which are involved in repetitive movements, the spindle is a transient structure. Its labile nature makes it easier for us to study the kinetics of fiber assembly and disassembly, the effects of drugs on these processes, and the specific structures that serve as organizing sites for fiber formation. These and other data can then serve as the basis for determining the mechanism by which directed chromosome movement occurs in dividing cells.

11.13
Organization and Dynamics of the Spindle _____

When mitosis begins, microtubules that radiate throughout the cytoplasm undergo disassembly and spindle microtubules begin to assemble (Fig. 11.31). The dynamic interchange between microtubule polymers

FIGURE 11-31
Electron micrograph of negatively stained microtubules from the cytoplasm just beneath the cell surface of newt (*Triturus viridescens*) erythrocytes. The heavy metal stain accumulates in the hollow center of the microtubule but does not bind to the tubule wall, which thus appears unstained. Spindle microtubules are identical in appearance and construction to the pictured cytoplasmic structures. ×56,000. (Photograph courtesy of J. G. Gall, from Gall, J. G., 1966, *J. Cell Biol.* **31**:639–643, Fig. 1.)

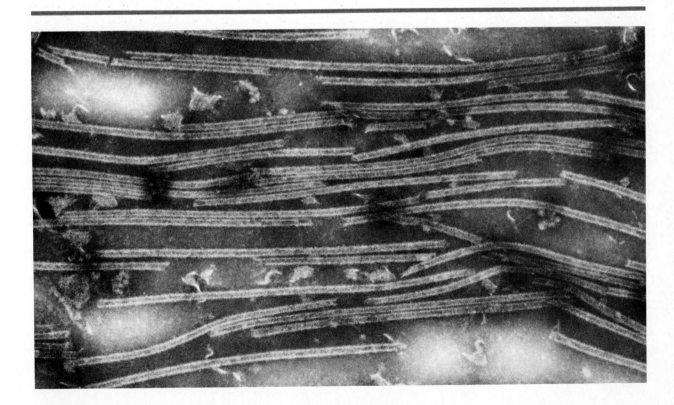

and the cytoplasmic pool of monomers is particularly sensitive to various drugs, which may prevent or encourage polymerization by binding to tubulin monomeric units. The alkaloid drug **colchicine**, extracted from the meadow saffron plant, has been known for many decades to prevent spindle formation or to cause it to disappear if it is already present in the cell. The drug, or its close relative *colcemid*, binds to tubulin dimers and prevents their polymerization, or causes existing fibers to depolymerize. When the drug is removed, the spindle is reconstituted in mitotic cells or is formed normally when cells begin mitosis. The drugs *vinblastine* and *vincristine* also prevent microtubule polymerization by binding to tubulin and causing the formation of paracrystalline aggregates of the monomer units. In contrast to these drugs, which interfere with polymerization, the drug *taxol* binds to polymers and stabilizes them so that depolymerization does not take place. Any of these drugs, whether they cause microtubule polymers to become more labile or more stable, interfere with the orderly assembly of the spindle and thereby inhibit chromosome alignment at metaphase and chromosome movement at anaphase. These drugs clearly demonstrate that the spindle is essential for orderly and directed chromosome movements in mitosis.

Efficient polymerization of microtubules requires the hydrolysis of guanosine triphosphate (GTP) to its GDP and P_i products. Each tubulin heterodimer has one bound GTP that is not involved in the polymerization reaction and whose function is unknown and one molecule of bound GTP that is hydrolyzed to GDP on the heterodimer. The kinetics of polymerization from heterodimers reveal the occurrence of an initial lag phase, a phase of rapid polymerization, and a final phase in which no further *net* change is detected in viscosity of the preparation; polymerization is monitored by viscosity measurements during the spontaneous

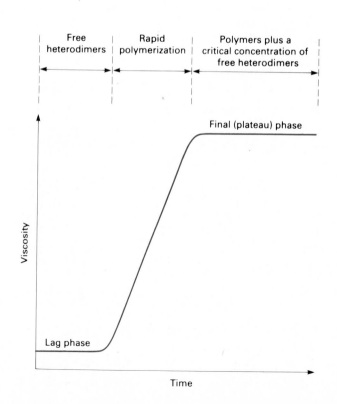

FIGURE 11-32
Kinetics of polymerization of microtubules from free heterodimers of tubulin, as determined by viscosity measurements. The initial lag phase is followed by a phase of rapid polymerization as heterodimers bind together to form microtubule structures. Polymerization reaches a plateau phase in which assembly and disassembly of free heterodimers occur at the same rate, as long as the free heterodimers occur in critical concentration in the monomer–polymer mixture.

assembly (or disassembly) process (Fig. 11.32). The initial lag phase probably reflects the binding together of the first heterodimers in a conformation that allows the rapid subsequent addition of more heterodimers; the initial binding step is referred to as *nucleation*. The final plateau phase of polymerization is due to the drop in tubulin heterodimer concentration to a level at which dimers are added to and released from the polymers at the same rate; this is the *critical concentration* of free subunits in a monomer–polymer suspension, below which polymerization will not proceed. Centrioles act as nucleation centers for microtubules in the spindle, cilia and flagella, peripheral cytoplasm, and elsewhere in the cell. Another nucleation center is found in the centrosome adjacent to the nucleus. We will discuss these centers shortly.

Microtubules have a *structural polarity*, which is essential for the production of organized, directional movement, and they resemble actin filaments and myosin filaments in this respect. When isolated dynein arms are added to a preparation of microtubules, all the arms point in the same direction on any one microtubule. These armed microtubules were shown to be functional because they could undergo cross-bridging interactions and bind to each other through their dynein arms. The oriented displays of decorated microtubules, like those of decorated actin filaments, provide clear evidence of structural polarity in assembled structures.

Microtubules bind and release heterodimers from both ends, but at very different rates at each end. If short nucleation segments of ciliary axoneme or of free microtubule fragments are incubated with tubulin heterodimers, one end elongates three times faster than the opposite end. The faster-growing end is referred to as the *(+) end* and the slower-growing one as the *(−) end* of the microtubule (Fig. 11.33). Lawrence Bergen and Gary Borisy further showed that the (+) end was located farthest away from the nucleation center, such as the ciliary centriole or centrosome, and that this (+) end was the place where new tubulin molecules were added to a growing cilium or spindle fiber. Similar studies with actin filaments, which also have a (+) and a (−) end, showed that the (+) end was embedded in the Z disc in striated muscle. It may very well be that the control over the direction and rate of growth of microtubules (and actin filaments) is determined in the cell by the particular proteins that bind to one or both ends of a fiber. In this way, assembly and disassembly at each end not only can occur independently of each other but can also be subject to independent controls. These features may contribute to the relative stability of fibers as well as to their spatial organization in the cytoskeleton and in motile systems within the cell. In addition, it is clear that the structural polarity of cytoskeletal protein fibers is a major determinant of the direction of movement of individual fibers and of aggregates of these structures.

11.14
Mechanism of Anaphase Movements

Spindle microtubules clearly are required for directed movement of chromosomes to the poles at anaphase of nuclear division. We mentioned earlier that disruption of microtubules by colchicine and other

FIGURE 11-33
Microtubule polarity. (a) Diagram to illustrate that heterodimers are bound and released at a faster rate at the (+) end of a free microtubule than at the (−) end of the structure. In the growing cilium or spindle fiber, tubulin heterodimers are added only to the (+) end of the microtubule, and this (+) end is located farthest away from the nucleation center, which is the centriole in the cilium and the centrosome in the spindle. (b) Electron micrographs of isolated flagellar axonemes from the alga *Chlamydomonas reinhardtii* before incubation with brain tubulin and (c) after 5 minutes of incubation at 30°C. The differential growth of microtubules at the (+) and (−) ends of the axoneme are strikingly apparent. ×7,300. (Photographs courtesy of L. G. Bergen and G. G. Borisy.)

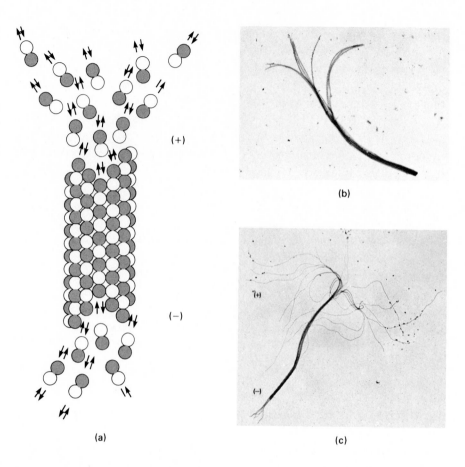

(a)

(b)

(c)

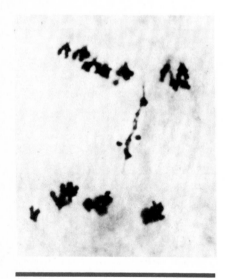

FIGURE 11-34
Photograph of a nucleus in the anaphase stage of division, after the two sets of chromosomes have moved to opposite poles of the cell. In the space between the two sets of chromosomes is a chromosome bridge and two dotlike acentric chromosome fragments on either side of the bridge. The chromosome bridge forms when the two centromeres of a dicentric chromosome move to opposite poles. Acentric chromosomes or fragments have no centromere and thus no means by which to move directionally to the poles. Such acentrics are usually not included in the daughter nuclei that are formed during the final stage of nuclear division. (Photograph courtesy of M. M. Rhoades.)

drugs abolished anaphase movement. We also know that an *acentric* chromosome or fragment (lacking the centromere, or spindle attachment point) does not move directionally to the poles along with normal chromosomes and may not ever reach the pole, even by random wanderings in an anaphase cell (Fig. 11.34).

Painstaking measurements of spindle fibers have shown that chromosomal fibers shorten but do not contract as chromosomes move slowly toward the poles. As chromosomes are *pulled* to the poles, the whole spindle figure often increases in length as the two halves of the spindle are *pushed* apart and polar spindle fibers become longer than they were in metaphase. These two concurrent events—shortening of chromosomal fibers and lengthening of polar fibers—must be explained, as well as the forces that pull chromosomes and push apart the two halves of the spindle figure during anaphase.

In 1967, Shinya Inoué proposed the **assembly–disassembly mechanism** in which the depolymerization of chromosomal microtubules led to shorter fibers and also generated the force that pulled chromosomes to the poles (Fig. 11.35). Chromosomes move to the poles rather slowly, at an average of 1 μm to 2 μm per minute, and very little force is calculated to be needed to move a chromosome the short distance it travels. When metaphase cells are treated under controlled conditions with depolymerizing agents, the chromosomal microtubules gradually disassemble at their polar ends and the chromosomes slowly move to the poles as their fibers shorten. Disassembly can thus generate sufficient force for chromosome movement, as Inoué had postulated. The addition

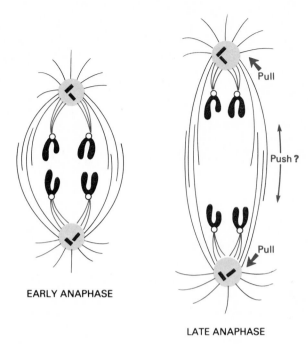

EARLY ANAPHASE

LATE ANAPHASE

FIGURE 11-35
According to the assembly–disassembly mechanism of anaphase movements proposed by S. Inoué, chromosomal spindle fibers (color) shorten because of microtubule depolymerization, and this disassembly process generates the force required to pull chromosomes to the poles of the spindle. Addition of tubulin monomers to the polar spindle fibers (black) would explain their lengthening during anaphase, but it is uncertain whether the process generates enough force to push apart the two halves of the spindle.

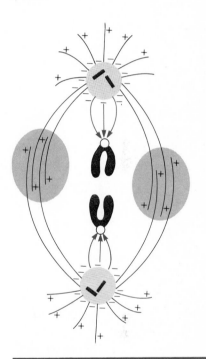

FIGURE 11-36
According to the sliding microtubule mechanism of anaphase movements proposed by J. R. McIntosh, separation of the two halves of the spindle is subsidized by the force generated as polar microtubules (black) of opposite polarity slide against each other in the region where the half-spindles overlap (color screen). Interactions between chromosomal fibers (color) and polar fibers are unlikely, however, because the two kinds of fibers have the same polarity in each half-spindle. The nucleation center for all the spindle microtubules (chromosomal, polar, and astral ray) is the centrosome (gray screen) at each pole, and microtubule assembly and disassembly take place at the (+) end, which is farthest from the nucleation center.

of tubulin monomers to polar microtubules would explain their lengthening, and perhaps enough force is generated to push apart the two halves of the spindle. (The experimental data are not so compelling in this regard as they are in support of disassembly causing chromosome movement.)

The **sliding microtubule mechanism** postulated in 1969 by J. Richard McIntosh was developed on the basis of the models of ciliary movement and muscle contraction. McIntosh proposed that chromosomal and polar microtubules had opposite structural and growth polarities in each half-spindle and that sliding of the two kinds of microtubules against each other generated the force by which chromosomes moved to the poles and the two halves of the spindle were pushed apart. Studies of microtubule growth, however, later showed that the chromosomal and polar fibers in each half-spindle had the same polarity because both had their slower-growing (−) ends closest to the poles. The faster-growing (+) end of the chromosomal microtubule was anchored in the kinetochore, and the (+) ends of the polar microtubules were near their region of overlap at the spindle center. Though inappropriate for chromosome movement, the sliding of polar microtubules of opposite polarity in each half of the spindle could take place and might very well cause the two halves to move apart (Fig. 11.36).

Some evidence exists for the presence of a dyneinlike protein in the mitotic spindle and for its role in causing the spindle halves to move apart during anaphase, perhaps through microtubule sliding. The protein can be extracted from spindles, but no projecting arms have been observed in electron micrographs of mitotic spindle fibers. When agents that immobilize dynein are added to isolated mitotic spindles, the spindle halves stop moving apart. These observations indicate that dynein or a dyneinlike protein serves as the force-generating crossbridge responsible for microtubule sliding that leads to separation of the two poles. The evidence that dynein or a similar protein is involved in chromosome movement to the poles is somewhat ambiguous, however. Dynein inhibitors do not necessarily stop chromosome movement to the poles in the same cells that experience inhibition of the separation of the two halves of the spindle figure. The two sets of movements may therefore be due to different force-generating mechanisms—or perhaps to some single mechanism that we have not yet discovered.

Other proposals have been made in addition to the assembly–disassembly and sliding microtubule mechanisms, and some of these proposals involve protein fibers other than microtubules as the possible force-generating systems that sponsor anaphase movements. The discovery of actin and myosin in the mitotic spindle led to suggestions that actin–myosin interactions generated the motive force and that spindle fibers were only passively involved in movement. When the suggestions were tested experimentally *in vivo* and *in vitro* by the use of inhibitory conditions for actomyosin-generated forces, however, chromosome movements and spindle separation remained unaffected.

At the present time we have good evidence for microtubule shortening and lengthening in relation to their known polarities in the anaphase cell. We do not yet have adequate evidence to decide for or against the various proposed force-generating systems involving microtubules directly or indirectly. Both the Inoué and McIntosh proposals remain viable at least to some degree, but neither proposal alone satisfies all the requirements for anaphase movements. The discovery of a dyneinlike MAP and its role in anaphase separation of the two halves of the spindle opens another avenue of investigation: the existence of other MAPs and, if they do exist, their role in spindle dynamics. A great deal remains to be done, but we have excellent model systems that will continue to provide guidelines for experimental studies just as they have in the past.

11.15
Microtubule Organizing Centers

When microtubules are depolymerized experimentally, they begin to reassemble from particular sites called **microtubule organizing centers** (MTOCs). Two centers have been identified: the *centrosome*, which is adjacent to the nucleus, and the *centriole* (*basal body*) at the base of cilia and flagella. In cells allowed to undergo regrowth of microtubules, the origin and direction of microtubule polymerization can be monitored by labeling the cells with fluorescent anti-tubulin antibodies after the cells have been fixed. The newly forming fibers first appear near the centrosome or basal body and gradually grow outward away from these centers. If the microtubules are decorated to determine their polarity, they are all found to have their (+) ends pointing away from the organizing centers.

Centrioles are barely visible as granules in the light microscope, but their microtubular construction is plainly evident in electron micrographs. Each **centriole**, whether serving as a basal body for a cilium or situated in the centrosome near the nucleus, is a cylindrical structure whose shape is defined by the display of nine sets of triplet microtubules that make up the wall or boundary of a centriole (Fig. 11.37). New

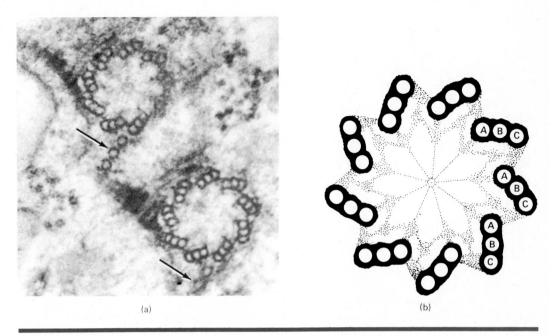

(a)

(b)

FIGURE 11-37
Microtubular organization of the
centriole. (a) Electron micrograph of a
cross section through two centrioles in
Paramecium. Nine sets of subfiber
triplets make up the centriole wall, and
a faint "cartwheel" is visible in the
centriole interior. Microtubules in
the adjacent cytoplasm (at arrows)
and in the centrioles are identical in
appearance. ×105,000. (b) Diagram
of centriole structure as seen in electron micrograph cross sections.
(Photograph courtesy of R. V. Dippell.)

centrioles usually form in the presence of pre-existing centrioles, but
they may arise *de novo* in the absence of any template structure. *De novo*
centriole formation has been documented in many kinds of cells and in
various sets of conditions. For example, the protozoan *Naegleria* may
exist either in an ameboid form or as a free-swimming flagellated cell.
Centrioles are absent in the ameboid form but they may appear within
30 minutes during the transition to the flagellated form. In ferns, ancient
gymnosperms such as cycads, and other species, centrioles are absent
from every cell, but they form *de novo* shortly before sperm production
begins and only in those cells that will give rise to sperm. In the cycad
Zamia, a cluster of up to 25,000 immature centrioles (*procentrioles*) arises
de novo in sperm-producing cells. During sperm production and differentiation, each of the 25,000 procentrioles matures to become a basal
body from which a flagellum will develop. Because new centrioles may
be formed in the absence of existing centrioles, their formation is
unlikely to involve a replication process and they are unlikely to carry
any of their own genetic information. DNA is absent from these
structures, but several studies have identified RNA in these organelles.
We have no idea what function, if any, this RNA specifies.

Centriole formation appears to follow much the same assembly
sequence in the several species that have been studied by electron
microscopy, whether or not a mature centriole is present. A ring of nine
singlet microtubules appears first, and these become the inner A
subfibers of the eventual triplets (Fig. 11.38). Next, the B subfibers
assemble onto the A singlets as "horseshoe"-shaped components made
only of 10 protofilaments instead of the 13 present in a completely
circular microtubule, such as the A subfibers. The assembly of
horseshoe-shaped C subfibers onto the B set then completes the
cross-sectional display of nine triplet microtubules. Once this procen-
triole has formed, it grows in length but usually maintains its original

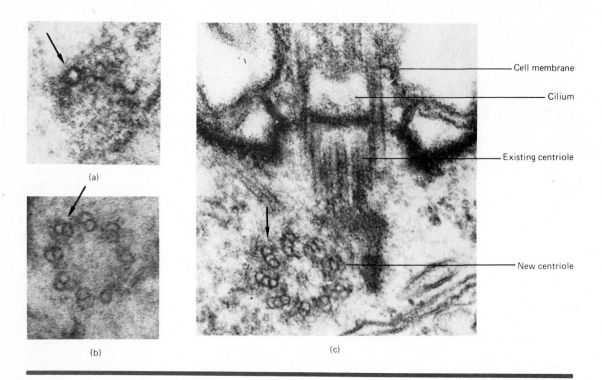

Cell membrane

Cilium

Existing centriole

New centriole

(a)

(b)

(c)

FIGURE 11-38
Electron micrographs of stages in centriole formation in *Paramecium*, as seen in cross section. (a) Single A-subfiber microtubules appear first and (b) become doublet when the B subfiber assembles onto the A subfiber. (c) The nine subfiber triplets are completed when the C subfiber assembles onto the doublet intermediates. The A subfiber is the innermost member of a triplet and the only member to be composed of a full complement of 13 protofilaments (note its fully circular outline). The new centriole (in cross section) forms near the proximal end of an existing centriole (longitudinal view) and at right angles to it. (a) ×104,000; (b) ×120,000; (c) ×120,000. (Photographs courtesy of R. V. Dippell.)

diameter during maturation. A mature centriole is about 160 nm to 230 nm in diameter but may vary in length from 160 nm to 5600 nm.

Cilia and flagella are formed only from centrioles, or basal bodies, situated just under the cell surface; they are never formed in the absence of basal bodies. If cilia are broken off, new cilia form as an outgrowth of the underlying basal body. If the basal body is destroyed or removed, the cilium degenerates and is not replaced unless another basal body replaces the one that was lost. In *Chlamydomonas*, the two centrioles migrate away from the cell periphery when the cell divides. Each flagellum degenerates, but at the end of mitosis new centrioles become established under the cell apex, and these proceed to sponsor new flagella.

The **centrosome** in animals and many lower organisms, but not in flowering plants or advanced gymnosperms (pines and others), is a relatively transparent region surrounded by short microtubules of the *aster* and harboring a pair of centrioles in its middle (Fig. 11.39). The *astral mitotic spindle* is indeed spindle-shaped, or lens-shaped, in contrast to an *anastral spindle*, which has a more cylindrical shape. Anastral spindles have no asters or centrioles and are typical of flowering plants and advanced gymnosperms. In well-developed astral spindles, astral microtubules and both chromosomal and polar microtubules emanate from the centrosome at each pole of the dividing cell. Although lacking astral microtubules and centrioles, anastral spindles also produce microtubules from the polar regions, and these consist of polar spindle fibers and chromosomal spindle fibers. Because microtubules arise from the polar regions whether or not asters or centrioles are present, neither of these components can serve as organizing centers for spindle fibers. Close inspection of well-developed asters and of the poles at each end of

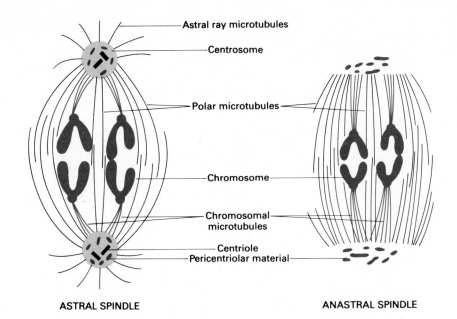

Astral ray microtubules

Centrosome

Polar microtubules

Chromosome

Chromosomal
microtubules

Centriole
Pericentriolar material

ASTRAL SPINDLE

ANASTRAL SPINDLE

FIGURE 11-39
The astral mitotic spindle has a pronounced bulging midline and tapered ends, whereas the anastral spindle is more cylindrical in shape. At each pole of the astral spindle is a centrosome surrounded by a radiating display of short microtubules that comprise the aster. Within the centrosome region at each pole is a pair of centrioles surrounded by densely staining pericentriolar material. Similar densely staining material occurs at the poles of the anastral spindle, but centrosome, centrioles, and astral ray microtubules are absent. The pericentriolar material at each pole of both types of spindles is believed to be a microtubule organizing center for all the kinds of microtubules present.

anastral spindles reveals that a densely staining **pericentriolar material** is present and that both polar and chromosomal spindle fibers originate in this material. The pericentriolar material must represent the actual microtubule organizing center at each pole of both astral and anastral spindles.

It seems puzzling at first that centrioles are MTOCs for ciliary microtubules but not for spindle microtubules. It is even more puzzling in view of the fact that the very same centrioles that serve as basal bodies and give rise to cilia may migrate to the poles of a cell and there become part of the centrosome of the mitotic spindle, yet these centrioles behave as MTOCs in the former case but not in the latter. Although it does not serve as an explanation, it is easy to see how a centriole with nine subfiber triplets can serve as a nucleation site for a cilium with nine subfiber doublets that are essentially a continuation of the sets of A subfibers and B subfibers of the centriole. In the spindle, however, hundreds or thousands of microtubules grow from the polar nucleation sites and are distributed radially in the cell. The geometry of centriole-cilium organization seems appropriate for the intimate relationship between the two structures, but centriole and spindle have very different microtubular geometries. We are at a loss to explain the different behaviors of the centriole at the cell surface and at the poles of mitotic cells. In fact, we don't know what function the centriole performs when it is in the middle of a centrosome. The only clear centriolar function is as a microtubule organizing center for ciliogenesis.

Nonmuscle Contractile Systems

The systems we have discussed involve interactions between two kinds of filaments (muscle contraction) or microtubules only (ciliary movement and anaphase movements), and at least in muscle and cilia the protein fibers exist in highly ordered displays. Because of these features it has been easier to study these systems than others of a more diverse nature or in which the motility components are labile and less ordered. Nevertheless, activities such as cytoplasmic streaming, particle transport within the cell, cellular locomotion on solid substrata, and cell displacement during growth (among others) can be studied by the use of many of the methods proven successful in the experimental analysis of muscle and cilia. A few examples of cellular and intracellular activities involving contractile fibers or filament–microtubule interactions will be discussed next, in order to broaden our perspective on motility phenomena and to seek common features underlying the diverse ways in which motility is expressed.

11.16
Cytoplasmic Streaming

Particles in suspension are in continuous motion because they are randomly bombarded by water molecules. Such random movement is called *Brownian motion* in honor of Robert Brown, who described the phenomenon in 1820. In contrast to undirected Brownian motion, cellular components and particles usually move in directed, nonrandom pathways. These directed movements are associated with the activities of one or more kinds of protein fibers.

In cells with rigid cell walls, such as plants and algae, **cytoplasmic streaming** is often observed, and the flow may alternate from clockwise to counterclockwise circuits and back again to clockwise, at frequent intervals. When granules are swept along in the streaming cytoplasm, the movement of the particles themselves is referred to as *cyclosis*. Large cylindrical cells of freshwater algae such as *Nitella* and *Chara* provide excellent material to study streaming. The outer layer of protoplasm is more gel-like and is referred to as **ectoplasm**, and the inner portion of the protoplasm, called **endoplasm**, is of a more fluid sol-like consistency. In these algae, the chloroplasts are embedded in the relatively

FIGURE 11-40

The fresh water alga *Nitella* (a) is composed of large cylindrical cells with clusters of smaller cells at the boundaries between adjacent large cells in a branch. (b) A detail of the system shows the central vacuole of a large cylindrical cell, surrounded by an inner protoplasmic layer of fluid endoplasm and an outer protoplasmic layer of gel-like stationary ectoplasm. Chloroplasts are embedded in the ectoplasm, but various kinds of particles flow with the streaming endoplasm in episodes of cyclosis.

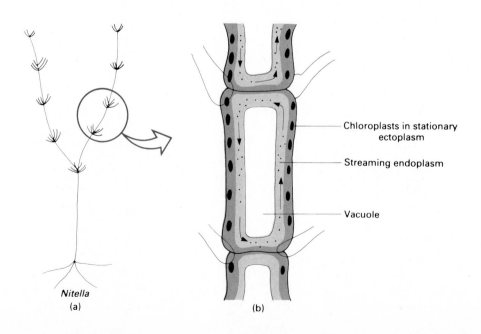

Chloroplasts in stationary ectoplasm

Streaming endoplasm

Vacuole

Nitella
(a)

(b)

stationary ectoplasm, whereas numerous granules flow with the endoplasmic stream in displays of cyclosis (Fig. 11.40).

Endoplasmic streaming apparently involves interactions between actin filaments and myosin filaments, and the motive force for streaming may be generated at the interface between the stationary ectoplasm and the moving endoplasm. Twisted bundles of 50 to 100 actin filaments at intervals along this interface are oriented parallel to the direction of streaming. Microtubules are found only in the ectoplasm, and because of their absence in the moving endoplasm they are believed to be unrelated to streaming events. Experimental support for the involvement of microfilaments but not microtubules in the streaming activity includes studies in which selective drugs were used. The drug **cytochalasin B**, an excretion product of various molds, specifically binds to one end of actin filaments and prevents the addition of G actin monomers to that end. In labile systems that involve continued assembly and disassembly of microfilaments, cytochalasin B causes disruption of existing fibers and prevents new ones from forming. Colchicine has no effect on microfilaments but it does cause disruption of labile microtubules. In a typical set of experiments in which these two drugs were used, Norman Wessells showed that cytochalasin B stopped cytoplasmic streaming in *Nitella* within one hour of treatment. Vigorous streaming resumed at the original rates when the drug was washed out of the cells. Colchicine, on the other hand, had no effect on streaming. These results with *Nitella* and other plant cells indicated that streaming required the participation of microfilaments but not of microtubules.

The interaction of actin filaments and myosin filaments as the contractile machinery for streaming has been suggested by different lines of experimental evidence. Myosin filaments that have been teased from *Nitella* endoplasm by microsurgery interact with actin to form actomyosin, just as in striated muscle. ATPase activity can be elicited in isolated preparations when these are supplied with appropriate levels of ATP and calcium ions, just as in muscle. Although such evidence is provocative, by itself it does not justify our concluding that endoplasmic streaming and muscle contraction both operate by the same contractile apparatus. The evidence is sufficient, however, to justify further experimental analysis based on the working hypothesis that a similar contractile system is involved in both phenomena.

11.17
Ameboid Movement

An ameba crawls along a solid surface by forming surface extensions, called *pseudopods*, in response to an internal flow of cytoplasm; such locomotion is referred to as **ameboid movement**. Similar types of movement based on cytoplasmic flow are characteristic of many unicellular organisms and of white blood cells within our own bodies. As the ameba extends a pseudopod, a forward flow of endoplasm into the pseudopod changes to a lateral flow near the tip of the extension and is there converted to stationary ectoplasm close to the cell surface. The conversion of endoplasm to ectoplasm at the tip of the pseudopod is matched by the reverse transformation of ectoplasm to endoplasm in the

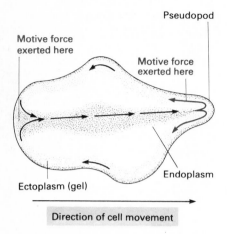

Pseudopod

Motive force
exerted here

Motive force
exerted here

Ectoplasm (gel)

Endoplasm

Direction of cell movement

FIGURE 11-41
Ameboid movement. As the cell
extends a pseudopod, a forward flow of
endoplasm (color) into the pseudopod
changes to a lateral flow near the tip
and is there converted to gel-like
ectoplasm. As ectoplasm is converted
to endoplasm in the rear of the ameba,
the endoplasm moves forward to
complete the pattern of cyclic flow. It is
uncertain whether a motive force is
exerted at the rear of the cell so that the
endoplasm is *pushed* forward or
whether the motive force is exerted at
the frontal zone of the cell so the
endoplasm is *pulled* forward. In either
case, the forward surge of endoplasm into a developing or extending
pseudopod accompanies cellular
movement along a solid surface.

rear of the ameba, and the endoplasm moves forward from the rear to complete the cyclic flow pattern. It is generally believed that the sol–gel changes of the cytoplasm are part of the mechanism involved in ameboid movement, particularly because the conversion of viscous ectoplasm to more fluid endoplasm by cold treatment or by application of high hydrostatic pressure to the ameba causes the cell to stop moving and to round up.

Although the available evidence supports the view that the more gel-like ectoplasm is somehow involved in generating a motive force, considerable disagreement exists about the nature of the force and the site at which it is produced. Two major theories have been proposed; each specifies a different end of the cell as the force-generating site, and each is supported by a large amount of data (Fig. 11.41). The earlier theory, first presented in the 1920s, proposed that the motive force was generated by the conversion of ectoplasm to endoplasm in the rear of the ameba and that, as the resulting hydraulic pressure was increased, the endoplasm was pushed forward toward the tip where the pressure was lower. The alternative theory, proposed by Robert Allen, states that the motive force is generated in a frontal zone near the tip of the advancing pseudopod as a result of contraction when the sol-to-gel conversion takes place. The frontal contraction exerts a force that pulls on the central column of endoplasm near the tip, and the pull exerted at its forward edge is sufficient to drag the remaining endoplasm forward and thereby to extend the pseudopod. The converted ectoplasm near the frontal zone then moves toward the rear of the ameba and, at the rear, is transformed again to the relaxed state to enter as endoplasm in the flowing central column.

In parallel with the system for muscle contraction, both actin filaments and myosin filaments have been identified in amebas and in similar pseudopodial organisms, such as slime molds. Cellular extracts show increased viscosity when added ATP is hydrolyzed to ADP and P_i, just like muscle actomyosin, and active contraction occurs when ATP and calcium or magnesium ions are added. The great difficulty we have in relating these observations to an actomyosin contractile mechanism that sponsors cytoplasmic flow is the lack of any orderly arrangement of the presumed contractile fibers—and the astonishing speed with which the labile structures assemble and disassemble in the living cell and during preparations for microscopical or biochemical study. Numerous actin microfilaments are present in the ectoplasm in particular, and occasional myosin filaments appear to be interspersed in this same peripheral ectoplasmic layer. Whether these fibers can undergo cyclic and orderly interactions is uncertain. We do know that at least the actin filaments are involved in cytoplasmic flow, because cytochalasin B interrupts the forward flow of endoplasm and, hence, pseudopod extension. The mechanism of ameboid movement thus remains a challenging problem.

11.18
Ruffled Membrane Movement of Cells in Culture

When cultured mammalian fibroblasts move along the surface of a dish, they inch along in an erratic fashion by alternately attaching and

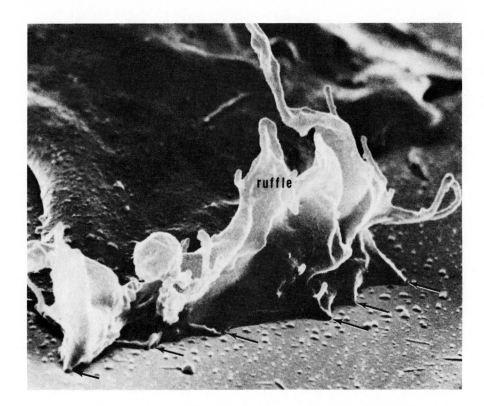

FIGURE 11-42
Scanning electron micrograph of a cultured mouse cell engaged in ruffled membrane movement on a solid surface. Ruffles are evident at the forward leading edge, as are a number of attachment points to the substratum (arrows). (Photograph courtesy of J. P. Revel.)

detaching the leading edge of the cell to the surface. As the leading edge advances and becomes attached, the trailing rear of the cell is ripped from its moorings and bounces forward to establish a new adhesion point on the dish. The entire moving cell has an elongated aspect due to the stretching and tension created by the forward advance of its leading edge. The edge itself has an undulating motion that produces a ruffled appearance in the advancing extension of the cell surface—hence the term **ruffled membrane movement** to describe the features of cultured-cell locomotion on a solid surface (Fig. 11.42). The flattened, fan-shaped surface protrusion at the leading edge is called a *lamellipodium*. As the rear of the cell adheres in a new position, a new lamellipodium can be formed and the cell can progress in the same or another direction.

When lamellipodia of different cultured fibroblasts make contact, movement stops almost immediately. The phenomenon of *contact inhibition of movement* was first described in 1954 by Michael Abercrombie, and it has since become an important diagnostic feature of normal versus transformed cells in culture. Normal cells stop moving when they make physical contact, and the cultured cells remain distributed as a single layer of confluent units. *Transformed cells*, which are considered cultured-cell equivalents of tumor cells in the organism, generally continue to move even after making physical contact with other cells, and the cells pile up on one another in disordered heaps (Fig. 11.43). The loss of contact inhibition represents the loss of one of the controls over orderly interactions between cells, which seemingly no longer respond to locomotor signals. Another distortion of normal cell–cell interactions in transformed cultures is the continued multiplication of cells to produce populations far larger than normal. Instead of ceasing mitotic activities

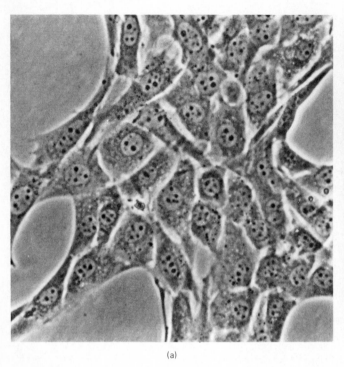

(a)

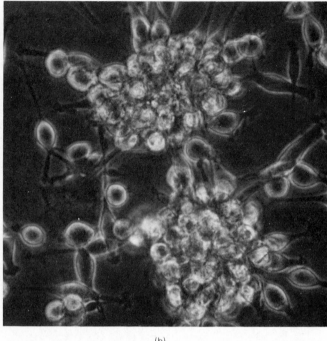

(b)

FIGURE 11-43
Mouse fibroblasts grown in cell culture.
(a) On a solid surface, normal cells stop
moving upon making physical contact
with other cells, and they remain
distributed as a single layer of confluent
(touching) cells. (b) Transformed cells
show no contact inhibition of movement
and they form heaps of disordered
cells, rather than confluent monolayers.

upon making contact, transformed cells continue mitosis because they no
longer respond to the control of *density-dependent* or *postconfluence inhibition of
mitosis*. By overriding the restraints on locomotion and mitosis, transformed cells and tumor cells migrate and multiply in uncontrolled fashion
in the culture dish and in the organism, respectively.

Cells in culture or in the developing embryo may migrate by means
of slender elongated processes called *filopodia*, by which contact is made
with the surface along which the cells move (Fig. 11.44). As filopodia
make and break contacts with a surface, the cell is pulled forward by the
contractile fibers within the slender extensions of the cell surface. In
both lamellipodia and filopodia, microfilaments and microtubules are
found in abundance, and each of these kinds of protein fibers makes a
contribution to movement. Although much of the experimental evidence
is somewhat ambiguous or even contradictory because of the failure to
standardize culture conditions (such as drug concentrations and time of
exposure to inhibitors), it seems that microtubules provide a cytoskeletal
framework or scaffolding by which the shape of a cell or its extensions is
maintained, whereas microfilaments constitute part of the contractile
machinery for locomotion. Two examples of experimental analysis will
illustrate these studies and the problems that plague them.

Norman Wessells showed that embryonic nerve cells stopped moving in the presence of cytochalasin; the lamellipodium at the leading
edge of the long axonal extension was retracted, but cell length was
unchanged (Fig. 11.45). Electron microscopy revealed that microfilaments had been disrupted but that microtubules and intermediate
filaments were unaffected by the drug. Cell movement resumed after the
drug was washed out, and microfilaments reassembled. In the presence

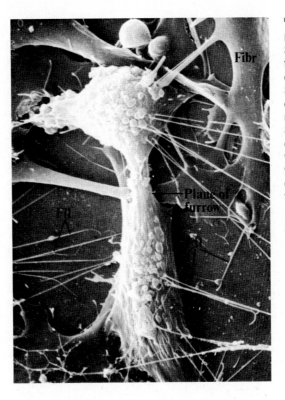

FIGURE 11-44
Scanning electron micrograph of a rat fibroblast in cell culture and about to divide in two at the plane of furrow. Surface blebbing is characteristic of cells in early interphase following nuclear division but prior to cell division. Slender filopodia make and break contact with the solid substratum along which the cells move. Contractile fibers within the filopodial extensions of the cell surface are responsible for pulling the cell forward to a new location. ×2250. (Photograph courtesy of K. R. Porter.)

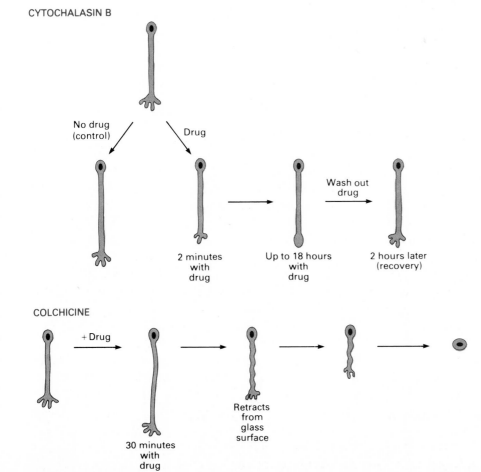

FIGURE 11-45
Effects of drugs on movement of embryonic nerve cells in culture. Cytochalasin B, which disrupts microfilaments, stops axonal movement within 2 minutes and leads to retraction of the lamellipodium at the leading edge, but cell length remains unchanged. Cells recover within 2 hours after the drug has been washed out. Colchicine, which disrupts microtubules, causes no visible change during the first 30 minutes of drug exposure. Exposure for more than 30 minutes leads to the retraction and final collapse of the axon into the body of the nerve cell. These results indicate that microfilaments are essential for cell movement, whereas microtubules contribute to cell shape in this system.

of colchicine, axonal extension continued for about 30 minutes, after which the axon gradually shortened and finally collapsed into the body of the nerve cell. These observations were interpreted as showing that microtubules were responsible for the maintenance of cell shape, whereas microfilaments were essential for locomotion. The role of the intermediate filaments was unresolved.

In a similar study with cultured fibroblasts, Robert Goldman found that colchicine prevented filopodium formation but had no effect on cell movement. Microtubules had been disrupted, but microfilaments were present at their usual location near the plasma membrane. Intermediate filaments remained near the nucleus instead of being dispersed throughout the cell. Goldman concluded that microtubules provided a cytoskeletal framework for cell shape and also aided in the dispersion of intermediate filaments within the cell. Microfilaments were undisturbed and movement continued to occur, so these fibers appeared to be responsible for cell locomotion. When cytochalasin B was used in low concentrations, microfilaments were unaffected but cell movement was inhibited. Microfilaments disappeared only when higher concentrations of cytochalasin were used, and cell movement was inhibited as before. Clearly, microfilaments alone cannot be responsible for cell locomotion, but they obviously participate in the process. Recent studies have provided clear indications that the Ca^{2+} concentration and appropriate levels of ATP are essential factors in contractility as the basis for movement in nonmuscle cells, just as they are in muscle itself. In addition, various *actin-binding proteins* have been implicated in the behavior, organization, and physical properties of actin filaments. We will briefly review these features next.

11.19
The Role of Calcium and Actin-Binding Proteins in Nonmuscle Contractility

Studies of isolated cytoplasm or cytoplasmic extracts from a variety of cells, such as ameba, macrophages, sea urchin eggs, and others, have shown that Ca^{2+} regulates ATP-dependent contractility in nonmuscle cells. If single ameba cells are ruptured under controlled conditions such that the free cytoplasm remains enclosed in an appropriate vessel, the consistency of the cytoplasm varies with the nature of the medium in which the cells are placed. In the presence of ATP and Ca^{2+}, orderly streaming may continue in a normal pattern. In media lacking ATP and Ca^{2+}, the released cytoplasm becomes rigid and inflexible so that streaming stops. If ATP is present but no Ca^{2+}, the cytoplasm remains in a fluid state. But, upon the addition of 7×10^{-7} M Ca^{2+} (or Ca^{2+} of greater concentration), the cytoplasm undergoes orderly streaming as contraction and relaxation (gel and fluid states, respectively) take place.

Although ATP-dependent contractility is regulated by calcium ions in muscle and in nonmuscle cells, different mechanisms are involved in each case. Muscle has an actin-linked system of calcium regulation, in which the ions promote conformational changes in the troponin–tropomyosin components bound to the actin filaments. In nonmuscle cells, it is believed that calcium regulation is myosin-linked, because

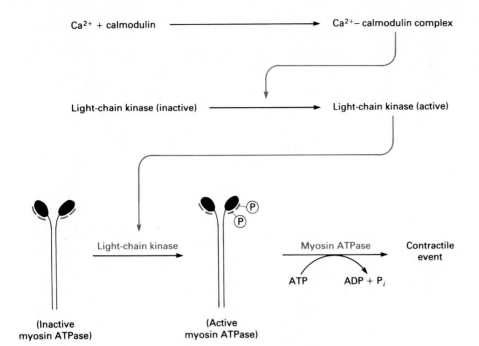

Ca^{2+} + calmodulin $\longrightarrow$ Ca^{2+}– calmodulin complex

Light-chain kinase (inactive) $\longrightarrow$ Light-chain kinase (active)

Light-chain kinase

Myosin ATPase   Contractile event

ATP   ADP + P_i

(Inactive myosin ATPase)   (Active myosin ATPase)

FIGURE 11-46
ATP-dependent contractility in non-muscle cells is regulated by Ca^{2+} on myosin directly, rather than through an actin-linked system as in striated muscle. Nonmuscle myosin is inactive unless one of its two pairs of light chains is phosphorylated. Phosphorylation is catalyzed by a light-chain kinase, which itself must be activated by prior binding with Ca^{2+}-loaded calmodulin. Once the kinase has catalyzed light-chain phosphorylation, myosin ATPase (myosin heads) is activated, ATP is hydrolyzed, and a contractile event can occur. In this way, nonmuscle myosin action is regulated in accordance with the concentration of free Ca^{2+} in the cytoplasm.

the ions affect the ability of myosin to hydrolyze ATP by virtue of conformational changes in the myosin molecules directly. In nonmuscle myosin, one of the pairs of light chains in the head region inhibits myosin ATPase activity, which is relieved when these light chains are phosphorylated. The phosphorylating enzyme is **myosin light-chain kinase**, whose activity is regulated in turn by the small calcium-binding protein *calmodulin* (Fig. 11.46). When the cytoplasmic calcium concentration increases, Ca^{2+} binds to calmodulin, which stimulates the kinase to phosphorylate myosin and thereby activate its ATPase. When the calcium level drops, the kinase activity stops and phosphoryl groups are removed from the myosin light chains by the action of a phosphatase enzyme. Cessation of kinase activity and removal of myosin light-chain phosphoryl groups presumably cause cytoplasmic contractility to stop. Regulation of free-Ca^{2+} concentration in the cytoplasm involves the release of calcium from membranous vesicles and the return of calcium into these vesicles, very much like sarcoplasmic reticulum control of calcium levels in striated muscle.

Three general classes of **actin-binding proteins** have been identified, each of which presumably has a different function in regulating nonmuscle contractility. These categories of proteins are referred to as *cross-linking proteins*, *capping proteins*, and *monomer-stabilizing proteins* (Table 11.1).

Cross-linking proteins have two or more actin-binding sites and can therefore link together two or more individual actin filaments into a three-dimensional network. Long, flexible proteins such as **filamin** and **α-actinin** can link actin filaments into loose networks with no particular orientations of the individual fibers. When even a small number of either of these cross-linking molecules is added to a suspension of actin filaments, the preparation changes rapidly from a fluid to a solid gel. Small cross-linking molecules such as **fimbrin** promote tight bundling of

TABLE 11-1
Major Types of Actin-Binding Proteins in Nonmuscle Cells*

Class	Protein	Mode of Action on Actin
Cross-linking proteins	α-Actinin	Links together actin filaments, producing a loose, unoriented network
	Filamin	Links together actin filaments, producing a loose, unoriented network
	Fimbrin	Links together adjacent actin filaments, producing tight bundles in parallel register
	Vinculin	Links actin filaments to plasma membrane
Capping proteins	Fragmin Gelsolin Villin	Bind to an end of actin filaments and thereby regulate change in filament length; Ca^{2+}-dependent fragmentation of actin filaments; may promote nucleation leading to actin filament assembly
Monomer-stabilizing proteins	Profilin	Binds to actin monomers and thereby prevents polymerization into filaments

*Nonmuscle myosin behaves much like muscle myosin in having ATPase activity and in interacting with actin filaments to produce movement.

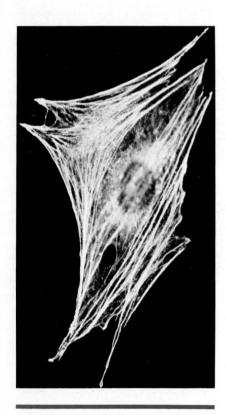

FIGURE 11-47
A cultured mouse cell stained with anti-actin antibodies coupled to a fluorescent dye. Bundles of actin microfilaments are bunched into stress fibers. (Photograph courtesy of K. Weber and M. Osborn.)

actin filaments in parallel register, very similar to the alignment found in stress fibers and so dramatically apparent in immunofluorescence photographs (Fig. 11.47). In addition to proteins that join actin filaments into aggregates, other proteins cross-link actin filaments to the plasma membrane or to specialized regions of the membrane. One of these binding proteins is **vinculin**, which is particularly evident in belt desmosomes and in the adhesion plaques that anchor stress fibers to the plasma membrane.

Capping proteins bind to one end or the other of an actin filament and thereby regulate the length of the actin polymer. If the (+) end is capped, for example, the filament will not lengthen and it may actually shorten because monomer disassembly will predominate at the uncapped, nongrowing (−) end. Few of these proteins have been well characterized, but among these are molecules that cause actin filaments to fragment into smaller fibers that become capped by the binding protein. When **gelsolin**, **fragmin**, or **villin** is added to actin filaments, the preparation exhibits a dramatic drop in viscosity. This change to a more fluid state is calcium-dependent, occurring only when the Ca^{2+} concentration is greater than 10^{-6} M. It has been suggested that these calcium-dependent binding proteins cause a cross-linked network of actin filaments to break up by virtue of the protein's binding so tightly to actin, in the presence of calcium, that the protein becomes inserted between actin monomers and thus leads to fragmentation of the filaments. Interestingly, these same binding proteins can promote *nucleation* of small numbers of actin molecules, leading to the formation of new actin polymers in a solution of free actin monomers. We are uncertain, however, whether these capping proteins function in the living cell primarily to initiate polymerization or to shorten existing actin filaments.

Monomer-stabilizing proteins bind to G-actin monomers and prevent their assembly into polymers. These proteins serve to stabilize the monomer pool in nonmuscle cells and thus control the monomer–

polymer equilibrium in the cells, where conditions typically favor polymerization. Changes in the activity of **profilin** and other monomer-stabilizing proteins can therefore determine whether assembly or disassembly of actin filaments is favored at a given time in a given cell.

Regulation of nonmuscle contractility involves a number of interacting sets of structural proteins, catalytic proteins, and binding proteins, together with ATP and calcium control systems. All these components (and perhaps others) contribute to the dynamic displays of cellular and intracellular motility, in all their variety of expression.

Organization of the Cytoskeleton

Although we have focused on the role of protein fibers as part of the machinery for cell movements, these fibers also provide a supporting framework, or "skeleton," for the cell and its contents, and they probably contribute to the organization of the cell interior. The component parts of differentiated cells maintain a characteristic distribution that varies from one kind of cell to another. The distinctive spatial order of subcellular organelles in a cell lineage indicates the nonrandom organization of the cell interior, which many believe to be due at least in part to cytoskeletal fibers. These fibers must help establish and maintain the basic subcellular architecture, but they must also allow the flexibility that is essential to movement, growth, and other vital processes. Photographs of the cell interior yield static images of protein fibers and other components, but we know the cell exists in a dynamic state of flux. The current unified approach to understanding the cell has come from the complementary investigations of microscopists and biochemists. Analysis of the cytoskeleton in particular has benefited considerably from information provided by each of these groups of investigators, who seek answers to similar problems and questions concerning the living cell.

11.20
Architecture of the Cytoskeleton

In order to gain a three-dimensional perspective on the cell interior, it is necessary to examine much thicker sections than can be used in conventional thin-section transmission electron microscopy. Typical thin sections usually fail to reveal connections between parts of the cell, particularly between fibers, but thick sections provide the depth and perspective we need to analyze the subcellular architecture. Especially useful views can be obtained for whole cells or very thick sections by the use of *high-voltage electron microscopy*, in which the energy beam of 1 million electron volts or more is able to penetrate the thickness of the preparation and permit photography (Fig. 11.48). Another useful procedure involves *quick freezing and deep etching* of the preparation, which is then used to form platinum replicas that can be photographed with the electron microscope. The fibers in this preparation are extensively interconnected by fine filamentous cross-links, which comprise the

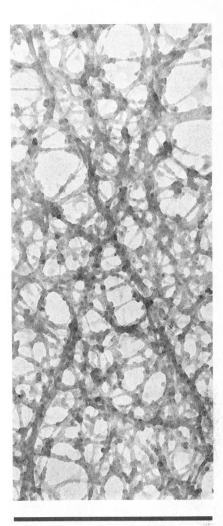

FIGURE 11-48
High voltage electron micrograph of cytoskeletal components in a cultured African green monkey kidney cell treated for 5 minutes with the detergent Brij 58. The detergent removes the plasma membrane without severely affecting the underlying cytoplasm. The network of filamentous strands has a characteristic microtrabelular appearance. ×125,000. (Photograph courtesy of M. Schliwa.)

microtrabecular lattice or network dispersed throughout the cytoplasm.

When cells are treated with a nonionic detergent, such as one of the Triton series, the membranous and soluble portions of the cytoplasm can be washed away while the cytoskeletal protein fibers remain in their original positions within the cell. The image of the cytoskeleton is quite different in detergent-treated preparations because the microtubules, intermediate filaments, and microfilaments are largely unconnected by cross-linking strands, which presumably have been removed by the detergent (Fig. 11.49). The difference between treated and untreated cells has led to uncertainty concerning the reality of the microtrabecular lattice. According to some, the lattice exists but is readily solubilized; according to others, the lattice is an artifact produced by the aggregation

FIGURE 11-49
Effect of the detergent Triton X-100 on the cytoskeleton of cultured cells. (a) High voltage electron micrograph of an African green monkey kidney cell treated for 1 minute with 0.1% detergent and labeled with myosin S1 to identify actin filaments. Intermediate filaments remain unlabeled. The fibrous cytoskeletal meshwork has a relatively open appearance and microtrabecular strands are not evident. ×96,000. (b) Electron micrograph of a platinum replica of freeze-dried cytoskeleton from a fibroblast treated for 30 minutes with 0.5% Triton X-100. Bundles of microfilaments oriented into stress fiber groups are evident, along with two microtubules and a diffuse filamentous network with attached ribosomes. ×70,000. (Photograph a courtesy of M. Schliwa; photograph b courtesy of J. Heuser.)

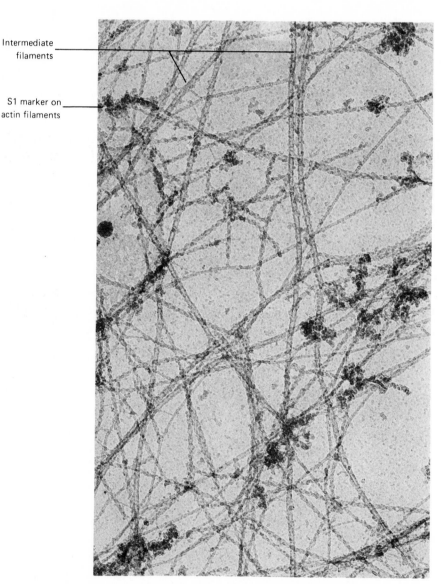

Intermediate filaments

S1 marker on actin filaments

(a)

of soluble macromolecules during fixation and dehydration procedures used in preparing cells for electron microscopy. Whether or not the major protein fibers are interconnected by microtrabeculae, we believe that some system of cross-linking does indeed characterize the cytoskeletal fibers and provides a physical basis for their interactions *in vivo*.

An excellent three-dimensional perspective on the cytoskeletal elements in a cell can be obtained by examination in the light microscope of whole cells that have been treated with a specific antibody preparation to which a fluorescent label has been added to make the antibody binding pattern visible. Anti-actin antibodies bind to actin filaments; anti-vimentin, anti-keratin, and other antibodies bind to intermediate filaments; and anti-tubulin antibodies bind to microtubules. Each of these visualized displays indicates that the cytoplasm is

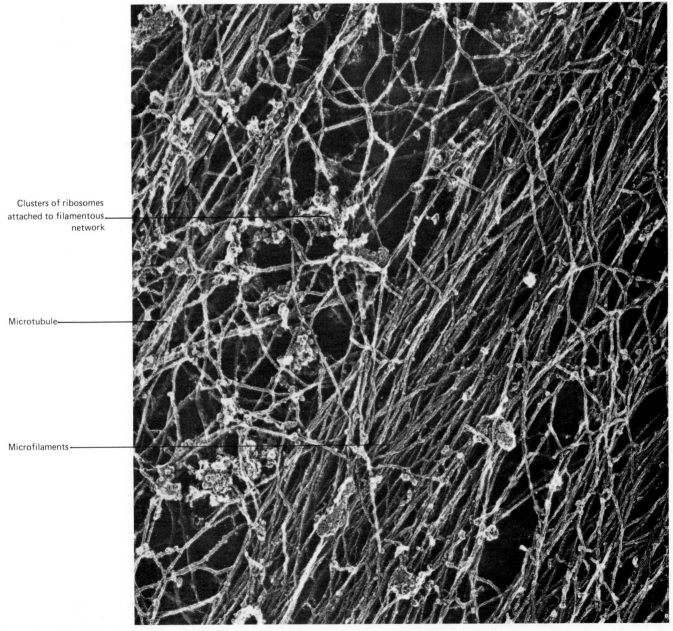

Clusters of ribosomes attached to filamentous network

Microtubule

Microfilaments

(b)

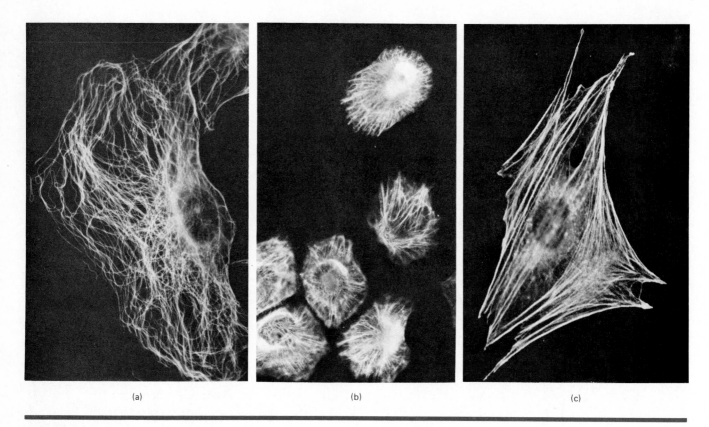

(a)   (b)   (c)

FIGURE 11-50
Immunofluorescence micrographs of cytoskeletal fibers in whole cultured mammalian cells. In each case the cells have been stained with an antibody preparation to which a fluorescent dye has been coupled. (a) Microtubules in a mouse cell exposed to anti-tubulin antibodies. Most of the fluorescent fibers correspond to single microtubules. (b) Intermediate filaments in human HeLa cells exposed to anti-keratin antibodies. (c) Actin microfilaments organized into stress fiber groups in a mouse cell exposed to anti-actin antibodies. (Photographs courtesy of M. Osborn and K. Weber.)

packed with fibers, although the amount and display pattern of each of the major fibers often varies from one cell type to another (Fig. 11.50). In many kinds of cells the actin filaments are bunched into stress fiber groups, intermediate filaments often but not always are particularly dense in the region around the nucleus, and microtubules often are concentrated around the nucleus but extend outward toward the cell periphery in all directions. Though most of the published photographs show only one of these three major fiber systems in any one cell, two different kinds of fibers can be seen in the same cell by the use of antibody preparations tagged with different fluorescent dyes. For example, if one antibody preparation is labeled with fluorescin and another antibody preparation is labeled with rhodamine, each display can be visualized separately in the same cell, because the two dyes have different absorption spectra and are visible only when illuminated by the appropriate wavelengths (Fig. 11.51).

Microscopic studies have familiarized us with the broad landscape of the cell interior, but not with the details that would show us the connections and molecular underpinnings by which different parts of the cell interact and coordinate their functions. These essential details have emerged from biochemical analysis, in conjunction with microscopy and other approaches.

11.21
Cytoskeletal Assemblies and Cell Shape

All three kinds of major protein fibers make some contribution to the overall shape of the cell and to a variety of projections from the cell surface. We have already discussed cilia and flagella, whose microtubular core determines the shape of the motility organelle during its growth, maintains this shape by virtue of tubule stability, but also provides the flexibility that allows changes in shape as the contractile fibers drive the locomotor apparatus. The ciliary microtubules are held together by nexin links, and the radial spokes emerging from the A subfibers make and break contact with the central sheath around the singlet microtubules. Both permanent and transient connecting proteins serve to hold the architecture in place and, at the same time, permit flexibility for the locomotor function of the organelles. The specific location and the number of individual cilia or flagella are determined by the position and number of basal bodies just under the cell surface. Each organelle is an outgrowth of a subtending basal body, or centriole.

In heliozoans—protozoa related to amebas—long, slender feeding processes called *axopods* contain hundreds of microtubules packed together in two interlocking spirals (Fig. 11.52). At very high resolutions it is often possible to see thin wisps of material between microtubules, and these materials are believed to hold the whole microtubular structure together as a unit. When the axopod is extended, the microtubular "skeleton" provides considerable structural support for the long protruding process. During feeding, the axopods can retract rapidly into the cell body, dragging along any attached prey and particles. According to experimental analysis, this retraction is due to depolymerization of the axopodial microtubules. Under controlled conditions, the microtubules depolymerize and the axopods retract when cells are exposed to low temperature or to calcium ions; both the microtubules and the axopods form again when the temperature is raised or Ca^{2+} is removed. In this example the change in shape is a consequence of cycles of

FIGURE 11-51
Immunofluorescence micrographs of a single cultured fibroblast doubly labeled with (a) rhodamine-coupled anti-vimentin antibodies to visualize vimentin intermediate filaments, and (b) fluorescin-coupled anti-tubulin antibodies to visualize microtubules. The correspondence of the two filament distributions may reflect the existence of some type of protein linkage between them. Because fluorescin and rhodamine have different absorption spectra, filaments labeled with these agents can be seen individually and separately when illuminated by the appropriate wavelengths. (Photographs courtesy of E. H. Ball, from Ball, E. H., and S. J. Singer, 1981, *Proc. Nat. Acad. Sci. U. S.* **78**:6986, Fig. 3A, B.)

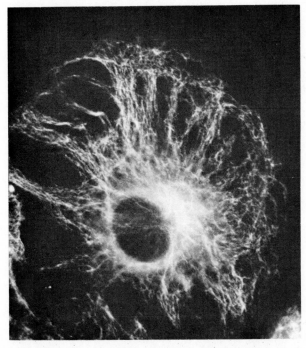

(a)

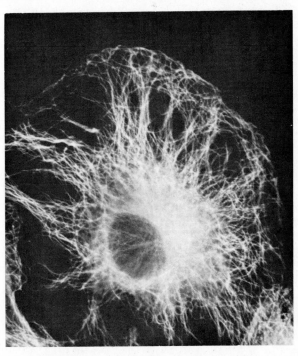

(b)

(a)   (b)

FIGURE 11-52
Heliozoan axopods. (a) Light
micrograph of the heliozoan
Actinosphaerium nucleofilum showing
many long, slender axopods extending
radially from the central body of the cell.
×80. (b) Electron micrograph of a cross
section through one axopod showing
the two interlocking, concentric spirals
of microtubules that make up the core
of the slender cellular extension.
(Photographs courtesy of L. G. Tilney.)

microtubule polymerization and depolymerization, and support is provided by the interlocking framework of polymerized microtubules in the
extended axopod.

In addition to providing contractility, actin filaments also may form
cross-linked aggregates that provide mechanical support and shape for
various parts of the cell. One of the best-known examples of cellular
structures supported by a stiff core of actin filaments are **microvilli**,
which are fingerlike projections that protrude from the exposed surfaces
of epithelial cells and increase the absorptive surface area of the tissue
(Fig. 11.53). The core of a microvillus consists of bundles of parallel
actin filaments, which terminate in a cap of amorphous material at the
apex of the structure and extend at their base into a network of
intermediate filaments and myosin—the *terminal web*. As shown by
decoration with myosin S1 fragments, all the actin filaments are oriented
with their (+) end at the tip of the microvillus. Not only are actin
filaments bound to the amorphous material at the tip of the microvillus,
but they are also bound by thin lateral links to the inside perimeter of the
microvillus membrane and to one another in the central core. Among
the actin-binding proteins in these cross-links are fimbrin and villin.

Transient displays of microfilaments are important influences in the
determination of cell shape or organ shape during development. When
an animal cell divides by furrowing, or cleavage, a bundle of filaments
called the *contractile ring* assembles spontaneously and by its contraction
causes the cell to pinch in two (Fig. 11.54). Both actin filaments and
myosin filaments are present in the contractile ring, and we believe that
sliding of actin filaments over myosin generates the force for contraction
leading to cleavage of the cell. When actin sites are blocked so that
attachment to myosin is prevented, cleavage stops. When anti-myosin
antibodies are injected into cleaving eggs, thereby preventing myosin
from binding to actin filaments, cleavage stops and the furrow disappears. The cleavage furrow disappears when cytochalasin B is

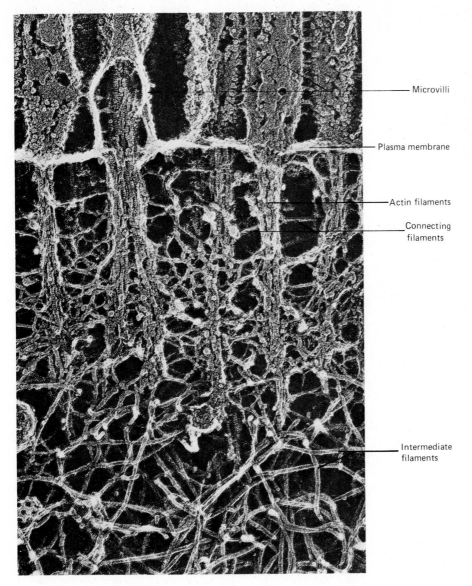

Microvilli

Plasma membrane

Actin filaments

Connecting
filaments

Intermediate
filaments

FIGURE 11-53
The core of each microvillus consists of
a bundle of actin microfilaments that
extend below the plasma membrane
into the underlying terminal web region
of the brush border of intestinal
epithelium. The terminal web is a
cytoskeletal region composed of
narrow myosin-containing strands
that connect adjacent bundles of
microfilaments to each other and to
the underlying bed of intermediate
filaments. (From Hirokawa, N., and J.
E. Heuser, 1981, *J. Cell Biol.* **91**:399,
Fig. 9. Copyright by Rockefeller Univ.
Press.)

injected into dividing eggs, and the furrow reappears when the drug is
washed out, as does the peripheral band of contractile-ring filaments.

Various morphogenetic changes during embryonic organ development appear to involve a "purse-string" contractile effect similar to the
one described for cell cleavage. In various embryonic organs, a region
may bulge outward or develop one or more infolds. Just before these
events occur, cells involved in the morphogenetic change begin to
assemble bundles of filaments that lie parallel to the surface and just
under the region where a kink later develops (see Fig. 6.5). Many of
these fibers are actin filaments (cytochalasin B prevents filament
assembly or disrupts existing filaments), and they simultaneously
inhibit the change in organ shape in the responsible regions. When
calcium ions are injected into young embryos, a dense region of
microfilaments can be seen at the site of calcium entry, and contraction
is observed to occur very rapidly. Calcium ions are ineffective in organs

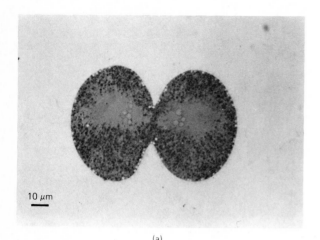

(a)

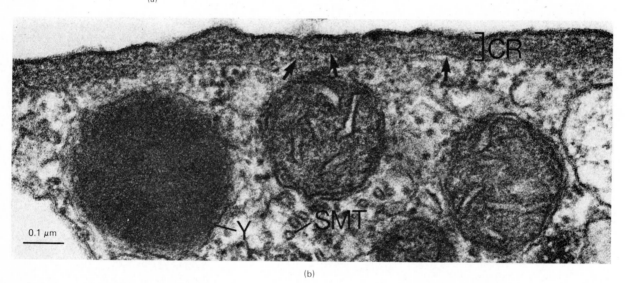

(b)

FIGURE 11-54

Cleavage of the fertilized egg of the sea urchin *Arbacia punctulata*. Shortly after (a) furrowing begins, a transient contractile ring develops perpendicular to the plane of the furrow, and (b) it consists of an assortment of components, the most prominent being actin microfilaments that completely encircle the furrow between the two daughter cells. In addition to microfilaments (at arrows) of the contractile ring (CR) adjacent to the plasma membrane, the cytoplasm contains yolk granules (Y), mitochondria, spindle microtubules (SMT), and other materials. (Photographs courtesy of T. E. Schroeder, from Schroeder, T. E., 1972, *J. Cell Biol.* **53**:419, Fig. 2a, 4c. Copyright by Rockefeller University Press.)

that were previously treated with cytochalasin B. The current interpretation is that actin and myosin filaments assemble at specific sites, perhaps in response to a Ca^{2+} gradient, and generate the contractile force that leads to deformation of cells and to change in organ shape.

In earlier chapters we discussed various features of the plasma membrane that were associated with erythrocyte shape (see Fig. 5.21) and cell–cell interactions via junctions (see Fig. 6.8), among other topics. In these cases it was clear that cytoskeletal protein fibers were bound by cross-linking proteins to the plasma membrane and thereby influenced cell-surface activities and properties. Similarly, protein mobility laterally within the plane of the membrane and interactions between adjacent cells or between cells and their external surroundings are believed to involve cytoskeletal protein fibers in a *transmembrane control system* that lies just under the cell surface (Fig. 11.55). It would appear that every aspect of cellular movement—whether of individual

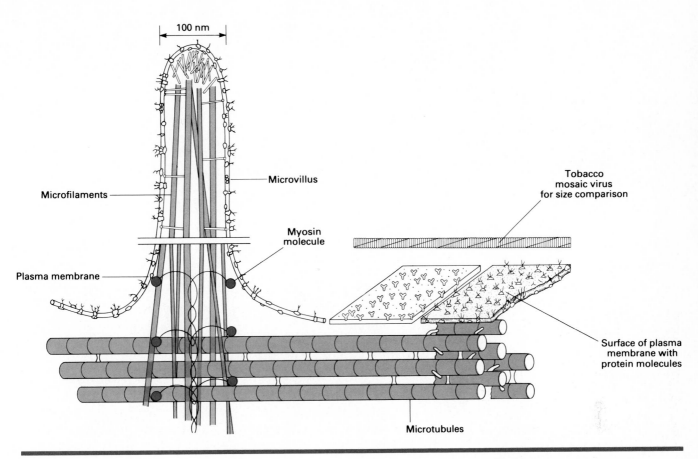

FIGURE 11-55
Scale model of the cytoskeletal framework associated with the plasma membrane, including one microvillus projecting at the surface. The cytoskeletal components include microtubules, microfilaments, and myosin molecules that underlie the inner surface of the plasma membrane. These components are believed to comprise a transmembrane control system governing the mobility of membrane proteins. A tobacco mosaic virus particle is shown for size comparison, and it is evident that the membrane molecules are tiny compared to the relatively enormous cytoskeletal structures. These size differences make it difficult to understand how the mobility of tiny proteins in the membrane can be influenced by huge cytoskeletal components, yet the evidence indicates that they are. (From Loor, F., 1976, *Nature* **264**:272.)

molecules, portions of the cytoplasm, or whole cells and organisms—requires the mechanical and contractile functions of sets of cytoskeletal protein fibers.

Summary

The organized system of protein fibers that is responsible for cell movement and contributes to cell shape in eukaryotes is referred to as the cytoskeleton. Several types of protein fibers are found in the cytoskeleton. Microtubules, formed from protofilament polymers of tubulin, are hollow cylinders 25 nm in diameter and indeterminate in length. Microfilaments, 6 nm in diameter, are formed of two intertwined filaments of F actin; each of which is a polymer of G actin. Intermediate filaments, 10 nm in diameter, are diverse but all types represent aggregates of particular monomers. Cellular formation of intermediate filaments may be irreversible in contrast to microtubules and microfilaments. The 15-nm-diameter myosin filament is an aggregate of myosin monomers, each of which has a globular head that binds actin and hydrolyzes ATP and a filamentous, rigid tail by which it associates with other monomers during filament assembly. Binding of the globular portion of monomeric myosin to actin filaments decorates them in a characteristic arrowhead fashion, revealing the polarity of the actin filaments that is necessary for muscle function. Microtubule associated proteins and microfilament accessory proteins regulate the stability and interaction of individual cytoskeletal elements.

Various aspects of cell motility involve the cytoskeleton. Best understood is the mechanism of contraction of the sarcomere of skeletal muscle. According to the sliding filament model, an interdigitating parallel array of thin actin filaments and thick myosin filaments can form cross-bridges in the presence of calcium ions and ADP. ATP binding to a myosin head causes it to release actin; the conformation of the head changes as ATP is hydrolyzed; and myosin with ADP binds to a new position on the actin filament. The concerted action of many myosin heads on a single actin filament serves to pull the actin filament toward the central part of the bipolar myosin filament. Because the actin filaments of each sarcomere are attached to the Z disc by actin-binding proteins, the contraction of each sarcomere produces an overall shortening of the muscle fiber. If calcium is not available, the site where myosin would bind to actin is sterically hindered by another protein, tropomyosin, so the muscle remains relaxed. Contraction is initiated by an action potential traveling along the sarcolemma and penetrating deep into the muscle fiber via the T system whose transverse sarcolemmal tubules interact with the sarcoplasmic reticulum. Released into the sarcoplasm from the sarcoplasmic reticulum lumen, calcium binds to troponin and induces a conformational change, allowing it to displace tropomyosin, expose the myosin-binding site on actin, and activate the myosin-ATPase. (In invertebrates the calcium activates the myosin directly by binding to one of its components.) When contraction is over, calcium is transported into the lumen of the sarcoplasmic reticulum from the sarcoplasm, and the muscle is once again relaxed.

Ciliary movement is also reasonably well understood. Cilia and flagella have axonemes constructed of microtubules in characteristic arrays: Two central microtubules are surrounded by 9 doublets of subfiber A and subfiber B microtubules. The ciliary doublets grow from the A and B subfibers of 9 microtubule triplets that make up a centriole (basal body) in the cytoplasm. Cilia and flagella will not form in the absence of centrioles (basal bodies), which serve as microtubule organizing centers (MTOCs). Tubulin is the major protein of all microtubules; however, microtubule-associated proteins (MAPs) stabilize the structure and promote its motility. These MAPs include dynein (with associated ATPase activity), nexin, proteins of radial spokes with knobs, and others. The machinery is entirely self-contained within the axoneme, permitting periodic beating in the presence of ATP. Mitochondria are the source of this ATP. During ciliary beating, motility occurs via a sliding microtubule mechanism in which dynein arms on one doublet undergo cyclic attachment to and detachment from an adjacent doublet as ATP is hydrolyzed, and this sliding is constrained to bending by cyclic interactions between the knobs of the radial spokes and the central sheath. Accessory fibers are found in sperm tail flagella, and sensory receptor cells contain modified cilia. Eukaryotic flagella are structurally and mechanistically different from bacterial flagella, which consist of protein filaments of polymerized flagellin. Movement of bacterial flagella is passive, powered by rotation of a disc structure in the cell membrane. A proton gradient directly powers this movement.

Microtubules also form the spindle that promotes anaphase separation of chromosomes. Spindle fibers assemble and disassemble rapidly in contrast to other fibers. Inhibitors of both microtubule assembly and disassembly interfere with the orderly function of the spindle. Like actin filaments, microtubules have structural polarity, and in the spindle they are oriented with the faster-growing (+) end farthest from the nucleation center in the centrosome. The polarity and the differential rates of growth of the two ends of each spindle fiber determine the direction of movement of chromosomes. For accurate distribution, a chromosome must be attached at its kinetochore to one class of spindle fibers (chromosomal fibers). Another class (polar spindle fibers) extends from the centrosome into the spindle equatorial region, where the fibers form an overlapping array. Movement probably involves both regulation of assembly and disassembly of the two sorts of microtubules and a sliding mechanism similar to that seen in cilia. A centriole in the centrosome region is not needed for formation of a spindle (higher plants lack centrioles), but other components of this microtubule organizing center are probably essential to organization and orientation of the spindle.

Microfilaments and microtubules are implicated in different types of nonmuscle-cell motility. In cytoplasmic streaming, actin and myosin are found in the sol-like endoplasm and at the interface between endoplasm and the more gel-like ectoplasm. Prevention of actin polymerization blocks streaming so a muscle-like contractile mechanism is postulated. Ameboid movement of certain unicellular organisms and of vertebrate white blood cells utilizes a similar system of sol–gel changes of the cytoplasm. Ameboid movement is inhibited by conditions that depolymerize microfilaments, but the precise nature and site of contractile force are not clear. Cultured cells move by successive attachment and detachment of their leading edge (ruffled membrane), containing microtubules that stabilize the structure and microfilaments that provide contractile force. Actin-binding proteins cross-link actin to promote gel formation, organized parallel arrays, or associations with the plasma membrane. These proteins can regulate the length of an actin filament by binding to one end and blocking further polymerization or by preventing polymerization of G-actin monomers. In some cases actin-binding proteins are regulated by calcium to promote ATP hydrolysis or binding.

As a whole the cytoskeleton has a complex architecture with filaments and tubules connected by a proposed microtrabecular lattice. Filament and microtubule formation and their characteristic distribution in a cell are subject to change with changing physiological conditions. In addition to movement and motility, the cytoskeleton also determines cell shape. Cytoskeletal structures are involved in providing the support for cilia, axopods, microvilli, and junctions; in forming the contractile ring in dividing cells; in promoting morphogenetic movement; and in other morphological phenomena.

Readings and References

Abercrombie, M., J. E. M. Heaysman, and S. M. Pegrum. 1970. The locomotion of fibroblasts in culture. II. Ruffling. *Exp. Cell Res.* **60**:437.

Afzelius, B. 1981. Genetic disorders of cilia. In *International Cell Biology 1980–1981*, ed. H. G. Schweiger, p. 440. New York: Rockefeller University Press.

Albrecht-Buehler, G. April 1978. The tracks of moving cells. *Sci. Amer.* **238**:68.

Albrecht-Buehler, G. 1980. Autonomous movements of cytoplasmic fragments. *Proc. Natl. Acad. Sci. U. S.* **77**:6639.

Allen, R. D. 1981. Cell motility. *J. Cell Biol.* **91**:148s.

Anderson, R. G. W., and A. K. Floyd. 1980. Electrophoretic analysis of basal body (centriole) proteins. *Biochemistry* **19**:5625.

Bajer, A. S., and J. Molè Bajer. 1982. Asters, poles, and transport properties within spindlelike microtubule arrays. *Cold Spring Harbor Sympos. Quant. Biol.* **46**:263.

Berg, H. C. August 1975. How bacteria swim. *Sci. Amer.* **233**:36.

Bergen, L. G., and G. G. Borisy. 1980. Head-to-tail polymerization of microtubules *in vitro*. Electron microscope analysis of seeded assembly. *J. Cell Biol.* **84**:141.

Bergen, L. G., R. Kuriyama, and G. G. Borisy. 1980. Polarity of microtubules nucleated by centrosomes and chromosomes of Chinese hamster ovary cells *in vitro*. *J. Cell Biol.* **84**:151.

Bessman, S. P., and P. J. Geiger. 1981. Transport of energy in muscle: The phosphorylcreatine shuttle. *Science* **211**:448.

Birchmeier, W. 1984. Cytoskeleton structure and function. *Trends Biochem. Sci.* **9**:192.

Brinkley, B. R. 1982. Organization of the cytoplasm. *Cold Spring Harbor Sympos. Quant. Biol.* **46**:1029.

Brinkley, B. R., *et al.* 1981. Tubulin assembly sites and the organization of cytoplasmic microtubules in cultured mammalian cells. *J. Cell Biol.* **90**:554.

Bridgman, P. C., and T. S. Reese. 1984. The structure of cytoplasm in directly frozen cultured cells. I. Filamentous meshworks and the cytoplasmic ground substance. *J. Cell Biol.* **99**:1655.

Brokaw, C. J., D. J. L. Luck, and B. Huang. 1982. Analysis of the movement of *Chlamydomonas* flagella: The function of the radial-spoke system is revealed by comparison of wild-type and mutant flagella. *J. Cell Biol.* **92**:722.

Cande, W. Z. 1983. Creatine kinase role in anaphase chromosome movement. *Nature* **304**:557.

Cande, W. Z., *et al.* 1974. A functional mitotic spindle prepared from mammalian cells in culture. *Proc. Natl. Acad. Sci. U. S.* **71**:1559.

Cheung, W. Y. June 1982. Calmodulin. *Sci. Amer.* **246**:62.

Cohen, C. November 1975. The protein switch of muscle contraction. *Sci. Amer.* **233**:36.

Cohen, C. 1979. Cell architecture and morphogenesis. I. The cytoskeletal proteins. *Trends Biochem. Sci.* **4**:73.

David-Pfeuty, T., and S. J. Singer. 1980. Altered distribution of the cytoskeletal proteins vinculin and α-actinin in cultured fibroblasts transformed by Rous sarcoma virus. *Proc. Natl. Acad. Sci. U. S.* **77**:6687.

DeRosier, D. J., L. G. Tilney, and E. Egelman. 1980. Actin in the inner ear: The remarkable structure of the stereocilium. *Nature* **287**:291.

Dustin, P. August 1980. Microtubules. *Sci. Amer.* **243**:66.

Euteneuer, U., and J. R. McIntosh. 1980. Polarity of midbody and phragmoplast microtubules. *J. Cell Biol.* **87**:509.

Evans, L., T. Mitchison, and M. Kirschner. 1985. Influence of the centrosome on the structure of nucleated microtubules. *J. Cell Biol.* **100**:1185.

Flanagan, M. D., and S. Lin. 1980. Cytochalasins block actin filament elongation by binding to high-affinity sites associated with F-actin. *J. Biol. Chem.* **255**:835.

Franzini-Armstrong, C., and L. D. Peachey. 1981. Striated muscle—contractile and control mechanisms. *J. Cell Biol.* **91**:166s.

Franzini-Armstrong, C., and K. R. Porter. 1964. Sarcolemmal invaginations constituting the T system in fish muscle fibers. *J. Cell Biol.* **22**:675.

Geiger, B. 1982. Involvement of vinculin in contact-induced cytoskeletal interactions. *Cold Spring Harbor Sympos. Quant. Biol.* **46**:671.

Gibbons, I. R. 1981. Cilia and flagella of eukaryotes. *J. Cell Biol.* **91**:107s.

Gibbons, I. R., and A. V. Grimstone. 1960. On flagellar structure in certain flagellates. *J. Biophys. Biochem. Cytol.* **7**:697. (Journal is now entitled *J. Cell Biol.*)

Goodenough, U. W., and J. E. Heuser. 1982. Substructure of the outer dynein arm. *J. Cell Biol.* **95**:798.

Haimo, L. T., and J. L. Rosenbaum. 1981. Cilia, flagella, and microtubules. *J. Cell Biol.* **91**:125s.

Haimo, L. T., B. R. Telzer, and J. L. Rosenbaum. 1979. Dynein binds to and crossbridges cytoplasmic microtubules. *Proc. Natl. Acad. Sci. U. S.* **76**:5759.

Harris, A. 1974. Contact inhibition of cell locomotion. In *Cell Communications*, ed. R. P. Cox, p. 147. New York: Wiley.

Heidemann, S. R., and J. R. McIntosh. 1980. Visualization of the structural polarity of microtubules. *Nature* **286**:517.

Heuser, J. E., and M. W. Kirschner. 1980. Filament organization revealed in platinum replicas of freeze-dried cytoskeletons. *J. Cell Biol.* **86**:212.

Hirokawa, N., T. C. S. Keller, III, R. Chasan, and M. S. Mooseker. 1983. Mechanism of brush border contractility studied by the quick-freeze, deep-etch method. *J. Cell Biol.* **96**:1325.

Huxley, H. E. 1969. The mechanism of muscle contraction. *Science* **164**:1356.

Hyams, J. 1982. Dynein in the spindle? *Nature* **295**:648.

Inoué, S. 1981. Cell division and the mitotic spindle. *J. Cell Biol.* **91**:131s.

Inoué, S., and H. Sato. 1967. Cell motility by labile association of molecules: The nature of mitotic spindle fibers and their role in chromosome movement. *J. Gen. Physiol.* **50**:259.

Kendrick-Jones, J., P. Tooth, K. A. Taylor, and J. M. Scholey. 1982. Regulation of myosin-filament assembly by light-chain phosphorylation. *Cold Spring Harbor Sympos. Quant. Biol.* **46**:929.

King, S. M., J. S. Hyams, and A. Luba. 1982. Absence of microtubule sliding and an analysis of spindle formation and elongation in isolated mitotic spindles from the yeast *Saccharomyces cerevisiae. J. Cell Biol.* **94**:341.

Lane, B., and B. Anderton. 1982. Focus on filaments: Embryology to pathology. *Nature* **298**:706.

Lazarides, E. 1981. Intermediate filaments—chemical heterogeneity in cellular differentiation. *Cell* **23**:649.

Lazarides, E., and J. P. Revel. May 1979. The molecular basis for cell movement. *Sci. Amer.* **240**:100.

Ledbetter, M. C., and K. R. Porter. 1963. A "microtubule" in plant cell fine structure. *J. Cell Biol.* **19**:239.

Lester, H. A. February 1977. The response to acetylcholine. *Sci. Amer.* **236**:106.

Loor, F. 1976. Cell surface design. *Nature* **264**:272.

Macnab, R. M. 1984. The bacterial flagellar rotor. *Trends Biochem. Sci.* **9**:185.

Margolis, R. L., and L. Wilson. 1981. Microtubule treadmills—possible molecular machinery. *Nature* **293**:705.

Margulis, L., L. To, and D. Chase. 1978. Microtubules in prokaryotes. *Science* **200**:1118.

Marx, J. L. 1983. Organizing the cytoplasm. *Science* **222**:1109.

McIntosh, J. R. 1984. Mechanisms of mitosis. *Trends Biochem. Sci.* **9**:195.

Mooseker, M. S., and L. G. Tilney. 1975. Organization of an actin filament–membrane complex. Filament polarity and membrane attachment in the microvilli of intestinal epithelial cells. *J. Cell Biol.* **67**:725.

Murray, J. M., and A. Weber. February 1974. The cooperative action of muscle proteins. *Sci. Amer.* **230**:58.

Nicklas, R. B. 1983. Measurements of the force produced by the mitotic spindle in anaphase. *J. Cell Biol.* **97**:542.

Omoto, C. K., and G. B. Witman. 1981. Functionally significant central-pair rotation in a primitive eukaryotic flagellum. *Nature* **290**:708.

Osborn, M., et al. 1982. Intermediate filaments. *Cold Spring Harbor Sympos. Quant. Biol.* **46**:413.

Osborn, M., and K. Weber. 1982. Intermediate filaments: Cell-type specific markers in differentiation and pathology. *Cell* **31**:303.

Peachey, L. D. 1965. The sarcoplasmic reticulum and transverse tubules of the frog's sartorius. *J. Cell Biol.* **25**:209.

Penman, S., et al. 1982. Cytoplasmic and nuclear architecture in cells and tissue: Form, functions, and mode of assembly. *Cold Spring Harbor Sympos. Quant. Biol.* **46**:1013.

Pickett-Heaps, J. D., D. H. Tippit, and K. R. Porter. 1982. Rethinking mitosis. *Cell* **29**:729.

Pollard, T. D. 1981. Cytoplasmic contractile proteins. *J. Cell Biol.* **91**:156s.

Pollard, T. D., and S. W. Craig. 1982. Mechanism of actin polymerization. *Trends Biochem. Sci.* **7**:55.

Pollard, T. D., and S. W. Craig. 1982. Actin binding proteins. *Trends Biochem. Sci.* **7**:88.

Porter, K. R., and C. Franzini-Armstrong. March 1965. The sarcoplasmic reticulum. *Sci. Amer.* **212**:72.

Porter, K. R., and J. B. Tucker. March 1981. The ground substance of the living cell. *Sci. Amer.* **244**:56.

Pratt, M. M., T. Otter, and E. D. Salmon. 1980. Dynein-like Mg^{2+}-ATPase in mitotic spindles isolated from sea urchin embryos (*Strongylocentrotus droebachiensis*). *J. Cell Biol.* **86**:738.

Prensier, G., E. Vivier, S. Goldstein, and J. Schrével. 1980. Motile flagellum with a "3 + 0" ultrastructure. *Science* **207**:1493.

Ris, H. 1985. The cytoplasmic filament system in critical point-dried whole mounts and plastic-embedded sections. *J. Cell Biol.* **100**:1474.

Satir, P. 1968. Studies on cilia. III. Further studies on the cilium tip and a "sliding filament" model of ciliary motility. *J. Cell Biol.* **39**:77.

Satir, P. October 1974. How cilia move. *Sci. Amer.* **231**:44.

Satir, P. 1982. Approaches to potential sliding mechanisms of cytoplasmic microtubules. *Cold Spring Harbor Sympos. Quant. Biol.* **46**:285.

Schliwa, M. 1981. Proteins associated with cytoplasmic actin. *Cell* **25**:587.

Schliwa, M., and J. van Blerkom. 1981. Structural interaction of cytoskeletal components. *J. Cell Biol.* **90**:222.

Scherson, T., et al. 1984. Dynamic interactions of fluorescently labeled microtubule-associated proteins in living cells. *J. Cell Biol.* **99**:425.

Schroeder, T. E. 1973. Actin in dividing cells: Contractile ring filaments bind heavy meromyosin. *Proc. Natl. Acad. Sci. U. S.* **70**:1688.

Schwartz, J. H. April 1980. The transport of substances in nerve cells. *Sci. Amer.* **242**:152.

Shay, J. W., ed. 1984. *Cell and Muscle Motility*, vol. 4. New York: Plenum.

Sloboda, R. D. 1980. The role of microtubules in cell structure and cell division. *Amer. Sci.* **68**:290.

Sluder, G., and C. L. Rieder. 1985. Experimental separation of pronuclei in fertilized sea urchin eggs: Chromosomes do not organize a spindle in the absence of centrosomes. *J. Cell Biol.* **100**:897.

Solomon, F. 1980. Organizing microtubules in the cytoplasm. *Cell* **22**:331.

Solomon, F. 1982. Organizing the cytoplasm for motility. *Cold Spring Harbor Sympos. Quant. Biol.* **46**:17.

Soltys, B. J., and G. G. Borisy. 1985. Polymerization of tubulin *in vivo*: Direct evidence for assembly onto microtubule ends and from centrosomes. *J. Cell Biol.* **100**:1682.

Sturgess, J. M., *et al.* 1979. Cilia with defective radial spokes. A cause of human respiratory disease. *New Engl. J. Med.* **300**:53.

Taylor, D. L., and Y.-L. Wang. 1980. Fluorescently labeled molecules as probes of the structure and function of living cells. *Nature* **284**:405.

Telzer, B. R., and J. L. Rosenbaum. 1979. Cell cycle-dependent, *in vitro* assembly of microtubules onto the pericentriolar material of HeLa cells. *J. Cell Biol.* **81**:484.

Tilney, L. G. 1968. Studies on the microtubules in heliozoa. IV. The effect of colchicine on the formation and maintenance of the axopodia and the redevelopment of pattern in *Actinosphaerium nucleofilum* (Barrett). *J. Cell Sci.* **3**:549.

Turksen, K., J. E. Aubin, and V. I. Kalnins. 1982. Identification of a centriole-associated protein by antibodies present in normal rabbit sera. *Nature* **298**:763.

Wang, K. 1983. Membrane skeleton of skeletal muscle. *Nature* **304**:485.

Warner, F. D., and P. Satir. 1974. The structural basis of ciliary bend formation. Radial spoke positional changes accompanying microtubule sliding. *J. Cell Biol.* **63**:35.

Weeds, A. 1982. Actin-binding proteins—regulators of cell architecture and cell motility. *Nature* **296**:811.

Wessells, N. K. October 1971. How living cells change shape. *Sci. Amer.* **225**:76.

Wheatley, D. N. 1982. *The Centriole: A Central Enigma of Cell Biology*. New York: Elsevier.

Wiche, G. 1985. High-molecular-weight microtubule-associated proteins (MAPs): A ubiquitous family of cytoskeletal connecting links. *Trends Biochem. Sci.* **10**:67.

Wilson, D. F., K. Nishiki, and M. Erecinska. 1981. Energy metabolism in muscle and its regulation during individual contraction–relaxation cycles. *Trends Biochem. Sci.* **6**:16.

Witman, G. B., J. Plummer, and G. Sander. 1979. *Chlamydomonas* flagellar mutants lacking radial spokes and central tubules. Structure, composition, and function of specific axonemal components. *J. Cell Biol.* **76**:729.

Wolosewick, J. J., and K. R. Porter. 1979. Microtrabecular lattice of the cytoplasmic ground substance. Artifact or reality. *J. Cell Biol.* **82**:114.

PART **IV**

Organization of the Genome

CHAPTER 12

Molecular Nature of the Genome

The **genome** is usually defined as the set of genes that contain the coded instructions for proteins that specify the structure, function, and regulatory processes in a life form. With the addition in recent years of molecular methods to those of conventional genetic analysis, we have come to view the genome as more than a bundle of individual genes. The means by which different life forms replicate, package, and organize their genomes vary from one group of organisms to another, just as these organisms vary in their life styles. In order to gain some appreciation of the relationship of the genome to the different needs (and kinds) of organisms, we will explore selected features of the genome as a system that provides the underlying foundations for the diversity we observe in the living world.

DNA Replication

As suggested in 1953 by Watson and Crick and proved in 1958 by Meselson and Stahl, each strand of the DNA double helix acts as a template for synthesis of a new, complementary partner strand. By this process of *semiconservative replication*, two identical DNA duplex molecules are produced from one parental duplex molecule (see Fig. 4.3). The remarkable accuracy of DNA replication depends on the structure and properties of the DNA molecule itself and on an ever-growing list of genes and gene products that make specific contributions to ensure the high fidelity of the replication process in making exact copies of all the genes in the genome, in every cell generation, in every organism throughout time.

12.1
The DNA Double Helix

Through complementary base pairing of adenines and thymines and of guanines and cytosines, the long unbranched polynucleotide chains of

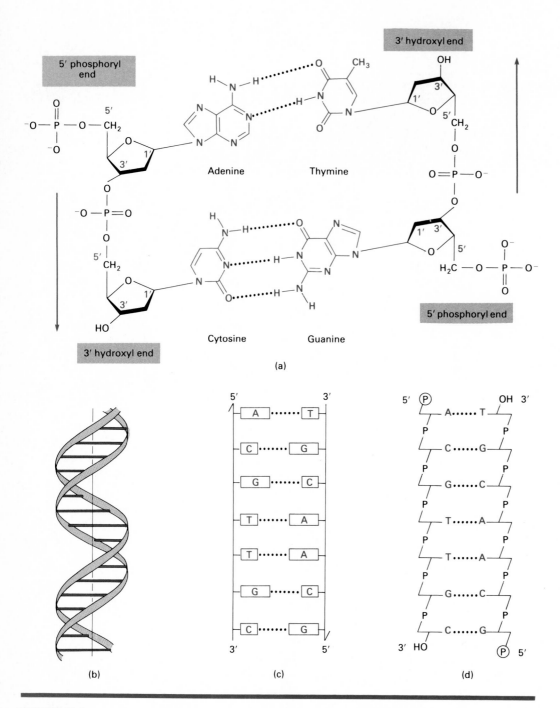

FIGURE 12-1
Molecular structure of the DNA double helix. (a) Each polynucleotide chain of the duplex consists of repeating nucleotide units joined by 3′,5′-phosphodiester bridges. The anti-parallel strands are hydrogen-bonded (dotted lines) between complementary base pairs. (b) The base pairs are stacked in the center of the molecule, between the two helically wound sugar–phosphate "backbones" of the polynucleotide chains. (c) The constant width of 2 nm for a duplex is due to the identical widths of all four possible complementary base pairs (A–T, T–A, G–C, C–G). Each base pair includes a larger purine (A or G) and a smaller pyrimidine (T or C) residue. (d) The DNA duplex is often depicted in the convention illustrated in this drawing, showing its major features of construction.

the **DNA double helix** are held in register in an *antiparallel* orientation. The nitrogenous base of each mononucleotide monomer is covalently bonded to deoxyribose, which is bonded in turn to a phosphate residue (Fig. 12.1). DNA molecules are relatively stable in the watery environment of the cell, primarily because of three major kinds of chemical bonds in polymer construction.

1. *Covalent bonds* link together atoms in each monomer unit, and they link mononucleotides in the long polymer chain via **3′,5′-phosphodiester bridges** between the 5′ carbon of one pentose sugar and the 3′ carbon of the pentose in the adjacent mononucleotide. These strong bonds in the sugar–phosphate "backbone" of each strand make the polynucleotide chains relatively resistant to breakage because of the high energy required for such an event.

2. The many weak *hydrogen bonds* within the DNA duplex are so arranged that most of them cannot break without many others breaking at the same time. This order of breakage is energetically unlikely to occur at cell temperatures, but it is readily accomplished *in vitro* to provide materials for many kinds of studies. Hydrogen bonding also takes place between virtually all the surface atoms in the sugar–phosphate chains and surrounding water molecules in the cell or test tube. These stabilizing forces help to maintain molecular shape, which is essential for genetic function.

3. *Hydrophobic interactions* occur between the flat surfaces of the aromatic nitrogenous bases stacked vertically along the length of the duplex molecule. These interactions lead to the exclusion of water molecules from the interior of the duplex so that water does not interfere or compete with hydrogen bonding between paired bases. Hydrophobic interactions thus contribute to molecular stability in the watery environment of the cell, and they also lend a considerable degree of stiffness to the DNA duplex.

The relative ease of separating and rejoining DNA strands permitted laboratory studies to characterize DNAs from different sources and to develop several important analytical methods. The two strands of native duplex DNA unwind and separate when the molecules are exposed to high temperature or to titration with acid or alkali. This **denaturation**, or **melting**, is the result of the disruption of hydrogen bonds between paired bases. One of the simplest ways to monitor DNA melting is to observe the change in absorbance of a preparation placed in a spectrophotometer set at a wavelength of 260 nm, the wavelength of maximum absorption of light energy by DNA. The stacked bases in duplex DNA absorb a given amount of light energy according to the concentration of molecules in a solution. When duplex DNA is melted, the bases in the single strands absorb more energy than the original duplex molecules at the *same* concentration (Fig. 12.2). The increase in absorbance of single-stranded versus duplex DNA at the same concentration of the molecules is called the **hyperchromic shift**. Thermal melting causes the bases to "unstack" and thus permits more light energy to be absorbed by the unhindered bases in single strands than in

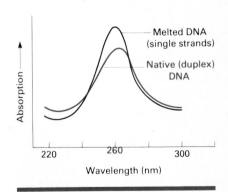

FIGURE 12-2

When melted DNA in solution is scanned at different wavelengths, there is greater absorbance at 260 nm than with the same concentration of duplex DNA in solution. This increase in absorbance of melted DNA is called the hyperchromic shift.

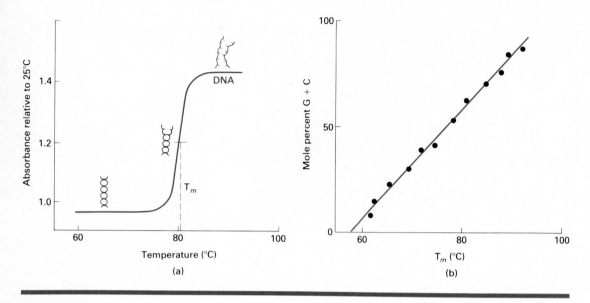

FIGURE 12-3
DNA melting. (a) Melting curve for duplex DNA in solution, with the increase in absorbance (the hyperchromic shift) plotted as a function of temperature. The T_m of a particular DNA is its midpoint melting temperature, at which half the denaturation has occurred in the sharp transition from the double-stranded to the single stranded state (shown diagrammatically in each of the three steps). When melting is completed, no further change in absorbance takes place (plateau). (b) T_m is dependent on the GC content of the DNA sample, as seen in the linear relationship for various DNAs (dots). More energy (higher temperature) is required to break triply hydrogen-bonded GC pairs than doubly hydrogen-bonded AT pairs.

double-stranded DNA. Because heated duplex DNA shows a hyperchromic shift and heated single-stranded DNA does not, this simple test permits us to identify the conformation of the molecules in any unknown sample.

GC pairs are triple-bonded and AT pairs are double-bonded in duplex DNA, so molecules with a higher mole percent of GC are more stable structures and require higher temperature or more alkaline pH in order to be melted. Acid affects purine bonds and is therefore not used routinely in denaturation studies, but alkaline conditions or high temperatures are widely used to melt native DNA. Chain unwinding during denaturation begins in regions higher in AT base pairs and moves progressively to regions of increasing GC content. Carefully controlled heating of DNA in solution is used to determine melting curves, which show the increase in absorbance during transition of duplexes to single-stranded chains. The beginning and end of melting in a duplex DNA preparation takes place over a very narrow range of temperature, which produces a characteristic sharp transition in the melting curve. The point at which the transition is 50% completed is called the **midpoint melting temperature**, or $\mathbf{T_m}$, and it is directly proportional to the GC content of the DNA molecules (Fig. 12.3). DNAs from different sources can thus be characterized by their T_m values, and because T_m and GC content are proportional, the GC content of a sample can be deduced from its T_m or vice versa.

The location of AT-rich sequences in a DNA molecule can be determined by **denaturation mapping**. AT regions melt sooner than GC regions in duplex DNA, so a sample can be heated at a temperature just high enough to melt AT regions but not GC-rich regions. In electron micrographs of such partially denatured preparations, intact GC duplex stretches contrast with opened-out, melted AT-rich portions of the molecule (Fig. 12.4). The method may seem somewhat crude today because we can quickly determine the exact nucleotide sequence in DNA molecules or regions that are thousands of nucleotides long. Denaturation mapping provides information that is useful when analyzing large genomes or as a preliminary to more detailed sequence analysis.

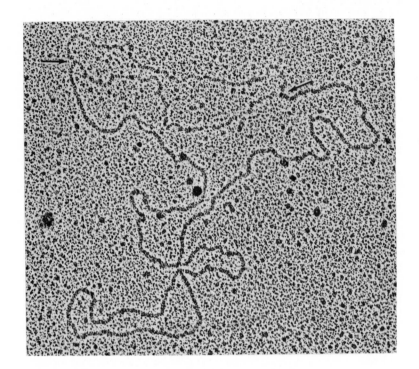

FIGURE 12-4
Electron micrograph of a mitochondrial duplex DNA molecule from *Drosophila melanogaster* eggs. The preparation was heated to 40°C for 10 minutes in a buffered solution of 10% formaldehyde, which leads to partial denaturation of the duplex molecules. Approximately one-fourth of the 6.1-μm-long circular molecule has denatured (between arrows), and this region is presumed to be richer in AT base pairs than the remainder of the molecule. Denaturation maps of AT-rich sequences can be constructed from such data. ×85,700. (Photograph courtesy of D. R. Wolstenholme and C. M.-R. Fauron.)

When melted DNA is incubated at a temperature about 25°C below its T_m, the two separated strands **renature**, or **reanneal**, to restore the original duplexes. Renaturation can be monitored by spectrophotometric readings of the decrease in absorbance at 260 nm, and in other ways. Information on the relatedness of different DNAs, the occurrence of deletions and nonhomologous regions in such DNAs, and similar features can be examined by **heteroduplex analysis**, in which single strands from the different sources undergo reannealing (Fig. 12.5). The kinetics of renaturation provide a measure of the size of the genome and

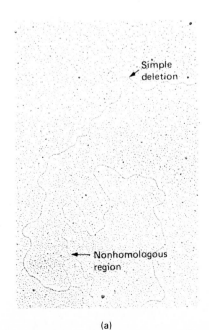

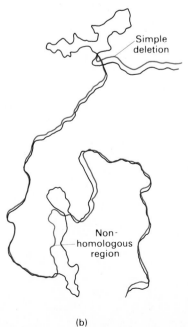

(a)   (b)

FIGURE 12-5
Heteroduplex DNA from annealed single strands of two phage λ strains, one of which (color) carried a simple deletion plus a second deleted region into which a short piece of nonhomologous DNA had been incorporated instead of its own much longer sequence. (a) Electron micrograph and (b) interpretative drawing showing that only one loop of single-stranded (unpaired) DNA occurs in the simple deletion site, but two unmatched single strands loop out in the second altered site. (Courtesy of B. Westmoreland and H. Ris; from Westmoreland, B. *et al.*, 1969, *Science* **163**:1343.)

of other genomic characteristics, which we will discuss later in this chapter and in the next chapter, along with the importance of renaturation and heteroduplex analysis in determining relationships between DNA and its RNA transcripts. In the next sections, however, we will concentrate on the replication of DNA and on the physical features of the double helix in relation to this process.

12.2
Origin and Direction of Strand Synthesis

DNA replication begins *in vivo* at a specific sequence of nucleotides called the **origin**. A single origin location occurs in prokaryotic genomes, but multiple origins are distributed along each linear chromosomal DNA molecule of eukaryotic genomes. Because of the complexity and multiplicity of eukaryotic chromosomes, most of our information has been obtained from the study of *E. coli* and other bacterial systems and of viral and plasmid DNAs, which are even simpler. From such studies of small DNAs it seems that the commitment to a new cycle of replication depends on the *recognition of an origin sequence* by a set of initiation proteins. Once the origin is recognized and strand synthesis is initiated, *synthesis proceeds* under the catalytic direction of another set of proteins. A third group of proteins is responsible for *suppression of the initiation of replication* elsewhere than at the origin to which initiation proteins are bound. In *E. coli*, the chromosomal origin of replication (*oriC*) consists of a unique sequence of 245 base pairs, which has been mapped at the 82-minute site on the 100-minute genetic map of the species.

In 1963 John Cairns provided the first experimental evidence showing that replication proceeds directionally away from the origin. He grew *E. coli* for one 30-minute generation period to label one strand of their duplex DNA with [³H]thymidine, as expected for semiconservative replication. The cells were then allowed to undergo a second 30-minute replication cycle during which time samples were removed at intervals and prepared for autoradiography. It was expected that there would be twice the density of label in regions of the DNA molecule that had undergone two rounds of replication. In other words, some parts of the molecule would have both strands labeled, whereas other parts

FIGURE 12-6

Diagrammatic interpretation of replicating duplex DNA in *E. coli*, based on observed distributions of radioactive label (colored dots) in autoradiographs (at right). The second DNA doubling has proceeded only for a short time, producing semiconservatively replicated segments A and B. Segment C has not yet replicated a second time.

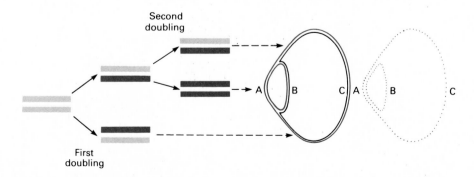

Interpretation based on semiconservative replication of DNA

Autoradiograph of *E. coli* chromosome

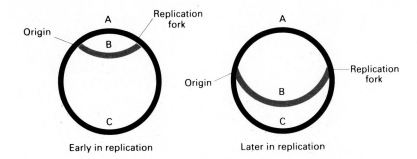

FIGURE 12-7
Theta forms of replicating circular duplex DNA show progressive lengthening of the equal-sized segments A and B, at the same time that segment C becomes shorter. These observations were interpreted to mean that replication proceeded unidirectionally around the circle, and that synthesis proceeded at a replication fork that moved farther and farther away from its point of origin. Segment B (color) is the portion of the replicating molecule that shows the greatest density of label in an autoradiograph (see Fig. 12.6).

would have only one labeled strand because its partner had not yet replicated in the second cycle (Fig. 12.6). In photographs the replicating DNA molecules resembled the Greek letter *theta* (θ); such circular replicating molecules have been called **theta forms** for this reason.

Theta forms were interpreted as showing that replication proceeded away from an origin, going around the circle until two semiconserved progeny duplexes were produced. Only one of the three segments of a theta form was very densely labeled, and this same segment changed in length during the second 30-minute replication cycle. Measurements of replicating molecules revealed that the denser segment became progressively longer at the same time that the initially long, less densely labeled segment became progressively shorter (Fig. 12.7). These data led to the proposal that replication proceeded unidirectionally around the circle and that the growth of new strands took place at a **replication fork** that moved farther away from the origin during the replication cycle.

The same θ figure could have arisen if replication had proceeded *in both directions* away from the origin, generating two replication forks. Later studies using *E. coli* indeed showed that *replication was bidirectional*, not unidirectional. DNA from most viruses, prokaryotes, and eukaryotes has now been shown to replicate by the more common bidirectional pattern.

The two patterns can be distinguished in autoradiographs if the regions between the two forks of the theta are examined for density of label (Fig. 12.8). In a molecule replicating unidirectionally the denser label is found only in the region of the one growing fork. If replication

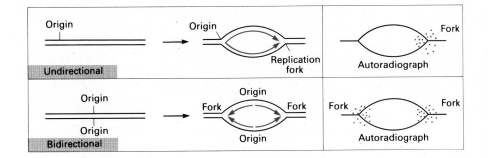

FIGURE 12-8
The autoradiographic pattern of label distribution can reveal whether replication proceeds in only one direction or in both directions away from the origin. Silver grains (colored dots) showing newly incorporated [³H] thymidine will be found in one place (one growing fork) in unidirectionally replicating DNA but in two places (two growing replication forks) if synthesis proceeds bidirectionally. The origin can then be located in relation to the presence of one or two forks in the replicating region. Each single line in the panel at the right represents a duplex region of DNA.

FIGURE 12-9
(a) Four replication bubbles are evident in this electron micrograph of a segment of purified chromosomal DNA from *Drosophila melanogaster.* Each replication bubble represents a replicon, which includes an origin at which replication is initiated. ×38,000 (b) The four replication bubbles are shown in color in this tracing. (Photograph courtesy of D. R. Wolstenholme, from Wolstenholme, D. R., 1973, *Chromosoma* **43** : 1–18, Fig. 6.)

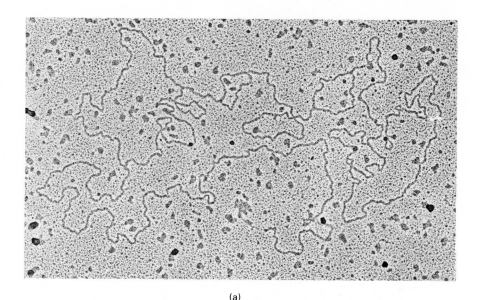

(a)

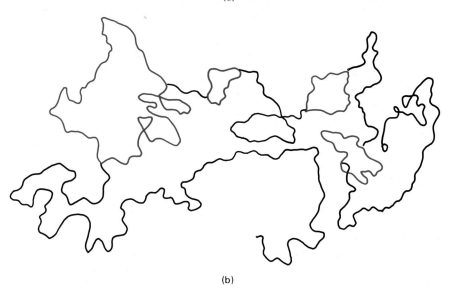

(b)

proceeds in both directions, there is denser label at *both* forks and less label between the forks.

Bacterial and viral genomes usually have only one location for the origin of replication, and the entire genome can be considered a **replicon**, or unit of replication. Eukaryotes have about 100 to 200 replicons per genome, as has been deduced from kinetic studies and from electron micrographs that show a number of *replication bubbles* along a single chromosomal DNA segment (Fig. 12.9). Each replication bubble presumably represents a single origin location from which chain synthesis has proceeded bidirectionally, creating two replication forks per bubble.

12.3
Synthesis of New Strands

The building blocks of DNA are deoxyribonucleoside 5'-*mono*-phosphates, which are derived from deoxyribonucleoside 5'-*tri*phosphate precursors. Triphosphate precursors are added onto a

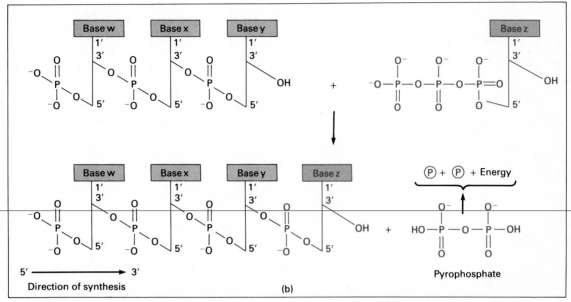

growing chain and are there hydrolyzed to monophosphates. During hydrolysis, pyrophosphate is released and the synthesis step is thereby driven to completion. Chain growth proceeds in the 5'→3' direction, as nucleoside triphosphates are added at the 3'-hydroxyl end of the growing strand (Fig. 12.10).

The two complementary strands of the DNA duplex are antiparallel, and chain growth proceeds along each strand only in the 5'→3' direction; the two strands must therefore grow in *opposite* directions at the replication fork. From genetic, biochemical, and electron microscopical studies, it has been suggested that the advance of a fork proceeds by continuous synthesis of one strand (the *leading* strand) and discontinuous synthesis of the other (the *lagging* strand). The short pieces of the lagging strand are subsequently bonded together during continued chain growth (Fig. 12.11). The first evidence of discontinuous DNA synthesis was provided in the late 1960s by R. Okazaki and colleagues, and the short pieces of the lagging strand are therefore referred to as **Okazaki fragments**.

Okazaki studied *E. coli* mutants that were defective for one of the enzymes needed to synthesize DNA. When such mutants were provided with labeled precursor in short pulses at low temperature (to slow down the reactions), almost all of the label was recovered in pieces of new DNA that were 1000 to 2000 nucleotides long. The synthesis of DNA apparently proceeded in bursts, but the Okazaki fragments were not hooked together to make whole chains because the mutants lacked the enzyme needed to catalyze the binding reaction. The enzyme is *DNA*

FIGURE 12-10
DNA synthesis. (a) New strand synthesis proceeds in the 5' → 3' direction through the addition of nucleoside 5-monophosphate residues derived from nucleoside triphosphate precursors. (b) Detail of synthesis showing the nucleoside triphosphate precursor (color) and its conversion by hydrolysis to a nucleoside monophosphate building block at the 3'-OH end of the growing chain. The release of pyrophosphate drives the reaction to completion.

FIGURE 12-11
Diagram of a replication fork during synthesis of duplex DNA. Chain growth proceeds in the 5′ → 3′ direction along each antiparallel template strand (black), but one new strand (the leading strand) is believed to be synthesized continuously and the other (the lagging strand) to be synthesized discontinuously. The short pieces (Okazaki fragments) of the lagging strand are later joined together to form a continuous covalently bonded chain.

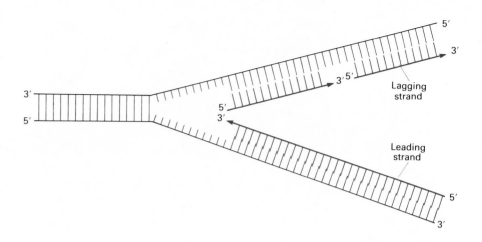

ligase, which guides the covalent bonding of the sugar–phosphate backbones of the replicated fragments. We will refer to this enzyme again when we discuss the sequence of events at the replication fork.

It was known for quite some time that the *initiation* of chain growth could not be accomplished by the same enzymes that catalyzed the elongation of an existing chain or Okazaki fragment. In 1970 Arthur Kornberg discovered that each DNA fragment could be initiated only by the synthesis of a short stretch of RNA, which primed the subsequent addition of DNA precursors. The **RNA primer** is made in a reaction catalyzed by an RNA polymerase that uses DNA as a template. Most of these enzymes are special polymerases called **RNA primases**, although in some cases the main cellular RNA polymerase may serve to guide synthesis of the short (about 4 to 10 residues) RNA sequence that primes covalent extension by DNA synthesis. The evidence for RNA priming of DNA chain growth was obtained by Kornberg in studies of phage M13. Mature M13 phage contain a single-stranded circular DNA molecule that is converted to a duplex replicating form when the virus infects host cells. The circular duplexes multiply during the infection cycle, and single-stranded DNA is later packaged in mature virus particles.

Kornberg found that, if the drug *rifampicin* was provided during the infection process, the single-stranded DNA in M13 phage was not converted to the duplex replicating form. If the drug was added about 5 minutes after infection, which is when the converted duplexes begin to synthesize new duplex DNA in the host cell, new duplex DNA was not produced. Because rifampicin specifically inhibits the initiation of RNA chains by RNA polymerase, the experimental data support the view that DNA synthesis is initiated by newly formed RNA primer sequences. Drugs that inhibit protein synthesis did not affect DNA synthesis, which showed that the RNA itself was important for DNA synthesis, not some protein(s) translated from that RNA.

RNA primase binds to the origin of a duplex DNA molecule, but it cannot begin to catalyze primer synthesis until the paired bases there are separated and the template surfaces of the strands are exposed. In addition, the strands of the double helix must be unwound as hydrogen bonds are disrupted between the two chains and a replication fork is established. As we discussed in Section 12.1, melting requires drastic conditions in the test tube, and these conditions are not encountered in

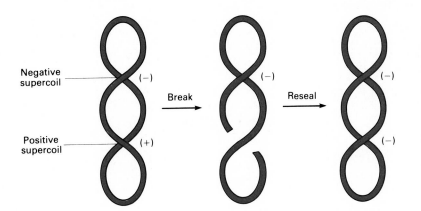

FIGURE 12-12
The enzyme topoisomerase II, or gyrase, can convert a positive (+) supercoil to a negative (−) supercoil conformation by breaking the duplex and resealing the broken ends in an inverted position. Supercoils are superimposed on the helically coiled duplex, whose double helix remains unchanged by supercoiling events.

the living cell. Strand separation requires the help of a number of specific proteins and energy from ATP hydrolysis. An enzyme called **topoisomerase II**, which is colloquially referred to as a **gyrase**, binds to the origin of replication and there induces double-stranded breaks and rejoinings, which causes negative *supercoiling* of the helically coiled duplex DNA (Fig. 12.12). The imposition of a second order of coiling by gyrase makes the DNA topologically accessible to **topoisomerase I**, which nicks and closes single strands and allows unwinding (relaxing) of the helical coil. As the helix unwinds, **helicase** breaks hydrogen bonds and thereby separates the two strands to establish a replication fork. Helicase action is driven by the energy of ATP hydrolysis, and the strand separation induced by this enzyme is then stabilized by **single-strand binding (SSB) proteins**. SSB proteins bind cooperatively to single strands or single-stranded regions of DNA and thus make them taut so that the exposed bases are accessible for pairing with new bases during DNA strand synthesis (Fig. 12.13). In addition, SSB proteins favor a helix-opening process by virtue of keeping an unzipped region open, so they are also referred to as helix-destabilizing proteins.

Once primed, DNA strand synthesis proceeds more or less continuously on the leading strand and discontinuously on the lagging strand. The *overall* direction of chain growth is 5′→3′ on the leading strand and 3′→5′ on the antiparallel lagging strand. The *actual* direction

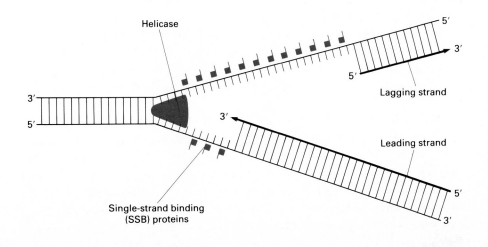

FIGURE 12-13
Diagram of selected events at the replication fork. As the double helix unwinds (by topoisomerase I action), the helicase enzyme breaks hydrogen bonds between paired bases and thereby separates the two strands and establishes a replication fork. The separated single-stranded regions are held taut by single-strand binding (SSB) proteins (color), which bind cooperatively to these regions. Such opened single-stranded segments are thus made accessible for pairing with new monomers during DNA synthesis.

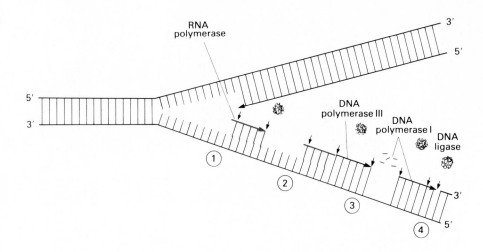

FIGURE 12-14
Discontinuous strand synthesis at the replication fork. (1) An RNA primer sequence (color) is added and hydrogen-bonded to the template by the action of RNA primase, at the replication fork. (2) Once primed, new strand synthesis may proceed as DNA monomers are added to the RNA primer by the catalytic action of DNA polymerase III. (3) The RNA primer is digested by exonuclease action of DNA polymerase I, and this enzyme then fills in the gap with deoxyribonucleotides. (4) After the Okazaki fragment has been entirely converted to DNA, the enzyme DNA ligase seals the 3′ end of the new fragment to the 5′ end of the previously synthesized DNA to make an uninterrupted sequence of new DNA. The pairs of arrows indicate the extent of the primer sequence in steps (1) and (2) and the space previously occupied by the primer in steps (3) and (4).

of chain growth, however, is only in the 5′→3′ direction on both strands. Each Okazaki fragment of the lagging strand is synthesized in the 5′→3′ direction, but when these fragments are stitched together, the entire strand is extended from the 3′ end to the 5′ end. The enzymes that catalyze strand synthesis are DNA polymerases, which can add new monomer units *only* to a 3′-hydroxyl end of a growing chain or fragment (see Fig. 12.10).

DNA polymerase III extends the growing chain from an RNA primer segment, and it is the main replicating enzyme. New strands contain no RNA upon completion, so the primers must be removed and the gaps filled in before a complete chain or sequence is produced. **DNA polymerase I** is the enzyme that fulfills both these functions—it removes RNA by exonuclease action and replaces ribonucleotides with deoxyribonucleotides, going from 5′ to 3′ (Fig. 12.14). When the Okazaki fragment has been converted entirely to DNA, the 3′ end of one fragment and the 5′ end of an adjacent fragment are joined together by the action of the enzyme **DNA ligase**. This enzyme uses energy from ATP hydrolysis to activate the exposed 5′ end and to join the two fragments covalently by formation of a phosphodiester link. The same event is repeated during synthesis until the strand is completed (Fig. 12.15).

In summary, DNA strand synthesis is initiated at the origin of replication by the action of bound proteins that include topoisomerase II and RNA primase. The gyrase nicks and closes duplex DNA, causing negative supercoiling after which the underlying helix can be unwound, and RNA primase catalyzes RNA primer synthesis. The replication fork for elongation of the chain is established by the action of topoisomerase I, which unwinds or relaxes the DNA helix, disruption of hydrogen bonds between paired bases by helicase action, and tautening of the opened single strands of the replication bubble by the binding of SSB proteins. DNA polymerase III adds deoxyribonucleotides to the RNA primer segment, in the 5′→3′ direction; DNA polymerase I excises RNA primers and fills the gaps with deoxyribonucleotides. The DNA segments are ligated by DNA ligase action, which catalyzes phosphodiester linkage to form an uninterrupted sugar–phosphate backbone in the new

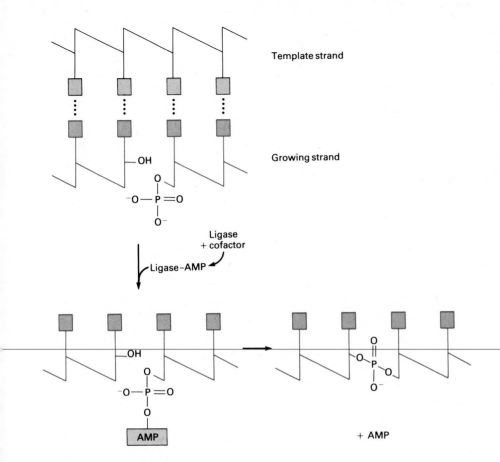

FIGURE 12-15
DNA ligase joins the 3'-OH terminus of one fragment to the 5'-phosphate terminus of an adjacent fragment with the help of a cofactor. In the first step of the sequence, the cofactor helps in the formation of an enzyme–AMP intermediate that activates the free 5' end of DNA by adding the AMP component there. The enzyme completes the 3',5'-phosphodiester link in the second step of the sequence and thereby joins the fragments into a continuous covalently bonded sequence. Upon completion of the second step, both the enzyme and AMP are released.

strand. The end result of all these events is production of two semiconserved duplex DNAs, each consisting of one parental template strand and one newly synthesized complementary partner strand. These events are summarized in Fig. 12.16 for one of the two replication forks in bidirectionally replicating DNA. The same events take place at each of the two forks of a replication bubble and are presumed to occur at the location of each origin of replication in eukaryotic DNA, just as at the location of the single origin in prokaryotic DNA.

DNA copying during replication is remarkably accurate. Only about one error is made per 10^9 base pairs, which is more than adequate to maintain large genomes such as those in mammals (about 3×10^9 base pairs of DNA). The high fidelity of copying is due largely to the *proofreading* mechanisms made possible by special properties of DNA polymerases. DNA polymerases cannot link together two nucleoside triphosphates to initiate a new chain or segment; they absolutely require a base-paired pre-existing segment with an available 3'-hydroxyl end onto which nucleotides can be added. If the available 3'-hydroxyl end is not paired because the wrong base has been added opposite the template, DNA polymerase I can remove the unpaired residue by hydrolysis and replace it with the correct matching base to regenerate a base-paired 3'-hydroxyl terminus. In fact, the polymerase performs its exonuclease function for any number of unpaired residues at the chain terminus, stopping when it reaches a base-paired point and at that point commencing its polymerase function to add correct monomers in

FIGURE 12-16
Schematic summary of dynamic events at the replication fork during synthesis of duplex DNA. Initial events (not shown) include nicking and closing of DNA by topoisomerase II to introduce negative supercoils in helically wound DNA as a prelude to the unwinding of the DNA double helix by topoisomerase I. When unwound, hydrogen bonds between paired bases are broken by helicase action, thus opening the replication fork; the opened regions are kept taut by bound single-strand binding (SSB) proteins. RNA primase catalyzes the addition of a short RNA primer, and the primed segment is extended by the addition of DNA monomers in reactions catalyzed by DNA polymerase III, the main replicating enzyme. DNA polymerase I removes the RNA primer by exonuclease digestion and then fills in the gap with DNA monomers to produce a continuous Okazaki fragment. DNA ligase seals adjacent Okazaki fragments to produce an uninterrupted sugar–phosphate backbone as the lagging strand undergoes discontinuous synthesis. Two semiconserved duplex DNAs are produced at the replication fork, each composed of one parental template strand and one newly synthesized complementary strand. The new strand may be synthesized continuously (leading strand) or discontinuously (lagging strand), according to available evidence. (Modified from Kornberg, A., 1984, *Trends in Biochem. Sci.* **9**(4):122–124, Fig. 1.)

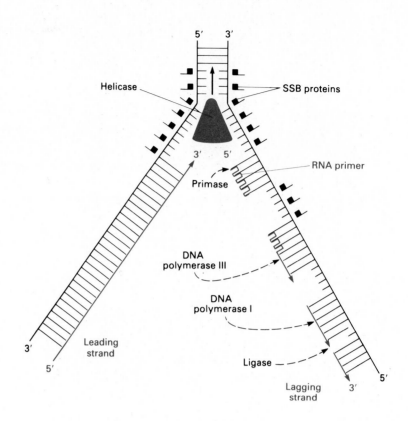

accordance with the template sequence (Fig. 12.17). The polymerase thus proofreads the growing chain for base-pair mismatches, or errors, and removes the unpaired erroneous base or sequence of bases through its exonuclease function. Upon reaching matched, paired bases, the enzyme performs its polymerase function and guides the synthesis of correct copy by catalyzing the $5' \rightarrow 3'$ incorporation of residues that are complementary to the template sequence.

All or most of the same replication proteins guide DNA synthesis during the *repair* of damaged DNA and during the breakage, rejoining, and repair events that characterize genetic *recombination*. We will discuss these topics later.

12.4
Replication in Viruses

The viral genome consists of a single linear or circular molecule of DNA or of RNA, and the molecule may be either single-stranded or double-stranded in any particular virus (Table 12.1). Replication in many viruses differs in various respects from the mode in prokaryotic and eukaryotic systems, as *in vitro* studies and studies of a variety of mutants have revealed. To gain some sense of viral diversity, we can examine a few examples to see their basic features and variations.

Replication of DNA viruses varies with the particular problems encountered in single-stranded versus double-stranded genomes and in circular versus linear DNA molecules. The mammalian virus SV40 (simian virus 40) replicates its circular duplex DNA genome by conventional bidirectional synthesis along both template strands, pro-

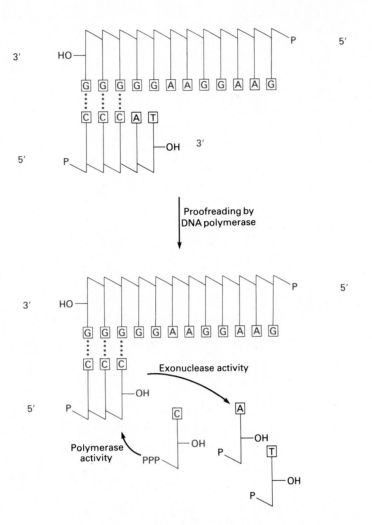

FIGURE 12-17
Relatively error-free copying of DNA during replication is largely due to proofreading by DNA polymerase I. By its exonuclease action, the enzyme removes incorrect residues (black) that have not undergone base pairing. And by its subsequent polymerase action, the enzyme adds correctly matched residues (color) to the base-paired 3'-OH terminus of the growing chain.

TABLE 12-1
Characteristics of Some Representative Viruses

Nucleic Acid	Virus	Main Host	Comments
DNA			
single-stranded	φX174	*Escherichia coli*	
	M13	*Escherichia coli*	
double-stranded	T2, T4, T6	*Escherichia coli*	
	adenoviruses	human	cause respiratory infections
	herpex simplex	human	causes "fever blisters" and genital herpes
	Epstein–Barr	human	causes infectious mononucleosis; associated with Burkitt's lymphoma
	cauliflower mosaic	cauliflower	transmitted by aphids
RNA			
single-stranded	tobacco mosaic	tobacco	
	poliovirus	human	
	measles virus	human	
	influenza A, B, C	human	
	retroviruses	mammals, birds	cause tumors
double-stranded	reoviruses	human	cause mild illness of respiratory or GI tract
	wound tumor virus	plants	transmitted by leafhoppers

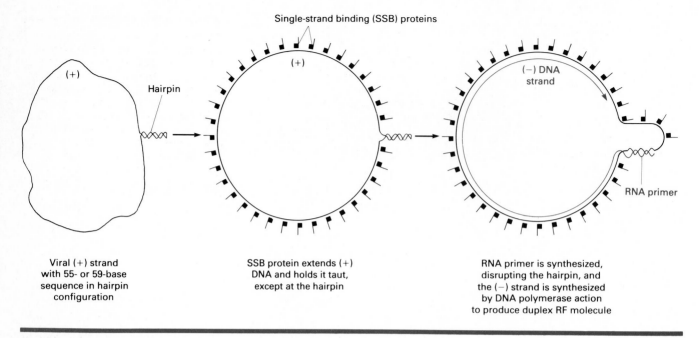

Single-strand binding (SSB) proteins

Hairpin

(+)

(+)

(−) DNA strand

RNA primer

Viral (+) strand
with 55- or 59-base
sequence in hairpin
configuration

SSB protein extends (+)
DNA and holds it taut,
except at the hairpin

RNA primer is synthesized,
disrupting the hairpin, and
the (−) strand is synthesized
by DNA polymerase action
to produce duplex RF molecule

FIGURE 12-18
During infection of *E. coli* by the single-stranded DNA phage φX174 or M13, the entering single (+) strand of the virus is coated with single-strand binding (SSB) proteins everywhere except in a 55- to 59-base sequence that exists in a hairpin configuration. A segment of RNA primer is synthesized at the hairpin region, and it is extended by DNA polymerase III action to form the complementary (−) strand of the duplex replicating form (RF) molecule. This duplex RF molecule produces (+) strands, using the (−) strand as a template, in repeated rounds of DNA synthesis.

ducing replication intermediates of the Cairns theta-form configuration just as *E. coli* does. Phage such as φX174 and M13 have a single-stranded circular DNA genome, which is converted to a double-stranded circular *replicating form* (RF) during the infection cycle in *E. coli* host cells. Although replication involves a duplex molecule, the RF DNA synthesizes only viral coding (+) strands for packaging in mature viruses, and the variation in replication deals with this special problem of selective strand synthesis.

The entering φX174 or M13 viral (+) strand is coated with host SSB proteins everywhere except in a 55- or 59-base sequence that forms a hairpin configuration. An RNA primer segment is synthesized at the hairpin region, and the primer is then extended by DNA polymerase III to form the complementary (−) strand of the duplex RF molecule (Fig. 12.18). The duplex RF proceeds to produce (+) strand, using the (−) strand as a template. Synthesis begins when the (+) strand of duplex RF is nicked at the site of the origin of replication, making a free 3'-hydroxyl end available for extension by DNA polymerase III. Synthesis proceeds around the circle and, as the replication fork advances, it extends the (+) strand along the (−) strand template, but it also displaces the previous (+) partner strand to produce a structure called a *rolling circle* (Fig. 12.19). In theory, any number of unit genomes can be synthesized by the **rolling circle mechanism**, each turn of the circle leading to displacement of the (+) strand that was synthesized in a previous cycle. When the unit genomes are cleaved from the displaced tail, the linear (+) strand sequence may be either converted to duplex RF for continued cycles of replication or circularized and packaged in virus particles for release from the infected cell. In the first case, the cleaved (+) strand would be coated with SSB protein in preparation for (−) strand synthesis to make duplex molecules; in the second case, the naked single strand would be enclosed in the viral protein coat, or *capsid*.

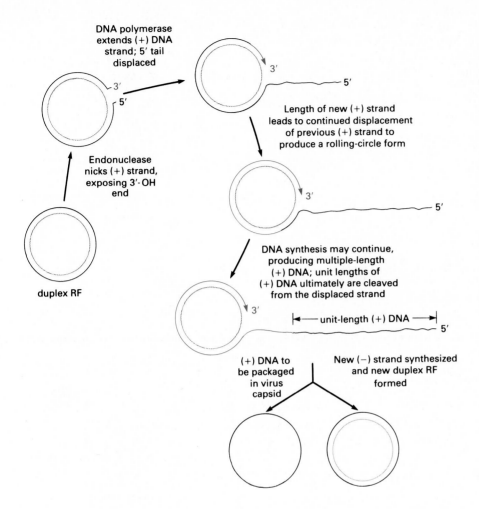

DNA polymerase extends (+) DNA strand; 5' tail displaced

Endonuclease nicks (+) strand, exposing 3'-OH end

duplex RF

Length of new (+) strand leads to continued displacement of previous (+) strand to produce a rolling-circle form

DNA synthesis may continue, producing multiple-length (+) DNA; unit lengths of (+) DNA ultimately are cleaved from the displaced strand

unit-length (+) DNA

(+) DNA to be packaged in virus capsid

New (−) strand synthesized and new duplex RF formed

FIGURE 12-19
The problem of selective strand synthesis can be solved through the rolling circle mechanism of single-stranded DNA synthesis, in which duplex replicating form (RF) DNA produces new (+) strand viral DNA (color) from (−) strand (dashed line) template information. The newly synthesized (+) DNA is produced in multiple lengths from a rolling circle form of the duplex. Unit genome lengths of (+) DNA are cleaved from the displaced tail of the rolling circle and may be circularized for packaging in the virus capsid or for continued cycles of (+) strand replication as part of new duplex RF molecules.

In ϕX174, the A protein encoded in the viral A gene is believed to bind to RF DNA and nick the (+) strand to initiate replication. The A protein is also believed to be involved in circularizing a linear unit genome cleaved from the tail of the rolling circle.

Replication of various linear duplex viral genomes poses the special problem of initiating DNA synthesis in the absence of an RNA priming process to provide the needed free 3'-hydroxyl terminus for chain elongation. In some phage and in the adenoviruses of animals, among others, the priming requirement is fulfilled by the action of special proteins that are covalently bound to the 5' terminal base of each strand of the duplex DNA molecule; the terminal protein is coded by the virus. In adenoviruses, mature DNA isolated from the viral particles has a 55,000-dalton protein bound to the 5' terminus of each strand, whereas replicating strands have a covalently bound 80,000-dalton protein at each 5' terminus of the duplex DNA. Presumably, the larger protein is involved in initiating replication and it is cleaved to the smaller size at some point during virus maturation. The 80K protein has a covalently linked cytidine with a free 3'-hydroxyl group, which primes the initiation of DNA chain synthesis by DNA polymerase. Chain synthesis proceeds independently at the two 5' ends of the duplex DNA, as the 80K protein displaces the homologous strands to which the 55K

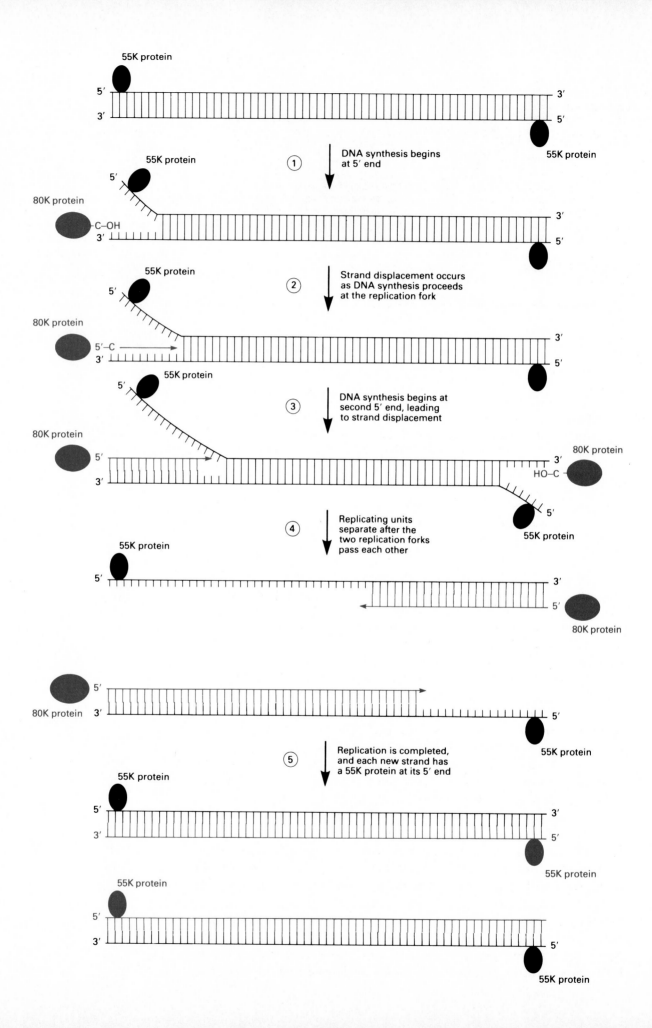

◄ **FIGURE 12-20**
Various linear duplex viral genomes utilize a special protein instead of RNA primer to provide a free 3′-OH terminus needed for the initiation of DNA synthesis. In adenoviruses, mature DNA has a 55,000-dalton (55K) protein at the 5′ end of each strand of the duplex. An 80,000-dalton (80K) protein with a free 3′-OH of its covalently bonded cytidine (C) primes DNA chain synthesis (color) and leads to displacement of the homologous strand to which the 55K terminal protein is bound. Chain synthesis proceeds independently at the two 5′ ends of the original duplex, and the two replicating units eventually separate but continue replication until completion. The new strand (color) in each semiconserved duplex product has a 55K protein at its 5′ end, presumably formed from the 80K protein sometime during virus maturation. Replication by strand displacement proceeds in the expected 5′ → 3′ direction along each template strand.

terminal protein is bound (Fig. 12.20). By this replication process of **strand displacement**, two new DNA strands are synthesized in the expected 5′→3′ direction, and each new semiconserved duplex has a terminal protein bound to each of its 5′ ends.

Many of the RNA viruses, whether single-stranded like polio virus or double-stranded like the reoviruses, have RNA-dependent RNA polymerases (*replicases*) that direct RNA replication. These replicases are coded by the virus genome, and new strands are synthesized in the 5′→3′ direction, beginning at the 3′ end of the template viral RNA strand(s). The replicase is often packaged in the mature viral particle so that viral RNA replication can begin immediately upon infection of the host cell. In the case of so-called *negative-strand* viruses such as influenza viruses, only the noncoding (−) strand is packaged so that replication is impossible unless the viral replicase is also present in the infecting particle. All the negative-strand viruses, in fact, have replicase packaged in the mature particles. During infection the coding (+) strand is synthesized, and new replicase proteins can be made from the information encoded in this strand, as well as replication of new (−) RNA strands for progeny viruses (Fig. 12.21).

A novel system of replication has been described for the single-stranded RNA tumor viruses of vertebrate animals. The Rous sarcoma virus (RSV) and others in the whole closely related group were prevented from replicating their RNA genome when DNA inhibitors were provided to host cells. This indication of the need for DNA synthesis in the multiplication of RNA tumor viruses was shown by David Baltimore and Howard Temin in 1970 to be due to the action of a very unusual polymerizing enzyme. The enzyme is an RNA-dependent DNA polymerase, which directs the synthesis of DNA from RNA templates. The reverse nature of the reaction from all other previously known DNA or RNA polymerases (which use DNA templates for DNA or RNA synthesis) led to the designation of the enzyme as **reverse transcriptase** and of these RNA tumor viruses as *retroviruses*.

In the case of Rous sarcoma virus, the first retrovirus to be described and one of the best known, the virus enters the cell and loses the membranous envelope that surrounds the encapsulated particle. The capsid coat is removed and the naked single-stranded RNA genome becomes accessible to the catalytic action of reverse transcriptase (Fig.

FIGURE 12-21
Influenza virus and other (−) strand RNA viruses package a replicase in the infecting particle, which guides synthesis in the host cell of the complementary coding (+) strand. The (+) RNA strand then serves as the template for new (−) strands for progeny viruses; it also serves as a messenger that guides translation from (+) information of new replicase and new capsid proteins for progeny viruses. If the replicase were not present in the entering virus, the noncoding (−) strand alone would be unable to subsidize virus multiplication after infection.

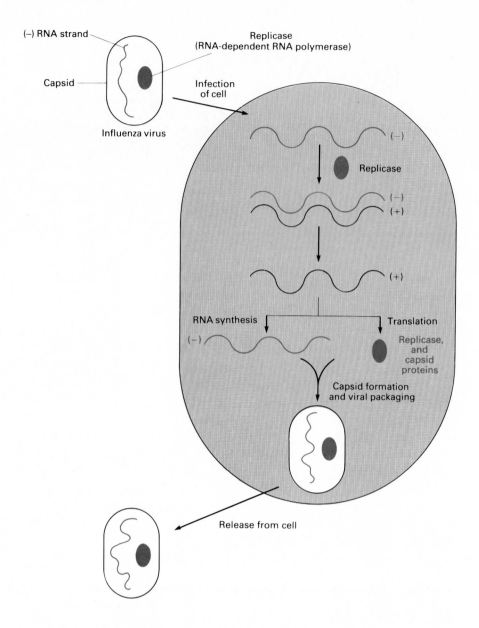

12.22). A DNA strand is copied from the RNA template, and the enzyme then catalyzes the synthesis of a DNA strand complementary to the first, thus producing a complete DNA double helix. The linear DNA somehow makes its way to the nucleus, where it is integrated into the host genome. The integrated **proviral DNA** is transcribed by the host apparatus to produce viral RNAs for packaging into mature viruses and for messengers from which viral proteins will be translated. One of the virally encoded proteins is the reverse transcriptase, from the viral *pol* gene, and molecules of the enzyme are packaged along with genomic RNA during retrovirus maturation.

In addition to exhibiting a variety of enzymatic tricks for replication, viruses differ in their degree of self-sufficiency for genomic multiplication. Some viruses (such as SV40) have no replication proteins of their own and rely entirely on the host machinery for replication. Some viruses have only a single gene that specifies one essential replication protein, and all the others are provided by the host. Retroviruses, for

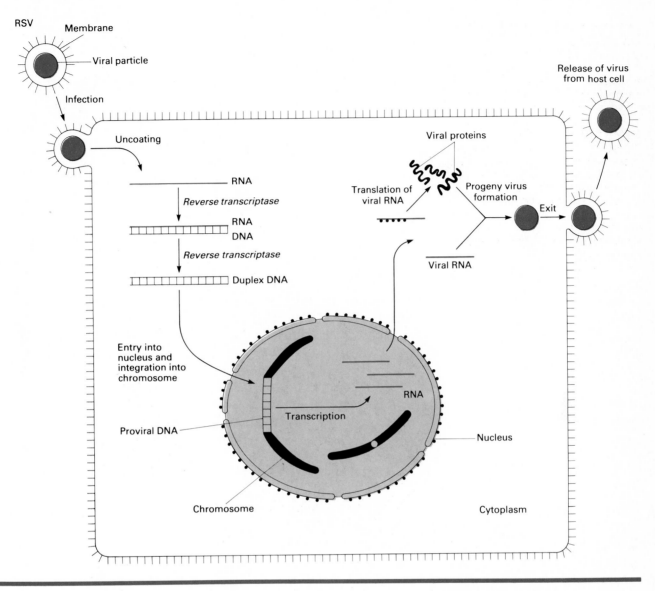

FIGURE 12-22
Infection cycle of the retrovirus RSV (Rous sarcoma virus). The infecting virus is uncoated and its RNA genome is copied into DNA by its own reverse transcriptase, an RNA-dependent DNA polymerase. The linear duplex DNA moves to the nucleus and is there integrated as proviral DNA in a host chromosome. In the host cell cytoplasm, some of the RNA transcripts of proviral DNA are translated into virus proteins (including the reverse transcriptase), and other RNA transcripts are packaged in progeny viruses. The virus is wrapped in a piece of host cell membrane upon its release from the cell, and it may initiate a new cycle of infection.

example, have three genes but only the *pol* gene encodes a replication protein (reverse transcriptase); the other two specify protein components of the core and the envelope of the mature virus. The linear duplex DNA genome of phage T4 of *E. coli* is very large (165,000 base pairs) and about 25 to 30 viral genes are involved in replication of the T4 genome in the infected host cell. In each case, regardless of the variations present, the virus is successful only if it can circumvent the cellular controls that would either prevent or limit its replication. Once established in the host, the virus must then initiate its own genomic replication selectively.

12.5
Replication in Mitochondria and Chloroplasts

The circular or linear duplex DNA genome in mitochondria and chloroplasts replicates semiconservatively, which was first shown in the 1960s for *Neurospora* mitochondrial DNA (**mtDNA**) and for *Chlamydomo-*

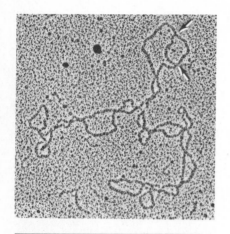

FIGURE 12-23
Electron micrograph of a theta-form replicating molecule of rat liver mitochondrial DNA, measuring about 5 μm in contour length of the supercoiled duplex. The theta form is evident from the fact that all segments, including the segments between the two replication forks (at arrows), are duplex. ×65,900. (Photograph courtesy of D. R. Wolstenholme, from Wolstenholme, D. R., et al., 1974, *Cold Spring Harbor Sympos. Quant. Biol.* **38**:267–280.)

nas chloroplast DNA (**ctDNA**) by the distribution of labeled and unlabeled strands after one or more doubling cycles (see Fig. 4.6). From electron microscopic studies, it appears the mtDNA and ctDNA may replicate on occasion by the rolling circle mechanism and by the formation of theta forms like those in *E. coli* (Fig. 12.23). Another, more typical replication pattern was first described in 1972 by Jerome Vinograd and has since been confirmed as the major process by which new circular or linear duplex DNA is synthesized in both kinds of organelles. The process is called **D-loop synthesis**, and its major feature is the staggered time at which copying begins along the two strands of the DNA duplex.

Replication begins at a specific origin along the light (L) strand, and some time later replication is initiated along the heavy (H) strand at its specific origin. As synthesis proceeds along the L-strand template, its original partner H strand is displaced as a single-strand loop. Hence the term *displacement loop*, or **D loop**, has been used to designate the replication process (Fig. 12.24). The newly synthesized short segment was identified from molecular hybridizations between these new pieces and L-strand DNA. The new pieces are readily isolated by mild treatment to break the hydrogen bonds that hold the segment and its L-strand template together.

As replication proceeds in the 5′→3′ direction around the L-strand template, the D loop becomes larger. When synthesis has proceeded to the point at which the H-strand origin becomes exposed in the expanded D loop, replication of the H strand is initiated and synthesis occurs in the 5′→3′ direction along the antiparallel template strand. Because synthesis along the L strand template begins earlier, one new semiconserved duplex is completed sooner than the other. The second duplex completes its replication after the first duplex has been released from the replication complex.

The unique feature of D loop synthesis is due to the presence of separate origins in different locations on the two strands of the duplex DNA. Even though a replication fork is initiated at one strand, the other strand is delayed in its replication until its specific origin is exposed. We would therefore expect the nature of the origins to be a determining feature of simultaneous versus staggered copying, and of unidirectional versus bidirectional replication. And so it is. The single replication fork of unidirectionally replicating DNA must be due to the existence of an origin on only one strand, which serves to initiate replication of both strands. The simultaneous formation of two replication forks in bidirectionally replicating duplex DNA must be due to the presence of the origins at the *same* location in *both* strands.

Packaging the Genome

The length of the DNA (or RNA) that comprises the genome is far greater than the size of the structure in which it resides. The nucleic acids must therefore be condensed by a very large factor in order to fit into the confined space of a virus capsid or a cell. The packaging

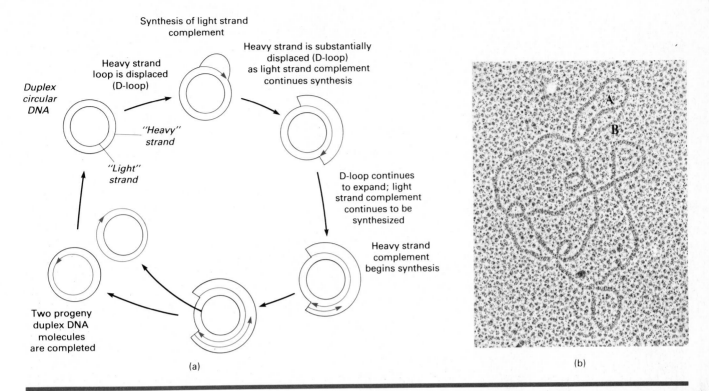

(a)

(b)

FIGURE 12-24
D-loop synthesis of mitochondrial DNA. (a) Diagram showing the heavy and light parental strands (gray) and the manner of their replication. The new heavy strand (color) is synthesized first, as a complement of the parental light strand, in the D-loop region. The new light strand (color), complementary to the parental heavy strand, begins its synthesis later. Each new strand is synthesized in the 5' → 3' direction along its template strand, yielding two semiconserved progeny duplex molecules. (b) Electron micrograph of a replicating rat liver mitochondrial DNA molecule in the early D-loop stage. The displace D-loop strand (B) is opposite the replicating duplex segment (A), and the remainder of the molecule has not yet replicated. × 65,900. (Photograph courtesy of D. R. Wolstenholme, from Wolstenholme, D. R., et al., 1974, *Cold Spring Harbor Sympos. Quant. Biol.* **38**:267–280.)

problem is particularly evident for the eukaryotic nucleus. In a typical human cell, for example, almost 2 million μm of DNA must be compressed into a nucleus whose diameter may only be 5 or 6 μm. The compact mass of DNA must carry out replication, transcription, and its other activities within this confined space. In general, condensation of the nucleic acid depends on binding of the acidic DNA or RNA to basic proteins.

12.6
Packaging Viral Genomes

The problem of condensing a viral genome to fit within its capsid coating is acute because the internal volume is often only slightly larger than the nucleic acid. The capsid is usually composed of identical subunits of one virally coded protein, which poses restrictions on the manner of coat assembly. The proteins may stack sequentially in a helical display that produces a rod-shaped or *filamentous* form, or they may form an *icosahedral* capsid that resembles a sphere but is actually a polyhedron (Fig. 12.25). The viral genome may be packaged in the capsid in one of two ways: during capsid assembly or by insertion into an empty coat. The genome is condensed by protein–nucleic-acid interactions as the capsid assembles around the nucleic acid, or it is condensed as it enters a finished but empty shell.

Packaging of the genome during capsid assembly is characteristic of filamentous phage, such as coliphage fd, and of single-stranded RNA viruses, such as tobacco mosaic virus (TMV). In TMV, assembly of the viral rod begins at a nucleation center in the form of a hairpin on the RNA strand. The single kind of protein subunit binds noncovalently to

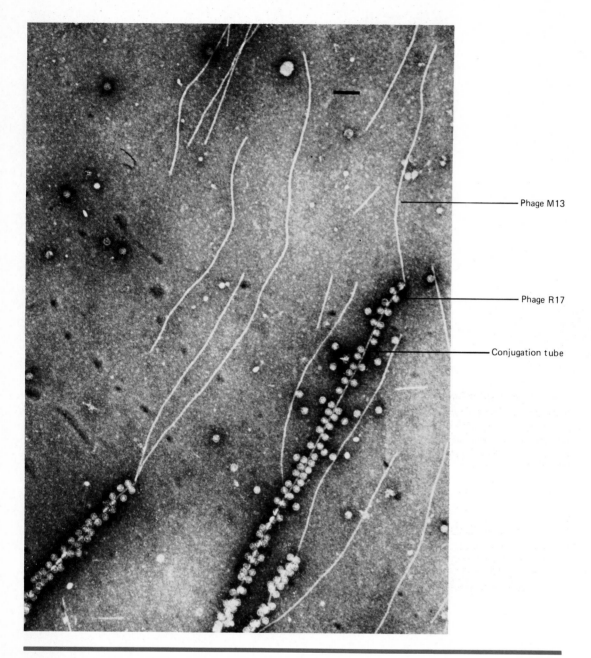

— Phage M13

— Phage R17

— Conjugation tube

FIGURE 12-25
Electron micrograph of two different phage attached to the long, thin conjugation tubes of *E. coli*. Icosahedral particles of phage R17 coat the sides of each conjugation tube, and filamentous phage M13 is attached to the tip of each tube. ×70,000. (Photograph courtesy of L. D. Simon.)

the RNA in such a way as to form bilayered disks consisting of 34 identical molecules. Each disk is a circular structure that becomes helical by interacting with the RNA. The stacking of the protein subunits creates a helical path for the RNA strand, which is completely enclosed in the mature virus (Fig. 12.26). TMV rods can be reconstituted from dissociated RNA and capsid proteins, which indicates that the construction of the virus is a spontaneous self-assembly process that depends on the geometry of the individual building units to guide the specific shape and size of the particle. Whether the capsid is filamentous as in TMV or spherical as in some of the other single-stranded RNA viruses depends entirely on the nature of the protein subunit. The

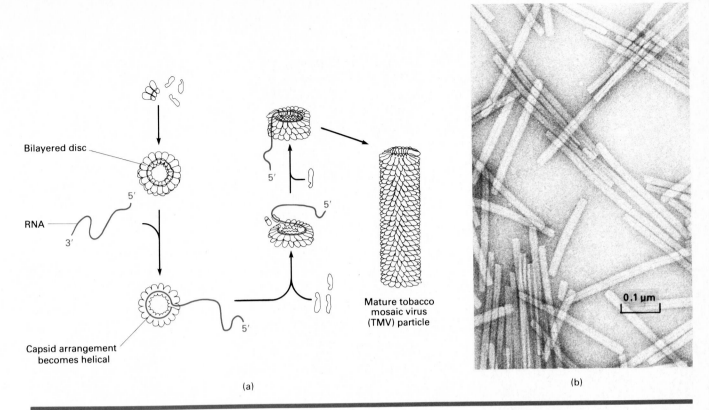

Bilayered disc

RNA

5'

3'

5'

5'

5'

5'

Capsid arrangement
becomes helical

Mature tobacco
mosaic virus
(TMV) particle

0.1 µm

(a)

(b)

FIGURE 12-26

Assembly of tobacco mosaic virus
(TMV). (a) Virus assembly from coat
protein units and single-stranded RNA
(color) occurs in a precise fashion to
produce a mature particle that consists
of 130 turns of the helically ordered
protein units, with $16\frac{1}{3}$ units per turn,
completely enclosing the RNA genome.
(From Stent, G. S., and R. Calendar,
1978, *Molecular Genetics: An Introductory Narrative*. Salt Lake City,
Utah: W.H. Freeman. Copyright ©
1978. (b) Electron micrograph of
rod-shaped TMV. × 100,000.
(Photograph courtesy of L.D. Simon.)

position of the RNA inside the capsid is determined by its binding interactions with coat proteins during viral morphogenesis.

Phage T4 and lambda are examples of viruses that insert their DNA into an empty shell that ultimately develops into the head of the lollipop-shaped, tailed viral particle. In each case the head is first assembled from a small set of interacting proteins, a specified amount of DNA is inserted, and the head undergoes structural changes leading to its mature form. The tail and other parts of the mature phage are subsequently added to the head after the DNA genome has been packaged (Fig. 12.27).

The T4 DNA to be packaged exists in the form of multiple genome sequences joined in tandem, and such a **concatamer** must be cleaved to single genome lengths for insertion into the empty head. Insertion begins at any point in the concatameric molecule and continues until a "headful" of DNA has been enclosed in the capsid. Some mechanism must exist for determining the correct amount of DNA to be included, but whatever the mechanism may be, it is somewhat imprecise because slightly more than the length of a unit genome is inserted. The encapsulated T4 DNA is therefore a *terminally redundant* molecule, but different DNAs may have different gene redundancies at each terminus of the linear duplex molecule (Fig. 12.28).

Phage lambda duplex DNA is also inserted into an empty head shell from concatamers, but these are cleaved at specific sequences called *cos* sites, which mark the two ends of the linear genome. Cleavage occurs at the *cos* site at the left in the standard gene map, which generates a free end for insertion into the capsid. DNA insertion continues until the *cos* site on the right is reached, and cleavage at this site produces the other

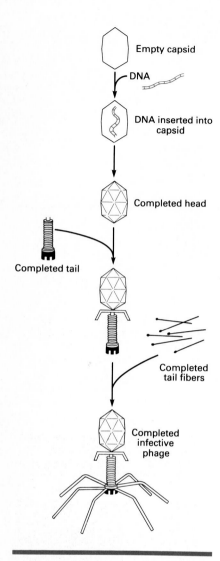

FIGURE 12-27
The *E. coli* phage T4 is produced by the action of many genes, which guide synthesis of capsid proteins and DNA of the phage head and proteins of the tail and tail fibers. A specified amount of phage DNA is inserted into an empty capsid, and the head is completed after a series of structural changes has occurred. The complex tail is added to the completed head, and tail fibers are then joined to the base of the phage tail to produce the completed infective virus particle.

free end of the lambda genome. Any DNA sequence between two *cos* sites can be packaged as long as it is neither much smaller nor much larger than the usual length of a lambda genome.

Little is known about the means by which a rather stiff rod of duplex DNA is folded inside the small volume of a capsid. It has been suggested that some of the proteins inside the capsid may provide a framework to which DNA binds and becomes condensed. If such an interaction does take place, it cannot be dependent on the particular nucleotide sequence because many kinds of modified genomes can be packaged just as effectively as any wild-type genome of appropriate length.

Packaging may be a very tricky and complicated phenomenon in viruses whose complete set of genetic information is partitioned among different molecules. In animal reoviruses, one copy of each of ten different duplex RNA molecules must be packaged together in a single capsid. In some plant RNA viruses, on the other hand, the genome consists of separate segments each of which is packaged in a different capsid. Infection by such plant viruses can succeed only if one of each type of particle enters the cell so that a complete genome is present. We know little or nothing about the selective processes for including different parts of a genome in a single capsid or for their insertion individually into different capsids. We would expect proteins to be involved in such selectivity, but our understanding of such systems is very limited at the present time.

12.7
The Bacterial Nucleoid

In bacteria the circular duplex DNA molecule is contained in a defined area of the cell called a **nucleoid** (Fig. 12.29). When the nucleoids are isolated from cells the DNA fibers exist in a very compact form, which can be unfolded to a less condensed state by treatment with agents that destabilize proteins or RNA. These observations indicate that the tight folding of DNA in the compact nucleoid is due to binding of the DNA to proteins and RNA. We have no experimental information on the role of RNA in stabilizing nucleoid structure, but we do know of several DNA-binding proteins, particularly in *E. coli*. All these proteins have a high content of basic amino acids, and some are very similar in amino acid composition to DNA-binding proteins of eukaryotic chromosomes. *E. coli* proteins H and HU resemble the chromosomal histones H2A and H2B, respectively, and protein P is similar to the basic protamines that bind to DNA in the head of certain animal sperm. Unfortunately, and despite a considerable amount of biochemical study, we do not know what structural roles these proteins play in folding the bacterial DNA genomes. Few mutants are known to have structural modifications in their DNA-binding proteins, so little can be done at present to compare nucleoid structure in wild-type and mutant strains.

The closed circle of duplex DNA is organized into a large number of loops, each of which can be modified independently of the others. Such loops are therefore considered to exist as *independent domains* in which events altering any one domain have no effect on the supercoiling of any

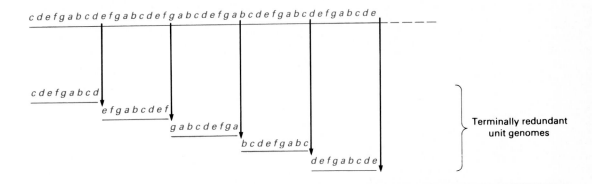

$$c\,d\,e\,f\,g\,a\,b\,c\,d\,e\,f\,g\,a\,b\,c\,d\,e\,f\,g\,a\,b\,c\,d\,e\,f\,g\,a\,b\,c\,d\,e\,f\,g\,a\,b\,c\,d\,e\,f\,g\,a\,b\,c\,d\,e$$

c d e f g a b c d

e f g a b c d e f

g a b c d e f g a

b c d e f g a b c

d e f g a b c d e

Terminally redundant
unit genomes

FIGURE 12-28
T4 DNA is synthesized as a concatamer of multiple genome lengths,
which must be cleaved to single
genome sequences for insertion
into the empty capsid. Cleavage is
imprecise, so more than one genome is
included in each unit length of cleaved
DNA. The DNA termini are redundant,
but different gene redundancies are
found in different packaged T4 DNA
molecules.

other domain. Each loop is believed to consist of duplex DNA condensed
by bound basic proteins in some undetermined way, and the condensed
fiber of each loop is considered to be held in place through unknown
forces that secure the ends of the loop (Fig. 12.30).

Nucleoid DNA loops seem to be *negatively supercoiled*, which creates
a state of torsional tension that can be relieved by unwinding the duplex
(Fig. 12.31). If the natural supercoils do allow the helix to unwind, then
the strands of the double helix will be accessible to interactions with
enzymes and other proteins that sponsor replication, transcription, and
regulation of DNA activities. Negative supercoiling and subsequent
unwinding in one or more of the looped domains would allow interactions of the DNA only in those loops and would have no effect on the
activities in neighboring loops. Different reactions could thus characterize one or more of the estimated 100 looped domains, depending on
the existence and location of negative supercoils in the domains. Part of
the spectrum of regulation of DNA activities, including gene action, may
therefore include the topological organization of the genome as well as
local molecular interactions and reactions. At the very least, the
condensation of DNA in a loop and the presence of numerous loops in
secured positions provide the physical basis for packing a large genome
into a small space. All of the 1300 μm of *E. coli* DNA is thus condensed
into about one-third of the volume of a cell that is only 1 μm or 2 μm
long and less than 1 μm wide!

12.8
Nucleosomes: Subunits of Chromosome Structure

Eukaryotic chromosomes are nucleoprotein fibers, also called **chromatin fibers**, that consist of a linear duplex DNA molecule complexed with
histone proteins and a variety of nonhistone proteins. Until 1974 we
had no clear idea of the way in which DNA and proteins were organized
in the chromatin fiber except that binding interactions between the
molecules were responsible for the condensation of enormously long
fibers into very compact chromosomes. In 1974 Roger Kornberg showed
that discrete particles, called **nucleosomes**, were released from chromatin that was subjected to controlled digestion by the enzyme *micrococcal
nuclease*. We now know that the chromatin fiber of the eukaryotic

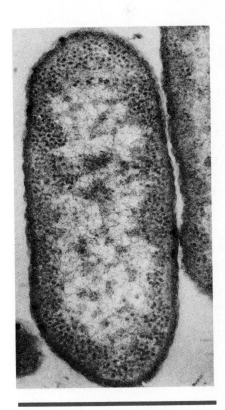

FIGURE 12-29
Electron micrograph of a section
through a bacterial cell showing
the central nucleoid in which DNA
(fine fibrils) is located. $\times$90,400.
(Photograph by H.-P. Hoffmann.)

FIGURE 12-30
The bacterial DNA duplex is organized into a number of loops, each of which exists as an independent domain secured at the base by unknown forces (gray). About 100 such domains are believed to occur in 1300-μm-long *E. coli* DNA, so that each domain consists a 13-μm-long loop, or about 40,000 base pairs. The helically coiled duplex DNA (black) in a loop is believed to be condensed by virtue of binding with basic proteins (color) in some undetermined way.

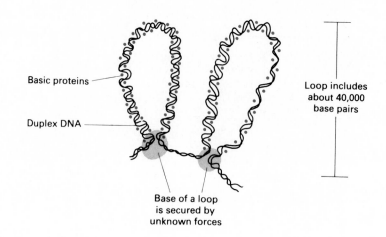

FIGURE 12-31
A negatively supercoiled DNA double helix can be relaxed by a nick in the duplex, rotation of the region near the nick, and sealing of the nick to produce an intact DNA double helix in which some of the supercoils are unwound. The unwound region of the molecule contains the same double-helical conformation of DNA as the super-coiled regions.

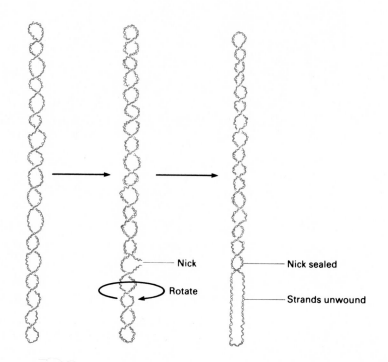

chromosome is organized as a series of regularly repeating nucleosome subunits, each of which consists of about 200 base pairs of the continuous thread of chromosomal duplex DNA in association with an octamer of four of the five known histone proteins (Table 12.2). Each octamer consists of two molecules each of histones H2A, H2B, H3, and H4. One molecule of the fifth kind of histone, H1, exists in association with each nucleosome but is not a contributor to nucleosome structure because the removal of H1 has no effect on the particle structure (Fig. 12.32).

If chromatin from different species is compared, the histone octamer is always recovered in nucleosomes, but the amount of associated DNA varies from a low of 154 base pairs to a high of 260 base pairs, with an average of 180 to 200 base pairs per nucleosome. Regardless of the total length of the nucleosomal DNA in the monomeric particles recovered early in the digestion treatment, continued digestion produces an

TABLE 12-2
Characteristics of Mammalian Histone Proteins

	Percentage of Basic Amino Acids		
Histone	Arginine	Lysine	Molecular Weight
H1	1	29	23,000
H2A	9	11	13,960
H2B	6	16	13,774
H3	13	10	15,342
H4	14	11	11,282

octamer core particle containing 146 base pairs of DNA. The **core DNA** is relatively resistant to further nuclease digestion, but the so-called **linker DNA** of the monomeric nucleosome obviously can be fragmented rather readily into smaller pieces. As the original length of nucleosomal DNA is reduced by continued digestion, histone H1 is also lost. Because H1 is lost only between the time of reduction from 160 to

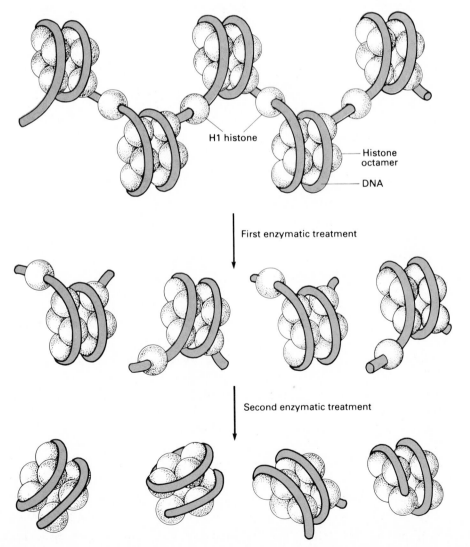

H1 histone

Histone octamer

DNA

First enzymatic treatment

Second enzymatic treatment

FIGURE 12-32
The nucleosome model of organization of the chromatin fiber was derived from controlled digestion experiments using the enzyme micrococcal nuclease. Mild digestion of the chromatin preparation yields particles that consist of about 200 base pairs of DNA complexed to one molecule of histone H1 and an octamer composed of two molecules each of histones H2A, H2B, H3, and H4. Upon further digestion of these particles, the octamer core bound to 146 base pairs of DNA is separated from H1 histone bound to the remaining (linker) DNA. These data and other information were interpreted as showing that the chromatin fiber is organized as a chain of repeating nucleosome subunits such that a continuous duplex DNA molecule is wound around histone octamer cores at regular intervals along its length, and that histone H1 is bound to a linker region of DNA between octamers.

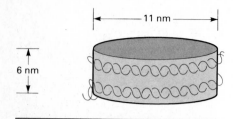

FIGURE 12-33

The nucleosome histone octamer is usually represented as a flat cylinder, 6 nm high and 11 nm wide, around which the DNA double helix makes two complete turns in the intact chromatin fiber or in isolated nucleosomes. About 67 nm of duplex DNA can be condensed in length to 11 nm by virtue of its being wrapped around the protein core of the nucleosome. This accounts in part for the condensation of chromosomal DNA in the nucleus.

170 base pairs and the final length of 146 base pairs, we believe that histone H1 is located in the portion of linker DNA that is right next to the core DNA.

Although we know little about nucleosome assembly during chromosomal replication, some insight into nucleosome organization has been obtained from chromatin extracts and from *in vitro* studies. The histone octamer may have a central component consisting of a tetramer of the arginine-rich histones ($H3_2H4_2$), to which two H2A · H2B dimers of the slightly lysine-rich histones become bound. These deductions are based on various kinds of data, including aggregation studies showing that $H3_2H4_2$ tetramers form rather readily whereas the predominant aggregate of the other two kinds of histones is a dimer; and the dissociation of isolated octamers from chromatin proceeds by an initial loss of one H2A · H2B dimer and the later loss of the second H2A · H2B dimer, leaving the $H3_2H4_2$ tetramer. The overall shape of the histone octamer is ellipsoidal, which is usually represented as a flat cylinder with a diameter of 11 nm and a height of 6 nm. We know nothing about the shapes of the individual histone molecules in the octamer or of the specific functions of different regions of these molecules in the various protein–protein and protein–DNA interactions.

Two different sets of data show that DNA is wound around the surface of the histone octamer. Biophysical studies indicate that the diameter of the DNA is larger than the diameter of the protein component of the nucleosome, and biochemical studies show that the DNA is susceptible to nuclease attack at regular intervals and therefore cannot be covered by proteins. It would seem, from biophysical measurements and from other data, that the helical coil of DNA makes two turns around the surface of the histone octamer (Fig. 12.33). About 67 nm of DNA can be condensed in length to 11 nm by virtue of being wrapped around the protein core. This slight reduction to 1/6 its fully extended length can account for only a minute amount of condensation of the chromosomal DNA, and we must still explain how the molecule can be converted to a compact structure about 1 μm to 5 μm long from an original length of hundreds, thousands, or tens of thousands of micrometers.

12.9

Looped Domains in Packed Chromatin

The *native* chromatin fiber has an average diameter of about 30 nm, whereas a stretched fiber or one depleted of histone H1 is only about 10 nm wide. The 10-nm fiber clearly consists of a string of nucleosomes, probably aligned edge to edge rather than face to face (Fig. 12.34). The **30-nm fiber** has a coiled structure as seen in electron micrographs, and about six nucleosomes are aligned in a helical coil for every turn along the axis of the fiber (Fig. 12.35). The *packing ratio* was 6 for DNA wound around individual nucleosomes (67 nm DNA on 11 nm of nucleosome length), which we can now increase to a packing ratio of 40 for the 30-nm fiber organization (40 μm of DNA per micrometer of fiber axis). Fiber compaction is increased even more by loops, which can be seen directly in electron micrographs of chromosomes that have been de-

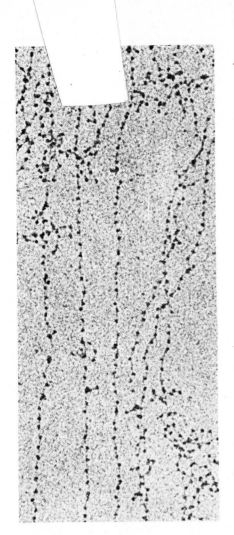

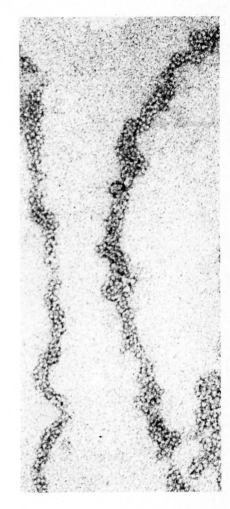

◀ **FIGURE 12-34**
Electron micrograph of chromatin fibers from mouse interphase nuclei. The 10-nm-wide fibers are in a partially unwound state, due to prior treatment in media of low ionic strength and the removal of histone H1. Each fiber is a continuous string of nucleosomes. ×90,000. (Photograph courtesy of B. A. Hamkalo.)

FIGURE 12-35 ▶
Electron micrograph of negatively stained chromatin fibers from mouse interphase nuclei. The 30-nm-wide fibers show closely appressed arrays of nucleosomes in coiled configurations. Two or three nucleosomes span the width of these native chromatin fibers. ×90,000. (Photograph courtesy of B. A. Hamkalo.)

pleted of their histones and most of their nonhistone proteins (Fig. 12.36). The remaining 8% of the chromosomal proteins apparently constitute a *scaffold* or framework from which the DNA loops appear to emerge and to which they presumably are bound. The dense network of scaffold fibers may be composed of nonhistone proteins complexed with metal ions because the scaffold can be disrupted by chelating agents and restored by the addition of copper ions and, to a less specific extent, by calcium ions. It would be interesting to know whether the scaffold metalloproteins are the means by which the bases of the DNA loops are secured in the chromosome.

The loops of naked DNA measure 10 μm to 30 μm in length, which means that each loop consists of 30,000 to 90,000 base pairs (1 μm of duplex DNA = 3000 bp). If we consider these loops as they existed in the original 30-nm fiber before protein depletion, and if the DNA packing ratio is 40 in the 30-nm fiber, then native chromatin loops in the intact fiber would be 1/40 the length of the naked DNA loops, or 0.25 to 0.75 μm. These dimensions are very close to the actual diameter of a chromosome. If a typical mammalian chromosome contains a DNA molecule 150,000,000 base pairs long (1.5×10^8 bp), and an average loop includes a sequence of 60,000 base pairs (6×10^4 bp), then the

chromosome would have about 2500 looped domains along the length of the chromatin fiber. Such a chromosome would be about 100 μm long and possibly could exist as such in the interphase nucleus, in which we know all the chromosomes are greatly extended and tangled (Fig. 12.37). Another order of condensation must take place during mitosis, however, when the long, stringy interphase chromosome is condensed to a length of 5 μm or less. It is possible that whole segments of the looped fiber fold back repeatedly, causing the condensed mitotic chromosome to be much wider as well as shorter than it was during interphase.

12.10
Replication of the Chromatin Fiber

Synthesis of new chromosomes requires not only the replication of DNA but also the production of new histone and nonhistone proteins and the assembly of these components into new chromatin fibers with characteristic nucleosomal organization. From labeling studies with nucleic acid

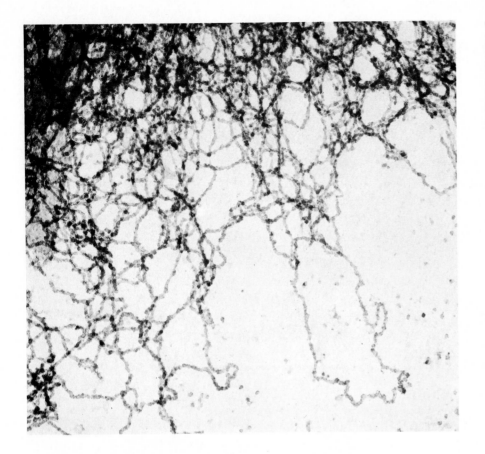

FIGURE 12-37
Electron micrograph of chromatin fibers
from an interphase nucleus of frog
erythrocyte. It is virtually impossible to
identify individual chromosomes in the
tangle of nuclear chromatin. ×50,000.
(Photograph courtesy of H. Ris.)

monomers or with amino acid monomers and from other data, we know
that DNA replication and histone synthesis are coordinated, each
process occurring during the S phase of the cell cycle in the premitotic
interphase nucleus. Furthermore, histones and DNA are synthesized in
stoichiometric amounts such that H2A, H2B, H3, and H4 are present in
equimolar amounts with about 100 base pairs of new duplex DNA.
Histone H1, however, is usually present in about half the amount of the
other histones, and nonhistone proteins vary in amounts as well as in
times of synthesis during the cell cycle. How are these molecules
assembled into polynucleosomal fibers? What happens to the nucleosomes of the parental chromatin fibers? Are they conserved or disassembled and reassembled?

The replication forks in replicating chromatin fibers progress fairly
rapidly away from their origins, and it has been difficult to study
molecular events in such transient structures. We do know from electron
micrographs that nucleosomes are present in recently replicated regions
along *both* daughter duplex DNA strands (Fig. 12.38). It seems most
likely that existing histone octamers are conserved and new octamers
formed during chromosome replication, these soon acting as the sites for
semiconserved DNA duplexes coiling around and binding to protein
regions. The strength of histone aggregation is considerable, judging
from the conditions required *in vitro* to separate the individual molecules
from the octamer cores, and from this viewpoint alone we would expect
existing octamers not to fall apart and be reassembled during chromosome replication. If the existing octamers are conserved, are they all

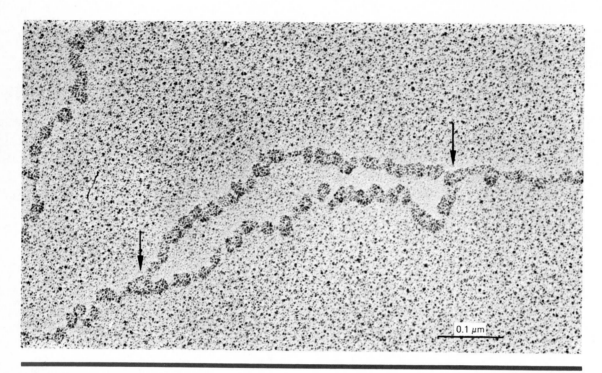

FIGURE 12-38
Electron micrograph of replicating chromatin from blastoderm cells of *Drosophila melanogaster* embryos. Nucleosomes occur on both daughter DNA duplexes in the replicated region between the two replication forks (at arrows). (Photograph courtesy of O. L. Miller, Jr., from McKnight, S. L., and O. L. Miller, Jr., 1977, *Cell* **12**:795, Fig. 4b. Copyright by M.I.T. Press.)

retained as part of one semiconserved strand and all new ones made for the other daughter strand, or are pre-existing and newly formed histone octamers distributed in some random fashion to both daughter strands? Either of these alternatives is possible, but evidence for or against these outcomes has been beyond our reach because of the technical problems of distinguishing the relatively small amount of newly synthesized components from the very large amount of pre-existing chromatin in replicating nuclei. However the new histone octamers are distributed to the daughter strands, information from labeling studies has shown that histones H3 and H4 become part of newly replicating chromatin first and that H2A and H2B are added later. These *in vivo* studies are consistent with *in vitro* assembly studies showing the initial formation of the $H3_2H4_2$ tetramer, to which two $H2A \cdot H2B$ dimers are subsequently bound.

About 500 different nonhistone chromosomal proteins can be detected by two-dimensional gel electrophoresis, but others may be present and not be detectable because of low concentration in chromatin. Except for polymerases, phosphatases, and some other enzymes, we know very little indeed about the diversity of nonhistone chromosomal proteins. Of the few such proteins that have been identified, one group has been singled out for study because its members seem to alter the conformation of chromatin or to stabilize altered conformations. These proteins are known as the **high-mobility group**, or **HMG proteins**, because they migrate rapidly in gels; that is, they show high electrophoretic mobility. This feature is the result of high levels of the charged basic amino acids lysine and arginine (about 25%) and of the charged acidic amino acids aspartate and glutamate (about 30%). The two sets of charged residues occupy different regions of the HMG protein molecules, which facilitates the simultaneous binding to DNA by the positively charged basic amino acids and binding to histones by the negatively charged acidic amino acid residues.

Four distinct species of HMG proteins have been extracted from chromatin of a diversity of eukaryotic organisms: HMG 1, 2, 14, and 17. HMG 1 and 2 are associated with histone H1 and linker DNA, whereas HMG 14 and 17 are associated with histones and DNA of the nucleosome core. HMG proteins are distributed nonrandomly in chromatin; they are concentrated in those regions of chromatin that are actively engaged in transcription. Actively transcribing chromatin is very sensitive to degradation by the enzyme DNase I, whereas inactive chromatin is not sensitive to low concentrations of the nuclease. When nuclei are exposed to low concentrations of DNase I to degrade active chromatin preferentially, HMG proteins are lost very rapidly. Chromatin is conformationally altered when it is actively transcribing RNA, so HMG proteins are believed to play a role in modifying the conformation of inactive chromatin or to stabilize actively transcribing chromatin in its altered form.

It is clear from this brief discussion that we have a long way to go before we can get a handle on replication of the chromosome, considering its complex composition and organization. Many specific questions can be asked about modifications in the composition and organization of replicating chromatin, and some answers have been obtained. But we must do more than enlarge the static picture of as dynamic a structure as a replicating chromosome. We must also concern ourselves with those processes that determine the exact spacing of nucleosomes, the segregation of new octamers into daughter strands, and the regulation of initiation and termination of the replication phase coordinately in all the chromosomes of a nucleus.

Organization of the Genome

The genetic information in prokaryotes and eukaryotes is based on a common genetic code, which specifies the primary structure of the polypeptide and RNA products of gene expression (see Fig. 4.11). The organization of the genome and its individual genes is fundamentally different in prokaryotes and eukaryotes, however, and these differences account in large part for the different processes by which gene expression is regulated in the two groups of organisms. In prokaryotes, all the genes are contained in a single molecule of duplex DNA, whereas the genes in eukaryotes are separated into different DNA molecules in chromosomes, which may vary in number from two to hundreds in a single genome (Fig. 12.39). Very little prokaryotic DNA is noncoding, but huge amounts of the eukaryotic genome may consist of DNA with no known coding function. Virtually all of the prokaryotic genome is made up of single copies of genes, whereas a large amount of the eukaryotic genome may consist of multiple copies of many kinds of sequences—that is, of *repetitive DNA*. Finally, as we have learned from recent molecular

FIGURE 12-39
The 46 chromosomes of a human somatic diploid cell. Each chromosome is made up of a single duplex DNA molecule and a variety of bound histone and nonhistone proteins. Each parent contributes one genome of 23 chromosomes to the individual (diploid) of the next generation, so the diploid has 23 pairs of chromosomes.

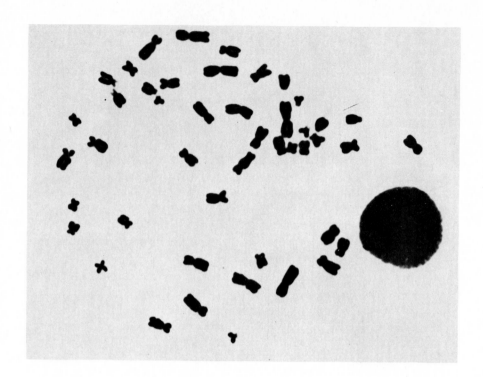

studies, the prokaryotic gene is organized as an uninterrupted coding sequence that is *colinear* with the amino acid sequence of the gene product, whereas genes in eukaryotes are organized into alternating coding and noncoding sequences, or *exons* and *introns* (see Section 4.6).

12.11
Genome Size and the C Value Paradox

Every species has a characteristic amount of DNA in its genome, which is called its **C value**. The C value may be expressed in picograms (pg) of DNA as determined by chemical measurements, or in base pairs or daltons of DNA as determined by the kinetics of renaturation of duplexes from single-stranded DNA fragments. The **C value paradox** refers to the great discrepancies between the size of the genome and the morphological complexity of the species—and even between some closely related species whose genome size may differ by a factor of 10 despite their morphological similarities. We might expect a corresponding increase in genome size and evolutionary ranking of organisms, if more genes are involved in specifying the increasingly complex systems of structure, development, and life style as we proceed from simple organisms to the more highly evolved life forms. Instead, we find a wide range of values in various groups of organisms and a considerable degree of overlap between groups of animals that represent very different levels of morphological complexity (Fig. 12.40). If more genes are needed to make a mammal than to make a fish, why do mammals have less DNA than many of the fishes? Why do some amphibians need nearly 10^{11} base pairs of DNA when others of similar morphological complexity can manage with about 10^9 base pairs, a hundredfold difference? It seems unlikely that some amphibians have 100 times more genes than others or

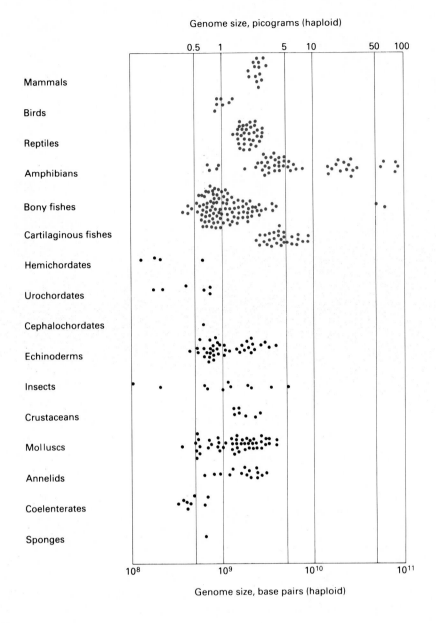

Genome size, picograms (haploid)

Genome size, base pairs (haploid)

FIGURE 12-40
C values expressed in picograms (upper scale) and in base pairs (lower scale) of DNA for various animal groups reveal a broad range in the amount of genomic DNA in some groups (such as amphibians) and a more restricted distribution in other groups (such as reptiles, birds, and mammals). No correspondence is evident between C values and the morphological complexity of these groups, a feature referred to as the C paradox. The C values for vertebrates are shown in color.

that a fish has more genes in its genome than there are in a mammalian genome. If the gene number is not much different between closely related species or is not higher in a fish than in a mammal, what can be the function of the excess DNA if it is not concerned with coding for proteins?

If we compare the C values over a broader range of organisms than the animal kingdom alone, there is some correspondence between increase in genome size and increase in morphological complexity (Fig. 12.41). It takes more DNA to make an alga or a fungus (2×10^7 to 10^8 base pairs) than to make a bacterium (6×10^5 to nearly 10^7 base pairs), and at least 10^8 base pairs are needed to assemble a multicellular plant or animal. The relationship between genome size and morphological complexity is obscured, however, once the quantum evolutionary leap to multicellularity has been achieved.

Some correspondence is evident between genome size (C value expressed in base pairs of DNA) and morphological complexity in a broad spectrum of organisms. It takes more DNA to make a eukaryotic alga or fungus (2×10^7 to 10^8 base pairs) than to make a prokaryotic bacterium (6×10^5 to nearly 10^7 base pairs), and at least 10^8 base pairs are required for a multicellular plant or animal. Each colored bar represents the range of C values recorded for each group of organisms listed.

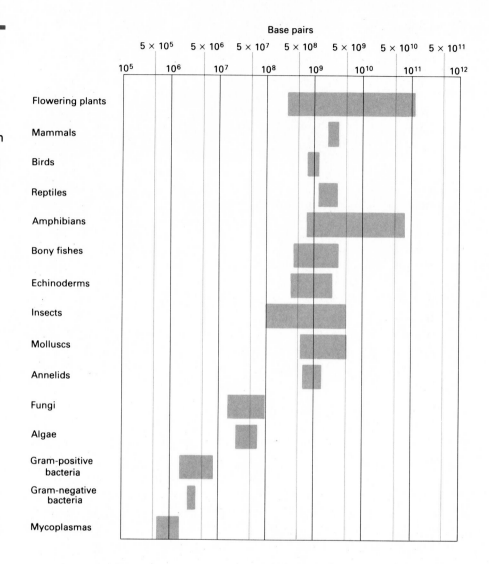

If all the DNA in a genome consisted of genes coding for proteins, a typical mammalian genome made up of 3×10^9 base pairs would include 600,000 genes of an average base-pair length of 5×10^3. This number of genes is considered to be a gross overestimate on the basis of at least two lines of evidence. From genetic studies of all the loci that can be mutated in the genome of *Drosophila melanogaster*, about 5000 essential genes have been inferred to be present in 10^8 base pairs of DNA. The estimated size of an average gene in this organism is about 2000 base pairs, which means that only 10^7 base pairs of the 10^8-base-pair-long genome is coded for proteins (5×10^3 genes $\times 2 \times 10^3$ bp per gene = 10^7 bp of DNA). Only one-tenth of the genomic DNA is represented by genes coding for proteins (10^7 bp genetic DNA $\div 10^8$ bp of total DNA = 10^{-1} of the total).

A more direct line of evidence for the determination of gene numbers in the genome is provided by estimates of the number of different mRNAs in different cell types of the organism. In mammals, about 10,000 different mRNAs are produced by gene expression in a given cell type, and most of these mRNAs are the same in most of the cells that have been studied. If we allow for some differences in gene expression in

the various types of cells, the total ~~~~~~~~~~ ~~~~~~~ pressed by
transcription in the organism might b~~~~~~~~~~~~~~ five times 10,000.
The gene number is more on the order of tens of thousands than of
hundreds of thousands per genome, according to these data, even
though we cannot provide an actual and unambiguous count.

What is the organization of coding sequences and of other components? Some answers have been obtained by analyzing the renaturation
kinetics of DNA, which we will discuss next.

12.12
Genome Analysis by the Use of Renaturation Kinetics _____

When duplex DNA is melted and the single strands are allowed to
reassociate by complementary base pairing, the rate of reassociation can
be monitored during an experiment by passing samples of the reaction
mixture over *hydroxyapatite columns* because only duplex DNA binds
selectively to hydroxyapatite crystals under appropriate conditions. The
conditions for a renaturation experiment are standardized for temperature of incubation, for ionic conditions, and for the length of sheared
fragments of single-stranded DNA from melted duplexes. In this way it
is possible to compare DNAs from different sources and different
experiments.

Renaturation of DNA depends on random collisions between complementary strands, and the progress of the reaction therefore follows
second-order kinetics, according to the equation

$$\frac{C}{C_0} = \frac{1}{1 + k \cdot C_0 t}$$

where C_0 is the initial DNA concentration at time $t = 0$, C is the
concentration of DNA that remains single-stranded at time t, and k is a
renaturation rate constant.

The renaturation of any DNA is usually described by its **Cot value**,
expressed in nucleotide moles $\times$ sec/liter. The progress of the reaction
takes the form of a *Cot curve* when the fraction of DNA that has
reassociated $(1 - C/C_0)$ is plotted against the log of the Cot. The four
genomes plotted in Fig. 12.42 all show the same sigmoidal curve
indicative of a second-order reaction, but each genome is characterized
by a different Cot measured at 50% reassociation $(Cot_{1/2})$. The $Cot_{1/2}$ of
a reaction indicates the total length of *different*, or *unique*, sequences that
are present, which is referred to as the **complexity** of the genome and is
usually expressed in base pairs. The $Cot_{1/2}$ of the renaturation of
genomic DNA is proportional to the complexity of that DNA, and the
value can be used to estimate the genome size. The complexity of *E. coli*
DNA is 4.2×10^6 base pairs, which coincides with data derived from
other methods of measurement. From renaturation kinetics, however,
we have the additional information that the *E. coli* genome is composed
almost entirely of unique sequences.

When genomic DNA of eukaryotic species is studied by renaturation
kinetics, a broad range of Cot values characterizes the reaction for any
species. The observed spread of Cot values indicates that genomic DNA
in eukaryotes is composed of different sets of sequences rather than one

FIGURE 12-42
Kinetics of reassociation by complementary base-pairing of single-stranded fragments of DNA monitored under standard conditions. (a) A sigmoidal Cot curve of the time course of renaturation is typical of second-order kinetics (according to the equation shown) as single-stranded DNA in the initial state undergoes reassociation into double-stranded DNA. The Cot measured at 50% reassociation (half-reaction) indicates the total length of unique sequences present, and this $Cot_{1/2}$ value thus describes the complexity of the genome. (b) Genome complexity based on $Cot_{1/2}$ values can be used to estimate genome size in base pairs (at arrows in the logarithmic scale above). The pairing kinetics of the artificial polymers poly(U) and poly(A) show the expected $Cot_{1/2}$ and unique-sequence complexity of one base pair. Phage MS-2 and T4 have smaller genomes than *E. coli* (4.2×10^6 base pairs) and mammalian species. The sigmoidal curve in each case indicates second-order kinetics and therefore shows that each sample was composed entirely of unique-sequence DNA. (From Britten, R. J., and D. E. Kohne, 1968, *Science* **161**:529–540. Copyright © 1968 by the American Association for the Advancement of Science.)

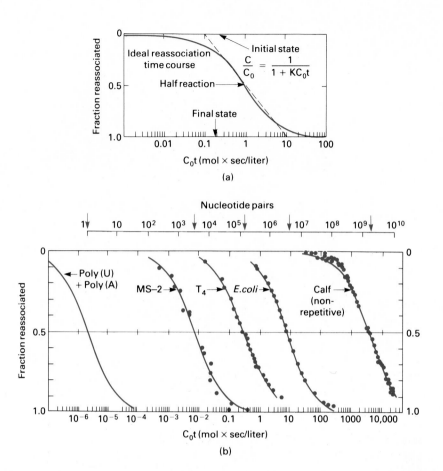

kinetically pure renaturing component as in prokaryotes or viruses (Fig. 12.43). Careful analysis reveals the existence of three major fractions of genomic DNA, each with its own rate of renaturation and, therefore, its own complexity. The fastest component to renature consists of relatively short sequences that occur in the genome in hundreds of thousands or millions of copies; that is, the component is **repetitive DNA**. Because of the very large number of repeated sequences present, this fraction of the genome is called **highly repetitive DNA**; it is also referred to as **simple sequence DNA** because any particular sequence may consist of 10 or fewer nucleotides and rarely more than a few hundred nucleotides. The component that renatures at Cot values between those of the fastest and those of the slowest renaturing fractions is **middle repetitive DNA**. There may be hundreds or thousands of copies of each of these sequences in a genome, and the sequences are usually intermediate in length. The slowest component to renature is **nonrepetitive DNA**. This slow component represents the unique sequences of the genome, and it constitutes the bulk of nuclear DNA (Table 12.3).

The different rates of renaturation for the major fractions of genomic DNA are due to their differences in complexity and in numbers of copies of the individual sequences. In a preparation of nuclear DNA from a population of cells, complementary copies of the numerous, short sequences of highly repetitive DNA "find" each other very quickly and renature. The somewhat longer and less numerous sequences of middle

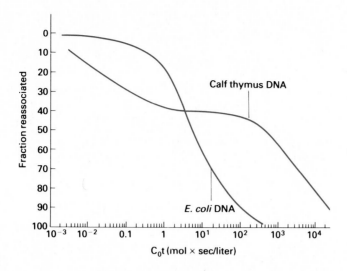

FIGURE 12-43
Genomic DNA in *E. coli* consists of one kinetically pure renaturing component, whereas eukaryotic DNA includes one or more components that reassociate faster than others. The heterogeneous population of eukaryotic DNA sequences includes a rapidly reassociating DNA with a lower Cot, which indicates that many copies of the same sequence are present. In addition, a slowly reassociating DNA typical of nonrepetitive unique-sequences is also present. (From Britten, R. J., and D. E. Kohne, 1968, *Science* **161**:529–540. Copyright © 1968 by the American Association for the Advancement of Science.)

repetitive DNA take longer to match up and pair, and the relatively small number of long unique-copy sequences require the most time to "find" a partner and renature.

Is the C value paradox due to a greater diversity of unique sequences (genes) in the larger genomes or to the presence of more copies of a similar number of genes in the larger genomes? We can

TABLE 12-3
Estimated Amounts of Unique-copy and Repetitive DNA Sequences in Representative Eukaryotic Genomes

Organism	Percent Unique-copy DNA	Repetitive DNA	
		Percent	Number of Copies
Paramecium aurelia (protozoan)	85	15	50–75
Dictyostelium discoideum (slime mold)	60	28	113
Neurospora crassa (true fungus)	80	20	60
Strongylocentrotus purpuratus (invertebrate: sea urchin)	50	27	10
		19	164
Nassaria obsoleta (invertebrate: gastropod)	38	12	20
		15	1,000
Bombyx mori (invertebrate: silkworm moth)	55	21	500
		24	50,000
Drosophila melanogaster (invertebrate: fruit fly)	78	15	35
		7	2,600
Xenopus laevis (vertebrate: amphibian; African clawed toad)	54	6	20
		31	1,600
		6	32,000
		3	high
Gallus domesticus (vertebrate: bird; chicken)	70	24	120
		3	330,000
		3	1,100,000
Bos taurus (vertebrate: mammal; cattle)	55	38	60,000
		2	1,000,000
		3	>1,000,000
Homo sapiens (vertebrate: mammal; human)	64	13	low
		12	intermediate
		10	high

answer this question by comparing the *kinetic complexity* of nonrepetitive DNA, as determined from renaturation analysis, with the *chemical complexity* of the genome, as determined from chemical measurements of the haploid DNA content. If a genome with more DNA contains more diverse sequences, we would expect a corresponding increase in kinetic complexity and chemical complexity. If a genome with more DNA has more copies of a similar number of genes, we would expect no correlation between the two sets of values because the kinetic complexity would not increase as the chemical complexity increases. When the two sets of complexity values are plotted, they show a good correlation (Fig. 12.44). This means that the larger genomes do contain a greater diversity of sequences. We are thus left with the dilemma of understanding why a simple organism may have more genes than a highly evolved, more complicated organism, and why two closely related species may differ tenfold in genome size.

What is the nature of repetitive DNA sequences: Are they coding or noncoding? How is repetitive and nonrepetitive DNA distributed in a chromosome, and how different is this distribution from one chromosome to another in the genome? What is the relative advantage of some sequences being repeated and others not? We will address these and other questions in later chapters, as each question becomes appropriate for discussion within the context of gene action and chromosome dynamics.

12.13
Clustered Genes, Scattered Genes, and Overlapping Genes _____

In prokaryotes, genes that code for proteins with related functions are often *clustered together in adjacent loci.* For example, the genes that specify enzymes of the biosynthetic pathway for the amino acid tryp-

FIGURE 12-44
The correspondence between kinetic complexity of nonrepetitive DNA, determined by reassociation kinetics, and chemical complexity, determined by chemical measurements of haploid DNA content, indicates that larger genomes contain a greater diversity of sequences rather than many copies of the same set of genes. The value for *E. coli* provides a reference point for prokaryotic genomes, but reasonably good correlation also exists for eukaryotic genomes (dots) across a broad range of values, except for polyploid species (x).

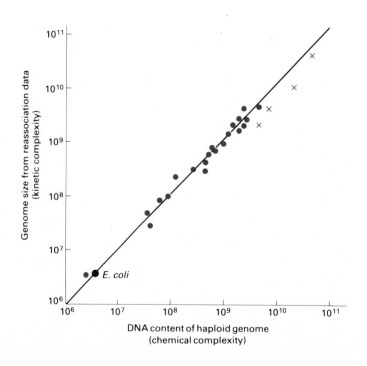

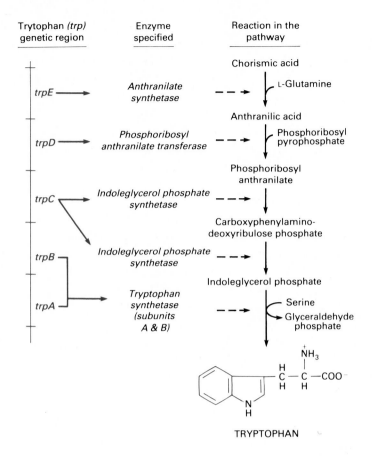

Tryptophan *(trp)* genetic region | Enzyme specified | Reaction in the pathway

FIGURE 12-45
The five genes clustered in the *trp* genetic region of *E. coli* specify four enzymes that catalyze the sequence of reactions for tryptophan synthesis. Coordinated regulation of action of the five adjacent genes contributes to the coordinated synthesis of enzymes required for the biosynthetic pathway.

tophan are found immediately next to each other in the *trp* genetic region of the genome map, and they occur in the sequence that corresponds to the sequence of steps in the reaction pathway in *E. coli* and other enteric bacteria (Fig. 12.45). The five *trp* genes are transcribed into a single mRNA molecule, or *polygenic transcript*, and they are all under the coordinated control of a common set of *regulatory genes* that influence the initiation of transcription. Such a group of coordinated regulatory genes and genes that code for enzyme structure, or *structural genes*, is called an *operon*. Operon organization in bacteria thus has important bearings on the coordination of gene action in producing proteins that must all be present and interact in a common biosynthetic pathway.

In eukaryotes, genes that code for proteins with related functions are generally *scattered among the different chromosomes of the genome*. Genes involved in virtually any one of the morphological or biochemical features of *Drosophila melanogaster* are scattered among the four chromosomes, or *linkage groups*, that comprise the genome (Fig. 12.46). The coordination of gene action in guiding the development of a eukaryotic structure must be quite different from the simpler prokaryotic scheme of activating a cluster of related genes through the device of a single common set of regulatory sequences. In some cases the genes encoding different polypeptide chains of a protein are far apart, and they may even be situated in different chromosomes. In humans the genes for the two globins of the hemoglobin molecule are in different chromosomes; the alpha-globin gene is in chromosome 16 and the beta-globin gene is in

FIGURE 12-46
Genes that affect the same character
(such as eye color, body color, wing
shape, bristle shape, and others) are
scattered among the four chromosomes of the haploid genome of
Drosophila melanogaster. Coordination
of gene action during eukaryotic
development must be much more
complex than in simpler prokaryotic or
viral systems. (From Strickberger, M.,
1976, *Genetics*, 2nd ed. New York:
Macmillan. Copyright © 1976 by
M. Strickberger.)

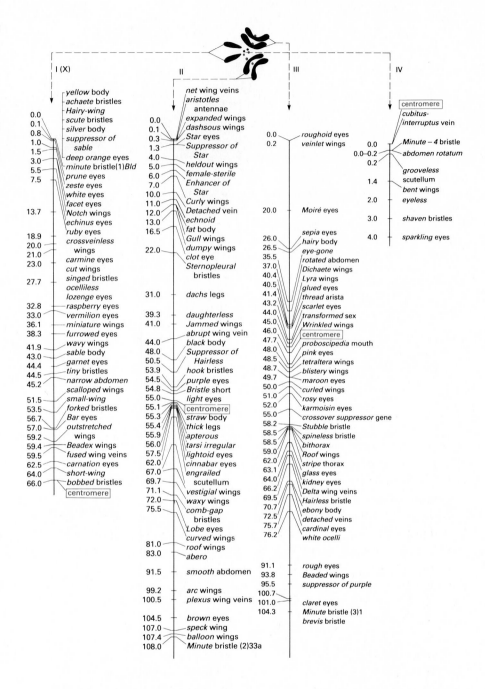

chromosome 11. The formation of hemoglobin, a tetramer of two
alpha-globin and two beta-globin chains, involves the coordination of
gene action in separate DNA molecules. As we will see in Chapter 14,
the mechanisms of regulating gene action in eukaryotes are more diverse
than those in prokaryotes, which we would expect intuitively on the
basis of gene distribution alone.

Genes are clustered according to their functions in viruses. The
linear genome of phage T7 consists of three distinct regions: (1) genes
that guide transcription early in the infection cycle; (2) genes that
specify phage replication of its DNA; and (3) genes that encode
structural proteins for the assembly of new phage progeny (Fig. 12.47).

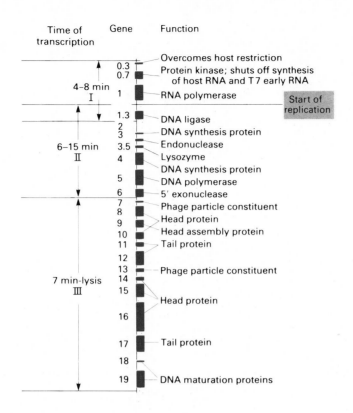

Time of transcription | Gene | Function

0.3 — Overcomes host restriction
0.7 — Protein kinase; shuts off synthesis of host RNA and T7 early RNA
4–8 min I
1 — RNA polymerase
Start of replication
1.3 — DNA ligase
2 — DNA synthesis protein
3 —
3.5 — Endonuclease
6–15 min II
4 — Lysozyme
 — DNA synthesis protein
5 — DNA polymerase
6 — 5′ exonuclease
7 —
8 — Phage particle constituent
9 — Head protein
10 — Head assembly protein
11 — Tail protein
12 —
13 — Phage particle constituent
7 min–lysis III
14 —
15 — Head protein
16 —
17 — Tail protein
18 —
19 — DNA maturation proteins

FIGURE 12-47
Genetic map of phage T7. The gene number is at the left and the gene function is at the right of each gene, whose relative size is indicated by the size of the colored bar. The roman numerals I–III mark off the early region (4–8 min), DNA replication genes (6–15 min), and the late genes (7 min–lysis), respectively. (After Kornberg, A., 1974, *DNA Synthesis*. Salt Lake City, Utah: W.H. Freeman.)

The ordered events of phage morphogenesis correspond to the ordered sequence of genes required for early, middle, and late steps in building new viruses during infection of the *E. coli* host. Similarly, phage lambda proceeds through an infection cycle by first transcribing genes that encode early functions (including DNA replication) and later transcribing genes that encode proteins for viral assembly later in the infection cycle. The synthesis of lambda head and tail proteins is accomplished via translation of a single operon, which includes about 20 genes for phage structural proteins. The operon is activated by the product of gene Q, which is made early in the infection cycle and without which later events will not take place. Lambda can exist indefinitely in a noninfectious *prophage* state as well as in a virulent infectious state. The prophage state persists as long as transcription of its early genes is blocked by a product of gene C_1. Later gene functions are not expressed because the necessary early gene products are not made. Control over the transcription of genes needed early in infection thus accounts for lambda's *lysogenic* nature—that is, its ability to be infectious *or* to remain in a noninfectious state under appropriate conditions.

All the foregoing information on gene distribution in a genome was obtained by conventional genetic mapping methods and by genetic and molecular analysis of transcription and translation products of gene action. A totally unexpected and surprising feature of a few viral genomes was the presence of **overlapping genes**, whose sequences coexisted in the same portion of the DNA strand. By base sequence analysis of the entire genome of 5386 nucleotides and of the mRNA transcripts of the individual genes, as well as amino acid sequences in

FIGURE 12-48

The genetic map of the circular genome of bacteriophage φX174 consists of ten genes (A–K) distributed among 5386 base pairs of DNA. Genes B, K, and E overlap with other genes in the genome and share some or all of the sequence involved. Four small regions of the genome (black) have no known coding function. These noncoding regions occupy fewer than 217 of the 5368 base pairs in this genome. (Data from M. Smith. 1979. *Amer. Sci.* **67**:57–67.)

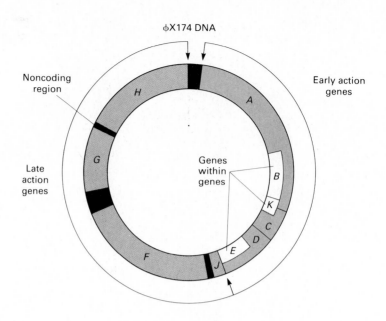

FIGURE 12-49

Different reading frames may be utilized in the same mRNA sequence of codon triplets to specify different amino acid sequences. Different proteins may thus be encoded in overlapping genes in a genome.

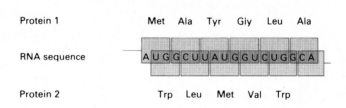

some of the protein products of these genes, three of the ten genes in the coliphage φX174 were found to be contained partially or entirely within the boundaries of three other genes (Fig. 12.48). Genes *F*, *G*, *H*, and *J* code for proteins that are made late in the infection cycle and become part of the mature phage particle; very short noncoding regions separate these genes from one another. The other six genes are active early in infection. Gene *B* is contained entirely within the sequence of gene *A*, gene *E* is within the sequence of gene *D*, and gene *K* is shared by part of the sequences of genes *A* and *C*.

Overlapping genes can be accommodated because the genetic code is based on triplets of nucleotides, and three different reading frames specifying three different proteins can coexist if each frame begins at a different one of the three nucleotides in the first triplet and proceeds thereafter in the standard three-by-three reading (Fig. 12.49). Overlapping genes have been found to exist in several phage and in some of the viruses with eukaryotic hosts, such as the simian virus SV40. The device of overlapping genes provides an economical means of packaging information into the smallest possible space. At the same time, the genome is less flexible because a single base-substitution mutation may lead to amino acid changes in two or even three genes instead of one gene. This problematical feature of overlapping gene organization may account for its rarity as a means of packaging a genome, even in cramped quarters.

Summary

The replication and expression of the DNA genome of all cells and many viruses involve the participation of enzymes and other proteins that stabilize packaging of DNA. *In vitro* the two antiparallel chains of nucleotides can be induced to separate by conditions that disrupt the hydrogen-bonded base pairs. AT-rich regions are more readily denatured than GC-rich regions. Observation of partially denatured DNA either electron microscopically or by changes in absorption of ultraviolet light can reveal distribution of bases, relative base composition, and (when DNA mixtures are reannealed) details of sequence homology.

Replication of DNA commences at an origin, a specific sequence of bases recognized by enzymes that proceed to use each strand as a template for synthesis of a new strand. The single strands are made accessible by topoisomerases and helicase, enzymes that relax the helix, and single-strand binding (SSB) proteins stabilize single-stranded regions. Replication is bidirectional from the origin and involves initial production of an RNA primer. Then deoxyribonucleotides are base paired to each template strand and covalently bonded by DNA polymerase III to the 3′ end of first the RNA primer and later the growing DNA strand. Because of the antiparallel structure of DNA and the specificity of DNA polymerase III, only one strand at each replication fork grows continuously. The other strand is synthesized in discontinuous fragments that are linked by DNA ligase after the gaps are filled in by DNA polymerase I. A proofreading function of DNA polymerase I ensures a low rate of error.

Many viruses have developed variations on this standard strategy in relation to the nature of the genome. Some replicate a circular duplex DNA genome in the same way as bacteria do. Some with single-stranded circular DNA genomes produce an intermediate duplex circular replicating form during infection that uses a rolling circle mechanism to produce multiple new copies of the single-strand viral genome. Some viruses with linear DNA genomes initiate replication on the appropriate strand at both 5′ ends of the genome, the newly synthesized strand displacing the parent strand. RNA viruses may have RNA-dependent RNA polymerase enzymes, but RNA tumor viruses (retroviruses) have an RNA-dependent DNA polymerase (reverse transcriptase) that synthesizes a DNA copy that can integrate into the host genome to become proviral DNA. Mitochondria and chloroplasts replicate their genomes in different ways—rolling circle, theta form, or D-loop synthesis—each of which involves semiconservative replication.

The limited space within a virus capsid or cell requires that there be a mechanism for packaging of the genome while allowing access to critical sequences for transcription and replication. Some viruses assemble the genome and capsid simultaneously; others insert the genome into a preassembled capsid. In bacteria, circular duplex DNA is held in compact form (the nucleoid) by binding to RNA and to proteins rich in basic amino acids. The circular genome is organized into negatively supercoiled looped domains that are independent from other such domains. Unwinding of the DNA helix allows access to enzymes.

In eukaryotes the genome is organized into independent chromosomes, each with several levels of packaging complexity. The simplest level is the nucleosome, an octamer of 4 kinds of histone proteins, in pairs, around which is wound 146 base pairs of DNA. Each nucleosome is connected to the next by a linker DNA segment of up to 114 base pairs. This packaging reduces the length of the DNA sixfold and looks in the electron microscope like a string of beads 10 nm in diameter. The nucleosomes coil, 6 per turn, into a 30-nm fiber, condensing it to 1/40 the length of naked DNA. Nonhistone proteins constitute a scaffold upon which the 30-nm fiber forms looped domains, the final structure of interphase chromosomes. Additional folding may permit further condensation at mitosis. Stoichiometric synthesis of histones occurs in proportion to DNA synthesis during the S phase of the cell cycle. Other protein components of chromatin include polymerases, phosphatases, and high-mobility group (HMG) proteins identified in regions active in transcription.

Neither the DNA content of the genome (C value) nor its sequence complexity bears an obvious relationship to the number of gene products an organism encodes. Analysis of renaturation kinetics allows classification of DNA according to its Cot value. Virtually all bacterial sequences are unique, represented once per genome. In addition to unique sequences, eukaryotes have highly repetitive DNA (short, millions of copies) and middle repetitive DNA (intermediate length, hundreds or thousands of copies). The function of most of these sequences is not known. The bulk of nuclear DNA is nonrepetitive, consisting of unique sequences. In prokaryotes genes with related function are frequently physically clustered at adjacent loci in the genome, where they are regulated and even transcribed as a unit. Eukaryotes may have genes for closely related functions, even separate subunits of a single protein, on different chromosomes. The viral genome may require an early gene product to activate expression of a cluster of later genes. Some viral genomes contain overlapping genes.

Readings and References

Abdel-Monem, M., and H. Hoffmann-Berling. 1980. DNA unwinding enzymes. *Trends Biochem. Sci.* **5**:128.

Adolph, K. W., S. W. Cheng, and U. K. Laemmli. 1977. Role of nonhistone proteins in metaphase chromosome structure. *Cell* **12**:805.

Baltimore, D. 1970. Viral RNA-dependent DNA polymerase in virions of RNA tumor viruses. *Nature* **226**:1209.

Bauer, W. R., F. H. C. Crick, and J. H. White. July 1980. Supercoiled DNA. *Sci. Amer.* **243**:118.

Bishop, J. M. March 1982. Oncogenes. *Sci. Amer.* **246**:80.

Borst, P., *et al.* 1984. Organelle DNA. *Trends Biochem. Sci.* **9**:128.

Britten, R. J., and E. H. Davidson. 1971. Repetitive and non-repetitive DNA sequences and a speculation on the origins of evolutionary novelty. *Quart. Rev. Biol.* **46**:111.

Britten, R. J., and D. E. Kohne. 1968. Repeated sequences in DNA. *Science* **161**:529.

Britten, R. J., and D. E. Kohne. April 1970. Repeated segments of DNA. *Sci. Amer.* **222**:24.

Burlingame, R. W., *et al.* 1985. Crystallographic structure of the octameric histone core of the nucleosome at a resolution of 3.3 Å. *Science* **228**:546.

Cairns, J. January 1966. The bacterial chromosome. *Sci. Amer.* **214**:36.

Chambon, P. May 1981. Split genes. *Sci. Amer.* **244**:60.

Cold Spring Harbor Symposia on Quantitative Biology
1978. *Chromatin.* Vol. **42**.
1979. *DNA: Replication and Recombination.* Vol. **43**.
1983. *DNA Structures.* Vol. **47**.

Cozzarelli, N. R. 1980. DNA gyrase and the supercoiling of DNA. *Science* **207**:953.

Craik, C. S., S. Sprang, R. Fletterick, and W. J. Rutter. 1982. Intron–exon splice junctions map at protein surfaces. *Nature* **299**:180.

Davidson, E. H., G. A. Galau, R. C. Angerer, and R. J. Britten. 1975. Comparative aspects of DNA organization in metazoa. *Chromosoma* **51**:253.

D'Eustachio, P., and F. H. Ruddle. 1983. Somatic cell genetics and gene families. *Science* **220**:919.

Earnshaw, W. C., and M. M. S. Heck. 1985. Localization of topoisomerase II in mitotic chromosomes. *J. Cell Biol.* **100**:1716.

Earnshaw, W. C., and U. K. Laemmli. 1983. Architecture of metaphase chromosomes and chromosome scaffolds. *J. Cell Biol.* **96**:84.

Falaschi, A., F. Cobianchi, and S. Riva. 1980. DNA-binding proteins and DNA-unwinding enzymes in eukaryotes. *Trends Biochem. Sci.* **5**:154.

Federoff, N. 1979. On spacers. *Cell* **16**:697.

Felsenfeld, G. 1978. Chromatin. *Nature* **271**:115.

Fersht, A. R. 1980. Enzymatic editing mechanisms in protein synthesis and DNA replication. *Trends Biochem. Sci.* **5**:262.

Fiers, W., *et al.* 1978. Complete nucleotide sequence of SV40 DNA. *Nature* **273**:113.

Fisher, L. M. 1981. DNA supercoiling by DNA gyrase. *Nature* **294**:607.

Freifelder, D. 1983. *Molecular Biology.* Boston: Jones and Bartlett.

Fuller, R. S., and A. Kornberg. 1983. Purified dnaA protein in initiation of replication at the *Escherichia coli* chromosomal origin of replication. *Proc. Natl. Acad. Sci. U. S.* **80**:5817.

Gall, J. G. 1981. Chromosome structure and the C-value paradox. *J. Cell Biol.* **91**:3s.

Gall, J. G., E. H. Cohen, and M. L. Polan. 1971. Repetitive DNA sequences in *Drosophila. Chromosoma* **33**:319.

Gilbert, W., and D. Dressler. 1969. DNA replication: The rolling circle model. *Cold Spring Harbor Sympos. Quant. Biol.* **33**:473.

Glikin, G. C,, G. Garguilo, L. Rena-Descalzi, and A. Worcel. 1983. *Escherichia coli* single-strand binding protein stabilises specific denatured sites in superhelical DNA. *Nature* **303**:770.

Goldman, M. A., *et al.* 1984. Replication timing of genes and middle repetitive sequences. *Science* **224**:686.

Hand, R. 1978. Eucaryotic DNA: Organization of the genome for replication. *Cell* **15**:317.

Harauz, G., and F. P. Ottensmeyer. 1984. Nucleosome reconstruction via phosphorus mapping. *Science* **226**:936.

Harland, R. 1981. Initiation of DNA replication in eukaryotic chromosomes. *Trends Biochem. Sci.* **6**:71.

Hübscher, U. 1984. DNA polymerase holoenzymes. *Trends Biochem. Sci.* **9**:390.

Jorcano, J. L., and A. Ruiz-Carrillo. 1979. H3-H4 tetramer directs DNA and core histone octamer assembly in the nucleosome core particle. *Biochemistry* **18**:768.

Kavenoff, R., L. Klotz, and B. Zimm. 1974. On the nature of chromosome-sized DNA molecules. *Cold Spring Harbor Sympos. Quant. Biol.* **38**:1.

Kolata, G. B. 1980. The 1980 Nobel prize in chemistry. *Science* **210**:887.

Kolodner, R., and K. K. Tewari. 1975. Chloroplast DNA from higher plants replicates by both the Cairns and the rolling circle mechanism. *Nature* **256**:708.

Kornberg, A. 1960. Biologic synthesis of deoxyribonucleic acid. *Science* **131**:1503 (Nobel lecture).

Kornberg, A. October 1968. The synthesis of DNA. *Sci. Amer.* **219**:64.

Kornberg, A. 1980. *DNA Replication.* San Francisco: Freeman.

Kornberg, A. 1984. DNA replication. *Trends Biochem. Sci.* **9**:122.

Kornberg, R. D. 1974. Chromatin structure: A repeating unit of histones and DNA. *Science* **184**:868.

Kornberg, R. D., and A. Klug. February 1981. The nucleosome. *Sci. Amer.* **244**:52.

Kriegstein, H. J., and D. S. Hogness. 1974. Mechanism of DNA replication in *Drosophila* chromosomes. Structure of replication forks and evidence for bidirectionality. *Proc. Natl. Acad. Sci. U. S.* **71**:135.

Laird, C. D., L. E. Wilkinson, V. E. Foe, and W. Y. Chooi. 1976. Analysis of chromatin-associated fiber arrays. *Chromosoma* **58**:169.

Laskey, R. A., and R. M. Harland. 1981. Replication origins in the eukaryotic chromosome. *Cell* **24**:283.

Laskey, R. A., and M. Mechali. 1982. Vive le replicon! *Nature* **300**:579.

Lawson, G. M., *et al.* 1982. Definition of 5′ and 3′ structural boundaries of the chromatin domain containing the ovalbumin multigene family. *J. Biol. Chem.* **257**:1501.

Leaver, C. J., and M. W. Gray. 1982. Mitochondrial genome organization and expression in higher plants. *Ann. Rev. Plant Physiol.* **33**:373.

Lehman, I. R. 1974. DNA ligase: Structure, mechanism, and function. *Science* **186**:790.

Lewin, B. 1978. *Gene Expression* **3**: *Plasmids and Phage.* New York: Wiley.

Lewin, B. 1980. *Gene Expression* **2**: *Eukaryotic Chromosomes.* 2nd ed. New York: Wiley.

Lewin, B. 1985. *Genes.* 2nd ed. New York: Wiley.

Lewin, R. 1982. Repeated DNA still in search of a function. *Science* **217**:621.

Lonberg, N., and W. Gilbert. 1985. Intron/exon structure of the chicken pyruvate kinase gene. *Cell* **40**:81.

Marsden, M., and U. K. Laemmli. 1979. Metaphase chromosome structure: Evidence for a radial loop model. *Cell* **17**:849.

Meselson, M., and F. W. Stahl. 1958. The replication of DNA in *E. coli*. *Proc. Natl. Acad. Sci. U. S.* **44**:671.

Mirkovitch, J., M.-E. Mirault, and U.K. Laemmli. 1984. Organization of the higher-order chromatin loop: Specific DNA attachment sites on nuclear scaffold. *Cell* **39**:223.

Mirzabekov, A. D. 1981. Nucleosome structure. *Trends Biochem. Sci.* **6**:240.

Mitra, S. 1980. DNA replication in viruses. *Ann. Rev. Genet.* **14**:347.

Moyne, G., R. Freeman, S. Saragosti, and M. Yaniv. 1981. A high-resolution electron microscopy study of nucleosomes from simian virus 40 chromatin. *J. Mol. Biol.* **149**:735.

Müller, U., H. Zentgraf, I. Eicken, and W. Keller. 1978. Higher-order structure of simian virus 40 chromatin. *Science* **201**:406.

Murray, A. W. 1985. Chromosome structure and behaviour. *Trends Biochem. Sci.* **10**:112.

Nathans, D. 1979. Restriction endonucleases, simian virus 40, and the new genetics. *Science* **206**:903 (Nobel lecture).

O'Brien, S. J., ed. 1984. *Genetic Maps 1984*, vol. 3. Cold Spring Harbor, N.Y.: Cold Spring Harbor Laboratory.

Ogawa, T., and T. Okazaki. 1980. Discontinuous DNA replication. *Ann. Rev. Biochem.* **49**:421.

Olins, D. E., and A. L. Olins. 1978. Nucleosomes: The structural quantum in chromosomes. *Amer. Sci.* **66**:704.

Pardue, M. L., and J. G. Gall. 1970. Chromosomal localization of mouse satellite DNA. *Science* **168**:1356.

Paulson, J. R., and U. K. Laemmli. 1977. The structure of histone-depleted metaphase chromosomes. *Cell* **12**:817.

Rattner, J. B., and B. A. Hamkalo. 1979. Nucleosome packing in interphase chromatin. *J. Cell Biol.* **81**:453.

Robberson, D. L., H. Kasamatsu, and J. Vinograd. 1972. Replication of mitochondrial DNA. Circular replicative intermediates in mouse L cells. *Proc. Natl. Acad. Sci. U. S.* **69**:737.

Salas, M., and E. Viñuela. 1980. Proteins covalently linked to viral nucleic acids. *Trends Biochem. Sci.* **5**:191.

Sanger, F. 1981. Determination of nucleotide sequences in DNA. *Science* **214**:1205 (Nobel lecture).

Sanger, F., *et al.* 1977. Nucleotide sequence of bacteriophage ϕX174 DNA. *Nature* **265**:687.

Schmid, C. W., and W. R. Jelinek. 1982. The Alu family of dispersed repetitive sequences. *Science* **216**:1065.

Saragosti, S., G. Moyne, and M. Yaniv. 1980. Absence of nucleosomes in a fraction of SV40 chromatin between the origin of replication and the region coding for the late leader RNA. *Cell* **20**:65.

Scovassi, A. I., P. Plevani, and U. Bertazzoni. 1980. Eukaryotic DNA polymerases. *Trends Biochem. Sci.* **5**:335.

Simons, K., H. Garoff, and A. Helenius. February 1982. How an animal virus gets into and out of its host cell. *Sci. Amer.* **246**:58.

Sinden, R. R., and D. E. Pettijohn. 1981. Chromosomes in living *E. coli* cells are segregated into domains of supercoiling. *Proc. Natl. Acad. Sci. U. S.* **78**:224.

Singer, M. F. 1982. SINEs and LINEs: Highly repeated short and long interspersed sequences in mammalian genomes. *Cell* **28**:433.

Smith, G. R. 1981. DNA supercoiling: Another level for regulating gene expression. *Cell* **24**:599.

Smith, M. 1979. The first complete nucleotide sequencing of an organism's DNA. *Amer. Sci.* **67**:57.

Takeda, Y., D. H. Ohlendorf, W. F. Anderson, and B. W. Matthews. 1983. DNA-binding proteins. *Science* **221**:1020.

Temin, H. M. January 1972. RNA-directed DNA synthesis. *Sci. Amer.* **226**:24.

Thoma, F., Th. Koller, and A. Klug. 1979. Involvement of histone H1 in the organization of the nucleosome and of the salt-dependent superstructures of chromatin. *J. Cell Biol.* **83**:403.

Wang, J. C. 1980. Superhelical DNA. *Trends Biochem. Sci.* **5**:219.

Wang, J. C. July 1982. DNA topoisomerases. *Sci. Amer.* **247**:94.

Wang, J. C., L. F. Peck, and K. Becherer. 1983. DNA supercoiling and its effects on DNA structure and function. *Cold Spring Harbor Sympos. Quant. Biol.* **47**:85.

Watson, J. D. 1976. *Molecular Biology of the Gene*. 3rd ed. Menlo Park, Calif.: Benjamin-Cummings.

Winnacker, E.-L. 1978. Adenovirus DNA: Structure and function of a novel replicon. *Cell* **14**:761.

Wolstenholme, D. R., K. Koike, and P. Cochran-Fouts. 1974. Replication of mitochondrial DNA: Replicative forms of molecules from rat tissues and evidence for discontinuous replication. *Cold Spring Harbor Sympos. Quant. Biol.* **38**:267.

Wood, W. B., and R. S. Edgar. July 1967. Building a bacterial virus. *Sci. Amer.* **217**:60.

Woodcock, C. L. F., L.-L. Y. Frado, and J. B. Rattner. 1984. The higher-order structure of chromatin: Evidence for a helical ribbon arrangement. *J. Cell Biol.* **99**:42.

Worcel, A., and E. Burgi. 1972. On the structure of the folded chromosome of *E. coli*. *J. Mol. Biol.* **71**:121.

CHAPTER 13

Gene Expression: Transcription and Translation

The genetic blueprint in a viral capsid, bacterial nucleoid, or eukaryotic nucleus is a store of information that can be utilized, or *expressed*, only when there is machinery to transcribe the information into molecules that can carry that information out to the cytoplasmic sites of protein synthesis, or translation. Gene sequences are transcribed into RNA copies, which function in association with the ribosomal apparatus to translate the coded nucleic acid sequence into a sequence of amino acids in the polypeptide chain. Various components in the cell oversee the accuracy of polypeptide chain synthesis; mistakes in the kinds or sequence of amino acids usually lead to protein dysfunction and to drastic consequences for the cell. The unity of all life is plainly evident in the underlying similarities of the processes and machinery for transcription and translation. Variations in particular features of these systems, on the other hand, reflect the ways in which different life forms have coped with unique problems during evolution.

The Genetic Template

Genetic studies of bacteria and phage showed that the gene and its protein product were **colinear** molecules; that is, the sequence of contiguous codons in the gene corresponded in location to the sequence of contiguous amino acids in the polypeptide chain. Colinearity was presumed to apply to eukaryotes as well, but this was shown to be incorrect in the 1970s when new molecular methods became available to determine the base sequences directly. Eukaryotic genes were found to be composed of interspersed coding and noncoding segments, whereas prokaryotic genes were indeed sequences of contiguous codons without noncoding interruptions. In addition, genes were shown to have sequences at their 5′ and 3′ ends that may or may not be transcribed and, if transcribed, may or may not be translated. The organization of the genetic template and the functions of its various portions have been studied by genetic and molecular methods, and we now have a substantial amount of information on these matters. From such information we have also gained considerable insight into the molecular basis for the regulation and precision of transcription and translation processes in cells.

13.1
The Organization of Gene Sequences

The colinearity of gene and polypeptide was demonstrated in the 1960s by molecular genetic analysis of the correspondence between the sites of mutations mapped in the gene and the sites of altered amino acids in the polypeptide product of the gene. Charles Yanofsky showed that the locations of mutated sites in the gene map of *trpA* and *trpB* in *E. coli* coincided with the locations of substituted amino acids in the A and B subunit polypeptide chains of the enzyme tryptophan synthetase (Fig. 13.1). The sequence of codons in the gene thus specified the kinds of amino acids and their sequence in the polypeptide. It was assumed—but not shown directly—that the codons were present in tandem, in an uninterrupted linear display.

Taking a somewhat different genetic approach, A. Sarabhai and colleagues provided evidence in support of colinear gene and polypeptide in the coliphage T4. The mutant strains all had a termination codon in place of an amino-acid–specifying codon within the gene sequence that coded for a head protein of the phage. These mutants therefore made shortened defective polypeptide chains because protein synthesis terminated prematurely at the site of the altered codon in the gene sequence. Mutation sites were mapped for all the strains, and the set was shown to be distributed all along the length of the gene. If the gene and the protein were colinear, the length of the defective protein would correspond to the length of the gene map between its beginning and the site of the mutant termination codon in each strain (Fig. 13.2). The defective protein would be progressively longer in mutants whose substituted codon was located progressively closer to the end of the gene

FIGURE 13-1
Colinearity of the gene and its protein product. Locations of mutations on the linear genetic map correspond to locations of amino acid substitutions in the linear TrpA polypeptides made by *trpA* mutants of *E. coli*. Each black square on the gene map represents a mutant site in a particular (numbered) strain, and each black dot on the polypeptide represents the site of the substituted amino acid in that mutant. Only a portion of the gene map and polypeptide are shown, and only 7 of the 268 amino acids in wild type and mutants are identified in the diagram. (After Yanofsky, C., *et al.*, 1967, *Proc. Nat. Acad. Sci. U.S.* **57**:296.)

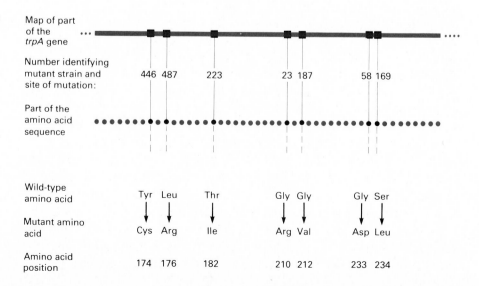

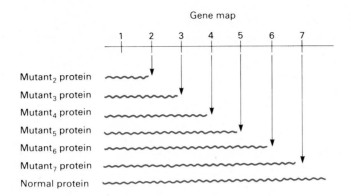

FIGURE 13-2
Summary of experimental data that showed that gene and protein are colinear in phage T4. The known position in mutant DNA of a termination codon in place of an amino-acid–specifying codon in normal DNA corresponded to the site of premature termination and the length of mutant polypeptides.

map. These predicted results were indeed found when the experiments were conducted, thus providing additional support for the concept of colinearity.

The uninterrupted coded sequence in bacteria and their viruses was presumed to characterize the gene in eukaryotes and their viruses. The sequence started with the initiation codon TAC (equivalent to the RNA codon AUG) and terminated with any one of the three known termination codons: ATT, ATC, or ACT (equivalent to RNA codons UAA, UAG, and UGA). This universal theme was upset in 1977 with the discovery that genes in eukaryotes and their viruses consisted of **coding sequences**, or **exons**, interspersed with noncoding **intervening sequences**, or **introns**, all sandwiched between the initiation and termination codons of the DNA sequence. The original information leading to this discovery came from comparisons of the structure of DNA and its corresponding messenger RNA, as we discussed earlier in Chapter 4 (see Fig. 4.17). The entire gene sequence is copied into a complementary RNA molecule that is a precursor of the final form of the messenger RNA. The precursor mRNA, or **pre-mRNA**, is unable to direct protein synthesis at the ribosomes. The introns must first be removed from pre-mRNA, and the exons must be *spliced* to make a continuous sequence of codons in the mature mRNA. Mature mRNA is colinear with the polypeptide. We will discuss these events later in the chapter.

The number of intervening sequences in the eukaryotic genetic message varies from one gene to another. The genes for the globin polypeptides of hemoglobin have only 2 intervening sequences between exons, whereas more than 50 intervening sequences are present between exons in the gene that specifies one of the collagen polypeptides. By direct base sequencing of restriction fragments of cloned ovalbumin genes from the chicken, investigators have established the size and order of the 8 exons and 7 introns. In this gene, as in others, the length of an exon or of an intron varies from fewer than 50 nucleotides to well over 1000 nucleotides (Fig. 13.3). The pre-mRNA molecule consists of 7564 nucleotides, but the mature mRNA of the ovalbumin gene retains only 1872 nucleotides after the 7 introns have been excised and the 8 exons have been spliced together into a continuous sequence.

Both the number and the length of intervening sequences vary to such an extent that it seems unlikely to have any obvious influence on gene organization. In fact, some eukaryotic genes lack introns altogether and are thus organized in the same manner as prokaryotic genes.

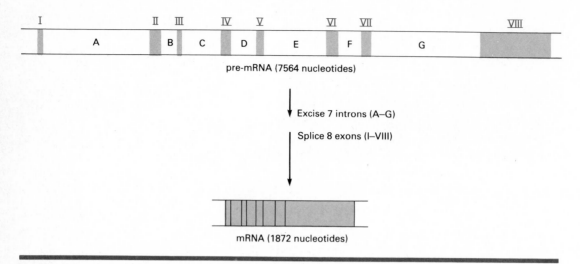

pre-mRNA (7564 nucleotides)

Excise 7 introns (A–G)

Splice 8 exons (I–VIII)

mRNA (1872 nucleotides)

FIGURE 13-3
Precursor mRNA (pre-mRNA) of the chicken ovalbumin gene consists of 8 exons (I–VIII, color) that alternate with 7 noncoding introns (A–G) of varied lengths in the total sequence of 7564 nucleotides. Excision of introns removes 5692 nucleotides, so that mature mRNA is comprised of the 8 exons spliced together into an uninterrupted sequence of 1872 nucleotides.

Examples of intronless eukaryotic genes are those for histone proteins and two of the three kinds of interferon that participate in immunity responses. On the other hand, when an intervening sequence from an interrupted gene is experimentally excised or altered substantially, the messenger RNA transcript of the altered gene is very unstable or even nonfunctional in guiding polypeptide synthesis. Eukaryotic genomes usually have altered duplicates of some genes, in which all the introns are missing or in which one or more of the introns are partially deleted. Such altered duplicates are called **pseudogenes**. Unlike their normal counterparts in the genome, pseudogenes are not transcribed. This observation indicates that intervening sequences of the gene are important features for normal gene expression, particularly in the transcription of DNA into RNA copies.

It is interesting to note that interrupted genes are characteristic of viruses that infect eukaryotic hosts, whereas uninterrupted genes occur in prokaryotes and their viruses. The correspondence between gene organization in the host and that in its viruses may reflect the fact that the same metabolic machinery is involved in both systems to transcribe and translate the genome. The host cell provides all or most of the transcriptional and translational systems for viral genes, as well as for its own genes.

13.2
The Organization of the mRNA Template

The immediate template for translation is the **messenger RNA** copy of the gene sequence. As stated in the previous section, *mature* mRNAs of prokaryotes, eukaryotes, and viruses are essentially the same in that they have a continuous sequence of triplet codons extending from the beginning to the end of the genetic message. In addition to this coding region, which specifies the amino acid sequence of the polypeptide, extra regions are present at both the 5′ and the 3′ end of the coded message. The sequence at the 5′ end preceding the coding region is called a **leader**, and the sequence at the 3′ end following the coding region is called a **trailer**. In general, neither of these flanking regions is trans-

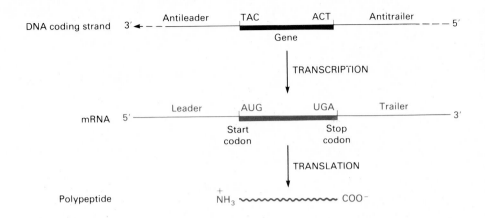

FIGURE 13-4
Flanking antileader and antitrailer regions at each end of the coded gene sequence are transcribed into the complementary mRNA copy, but a region 3′ to the antileader and another region 5′ to the antitrailer (shown by dashed lines) are not transcribed. During mRNA translation, neither leader nor trailer is translated. The coded gene sequence between the Start codon AUG and the Stop codon UGA (or UAA or UAG) is translated into polypeptide, proceeding from the amino terminus to the carboxyl terminus of the amino acid sequence. The steps involved in intron excision and exon splicing as they occur in eukaryotes have been omitted here, for purposes of simplicity.

lated into protein, even though they form parts of the gene transcript (Fig. 13.4).

Most eukaryotic mRNAs have a stretch of adenylic acid residues, or polyadenylic acid, at their 3′ terminus. This **poly(A) tail** is not coded in the gene but is added to the RNA molecule in the nucleus as a posttranscriptional event in stepwise reactions catalyzed by the enzyme poly(A) polymerase. The process is called **polyadenylation**. The number of adenine residues that are added to the RNA varies among groups of organisms and may include about 200 in mammalian species. Whatever its original length in the nucleus, the poly(A) tail is gradually shortened after the mRNA has entered the cytoplasm. In a few cases we know that mRNAs are less stable if polyadenylation is prevented or if a shorter poly(A) tail is present, but no generalization can be made. In fact, histone gene mRNAs are not polyadenylated and mRNAs of other genes may or may not be polyadenylated. When poly(A)$^+$ and poly (A)$^-$ fractions of mRNA are isolated, histone mRNAs constitute a large portion of the poly(A)$^-$ fraction and are not found in the poly(A)$^+$ fraction. Other mRNA components, however, may be found in both poly(A)$^+$ and poly(A)$^-$ fractions. In view of the functional efficiency of both kinds of mRNAs in guiding translation, their similar stabilities, and their equivalence in being transported from the nucleus to the cytoplasm, we are unable to ascribe a general significance to the presence or absence of a poly(A) tail on mRNA molecules or to the length of the polyadenylated sequence in poly(A)$^+$ populations.

The 5′ end of eukaryotic mRNA is also modified posttranscriptionally, by the addition of a **cap** that consists of a residue of *7-methylguanosine*. Capping takes place shortly after transcription of the RNA has begun; most of the isolated RNAs already have a methylated cap, and very little of the original 5′ end is found in nuclear RNA fractions. The 5′ terminal cap is added in two or more steps, each catalyzed by a specific enzyme. The first step involves the condensation between guanosine monophosphate and the original 5′ nucleoside triphosphate terminus of the RNA in a 5′-5′ linkage, and the next step is the addition of a methyl group to the 7 position of the terminal guanine (Fig. 13.5). No other bases in unicellular eukaryotes are methylated at the terminal region of the primary transcript, but in multicellular eukaryotes the original first base of the RNA (now second in position) is also methylated, usually at the 2 position of the residue. Still other

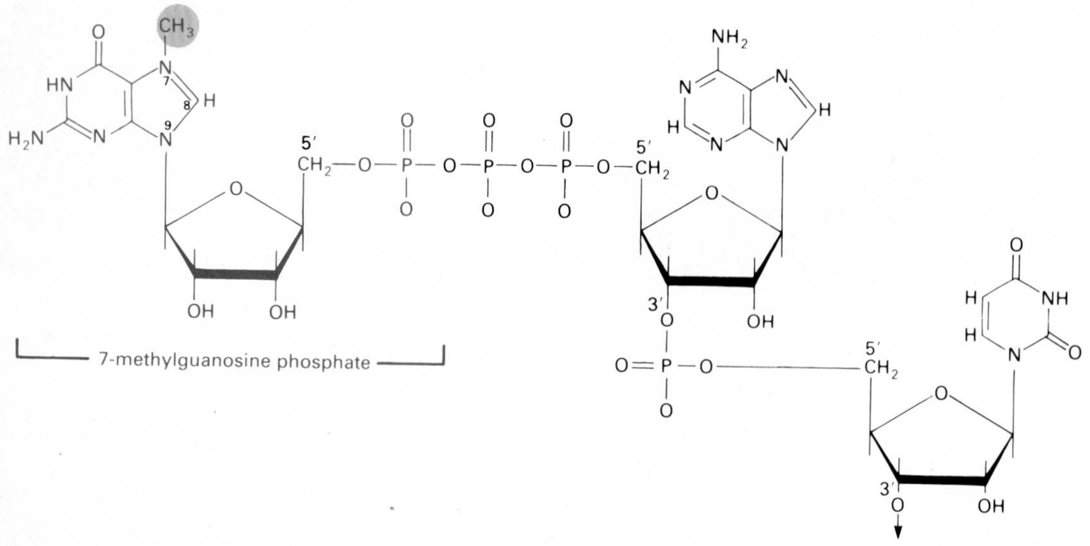

FIGURE 13-5
The 5' end of eukaryotic mRNA is capped by the addition in a 5'–5' linkage of 7-methylguanosine to the original terminus of the messenger shortly after transcription has begun. In the two-step capping process, guanosine monophosphate is linked to the mRNA 5' terminus, and afterward a methyl group (color screen) is added to the N at position 7 of the guanine ring. The 5'–5' linkage blocks the 5' end of the mRNA and prevents other changes at this terminus.

methylations may occur at the second or third bases of the capped RNA, but such events involve only about 10 to 15% of the total population. Every RNA molecule is capped in the nucleus of all the eukaryotes that have been studied. The significant feature of the cap is its 5'-5' linkage with the adjacent residue, in a reverse orientation from all the other nucleotides of the transcript. Because of its particular linkage, the 7-methylguanosine cap effectively blocks the 5' end of the RNA and prevents any change from taking place at this terminus.

The primary RNA transcript of viruses with eukaryotic hosts is capped and polyadenylated, just like the host RNA. In prokaryotes and their viruses, however, neither capping nor polyadenylation of RNA takes place. The situation varies in the case of mitochondria and chloroplasts. RNA transcripts remain uncapped in both kinds of organelles, for reasons that are uncertain, whereas polyadenylation characterizes chloroplasts and some mitochondria but not others. Mitochondrial RNA transcripts are posttranscriptionally polyadenylated in mammalian species, but not in fungi such as yeasts. In mammalian mitochondria the addition of a short poly(A) tail is an essential feature for completion of the termination codon UAA, the only one of the termination codons known to be utilized in these systems. The mammalian mitochondrial gene sequence often ends with A or AT, which is transcribed as U or UA at the mRNA 3' end. Upon addition of A residues, the complete UAA termination codon is made, as well as a length of poly(A) as the 3' terminus of the messenger molecule.

The mature mRNA template for polypeptide synthesis thus includes regions that flank the coding sequence proper. The 5' leader and the 3' trailer are transcribed into RNA from the gene sequence, but a 5' cap and a 3' poly(A) tail are added to the primary transcript afterward in eukaryotes and their viruses. These events in eukaryotes occur in addition to the posttranscriptional processing steps involving excision of introns and splicing of exons in the region between leader and trailer segments. These topics will be discussed shortly.

Transcription of DNA into RNA

In the process of **transcription**, the sequence of deoxyribonucleotides in DNA provides the template for synthesis of a complementary sequence of ribonucleotides in RNA. Three major functional types of RNA molecules are transcribed from genes, each with a particular role to play in gene expression; these molecules are messenger RNA (mRNA), ribosomal RNA (rRNA), and transfer RNA (tRNA). All three kinds of RNAs interact in the processes of translating informational DNA into protein.

RNA may be synthesized by means other than transcription in RNA viruses. In these viruses, RNA is synthesized from RNA templates to make copies of the viral RNA genome in a replication process, as well as to make mRNA transcripts for the infection process itself. In the vertebrate retroviruses, as discussed in the previous chapter, the viral RNA serves as a template to make a DNA copy in a reverse transcription sequence (see Fig. 12.22).

The transcription of RNA requires the catalytic action of *RNA polymerases*, whose subunits may perform different, specific functions in the overall process. In addition to guiding the base pairing between monomer ribonucleotides and DNA and catalyzing phosphodiester bonding along the new RNA strand, components of the enzyme may also be active in the initiation and termination of RNA synthesis. All these events require the recognition by RNA polymerase of the different portions of the DNA template, and coordinated interactions between the polymerase and the template that serves as its means of guidance for synthesis.

13.3
Composition and Action of RNA Polymerases

RNA synthesis proceeds in the $5' \rightarrow 3'$ direction along the DNA template strand, and ribonucleotides (like deoxyribonucleotides) can be added only to an available 3'-hydroxy group by the enzyme **RNA polymerase**. Because the template DNA and the growing RNA chain are antiparallel, the startpoint of RNA chain synthesis must be at the 3' end of the gene. Polymerization proceeds from the 3' end to the 5' end of the gene, and the RNA transcript grows in the antiparallel $5' \rightarrow 3'$ direction by the addition of four kinds of ribonucleotide monomers (Fig. 13.6). Each ribonucleotide monomer has a nitrogenous base covalently bonded to the pentose sugar D-ribose at the carbon-1 position, and a phosphate residue bound to carbon-5 of the sugar. As monomers are bonded together to lengthen the chain, phosphodiester links are formed to join the phosphate at carbon-5 of one monomer with the available 3'-hydroxyl of the adjacent monomer. The nitrogenous bases include adenine, guanine, and cytosine, just as in DNA, but uracil instead of thymine is the fourth kind of base in RNA. Complementary base pairing between cytosine and guanine is the same in DNA–RNA duplex regions as in any other duplex nucleic acid. Adenine in DNA

FIGURE 13-6
RNA synthesis proceeds in the 5' → 3' direction (arrow) along the antiparallel 3' → 5' DNA coding strand. RNA monomers (color) include uracil instead of thymine, but the other three kinds of bases are the same in DNA and RNA chains. Complementary base-pairing provides the guide for copying the correct sequence in the RNA transcript.

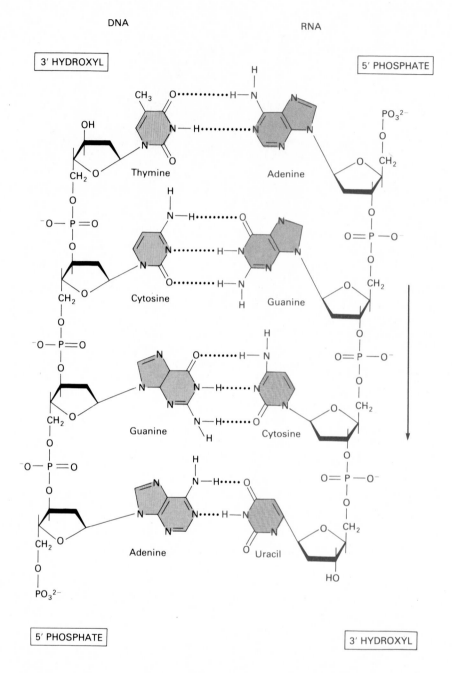

DNA   RNA

3' HYDROXYL   5' PHOSPHATE

5' PHOSPHATE   3' HYDROXYL

pairs with uracil in RNA, and thymine in DNA pairs with adenine in RNA. A region of DNA template with the sequence 3'-TACGGCAT-5' directs the incorporation into an RNA copy of the sequence 5'-AUGCCGUA-3'.

Transcript molecules have particular 5' and 3' ends, so RNA chains must be initiated and terminated at particular sites on the DNA. The RNA polymerase binds to a region of DNA that includes the first base to be copied. The entire region immediately *upstream* of the gene (preceding its 3' end) that is involved in the initiation of transcription is called the **promoter**. The point at which the first nucleotide is copied is called the **startpoint** of transcription. Once initiated, the RNA chain is elongated by polymerase action, and the chain is then terminated at a region of the DNA *downstream* of the gene (following its 5' end), which is called the

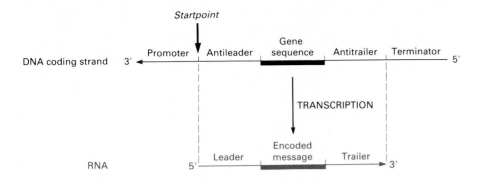

FIGURE 13-7
The promoter region immediately upstream of the gene is involved in binding RNA polymerase in the initiation of transcription, and the terminator region downstream of the gene is a recognition sequence for the termination of transcription. Neither of these two regions is transcribed. Transcription proceeds from the DNA startpoint, where the first nucleotide is copied, to the end of the antitrailer sequence. The transcript is thus synthesized in the expected 5′ → 3′ direction, and it includes leader, encoded message, and trailer sequences.

terminator. At the terminator, the polymerase action stops and the enzyme separates from the DNA strand as the finished RNA transcript is released. The relationship between the DNA template and its RNA transcript is shown in Fig. 13.7.

Only one kind of RNA polymerase is involved in the transcription of all the three functional types of RNA in prokaryotes, phage, and organelles, whereas eukaryotes have three distinct RNA polymerases. Each eukaryotic polymerase is found in a particular region of the nucleus, and each transcribes a different set of genes (Table 13.1). About 50 to 70% of the RNA-synthesizing activity is carried out in the *nucleolus* by RNA polymerase I, which transcribes the genes for the major ribosomal RNAs. The other two enzymes are active in the *nucleoplasm*, which is the portion of the nucleus exclusive of the nucleolus. RNA polymerase II transcribes pre-mRNA from the genes encoding the cellular proteins, which represents about 20 to 40% of the cellular RNA synthesized. RNA polymerase III accounts for only 10% of cellular RNA synthesis activity, and the enzyme is responsible for transcription of small, stable molecules—particularly the tRNAs and the 5S RNA of the ribosome.

The three eukaryotic RNA polymerases are distinguished by their responses to the mushroom poison **α-amanitin**. RNA polymerase I is essentially resistant to inhibition by the drug. RNA polymerase II is very sensitive; its activity is inhibited at very low concentrations of α-amanitin (about 0.03 μg/ml). RNA polymerase III is inhibited only at levels of about 20 μg/ml of the drug, or higher. When presented with high levels of α-amanitin, therefore, cells continue to transcribe the major rRNAs but none of the others. At the lowest concentrations, mRNA precursors are the only transcripts that fail to be synthesized; at moderate concentrations of α-amanitin, the small, stable RNAs as well as the mRNAs stop being made.

TABLE 13-1
Characteristics of RNA Polymerases from Animal Nuclei

Polymerase	Nuclear Location	RNAs Transcribed	Response to α–Amanitin
I	Nucleolus	28S, 18S, 5.8S rRNA	Resistant
II	Nucleoplasm	pre-mRNA, mRNA	Very sensitive
III	Nucleoplasm	5S rRNA, tRNAs	Somewhat sensitive

Like the bacterial polymerase, all three of the eukaryotic enzymes are large proteins of 500,000 daltons or more and consist of a number of polypeptide subunits. The bacterial enzyme, which has been studied in greatest detail in *E. coli*, is composed of five polypeptide subunits, whereas the eukaryotic RNA polymerases have about 10 subunits. We know very little at present about the functions of the subunits of the eukaryotic polymerases because it has not yet been possible to reconstitute active enzymes from preparations of subunits, and few polymerase mutations have been found. In *E. coli*, on the other hand, the complete enzyme (holoenzyme) can be separated biochemically into the **core enzyme** and the **sigma factor**. The core enzyme has two α polypeptides, one β polypeptide, and one β' polypeptide subunit, which are encoded in the genes *rpoA*, *rpoB*, and *rpoC*, respectively. The sigma factor is the σ polypeptide encoded by the gene *rpoD*.

The holoenzyme ($\alpha_2\beta\beta'\sigma$) can initiate transcription at the promoter site of the DNA sequence and catalyze the formation of phosphodiester bonds in the elongation of the RNA transcript. If the sigma factor is removed from the catalyst, the remaining core enzyme initiates transcription at random along the DNA template, and it copies both strands of the DNA duplex instead of the coding strand alone. When the σ polypeptide is restored to make the holoenzyme, transcription is properly initiated at the promoter, and only the coding DNA strand is transcribed. From these and other molecular and genetic data, it is clear that the sigma factor recognizes the initiation site for transcription, on the coding strand, and that the core enzyme has the ability to direct synthesis of the RNA polymer. In fact, once transcription has been initiated *in vivo* or *in vitro*, the σ polypeptide is released and only the core enzyme carries out polymerization of the RNA chain (Fig. 13.8).

We have some general information about the roles of the individual subunits of the core enzyme in catalyzing RNA chain synthesis, particularly from reconstitution studies using subunits from mutant and wild-type strains or from treated preparations. The α subunits may be involved in promoter recognition, because specific modification of an arginine residue leads to a reduced affinity for the promoters that are usually recognized by the holoenzyme. The β' subunit probably plays a role in binding the polymerase to the DNA template because it is the most basic of the polypeptide subunits. In addition, transcription is inhibited *in vitro* when the polyanion *heparin* is present, and heparin binds specifically to the β' subunit of the enzyme. Heparin binds strongly to DNA, so its interaction with the β' subunit indicates that the subunit is also capable of binding strongly to the DNA template and that heparin prevents transcription by preventing the β' subunit from binding the enzyme to promoter DNA. Finally, the β subunit may be involved in binding the substrates of RNA synthesis because nucleoside phosphate incorporation is inhibited by antibiotics of the *rifamycin* and *streptolydigin* groups only when a reconstituted enzyme has a β subunit from antibiotic-sensitive strains—not when the enzyme's β subunit has come from antibiotic-resistant mutant strains.

Termination of transcription requires the intervention of yet another gene product, which is called the **rho protein**. This protein binds to the

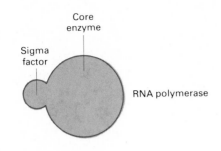

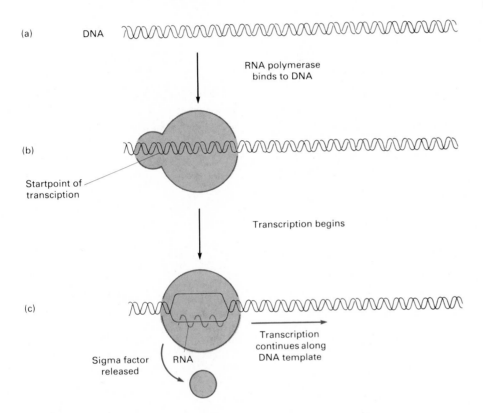

(a)   DNA

RNA polymerase
binds to DNA

(b)

Startpoint of
transcription

Transcription begins

(c)

Sigma factor
released   RNA

Transcription
continues along
DNA template

FIGURE 13-8
The RNA polymerase holoenzyme
in *E. coli* consists of a sigma-factor
polypeptide and a core component
made up of four polypeptide subunits.
Sigma factor is required to initiate
transcription correctly at the promoter
of the DNA coding strand, but the core
enzyme alone carries out subsequent
polymerization when sigma factor is
released from the complex.

terminator region at the 5′ end of the gene and sponsors dissociation of the RNA polymerase from the DNA template. In addition to the influence of rho protein on dissociation of the enzyme from the template, it is possible that the nature of the gene terminus itself may be involved in release of the enzyme. Prokaryotic genes usually have a string of GC base-pairs followed by a string of AT pairs at the 5′ end of the antitrailer just preceding the terminator region. It has been suggested that the physical difference between stronger triple-bonding in GC stretches and the looser double-bonding in AT stretches acts as a signal for dissociation of RNA polymerase from DNA. Unfortunately, we know relatively little about the precise details of the transcription termination process, but considerable attention is now being directed toward understanding interactions between proteins and nucleic acids. We may look forward very soon to learning the nature of these molecular interactions in the processes of transcription and for other aspects of the genetic apparatus leading from gene to protein.

13.4
Promoters: Sites of Transcription Initiation

The promoter is located adjacent to the 3′ end of a gene and its function is to be recognized by proteins, one of which is RNA polymerase. The promoter is not transcribed or translated, so its function resides in the DNA sequence itself, and its influence is exerted only on sequences with which it is physically contiguous in the same DNA strand. The region between the startpoint and the end of transcription is defined as the **transcription unit**, and this region lies between the promoter and the terminator (Fig. 13.9). The transcription unit may include one or more genes, depending on the system. Polygenic transcription units are commonly found in prokaryotic, viral, and organelle genomes but rarely in eukaryotic systems.

By convention, nucleotides are numbered in relation to the startpoint of a sequence, which is given the value of +1. Nucleotides to the right of the startpoint, or downstream, are assigned increasing positive values. Nucleotides to the left of the startpoint, or upstream, are assigned negative values from −1 and increasing away from the startpoint. A sequence is written proceeding from left to right, which is the 5′ → 3′ direction of transcription along the antiparallel 3′ → 5′ gene sequence, and the nucleotides are numbered in both directions away from the startpoint (Fig. 13.10). In these terms, the DNA region to which RNA polymerase binds in a stable initiation complex encompasses about 40 nucleotides, between −20 and +20 of the sequence. In order to determine the features of DNA required for RNA polymerase binding, we compare the sequences of different promoters to identify the signal recognized by the enzyme. Any sequence that is present in all or most promoters is a likely candidate for such a recognition signal.

An astonishing discovery that emerged from base-sequence analysis of more than 50 different promoters in *E. coli* was the absence of sequence homology or identity over most of the DNA region to which the polymerase binds. Just upstream of the startpoint, however, is a hexanucleotide with a sequence closely related to TATAAT in all the promoters. The TATAAT sequence as such is found rarely, but it is a *consensus sequence* that includes the bases most often found at each of the six positions. The sequence is often called the Pribnow box in recognition of the person who first described its occurrence. The center of the Pribnow box is about 10 bases upstream from the startpoint, and the hexanucleotide most often occurs from position −14 to position −8. Another consensus sequence occurs farther upstream, with its center at about position −35; the predominant bases are TTGACA. Both of these

FIGURE 13-9
The transcription unit includes the DNA sequence between the startpoint nucleotide and the end of transcription just preceding the terminator. Because the promoter and terminator sequences are not transcribed, they are not part of the DNA transcription unit.

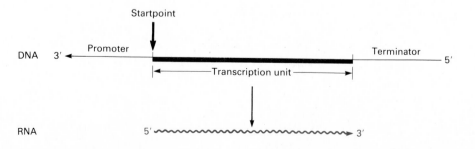

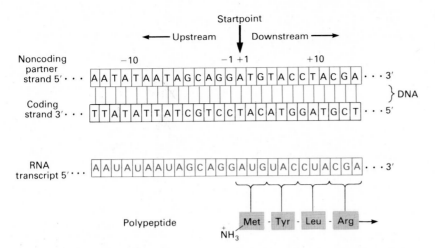

consensus sequences are believed to act as recognition signals for the binding of RNA polymerase, although the Pribnow box is the only one of the two sequences that remains tightly associated with the enzyme after digestion with DNase of all the bases that are not protected by the covering enzyme protein molecule. In other words, when digestion with DNase is performed to see which segment of DNA is covered by bound enzyme and is therefore safe from degradation, the DNA region from about −20 to +20 is retained intact, whereas the −35 sequence is degraded by DNase. In addition, some promoters lack the −35 sequence. Because of these variations, it has been suggested that the −35 sequence is involved in raising the efficiency with which RNA polymerase recognizes a particular promoter, whereas the −10 sequence, or **Pribnow box**, is the actual site of stable binding of the enzyme in the formation of an initiation complex for the start of transcription (Fig. 13.11).

FIGURE 13-10
The nucleotides of a DNA sequence are numbered in relation to the startpoint, which is nucleotide +1. All nucleotides upstream of the startpoint are assigned consecutive negative numbers, and all nucleotides downstream of the startpoint are assigned consecutive positive numbers; the numbers increase progressively in both directions away from the startpoint. The transcription unit includes all the positively numbered nucleotides, beginning with +1. In discussions of the gene sequence, it is conventional to refer to the noncoding DNA partner strand rather than to the coding strand itself. The advantage of this convention is that knowledge of the 5′ → 3′ noncoding strand allows us to write the 5′ → 3′ RNA sequence directly, changing only each T in the DNA to U in the RNA sequence (for example, the DNA Start codon ATG in the noncoding strand becomes AUG in the transcript). Each codon in the 5′ → 3′ noncoding DNA strand or the 5′ → 3′ RNA transcript can then be read to determine its corresponding amino acid unit of the polypeptide translation.

FIGURE 13-11
In *E. coli* and other prokaryotes, the −10 sequence, or Pribnow box, includes a hexanucleotide consensus sequence. The hexanucleotide TATAAT (or one similar to it) occurs in the Pribnow box of all sequenced prokaryotic promoters. The Pribnow box is the region to which RNA polymerase binds in a stable complex for the start of transcription at nucleotide +1. The −35 sequence farther upstream is more variable, but it is believed to increase the efficiency with which RNA polymerase recognizes the promoter prior to stable binding at the −10 sequence. Note that all references to DNA sequence are based on the 5′ → 3′ noncoding partner strand of the duplex DNA molecule.

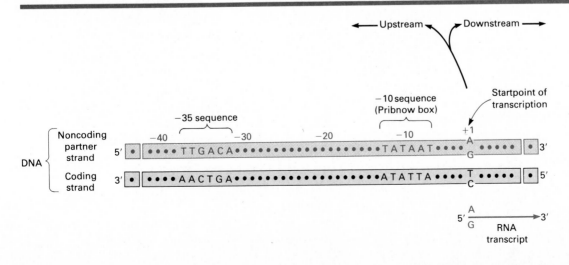

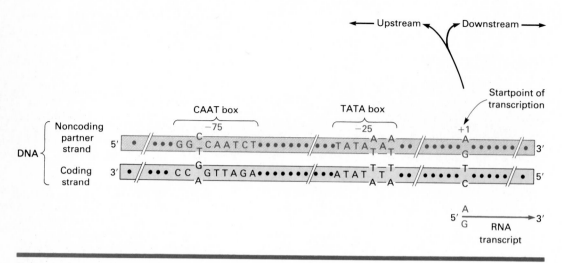

FIGURE 13-12

Two different regions have been identified in eukaryotic promoters recognized by RNA polymerase II, the enzyme that catalyzes transcription of genes encoded for polypeptides. The TATA box is positioned around nucleotide −25 and consists of seven nucleotides with a consensus sequence of TATA^A_TA^A_T. The TATA box in eukaryotes functions like the Pribnow box in prokaryotes in that they both sponsor the accurate initiation of transcription at the +1 startpoint nucleotide. The CAAT box positioned around nucleotide −75 farther upstream consists of nine nucleotides with a consensus sequence of GGCCAATCT or GGTCAATCT, and it is present in many (but not all) eukaryotic promoters. Its function may be to aid in the initiation of transcription of some genes, because initiation is severely reduced in deletion mutants that lack the CAAT box sequence.

The identities of eukaryotic promoters were inferred from the occurrence of base-sequence homologies in regions upstream from the startpoints of various genes in different organisms. The emphasis has been on genes transcribed by RNA polymerase II, because these are the most varied and numerous elements in a genome. RNA polymerase I transcribes only identical rRNA genes, and RNA polymerase III transcribes only a small number of genes in any one organism (32 tRNA genes and the 5S rRNA gene). Two different regions of nucleotide homologies have been located upstream of the startpoint—one region centered at about −25 and the other centered at about −75. The −25 sequence consists of seven AT base-pairs with a consensus sequence of TATA^A_TA^A_T in the great majority of cases; it is referred to as the **TATA box** or the **Hogness box**. The −75 sequence consists of nine nucleotides with a consensus ordering of GG^C_TCAATCT, and it is sometimes called the **CAAT box**.

Except for its location at −25 instead of −10 and for the presence of a seventh AT base-pair, the TATA box in eukaryotic promoters is virtually identical to the Pribnow box in prokaryotic promoters (Fig. 13.12). Deletion or specific base modifications of the TATA box reduce the *accuracy* of initiating transcription at the startpoint. Both the TATA box and the Pribnow box regions serve to ensure the accuracy of transcribing the +1 nucleotide first. They do so by tightly binding RNA polymerase and thereby sponsoring the formation of a stable initiation complex in the correct place on the DNA template. In addition, these AT-rich regions are flanked by GC-rich regions with stronger triple hydrogen bonding, which remain in the bonded duplex conformation when the more loosely bonded AT pairs melt and unwind as transcription begins along the coding template strand (Fig. 13.13).

The −75 sequence may not generally be required to initiate transcription because the sequence is not present in all promoters. The CAAT box may be required for certain classes of genes, however, because its deletion may lower the efficiency of initiating transcription of the gene to 2% of the normal level.

Both the TATA box and the CAAT box regions are absent upstream of the 5S rRNA gene in the clawed toad *Xenopus laevis*. In fact,

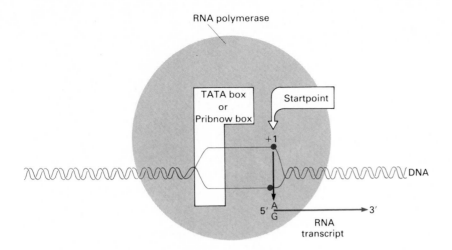

FIGURE 13-13
RNA polymerase (gray) binds tightly to the AT-rich TATA box region in eukaryotic promoters, or to the Pribnow box in prokaryotic promoters, and is thereby assured of being in the correct location to transcribe the +1 startpoint nucleotide first.

the promoter for this gene lies *within* the transcription unit, between positions +55 and +80, and RNA polymerase III binds to this region in the initiation of transcription. Although we are still uncertain about how the bound polymerase accurately initiates transcription more than 50 bases upstream, at the +1 startpoint, it has been suggested that RNA polymerase III is a large enough molecule to cover the startpoint and the promoter regions at the same time. Where the promoter lies was determined from studies in which deletions were introduced into the gene and its surrounding regions from both the upstream and downstream directions. The 5S rRNA transcript continues to be produced when the entire upstream sequence is deleted, indicating the absence of a promoter at the expected 3′ end of the gene, and shortened transcripts continue to be synthesized as long as the deletion does not extend to the +55 base. Transcription does *not* take place when the deletion goes past the +55 base in the downstream direction, nor does it occur when deletions are introduced from the 5′ end of the gene and extend upstream of base +80. As long as the region +55 to +80 remains intact, transcription occurs, so the promoter must lie between positions +55 and +80 (Fig. 13.14).

Promoters for other genes transcribed by RNA polymerase III may also be located within the transcription unit, since a number of tRNA genes have been found to have one or two internal promoters. In the case of the *Xenopus* 5S rRNA gene, but not for the few tRNA genes thus far examined, RNA polymerase III can initiate transcription only if a particular 37,000-dalton protein is also present and is bound to the DNA from +45 to +96. The *efficiency* of transcription appears to be related to the nature of the flanking upstream region of the gene, however, since differences in this region lead to different rates of transcription for genes with identical transcription unit sequences.

In the virus SV40 genome there occur two identical sequences of 72 base-pairs each, which influence the rate of transcription. Deletion experiments have shown that transcription is unaffected when one of these sequences is removed, but the removal of both repeats leads to a greatly reduced rate of transcription. The repeat sequences need not be present in their usual location to influence transcription. When the

FIGURE 13-14

FIGURE 13-14
Transcription by RNA polymerase III of the 5S rRNA gene in *Xenopus laevis.* (a) The 120 nucleotides of the 5S rRNA transcription unit (+1 to +120) include an internal promoter region (+55 to +80) rather than an upstream promoter. The upstream TATA box and CAAT box are absent. When it binds to DNA, RNA polymerase III (gray) is a large enough molecule to cover the region containing the startpoint and the internal promoter. (b) DNA with upstream deletions that do not extend past the +55 nucleotide is transcribed, but the RNA copies are shorter than normal. Such data indicate the absence of an upstream promoter. (c) Transcription fails to occur if deletions include all or part of the +55 to +80 region of the gene. Such data indicate that the promoter must lie between +55 and +80 of the gene sequence.

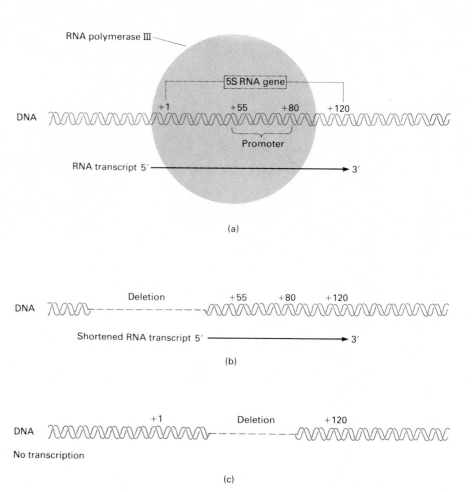

repeat sequence is transposed to *any* part of the genome, transcription continues normally. In fact, when certain mammalian genes, such as the β-globin gene, are placed in the same DNA molecule with the 72-base-pair repeat, the transcription of the gene may increase 200-fold. On the other hand, the SV40 repeat sequence has no effect on some other genes, such as the α-globin gene. The repeat sequence is called an **enhancer** because it may exert a stimulating influence on gene transcription. It is not considered part of a promoter because the enhancer sequence may affect transcription even when it occurs some thousands of bases away from the startpoint, in either the upstream or the downstream region. Investigations are in progress to determine how the enhancer exerts its influence and how it can work over very large distances in the genome. Although enhancers have not been found in prokaryotic or eukaryotic systems, several viruses in addition to SV40 appear to have enhancer-like elements in the genome. No sequence homology occurs, however, and the nature of the enhancer-like elements has been inferred in other viral genomes by experiments in which such an element has been found to substitute in SV40 for the virus's own known enhancer. Interestingly, the enhancer-like sequence in retroviruses is known to be involved in activating cellular genes in the host.

The enhancer might have been considered part of the promoter if data had been obtained only from deletion experiments. But, from transposition experiments devised to place the enhancer in other parts of the SV40 genome and in genomes or DNAs from other sources, we know that the enhancer influences the promoter but is not a part of it.

Promoters play a vital role in gene expression, and they are a primary site for processes by which such expression is controlled. In fact, the principal means for regulation of gene expression is control over the start of transcription and the rate of transcription of each gene in the genome. We will discuss transcriptional controls and other controls over gene expression in the next chapter.

13.5
tRNA Transcripts

Mature tRNAs function as carriers of amino acids to the ribosomal sites of translation. The **tRNA** transcripts synthesized by RNA polymerase III are precursor molecules only slightly longer than the mature forms. During processing of **pre-tRNA**, the short 5′ leader sequence is removed, the 3′ end of the molecule is extended by the addition of 3′-ACC-5′, and introns are removed. Once the remaining exons are spliced together, the mature tRNA is available to accept a specific amino acid and carry it to the translational machinery for incorporation into polypeptide. The steps involved in processing precursor to mature tyrosine-carrying tRNA (tRNA^{Tyr}) in yeast are shown in Fig. 13.15. The single-stranded tRNA molecule is usually depicted in its secondary-structure cloverleaf configuration. Note that only the expected bases U, A, G, and C are incorporated into the initial transcript but that base modifications occur as posttranscriptional events in tRNA maturation.

FIGURE 13-15
Processing of precursor tRNA to mature tRNA is illustrated for yeast tRNA^{Tyr}. The 5′ leader sequence is removed first; the single intron is excised from the shortened precursor, to which 3′-ACC-5′ has been added at the 3′-OH end of the molecule; and the two exons are spliced together to produce the mature tRNA. The anticodon triplet (underlined) 5′-GUA-3′ is modified to 5′-GψA-3′ when uridine is changed to pseudouridine in the mature tRNA. Other nucleotides are modified posttranscriptionally, including C and A residues that are methylated at carbons 1, 2, or 5 (m^1, m^2, m^5). (From DeRobertis, E. M., and M. V. Olson, 1979, *Nature* **278**:137, Fig. 7.)

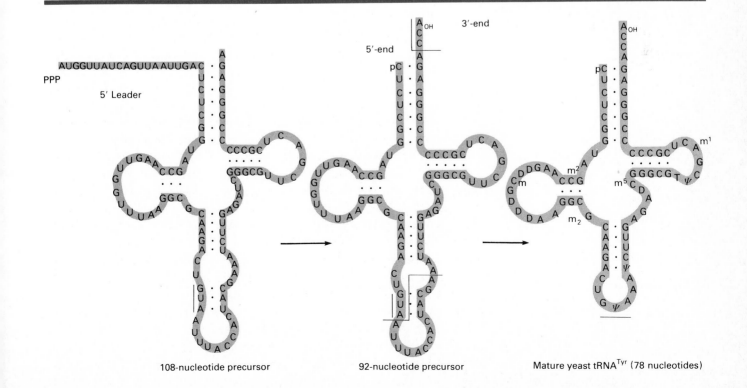

108-nucleotide precursor   92-nucleotide precursor   Mature yeast tRNA^{Tyr} (78 nucleotides)

FIGURE 13-16
Molecular structure of transfer RNA (tRNA). (a) Generalized cloverleaf model of the secondary structure of the single-stranded RNA molecule. Solid circles represent bases in the hydrogen-bonded helical regions, and open circles stand for unpaired bases. Unusual bases include ribothymidine (T), pseudouridine (ψ), and others. (b) Schematic model of the tertiary structure of yeast tRNA^{Phe}. (From Kim, S. H., et al., 1974. Science **185**:435.) (c) Secondary structure of yeast tRNA^{Ser} in which inosine occupies the 5' position in the anticodon 3'-AGI-5'. (d) Secondary structure of yeast tRNA^{Ala}, the first nucleic acid to be completely sequenced, by Robert Holley in 1965. The 3'-CGI-5' anticodon should pair with mRNA codons 5'-GUA-3', 5'-GCU-3', and 5'-GCC-3', according to the wobble concept (see Fig. 13.17).

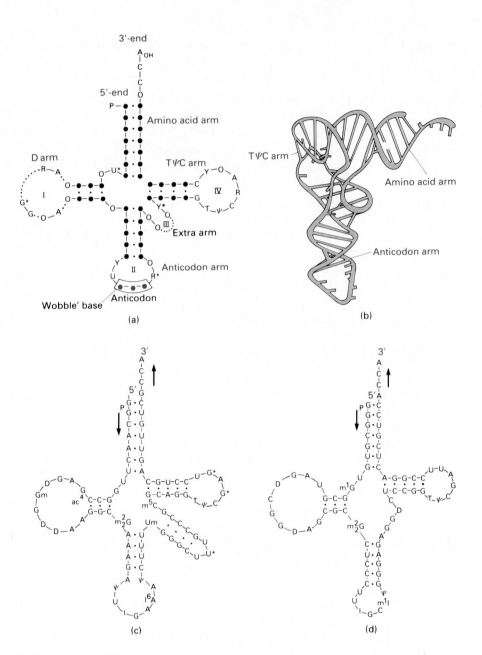

Among the modified bases are such unusual residues as ribothymidine, pseudouridine, inosine, and others. Inosine, for example, is derived posttranscriptionally from adenine, by deamination at carbon-6.

Various parts of the tRNA molecule carry out specific functions, such as the amino acid arm at the 3' end to which the amino acid is bound and the anticodon arm that includes the base-triplet recognition site, or **anticodon**, that interacts by complementary base-pairing with the mRNA codon during translation (Fig. 13.16). According to the genetic code we would expect 61 different tRNAs, each with a unique anticodon, to interact with 61 unique mRNA codons that specify amino acids. Instead, only 32 different tRNAs are produced and these tRNAs are all that are needed to handle 61 different mRNA codons. The occurrence of only 32 different tRNAs, and the presence of modified bases such as inosine in the anticodon triplet itself, were explained by Francis Crick in the **wobble hypothesis**. Crick suggested that the 5' base of the anticodon can pair in certain cases with more than one kind of complementary 3′ base in the mRNA codon. This 5′ anticodon residue is the *wobble base*, which means that its pairing properties are less restricted. According to the wobble concept, the tRNA anticodon 3′-AGU-5′ can pair as expected with the mRNA codon 5′-UCA-3′ and with the mRNA codon 5′-UCG-3′ as well. The 5′-U wobble base in the anticodon can recognize both A and G in the 3′ site of the mRNA codons. A single kind of tRNA can thus interact with two different mRNA codons. In addition to 5′-U, other wobble bases at the 5′ position of an anticodon are guanine and inosine; G can pair with U or C in a codon, and I can pair with A, U, or C (Fig. 13.17). In every case, however, pairing is restricted to G–C and A–U for the middle base and the 3′ base of any anticodon; only the 5′ base has wobble, and only U, G, and I are in this category.

The wobble hypothesis drew on certain observed features of the synonymous mRNA codons for amino acids as conventionally shown in the 64-box display (see Fig. 4.11). Codon synonyms have the same initial doublet but differ in their 3′ base. The four alanine codon synonyms, for example, are GCU, GCC, GCA, and GCG. The exceptions to this rule are methionine and tryptophan (which are each specified by a single codon) and serine, leucine, and arginine (each of which has six codon synonyms). In the case of the latter three amino acids, however, four of the six codons have the same initial doublet, and the other two codons have a different identical doublet at the 5′ and middle positions. The occurrence of different 3′ bases in codons with

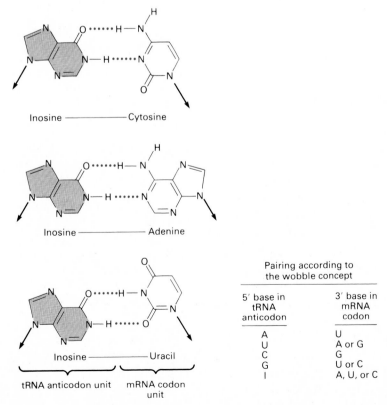

(a)

Pairing according to the wobble concept	
5′ base in tRNA anticodon	3′ base in mRNA codon
A	U
U	A or G
C	G
G	U or C
I	A, U, or C

(b)

FIGURE 13-17
Wobble in the tRNA anticodon. (a) When inosine is present as the 5′ base in an anticodon, it can pair with cyosine, adenine, or uracil in the 3′ position of mRNA codons. Less restricted base-pairing, or wobble, is characteristic of certain bases when these are located at the 5′ end of a tRNA anticodon triplet. (b) In addition to inosine, uracil and guanine may be 5′ wobble bases in anticodons, and they show less restricted base-pairing properties. Wobble is not associated with adenine or cytosine when either base occupies the 5′ end in the tRNA anticodon triplet.

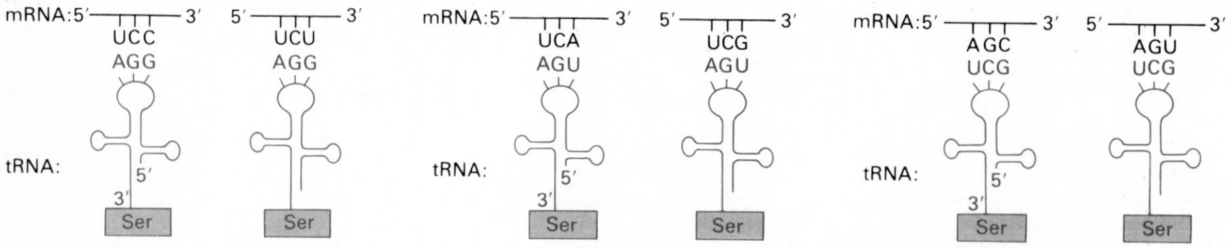

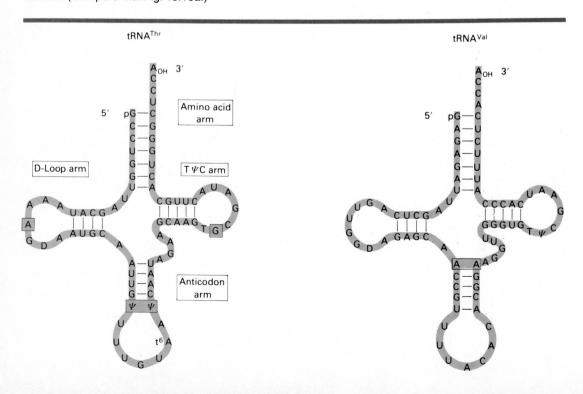

FIGURE 13-18

Six different serine mRNA codons can be handled by three different tRNA^Ser anticodons because of wobble in the 5' base of the anticodons (AGG, AGU, UCG). Wobble base 5'-G can pair with C or U in the mRNA codons UCC/UCU and AGC/AGU, and wobble base 5'-U can pair with A or G in the mRNA codons UCA/UCG.

FIGURE 13-19

Secondary-structure cloverleaf configurations for two mitochondrial tRNAs from *Neurospora crassa* show some of the unusual features of these mitochondrial gene transcripts. In tRNA^Thr, an A residue is present instead of the standard G residue in the D-loop arm, G is present instead of ψ in the TψC arm, and an unbonded ψ base pair replaces the standard hydrogen-bonded fifth base pair in the stem of the anticodon arm. In tRNA^Val, the fifth pair of bases (AA) in the stem of the anticodon arm is not hydrogen-bonded. (Compare with Fig. 13.16a.)

identical initial doublets provided the clue to the possibility of wobble in the 5' base of the anticodon.

Experimental support for the wobble hypothesis was first obtained in studies showing that the six serine codons were served by the predicted minimum number of three tRNAs, each with a 5' wobble base in the anticodon (Fig. 13.18). Although these and other data have verified the basic premise of the wobble concept in explaining the existence of fewer than 61 kinds of tRNAs, other factors may be influential in reducing the restrictions for complementary base-pairing between codon and anticodon triplets. Studies of mitochondrial tRNAs may produce important insights into tRNA–mRNA interactions, because only 22 to 25 tRNAs are encoded in mitochondrial genomes and these tRNAs have some interesting variations in their molecular structure. Instead of having five complementary base-pairs, some tRNAs have only four such pairs in the hydrogen-bonded stem of the anticodon arm, and some mitochondrial tRNAs have eight bases instead of the conventional seven in the loop of the anticodon arm (Fig. 13.19). These features, among others, may be involved in the ability of a single kind of tRNA to recognize and pair with as many as four codons, each with the same initial doublet but a different 3' base (Fig. 13.20). By ana-

UUU	Phe	AAG	UCU		UAU	Tyr	AUG	UGU	Cys	ACG
UUC			UCC	Ser	AGU	UAC		UGC		
UUA	Leu	AAU	UCA			UAA	Ter	UGA	Trp	ACU
UUG			UCG			UAG		UGG		

CUU			CCU			CAU	His	GUG	CGU		
CUC	Thr	GAU	CCC	Pro	GGU	CAC			CGC	Arg	GCA
CUA			CCA			CAA	Gln	GUU	CGA		
CUG			CCG			CAG			CGG		

AUU			ACU			AAU	Asn	UUG	AGU	Ser	UCG
AUC	Ile	UAG	ACC	Thr	UGU	AAC			AGC		
AUA			ACA			AAA	Lys	UUU	AGA	Arg	UCU
AUG	Met	UAC	ACG			AAG			AGG		

GUU			GCU			GAU	Asp	CUG	GGU		
GUC	Val	CAU	GCC	Ala	CGU	GAC			GGC	Gly	CCU
GUA			GCA			GAA	Glu	CUU	GGA		
GUG			GCG			GAG			GGG		

FIGURE 13-20
The coding dictionary for yeast mitochondrial mRNA codons (5′ → 3′, left) and tRNA anticodons (3′ → 5′, color). The 5′ wobble base of each anticodon is underlined. Unmixed codon families, in which all four codons with the same initial doublet specify the same amino acid, generally interact with a single anticodon whose 5′ wobble base is U. The only exception to this feature is the unmixed codon family for arginine (CGU, CGC, CGA, CGG), which interacts with the anticodon 3′-GCA-5′. (From Bonitz, S. G., *et al.*, 1980, *Proc. Nat. Acad. Sci. U.S.* **77**:3167-3170, Fig. 2.)

lyzing the features and capacities of mitochondrial tRNAs, therefore, we may be able to better understand how these molecules function generally in any system. The more invariant nature of cytoplasmic tRNAs and their highly conserved sequences and construction, along with a minimum number of useful mutations, has restricted our ability to pursue the full spectrum of studies deemed necessary.

An interesting situation exists in mammalian mitochondria, where the 22 tRNA genes are scattered all around the organelle genome but occur at the terminus of almost every rRNA and polypeptide-specifying gene (Fig. 13.21). From extensive molecular analyses of RNA tran-

FIGURE 13-21
Gene maps for each strand of human duplex mitochondrial DNA, as determined with HeLa cells. The maps have been linearized for easier reference to the genes distributed along 16.58 kilobases in each strand of the circular duplex molecule. Eight tRNA genes are encoded in the light strand, and the remaining 14 tRNA genes are encoded in the heavy strand along with genes that specify rRNA and polypeptides (symbolized below). Note that a tRNA gene is located at the terminus of nearly every gene encoded in the heavy strand. (From Ojala, D., *et al.*, 1981, *Nature* **290**:470–474, Fig. 1.)

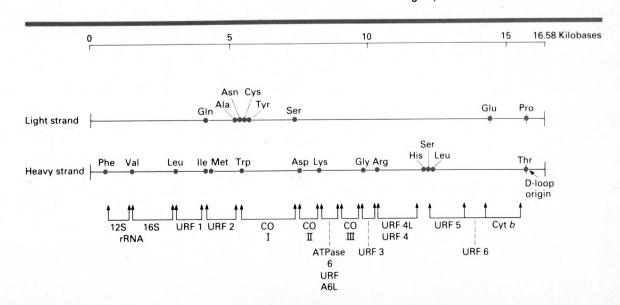

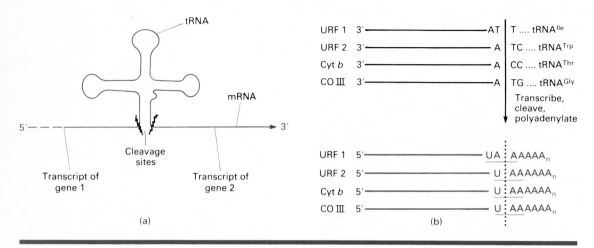

(a)

(b)

FIGURE 13-22
Proposed model of tRNA punctuation processing of the polygenic mRNA transcript of the heavy strand in human mitochondrial DNA. (a) The tRNA regions of a polygenic transcript may loop out and thereby provide signals for cleavage at tRNA termini in a transcript. (b) Incomplete termination codons AT or A in the four genes shown are transcribed into complementary UA or U, respectively, in the primary transcript. Cleavage of the transcript at this incomplete terminus is followed by polyadenylation, which adds adenine residues and thereby simultaneously completes the UAA Stop codon (underlined) and provides a short poly(A) tail at the 3' end of the active mRNA molecule.

scripts and of their alignments with DNA sequences of the human mitochondrial genome, Giuseppe Attardi and others have postulated that the tRNA regions are involved in processing the single polygenic RNA transcript of the main coding strand. The **tRNA punctuation processing model** proposes that the tRNA regions loop out from the polygenic transcript and thereby provide signals for cleaving the transcript at the termini of the tRNA sequence (Fig. 13.22). Once the tRNAs are cut out, the mRNAs and rRNAs that flank the tRNA sites will be separated out at the same time. The liberated transcripts may undergo further processing before carrying out their functions in the mitochondrial genetic apparatus. One of these posttranscriptional processing steps is the addition of a poly(A) sequence to the 3' end of the freed RNA transcript in the case of certain genes. Genes with incomplete termination codons, such as 5'-A or 5'-AT, produce mRNA transcripts with 3'-U or 3'-UA termini. Upon being polyadenylated, the UAA termination codon is produced, as is a short poly(A) tail that becomes the 3' terminus of the finished mRNA molecule. Genes that already possess a complete UAA termination codon may also be polyadenylated, but addition of the poly(A) tail serves no function in completing a coding sequence.

These unusual features of the mammalian mitochondrial system do not necessarily apply to other mitochondrial genomes. In yeast mitochondria, for example, genes have a complete termination codon plus a noncoding trailer sequence at the 3' end. In addition, the available evidence indicates that yeast mitochondrial mRNA transcripts are not polyadenylated. Interestingly, the tRNA genes are not scattered around the genome but instead are present predominantly in a cluster between the genes for 21S rRNA and cytochrome oxidase subunit II (see Fig. 9.34). We can see from these systems, and from other information discussed in Chapter 12, that the organization of the genome often has an important bearing on the processes of gene expression.

Genes for tRNAs are present in single copies in organelle genomes, but several tRNA gene copies may occur in prokaryotic genomes. Eukaryotic genomes, however, have hundreds of copies of the different tRNA genes. These repeat sequences constitute part of the middle-repetitive DNA of the eukaryotic genome. All the genes may be clustered in a single chromosome, as in *Drosophila melanogaster*, or they may be present in all or some of the chromosomes of the genome. The reasons for these variations are unclear, nor do we know whether any advantages are conferred by one arrangement or another.

13.6
rRNA Transcripts

Ribosomal RNA (**rRNA**) molecules vary in size from several thousands of nucleotides in the single strand to about 120 nucleotides in the smallest of the several kinds of these transcripts. By comparison, tRNAs are 70 to 80 nucleotides long; nuclear pre-mRNAs may include as many as 10,000 residues or even more; and mature mRNAs are generally 1000 to 2000 nucleotides long, though they vary considerably according to the length of a particular genetic instruction and the regions flanking the coding sequence. It is conventional to describe and refer to rRNAs and to the ribosomes in terms of their sedimentation coefficient, expressed in *Svedberg units* (**S**). These coefficients are calculated from analyses of molecule or particle sedimentations in sucrose-gradient centrifugation.

A whole ribosome consists of two unequal-sized **ribosome subunits**, each of which contains one or more specific rRNAs. The prokaryotic ribosome is a 70S particle whose larger 50S subunit includes one 23S and one 5S RNA molecule, whereas the smaller 30S subunit has only a 16S rRNA (Table 13.2). The eukaryotic ribosome is an 80S particle whose larger 60S subunit contains one 25S to 28S, one 5.8S, and one 5S RNA, and the smaller 40S subunit has one 18S rRNA molecule. Because molecule or particle shape and molecular weight are determining factors in sedimentations, the sum of the S values for two subunits is greater than the observed S value of the whole ribosome. Similarly, the 23S rRNA is twice the length of the 16S rRNA, but the precise difference between their lengths is not reflected in their S values.

The initial rRNA transcript is a precursor molecule, or **pre-rRNA**. Apart from this similarity, other features of the process and its products are different in prokaryotes and eukaryotes. In *E. coli*, for example, each of the seven copies of the rRNA gene (*rrn*) may be transcribed into a 30S pre-rRNA molecule. The whole 30S precursor is rarely isolated, however, presumably because the molecule is processed *during* transcription or very shortly afterward. In mutants that are deficient in ribonuclease III (the enzyme that cleaves the pre-rRNA at specific sites), the 30S precursor accumulates. When the precursor is incubated *in vitro* with

TABLE 13-2
Characteristics of Cytoplasmic Ribosomes

Source	Ribosome Monomer	Ribosome Subunits	rRNA Present in Subunit	Number of Proteins in Subunit
Prokaryotes	70S	30S	16S	21
		50S	23S, 5S	31
Eukaryotes	80S	40S	18S	33
		60S*	25–28S, 5.8S, 5S	49

*The large rRNA is 28S in animals and 25–26S in protists, fungi, and plants.

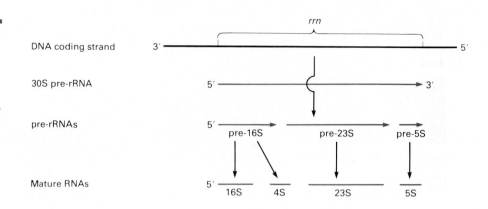

FIGURE 13-23
Processing of the pre-rRNA transcript of a rRNA gene (*rrn*) in *E. coli* results in 16S, 23S, and 5S rRNAs, as well as one tRNA molecule (4S). The entire 30S pre-rRNA transcript is rarely found, presumably because it is processed during transcription or immediately afterward. Whole 30S rRNA transcripts can be isolated from mutants deficient in the cleaving enzyme ribonuclease III. When such 30S pre-rRNA is incubated with the enzyme *in vitro*, pre-16S, pre-23S, and pre-5S fragments are produced. In normal cells these precursor fragments are trimmed at their 5′ and 3′ ends to form mature rRNAs and the one kind of tRNA encoded within this sequence.

RNase III, cleavages take place and individual precursors to the mature 16S, 23S, and 5S rRNAs are produced (Fig. 13.23). The 5′ → 3′ order of the different species in the 30S precursor transcript is 16S—23S—5S. Each of the individual 16S, 23S, and 5S precursors is slightly longer than its mature form and must be processed at both the 5′ and the 3′ end in order to emerge as a mature rRNA for incorporation into the ribosomal subunits. The location of each kind of mature rRNA is readily determined by analyzing the components isolated from preparations of pure ribosomal subunits (Fig. 13.24).

The absolute size of the eukaryotic pre-rRNA varies according to the group of organisms; it is 37S in insects, 40S in amphibians, and 45S in mammals. In every case, however, eukaryotic pre-rRNA is processed to generate the 18S, 25S to 28S, and 5.8S rRNAs, but not the 5S molecules. The 5S rRNA of the large subunit is transcribed from its own genes, which may or may not be situated near the major rRNA genes in a genome. Processing of pre-rRNA can be followed in some detail,

FIGURE 13-24
Separation of ribosomes and rRNAs from the cytoplasm of prokaryotic and eukaryotic cells by centrifugation in sucrose gradients. Centrifugation of particles yields 70S or 80S whole ribosomes along with free 50S + 30S or 60S + 40S subunits, respectively. Purified RNA from whole-ribosome preparations separates into distinct subpopulations of rRNAs, each of which can be traced to the particular subunit if the rRNAs are purified from separate populations of large subunits and small subunits rather than from intact whole ribosomes.

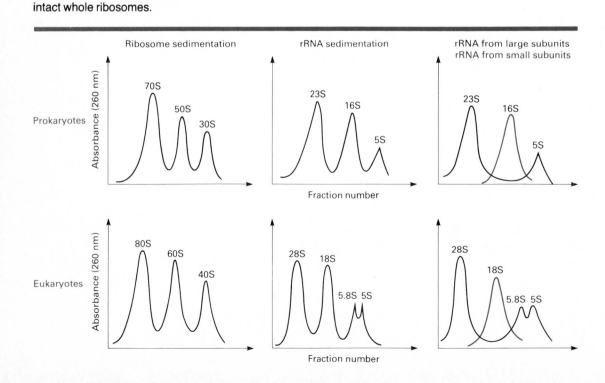

TABLE 13-3
Types of Labeled rRNA Collected from Subcellular Fractions During a Chase with Cold Uridine Following a 10-Minute Pulse with [³H]uridine

Subcellular Fraction	Collection Time During Chase Period			
	0 min	10 min	30 min	60 min
Nucleus	45S	41S	36S	–
Cytoplasm	–	–	18S	28S, 5.8S

because the initial transcript matures rather slowly through a series of intermediates, all within the nucleus, and the mature rRNAs appear in cytoplasmic ribosomes between 30 and 60 minutes after synthesis of the initial 45S transcript. Via **pulse–chase** radioactive labeling, the time course and the sequence of events can be determined in a relatively straightforward manner. In such experiments, an initial *pulse* of [³H]uridine is provided to cells and a large amount of unlabeled (cold) uridine is introduced a short time later as the *chase*. After withdrawing samples from the incubation mixture at intervals, investigators can determine the pathway of the processing of primary to mature rRNA by noting the kinds of RNA fragments produced from the 45S RNA and their times and places of appearance.

The first transcription product to be labeled is 45S rRNA, perhaps 10 minutes after the radioactive label has been provided. In the ensuing chase period, the incorporated labeled residues from 45S pre-rRNA first appear in a 41S fragment, which is cleaved to produce 18S rRNA plus a 36S pre-rRNA molecule. The labeled 18S rRNA is found in cytoplasmic ribosomes long before the other labeled rRNAs (Table 13.3). The 36S pre-rRNA is cleaved to a 32S fragment, which is then cleaved to yield the 28S and 5.8S rRNAs of the large ribosomal subunit. The 5S rRNA encoded elsewhere in the genome is packaged together with 28S and 5.8S rRNAs in the larger subunit, under controls we do not yet understand (Fig. 13.25). All the rRNAs appear as ribonucleoproteins, rather than as naked RNA molecules, and are transported from the nucleus to the cytoplasm in this form. The nuclear ribosomal ribonucleoproteins are inactive or precursor particles, which are somehow transformed into active ribosomal subunit packages on leaving the nucleus. We know little about the processes of ribosomal subunit maturation, but we believe that they occur either at the nuclear envelope or in the cytoplasm immediately adjacent to the nucleus.

Numerous copies of the 5S and major rRNA genes are present in a eukaryotic genome; these genes form part of middle-repetitive DNA. The hundreds or thousands of copies of the major rRNA gene are referred to as **ribosomal DNA**, or **rDNA**, and they are clustered in the *nucleolar organizing region* (**NOR**) of one or more chromosomes in the genome. In stunning electron micrographs of actively transcribing rDNA isolated from nucleoli of amphibian oocytes, Oscar Miller, Barbara Hamkalo, and others have shown that many transcripts are

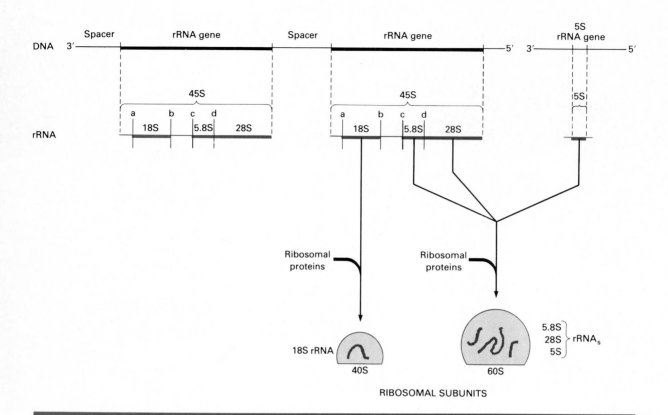

FIGURE 13-25
Processing and packaging of rRNAs into ribosome subunits in eukaryotes. The primary 45S rRNA transcript of the rRNA gene is cleaved into fragments over a period of time during its processing in the nucleus. The first cut (a) removes the leader and leaves a 41S fragment; the second cut (b) produces 18S rRNA and a 36S fragment from the 41S remainder; the third cut (c) in the 36S fragment removes a short sequence and yields a 32S fragment; and processing of the 32S fragment (d) produces 28S rRNA and 5.8S rRNA. The 5S rRNA is coded elsewhere in the genome, and it is packaged along with 28S rRNA and 5.8S rRNA in the 60S large subunit; 18S rRNA alone is present in the small subunit.

synthesized at the same time from a single rRNA gene and that all the rRNA genes in tandem on the rDNA strand are simultaneously engaged in transcription (Fig. 13.26).

The individual rRNA genes are separated by so-called **spacer DNA**, which remains bare of transcript RNA. The molecular features of spacers in rDNA have been analyzed by Donald Brown, Igor Dawid, and others by the use of *denaturation mapping* and *heteroduplex analysis* in conjunction with electron microscopy. When rDNA is exposed to mild denaturation conditions, AT-rich regions melt, whereas GC-rich regions retain their paired duplex configuration because of the stronger triple-hydrogen bonds between G and C and the looser double-hydrogen bonds between A and T. Measurements of partially denatured amphibian oocyte rDNA in electron micrographs showed that GC-rich regions about 0.8 μm long alternated with AT-rich regions about 4 μm long (Fig. 13.27). These values corresponded to the short rRNA genes alternating with the long spacer DNA regions in photographs of transcribing rDNA from the same material (see Fig. 13.26). From these and other molecular data, we know that rDNA is organized as a tandem array of rRNA gene repeats that alternate with long AT-rich spacer sequences.

The 0.8-μm length of the GC-rich rRNA gene sequence corresponded to the length expected for a gene that is transcribed into a 40S pre-rRNA molecule in amphibians. No RNA transcript complementary to spacer DNA can be found, so it would appear that the spacer itself is not transcribed. Interestingly, spacer DNA from different but related species showed a strikingly high degree of nonhomology, according to base composition analysis, whereas rRNAs from these same species were

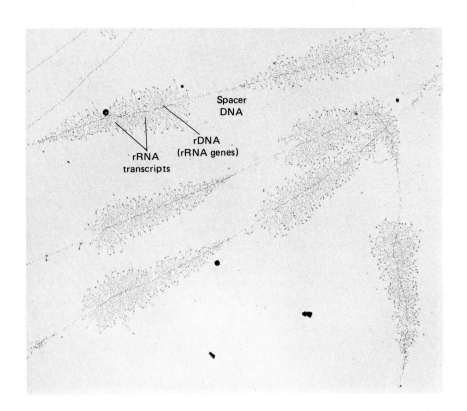

FIGURE 13-26
Electron micrograph of actively transcribing rDNA isolated from oocyte nucleoli of the spotted newt (*Triturus viridescens*), an amphibian. Each arrowhead-shaped region represents one rRNA gene with rRNA transcripts "peeling off" during transcription. The shortest transcripts in a cluster are near the 3' end of the gene, and the transcripts lengthen as transcription proceeds toward the 5' end of the gene, in the 5' → 3' direction along the antiparallel rDNA template. The rRNA genes occur as tandem repeats that are separated by untranscribed spacer DNA sequences. (Photograph courtesy of O. L. Miller, Jr., from Miller, O. L., Jr., and B. Beatty, 1969, *Science* **164**:955, Fig. 2.)

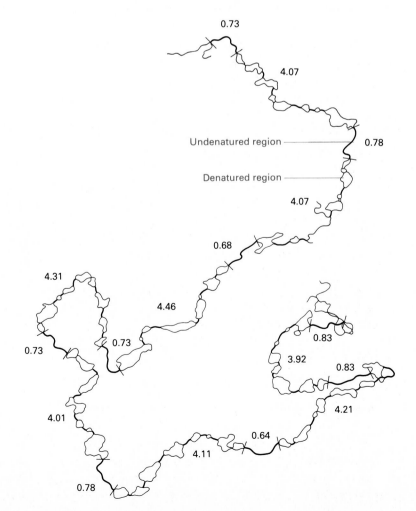

FIGURE 13-27
Tracing of an electron micrograph of one partly denatured segment of amplified rDNA from nucleoli of the toad *Xenopus mulleri*. This 42-μm-long piece includes eight complete repeats of the sequence encoded for 40S pre-rRNA. The short paired regions (solid, thicker lines) correspond to rRNA genes and alternate with longer AT-rich spacer DNA that has undergone partial denaturation and appears as sets of open loops. The paired gene sequences measure 0.64 to 0.83 μm in length, and the alternating spacer DNA regions measure 3.92 to 4.46 μm in length. (From Brown, D. D., P. C. Wensink, and E. Jordan, 1972, *J. Mol. Biol.* **63**:57, Plate 11b.)

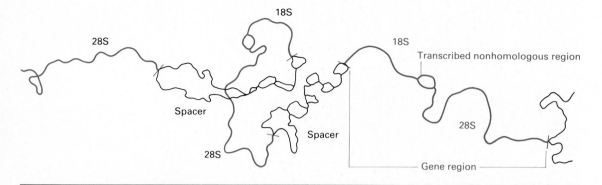

FIGURE 13-28

Tracing of an electron micrograph of heteroduplex DNA composed of one strand of rDNA from *Xenopus laevis* and the other from *X. mulleri*. A high degree of homology is apparent from the close pairing in the coded region that specifies 18S and 28S rRNA (color), but little homology exists between spacer-DNA regions in the two species (black), as evident from unpaired loops. It is clear that, in the same evolutionary time interval, the spacers have diverged in sequence in the two species, whereas the rRNA sequence itself has been greatly conserved. (From "The Isolation of Genes" by D. D. Brown. Copyright © 1973 by Scientific American, Inc. All rights reserved.)

highly homologous in base sequences. When rDNAs from *Xenopus laevis* and *X. mulleri* were melted to single strands and then allowed to reanneal to form duplexes consisting of one strand from each species, these heteroduplexes could be analyzed by electron microscopy to determine regions of homology and nonhomology. Homologous paired regions appeared as thicker duplex segments, whereas nonhomologous regions remained unpaired and were recognized as bubbles or loops of single-stranded DNA (Fig. 13.28). As predicted from base-sequencing data, both the 18S and 28S rDNA sequences were closely paired and therefore homologous. The long spacers, however, were essentially unpaired, which indicated their lack of base-sequence homology. These studies were among the earliest to demonstrate the conservation during evolution of homology in coding sequences but a substantial amount of divergence in noncoding regions of the *same* molecules. Similar observations were later made for other tandemly repeated gene clusters, including genes coding for 5S rRNA and for histone proteins.

The localization of rRNA genes in the nucleolar organizing region(s) of the eukaryotic genome was first established in 1965 by F. M.

FIGURE 13-29

Demonstration that rDNA in *Drosophila melanogaster* is located at the nucleolar organizing region (NOR) of the chromosome. Hybridization of purified rRNA to DNA from flies carrying from 1 to 4 NORs per cell (2 NORs is the normal number) is shown. Horizontal lines indicate the hybridization plateau values predicted for 1, 3, or 4 NORs, on the basis of the normal plateau value of 0.270% for 2 NORs. In these saturation hybridizations, increasing amounts of RNA (μg) are added to hybridization mixtures containing a fixed amount of DNA. Once all the complementary DNA has been saturated by pairing with RNA, no additional hybrids form because no more DNA is available for hybridization regardless of the amount of RNA present. (From Ritossa, F. M., and S. Spiegelman, 1965, *Proc. Nat. Acad. Sci. U.S.* **53**:737.)

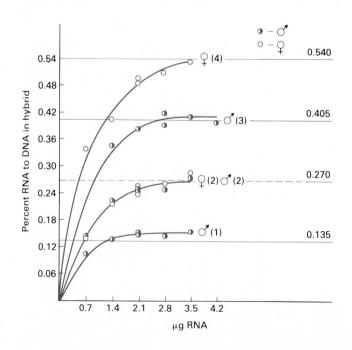

Ritossa and Sol Spiegelman, who studied *Drosophila melanogaster*. Earlier studies by Donald Brown, John Gurdon, and others had shown that an anucleolate mutant of *Xenopus laevis* failed to synthesize rRNA or ribosomes in the absence of the nucleolus and of the chromosomal NOR to which the nucleolus was attached. These observations implicated the nucleolus and the NOR as the sites for rRNA synthesis, but direct evidence was needed to confirm the supposition. Ritossa and Spiegelman therefore sought molecular evidence for the localization of rRNA genes at the NOR, using four strains of *D. melanogaster* that had from one to four NORs in an otherwise similar genomic background. After adding radioactively labeled uridine to identify new rRNA in the flies, they purified the newly synthesized rRNA from isolated ribosomes. The labeled rRNA was then incubated with melted strands of chromosomal DNA in molecular hybridization assays to determine the percentage of DNA–rRNA hybrid molecules formed in each strain. The prediction was simple: If rRNA genes are located at the NOR, the percentage of DNA–rRNA hybrids should parallel the number of NORs per strain. This prediction was confirmed by the assays. Strains with four NORs yielded four times the molecular hybrids as strains with one NOR; strains with three NORs and strains with two NORs yielded three times and two times the base value, respectively (Fig. 13.29). The parallel between the number of NORs (sets of rRNA genes) and the amount of rRNA that was synthesized definitively demonstrated that rRNA genes are present at the nucleolar organizing region(s) of the chromosomes. We will discuss other features of rDNA and the chromosomal NOR in other chapters, in relation to chromosomal organization and the regulation of rRNA gene expression.

13.7
Posttranscriptional Processing of mRNA in Eukaryotes

In Section 13.2 we discussed two of the posttranscriptional modifications in precursors of eukaryotic mRNA: *capping* and *polyadenylation*. In this section we will pay particular attention to the *removal of introns* and the *splicing of exons* to produce the uninterrupted coding sequence of the mRNA prepared to function as an instructional template in translation. These processing events are remarkably precise, so we would expect specific signals by which boundaries are delineated and recognized during RNA cutting and splicing.

The removal of introns appears to proceed in a preferred order along the pre-mRNA strand rather than at random. This feature is the most reasonable inference from studies of primary transcripts, mature mRNAs, and intermediates of processed nuclear RNA for several well-known genes, including the ovomucoid and ovalbumin genes of the chick. Each of these two genes has seven introns alternating with eight exons. When investigators fractionate nuclear RNA on gels and allow it to hybridize with intact genic DNA or partial sequences of the gene in order to identify the composition of the RNA bands, only a relatively few discrete bands are present (Fig. 13.30). This indicates the removal of introns in some preferred order, because more than 300 precursor intermediates would be generated by completely random excisions and a

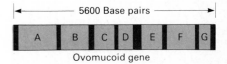
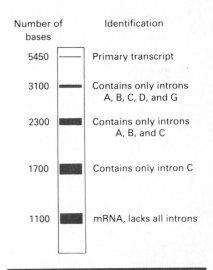

FIGURE 13-30
Preferred order of intron excision during posttranscriptional processing of ovomucoid pre-mRNA. (a) The chicken ovomucoid gene is organized into 8 exons (black) and 7 introns (A–G, color) over a span of 5600 base pairs of DNA. (b) Gel electrophoresis of precursor and mature mRNAs shows 5 major bands, each identified by hybridization with radioactively labeled DNA probes containing particular exon and intron sequences. All 7 introns are present in the largest molecules, which must be the primary transcript, and no introns are present in mature mRNA. The intermediate forms become progressively shorter as specific introns are excised, but the order of excision is not random. In this case, introns E and F are excised first, D and G next, A and B next, and intron C last of all.

few discrete RNA bands would not be found. The size of the intermediate indicates the particular introns that have been removed, but verification of the lost introns can be made from electron micrographs of each RNA intermediate complexed with intact genic DNA. Any intron that has been removed in the RNA shows up as a loop in the DNA strand of the hybrid duplex molecule (see Fig. 4.17). Although different combinations of introns can be found in these RNA intermediates, the frequency of loss of individual introns indicates the existence of some preferred pathway for excisions. For the ovomucoid RNA, introns E and F are lost first, D and G are lost next, then B is lost, and A and C are removed last (Fig. 13.31). Furthermore, because all of these intermediates are polyadenylated, it would appear that the poly(A) tail is added after completion of the primary transcript but before there has been any (or any appreciable) excision and splicing.

What kind of signal might we expect for precise intron excision in virtually every eukaryotic messenger transcript? It is unlikely that each gene has its own unique signal—far more likely that some ubiquitous sequence is present at exon–intron junctions in all or most cases, because excision and splicing are ubiquitous processes. By comparing the nucleotide sequence of mRNA with the sequence of the intact gene, we find that no *extensive* sequence homology exists. Instead, *very short sequences* are found in virtually every exon–intron junction that has been examined. These conserved sequences are called **consensus sequences**, and they are characterized at the least by the presence of a particular nucleotide doublet at each end of an intron. Proceeding from the 5′ to the 3′ direction along the gene, the dinucleotides GT and AG mark the

FIGURE 13-31
The order of intron excision from the primary RNA transcript (color) of the chicken ovomucoid gene can be determined from electron micrographs of heteroduplexes composed of the DNA coding strand and RNA intermediates. Each intron loop in the DNA strand indicates the absence of a complementary sequence at that site in the RNA transcript and shows, therefore, that the particular intron copy has been excised from the transcript. A preferred order of intron excision, rather than random removal, is evident from such data.

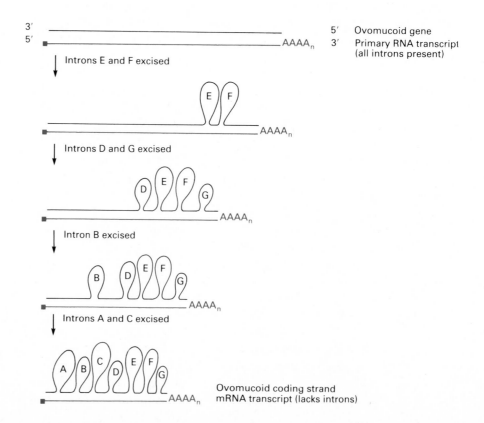

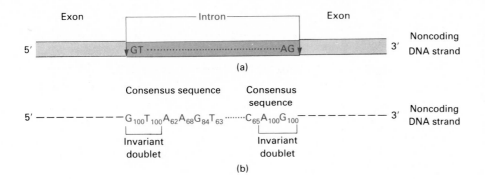

FIGURE 13-32
Signals for precise removal of introns from nuclear gene transcripts are found at the termini of the intron sequence itself. (a) Base sequence analysis of the noncoding 5′ → 3′ DNA strand, which is identical to the 5′ → 3′ RNA transcript sequence when U is substituted for T (GU—AG in RNA), reveals an invariant GT doublet at the 5′ end and an invariant AG doublet at the 3′ end of the intron. (b) These doublets occur in 100% of introns examined, whereas other bases in the consensus sequences are found in fewer introns (percentages are shown by subscript numbers). Only the bases in highly homologous consensus sequences are shown, because the intervening bases are highly variable in different introns.

5′ and 3′ boundaries of the intron and are present in all the polypeptide-specifying genes we know about (Fig. 13.32). These consensus sequences are not present, however, in mitochondrial or chloroplast interrupted genes, which may indicate some fundamental difference in splicing mechanisms in organelles as compared with those in the nucleus.

The importance of consensus sequences in excision and splicing is evident from studies of mutations that delete or modify the exon–intron boundaries and lead to splicing failure or mislocation or cause a substantial reduction in the efficiency of splicing. Improperly spliced or unspliced RNA tends to be unstable and may be degraded in the nucleus. Even if the aberrant RNA leaves the nucleus and enters the cytoplasm, it may not become involved in translation. Should such an RNA be translated, however, an aberrant polypeptide would probably be synthesized and adversely affect cellular function and behavior.

We do not know how the consensus sequences are recognized as exon–intron boundaries, but there is some basis for believing that the cutting enzyme recognizes the junctions by virtue of *secondary structures at these RNA sites*. Such secondary structure might arise as the result of base pairing between an RNA molecule and the consensus sequences, which would bring together the two ends of an intron and thereby facilitate their cleavage by a processing enzyme (Fig. 13.33). The so-called **small nuclear RNAs (snRNA)** are likely candidates for base-pairing with transcript junctions because at least one of these snRNAs, *U1*, is complementary to the consensus sequences at the splicing junctions, and various snRNAs share some sequence homologies. A large number of snRNAs are present in the nucleus—perhaps 10^5 to 10^6 molecules per cell, in the form of ribonucleoproteins that range in size from 100 to 300 nucleotides. Most of the U1 snRNA molecule can base-pair to produce duplex hairpin regions, but its 5′ terminus is single-stranded and available for pairing with splicing junctions. Experimental evidence in support of U1 or other snRNAs as components in the splicing reactions is rather fragmentary at present, but the data are tempting enough to urge pursuit of the question in some detail in a variety of systems.

Many other questions remain to be answered. What accounts for removal of the two consensus sequences of the *same* intron when all the introns have the same two boundaries? How precise is the processing reaction—do we see only the correctly spliced mRNAs from among a population of molecules that also includes inaccurately processed RNAs, or is the reaction largely error-free? We have no data to answer these

FIGURE 13-33
Small nuclear RNAs (snRNA), such as U1 snRNA, may be involved in the recognition by cutting enzymes of exon–intron boundaries in pre-mRNA. U1 and other snRNAs have an unpaired terminus that includes doublets of bases complementary to splice-junction doublets, and snRNA may thus pair with pre-mRNA at these regions. On pairing, secondary structure may develop and bring together the two ends of an intron such that a cutting enzyme would recognize the cleavage sites by their conformation and cut out the intron sequence between two exons. Once the intron has been removed, the exons would be spliced together to make an uninterrupted mRNA coding sequence.

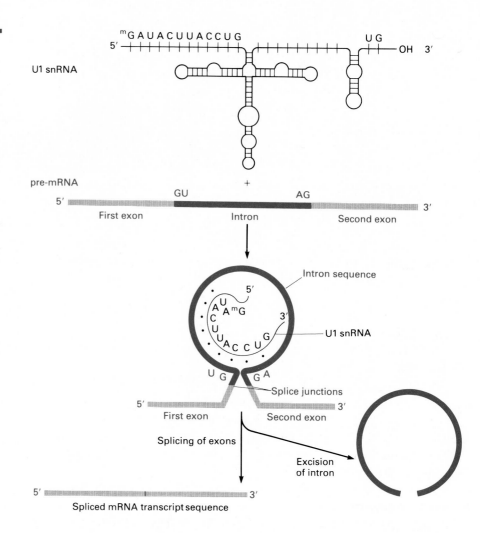

questions at the present time, but they can be investigated experimentally with available molecular methods.

In summary, the typical gene in eukaryotes is copied into a primary transcript that includes flanking leader and trailer sequences and alternating coding and noncoding segments between initiation codon AUG and termination codon UAA, UAG, or UGA. The pre-mRNA is capped by a 7-methylguanosine residue almost immediately after transcription begins and is polyadenylated at its 3′ end only after the primary transcript has been synthesized. Once synthesized, pre-mRNA undergoes removal of introns and splicing of exons in some limited nonrandom order, and the completed mRNA is released in ribonucleoprotein form to enter the cytoplasm from the nucleus. Once in the cytoplasm, mRNA can function in translation of the genetic message only in association with ribosomes. These events are illustrated in Fig. 13.34.

In certain cases, RNA processing may not follow the orthodox pattern just summarized but may include one or more variations in which different RNAs are generated from the same DNA sequence. One such example concerns two varieties of *immunoglobulins* of class M, one of the five known classes of these antibody molecules. Immunoglobulins (Ig) are synthesized in B lymphocytes (a B lymphocyte is a kind of white blood cell), which differentiate from progenitor cells in the bone marrow.

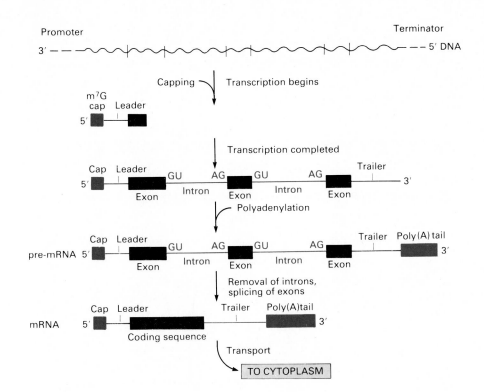

FIGURE 13-34
Schematic summary of transcription and of transcript processing in eukaryotes. Capping of the 5' end with 7-methylguanosine (m⁷G) occurs shortly after transcription has begun, and the entire primary transcript is then completed. The transcript includes leader, exons, introns, and trailer, but the promoter and terminator regions of the gene are not transcribed. The 3' end of the transcript is polyadenylated to form pre-mRNA, after which introns are excised and exons are spliced together to produce an uninterrupted coding sequence. Mature mRNA, in ribonucleoprotein form, leaves the nucleus and enters the cytoplasm, where translation occurs at the ribosomes.

During their earlier development, B lymphocytes synthesize a membrane-bound M immunoglobulin (IgM). This IgM molecule binds to the cell surface by virtue of a highly hydrophobic sequence of 41 amino acids at its carboxy terminus. Later in their development, B lymphocytes become plasma cells that actively secrete a different IgM. The secreted IgM differs from the membrane-bound IgM molecule in having a hydrophilic carboxy terminus of 20 amino acids instead of the hydrophobic set of 41 amino acids in this location. The hydrophilic carboxy terminus probably accounts for the ability of the new IgM variety to pass through the membrane.

Different mRNAs specify the membrane-bound IgM and the secreted IgM, but both IgM proteins are specified by the same DNA sequence and by the primary transcript copied from this sequence. The production of one mRNA or the other depends on how the primary transcript is processed in the nucleus. The membrane-bound IgM is produced from mRNA spliced together from 6 exons of the gene sequence, the last 2 exons encoding the 41 amino acids of the hydrophobic carboxy terminus. The secreted IgM is translated from mRNA with only the first 4 exons present, plus a portion of the intron downstream of the last of these exons (Fig. 13.35). The 20 amino acids of the hydrophilic carboxy terminus are present in this intron, which is excised when the membrane-bound IgM transcript is spliced together from 6 exons. The formation of one mRNA or the other therefore depends on whether the one splicing signal within the intron is utilized in processing. We have only limited evidence at present, but it is possible that control over the kind of mRNA to be produced depends on the availability of the intron splicing signal, not on some mechanism that requires choosing between splicing signals.

The immunoglobulin M (IgM) primary RNA transcript is processed in two different ways to generate mRNA transcripts encoded for membrane-bound IgM and secreted IgM. Membrane-bound IgM is translated from an RNA transcript whose introns (pale color) have been removed and its six exons (numbered above) spliced together. The hydrophobic terminus (black) of the protein is translated from exons 5 and 6 (darkest color), and this terminus contributes to the membrane-binding properties of the Ig molecule. The secreted IgM, made at a later time in B lymphocyte development, is translated from a shorter processed transcript that includes only exons 1–4 (not 5 or 6) plus a small portion of the intron adjacent to exon 4. This intron sequence encodes a hydrophilic terminus in secreted IgM molecules, which helps account for passage of these proteins across the membrane.

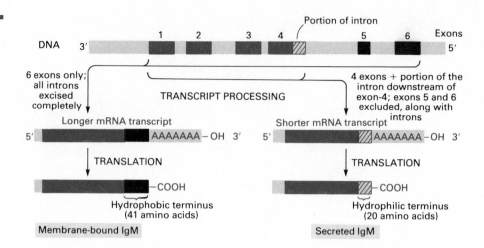

In the case of the two IgM, as in similar examples, the interrupted organization of the eukaryotic gene provides a degree of genetic flexibility in gene expression. The same DNA sequence can yield different but related molecules, because different parts of the sequence are incorporated into mRNA during RNA processing, at different stages of development. We will pursue this matter further in Chapter 14.

Translation of the Genetic Message

Accurate translation of the encoded genetic message in mRNA requires appropriate interactions of all three kinds of RNA and a number of catalytic, regulatory, and structural proteins. The molecular processes involved in protein synthesis are complex and, although we know quite a bit about many of these processes individually, we are not really able to put all the pieces together and understand the whole fabric of translation in its entirety. The omission of any component, or its malfunction, can prevent protein synthesis or cause the polypeptide to be nonfunctional for one or more reasons. This observation alone clearly shows that all the parts of the translation machinery act in concert to ensure the accurate synthesis of an encoded gene product. In the following sections we will explore the processes and machinery that underlie translation in all living cells.

13.8
Amino Acids, tRNAs, and Aminoacyl-tRNA Synthetases _____

Free amino acids cannot participate in protein synthesis until they have been raised to a sufficiently high energy level for polymerization reactions. In addition, the insertion of the correct amino acid in its correct location in a growing polypeptide chain takes place through the agency of its specific tRNA, which provides one component of the recognition mechanism that underlies translational accuracy. The reaction that energizes, or activates, the amino acid to its higher-energy **aminoacyl** form and the reaction that binds the aminoacyl residue to its

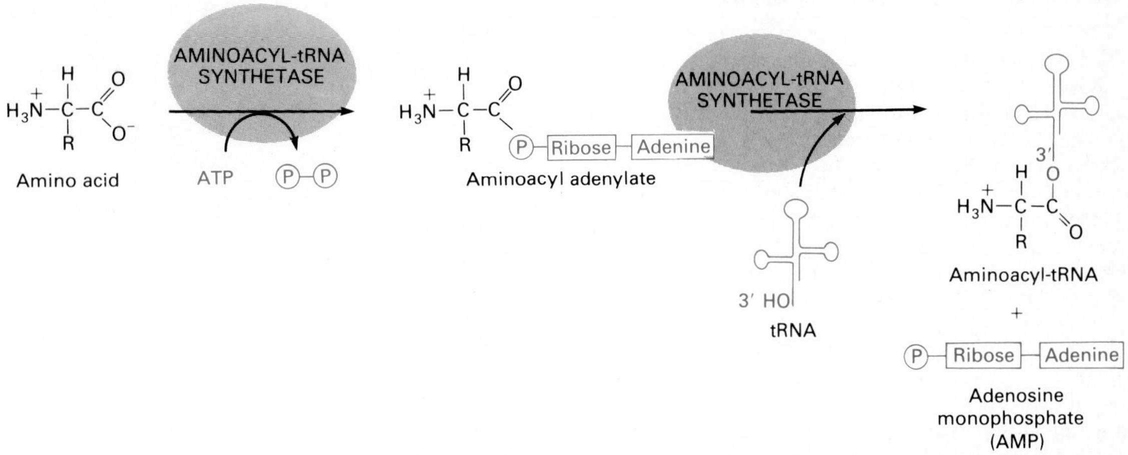

FIGURE 13-36
Free amino acids must be energized and must be bound to a recognition component before they can participate in protein synthesis. Both requirements are taken care of by the catalytic action of a particular aminoacyl-tRNA synthetase specific for a particular amino acid. In the first process the amino acid is activated to become an aminoacyl adenylate whose AMP residue is provided by coupled hydrolysis of ATP. In the second process AMP is released as the tRNA binds at its 3'-OH end to the amino acid it will carry to the ribosome for incorporation into a growing polypeptide chain.

specific tRNA carrier are both catalyzed by the same enzyme, called an **aminoacyl-tRNA synthetase**. At least one synthetase exists for each of the 20 amino acids in the genetic code.

The synthetase drives the first reaction through coupling with the hydrolysis of ATP to produce a high-energy intermediate called an aminoacyl-adenylate. This intermediate remains bound to the enzyme until the second reaction, in which the carboxyl group of the aminoacyl residue is bonded to the A nucleotide at the 3' terminus of the tRNA (Fig. 13.36). A particular tRNA is designated by the amino acid it can carry; for example, tRNA^{Leu} is a leucine-carrying tRNA. Each aminoacyl-tRNA is identified by its aminoacyl residue and its tRNA; for example, Leu–tRNA^{Leu} is the leucyl–tRNA that is transported to the ribosome for the incorporation of leucine into the growing polypeptide chain.

We know very little about the features of the different synthetases, and thus we know little about the specificities that lead a particular synthetase to couple only one kind of amino acid to a tRNA specific for that amino acid. The fact that every tRNA has 3'-ACC at the end of its amino acid accepting arm only deepens our dilemma as we try to sort out selective features involved in these reactions. We do know, however, that it is the tRNA anticodon (not the amino acid) that is responsible for recognition of mRNA and for insertion of the proper amino acid in its assigned location in the growing chain. This fact was first demonstrated in 1961 by experiments in which cysteine in Cys–tRNA^{Cys} was chemically converted to alanine to produce Ala–tRNA^{Cys} (Fig. 13.37). If the tRNA^{Cys} recognized the mRNA codons, alanine would be inserted into every site that was usually occupied by a cysteine residue in the polypeptide synthesized *in vitro*. If the amino acid was a recognition component, however, alanine would be inserted only in its correct sites and cysteine would be inserted only in its correct sites, regardless of the tRNA carrier to which the amino acid was bound. Alanines replaced cysteines in tests that used Ala-tRNA^{Cys}, which clearly showed that the meaning of mRNA codons was recognized by tRNA, through its anticodon, and not by its amino acid.

FIGURE 13-37
Evidence showing that mRNA codon meaning is recognized by the tRNA anticodon and not by the amino acid carried by the tRNA was provided by studies of tRNA^{Cys} carrying its normal cysteine residue (Cys–tRNA^{Cys}) or carrying an alanine residue (Ala–tRNA^{Cys}) produced by chemical desulfuration of Cys-tRNA^{Cys}. Because alanine was inserted into every site usually occupied by cysteine in the polypeptide, the tRNA^{Cys} must have recognized the mRNA codon and thus inserted any amino acid it carried into the polypeptide. If the amino acid were part of the recognition system, Ala–tRNA^{Cys} would have put alanines only where alanines belonged and not where cysteine belonged in the growing polypeptide chain.

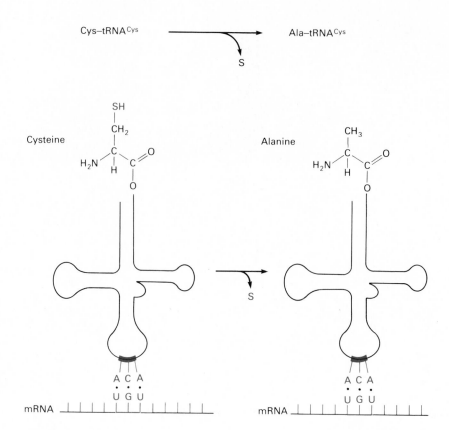

13.9
Ribosomes

The **ribosome** is a small but compact ribonucleoprotein particle composed of two unequal-sized subunits, which act in concert to catalyze and coordinate translational processes. The smaller 70S ribosome in prokaryotes consists of three different rRNA molecules and 52 proteins that are unrelated to each other and occur in one copy per ribosome, with only three exceptions. Among the 21 proteins of the small subunit (numbered S1 to S21), protein S6 is present in two copies. Among the 31 proteins of the large subunit (each prefixed by the letter L), proteins L7 and L12 are present in two copies each. The 80S cytoplasmic ribosome, or **cytoribosome**, in eukaryotes has four different rRNAs plus about 82 proteins (see Table 13.2). In chloroplasts the organelle ribosome is virtually indistinguishable from bacterial ribosomes in many of its features, whereas mitochondrial ribosomes vary from 60S particles in animals to 80S particles in plants and fungi.

Although ribosomal subunits are often depicted as flattened ellipsoidal structures, recent physical and electron microscopic studies of ribosomal subunit structure have yielded images of greater morphological complexity. In bacteria, the 30S ribosomal subunit appears to have a large rounded *base* that is separated from the narrower *head* by a constricted region, and a *cleft* separates the head from a *platform* region. The 50S subunit has a narrow *stalk* and a *central protuberance* emerging from the broad rounded *base* of the particle. Although we are not certain about this, the two subunits may be held together in a 70S ribosome by associations between the cleft of the 30S subunit and the central protuberance of the 50S subunit—perhaps leaving a space or groove

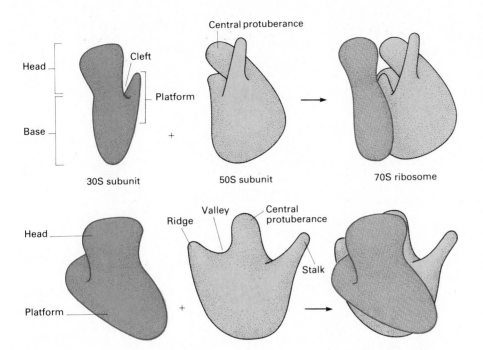

FIGURE 13-38
The three-dimensional model of the bacterial ribosome gives an asymmetric shape to the two ribosome subunits. The 30S subunit includes a narrow head and large rounded base separated by a constricted region, and a cleft between the head and the platform region of the particle. The 50S subunit has a central protuberance between a ridge on one side and a stalk on the other, all emerging from a broad rounded base. The orientations are shown of the models for each subunit and the whole 70S ribosome. A ribosome is about 25 nm long. (From Lake, J. A., 1985, *Ann. Rev. Biochem.* **54**:507, Fig. 1.)

between them (Fig. 13.38). Preliminary analyses of 80S eukaryotic cyto-ribosomes indicate that the eukaryotic and bacterial small subunits are similar in conformation but that some degree of difference characterizes the structures of the eukaryotic and bacterial large subunits.

The greatest interest in subunit conformation and structure revolves around the locations of mRNA and tRNAs at the ribosome surface and around the organization of rRNAs within the ribosomal subunits. These features have important predictive implications for our understanding of molecular interactions during translation, and they involve the roles of ribosomal proteins as well as all the kinds of RNA. On the basis of biochemical, molecular, and electron microscopical studies, the 3′ terminus of 16S rRNA in the bacterial small subunit has been located in the platform on the other side of the cleft from the bulging head region. This 3′ end contains a sequence of about six nucleotides that is complementary to a sequence of bases found in all known leaders of mRNA in prokaryotes and their viruses (Fig. 13.39). This sequence

ø X gene	Sequence of mRNA leader and initiator regions (5′ → 3′)
A	C A A A U C U U **G G A G G** C U U U U U U *A U G* G U U
B	A A A G G U C U **A G G A G** C U A A A G A *A U G* G A A
D	C C A C U A A U **A G G U** A A G A A A U C *A U G* A G
E	C U G C G U U **G A G G** C U U G C G U U U *A U G* G U
F	C C C U U A C U U G **A G G A** U A A A U U *A U G* U C U
G	U U C U G C U U **A G G A G** U U U A A U C *A U G* U U U
J	C G U G C G G **A A G G A G** U G A U G U A *A U G* U C U
16S rRNA (3′ end only)	ₕₒA U U C C U C C A G U A G ••••• 3′ → 5′

FIGURE 13-39
The leader sequences of various genes in the coliphage φX174 show some degree of homology with one another, and in one region (colored letters) they are complementary with all or some of six bases at the 3′-OH end of 16S rRNA. Such complementarity may promote the binding of the 5′ end of mRNA to the exposed 3′ end of 16S rRNA in the small subunit of the ribosome, preparatory to the initiation of translation. Note that the Start codon AUG (underlined) is only a short distance downstream of the bases believed to pair with 16S rRNA.

FIGURE 13-40
The proposed secondary structure of *E. coli* 16S rRNA consists of many short regions in hairpin conformation that result from hydrogen bonding between bases in the single-stranded molecule. The molecule appears to be organized into four general domains, each with its own particular functions or properties in relation to subunit assembly and translation. The 3′ minor domain includes the 3′-OH terminus of 16S rRNA; it is important in binding mRNA and in the selection of translation initiation sites in bound mRNA.

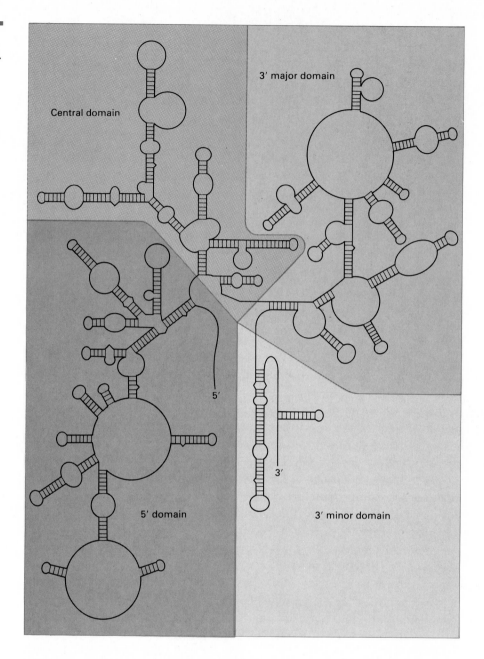

complementarity indicates that binding between mRNA leader and 3′ rRNA terminus at the ribosome surface can take place and that it may serve to position the 5′ end of mRNA for sequential translation of the 5′ → 3′ encoded message. Unfortunately, we have no clear information yet on the location of mRNA during translation at the ribosome. The 40 or so bases of an mRNA strand that can fit along the ribosome may be situated in the groove between the two subunits, as some have suggested, or they may be located superficially along the surface. Similarly, we can calculate that the ribosome is large enough to accommodate two tRNAs at the same time, but we have no idea whether the tRNAs are inserted in openings made by clefts at the ribosome surface or elsewhere on the structure.

Ribosomal subunits form by a **self-assembly** process in which all the information needed to bind together the rRNA(s) and ribosomal proteins resides in these molecules themselves. No other guidance system is required, as has been amply demonstrated by *in vitro* studies of bacterial ribosome assembly and disassembly. All or most of the ribosomal proteins can bind to 16S rRNA, although the binding is stronger for some proteins than for others. The rRNA binding sites are clustered predominantly in the 5′ half of the molecule, and they share the common feature of having a secondary structure derived from base-pairing to form hairpins that have bulging unpaired regions in their duplex stems (Fig. 13.40). Similar secondary structure characterizes both 23S and 5S rRNA in the bacterial large subunit. We know little about the situation in eukaryotic ribosomes, which are larger and more complex and thus more difficult to analyze. There is every reason to suppose, however, that eukaryotic cytoribosomes share the same fundamental features of rRNA secondary structure and binding of ribosomal proteins to specific regions of rRNA.

13.10
Studies of Ribosome Disassembly and Reassembly

Ribosomal subunits can be collected in separate fractions after centrifugation of monomer ribosomes in media of appropriate Mg^{2+} concentration. Subunits dissociate when bacterial ribosomes are provided with less than 5 to 10 millimolar Mg^{2+} or when eukaryotic cytoribosomes are in media with less than 1 millimolar Mg^{2+}, and when other conditions (pH, K^+ concentration, and so on) are regulated. Purified subunit fractions can then be analyzed *in vitro* to determine their composition and manner of dissociation and reconstitution.

When bacterial ribosome subunits are centrifuged in CsCl or LiCl, a discrete group of **split proteins** is lost from both kinds of subunits, leaving 23S and 42S particle **cores** from the 30S and 50S subunits, respectively. In higher concentrations of CsCl or LiCl, the 23S core dissociates to yield 16S rRNA and **core proteins**, and the 42S core dissociates to yield 23S and 5S rRNA plus core proteins (Fig. 13.41).

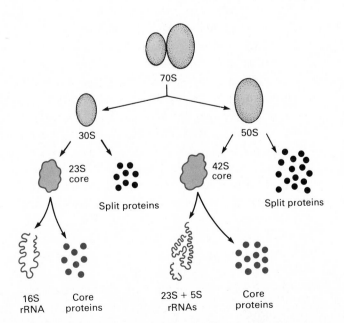

FIGURE 13-41
During centrifugation in LiCl or CsCl, each subunit of the 70S bacterial ribosome is dissociated into two discrete groups of proteins plus rRNAs. Lower salt concentrations produce split proteins and a residual core, and higher salt concentrations separate the rRNA from a set of core proteins. Loss of sets of proteins, rather than a progressive diminution, indicated the existence of coordinated groups of proteins in the ribosome.

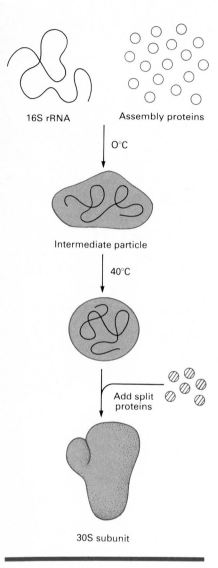

16S rRNA   Assembly proteins

0°C

Intermediate particle

40°C

Add split
proteins

30S subunit

FIGURE 13-42
On removal of CsCl from and addition of Mg^{2+} to a disassembled preparation, the 30S ribosome subunit reassembles by the stepwise addition of 2 sets of proteins to 16S rRNA. In the cold, 16S rRNA associates with 15 of the 21 subunit proteins to form an intermediate particle. When this preparation of particles is heated, the particles become more compact and are then able to bind the remaining 6 split proteins and thus reconstitute the 30S subunit.

Proteins are lost together in groups rather than their numbers dwindling gradually in successive disruptions. Hence it would appear that each subunit has particular sets of proteins organized in some cooperative manner so that each stepwise disruption leads to the loss of all the members of a set at the same time.

Disruptions can be reversed if CsCl is removed and Mg^{2+} is added to a preparation of dissociated subunit components. Reassembly of the 30S subunit also involves stepwise events, but different temperatures are required for each event. In the initial stage of reassembly, 16S rRNA associates with about 15 proteins if placed in the cold. The remaining 6 proteins will bind only if the initial intermediate particle is heated (about 40°C). Chemical analyses have revealed that heating the initial intermediate particle leads to its becoming more compact, and this more compact intermediate particle is then able to bind the last set of (split) proteins (Fig. 13.42). Once reassembled, the 30S subunits can participate actively in protein synthesis *in vitro*, but particles in intermediate stages of reassembly are inactive. Reassembly of 50S subunits follows a similar course of stepwise reconstitution.

Investigators have analyzed the role of the individual molecules in subunit assembly by omitting one kind of molecule at a time from the reconstitution system. Reconstitution absolutely requires a scaffold of 16S rRNA (or 23S and 5S rRNAs) to which particular proteins must bind initially. Once the initial set of proteins has been bound to rRNA, other proteins can bind. By systematically omitting one protein at a time and determining the effect on the binding of other proteins and on the structure and activity of the reconstituted particle, investigators have shown that ribosomal proteins must bind to the assembling structure in a certain order. The *in vitro* **assembly map** constructed for the bacterial 30S subunit is based on reconstitution data showing which proteins must be bound to 16S rRNA before other proteins can bind and showing the relative dependence of some proteins on others to help them bind (Fig. 13.43). A similar process has yielded information for the *in vitro* assembly map for the 50S bacterial ribosome subunit.

Although the timing and pattern of binding to rRNA reveal important relationships between subunit proteins, and although inferences can be made concerning their arrangements in the structure, more specific information in this regard has come from direct analysis using biochemical and electron microscopical methods. Antibodies can be prepared against each of the subunit proteins and bound to the intact subunits. The sites of antibody binding can then be observed by electron microscopy. Almost all of the 30S subunit proteins and many of the 50S proteins have been localized in this way in the intact subunit structure. Other methods have also been used, such as neutron scattering and protein cross-linking to each other and to rRNA, and all these methods have led to a relatively similar picture in which each ribosomal protein has been located in the 30S subunit. We must still pursue the details of molecular organization in the subunits, but considerable progress has already been made, at least for the 30S bacterial ribosome subunit.

How is the ribosome formed in the living bacterial cell? We can only surmise the probable sequence of events, largely on the basis of re-

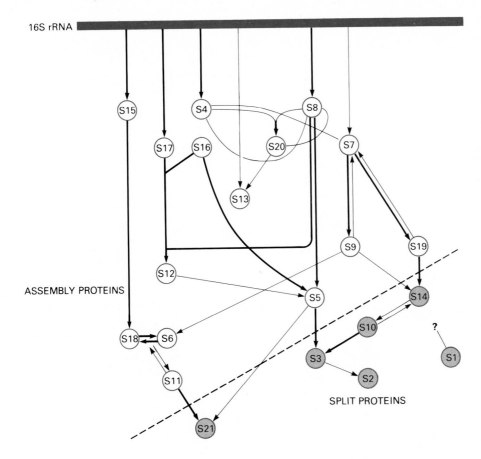

16S rRNA

ASSEMBLY PROTEINS

SPLIT PROTEINS

FIGURE 13-43
The *in vitro* assembly map for the *E. coli* 30S ribosome subunit is based on reconstitution studies that traced the sequence and dependence of the binding of 15 assembly proteins (open circles) and 6 split proteins (colored circles) to 16S rRNA and to each other. Arrows indicate the facilitating effect on binding of one protein to another and to rRNA. A thick arrow indicates a strong effect and a thin arrow indicates a weaker effect. Certain of the assembly proteins (S15, S17, S4, S20, S8, and S7) bind early to 16S rRNA, and other specific proteins are added afterward until all 15 assembly proteins are bound in the intermediate particle. The 6 split proteins (color) are added later, when the temperature is raised from 0°C to 40°C (see Fig. 13.42). Some uncertainty exists concerning the protein to which split protein S1 binds. (Based on studies by M. Nomura.)

constitution studies, because the only 30S intermediate found so far is a particle with most of the proteins already attached to a pre-16S rRNA molecule. We might expect the proteins that bind very tightly to rRNA at the 5′ end of the transcript to be attached shortly after transcription has begun. The presence of these proteins induces a conformational change in the rRNA, which allows other proteins to bind (Fig. 13.44). Mature 16S rRNA in functional 30S subunits is 1541 bases long and highly methylated, whereas pre-16S rRNA is a longer molecule and has relatively few methylated nucleotides. Cleavage of the extra nucleotides and methylations of nucleotides probably induces further conformational changes in the rRNA of the intermediate particle, which influence the topology of the bound proteins and may allow the remaining proteins to bind and thus to complete the structure. Similar events undoubtedly characterize the formation of 50S ribosome subunits.

How similar are ribosomes from different bacterial species? We know from reconstitution studies that proteins from 30S subunits bind only to 16S rRNA and that proteins from 50S subunits bind only to 23S rRNA. But apart from these restrictions, functional subunits can reassemble even if the rRNAs and proteins are taken from widely different bacterial species. These molecules have a wide range of differences in their base sequences, but an overall similarity characterizes subunit structure in all these species. The components probably are functionally homologous, even though their overall composition and

FIGURE 13-44
Schematic summary of the possible mode of assembly of the 30S ribosome subunit *in vivo*. Assembly proteins are shown as open circles and split proteins as hatched circles.

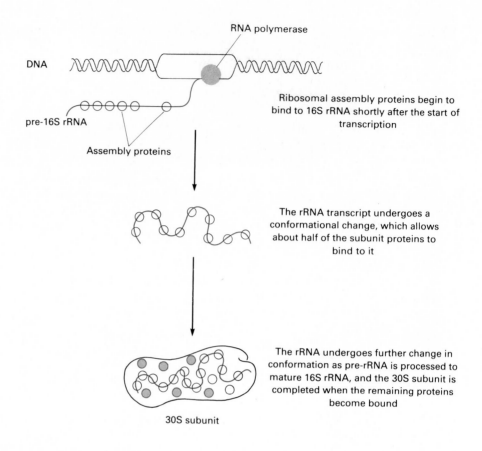

RNA polymerase

DNA

pre-16S rRNA

Assembly proteins

Ribosomal assembly proteins begin to bind to 16S rRNA shortly after the start of transcription

The rRNA transcript undergoes a conformational change, which allows about half of the subunit proteins to bind to it

The rRNA undergoes further change in conformation as pre-rRNA is processed to mature 16S rRNA, and the 30S subunit is completed when the remaining proteins become bound

30S subunit

sequences are different. Studies of hybrid ribosomes have provided additional support for the occurrence of functionally homologous ribosomal components. When 30S and 50S subunits from different species are put into *in vitro* systems, the hybrid 70S ribosomes function properly in protein synthesis.

Neither molecules nor subunits are chemically or functionally homologous when prokaryotic and eukaryotic ribosomes are compared. Ribosomal RNAs from rat or yeast cells cannot bind to ribosomal proteins from bacterial cells. Hybrid ribosomes consisting of one 30S and one 60S, or of one 40S and one 50S subunit, cannot subsidize protein synthesis *in vitro*.

Interestingly, chloroplast ribosomes are highly homologous with *E. coli* ribosomes. Both have 70S ribosomes, with 16S rRNA in the 30S subunit and 23S plus 5S rRNA in the 50S subunit, and hybrid ribosomes function very well in guiding protein synthesis *in vitro*. There are 1144 positions (74%) in 16S rRNA from chloroplast ribosomes in maize (*Zea mays*) that are identical in *E. coli* 16S rRNA, which indicates a very close evolutionary relationship between chloroplasts and prokaryotes. Mitochondrial ribosomes, on the other hand, are highly variable, and little or no homology is evident with prokaryotic rRNA or subunits or with these components in chloroplasts.

In the next sections we will discuss the processes of protein synthesis and the role of ribosomes in catalyzing and coordinating the translation of mRNA.

13.11
Monosomes and Polysomes _____

Until 1962 it was generally believed that proteins were synthesized on single, free ribosomes. The true picture was discovered by Alexander Rich and co-workers, who showed that polypeptides were made at groups of ribosomes, called polyribosomes, or **polysomes**. The polysome is a complex composed of a variable number of individual ribosomes, which we can refer to as **monosomes**, held together by a strand of mRNA. The length of a polysome is usually proportional to the length of the bound mRNA, or genetic message.

Rich's experiments involved rabbit reticulocytes, which, like other mammalian red blood cell precursors, are virtual factories for hemoglobin synthesis and little else. The advantages of this system, therefore, were (1) suitability for bulk biochemical analysis from relatively homogeneous cell populations and (2) almost a single polypeptide synthesis reaction that could be studied without screening out interference from many other polypeptides being made at the same time.

Reticulocytes were incubated in media containing radioactively labeled amino acids, and after a suitable time the cells were broken and the cell-free lysates were separated into different fractions by centrifugation. The prediction was that growing globin chains would be found in the fractions that were actually engaged in their synthesis, and that they could be identified by their radioactive label (Fig. 13.45). The fraction in which most of the radioactive globin fragments were found consisted of 5-ribosome groups, not the monosome fraction.

In another experiment it was shown that the labeled polypeptides were truly in the process of synthesis and were functionally associated with polysomes, rather than randomly associated or present by accident. When the drug **puromycin**, which acts as an analog of tRNA, is added to an actively synthesizing system, chain growth is terminated *prema-*

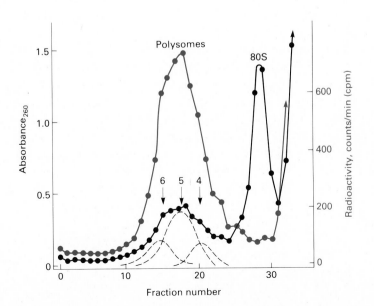

FIGURE 13-45
Sedimenting positions of a ribosomal preparation from rabbit reticulocytes to which [^{14}C] amino acids had been added for 45 seconds to determine the location of nascent polypeptides into which these amino acids were incorporated. Black circles indicate absorbance readings (optical density) at 260 nm in the 36 fractions. The bulk of the radioactivity (color) occurs in the polysome region of the gradient, where aggregates of 4, 5, and 6 ribosomes are found (each is indicated by dashed lines). Little radioactivity is present in the monosome peak (80S). (From Warner, J. S., A. Rich, and C. E. Hall, 1962, *Science* **138**:1399.)

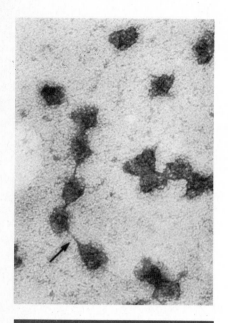

FIGURE 13-46
Electron micrograph of polysomes from rabbit reticulocytes. One pentamer is visible, and the five ribosomes in such aggregates are held together by a thin strand of mRNA (arrow) coded for a hemoglobin polypeptide. × 300,000. (From Slayter, H. S., et al., 1963, *J. Mol. Biol.* **7**:652-657, Plate IIIa.)

turely and incomplete molecules are released from the ribosomes–mRNA complex. Such *nascent* (growing) chains would then disappear from the polysome fraction and be found in the fluid supernatant phase of the system; they could be recognized by their radioactive label. In this way, it was verified that chain growth takes place at the polysomes, because only nascent polypeptides are affected by puromycin.

Supporting evidence for globin synthesis at polysomes was obtained by Rich from electron micrographs of various gradient fractions (Fig. 13.46). In the 5-ribosome fraction, groups of five ribosomes were seen to be held together by a thin strand. This strand was presumed to be mRNA because it was digested by RNase and the polysomes then dissociated into monosome units. The length of the presumed mRNA was about right for a message that should be long enough to code for 141 amino acids in α-globin or 146 amino acids in β-globin. There would be at least 146×3 nucleotides for the whole set of codons in the message, and its dimension would be about 1500 Å (the Watson–Crick model indicated a dimension of about 10 Å per 3 nucleotides in a polynucleotide chain). This is exactly what the 1500-Å-long polysomal mRNA was found to be.

Interactions between amino acids during growth of the polypeptide chain at the polysomes uniformly involve **peptide bond** formation between the α-amino of one unit and the α-carboxyl of the adjacent unit, leading to the —C—N— peptide linkage (Fig. 13.47). When two or more amino acid units are thus bonded together, the product is a *peptide*. A polypeptide contains many amino acid units, whose linear sequence corresponds to the *primary structure* of the molecule. Essentially the same processes are involved in the translation of any genetic message, regardless of the polypeptide synthesized.

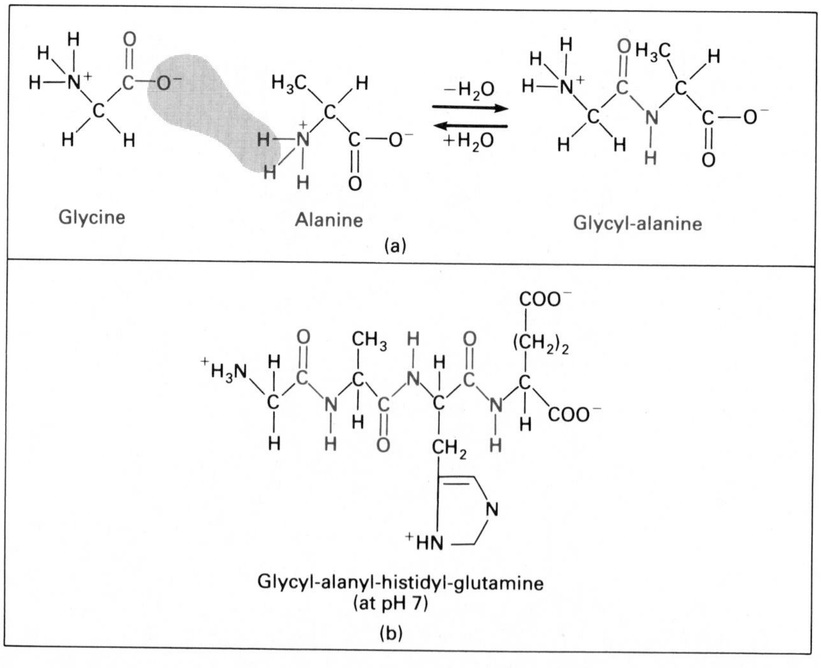

FIGURE 13-47
Peptide bond formation during protein synthesis. (a) A dipeptide is produced from two free amino acids in a dehydration reaction. The same reaction would join a free amino acid to a peptide of any length. (b) Adjacent aminoacyl residues are joined by peptide bonds throughout a peptide or polypeptide chain. Differences along the linear polypeptide are largely due to aminoacyl side-chains and not to the invariant zigzag backbone of the molecule.

Glycine   Alanine   Glycyl-alanine

(a)

Glycyl-alanyl-histidyl-glutamine
(at pH 7)

(b)

FIGURE 13-48 ▶

Formation of the initiation complex preparatory to protein synthesis in prokaryotes. (a) The mRNA binds at its 5' end to the 30S small subunit in the presence of one or more initiation factors (IF), and (b) fMet–tRNA^{Met} binds through its complementary anticodon to the Start codon AUG of mRNA to complete the initiation complex. (c) After the large 50S subunit binds to the initiation complex, initiation factors are released and polypeptide chain elongation may proceed.

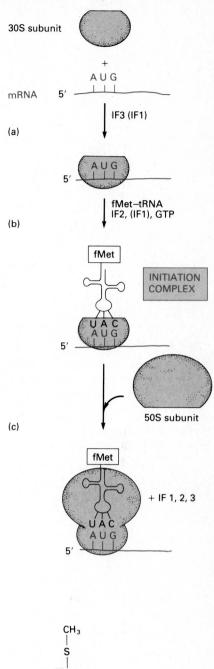

13.12
Polypeptide Chain Initiation

The initiation of translation requires formation of an **initiation complex**, which consists of the small ribosome subunit, mRNA, and the specific initiator aminoacyl-tRNA (Fig. 13.48). In addition, protein **initiation factors** must be present and bound to the small ribosome subunit—a requirement discovered after it was found that washed subunits could not initiate new chains. The initiation factors were washed away, because they are loosely bound to the subunit. Three initiation factors (IF1, IF2, and IF3) are present in bacterial cells, but eight or more of these proteins have been found in mammalian reticulocytes (all eukaryotic initiation factors are designated by the prefix "e", as in eIF1).

The specific **initiator aminoacyl-tRNA** carries methionine (Met) in eukaryotes, but a modified methionine called *N*-**formylmethionine (fMet)** is carried in prokaryotes and in mitochondria and chloroplasts. The initiator tRNA^{Met} is different from the tRNA^{Met} that recognizes AUG codons at *internal* sites of the mRNA. The methionyl residue can be formylated by a formylase enzyme when it is bound to tRNA$_f^{Met}$ but not when it is bound to tRNA$_m^{Met}$ either *in vivo* or *in vitro* in the case of bacteria. Formylation fails to occur *in vivo* in eukaryotes, however, because the formylase is absent from their cytoplasm. The subscripts f and m identify the initiator and noninitiator tRNAs, respectively. Although Met or fMet is the first amino acid to be installed, these residues may later be cleaved or modified by specific enzymes (deformylase and aminopeptidase, respectively). The amino terminus of a polypeptide chain may therefore have some amino acid other than Met or fMet present, depending on post-initiation events.

The codon GUG may occasionally serve as the initiating mRNA codon, instead of AUG, and bind Met-tRNA$_f^{Met}$ or fMet-tRNA$_f^{Met}$. Internal GUG codons, however, bind only valyl–tRNA^{Val}. Whether it binds to AUG or GUG, fMet can engage only in peptide bond formation through its free α-carboxyl group, because its α-amino group is blocked by the formyl residue (Fig. 13.49).

FIGURE 13-49

N-formylmethionine (fMet) is the amino acid carried by the initiator tRNA in prokaryotic protein synthesis. The presence of a formyl residue (color) at the α-amino group effectively blocks peptide bond formation there and leaves only the free carboxyl group for bonding to another amino acid.

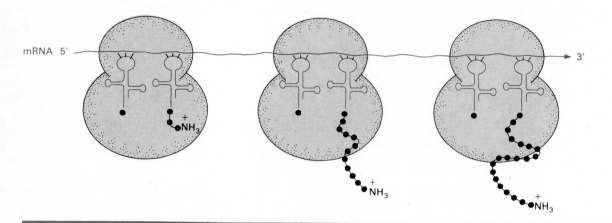

mRNA 5'

3'

FIGURE 13-50
Polysomes form as ribosomes are added to the available 5' end of mRNA engaged in translation. The ribosomes move in convoy toward the 3' end of the message, and each ribosome is active in all the processes of protein synthesis. Though it is not shown here, each new ribosome proceeds through formation of the initiation complex before the large subunit is added to complete the ribosome monomer that functions in chain elongation.

We are somewhat uncertain about the role of IF1 in bacterial chain initiation, but IF2 sponsors placement of the initiator aminoacyl-tRNA at the correct site on the 30S subunit–mRNA complex in bacteria, and IF3 is required for the 30S subunit to bind only to the mRNA initiation site and not elsewhere. All three initiation factors dissociate from the complex after the large subunit binds to the initiation complex and the stage is set for chain elongation. As the ribosome moves from the initiator mRNA codon to the next codon triplet in the $5' \rightarrow 3'$ direction, the mRNA can continue to participate in the formation of new initiation complexes as long as its 5' end is free. Polysomes thus form as additional ribosomes join the mRNA strand and move toward the 3' end of the message (Fig. 13.50).

13.13
Polypeptide Chain Elongation

Each ribosome has two active centers that span the monosome particle; these are called the **A site** (amino-acid–entering site) and the **P site** (peptidyl site). The initiator aminoacyl-tRNA is the only one that binds first to the P site, or partial P site, on the small ribosome subunit. All other aminoacyl-tRNAs enter only at the A site of the whole ribosome monomer during chain elongation (Fig. 13.51).

The second amino acid in the coded sequence is brought to the A site of the ribosome by its carrier tRNA, and the Met or fMet residue from the P site is then linked to the newly arrived aminoacyl-tRNA to form a dipeptidyl-tRNA. The free tRNA^{Met} is discharged from the P site, which becomes available to accept the dipeptidyl-tRNA after a translocation reaction has occurred. Upon translocation of the dipeptidyl-tRNA to the P site, the open A site is free to accept the next incoming aminoacyl-tRNA. The processes of *peptide bond formation* and *translocation* are coordinated and catalytically assisted by ribosomal proteins and RNAs. Peptide bond formation is catalyzed by **peptidyl transferase**, which is situated on the large subunit, and translocation is mediated by an elongation factor that functions as a **translocase** and is bound to the large subunit during the event.

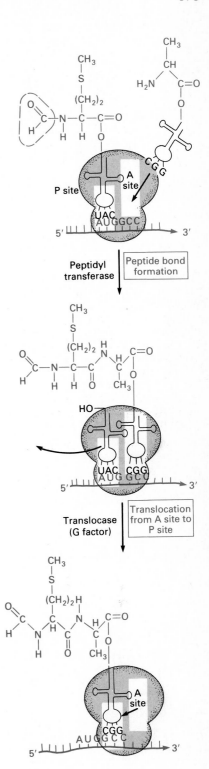

FIGURE 13-51 ▶
Polypeptide chain elongation at the ribosome. Incoming aminoacyl-tRNA enters at the A site; peptide bond formation takes place catalyzed by peptidyl transferase, making the peptidyl chain one unit longer. The tRNA is discharged from the P site after giving up its peptidyl chain to the incoming unit, and the new peptidyl-tRNA is translocated from the A to the P site in a reaction requiring translocase (G factor). The A site is now open for the next aminoacyl-tRNA specified by the coded sequence in mRNA. These same steps are repeated for each amino acid residue until chain termination occurs.

Two **elongation factors** have been identified in cells. In bacteria these are called EF-Tu and EF-Ts; their equivalents in eukaryotes are designated eEF1 and eEF2. Both factors undergo cyclic association and dissociation with the ribosome, and they serve to mediate the entry of aminoacyl-tRNA to the A site and to sponsor the translocation of peptidyl-tRNA from the A site to the P site (Fig. 13.52). A total of three high-energy bonds must be cleaved for each amino acid added to the growing polypeptide chain during elongation. One hydrolysis takes place when ATP is cleaved during the charging of tRNA with its amino acid, in the formation of aminoacyl-tRNA. The other two high-energy bonds are provided by GTP hydrolysis during chain elongation: (1) GTP is cleaved after an aminoacyl-tRNA is bound to the A site, and (2) another GTP is hydrolyzed when the ribosome translocates to the next triplet codon along the mRNA. The translocation reaction is sponsored when EF-G or eEF2 binds to the ribosome, and, upon GTP hydrolysis, the peptidyl-tRNA is translocated to the P site and the elongation factor is released to recycle. The same sets of events and factors are involved in each step of chain elongation, regardless of the particular polypeptide being synthesized, which is a very economical and elegant device indeed.

13.14
Polypeptide Chain Termination

Termination of chain synthesis requires the catalytic action of protein **release factors** (RF), which cause the ribosome to bind to termination codon triplets. A single release factor (eRF) has been identified in eukaryotic cells, but three different factors are present in bacterial cells. Polypeptidyl-tRNA must be in the P site, because RF acts only at the A site of the ribosome. In bacteria, factor RF1 recognizes termination codons UAA and UAG, RF2 recognizes codons UAA and UGA, and RF3 stimulates the action of both the other RFs.

The termination sequence involves a number of separate reactions: (1) release of the polypeptide from the terminal tRNA, probably in conjunction with GTP hydrolysis; (2) removal of the tRNA from the ribosome; and (3) separation of the ribosome from the mRNA strand. Upon the release of a ribosome, the two subunits dissociate and return to the cytoplasmic pool of subunits for other cycles of protein synthesis. Intact monosomes are not usually found in active cells, except as parts of polysomes. In fact, if the subunits fail to dissociate, protein synthesis

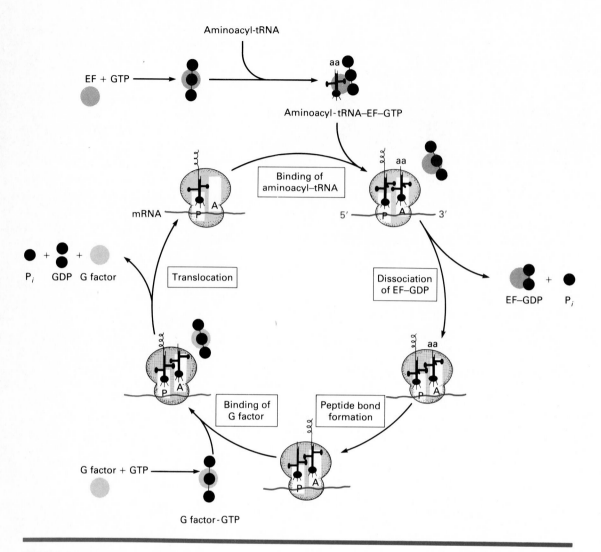

FIGURE 13-52
Polypeptide chain elongation at the
ribosome. Entry of aminoacyl-tRNA
to the A site of the ribosome is mediated by elongation factor (EF) and
guanosine triphosphate (GTP). GTP is
hydrolyzed to guanosine diphosphate
(GDP) and P_i after the aminoacyl-
tRNA is bound at the A site, and the
new residue is then added to the
growing peptidyl chain by peptide
bond formation. Translocation of the
peptidyl-tRNA to the P site requires G
factor and GTP. Hydrolysis of GTP
provides energy for this event, as for
the earlier binding of aminoacyl-tRNA
to the ribosome. When the A site is
again open, another cycle of chain
growth can take place. These same
events occur repeatedly until the entire
polypeptide chain has been translated.

slows down or even stops due to the deficiency of free small subunits for
initiation and of large subunits for elongation events. One of the
initiation factors, IF3, appears to aid the dissociation of monosomes into
subunits by binding to the small subunit. IF3 thus helps to dissociate
monosomes at the same time that it prepares the ribosomal small
subunit to undergo another round of polypeptide chain initiation.

Chain termination does require termination codon UAA, UAG, or
UGA to be present, as has been demonstrated in numerous *missense*
mutants in which a Stop codon is altered to one that specifies an amino
acid. In such mutants the polypeptide is longer than the wild-type
product, due to translation of normally untranslated codons in the
trailer at the 3′ end of mRNA. In several α-globin variants of human
hemoglobin, for example, the α-globin has more than the normal 141
amino acids. Hemoglobin Constant Spring (Hb CS) has 31 extra amino
acids at its carboxy terminus, but amino acids 1 to 141 are identical with
the residues in normal α-globin. *Glutamine* is amino acid 142 in Hb CS,
so the most reasonable explanation is that the normal UAG Stop codon
has been changed to CAG because of a base substitution in the α-globin

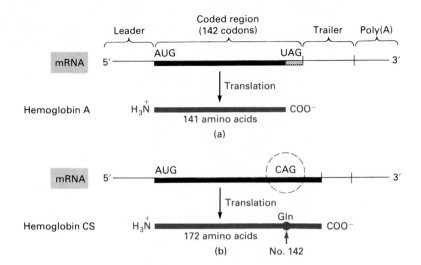

FIGURE 13-53
Effect of mutation in the Stop codon of the human α-globin gene. (a) Normal hemoglobin A contains α chains that are 141 amino acids long, whereas (b) hemoglobin CS (Constant Spring) has α chains that are 172 amino acids long. The missense mutant α chain is longer because the UAG Stop codon has been altered to glutamine-specifying CAG, and translation therefore proceeds past this codon into the trailer region of mRNA. Chain termination occurs in the mutant when a Stop codon is reached in the trailer sequence, yielding an α-globin chain longer by 31 amino acids than the normal α-globin chain.

gene. Translation therefore proceeds in the mutant beyond codon 141, until a Stop codon is reached in the trailer sequence of the mRNA (Fig. 13.53).

13.15
Chemical Inhibitors of Protein Synthesis

A number of chemical agents, including various antibiotics, interfere with protein synthesis at one or more stages of the process. Some of these drugs are particularly useful therapeutic agents because they selectively inhibit bacterial protein synthesis without affecting cytoplasmic protein synthesis in the human or other eukaryotic host (Table 13.4). Care must be taken in the case of some antibiotics, however, because they may inhibit protein synthesis in mitochondria of the same host cells that

TABLE 13-4
Characteristic Action of Some Inhibitors of Protein Synthesis

Synthesis Stage Inhibited	Inhibitor	Mode of Action of Inhibitor	Effective in Prokaryotes	Effective in Eukaryotes
Initiation	Aurintricarboxylic acid	Prevents association of ribosomal sub-unit with messenger RNA	+	+
	Streptomycin	Releases bound fMet-tRNA from initiation complex	+	−
Elongation	Streptomycin	Inhibits binding of aminoacyl-tRNA to ribosome; inhibits translocation on the ribosome	+	−
	Chloramphenicol	Stops amino acid incorporation by inhibiting peptidyl transferase	+	−
	Cycloheximide	Inhibits tRNA movement on the ribosome	−	+
	Puromycin	Acts as amino acid analog and causes premature polypeptide chain termination	+	+
Termination	Various drugs	Inhibit releasing factors; inhibit ribosome release from messenger RNA of polysome	+	+

FIGURE 13-54
Results of experiments designed to identify the cellular compartments in which chloroplast thylakoid membrane proteins are produced in *Chlamydomonas reinhardi*. The total protein complement was determined by absorbance of preparations of extracted proteins (upper line), and the identification of those proteins made in the cytoplasm and those made in the chloroplast was determined by different radioactive labels provided to cells grown in media containing cycloheximide (cytoplasmic inhibitor) or chloramphenicol (chloroplast inhibitor). Proteins made in the cytoplasm (colored line below) were labeled with [^{14}C]arginine, provided while the cells were in media containing chloramphenicol, and proteins made in the chloroplast (black line below) were labeled with [^{3}H]arginine while cells were in media containing cycloheximide. Comparable studies have shown that some mitochondrial membrane proteins are synthesized at ribosomes in the cytoplasm and others at ribosomes within the mitochondrion. (From Hoober, J. K., 1970, *J. Biol. Chem.* **245**:4327, Fig. 6.)

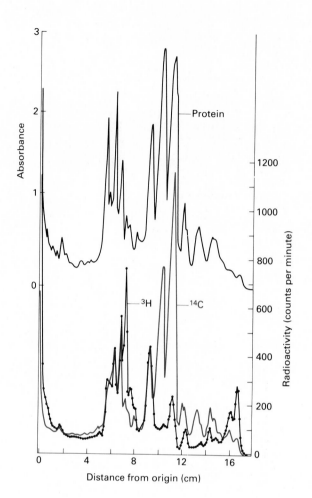

continue to translate polypeptides on cytoribosomes. In plants, chloroplast protein synthesis is usually shut down at the same time as mitochondrial protein synthesis. The translational apparatus of both kinds of organelles responds in a prokaryotic fashion to a variety of drugs, as shown in studies with isolated organelles or with intact eukaryotic cells.

In a typical experiment with eukaryotic cells, the differential effects of **cycloheximide** and **chloramphenicol** can be assessed by determining the patterns of polypeptide synthesis, using different radioactive labels in media with the different inhibitors present. One set of organelle proteins is made only in the presence of cycloheximide and another set only in the presence of chloramphenicol (Fig. 13.54). Proteins known to be encoded by nuclear genes and translated on cytoribosomes are not made in cells that are incubated in cycloheximide, but proteins encoded in organelle genes and made on organelle ribosomes continue to be synthesized in the same cells. The reverse is true for cells incubated in media containing chloramphenicol; organelle translation is shut down, whereas cytoribosomal translation continues more or less normally. Experiments of this same design can provide information concerning the specific cellular compartments in which the various polypeptides of a functional protein, such as cytochrome oxidase or ribulose 1,5-bisphosphate carboxylase, are made and therefore encoded.

Cells, or their organelles, are generally sensitive to antibiotics and other drugs. Drug-resistant mutants can provide information on the processes of translation and on the molecular nature and function of ribosomal components. Chloramphenicol, for example, interferes with the peptidyl transferase reaction. Because bacterial mutants have altered 50S subunit proteins and mitochondrial mutants have altered bases in the 3' end of the larger rRNA, the peptidyl transferase reaction must be localized to the 50S subunit, or to its equivalent in mitochondria.

The localization of **streptomycin** effects in drug-sensitive bacteria was determined by various experimental procedures involving mixed ribosome subunit reconstitution, translational accuracy *in vitro*, and subunit reassembly. When subunits from streptomycin-sensitive (*str-s*) and streptomycin-resistant (*str-r*) strains of *E. coli* were mixed in all possible paired combinations and studied *in vitro* with poly(U) as the mRNA, polyphenylalanine was made in the presence of streptomycin only when the 30S subunit came from the *str-r* strain. The source of the 50S subunit was irrelevant. The specific change in *str-r* 30S subunits was traced to an alteration in protein S12, in mixed reconstitution experiments involving purified 16S rRNA and 30S ribosome subunit proteins. Masayasu Nomura showed that the only reconstituted 30S subunits that could function normally in the presence of streptomycin were those containing S12 from the *str-r* strain, regardless of the source of all the other subunit proteins and 16S rRNA (Fig. 13.55). From later studies it was learned that the principal effect of the antibiotic in *str-s* cells was to prevent the progress from polypeptide chain initiation to chain elongation. Streptomycin causes fMet-tRNA$_f^{Met}$ to be released from the initiation complex just after the 50S subunit has become attached. The 70S ribosome dissociates from the mRNA and accumulates in monosome form in the drugged cell, because initiation factor IF3 is no longer present to aid dissociation into subunits. The decline in subunits leads to a decline in new chain initiation and, eventually, to cell death.

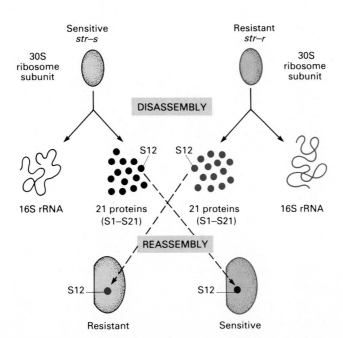

FIGURE 13-55
Schematic summary of mixed reconstitution experiments that showed that the only component responsible for sensitivity or resistance of *E. coli* to streptomycin is protein S12 of the 30S ribosome subunit.

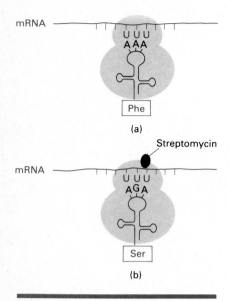

FIGURE 13-56
Misreading of mRNA codons in streptomycin-sensitive *E. coli*. (a) In the absence of streptomycin, the mRNA codon UUU is read as phenylalanine (Phe) by the Phe-tRNA^{Phe} anticodon AAA, as expected. (b) When streptomycin is present, UUU is often misread as UCU and pairs with the AGA anticodon of Ser-tRNA^{Ser}, which leads to insertion of a serine residue where a phenylalanine ought to be located in the polypeptide translation.

Streptomycin studies also revealed the role of the ribosome in guiding the accuracy of translation. In the presence of low concentrations of the antibiotic, *str-s E. coli* synthesizes faulty polypeptides. When poly(U) is provided *in vitro* as the mRNA for *str-r* ribosomal translation, polyphenylalanine is made as expected. Polypeptides made along *str-s* ribosomes, however, contained isoleucine and serine residues as well as phenylalanines. The drug causes **misreading** of mRNA codons, such that U is misread as C and C as U, and either U or C is occasionally misread as A (Fig. 13.56). The pattern of misreading was evident from the nature of the substituted amino acids and thus of their known codons, and from studies using poly(C) artificial messengers. In the presence of poly(C) and streptomycin, *str-s* ribosomes promoted the incorporation of serine, histidine, and threonine, as well as the expected prolines (see Fig. 4.11). Misreading is not the primary lethal effect of streptomycin, however, because protein synthesis was inhibited in the absence of misreading when certain artificial messengers were tested (those lacking U or C). The principal cause of lethality induced by streptomycin is the failure of chain initiation to proceed to the stage of dipeptidyl formation and chain elongation.

The molecular events of gene expression during transcription and translation thus determine whether a polypeptide will be synthesized and the rate of protein synthesis. Clearly, regulation of gene expression can be effective at any stage of either transcription or translation, as well as before or after these processes have been set in motion in the cell. In the next chapter we will discuss a number of the control mechanisms by which gene expression is regulated in prokaryotes and eukaryotes. These controls allow us to understand why genetically identical cells in a population or an organism express different genes at different times and thus develop a multiplicity of phenotypes from a single set of genetic blueprints encoded in the genome.

Summary

In bacteria and bacteriophage the gene is colinear with its protein product. In eukaryotes and their viruses, however, coding sequences (exons) in the gene are interrupted by noncoding intervening sequences (introns) of variable number and length that are faithfully transcribed by RNA polymerase into precursor mRNA but are not translated into protein. The splicing out of the noncoding segments is an essential part of the maturation process of mRNA. Duplicate genes in eukaryotic genomes (pseudogenes) lack the normal introns and are not transcribed. In all mRNAs the protein coding sequence is flanked by a characteristic leader sequence upstream and by a trailer downstream. After transcription, in addition to being correctly spliced, eukaryotic mRNA must be provided with a 7-methylguanosine cap at the 5′ end and a poly(A) tail of up to 200 residues at the 3′ end.

RNA polymerases catalyze the transcription of DNA into RNA, beginning at the 3′ end of the region to be transcribed (the 5′ end of the RNA) and successively adding ribonucleotide monomers to the 3′ end of the growing chain. A DNA promoter sequence upstream of the gene binds RNA polymerase and is a signal to start transcription. A terminator sequence at the other end of the gene stops polymerase action with the aid of rho protein. Three kinds of RNA polymerases function in eukaryotic cells: Polymerase I produces ribosomal RNA precursors, polymerase II transcribes pre-mRNA, and polymerase III transcribes small, stable RNA species such as tRNA and 5S rRNA. Bacteria contain a single RNA polymerase. RNA polymerase enzymes have multiple subunits, some of which recognize the promoter, some of which bind to the template, and some of which bind to the substrate.

The promoter region in the DNA is not itself transcribed. No single sequence is always found in a promoter, but a consensus sequence (Pribnow box or TATA box) rich in A and T nucleotides is usually located shortly upstream from the startpoint of transcription and within the region to which RNA polymerase binds.

Once transcribed, all eukaryotic RNAs undergo processing before they are functional. Excision of introns from precursor mRNA follows polyadenylation and occurs in a specific sequence. Consensus sequences mark the intron–exon junction and are essential to excision and splicing to produce functional mRNA. The splicing mechanism may involve base pairing with small ribonucleoproteins. Changes in splicing patterns are associated with developmental changes in gene expression. Processing of tRNA precursors involves removal of a short leader at the 5′ end, addition of ACC to the 3′ end, removal of introns, and modification of certain bases to ensure a stable, internally base-paired secondary structure. Eukaryotic cells produce only 32 tRNAs, but 61 codons must be translated. The wobble hypothesis proposes that there are several alternative possibilities for pairing of the 5′ base of the tRNA anticodon. Mitochondrial genomes encode only 22 to 25 tRNA species, different in structure from their cellular counterparts and probably subject to somewhat different rules for codon–anticodon pairing. Organelles have only a single copy of each tRNA gene, but prokaryotes have several and eukaryotes may have hundreds.

Successive cleavages of the initial ribosomal RNA transcript release the mature rRNA species: 23S, 5S, and 16S in prokaryotes, 25-28S, 5.8S, and 18S in eukaryotes. (The 5S eukaryotic rRNA is transcribed from genes located elsewhere in the genome by polymerase III.) In the nucleus, protein components are added to rRNAs, and eukaryotic ribosomal subunits are transferred from the nucleus to the cytoplasm. Hundreds or thousands of ribosomal genes are clustered on one or several chromosomes, where they form the nucleolar organizing regions. Within a cluster each rRNA gene is separated from the next by nontranscribed spacer DNA.

Ribosomal proteins (52 in prokaryotes, 82 in eukaryotes) assemble with rRNA *in vitro* in a precise sequential way. Both types of ribosomes are complex morphologically. Binding sites are available for 2 tRNA molecules and up to 40 nucleotides of mRNA. The prokaryotic 16S rRNA of prokaryotes includes a sequence that is complementary to the leader portion of mRNA, helping to position mRNA on the small subunit. Specific ribosomal proteins are also implicated in functions such as antibiotic resistance, peptide bond synthesis, and translocation of the ribosome along the message. Any prokaryotic ribosomes can interchange parts and remain functional; however, prokaryotic–eukaryotic hybrid ribosomes are not functional. Several ribosomes in convoy simultaneously translate a single mRNA. When not translating, ribosomal subunits are free in the cytoplasm.

Once in the cytoplasm, all three kinds of RNA cooperate in protein synthesis, the translation of the coded mRNA. A necessary preceding event is generating activated amino acids (using energy from ATP) and coupling them to the 3′ end of tRNAs bearing the appropriate anticodons. Protein synthesis is initiated by the formation of a complex of the mRNA, a ribosome small subunit, and a particular initiator tRNA bearing methionine in eukaryotes or *N*-formylmethionine (fMet) in prokaryotes. The initiator tRNA binds by its anticodon to the initiating codon (AUG) of the mRNA. Now the ribosome's large subunit joins the complex, and polypeptide synthesis proceeds. Each incoming aminoacyl-tRNA is positioned at the A site, according to base pairing between its anticodon and the next codon on the mRNA. A peptide bond joins the peptidyl chain to the amino acid, leaving both joined to the tRNA at the A site. The empty tRNA is discharged from the P site. The lengthened peptidyl-tRNA is translocated to the P site and the A site is open to the next aminoacyl unit of the chain. The ribosome moves in the 3′ direction along the mRNA, and the cycle recurs to elongate the peptide. When one of the three termination codons is positioned on the ribosome opposite the A site, release factors act to liberate the polypeptide from the final tRNA and discharge it and the mRNA from the ribosome. Binding of initiation factors in preparation for another round of translation assists in dissociating the ribosomal subunits. Though all translation occurs by the same mechanism, ribosomal differences confer different drug sensitivity on eukaryotes than on prokaryotes, mitochondria, or chloroplasts.

Readings and References

Attardi, G. 1981. Organization and expression of the mammalian mitochondrial genome: A lesson in economy. *Trends Biochem. Sci.* **6**:86, 100.

Bogenhagen, D. F., S. Sakonju, and D. D. Brown. 1980. A control region in the center of the 5S RNA gene directs specific initiation of transcription. II. The 3′ border of the region. *Cell* **19**:27.

Bonitz, S. G., *et al*. 1980. Codon recognition rules in yeast mitochondria. *Proc. Natl. Acad. Sci. U. S.* **77**:3167.

Brenner, S., F. Jacob, and M. Meselson. 1961. An unstable intermediate carrying information from genes to ribosomes for protein synthesis. *Nature* **190**:576.

Brody, E., and J. Abelson. 1985. The "spliceosome": Yeast pre-messenger RNA associates with a 40S complex in a splicing-dependent reaction. *Science* **228**:963.

Broker, T. R., and L. T. Chow. 1980. Patterns and consequences of adenoviral RNA splicing. *Trends Biochem. Sci.* **5**:174.

Brown, D. D. August 1973. The isolation of genes. *Sci. Amer.* **229**:20.

Brown, D. D., and J. B. Gurdon. 1964. Absence of ribosomal RNA synthesis in the anucleolate mutant of *Xenopus laevis*. *Proc. Natl. Acad. Sci. U. S.* **51**:139.

Caskey, C. Th. 1980. Peptide chain termination. *Trends Biochem. Sci.* **5**:234.

Chambon, P. May 1981. Split genes. *Sci. Amer.* **244**:60.

Chomyn, A., *et al*. 1985. Six unidentified reading frames of human mitochondrial DNA encode components of the respiratory-chain NADH dehydrogenase. *Nature* **314**:592.

Clark, B. 1980. The elongation step of protein biosynthesis. *Trends Biochem. Sci.* **5**:207.

Clayton, D. A. 1984. Transcription of the mammalian mitochondrial genome. *Ann. Rev. Biochem.* **53**:573.

Crick, F. H. C. 1966. Codon–anticodon pairing: The wobble hypothesis. *J. Mol. Biol.* **19**:548.

Crick, F. H. C. 1979. Split genes and RNA splicing. *Science* **204**:264.

Daneholt, B. 1975. Transcription in polytene chromosomes. *Cell* **4**:1.

Darnell, J. E., Jr. October 1983. The processing of RNA. *Sci. Amer.* **249**:90.

Davison, B. L., J.-M. Egly, E. R. Mulvihill, and P. Chambon. 1983. Formation of stable preinitiation complexes between eukaryotic class B transcription factors and promoter sequences. *Nature* **301**:680.

Deutscher, M. P. 1984. The eucaryotic aminoacyl–tRNA synthetase complex: Suggestions for its structure and function. *J. Cell Biol.* **99**:373.

Dickerson, R. E. December 1983. The DNA helix and how it is read. *Sci. Amer.* **249**:94.

Dingwall, C. 1985. The accumulation of proteins in the nucleus. *Trends Biochem. Sci.* **10**:64.

Domdey, H., *et al.* 1984. Lariat structures are *in vivo* intermediates in yeast pre-mRNA splicing. *Cell* **39**:611.

Early, P., *et al.* 1980. Two mRNAs can be produced from a single immunoglobulin μ gene by alternative RNA processing pathways. *Cell* **20**:313.

Garrett, R. 1983. Antibiotics and active ribosomal RNA sites. *Trends Biochem. Sci.* **8**:189.

Gilbert, W. 1981. DNA sequencing and gene structure. *Science* **214**:1305 (Nobel lecture).

Gorini, L. April 1966. Antibiotics and the genetic code. *Sci. Amer.* **214**:102.

Greer, C. L., and J. Abelson. 1984. RNA splicing: Rearrangement of RNA sequences in the expression of split genes. *Trends Biochem. Sci.* **9**:139.

Grosveld, G. C., E. de Boer, C. K. Shewmaker, and R. A. Flavell. 1982. DNA sequences necessary for transcription of the rabbit β-globin gene *in vivo*. *Nature* **295**:120.

Gruissem, W., *et al.* 1982. Transcription of *E. coli* and *Euglena* chloroplast tRNA gene clusters and processing of polycistronic transcripts in a HeLa cell-free system. *Cell* **30**:81.

Hall, B. D., S. G. Clarkson, and G. Tocchini-Valentini. 1982. Transcription initiation of eucaryotic transfer RNA genes. *Cell* **29**:3.

Hall, B. D., L. Haarr, and K. Kleppe. 1980. Development of the nitrocellulose filter technique for RNA–DNA hybridization. *Trends Biochem. Sci.* **5**:254.

Hatfield, D. 1985. Suppression of termination codons in higher eukaryotes. *Trends Biochem. Sci.* **10**:201.

Hoober, J. K. 1970. Sites of synthesis of chloroplast membrane polypeptides in *Chlamydomonas reinhardi* y-1. *J. Biol. Chem.* **245**:4327.

Horowitz, H., and T. Platt. 1982. A termination site for *lac*I transcription is between the CAP site and the *lac* promoter. *J. Biol. Chem.* **257**:11740.

Hunt, T. 1980. The initiation of protein synthesis. *Trends Biochem. Sci.* **5**:178.

Ingram, V. I. January 1958. How do genes act? *Sci. Amer.* **198**:68.

Johnson, P. F., and J. Abelson. 1983. The yeast tRNA[Tyr] gene intron is essential for correct modification of its tRNA product. *Nature* **302**:681.

Kaempfer, R. 1970. Dissociation of ribosomes on polypeptide chain termination and origin of single ribosomes. *Nature* **228**:534.

Keller, W. 1984. The RNA lariat: A new ring to the splicing of mRNA precursors. *Cell* **39**:423.

Konarska, M. M., P. J. Grabowski, R. A. Padgett, and P. A. Sharp. 1985. Characterization of the branch site in lariat RNAs produced by splicing of mRNA precursors. *Nature* **313**:552.

Konkel, D. A., S. M. Tilghman, and P. Leder. 1978. The sequence of the chromosomal mouse β-globin major gene: Homologies in capping, splicing, and poly(A) sites. *Cell* **15**:1125.

Korn, L. J. 1982. Transcription of *Xenopus* 5S ribosomal RNA genes. *Nature* **295**:101.

Kozack, M. 1981. Possible role of flanking nucleotides in recognition of the AUG initiator codon by eukaryotic ribosomes. *Nucleic Acids Res.* **9**:5233.

Laird, C. D., and W. Y. Chooi. 1976. Morphology of transcription units in *Drosophila melanogaster*. *Chromosoma* **58**:193.

Leaver, C. J., and M. W. Gray. 1982. Mitochondrial genome organization and expression in higher plants. *Ann. Rev. Plant Physiol.* **33**:373.

Lake, J. A. August 1981. The ribosome. *Sci. Amer.* **245**:84.

Lewin, B. 1980. *Gene Expression, 2: Eukaryotic Chromosomes.* 2nd ed. New York: Wiley.

Lewin, B. 1985. *Genes.* 2nd ed. New York: Wiley.

Lewin, R. 1985. More progress in messenger RNA splicing. *Science* **228**:977.

Lipmann, F. 1969. Polypeptide chain elongation in protein biosynthesis. *Science* **164**:1024.

Maniatis, T., E. F. Fritsch, J. Lauer, and R. M. Lawn. 1980. The molecular genetics of human hemoglobins. *Ann. Rev. Genet.* **14**:145.

Mantei, N., and C. Weissmann. 1982. Controlled transcription of a human α-interferon gene introduced into mouse L cells. *Nature* **297**:128.

Maurer, R. A., C. R. Erwin, and J. E. Donelson. 1981. Analysis of 5′ flanking sequences and intron–exon boundaries of the rat prolactin gene. *J. Biol. Chem.* **256**:10524.

McKnight, S. L., and R. Kingsbury. 1982. Transcriptional control signals of a eukaryotic protein-coding gene. *Science* **217**:316.

Miller, O. L., Jr. March 1973. The visualization of genes in action. *Sci. Amer.* **229**:34.

Miller, O. L., Jr. 1981. The nucleolus, chromosomes, and visualization of genetic activity. *J. Cell Biol.* **91**:15s.

Mount, S. M., and J. S. Steitz. 1981. Sequence of U1 RNA from *Drosophila melanogaster*. Implications for U1 secondary structure and possible involvement in splicing. *Nucleic Acids Res.* **9**:6351.

Noller, H. F. 1984. Structure of ribosomal RNA. *Ann. Rev. Biochem.* **53**:119.

Noller, H. F., and C. R. Woese. 1981. Secondary structure of 16S ribosomal RNA. *Science* **212**:403.

Nomura, M. January 1984. The control of ribosome synthesis. *Sci. Amer.* **250**:102.

O'Farrell, P. Z., *et al.* 1978. Structure and processing of yeast precursor tRNAs containing intervening sequences. *Nature* **274**:438.

Ogden, R. C., *et al.* 1981. The mechanism of tRNA splicing. *Trends Biochem. Sci.* **6**:154.

Ojala, D., J. Montoya, and G. Attardi. 1981. tRNA punctuation model of RNA processing in human mitochondria. *Nature* **290**:470.

Padgett, R. A., P. J. Grabowski, M. M. Konarska, and P. A. Sharp. 1985. Splicing messenger RNA precursors: Branch sites and lariat RNAs. *Trends Biochem. Sci.* **10**:154.

Padgett, R. A., *et al.* 1984. Lariat RNAs as intermediates and products in the splicing of messenger RNA precursors. *Science* **225**:898.

Pederson, T. 1983. Nuclear RNA–protein interactions and messenger RNA processing. *J. Cell Biol.* **97**:1321.

Perry, R. P. 1981. RNA processing comes of age. *J. Cell Biol.* **91**:28s.

Pribnow, D. 1975. Nucleotide sequence of an RNA polymerase binding site at an early T7 promoter. *Proc. Natl. Acad. Sci. U. S.* **72**:784.

Proudfoot, N. J. 1980. Pseudogenes. *Nature* **286**:840.

Proudfoot, N. J. 1982. The end of the message. *Nature* **298**:516.

Rich, A. December 1963. Polyribosomes. *Sci. Amer.* **209**:44.

Rich, A., and S. H. Kim. January 1978. The three-dimensional structure of transfer RNA. *Sci. Amer.* **238**:52.

Ritossa, F. M., and S. Spiegelman. 1965. Localization of RNA complementary to ribosomal RNA in the nucleolus organizer region of *Drosophila melanogaster*. *Proc. Natl. Acad. Sci. U. S.* **53**:737.

Roberts, R. 1980. Small RNAs and splicing. *Nature* **283**:132.

Rodriguez, J. R., C. W. Pikielny, and M. Rosbash. 1984. *In vivo* characterization of yeast mRNA processing intermediates. *Cell* **39**:603.

Rogers, J., and R. Wall 1980. A mechanism for RNA splicing. *Proc. Natl. Acad. Sci. U. S.* **77**:1877.

Sakonju, S., D. F. Bogenhagen, and D. D. Brown. 1980. A control region in the center of the 5S RNA gene directs specific initiation of transcription. I. The 5′ border of the region. *Cell* **19**:13.

Sanger, F. 1981. Determination of nucleotide sequences in DNA. *Science* **214**:1205 (Nobel lecture).

Sarabhai, A. S., A. O. W. Stretton, S. Brenner, and A. Bolle. 1967. Colinearity of gene with the polypeptide chain. *Nature* **210**:14.

Schwarz, Z., and H. Kössel. 1980. The primary structure of 16S rDNA from *Zea mays* chloroplast is homologous to *E. coli* 16S rRNA. *Nature* **283**:739.

Siekevitz, P., and P. C. Zamecnik. 1981. Ribosomes and protein synthesis. *J. Cell Biol.* **91**:53s.

Subramanian, A. R. 1984. Structure and functions of the largest *Escherichia coli* ribosomal protein. *Trends Biochem. Sci.* **9**:491.

Swanson, R. F., and I. B. Dawid. 1970. The mitochondrial ribosome of *Xenopus laevis*. *Proc. Natl. Acad. Sci. U. S.* **66**:117.

Tilghman, S. M., *et al.* 1978. The intervening sequence of a mouse β-globin gene is transcribed within the 15S β-globin mRNA precursor. *Proc. Natl. Acad. Sci. U. S.* **75**:1309.

Treisman, R., S. H. Orkin, and T. Maniatis. 1983. Specific transcription and RNA splicing defects in five cloned β-thalassemia genes. *Nature* **302**:591.

Warner, J. R., A. Rich, and C. E. Hall. 1962. Electron microscope studies of ribosomal clusters synthesizing hemoglobin. *Science* **138**:1399.

Wasylyk, B., and P. Chambon. 1981. A T-to-A base substitution and small deletions in the conalbumin TATA box drastically decrease specific *in vitro* transcription. *Nucleic Acids Res.* **9**:1813.

Weiss, R., and J. Gallant. 1983. Mechanism of ribosome frameshifting during translation of the genetic code. *Nature* **302**:389.

Woo, S. L. C., *et al.* 1981. Complete nucleotide sequence of the chicken chromosomal ovalbumin gene and its biological significance. *Biochemistry* **20**:6437.

Yanofsky, C. May 1967. Gene structure and protein structure. *Sci. Amer.* **216**:80.

Zeitlin, S., and A. Efstratiadis. 1984. *In vivo* splicing products of the rabbit β-globin pre-mRNA. *Cell* **39**:589.

Zieve, G. W. 1981. Two groups of small stable RNAs. *Cell* **25**:296.

CHAPTER 14

Regulation of Gene Expression

Structural, functional, and behavioral characteristics of any cell are largely due to **gene expression**—that is, to the transcription of genetic information and its translation into proteins. Strikingly different kinds of cells may arise in populations with identical genomes, however, which is plainly evident in a multicellular individual whose varied kinds of cells can all be traced back to a single fertilized egg. If all these kinds of cells in the individual were produced by mitosis, which yields genetically identical nuclei in descendant lineages, how can we explain the observed cellular variety? The answer to this central question in biology has come from many different experimental approaches. In this chapter we will concentrate on the mechanisms that *regulate* gene expression, such that only a fraction of the genome is expressed in any one cell type and such that different genes are expressed in different cells. With a basic understanding of molecular controls over gene expression, we are in a better position to attack the equally basic questions concerning development and differentiation of specific cell types in specific locations in the organism. In other words, we ultimately wish to know why one kind of cell becomes part of the nervous system or liver, whereas another kind of cell differentiates into skin or blood components. Armed with methods and information from molecular cell biology and molecular genetics, we can now approach fundamental and challenging questions in developmental biology more specifically.

Differential Gene Expression

We know that different cell types arise from the fertilized egg in multicellular organisms and that each kind of cell in turn gives rise only to other cells like itself in the mature individual. How can we explain these two phenomena—the phenotypic differentiation of genetically homogeneous cells during embryogenesis and the *heritability* of each cellular phenotype in the mature organism? Attempts to explain both phenomena with a single theory centered on the possibility that the genome was altered differently in the various cell lineages and that these alterations were permanent. If the genome remained intact, however, other explanations were required and these explanations centered on differential gene expression. By **differential gene expression** we mean that only some of the genes are turned on, or expressed, and that other genes in the same cell are turned off, or not expressed.

14.1
Totipotent Nuclei in Differentiated Cells

The nucleus of a fertilized egg is **totipotent**; it can provide all the genetic information needed for the development and differentiation of the many kinds of cells that constitute an organism. If genes were lost or

FIGURE 14-1
Schematic summary of nuclear transplantation procedures designed to test whether or not nuclei from differentiated cells have retained totipotency and can guide normal development and differentiation. Nuclei from dissociated cells of blastula or gastrula stages of embryonic development are transplanted into egg cells that have been enucleated or irradiated, so that the transplanted nucleus serves as the exclusive genetic system for subsequent events. In some amphibians, such egg systems undergo normal development and differentiation, which indicates that the transplanted nucleus is totipotent and, therefore, that neither gene loss nor mutation can be primarily responsible for development and differentiation of the multicellular organism.

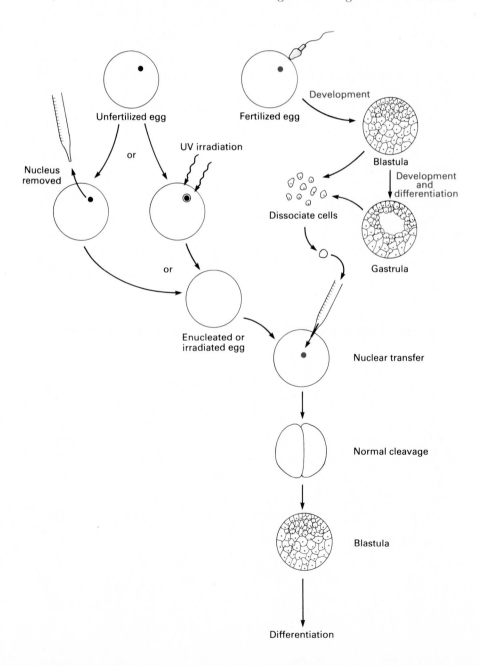

underwent mutations during differentiation, then, because of genome alterations, the nucleus of a differentiated cell would no longer support the development of an organism. In order to test the totipotency or genetic capacity of nuclei from differentiated cells, Robert Briggs and Thomas King devised methods for **nuclear transplantation** of somatic cell nuclei into enucleated or irradiated egg cells from frogs (Fig. 14.1). They found that normal development occurred when nuclei from preblastula embryonic cells were transplanted into egg cells, but not when nuclei from postblastula embryonic cells were used. Postblastula nuclei were no longer totipotent, which indicated that some irreversible change had occurred by the time of gastrulation in the frog embryo. In similar studies using toads, however, John Gurdon and others found that nuclei from embryonic intestinal cells remained totipotent long after gastrulation. In many cases normal adult toads were produced, and these were fully fertile animals capable of producing normal progeny.

Despite these differences between amphibians, which are not well understood, both sets of studies showed that a complete set of functional genes must have been retained for a considerable time after differentiation, because a differentiated cell nucleus in an egg cell could guide development of the animal.

In the early 1960s, shortly after the reports by Briggs and King, nuclear totipotency was also shown to characterize plants. Frederick Steward showed that isolated cells that had been dissociated from carrot roots could give rise to whole plants when grown in specially supplemented culture media (Fig. 14.2). Single differentiated cells could produce normal plants that flowered and reproduced, so the entire genome must have been retained its original genetic state.

Molecular hybridization experiments have repeatedly shown that complete and essentially identical genomes are present in the differentiated tissues of an individual. In these studies the DNAs from different tissues are isolated, purified, and melted to single strands. When DNAs

FIGURE 14-2
Schematic summary of experiments that showed that nuclei from carrot root cells retain totipotency. Isolated root cells undergo initial growth and development in culture and differentiate into plantlets. Long-term growth leads to mature flowering plants that are normal in every respect.

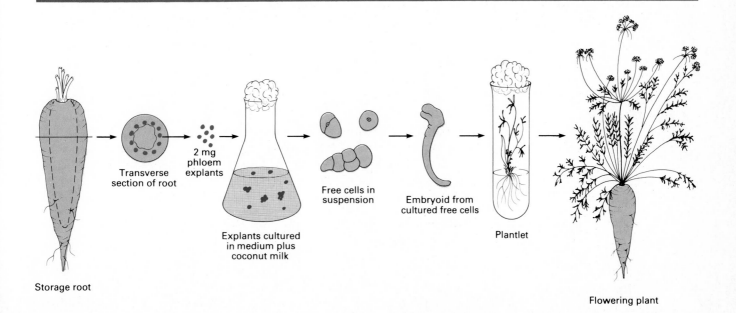

Storage root

Transverse section of root

2 mg phloem explants

Explants cultured in medium plus coconut milk

Free cells in suspension

Embryoid from cultured free cells

Plantlet

Flowering plant

from different tissues are allowed to reanneal to form hybrid DNA–DNA duplexes, the extent of hybridization indicates the extent of sequence complementarity among the genomes from the various sources. When liver DNA is labeled with ^{3}H, and brain or kidney DNA is labeled with ^{14}C or ^{32}P, hybrid duplexes can be identified by the presence of double labeling (one strand carrying one isotopic marker and the partner strand carrying the other isotopic label). Data from these and similar experiments regularly show that the different tissues of an individual are genomically the same.

Of course, exceptions have been found to the general rule that genomes remain in their intact or original state in all the cells of an individual. In various invertebrates, such as the roundworm *Ascaris*, genes are lost by diminution of chromosomes during somatic cell development, whereas the genome remains intact in germ-line cells set apart during development. Ribosomal RNA genes become methylated in somatic cells but not in oocytes of the toad *Xenopus*, showing that genes may be modified during development and differentiation. Studies of immunoglobulins in mammalian species reveal that mutations may alter certain genes in somatic cell lineages. New kinds of immunoglobulin molecules appear to be the result of mutations in some instances and of changes in the genes or in gene products by transcriptional processing in other instances, as we shall see later in this chapter.

In the great majority of organisms and cell types, differential gene expression appears to be responsible for phenotypic differences in genetically identical cells. The most direct evidence in support of this premise has come from molecular hybridization studies of such differentiated cells as reticulocytes. Globin genes are present in all the body cells, judging from the hybrid duplex formation observed between cloned globin genes or globin mRNA and nuclear DNA from various cells. DNA–mRNA hybridizations show, however, that globin mRNA is found only in hemoglobin-synthesizing blood cells and not in other kinds of cells. In reticulocytes and in other cells that have been analyzed, the genes are present but are expressed only in particular cells and not in others.

If all the genes are present but are active only at certain times in certain cells, what regulates genic activity or inactivity? The first important evidence pointing toward the nature of controls over gene expression was obtained in the 1960s in studies of *E. coli*. These and other studies showed that control mechanisms operated predominantly at the level of transcription. Genes were expressed if transcription took place, but they were not expressed when transcription was blocked. We will discuss the studies of transcriptional control in bacteria first; these are the most detailed analyses and the ones that opened new avenues of experimentation into all organisms.

14.2
Repressor Control of Transcription in Bacteria

In *E. coli* and other bacteria, many of the genes are expressed only if transcription takes place. In the 1950s and 1960s, Francois Jacob and Jacques Monod provided elegant genetic evidence showing that control

TABLE 14-1
Regulatory and Structural Genes of the *lac* Region in *E. coli*

Component	Symbol	Function	Protein Product
Structural genes	*lacZ*	Codes for enzyme protein	β-galactosidase
	lacY	Codes for membrane protein	Galactoside permease
	lacA	Codes for enzyme protein	Thiogalactoside transacetylase
Regulatory genes			
Operator	*lacO*	Binding site for repressor protein	None
Promoter	*lacP*	Binding site for RNA polymerase	None
Repressor gene	*lacI*	Codes for repressor protein	*lac* repressor

over transcription depended on **repressor proteins** that interacted with the **operator** immediately adjacent to genes coding for enzymes and for other proteins needed for metabolism. In the case of the *lac* region of the *E. coli* genome, they identified a cluster of three genes that specified the primary structures of the lactose-metabolizing enzyme β-galactosidase (*lacZ*); a membrane protein called galactoside permease, which helps lactose to cross the cell membrane (*lacY*); and the enzyme thiogalactoside transacetylase, whose function remains uncertain (*lacA*). These three genes were mapped next to each other in the order *lacZ-lacY-lacA*. These were **structural genes**; mutations in any one of them caused structural alterations in the protein product. Mutations in the operator, however, influenced the expression of all three *lac* genes coordinately but did not affect protein structure. The operator (*lacO*) in turn responded to the lactose repressor protein, which was the product of repressor gene *lacI*. Because *lacO* and *lacI* influenced the amounts made of the structural proteins but not the structure of these proteins, both the operator and the repressor were **regulatory genes**. Some time later, the **promoter** (*lacP*) was defined as a regulatory gene and mapped next to the operator, on the opposite side from the structural gene loci (Table 14.1).

These and other genetic data led Jacob and Monod to formulate the **operon concept** of gene expression and its regulation. Structural genes code for enzymes and other proteins needed for metabolism and cell structure, and regulatory genes govern the expression of structural genes via their control over structural gene transcription. The structural and regulatory genes that are involved in a particular cell function and are clustered together on the genetic map constitute a *coordinated* set of genes called an **operon**. Repressor control over structural gene transcription is exerted through interactions between the repressor protein and its specific operator. When repressor is bound to operator DNA, the RNA polymerase at the promoter site is prevented from moving along the DNA template, and transcription is blocked. When repressor does not bind to the operator, transcription can occur because RNA polymerase can move past the operator and catalyze transcription of all three structural genes coordinately. Whether or not the repressor protein binds to the operator is determined by the presence or absence of lactose and other β-galactoside substrates of the *lac* gene products (Fig. 14.3).

The *lac* system is an example of control over the synthesis of **inducible enzymes**, which are synthesized only when the substrate is present, not in its absence. When the substrate is present, it binds to

FIGURE 14-3
The operon model of control over *lac* gene expression for three inducible enzymes involved in lactose metabolism in *E. coli*. (a) In the absence of inducer (lactose), the *lac* repressor protein binds to *lacO* (operator) and blocks movement of RNA polymerase toward *lacZYA*. Enzymes are not synthesized because mRNA transcripts are not available for translation. (b) In the presence of inducer, repressor protein binds to lactose and is rendered incapable of binding to *lacO*. RNA polymerase can move along the DNA template, from its *lacP* (promoter) binding site, and can catalyze transcription of *lacZYA*. Translation from mRNA can now take place to produce the three inducible enzymes.

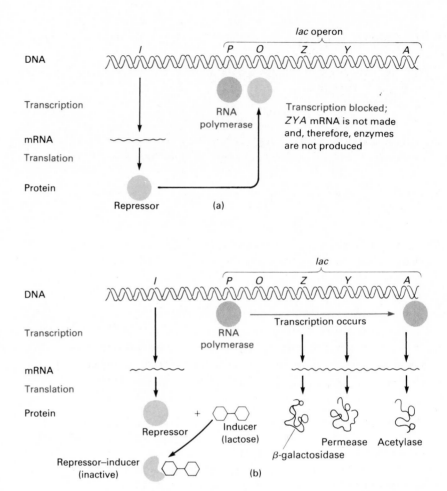

repressor protein and alters the conformation of the protein such that it can no longer bind to operator DNA. In the absence of the substrate, repressor protein exists in a conformation suitable for binding to its operator DNA. The repressor is specific for its own operon, and different operons are regulated by different repressor genes. The repressor need not be physically adjacent to the operon; repressor protein is a diffusible product. The promoter and operator, however, are parts of an operon and must be physically adjacent to the structural genes in the same DNA strand. These features were established by genetic analysis of regulatory gene mutations and structural gene mutations in *E. coli* strains.

Repressor control may also characterize the synthesis of **repressible enzymes**, which are made only when the metabolite is absent or in low concentration in the cell. In such a system, the repressor protein cannot bind to operator DNA unless its conformation is altered by the specific metabolite. When little or no metabolite is present, therefore, transcription and translation of the structural genes can occur because repressor alone cannot block the operator (Fig. 14.4). When metabolite is present in high concentration, the molecule binds to repressor protein and helps it bind to the operator, thus blocking transcription. The repressing metabolite is called a **corepressor** because it helps block transcription of structural genes in the operon. Repressible enzymes usually catalyze biosynthetic reactions, whereas inducible enzymes usually catalyze the breakdown reactions of metabolism.

Whether enzyme synthesis is inducible or repressible, transcription is turned off when repressor proteins bind to operator DNA. Transcription is turned on only when the repressor is removed from operator DNA. Both cases of transcriptional regulation reflect the same principle of **negative control**, because repressor protein must be removed before gene expression can occur. Examples of **positive control** over transcription are known, in which some molecule binds to regulatory DNA and stimulates transcription. One of the best known systems of positive control in bacteria involves the cyclic nucleotide **cyclic AMP (cAMP)**, which influences the *lac* operon and a number of other operons involved in the synthesis of inducible enzymes of carbohydrate metabolism.

Control by cAMP occurs only when it is bound in a complex to catabolite activator protein (CAP), which is a structural gene product. Neither cAMP nor CAP can function alone, as shown by mutants defective in CAP synthesis or in the synthesis of adenylcyclase, the enzyme that converts ATP to cAMP (Fig. 14.5). The cAMP–CAP control mechanism acts independently of repressor control, as demonstrated by the fact that wild-type and repressor-mutant strains respond equally well to cAMP in the growth medium. From studies using isolated *lac*

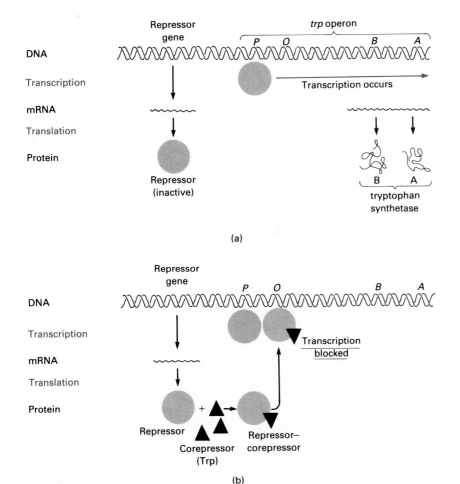

(a)

(b)

FIGURE 14-4
Differential gene expression in the case of a repressible enzyme coded by genes *A* and *B* of the *trp* operon. (a) In the absence of tryptophan (Trp), the end product of the pathway catalyzed by tryptophan synthetase and other enzymes, gene expression is turned on. Repressor cannot bind alone to *trpO*, and RNA polymerase moves from its binding site at the promoter (*trpP*) to catalyze transcription. The A and B polypeptides are translated, and they combine to form the active enzyme tryptophan synthetase that leads to tryptophan synthesis in the cell. (b) When Trp is present, it acts as a corepressor by binding to repressor protein and thereby helps the repressor bind to *lacO* and block RNA polymerase movement. In the absence of mRNA, proteins are not synthesized and Trp biosynthesis stops.

FIGURE 14-5
Cyclic AMP (adenosine 5′-mono-
phosphate) is derived from ATP in
a reaction catalyzed by the enzyme
adenylcyclase.

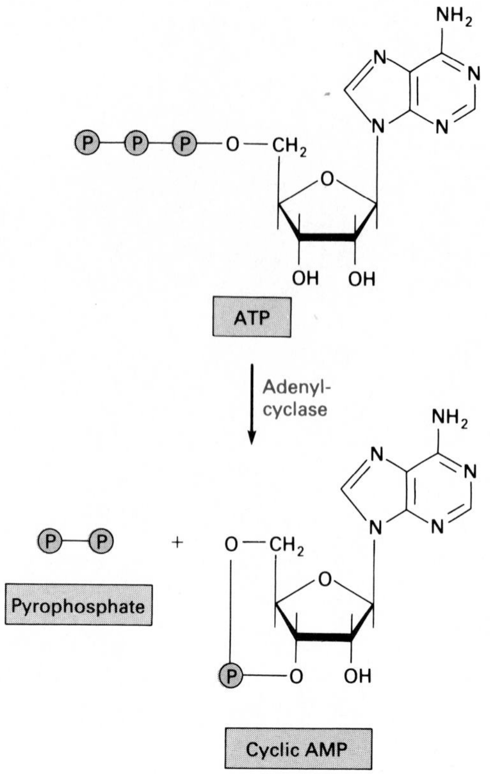

FIGURE 14-6
Base sequence of the regulatory region
of the *lac* operon in *E. coli*, from the
terminus of the repressor gene *lacI* to
the start of the structural gene *lacZ*.
The binding of RNA polymerase to
the promoter (*lacP*) is enhanced
when cAMP–CAP is also bound to the
promoter. Interaction between
cAMP–CAP and RNA polymerase
does not interfere with the interaction
between repressor protein and the
operator (*lacO*), because these regions
are spatially separated in the *lac*
region. (From Dickson, R. C., et al.,
1975, *Science* **187**:27.)

operon DNA, we know that RNA polymerase binds to the promoter
infrequently, even in the absence of repressor protein, but binding of the
polymerase is greatly enhanced when cAMP–CAP is also bound to the
promoter. Bound cAMP–CAP is believed to permit RNA polymerase
and promoter DNA to interact sterically in a more effective manner than
is otherwise possible. Bound cAMP–CAP does not interfere with
interactions between repressor protein and operator DNA, which are at
the other end of the regulatory region from the cAMP–CAP binding site
(Fig. 14.6).

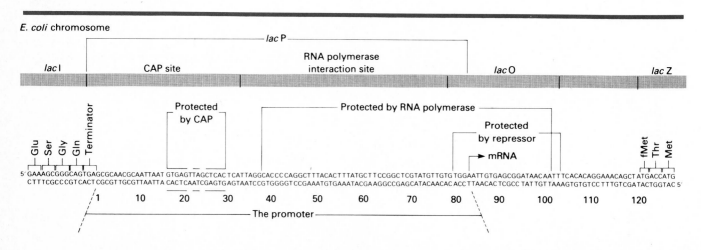

14.3
Attenuation Control of Transcription in Bacteria _____

A number of operons that are coded for enzymes that catalyze pathways for amino acid synthesis are regulated by a mechanism that is independent of repressor control. The control mechanism called **attenuation** regulates gene expression by *terminating transcription* after the process has been initiated but before RNA polymerase reaches the structural genes of the operon. Repressor control, on the other hand, regulates the *initiation* of transcription. Both of these control mechanisms may influence transcription of the same genes.

Although repressor control was believed to apply to all bacterial operons, repressors for the histidine (*his*) operon and certain other operons simply could not be found. Studies by Charles Yanofsky of deletion mutants provided important clues to the existence of the attenuation control mechanism. Some *E. coli* mutants with deletions near to, but distinct from, the promoter–operator region of the tryptophan operon (*trpP–trpO*) showed an *increase* in expression of the five structural genes (*trpE–trpD–trpC–trpB–trpA*) that specify the enzymes of the tryptophan biosynthetic pathway (Fig. 14.7). The deletions,

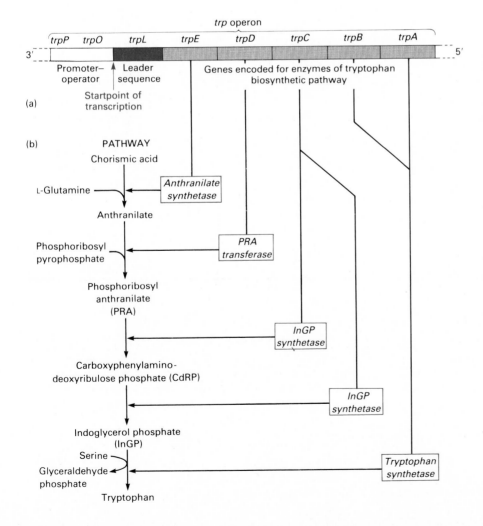

(a)

(b)

FIGURE 14-7
Organization and functions of the *trp* operon in *E. coli*. (a) The leader sequence (*trpL*) adjacent to the operator (*trpO*) is transcribed along with the five structural genes (*trpE* to *trpA*) of the operon. (b) Enzymes encoded in the *trp* structural genes catalyze reactions of the pathway that lead to synthesis of the amino acid tryptophan.

FIGURE 14-8
Nucleotide sequence of the 5' end of *trp* messenger RNA, including the 162 nucleotides of the regulatory leader sequence and a few of the codons specifying the *trpE* polypeptide. Part of the leader sequence encodes a leader peptide 14 amino acids long, from the AUG Start codon at nucleotides 27 to 29 through the UGA Stop codon at nucleotides 69 to 71. The non-terminated transcript is shown. If transcription had been terminated at the attenuator, a transcript sequence of only 140 nucleotides would have been made (its 3' terminus is marked by an arrow). (Reprinted by permission from C. Yanofsky. 1981. *Nature* **289**:751–758. Copyright © 1981 Macmillan Journals Limited.)

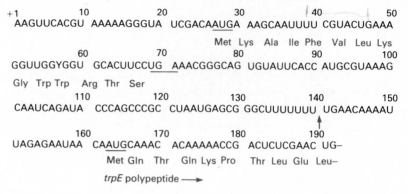

Leader peptide sequence

```
+1          10          20          30        | 40 ——— |    50
    AAGUUCACGU AAAAAGGGUA UCGACAAUGA AAGCAAUUUU CGUACUGAAA
                                     Met Lys Ala Ile Phe  Val Leu Lys
            60          70          80          90          100
    GGUUGGYGGU GCACUUCCUG AAACGGGCAG UGUAUUCACC AUGCGUAAAG
    Gly Trp Trp  Arg Thr Ser
            110         120         130         140         150
    CAAUCAGAUA CCCAGCCCGC CUAAUGAGCG GGCUUUUUUU UGAACAAAAU
                                                ↑
            160         170         180         190
    UAGAGAAUAA CAAUGCAAAC ACAAAAACCG ACUCUCGAAC UG–
              Met Gln Thr  Gln Lys Pro  Thr Leu Glu Leu–

    trpE polypeptide ——→
```

which lay between *trpO* and *trpE*, apparently removed a regulatory site involved in an independent system, because all the mutants were quite capable of normal repressor control over transcription. Further analysis, particularly base sequencing of mRNA transcripts, revealed the presence of a **leader sequence** comprised of about 160 nucleotides at the 5' end of the mRNA, immediately preceding *trpE*. The operon site encoding the leader sequence is *trpL*.

To determine the relationship of *trpL* to transcription, investigators compared the frequency of transcription of *trpL* and that of the *trpB–trpA* region at the opposite end of the transcription unit. These studies revealed that about 15% of the transcription events produce copies of the entire transcription unit, including *trpB–trpA*. But in about 85% of the cases, *trpL* was transcribed but *trpB–trpA* were not transcribed, nor were *trpE*, *trpD*, or *trpC*. Therefore, in the great majority of transcription events, transcription terminated before the structural genes were reached by RNA polymerase.

Sequence analysis of the leader region of the mRNA transcript provided important information about the structure and function of the site at which transcription is terminated, which is called the **attenuator**, and about the role of the attenuator in the regulation process. Two observations were particularly significant. First, the leader included a ribosome-binding site near its 5' end and enough codons to specify a polypeptide consisting of 14 amino acids. The encoded region included an AUG initiation codon and the Stop codon UGA, and two of the internal codons in tandem specified tryptophan (Trp) residues. The nucleotide sequence of the leader, including the **leader peptide** region, and part of the abutting *trpE* sequence are shown in Fig. 14.8.

The second observation was that the nucleotide sequence of the leader region immediately 3' to the leader peptide Stop codon allowed base-pairing to produce extensive *stem-and-loop secondary structures*. In fact there were two regions capable of such secondary structure. But, because they overlapped to some degree, it would be sterically impossible for both regions to form stem-and-loop structures at the same time; the two regions were mutually exclusive (Fig. 14.9). The more GC-rich secondary structure, nearest to *trpE*, is followed by eight uridine residues. Similar base sequences have been identified near transcription termination sites in other bacterial operons under attenuation control.

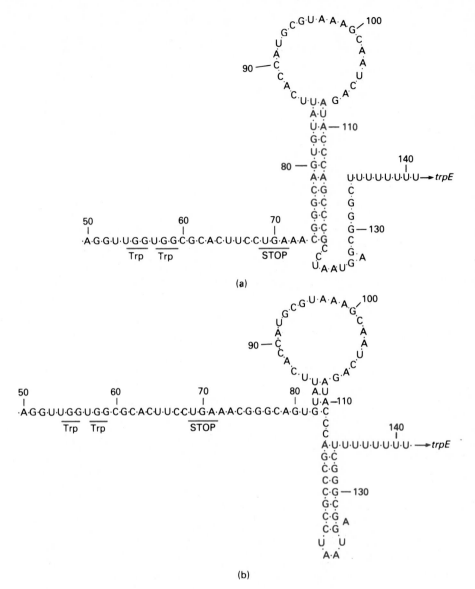

(a)

(b)

FIGURE 14-9
Secondary-structure alternatives in the *trp* leader section of the mRNA transcript. (a) Stem-and-loop structure is believed to permit continued transcription beyond nucleotide 140 into the structural gene region. Formation of a locally double-bonded stem (color) near the leader peptide sequence prevents attenuator stem-and-loop formation because the two secondary structures are mutually exclusive. (b) Formation of stem-and-loop secondary structure in the attenuator region (color) leads to termination of transcription in the poly(U) segment preceding *trpE*. (Reprinted by permission from C. Yanofsky. 1981. *Nature* **289**:751–758. Copyright © 1981 Macmillan Journals Limited.)

It is now clear that the attenuator is the GC-rich sequence followed by a segment of poly(U), all at the 3' end of the leader. If the attenuator can develop its stem-and-loop secondary structure, RNA polymerase dissociates from the template on reaching the poly(U) segment, and transcription stops. If the attenuator does not assume its secondary structure because the mutually exclusive secondary structure has already formed ahead of it, RNA polymerase remains bound to the template and continues to catalyze transcription of all the structural genes in the unit (Fig. 14.10).

The activation of attenuation control depends primarily on the utilization of tryptophan in protein synthesis. If Trp is present in low concentration, there is not enough Trp–tRNA^{Trp} to allow translation of the leader peptide. The ribosome stalls at the tandem Trp codons in leader mRNA, thereby allowing secondary-structure development of the upstream sequence, which prevents the mutually exclusive attenuator sequence from forming a stem and loop. Transcription readthrough

FIGURE 14-10

Simplified diagram of the *trp* leader sequence in the mRNA transcript. (a) If a stem-and-loop secondary structure develops in the segment early in the leader sequence, the mutually exclusive attenuator stem and loop car not develop in the same molecule. In the absence of an attenuator stem and loop, RNA polymerase can proceed along the template and catalyze transcription of the structural genes *trpE* to *trpA*. (b) Formation of the attenuator stem-and-loop secondary structure in the leader region of the mRNA transcript leads to dissociation of RNA polymerase just past the poly(U) portion of the transcript, and transcription is prematurely terminated at this point. Attenuation control thus leads to premature termination of transcription such that none of the structural genes is transcribed. In the absence of a complete transcript of the *trp* operon, the enzymes cannot be made and tryptophan synthesis stops.

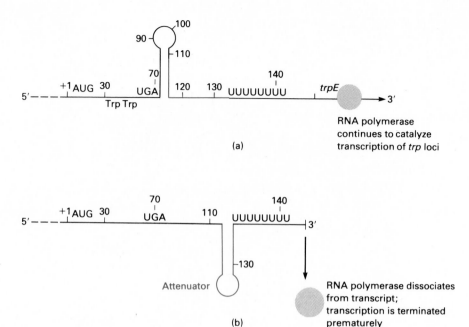

therefore takes place, the structural gene transcripts are translated, and Trp is synthesized in the cell. Synthesis of the repressible enzymes of Trp synthesis thus occurs in typical fashion: when the end product of the pathway is limiting.

When Trp is present in excess, enough Trp–tRNA^{Trp} is available for synthesis of the leader peptide. The ribosome moves along the mRNA transcript, right behind RNA polymerase, and the leader peptide is translated. The proximal stem-and-loop structure cannot develop because the bound ribosome blocks the site, and the attenuator is free to assume its stem-and-loop conformation. With the attenuator secondary structure present, the ribosome dissociates at the leader UGA Stop codon, and RNA polymerase dissociates from the transcript poly(U) segment. Trp biosynthesis stops because transcription is prematurely terminated, before the structural genes have been transcribed. The responsiveness of attenuation control in relation to the concentration of Trp in the cell is illustrated in Fig. 14.11.

Bacterial biosynthetic operons may have both repressor control and attenuation control mechanisms, such as the *trp* operon, or only attenuation control, such as the operons encoded for enzymes of the biosynthetic pathways leading to the amino acids histidine, leucine, and threonine. When both control mechanisms are available, repressor proteins can turn off transcription with the help of corepressors if the metabolite is in excess. Should the RNA polymerase escape repressor control, the enzyme will initiate transcription of the operon. Attenuation control may then be activated, depending on the availability of Trp–tRNA^{Trp} inside the cell. The repressor control is responsive to supplies of Trp (as corepressor), whereas attenuation control is responsive to supplies of Trp–tRNA^{Trp}, which fluctuate with the rate of protein synthesis. Viewed in this way, attenuation emerges as a mechanism that fine-tunes gene expression of bacterial biosynthetic operons.

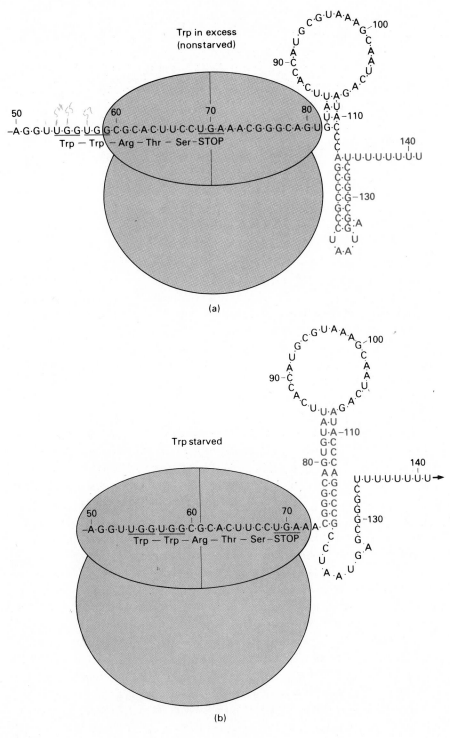

FIGURE 14-11

Responsiveness of the attenuation control is determined partly by the use of tryptophan (Trp) in protein synthesis. (a) When Trp is in excess, leader peptides are translated as the ribosome moves along the mRNA transcript right behind RNA polymerase. The ribosome blocks development of the first stem-and-loop alternative and thereby allows formation of the attenuator stem-and-loop secondary structure (color). Trp is not made in the cell because the ribosome and the RNA polymerase dissociate from the mRNA transcript before the structural genes are reached. (b) A deficiency of Trp in cells leads to formation of the first stem and loop (color) and prevents formation of the mutually exclusive attenuator stem and loop. Transcription continues into the structural gene region, and Trp is synthesized once the biosynthetic enzymes are translated from *trpE–trpA* encoded instructions. The outcome is typical of repressible enzyme synthesis, occurring when the end product of the pathway (Trp) is limiting but not when it is present in excess. (Reprinted by permission from C. Yanofsky. 1981. *Nature* **289**:751–758. Copyright © 1981 Macmillan Journals Limited.)

14.4

Transcriptional Control in Eukaryotes

Transcriptional controls are the predominant mechanisms by which gene expression is regulated in prokaryotes and many viruses, and they probably are the principal mechanisms in eukaryotes as well. The mechanisms differ in the two groups of organisms, however, because neither repressor control nor attenuation control has been demonstrated in eukaryotic species. By using cloned DNA as *probes* to identify specific mRNA transcripts in different kinds of cells, we can readily show that many kinds of transcripts are present in one or a few cell types and not in others, even though all these cells carry the genes in question.

In the specific case of chicken oviduct, some of the details of transcriptional control have been obtained by molecular analysis of organs cultured *in vitro*. The estrogenic steroid hormone *estradiol* turns on the transcription of previously inactive ovalbumin genes in immature chick oviduct or in uninduced hen oviduct. If ovalbumin DNA probes are used in DNA–RNA hybridization tests, virtually no molecular hybrids are formed with RNA from oviduct tissues that have not been provided with estradiol. When estradiol is provided, large quantities of pre-mRNA and mature mRNA can be recovered and identified in DNA–RNA hybrid duplexes. Furthermore, ovalbumin protein is synthesized only in hormonally induced oviduct, which indicates that the hormone stimulates transcription and that the transcripts are available for translation. In cultures to which the drug *actinomycin* has been added to hormonally induced oviducts, transcription stops even though estradiol was provided. Actinomycin specifically inhibits RNA polymerase II, the enzyme that catalyzes messenger RNA transcription, and thus provides independent confirmation that the hormone turns on ovalbumin gene transcription.

Ovalbumin synthesis is regulated by a positive transcriptional control mechanism; transcription is turned on when estradiol is added. We know relatively little about these hormone-mediated controls, but it appears that the hormone binds to specific protein receptors in the cytoplasm, and the estradiol–receptor complexes pass through the nuclear envelope and bind to chromatin. The nature of the specific binding reaction, the recognition of ovalbumin DNA sites, and other molecular features of these and similar transcriptional controls are largely unknown. The physical and chemical complexity of chromosomes and the large size of eukaryotic genomes have made the necessary molecular and biophysical analyses more difficult to perform than similar studies of the relatively small, naked DNA molecule in a prokaryote or a virus.

Among the most dramatic observations of positive transcriptional control stimulated by steroid hormones are those made on giant polytene chromosomes of *Drosophila*, *Chironomus*, and other dipteran insects. During larval development, the chromosomes become multi-stranded, or **polytene**, as the result of numerous, repeated DNA replications without subsequent mitotic separations. Each chromosome appears banded, even in unstained preparations, and many of the bands coincide with mapped genes. As the larva develops toward the pupal stage of the life cycle, specific chromosome bands expand by puffing and later regress. A **puff** is a chromosome region, usually associated with one chromosome band, at which the chromatin is unfolded and greatly extended (Fig. 14.12). RNA synthesis occurs at puffs; we know this from autoradiography, the binding of RNA polymerase II, and other molecular information.

The steroid hormone **ecdysone** plays a major role in turning on transcription, which can be monitored by puff development. Ecdysone is

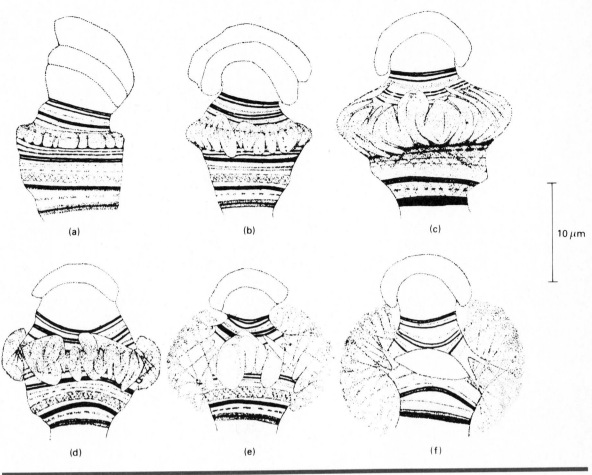

(a)   (b)   (c)

10 μm

(d)   (e)   (f)

FIGURE 14-12
Diagrams of puff development in a polytene chromosome. The puff first appears as a locally limited decondensation, probably of one specific band, and the chromatin undergoes greater and greater unfolding or decondensation (a through f). A very large and well developed puff is often called a Balbiani ring. (From Beermann, W., 1952, *Chromosoma* **5**: 139.)

a growth hormone produced in the prothoracic gland of young larvae, and the hormone is released into the bloodlike hemolymph in which it circulates throughout the organism. When young larvae are injected with ecdysone, existing puffs regress and new puffed sites appear within five minutes. Over a period of several days, about 125 different and specific chromosome bands undergo puffing, with each puff appearing and regressing at regular intervals during development (Fig. 14.13). The earlier puffs to appear in this developmental cascade probably form in direct response to the hormone; puffing is not abolished by prior treatment with cycloheximide or other drugs that inhibit protein synthesis. If protein synthesis is inhibited after ecdysone injection, however, late-developing puffs fail to appear.

Each *target cell* of hormonal induction contains thousands of protein receptor molecules in the cytoplasm before hormone exposure, as revealed by data from assays of binding between the hormone and cytoplasmic proteins extracted from uninduced cells. After hormonal induction, cytoplasmic protein extracts no longer bind to hormone molecules, whereas chromatin extracts do bind. These observations indicate that protein receptors are already present in the target cell cytoplasm before hormonal induction and that hormone–receptor complexes move into the nucleus afterward and there bind to chromatin.

RECTUM CELL

SALIVARY GLAND CELL

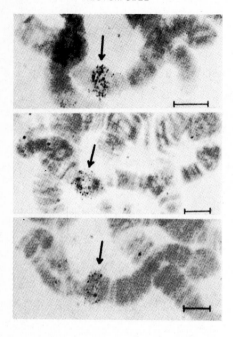

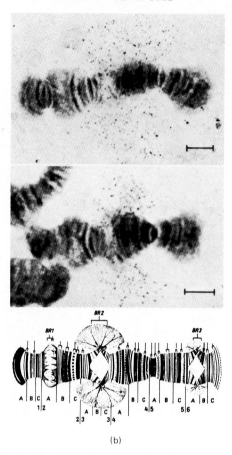

(a)

(b)

FIGURE 14-13

Differential gene action as seen in puffing of chromosome IV of the midge *Chironomus tentans*. (a) Polytene chromosome IV from rectum cell nuclei undergoes little puffing at the BR2 locus (at arrow), which is identified by hybridization with radioactively labeled BR2 mRNA. (b) In salivary gland nuclei from the same larvae, however, a large expanded Balbiani ring is evident at the BR2 locus on chromosome IV. The locus can be recognized by the Balbiani ring and by the presence of silver grains in autoradiographs of chromosomes hybridized with radioactively labeled BR2 mRNA. (From Lambert, B., 1975, *Chromosoma* **50**:193.)

Presumably the chromatin contains specific sites that accept specific hormone–receptor complexes, and the protein receptors are the actual positive-control elements that turn on transcription at the sites to which they bind.

The relationship of ecdysone to puffing and the relationship of puffing to tissue differentiation can be explored by applying a ligature to the insect larva in such a way that part of the salivary glands can be tied off from the remainder of these glands. Polytene chromosomes in salivary glands are particularly well developed and readily studied. In fact, polytene chromosomes are often referred to colloquially as "salivary gland chromosomes" because larval salivary glands have been studied far more often than other larval organs. In such ligatured larvae, the salivary gland cells that can continue to receive ecdysone from the neighboring prothoracic gland undergo normal puffing and tissue differentiation. Salivary gland cells on the other side of the ligature, however, receive no ecdysone, and these cells undergo very little puffing and no tissue differentiation. From these and other studies, it is clear that ecdysone turns on the transcription of specific genes that underlie the normal program of development leading from the larval to the pupal stage.

Investigators can conduct an independent assay for differential gene activation by using fluorescent-tagged antibodies prepared against a

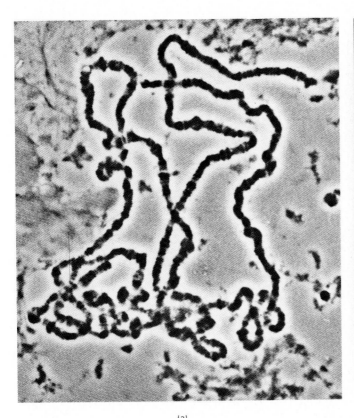

(a)

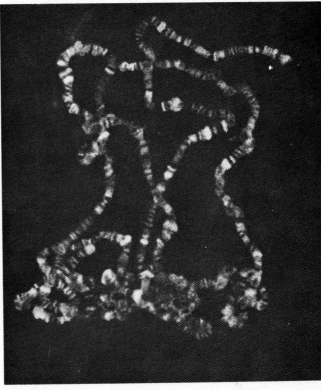

(b)

FIGURE 14-14
Differential gene action in polytene chromosomes of *Drosophila melanogaster* is evident from immunofluorescence after the application of fluorescent-labeled antiserum prepared against RNA polymerase.
(a) Bands of salivary gland chromosomes seen with phase-contrast optics can be related to the same chromosomes seen with (b) fluorescence optics in light microscopy. The bright fluorescent bands are the sites of bound antiserum, which indicates that RNA polymerase is present and presumably is engaged in catalyzing transcription only of these genes, not of others in the same cell. (Photographs courtesy of L. M. Silver.)

subunit of RNA polymerase II. The immunofluorescent preparation is allowed to bind to chromosomes or to chromosomal or cloned DNA. The tagged antibodies bind only to some of the chromosomal or DNA sites and not to others, thereby revealing the presence of the transcription enzyme wherever binding occurs. Presumably these sites are actively involved in transcribing pre-mRNA, whereas the remainder of the DNA is not being transcribed. When polytene chromosomes are treated in this way and examined by fluorescence microscopy, specific bands (genes) can be identified as being transcriptionally active at the same time that other bands (genes) are turned off (Fig. 14.14).

14.5
Posttranscriptional and Translational Controls in Eukaryotes

Gene expression may be regulated after transcription has been completed, by modifying the transcript molecule in various ways or, in some cases, by modifying the RNA degradation system that determines the relative stability (lifetime) of the mRNA that guides translation. These aspects of control are of greater importance in eukaryotes than in prokaryotes, perhaps in part because of the different logistics involved in transcription and translation in these two groups of organisms. In bacteria, ribosomes bind to mRNA and translation begins while transcription is still in progress (Fig. 14.15). There is little time available for any extensive modification or processing, and bacterial genes lack introns to be excised and exons to be spliced together. In eukaryotes, on

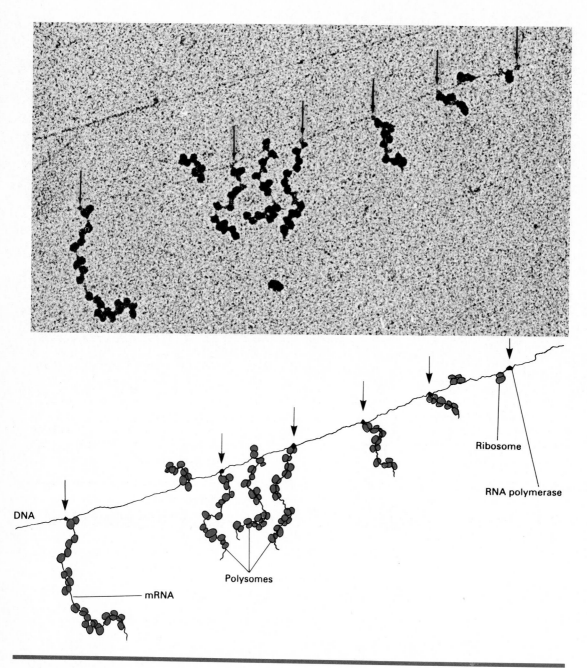

FIGURE 14-15

Electron micrograph of *E. coli* DNA with active transcription–translation complexes distributed along its length. Ribosomes bind to mRNA as the transcript "peels off" the template DNA during transcription, seen here by the increasing length of the polysome groups when viewed from right to left. Molecules of RNA polymerase (at arrows) catalyze transcription. An explanatory tracing of the photograph is shown below. (Photograph courtesy of O. L. Miller, Jr., from Miller, O. L., et al., 1970, *Science* **169**:392–395.)

the other hand, transcription takes place in the nucleus and translation takes place in the cytoplasm. Transcript processing is a more leisurely event in the nucleus, and various posttranscriptional changes occur to convert pre-mRNA to mature mRNA. Furthermore, mRNA must be transported from the nucleus to the cytoplasm. All in all, the greater variety and complexity of gene regulation in eukaryotes are the outcome of the more varied and complex processes involved in information flow from DNA to protein.

Gene expression may be modified by **posttranscriptional controls** exercised through any of the major steps in processing pre-mRNA: (1) capping the 5′ end with 7-methylguanosine, (2) excision of introns and splicing of exons, and (3) polyadenylation of the 3′ terminus. In addition, different conditions may determine the relative success and efficiency of transporting processed mRNA from the nucleus to the cytoplasm, the availability of ribosome subunits for translation, and the rate of turnover of transcript molecules (Fig. 14.16).

From studies of variant genes and transcripts we know that a complete pre-mRNA transcript usually must be synthesized and processed for translation. Pseudogene duplicates of functional genes are missing some or all of the normal introns, and these defective genes are not transcribed even though all the coding sequences are present. Modifications can be made in gene sequences of cloned DNA to determine the effects of various alterations on translation of the mRNA transcribed from such sequences. If intervening sequences are partially or totally deleted from the gene, pre-mRNA is not processed properly and fails to be translated. Pre-mRNA transcripts lacking a cap are generally nonfunctional, and transcripts without their usual poly(A) tail are often less stable than polyadenylated mRNAs.

Because an average pre-mRNA transcript is about 5 to 10 times longer than the processed mRNA, we might expect a fivefold to tenfold difference between total messenger RNA in the nucleus and in the cytoplasm. Instead, only about one-twentieth of this mass of RNA enters the cytoplasm from the nucleus. Whether these values reflect the results of processing and export controls or other factors has not yet been resolved by experimental analysis.

Stable mRNA underlies one of the important eukaryotic **translational controls**. Continued synthesis of particular proteins can occur

FIGURE 14-16
Gene expression in eukaryotes may be modified at any of various steps during information flow from gene to protein. Control may be exerted so that transcription may or may not occur or in the posttranscriptional processes of capping, polyadenylation, intron excision, and exon splicing of the pre-mRNA. In addition, gene expression is influenced by the relative efficiency of mRNA transport to the cytoplasm from the nucleus, the availability of ribosome subunits for translation, turnover of mRNA, and other cellular activities.

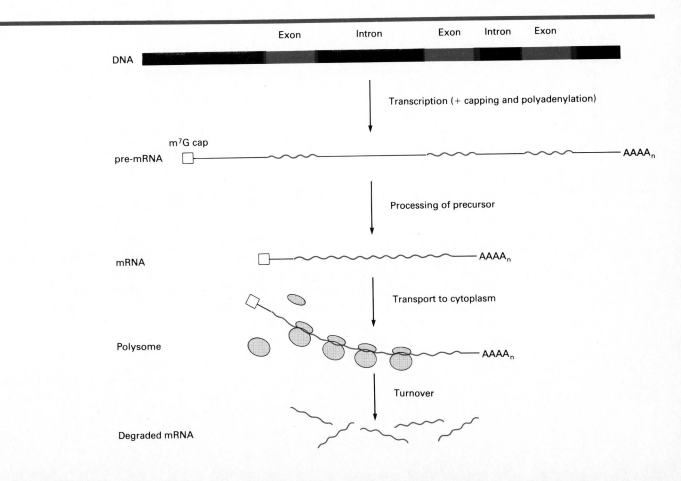

because the same mRNA molecules participate in numerous rounds of translation without being degraded so rapidly as the average mRNA. Because mammalian reticulocytes lose their nucleus, new transcripts cannot be synthesized. Hemoglobin continues to be synthesized in these cells for weeks, however, because globin mRNAs are very stable molecules with a relatively long lifetime. Control is exerted here at the level of translation.

Silk is fashioned from the protein *fibroin*, which is made in the silk gland of silkworm larvae (*Bombyx mori*). Owing to a high rate of transcription and the efficient utilization of stable mRNA molecules, a single fibroin gene can subsidize the synthesis of about 10 billion molecules of this protein in just a few days. About 100,000 mRNA molecules can be transcribed from the one fibroin gene, and each mRNA can guide the synthesis of 100,000 fibroin molecules in translation.

The relative stability of a particular mRNA may be under hormonal control in some cases. The milk protein *casein* is synthesized in mammary glands, and its rate of synthesis is decreased if the hormone *prolactin* is not provided. The mRNA transcripts made in mammary glands provided with prolactin were found to have a significantly longer half-life than casein transcripts made in hormonally deprived glands. In this example, a hormone appears to activate a translational control, whereas in oviduct tissue a hormone activates a transcriptional control.

The group of control mechanisms we have discussed in the chapter so far are examples of regulation by *modulation* of gene expression. In the next sections we will discuss the second major group of control mechanisms, which act by *alteration* of the genes themselves.

Genomic Alterations and Gene Expression

From the earliest days of cytogenetic studies, we knew that structural changes in chromosomes could influence phenotype expression and development. What we have learned only recently is that chromosomal and genic alterations are not necessarily rare events and that such changes provide the basis for at least some of the developmental patterns that characterize particular cells, tissues, organs, and organisms. In addition, we now have a concept of **genomic flux**—that is, of the genome existing in a dynamic and changing state rather than as a stable and passive set of genes occupying fixed locations and destined only to be translated into the single kind of polypeptide encoded in each base sequence. Our new awareness of the dynamic genome has come from the powerful new molecular methods developed barely ten years ago and from an extensive fund of information gathered over many decades of biological research.

14.6
Gene Amplification

Large amounts of a particular protein can be synthesized for days or weeks at a time in cells that have stable mRNAs, as we discussed above. Such cells are often devoted to one special function and to the synthesis

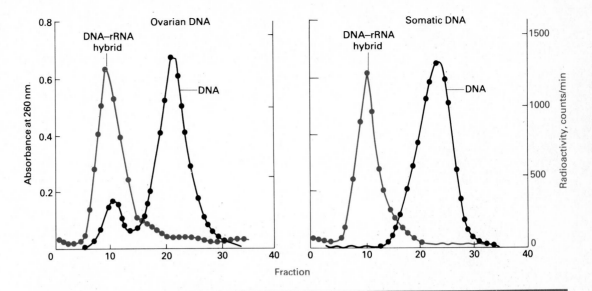

FIGURE 14-17
Identification of a satellite DNA as rDNA, and amplification of rDNA in oocyte nuclei. DNA–rRNA hybrids sediment in the same region of the gradient as a satellite DNA from oocytes in ovarian preparations, indicating that the satellite is rDNA. Although the satellite is not evident in the absorbance curve in somatic nuclear DNA preparations, rDNA is present; molecular hybrids between rRNA and DNA from this satellite region of the DNA do form and do sediment where expected in the gradient. The increased amount of rDNA in oocytes provides evidence for gene amplification—that is, replication of certain DNA while most of the nuclear DNA does not replicate.

of one or a few proteins, to the exclusion of many other proteins. Reticulocytes, silk glands, mammary tissue, and similar systems amplify the synthesis of their special proteins at the expense of other proteins, which are not needed to carry out this single, specialized function. Specialized cells devote most of their energies to the one service they perform.

In contrast to these systems, some generalized cell types gear up to serve a particular function for a finite period of time by the process of **gene amplification**, in which some genes are replicated while the remainder of the genome remains unreplicated. Gene amplification therefore involves *differential replication*. When the number of copies increases, large quantities of the gene product can be produced from the amplified sequence(s). One of the earliest and best known examples of gene amplification involves the repeated major ribosomal RNA gene (rDNA) in oocytes of insects and amphibians.

Amplification of rDNA in the toad *Xenopus laevis* takes place only in oocytes and only during an early stage of meiosis, as determined by microscopy and by molecular hybridization assays (Fig. 14.17). The original number of about 900 copies of the rRNA gene in the diploid oocyte is increased to 600 to 1600 *times* 900, and the newly replicated middle-repetitive rDNA sequences are separated from the chromosomal NOR and housed in new, individual nucleoli that fill the nuclear space. Amphibians are the only species known to produce extra nucleoli to sequester the extra rDNA. Other species keep all the rDNA in the usual number of nucleoli characteristic for the species (Fig. 14.18). Interestingly, the few plants that have been studied do not amplify the thousands of copies of the rRNA gene that are normally present at the NOR sites of the genome, whereas a wide range of protozoa and animals amplify their rDNA at specific times in development and in specific cells.

In the amphibian oocyte, the amplified rDNA is transcribed into rRNA that becomes incorporated into large numbers of new ribosomes for the egg cell. These extra rRNA genes become inactive after oogenesis, but the store of ribosomes created earlier subsidizes all the

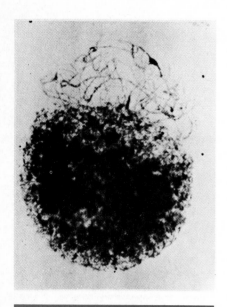

FIGURE 14-18
Light micrograph of an oocyte nucleus of a beetle (*Dytiscus marginalis*). A large cap of amplified rDNA is at the bottom, comprising about 90% of the nuclear DNA at this stage of early prophase in meiosis. In this system there is no increase in nucleoli to accommodate the large amount of extra DNA. ×1000. (Photograph courtesy of J. G. Gall, from Gall, J. G., and J.-D. Rochaix, 1974, *Proc. Nat. Acad. Sci. U.S.* **71**:1819, Fig. 1.)

protein synthesis that occurs in the egg and the embryo, up to the time of gastrulation. Even the anucleolate mutant that makes no ribosomes is able to proceed through embryogenesis by utilizing the ribosomes that are present in the fertilized egg and partitioned into embryonic cells during mitosis. The mutant dies at about the time of gastrulation, because it cannot continue to synthesize all the proteins it needs when the maternal supply of ribosomes is spread thin in all the embryonic cells produced from the fertilized egg.

In amphibians and other species whose rDNA is amplified, replication proceeds by the *rolling circle mechanism*. As we discussed earlier for φX174 replication (see Fig. 12.19), multiple lengths of DNA are synthesized and then are cut by nuclease action. The linear rDNA molecule is circularized when its "sticky" ends undergo base pairing and DNA ligase catalyzes phosphodiester bonding to seal the circle. Replication continues along the rolling circle all the time that rDNA sequences are released upon completion of their synthesis. The great advantage of this replication mechanism is its speed; huge numbers of ribosomes must be made during the brief time of oocyte development. We are not yet able to explain how the first rDNA circles are formed from regions that are part of a continuous chromatin fiber, nor do we know the signals that switch gene amplification on and off in those cells that are singled out for such a discriminating activity.

Until 1980 there was no evidence for amplification of genes other than rDNA during normal development. Allan Spradling and Anthony Mahowald first showed that *chorion* genes in *Drosophila* were amplified tenfold in egg chambers and not in other somatic cells. Chorion proteins form part of the egg shell and are made in larger quantities during the brief period of time when they are utilized in egg formation. In this situation, as with rDNA amplification in oocytes, large amounts of gene product are needed for limited and specified times during development, rather than being needed indefinitely for an ongoing function of a specialized cell. These finite needs are better met by a gene-amplification control than by stable mRNAs or some other control that modulates gene expression on a long-term basis.

14.7
The Generation of Antibody Diversity

One of the most remarkable systems for regulating gene expression through **gene rearrangements** has been described for genes that specify **antibodies**, or **immunoglobulins**, which are synthesized in B lymphocytes (plasma cells). Immunoglobulins (Ig) bind to foreign substances, called **antigens**, in immune responses that constitute a major body defense against infection and disease. An animal can generate over a million different immunoglobulins to confront more than a million different antigens it may encounter in its lifetime, but fewer than a thousand Ig genes are encoded in the genome. How can so few genes be responsible for generating such a diversity of specific antibodies? New molecular methods have made possible astonishing progress in efforts to provide answers to this question and others related to immunoglobulin synthesis and variety.

Each Ig molecule consists of four polypeptide chains—two designated as **heavy** (H) and two **light** (L)—that are held together by disulfide bonds. The H chains are identical and the L chains are identical in any single Ig molecule. Each H chain and each L chain are made up of functionally different regions: Both contain a **constant** (C) **segment** and a **variable** (V) **segment** linked by a **joining** (J) **segment**, but each H chain also has a fourth segment of considerable **diversity** (D) between the V and J regions (Fig. 14.19). Five different classes of Ig molecules can be defined according to their different H chains (Table 14.2). All these classes of Ig interact with antigens through binding at their two identical *antigen combining sites*, situated at the variable N-termini of the four polypeptide chains.

The organization of Ig molecules is reflected in the organization of Ig genes. In mammalian germ-line DNA from sperm or other sources, each of the three **multigene families** is situated in a different chromosome of the genome. Two of these families of multiple genes code for the two kinds of L chains, kappa (κ) and lambda (λ), and the third set of genes encodes all the kinds of H chains (γ, μ, α, δ, and ε). Each family of genes consists of *C*, *J*, and *V* gene clusters, plus a cluster of *D* genes in the H-chain family on the chromosome (Fig. 14.20). To distinguish the different gene clusters and their corresponding polypeptide segments in the Ig molecule, subscripts are used. Light-chain components bear the subscript L (V_L, J_L, and C_L), or kappa and lambda subscripts to designate the two kinds of L chains (V_κ, J_κ, and C_κ or V_λ, J_λ, and C_λ). Heavy-chain components have the subscript H (V_H, D_H, J_H, and C_H).

Two functionally and mechanistically different Ig-gene rearrangements occur during the differentiation of B lymphocytes from germ-line precursor cells:

1. In *V-gene translocation*, a particular *V* gene becomes associated with a *C* gene to produce a functional Ig gene that determines the antigenic specificity of that B lymphocyte cell and all its mitotic descendants. The rearrangement takes place independently of any contact with the specific antigen involved.

2. In **heavy-chain class switching**, the expressed V_H gene is linked to a different C_H from the one originally joined to it, without a change in antigenic specificity of the Ig produced. The Ig retains its original

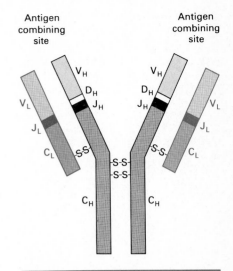

FIGURE 14-19

The immunoglobulin molecule is made up of one pair of identical heavy chains and one pair of identical light chains, all held together by disulfide bonds. Each heavy chain has a variable (V_H), diversity (D_H), joining (J_H), and constant (C_H) segment, and each light chain has three such segments (V_L, J_L, and C_L) but lacks a diversity region. The two identical antigen combining sites are located in the variable regions, at the N-termini of the four chains. The greater molecular weight of the heavy chain is due to the fact that the constant segment in the heavy chain is longer than its equivalent in the light chain.

TABLE 14-2
Types of Human Immunoglobulins

Immunoglobulin Class	Light Chain Present	Heavy Chain Present	Molecular Weight	Functions
IgA	κ or λ	α (alpha)	144,000	main antibody in saliva and intestinal fluids
IgD	κ or λ	δ (delta)	156,000	cell-surface receptor on immature B lymphocytes
IgE	κ or λ	ε (epsilon)	166,000	antiparasitic immune response, releases histamine from mast cells
IgG	κ or λ	γ (gamma)	144,000	main serum antibody, activates complement
IgM	κ or λ	μ (mu)	160,000	cell-surface receptor, serum antibody (early), activates complement

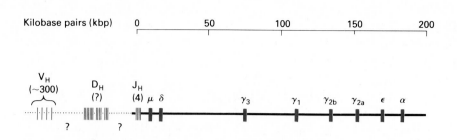

FIGURE 14-20

Organization of mouse immunoglobulin heavy-chain genes in germ-line DNA. The multigene family encodes all the components of all the H-chain classes (IgM, IgD, IgG, IgE, and IgA) and includes about 300 V_H genes, about 12 D_H genes, 4 J_H genes, and 8 C_H genes (one μ, one δ, four γ, one ε, and one α). The region encompassing J_H and C_H genes and spacer DNA is about 200 kbp long, but we are uncertain about the lengths of regions that include V_H and D_H genes.

antigenic specificity because its V region is unaltered, but the Ig class may change because of the switch in the C_H component of the antibody molecule. The switch in the C_H component may lead to a different biological activity for the Ig molecule (see Table 14.2).

The events leading to these gene rearrangements have been analyzed by molecular studies of DNA and RNA sequences and of amino acid sequences of Ig molecules during development in different B lymphocyte populations. In each of these phenomena, alterations in the DNA sequences are followed by processing of the RNA transcripts copied from the rearranged Ig genes. We will first consider the events of V gene translocation leading to L-chain gene assembly and to H-chain gene assembly, and then discuss heavy-chain class switching.

During **light-chain gene assembly**, a V gene joins with a J gene in the differentiating B lymphocyte. V/J joining is achieved by deletion of germ-line DNA sequences between any one of the V genes and any one of the J genes in either the kappa or the lambda multigene family. The DNA spacer sequence between VJ and the C gene region is transcribed along with the VJ and C segments of the chromosome. This spacer is

FIGURE 14-21

Light-chain gene assembly. In the differentiating B lymphocyte, original germ-line DNA is rearranged by deletions between any of the V genes and any of the J genes and by V-J joining afterward in either the κ (shown here) or λ multigene family. After transcription into pre-mRNA of the C gene and the retained V and J genes, transcribed spacer regions are excised and the three encoded segments are spliced together to produce an uninterrupted sequence in mature mRNA.

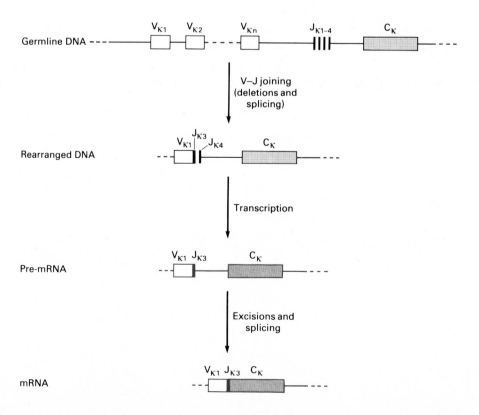

later excised from the pre-mRNA transcript, and the VJ and C regions are spliced together. Expression of the L-chain component of an Ig molecule thus depends on two key processes: *V/J* joining in DNA and VJ–C splicing in pre-mRNA to produce mRNA for translation (Fig. 14.21).

During **heavy-chain gene assembly** in a differentiating B lymphocyte, one *V*, one *D*, and one *J* gene from their respective clusters join to the whole set of C_H genes in the same chromosome. The *VDJ* joining requires deletion of all the other alternatives in the three clusters and of any spacer DNA between the retained three genes. This rearranged DNA is transcribed into pre-mRNA, which is then processed to excise the spacer between VDJ and C segments. In some differentiating B lymphocytes, C_μ is also excised from pre-mRNA, leaving the C_δ sequence adjacent to VDJ in the processed mRNA. In other B lymphocytes, C_μ is not excised. Any one immature lymphocyte synthesizes either IgM (C_μ retained) or IgD (C_μ removed), just as any one lymphocyte makes Ig carrying either the κ or the λ light chain (Fig. 14.22).

Heavy-chain class switching involves deletions and rearrangements of DNA in activated **B lymphocytes**, or **plasma cells**, after antigenic stimulation has taken place. Through these rearrangements, plasma cells that initially produced IgM or IgD may switch to produce IgG, IgE, or IgA, which fulfill different functions in the immune system. If most of the C_H cluster is deleted, leaving C_ϵ' and C_α, the plasma cell secretes IgE from the RNA transcribed along the rearranged DNA sequence (Fig. 14.23). No change occurs in the *VDJ* sequence that was established earlier in the immature stage of the lymphocyte, so no change occurs in the antigenic specificity of the cell; the variable sequence is retained in its original state. The only change is in the constant region of the H chain.

Heavy-chain class switching depends on the presence of **multiple switch sites**, which base sequencing has shown to be tandemly repeated homologous regions immediately preceding almost every C_H gene in the cluster (Fig. 14.24). Conventional recombination may lead in some cases to the rearrangement of C genes, but in other cases some different

FIGURE 14-22
Heavy-chain gene assembly. In the differentiating B lymphocyte, germ-line heavy-chain genes are rearranged by deletions and subsequent joining of one each of the *V*, *D*, and *J* genes to the set of *C* genes in the multigene family. Transcription of rearranged DNA into pre-mRNA is followed by differential excision and splicing reactions to produce two classes of heavy-chain mRNA. These messengers guide the synthesis of either IgM or IgD heavy chains, but any one lymphocyte makes only one of these types of heavy chains.

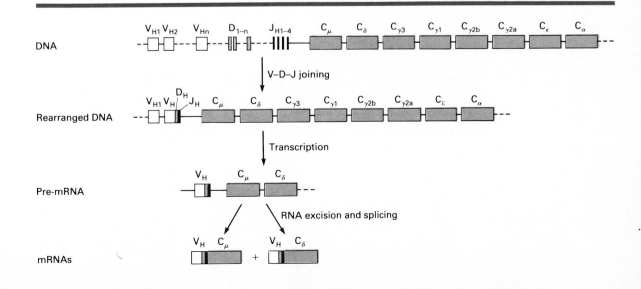

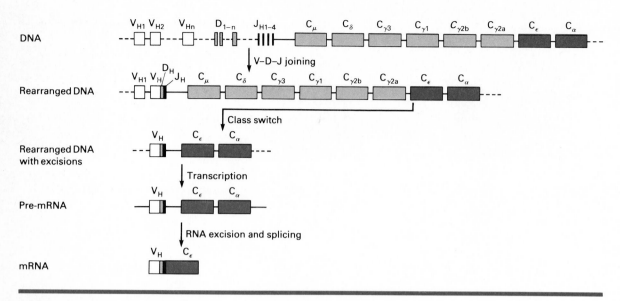

FIGURE 14-23

Heavy-chain class switching. Antigenic stimulation in developing B lymphocytes leads to secretion of IgG, IgE, or IgA in cells previously active in making IgM. To switch expression from IgM to another class, deletions of *C* genes and splicing of remaining *C* segments to *VDJ* genes must take place. In the

example shown, six *C* genes are excised and the two remaining *C* genes are spliced to *VDJ* in a rearranged DNA sequence. After transcription of pre-mRNA, the transcript is processed further to produce a functional mRNA that will guide translation of IgE heavy-chain polypeptide.

FIGURE 14-24

In heavy-chain class switching, the switch sites (color) that precede C_H genes (except for δ) are responsible for rearrangements in the active gene cluster, so that new classes of heavy chains may be produced in activated B lymphocytes (plasma cells) after antigenic stimulation. Antigenic specificity remains unchanged because the VDJ segments are unchanged, but functionally different Ig will be made depending on the C_H genes retained and spliced to *VDJ* after the intervening C_H genes have been deleted.

mechanism appears to be involved. The nature of these mechanisms is not yet clear. We know that the switch sites are necessary from studies of B lymphocyte populations that undergo no class switching and continue to secrete IgM exclusively. In these cells a large segment 5′ to the C_μ locus, which includes the C_μ switch sites, has been deleted.

Through gene rearrangements and RNA processing, over a million different and specific kinds of B lymphocytes can be generated from combinations of *V*, *J*, and *C* genes for κ and λ L chains and of *V*, *D*, *J*, and *C* genes for H chains of individual Ig molecules. Each B lymphocyte produces a single, specific antibody type that permits interaction through its antigen combining site with a single kind of invading

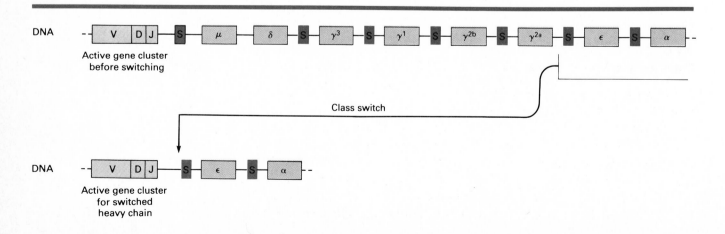

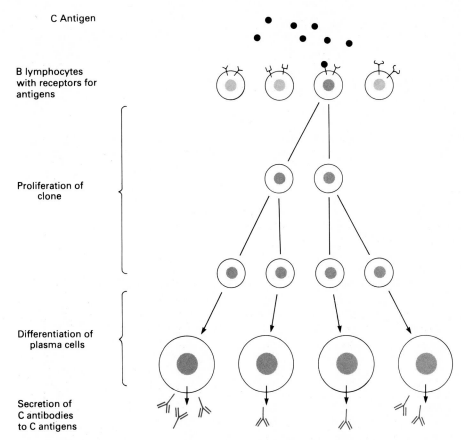

C Antigen

B lymphocytes
with receptors for
antigens

Proliferation of
clone

Differentiation of
plasma cells

Secretion of
C antibodies
to C antigens

FIGURE 14-25
Clonal selection. Various sensitized B lymphocytes arise in the body before exposures to particular antigens. When such an antigen, perhaps C antigen, invades the body, sensitized B lymphocytes of the anti-C variety are stimulated to develop into activated plasma cells. These plasma cells proliferate into clones of identical cells that secrete C antibodies that act specifically against the invading C antigens.

antigen. Antigenic specificity is determined by V gene translocation events in the immature B lymphocyte before confrontation with that antigen has occurred. Once stimulated by its antigen, a particular and specific B lymphocyte proliferates and synthesizes quantities of the pertinent Ig molecule that engages the antigen to produce an immune response in the organism (Fig. 14.25). In this way the animal can generate an enormous and diverse repertory of antibodies from fewer than a thousand gene sequences. Hence it is genetically prepared to handle virtually any antigen it may encounter in a lifetime, long before the encounter even takes place. In addition, heavy-chain class switching provides a mechanism for altering the biological function of the Ig molecule without altering its antigenic specificity. The same antigenically specific Ig may thus act in different parts of the body and engineer more than one kind of response to a particular antigen.

14.8
Transposable Genetic Elements

Transposable genetic elements are unique DNA segments that can move from place to place in the genome through insertion and excision events governed by unusual features of sequence organization. Transposable elements occur in viral, prokaryotic, and eukaryotic genomes, and they may influence gene expression, lead to rearrangements in genomic sequences, and sometimes induce mutations near the site of transposition. Studies of these movable genetic elements in recent years have contributed to our current view of the dynamic state of the genome (in contrast to the view derived from classical genetics of a relatively stable genome). Only some examples of these interesting systems will be discussed here, but the literature is quite large and is increasing at a rapid rate.

Simpler **insertion sequences (IS)** and more complex **transposons (Tn)** are movable genetic elements that can be distinguished by their size and their gene functions. IS elements are less than 2000 base-pairs long and contain genes that are involved only in the function of insertion into DNA, whereas Tn elements are much longer and contain genes that are unrelated to insertion as well as insertion genes. IS elements may be part of transposon DNA, but, whether singly or in combination, both IS and Tn elements can move onto and off the chromosome and from one place in the genome to another with considerable frequency. They have sometimes been called "jumping genes."

Heteroduplex analysis of DNAs from genetically or phenotypically different strains provides a general means of tracing the movement, insertion, and removal of transposable elements. If one strand has an IS or Tn element and the other strand of the heteroduplex does not, the unpaired element will be evident as a single-stranded loop in a particular location of the otherwise paired duplex (Fig. 14.26). The length of the unpaired region can be measured directly in micrometers, which can then be converted to terms of molecular weight ($1\mu m = 2 \times 10^6$ daltons) or base-sequence length (1 μm = about 3000 bases, or 3 kilobases). Genetic analysis, of course, is an essential component of any of these studies.

Transposons have at least two genes of their own, in addition to any genes they may capture from the genome of a cell in which they resided. One transposon gene encodes a *transposase* enzyme that initiates the insertion or excision of the element, and a second gene encodes a *resolvase* enzyme that helps complete the insertion or excision. The resolvase also functions as a repressor of transcription of both genes

FIGURE 14-26
Heteroduplex analysis of cloned maize DNA reveals an unpaired loop in the strand from a waxy mutant hybridized with homologous DNA from a strain carrying the normal waxy gene. The single-stranded loop consists of the transposable element called *Activator* (*Ac*), which upon insertion into the chromosome near the *waxy* locus causes an altered phenotype to develop. *Ac* is a transposon that enters and leaves various sites on the chromosome, and is responsible for mutation or instability of nearby genes. As shown in the interpretive drawing of the electron micrograph, the paired homologous DNAs produce a thicker region than is evident for the unpaired *Ac* insertion or the unpaired strands of the vector DNA to which the maize fragments were spliced to produce recombinant DNA for cloning. (Photograph courtesy of N. Federoff, from Federoff, N., S. Wessler, and M. Shure, 1983, *Cell* **35**:235, Fig. 1. Copyright by M. I. T. Press.)

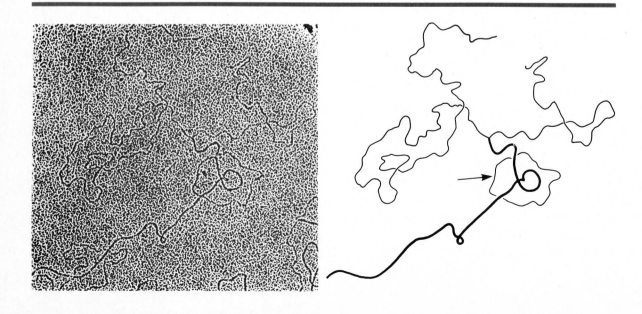

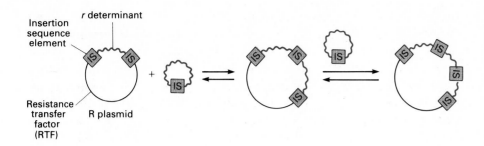

Insertion sequence element

r determinant

Resistance transfer factor (RTF)

R plasmid

FIGURE 14-27
R plasmids are composed of one or more *r* determinants carrying antibiotic-resistance genes and a resistance transfer factor (RTF) that mediates plasmid transfer between cells. The *r* determinants are transposons with insertion sequence (IS) elements at their termini. Insertion or removal of *r* determinants may lead to R plasmids carrying different numbers of drug-resistance genes.

when it binds between them on the DNA strand. The discovery of transposable genetic elements in bacteria, in the 1970s, provided an explanation for the puzzling phenomenon of the rapid spread of multiple antibiotic resistances in pathogenic bacteria. Because antibiotic therapy is a major component of modern health care, the sudden ineffectiveness of this therapy presented serious problems in the treatment of infections.

The genes governing antibiotic resistance in pathogenic enteric bacteria, such as *Salmonella* and *Shigella*, are carried in **R plasmids** that, like other plasmids, exist as DNA circles in the cytoplasm or as part of the bacterial chromosome. R plasmids consist of two kinds of DNA sequences: **r determinants**, which carry antibiotic-resistance genes and others, and **resistance transfer factors** (RTF), which mediate intercellular transfer. The *r* determinants are transposons with IS elements at their termini (Fig. 14.27). By the insertion of transposons in which each element may carry one or more genes, a single R plasmid may carry one or more antibiotic-resistance genes during its travels between cells. Because transpositions can expand the number of drug-resistance genes carried by R plasmids in bacterial cells, and because any or all of these genes can be picked up from a bacterial chromosome or be inserted into the chromosome, strains with multiple drug resistances can arise and spread rapidly to render drug therapy ineffective in patients.

The *r* determinants of R plasmids apparently have evolved as a collection of transposons. Transposons of different types have no base-sequence homologies, nor is there any homology between R plasmid transposons and the bacterial chromosome or other genetic molecules. The lack of sequence homology means that conventional recombination events are unlikely to underlie the integration and removal of transposons that lack IS elements. Molecular models for these processes have been proposed, but many details remain to be elucidated.

Transposable genetic elements were first described as "controlling elements" in maize by Barbara McClintock, who has studied these materials by genetic methods since the 1940s. From her study of pigment patterns on kernels of the maize cob, McClintock inferred the existence of movable elements and their roles in causing unstable mutations and chromosomal rearrangements that influenced gene expression. Similar mobile elements were presumed to influence gene expression and to cause genomic rearrangements in *Drosophila*, but few molecular methods were available in the 1960s and the genetic data could not be complemented by molecular information on the nature and abundance of these elements. With the introduction of recombinant DNA methods and of rapid base sequencing in the 1970s, and with the emergence of data showing that mobile genetic elements were also present in bacteria and viruses, transposable genetic elements assumed their rightful place as ubiquitous agents of genomic flux and of influence over gene expression.

Mobile genetic elements exist in the genome in *families of dispersed sequences* that are *repeats* of at least part of a basic sequence common to all the members of the same family. In *Drosophila*, about 20 to 30 such families are believed to be present, accounting for 1% to 5% of the nuclear DNA in different strains. One of the best characterized of these families in *Drosophila* is *copia*, whose repeat members are found at 20 to 60 different sites in a genome, depending on the strain studied. The variability in numbers of repeats and in their locations in any strain or individual fly can be determined by hybridizations between a genomic library of cloned DNA and *copia* mRNA or cDNA probes, restriction fragment analysis, heteroduplex analysis, and other means. Sequence variations in these repeats are revealed by base sequencing, the size of unpaired loops in heteroduplexes, and other data.

Transposable elements range in size from about 4500 to 7000 base pairs, and all the ones that have been studied share a common plan of organization. The resolvase and transposase genes, plus one or more genes carried as passengers, are flanked by repeat sequences at each end of the element. A *long direct repeat* of about 300 to 500 base pairs, bordered by a *short inverted repeat* on each side, is present at each end of the element, and a *short direct* (noninverted) *repeat* is present next to each of these at the termini (Fig. 14.28). An intriguing observation is that the chromosomally integrated form of vertebrate retroviruses is organized in the same manner as a transposable genetic element. Whether or not these similarities reflect the evolutionary origin of proviruses from transposable elements remains to be seen, but the suggestion can be tested experimentally and is now under investigation.

Bacterial transposons are predominantly site-specific and therefore influence particular genes. Eukaryotic transposable elements, however, seem to wander from place to place in the genome and influence genetic events on a random basis. These elements influence genomic organization and the expression of established genes in the organism through their abilities to integrate and to leave DNA rather than because of any protein that may be encoded by a native transposon gene. In fact, in *copia* and other elements that do produce some polypeptides, we know of no function for the gene products. In the case of *copia*, copious quantities of RNA (hence the name *copia*) are transcribed nevertheless.

At the present time we are uncertain about the functional and evolutionary significance of transposable genetic elements. We are certain, however, that these elements contribute to genomic flux and that the dynamic state of the genome may very well be important in the changes that characterize differentiation of multicellular organisms— and evolution itself. In other words, transposable genetic elements may play a role in the regulation of complex events rather than merely specifying a few polypeptides of short-term significance to the organism or the species.

Despite the fact that the genome is somewhat labile, wholesale genomic rearrangements rarely take place. The vast majority of cells continue to harbor a set of genes that occupy mappable locations in a

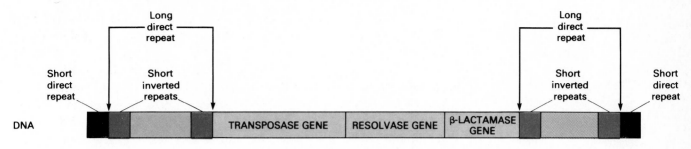

Bacterial transposon 3 (Tn3)

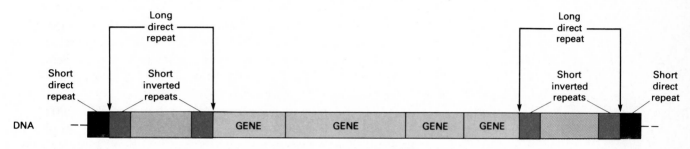

Integrated retroviral DNA

FIGURE 14-28
Transposable genetic elements and integrated retroviral DNA are organized in very similar fashion. Three kinds of repeat sequences border the gene region at each terminus in both kinds of DNA. Transposons carry a transposase gene and a resolvase gene, which encode enzymes that aid in transposition, plus one or more additional genes that are not related to transposability. In bacterial transposon 3, the β-lactamase gene encodes the enzyme that inactivates the β-lactam antibiotic ampicillin.

fixed number of linkage groups that exist in both germ-line and somatic cells throughout development. The primary controls over gene expression are those that modulate transcription and translation of genes in these linkage groups. Only a small percentage of differential gene expression events can be traced to alterations in the genome, but such alterations may certainly lead to profound changes in development and, perhaps, in evolution.

Summary

Not all the genes in any genome are equally active, nor do they maintain the same level of activity throughout the existence of the virus or of the cell and its descendants. In multicellular organisms, the totipotency of cells at early embryonic stages usually becomes restricted at some point in development, after which it is difficult if not impossible to restore, despite the retention in most organisms of a complete genome. The phenotypic differences that arise primarily reflect changes in the transcription of mRNA, through either modulation of gene expression or changes in the genes themselves.

Regulation of gene expression is better understood in prokaryotic systems. The classic example of regulation by negative control concerns the operon, a coordinated unit consisting of a set of regulatory genes adjacent to a set of structural genes encoded for cellular or viral proteins. The promoter is the site of binding of RNA polymerase, which catalyzes transcription of the structural genes. The operator, between the promoter and structural genes, is the site of binding of a repressor protein that can block transcription by blocking movement of the RNA polymerase from promoter to structural genes. The gene for the repressor is located outside the operon region. Each operon has its own repressor gene and protein. Certain metabolites prevent repressor binding and thereby promote synthesis of the corresponding mRNA; in other cases a metabolite facilitates repressor binding and stops operon mRNA synthesis. Examples of positive control are also known, in which RNA polymerase binds more efficiently to promoters in the presence of controlling substances, such as cyclic AMP and its receptor protein. Bacteria can exhibit attenuation control, a fine-tuning mechanism in which the rate of structural-gene mRNA synthesis is regulated by the rate of translation of a leader peptide-coding sequence. If translation of the leader peptide is slow or absent, the mRNA forms a secondary structure called the attenuator, which blocks further progress of the RNA polymerase and causes the premature termination of transcription before the structural genes have been reached.

In eukaryotes, neither attenuation nor an operator–repressor control has been demonstrated, but gene expression is still regulated primarily by transcriptional control mechanisms. In many cases steroid hormones induce the synthesis of specific mRNAs by binding to cytoplasmic receptors, migrating into the nucleus, and binding to chromatin to activate the transcription of selected genes. (This mechanism has been studied in chick oviduct stimulated by estradiol and in dipteran larvae stimulated by ecdysone.) In the latter case, the characteristic puffing of specific sites on the polytene chromosomes of the larvae indicates increased transcription of the genes in those regions. Other regulatory mechanisms for eukaryotes that are unavailable to prokaryotes involve posttranscriptional control over maturation of pre-mRNA to mRNA, conditions for transport of mature mRNA to the cytoplasm, the stability of the mRNA itself (its functional lifetime), the availability of ribosome subunits for translation, and other features.

In some cases the genome is physically altered to produce changes in gene expression without compromising the overall constancy of the organism's phenotype. For example, in amphibian oocytes there is a selective and dramatic 900-to-1600-fold increase in rRNA genes (rDNA) when other genes are not replicating (gene amplification). These extra rRNA genes prepare ribosomes to support the intense protein synthesis of the early embryo, and they disappear later in embryogenesis.

A different sort of programmed alteration occurs during differentiation of B lymphocytes and during their subsequent maturation into antibody-producing plasma cells of the immune system. Multiple-gene families in the germ-line genome encode variable (V), joining (J), and constant (C) segments of the pair of heavy (H) and the pair of light (L) polypeptide chains of all antibodies [a diversity (D) segment is also present in H chains but not in L chains]. During the differentiation of B lymphocytes, V and J (and D) genes are rearranged and translocated next to the set of C genes, and DNA between selected V and J (and D) genes is deleted so that each H or L chain consists of one V, one J, (one D), and all the C genes. The N-terminal V regions of the H and L chains form a pair of unique and specific antigen-binding sites on the Y-shaped antibody molecule. Because of the variety of possible choices for each segment of the H and L polypeptide chains, fewer than 1000 genes can generate over a million different, specific antibody molecules. The unstimulated B lymphocyte synthesizes a particular receptor protein, which projects from the plasma membrane. Upon encountering an antigen that binds to its receptor, the lymphocyte proliferates and its clonal descendants mature to plasma cells. Each lymphocyte clone synthesizes only one specific antibody type. During maturation, heavy-chain class switching occurs as one or more C genes are deleted and new C-gene regions are spliced to VDJ sequences. It is the C-gene region that determines the class of antibody being produced—IgM, IgD, IgG, IgE, or IgA.

Transposable genetic elements moving in the genome influence gene expression in both prokaryotes and eukaryotes. Insertion sequences (IS) are mobile elements that contain only genes necessary for their insertion into and removal from the genome. Transposons (Tn) are larger mobile elements than IS, and they may capture adjacent genes of the host. By returning these genes to unfamiliar locations or even carrying them into different cells, these transposons may change the phenotypic properties of the cell.

Readings and References

Adhya, S., and S. Garges. 1982. How cyclic AMP and its receptor protein act in *Escherichia coli*. *Cell* **29**:287.

Alt, F. W., *et al.* 1982. Immunoglobulin heavy-chain expression and class switching in a murine leukaemia line. *Nature* **296**:325.

Beermann, W., and U. Clever. April 1964. Chromosome puffs. *Sci. Amer.* **210**:50.

Bernards, A. 1982. Transposable genes for surface glycoproteins in trypanosomes. *Trends Biochem. Sci.* **7**:253.

Briggs, R., and T. J. King. 1952. Transplantation of living nuclei from blastula cells into enucleated frogs' eggs. *Proc. Natl. Acad. Sci. U. S.* **38**:455.

Brown, D. D. 1981. Gene expression in eukaryotes. *Science* **211**:667.

Brown, D. D. 1984. The role of stable complexes that repress and activate eucaryotic genes. *Cell* **37**:359.

Brown, D. D., and I. B. Dawid. 1968. Specific gene amplification in oocytes. *Science* **160**:272.

Bukhari, A. I., J. A. Shapiro, and S. L. Adhya, eds. 1977. *DNA: Insertion Elements, Plasmids, and Episomes*. Cold Spring Harbor, N.Y.: Cold Spring Harbor Laboratory.

Calabretta, B., *et al.* 1982. Genome instability in a region of human DNA enriched in *Alu* repeat sequences. *Nature* **196**:219.

Clowes, R. C. April 1973. The molecule of infectious drug resistance. *Sci. Amer.* **229**:18.

Cohen, S. N., and J. A. Shapiro. February 1980. Transposable elements. *Sci. Amer.* **242**:40.

Cold Spring Harbor Symposia on Quantitative Biology. 1981. *Movable Genetic Elements*, vol. 45.

Coleclough, C. 1983. Chance, necessity, and antibody gene dynamics. *Nature* **303**:23.

Darnell, J. E., Jr. 1982. Variety in the level of gene control in eukaryotic cells. *Nature* **297**:365.

DeRobertis, E. M., and J. B. Gurdon. December 1979. Gene transplantation and the analysis of development. *Sci. Amer.* **241**:74.

DiBerardino, M. A., N. J. Hoffner, and L. D. Etkin. 1984. Activation of dormant genes in specialized cells. *Science* **224**:946.

Dickson, R. C., J. Abelson, W. M. Barnes, and W. S. Reznikoff. 1975. Genetic regulation: The *lac* control region. *Science* **187**:27.

Donelson, J. E., and M. J. Turner. February 1985. How the trypanosome changes its coat. *Sci. Amer.* **252**:44.

Döring, H.-P., and P. Starlinger. 1984. Barbara McClintock's controlling elements: Now at the DNA level. *Cell* **39**:253.

Federoff, N. June 1984. Transposable genetic elements in maize. *Sci. Amer.* **250**:84.

Gall, J. G. 1968. Differential synthesis of the genes for ribosomal RNA during amphibian oogenesis. *Proc. Natl. Acad. Sci. U. S.* **60**:553.

Gancedo, J. M., M. J. Mazón, and P. Eraso. 1985. Biological roles of cAMP: Similarities and differences between organisms. *Trends Biochem. Sci.* **10**:210.

Groner, B., and N. E. Hynes. 1982. Long terminal repeats provide regulatory signals at the ends of retroviral genes. *Trends Biochem. Sci.* **7**:400.

Herberman, R. B., and J. R. Ortaldo. 1981. Natural killer cells: Their role in defenses against disease. *Science* **214**:24.

Hobbs, A. A., D. A. Richards, D. J. Kessler, and J. M. Rosen. 1982. Complex hormonal regulation of rat casein gene expression. *J. Biol. Chem.* **257**:3598.

Hochschild, A., N. Irwin, and M. Ptashne. 1983. Repressor structure and the mechanism of positive control. *Cell* **32**:319.

Hourcade, D., D. Dressler, and J. Wolfson. 1973. The amplification of ribosomal RNA genes involves a rolling circle intermediate. *Proc. Natl. Acad. Sci. U. S.* **70**:2926.

Jacob, F. 1966. Genetics of the bacterial cell. *Science* **152**:1470 (Nobel lecture).

Jacob, F., and J. Monod. 1961. Genetic regulatory mechanisms in the synthesis of proteins. *J. Mol. Biol.* **3**:318.

Johnsrud, L. 1978. Contacts between *Escherichia coli* RNA polymerase and a *lac* operon promoter. *Proc. Natl. Acad. Sci. U. S.* **75**:5314.

Johnsrud, L. 1979. DNA sequence of the transposable element IS1. *Molec. gen. Genet.* **169**:213.

Kindt, T. J., and A. Coutinho. 1983. More sources of antibody diversity. *Nature* **304**:306.

King, W. J., and G. L. Greene. 1984. Monoclonal antibodies localize oestrogen receptor in the nuclei of target cells. *Nature* **307**:745.

Korge, G. 1977. Direct correlation between a chromosome puff and the synthesis of a larval saliva protein in *Drosophila melanogaster*. *Chromosoma* **62**:155.

Lamb, M. M., and B. Daneholt. 1979. Characterization of active transcription units in Balbiani rings of *Chironomus tentans*. *Cell* **17**:835.

LaPorte, D. C. 1984. Antisense DNA: A new mechanism for the control of gene expression. *Trends Biochem. Sci.* **9**:463.

Leder, P. May 1982. The genetics of antibody diversity. *Sci. Amer.* **246**:102.

Lewin, B. 1980. *Gene Expression, 2: Eucaryotic Chromosomes*. 2nd ed. New York: Wiley.

Lewin, B. 1985. *Genes*. 2nd ed. New York: Wiley.

Lewin, R. 1983. A naturalist of the genome. *Science* **222**:402.

Maniatis, T., and M. Ptashne. January 1976. A DNA operator–repressor system. *Sci. Amer.* **234**:64.

Matthews, B. W., *et al.* 1983. How does cro repressor recognize its DNA target sites? *Trends Biochem. Sci.* **8**:25.

Maurer, R. A. 1982. Estradiol regulates the transcription of the prolactin gene. *J. Biol. Chem.* **257**:2133.

McClintock, B. 1984. The significance of responses of the genome to challenge. *Science* **226**:792 (Nobel lecture).

McKnight, S. L., and R. Kingsbury. 1982. Transcriptional control signals of a eukaryotic protein-coding gene. *Science* **217**:316.

Miesfeld, R., *et al.* 1984. Characterization of a steroid hormone receptor gene and mRNA in wild-type and mutant cells. *Nature* **312**:779.

Miller, O. L., Jr., B. A. Hamkalo, and C. A. Thomas, Jr. 1970. Visualization of bacterial genes in action. *Science* **169**:392.

Nevers, P., and H. Saedler. 1977. Transposable genetic elements as agents of gene instability and chromosomal rearrangements. *Nature* **268**:109.

North, G. 1984. Multiple levels of gene control in eukaryotic cells. *Nature* **312**:308.

Ohlendorf, D. H., *et al.* 1982. The molecular basis of DNA-protein recognition inferred from the structure of the cro repressor. *Nature* **298**:718.

O'Malley, B. W., ed. 1982. *Gene Regulation*. New York: Academic Press.

O'Malley, B. W., S. L. C. Woo, and M.-J. Tsai. 1981. Structure and hormonal regulation of the ovalbumin gene cluster. *Curr. Top. Cell Regul.* **18**:437.

Pastan, I. August 1972. Cyclic AMP. *Sci. Amer.* **227**:97.

Philipson, L, and U. Pettersson. 1980. Control of adenovirus gene expression. *Trends Biochem. Sci.* **5**:135.

Ptashne, K., and S. N. Cohen. 1975. Occurrence of insertion sequence (IS) regions on plasmid deoxyribonucleic acid as direct and inverted nucleotide sequence duplications. *J. Bacteriol.* **122**:776.

Ptashne, M. 1984. Repressors. *Trends Biochem. Sci.* **9**:142.

Ptashne, M., A. D. Johnson, and C. O. Pabo. November 1982. A genetic switch in a bacterial virus. *Sci. Amer.* **247**:128.

Rechavi, G., D. Givol, and E. Canaani. 1982. Activation of a cellular oncogene by DNA rearrangement: Possible involvement of an IS-like element. *Nature* **300**:607.

Reif, H.-J., and H. Saedler. 1977. Chromosomal rearrangements in the *gal* region of *E. coli* K12 after integration of IS1. In *DNA: Insertion Elements, Plasmids, and Episomes*, ed. A. I. Bukhari, J. A. Shapiro, and S. L. Adhya, p. 81. Cold Spring Harbor, N.Y.: Cold Spring Harbor Laboratory.

Reudelhuber, T. 1984. Upstream and downstream control of eukaryotic genes. *Nature* **312**:700.

Robertson, M. 1982. Gene rearrangement and the generation of diversity. *Nature* **297**:184.

Sakano, H., Y. Kurosawa, M. Weigert, and S. Tonegawa. 1981. Identification and nucleotide sequence of a diversity DNA segment (D) of immunoglobulin heavy-chain genes. *Nature* **290**:562.

Schimke, R. T. November 1980. Gene amplification and drug resistance. *Sci. Amer.* **243**:60.

Shapiro, J. A. 1979. Molecular model for the transposition and replication of bacteriophage Mu and other transposable elements. *Proc. Natl. Acad. Sci. U. S.* **76**:1933.

Shiba, T., and K. Saigo. 1983. Retrovirus-like particles containing RNA homologous to the transposable element *copia* in *Drosophila melanogaster*. *Nature* **302**:119.

Shimotohno, K., S. Mizutani, and H. M. Temin. 1980. Sequence of retrovirus provirus resembles that of bacterial transposable elements. *Nature* **285**:550.

Silver, L. M., and S. C. R. Elgin. 1977. Distribution patterns of three subfractions of *Drosophila* nonhistone chromosomal proteins: Possible correlations with gene activity. *Cell* **11**:971.

Sluyser, M. 1983. Interaction of steroid hormone receptors with DNA. *Trends Biochem. Sci.* **8**:236.

Spradling, A. C., and A. P. Mahowald. 1980. Amplification of genes for chorion proteins during oogenesis in *Drosophila melanogaster*. *Proc. Natl. Acad. Sci. U. S.* **77**:1096.

Stark, G. R. 1984. Gene amplification. *Ann. Rev. Biochem.* **53**:447.

Starlinger, P. 1984. Transposable elements. *Trends Biochem. Sci.* **9**:125.

Steward, F. C., M. O. Mapes, and K. Mears. 1958. Growth and organized development of cultured cells. *Amer. J. Bot.* **45**:705.

Stroynowski, I., and C. Yanofsky. 1982. Transcript secondary structures regulate transcription termination at the attenuator of *S. marcescens* tryptophan operon. *Nature* **298**:34.

Tonegawa, S. 1983. Somatic generation of antibody diversity. *Nature* **302**:575.

Ullmann, A., and A. Danchin. 1980. Role of cyclic AMP in regulatory mechanisms in bacteria. *Trends Biochem. Sci.* **5**:95.

Watson, M. D. 1981. Attenuation: Translational control of transcriptional termination. *Trends Biochem. Sci.* **6**:180.

Williams, A. F. 1984. The immunoglobulin superfamily takes shape. *Nature* **308**:12.

Yanofsky, C. 1981. Attenuation in the control of expression of bacterial operons. *Nature* **289**:751.

Yanofsky, C., and R. Kolter. 1982. Attenuation in amino acid biosynthetic operons. *Ann. Rev. Genet.* **16**:113.

CHAPTER 15

The Nucleus

The **nucleus** is the control center of the eukaryotic cell. Genetic instructions for growth and development are encoded in the DNA that constitutes part of the chromosomal nucleoprotein fiber. Replication of DNA and its transcription into RNA take place in the nucleus, and the different forms of RNA must then be processed in the nucleus before being channeled to their sites of activity in the cytoplasm. Chromosomes package the genes, participate in the regulation of gene expression, and provide the physical and chemical framework by which replicated genes are distributed to progeny nuclei during reproduction. In addition to the chromosomes, the nucleus includes one or more nucleoli in which ribosome subunits are assembled, a fibrillar network that may serve to orient the chromosomes within the nuclear space, a relatively fluid nucleoplasm in which solutes and small particles are suspended or dissolved, and an enveloping double-membrane system that participates in dynamic exchanges of particles and molecules and thereby helps to coordinate the entire nucleocytoplasmic system of the living cell.

Nuclear Organization

The membrane-bounded nucleus is the principal trademark of a eukaryotic cell (Fig. 15.1). Except for the nuclear envelope, however, there are no permanent membranes in the nucleus. Cells may have one nucleus (uninucleate), two nuclei (binucleate), or more than two nuclei (multinucleate), but the cells of higher organisms are characteristically uninucleate. As a general rule, the cell cannot survive if the nucleus has been lost or extensively damaged. Certain exceptions are known, however, in which cell death does not occur upon loss of the nucleus. Mature mammalian erythrocytes may survive for a few months after the nucleus has disappeared, and food-conducting cells in phloem tissues of flowering plants continue to function for years after nuclear degeneration. In the latter case, the anucleate phloem cells are maintained largely

Nucleus

Nucleoli

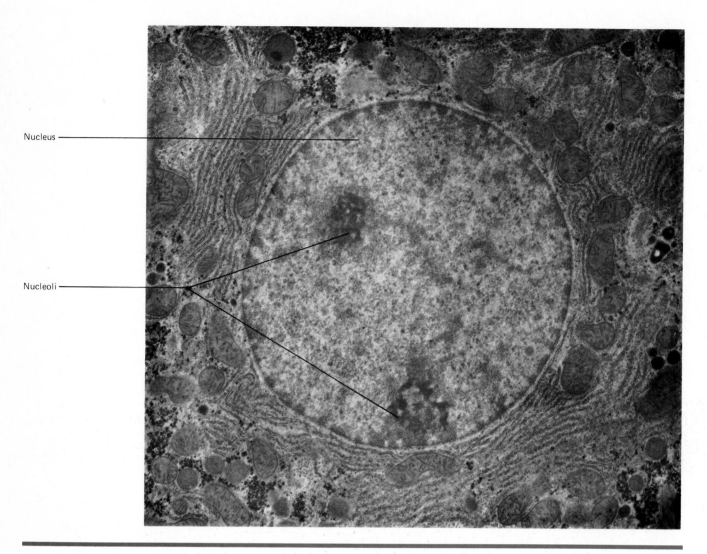

FIGURE 15-1
Electron micrograph of a section through part of a rat liver cell, showing the nucleus surrounded by cytoplasmic structures. Two nucleoli are visible in the nucleus. ×8700. (Photograph courtesy of K. R. Porter.)

because they receive essential materials from adjacent nucleated cells in the tissue.

Of the major types of macromolecules in the nucleus, DNA is confined to chromosomes, RNA occurs mainly in the nucleolus and nucleoplasm, lipids (mostly phospholipids) are parts of the nuclear envelope, and proteins are found everywhere in the nucleus. Very little carbohydrate is present in the nucleus.

15.1
The Nuclear Envelope

The interior of the nucleus is separated from the surrounding cytoplasm by two functionally distinct membranes that together constitute the **nuclear envelope**. The two lipid bilayer membranes are separated by a *perinuclear space* of variable size, but generally within the range of 10 to 50 nm. The membranes are fused locally at regions called *nuclear pore complexes*, which consist of a narrow opening bordered by large protein granules arranged radially on each of the two membranes of the envelope. Adjacent to the nucleoplasmic surface of the inner membrane is a fibrous protein meshwork called the *nuclear lamina*, which binds to

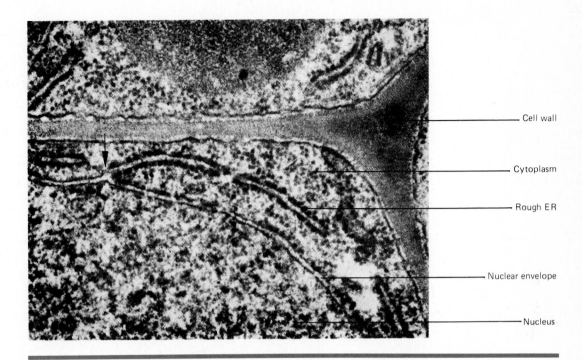

Cell wall

Cytoplasm

Rough ER

Nuclear envelope

Nucleus

FIGURE 15-2
Electron micrograph of a section
through part of a root cell from the
plant *Lythrum salicaria*. A continuity
is visible (at arrow) between the
ribosome-studded outer membrane of
the nuclear envelope and an element of
the rough endoplasmic reticulum
(rough ER) in the cytoplasm. The two
membranes of the nuclear envelope
are separated by a perinuclear space.
×46,000. (Photograph courtesy of
M. C. Ledbetter.)

the membrane on one side and to condensed chromatin on the other side
by different sets of proteins. Because of the complexity and physical
continuity of the system, we must view the whole structure as an
envelope rather than as two membranes.

The outer membrane of the nuclear envelope is studded with
numerous ribosomes on its cytoplasm-facing surface. This membrane is
functionally and chemically like the rough endoplasmic reticulum
(RER), with which it appears to be continuous when viewed in favorable
electron micrographs (Fig. 15.2). In addition to their capacity for
protein synthesis at ribosomes, the outer nuclear membrane and the
RER can pinch off vesicles and otherwise assist in the transport of
materials from one compartment to another in the cell. In fungi and
other organisms with minimal ER development, the nuclear envelope
may assume varied functions ordinarily carried out by the RER in more
abundantly endowed cells.

Each **nuclear pore complex** consists of a narrow opening, or **pore**,
surrounded by a ringlike **annulus** on the outer surface of the nuclear
envelope, and another annulus on the nucleoplasmic surface of the
envelope. A typical mammalian cell may have several thousand nuclear
pore complexes distributed within the area of the nuclear envelope (Fig.
15.3), but some cell types are exceptional in being nonporous. In mature
oocytes, tumor cells, and some other kinds of cells that are very active in
protein synthesis, nuclear pore complexes occur in stacks of cytoplasmic
membranes called *annulate lamellae*. We know nothing about the significance of these components, nor do we know whether these cytoplasmic
membranes are in any way related to nuclear envelope construction in
the numerous and rapid mitotic divisions that characterize embryo and
tumor growth and development.

The local fusion of outer and inner membranes defines a nuclear
pore region with a diameter of about 70 to 80 nm (Fig. 15.4). The pore

FIGURE 15-3
Electron micrograph of a freeze-fracture preparation, showing numerous nuclear pore complexes distributed over the surface of the nuclear envelope. ×48,000. (Photograph courtesy of D. Branton.)

channel through which molecules pass between nucleus and cytoplasm, however, is probably only 9 nm wide. The dimensions of this narrow passageway have been inferred from studies of the rate of entry of labeled molecules with different masses. Molecules of 5000 or fewer daltons cross the nuclear envelope very rapidly after they have been injected into the cytoplasm. Slightly larger molecules take longer to enter the nucleus, and those with a molecular weight of 60,000 or more barely penetrate the nuclear envelope even when periods of an hour or more are allowed for equilibration. From such data, the opening in the nuclear pore complex has been inferred to be a narrow (9 nm) aqueous channel that provides a direct passageway for small, water-soluble molecules to move from one cellular compartment to the other.

This same passageway also serves for the movement through the nuclear envelope of larger particles, including granular protein and nucleoprotein materials. Such materials can often be seen squeezing through the center of nuclear pore complexes. Although the dimensions

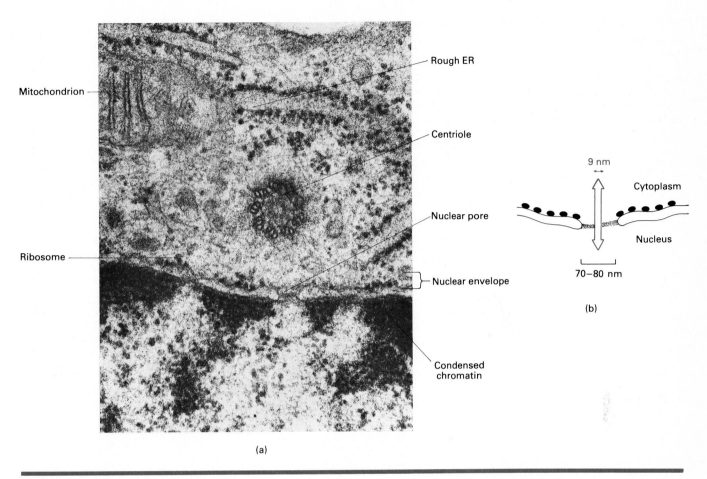

(a)

9 nm

Cytoplasm

Nucleus

70–80 nm

(b)

Mitochondrion

Ribosome

Rough ER

Centriole

Nuclear pore

Nuclear envelope

Condensed chromatin

of many macromolecules or aggregates are less than 9 nm, their passage appears to depend on interactions with cytoplasmic and nuclear proteins and not on their permeability properties. Evidence in support of this deduction has come from various studies, including the observation that an oocyte whose nuclear envelope has been grossly damaged accumulates about the same amount of labeled cytoplasmic proteins as an oocyte with an intact nucleus. The distribution of proteins and ribonucleoproteins between the nucleus and cytoplasm is therefore more likely to be determined by the properties of these molecules and particles themselves and of their specific interactions with nuclear and cytoplasmic components. In this way, nuclear and cytoplasmic proteins and nucleoproteins become concentrated in their respective compartments, regardless of their original sites of synthesis.

The annulus that borders a pore on each surface of the nuclear envelope is composed of eight protein granules arranged in a radially symmetric pattern (Fig. 15.5). These granules are quite distinct from the amorphous, electron-dense "plug" of material that often fills the pore channel and that probably consists of material in transit between nucleus and cytoplasm. This plug is often attached by ill-defined fibrils to the annular granules or to the bordering membrane of the pore complex. Whether these fibrils aid in the passage of the central plug of material is unknown, but it is a reasonable suggestion in view of the discussion in the preceding paragraph.

FIGURE 15-4
Nuclear pore complex. (a) Electron micrograph of a section through part of a rat bone cell, showing a distinct nuclear pore defined by locally fused ribosome-studded outer membrane and ribosome-free inner membrane of the nuclear envelope. The presence of condensed chromatin identifies the nucleus in the lower portion of the photograph, and the presence of a centriole, a mitochondrial profile, and elements of rough ER identify cytoplasm in the upper portion of the photograph. ×51,700. (Photograph courtesy of M. Federman.) (b) The nuclear pore is about 70–80 nm wide, but the pore channel through which molecules pass between nucleus and cytoplasm is believed to be only 9 nm in diameter.

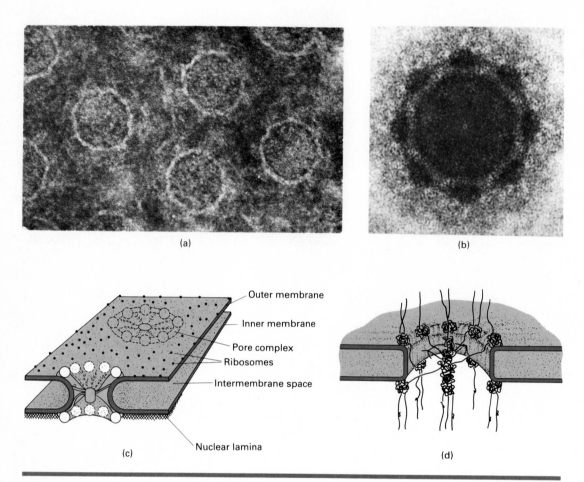

FIGURE 15-5
Nuclear pore complex. (a) Electron
micrograph of a negatively stained
preparation from a newt cell showing
circular pore complexes of the nuclear
envelope. ×200,000. (b) Electron
micrograph showing the eightfold
symmetry of the pore complex, which
has been made evident by rotational
enhancement during photography.
×350.000. (c) Diagram, based on
electron microscopy, showing a portion of nuclear envelope and the
organization of a pore complex. The
annulus bordering a pore is composed
of eight protein granules arranged in a
radially symmetric pattern, and one
annulus is present on each surface of
the nuclear envelope. A central plug of
material is attached to the annulus
proteins by ill-defined fibrils of uncertain
function. A nuclear lamina associated
with the inner surface of the nuclear
envelope forms a continuous sheath
and is composed of a meshwork
of proteins. (d) According to some
interpretations of microscopical data,
the encircling annulus proteins and the
pore plug are composed of fibrous
rather than globular proteins. (Photographs courtesy of J. G. Gall, from
Gall, J. G., 1967, *J. Cell Biol.* **32**:391–
400, Figs. 2, 10c.)

Interestingly, nuclear pore complexes retain their shape, numbers,
and pattern of distribution even after the phospholipid bilayers have
been dissolved away by mild detergents. Retention of nuclear shape and
of the nuclear pore complexes is the result of the **nuclear lamina** that
underlies the nuclear envelope (Fig. 15.6). The proteins that form the
lamina meshwork are not well defined, but at least three major
polypeptides of 60,000 to 70,000 in molecular weight have been identified in vertebrates. These polypeptides assemble spontaneously into a
continuous meshwork, which is believed to bind to inner membrane

proteins and thereby to form a continuous sheath that abuts the inner surface of the nuclear envelope. Other proteins of an undetermined nature are believed to bind condensed regions of chromatin to the innermost face of the nuclear lamina (see Fig. 15.4).

The lamina proteins may thus serve to organize the nuclear pore complexes of the envelope and to hold condensed, inactive chromatin near the nuclear periphery and away from the unfolded, active chromatin in the remainder of the nucleus. The three lamina proteins that bind to the nuclear envelope can be phosphorylated and dephosphorylated. Transient episodes of reversible phosphorylation may allow these lamina proteins to participate in the disassembly and reassembly of the nuclear envelope during mitosis. This speculation is based on the observation that the lamina proteins are reversibly phosphorylated during mitosis and that the proteins become distributed independently of membrane phospholipids just before metaphase of mitosis but reassociate during reorganization of the nuclear envelope in the telophase stage of the division process.

The nuclear envelope is a dynamic structure, which is differentiated into various components that carry out a number of cellular functions. In addition to providing a boundary that separates nuclear and cytoplasmic components and activities, the nuclear envelope allows for a dynamic exchange between the two major cellular compartments and provides a flexible structure that can disassemble and reassemble during nuclear division and nuclear reorganization.

15.2
The Nucleolus

The **nucleolus** is a spherical structure surrounded by nucleoplasm but not separated from it by a membrane. Each nucleolus is produced from, and attached to, a specific **nucleolar-organizing region** (NOR) located at a specific site on a specific **nucleolar-organizing chromosome**. A genome may include one or more nucleolar-organizing chromosomes and, therefore, one or more nucleoli may be present in the same nucleus. Nucleoli often fuse together, however, so a count of nucleoli is not an indication of the number of nucleolar-organizing chromosomes in a complement of chromosomes. In many cases the NOR is located near the terminus of a chromosome, and a small knob or *satellite* of the chromosome projects beyond the NOR. In the human chromosome complement, chromosomes 13, 14, 15, 21, and 22 are nucleolar-organizing, and each of these chromosomes is decorated with a satellite at the end of the shorter of the two chromosome arms (Fig. 15.7). In a typical diploid human cell, because of fusion of the five pairs of nucleoli, the interphase nucleus usually has only one large nucleolus.

The nucleolus is a virtual factory for the synthesis of ribosomal RNAs and the assembly of ribosome subunits in precursor form, as we discussed earlier in Chapter 13. The ribosomal RNAs synthesized in the nucleus are transcribed from rRNA genes (rDNA) clustered in tandem repeats at the NOR. Pre-rRNA, which is a 45S transcript in mammals, is processed to mature 18S, 25S to 28S, and 5.8S rRNA molecules in the nucleolus. These rRNAs assemble with 5S RNA made in the nucleo-

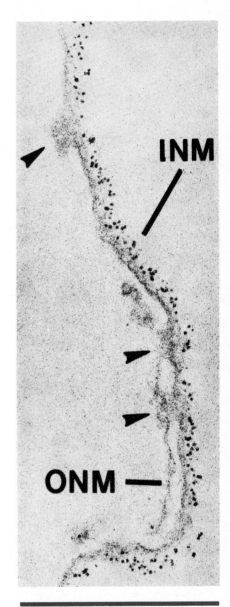

FIGURE 15-6
Electron micrograph of a cross section through isolated rat liver nuclear envelope after labeling with electron-dense ferritin coupled to antibodies against two of the proteins in the nuclear lamina. The label is localized under the inner nuclear membrane (INM) and is absent from the surfaces of the outer nuclear membrane (ONM) of the envelope. Three nuclear pore complexes (at arrowheads) are present in this section. ×315,000. (Photograph courtesy of L. Gerace, from Gerace, L., and Blobel G., 1982, *Cold Spring Harbor Sympos. Quant. Biol.* **41**: 967, Fig. 4A.)

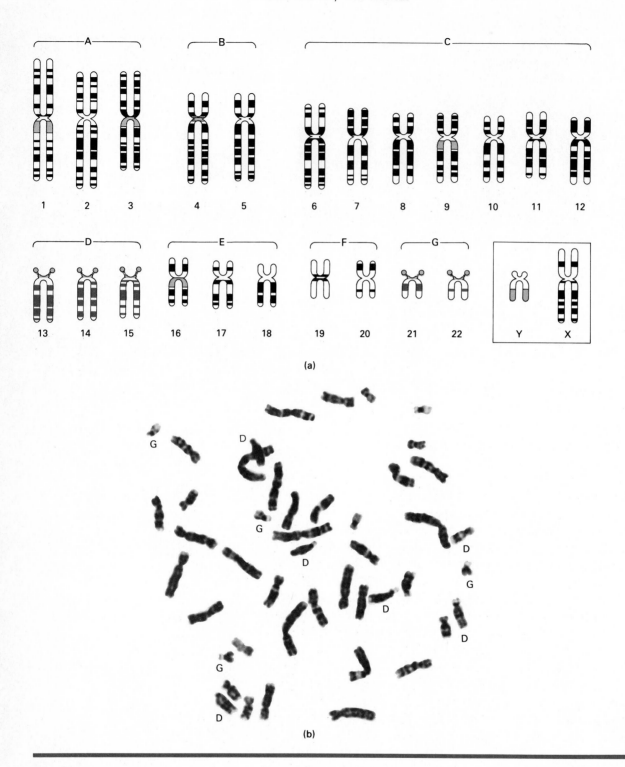

(a)

(b)

FIGURE 15-7

(a) standard representation of the human chromosome complement of 22 nonsex chromosomes and the X and Y sex chromosomes. Chromosomes 13, 14, 15, 21, and 22 (D group and G group) are nucleolar-organizing chromosomes, and they possess the distinctive terminal satellite knobs adjacent to the nucleolar-organizing region of the chromosome. Each metaphase chromosome is here depicted as a replicated structure whose two halves are held together at a common centromere region.
(b) Satellite Knobs are visible on some of the six D and four G chromosomes in this photograph of a metaphase spread.

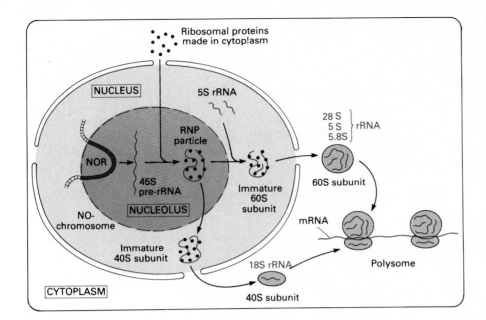

FIGURE 15-8
Schematic diagram of rRNA synthesis and ribosome subunit formation in the nucleus. In the nucleolus the 45S pre-rRNA transcript of NOR-localized DNA is cleaved and processed to mature 18S, 28S, and 5.8S rRNAs (see Fig. 13.25). These rRNAs plus 5S rRNA made elsewhere in the nucleus assemble with ribosomal proteins imported from the cytoplasm to form immature ribosome subunits. The larger 60S and smaller 40S subunits mature at the nuclear boundary or in the immediately adjacent cytoplasm, and they can then participate in protein synthesis as part of ribosome monomers in polysome aggregates.

plasm and ribosome subunit proteins imported from the cytoplasm, to form precursor ribosome subunits in the nucleolus. The subunits mature at the nuclear boundary, or in the immediately adjacent cytoplasm once they have been transported out of the nucleus (Fig. 15.8).

The structural organization of the nucleolus reflects its chromosomal attachment and its functions in ribosome subunit production. In electron micrographs of cell thin sections, four different components can be resolved: (1) a *granular zone* containing fuzzy particles about 15 nm wide, which represent ribosome subunits nearing completion; (2) a *fibrillar zone* with indistinct fibrils of RNA transcripts in nucleoprotein form, measuring about 5 nm in diameter; (3) a zone of *nucleolar chromatin* consisting of 10-nm-wide chromosomal loops extending out from their point of attachment in the NOR of the chromosome; and (4) a structureless *nucleolar matrix* in which all these materials are distributed (Fig. 15.9). The nucleolus may enlarge in active cells and become reduced in size in inactive cells, principally due to expansion or reduction in the extent of the granular zone. These changes in dimensions undoubtedly result from different rates of ribosome subunit production in relation to cellular biosynthetic activities.

The chemical nature of nucleolar components can be determined by specific stains in light microscopy and fluorescence microscopy; by carefully controlled ultrastructural cytochemistry using DNAase, RNAase, and proteases to observe the erosion of DNA, RNA, and proteins in cell thin sections viewed with the electron microscope; and by autoradiography. Nucleolar chromatin is distinguished by its magenta color after staining with the *Feulgen reagent* or by its pale green fluorescence after staining with *acridine orange*. In the same preparations, the RNA in the remainder of the nucleolus is colorless after Feulgen staining and bright orange after staining with acridine orange. In electron micrographs of sections exposed to different enzymes, the nucleolar chromatin is degraded by DNAase, whereas RNAase digests

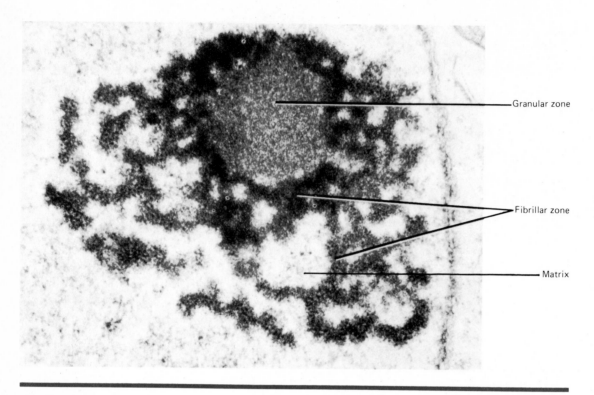

Granular zone

Fibrillar zone

Matrix

FIGURE 15-9
Electron micrograph of a section through the nucleolus of an opossum spermatogonial cell. The granular and fibrillar zones are evident in the matrix of the nucleolus, but the nucleolar chromatin is not included in the particular plane of this section. ×30,000. (Photograph courtesy of D. W. Fawcett.)

the other parts of the nucleolus. Proteases erode all those components, indicating their nucleoprotein nature.

The static picture provided by stains or enzyme digestions can be animated by studies of the incorporation of labeled precursors during macromolecular synthesis. When [³H]uridine is provided to cells to determine the sites of RNA synthesis, the silver grains in the overlying emulsion are found to be in the densest concentration over the nucleolus (Fig. 15.10). This observation is compatible with kinetic data showing that the rate of rRNA transcription by RNA polymerase III far exceeds the rates of tRNA and mRNA synthesis. The identification of rRNA in the nucleolus and the sequence of processing and transport of pre-rRNA and its derivatives have been determined by molecular studies of isolated nucleoli and nucleoplasm following centrifugation and isolation of the radioactively labeled molecules (see Section 13.6).

Proteins are not synthesized in the nucleolus or in any other part of the nucleus. Mature ribosomes are absent from the nucleus, so no machinery is available for the synthesis of nuclear proteins. All the nuclear proteins are made at cytoplasmic ribosomes and must be transported across the nuclear envelope into the nucleus. The imported proteins become parts of chromosomes, ribosome subunits, nuclear lamina, and other nuclear structures, or they serve a catalytic or regulatory function in DNA replication and transcription.

During nuclear division by mitosis or meiosis, the nucleoli disappear by the time of metaphase and reappear during nuclear reorganization in telophase. All synthesis of macromolecules stops, including RNA synthesis, when chromosomes condense and nucleoli disappear in dividing cells. When telophase begins, small nucleoli form at the NOR of each nucleolar-organizing chromosome, enlarge, and fuse to form one or more

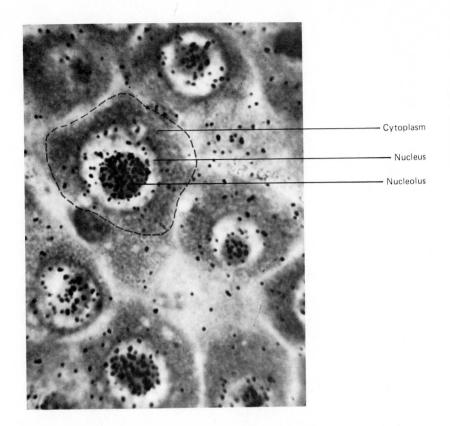

Cytoplasm

Nucleus

Nucleolus

FIGURE 15-10
Light-microscopic autoradiograph of rat liver cells, showing the high density of silver grains localized in the nucleolus after the incorporation of [³H]uridine into newly synthesized (ribosomal) RNA. A scattering of background silver grains occurs in the remainder of the nucleus and surrounding cytoplasm. (Photograph courtesy of S. Koulish, from Koulish, S., and R. G. Kleinfeld, 1964, *J. Cell Biol.* **23**: 39–51, Fig. 8.)

large nucleoli. Macromolecular syntheses resume and continue throughout the interphase between divisions of the cell nucleus—that is, in the G_1, S, and G_2 phases of the cell cycle (see Fig. 4.28).

15.3
The Chromosome Complement

Chromosomes were described in the 1880s as vividly staining rod-shaped bodies that were always present between the two poles of dividing plant and animal cells. Although permanently condensed chromosomes occur in various protists, fungi, and other simple eukaryotic organisms, the condensed bodies of dividing nuclei usually become greatly extended and appear as a network of tangled fibers in nondividing interphase nuclei (Fig. 15.11). These stainable chromatin fibers are deoxyribonucleoproteins that constitute the basic structural units of the set of chromosomes, or **chromosome complement**, of the eukaryotic cell. Each chromosome is a single deoxyribonucleoprotein strand consisting of one duplex DNA molecule bound to histone and nonhistone proteins in repeating nucleosomal subunit organization (see Section 12.8).

Studies of the chromosome complement are most easily pursued by assembling all the photographed somatic chromosomes into an ordered arrangement called a **karyotype**. The usual preparations are made of metaphase nuclei obtained from cells in culture or from actively dividing tissues such as root tips in plants (Fig. 15.12). Metaphase chromosomes are the most condensed found in any division stage, and are more likely

FIGURE 15-11
Electron micrograph of chromatin fibers from interphase nuclei of frog erythrocytes. The material was spread on a nonchelating buffer and was air-dried before photography. ×50,000. (Photograph courtesy of H. Ris.)

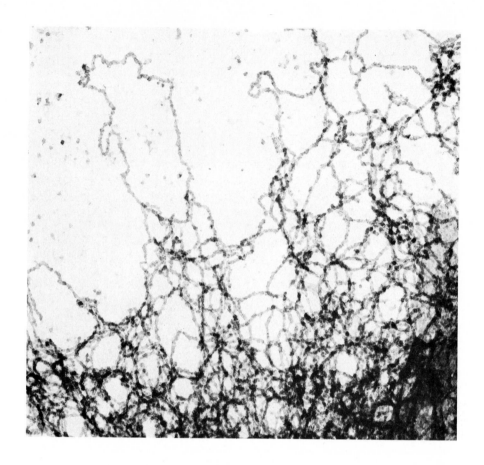

FIGURE 15-12
Spread of the 46 chromosomes from a dividing human diploid nucleus. The replicated halves of each chromosome are held together at the centromere region. (Photograph courtesy of L. J. Sciorra.)

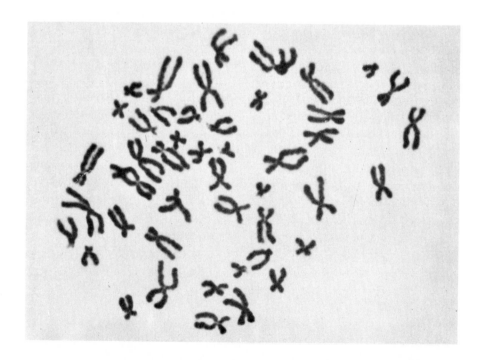

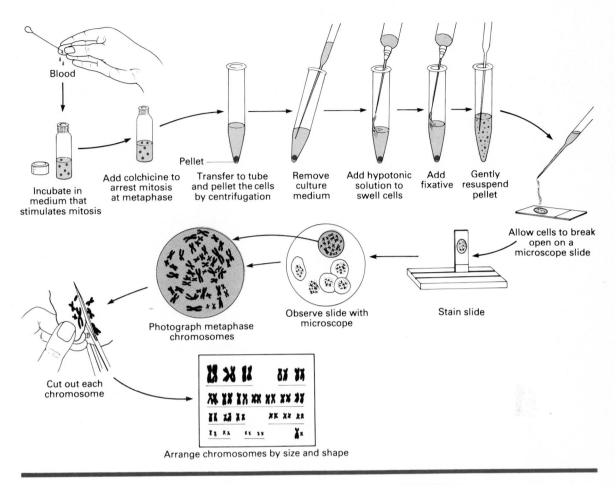

Blood

Incubate in medium that stimulates mitosis

Add colchicine to arrest mitosis at metaphase

Pellet

Transfer to tube and pellet the cells by centrifugation

Remove culture medium

Add hypotonic solution to swell cells

Add fixative

Gently resuspend pellet

Allow cells to break open on a microscope slide

Stain slide

Observe slide with microscope

Photograph metaphase chromosomes

Cut out each chromosome

Arrange chromosomes by size and shape

FIGURE 15-13
Flow diagram illustrating the procedures involved in karyotype preparation.

to be identified and counted than in division stages where they are longer and more tangled. Cells in culture, usually lymphocytes or fibroblasts in mammalian species, are stimulated to undergo mitosis by the addition of a mitogenic agent, and colchicine is added later to disaggregate the spindle and thereby arrest mitotic nuclei in the metaphase stage. Well-spread metaphase chromosomes in arrested nuclei are stained and photographed, and each chromosome is then cut out of the photograph (Fig. 15.13). The individual chromosomes are positioned according to established convention, proceeding from the largest to the smallest chromosomes, with the centromeres aligned to emphasize the differences in arm length on each side of the centromere of each chromosome.

Chromosomes can be described morphologically in accordance with their size and centromere location. Chromosomes of any size may be **metacentric** (the centromere is median and the two chromosome arms are therefore of equal size), **submetacentric** (the centromere is closer to one end of the chromosome than to the other and the arms are therefore of unequal size), **acrocentric** (the centromere is very close to one end of the chromosome and the two arms are of greatly unequal size), or **telocentric** (the centromere is at one end of the chromosome and only one chromosome arm is defined). Telocentric chromosomes are rarely found, and the relative preponderance of one morphological type or another varies in different species and different groups of organisms. In

FIGURE 15-14
Five pairs (at arrows) of the 23 pairs of human chromosomes are acrocentric (chromosomes 13, 14, 15, 21, and 22; see Fig. 15.7), whereas all 20 pairs of mouse chromosomes are acrocentric (see Fig. 15.23). (Photograph courtesy of L. J. Sciorra.)

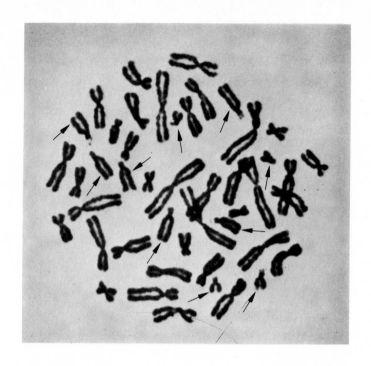

FIGURE 15-15
Karyotype of a human male, showing the chromosomes arranged into seven groups (A–G) according to chromosome length and centromere location. Group A consists of large metacentrics; B, large submetacentrics; C, intermediate-size submetacentrics; D, acrocentrics (nucleolar-organizing); E, small submetacentrics; F, small metacentrics; and G, smallest acrocentrics (nucleolar-organizing). On the basis of their morphology, the X chromosome can be put into group C and the Y chromosome into group G.

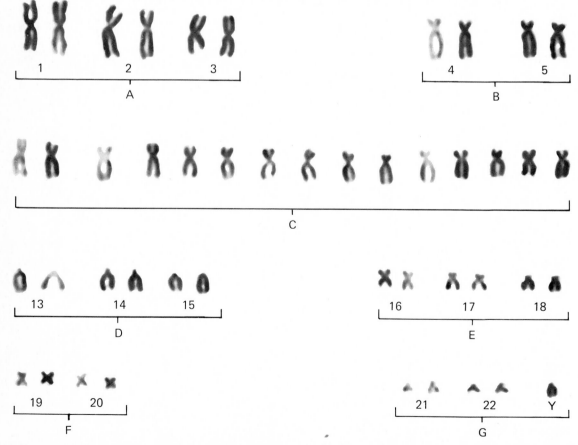

X Chromosomes occupy the second position in the C group

the mouse, for example, all twenty chromosomes of the haploid complement are acrocentric, whereas only five of the human chromosomes are acrocentric (Fig. 15.14).

When human metaphase chromosomes are arranged in a standard karyotype, seven different morphological groups can be identified, each of which is designated by a letter from A to G. The three group-A chromosomes are the largest and each is metacentric, two group-B chromosomes are the largest of the submetacentric chromosomes, seven smaller submetacentrics constitute group C, the three larger acrocentrics form group D, the two smaller acrocentrics are in group G, and groups E and F consist of three small submetacentrics and two small metacentrics, respectively (Fig. 15.15). The human sex chromosomes have different morphologies: The X chromosome is a C-type submetacentric, and the Y chromosome is a G-type acrocentric. The autosomal chromosomes of the D and G groups, all acrocentrics, are nucleolar-organizing chromosomes in humans.

When the karyotype convention was first established in 1960, it was necessary to define groups of chromosomes because the individual chromosomes of the same morphology and size were indistinguishable by ordinary staining procedures; all chromosomes of the same size and morphology presented the same opaque image. In 1969 T. C. Hsu and others introduced new methods of staining chromosomes to reveal patterns of stained bands and lightly stained interbands. These techniques enabled investigators to recognize and identify each chromosome of the complement (Fig. 15.16). Although each of the 22 autosomes and 2 sex chromosomes can be identified unambiguously after banding, it is still convenient to retain the references to human chromosome groups A to G for general discussion or for particular instances in which any of the chromosomes in a particular group may be involved. For example, we often refer to the occurrence of D/G translocations in certain patients with Down syndrome or in their relatives, even though we know now that the G chromosome is chromosome 21. Any of the D-group chromosomes 13, 14, and 15, however, may be involved in chromosome breakage and relocation, though in significantly different frequencies (Fig. 15.17).

The most useful and routinely used method of staining chromosomes is **G-banding**, which requires no special preparation to reveal bands after staining with *Giemsa* reagent. A closely related banding pattern is produced by **Q-banding**, after staining with *quinacrine* and other fluorescent agents. Fluorescent stains fade after a short time, and fluorescence optics and UV illumination are required to observe the preparations. Giemsa-stained preparations are more permanent and require ordinary light-microscope optics and white-light illumination, so G-banding is used routinely in preference to Q-banding. Another useful method is *C-banding*, which produces fewer bands but highlights highly repetitive DNA. We will discuss C-banding later in the chapter, in relation to the organization of the centromere region.

Although we know the basis for differential staining in C-banding, we have not been able to ascertain the chemical or structural basis for G-banding and we have limited information on Q-banding. Many suggestions have been made and many analyses reported, but the

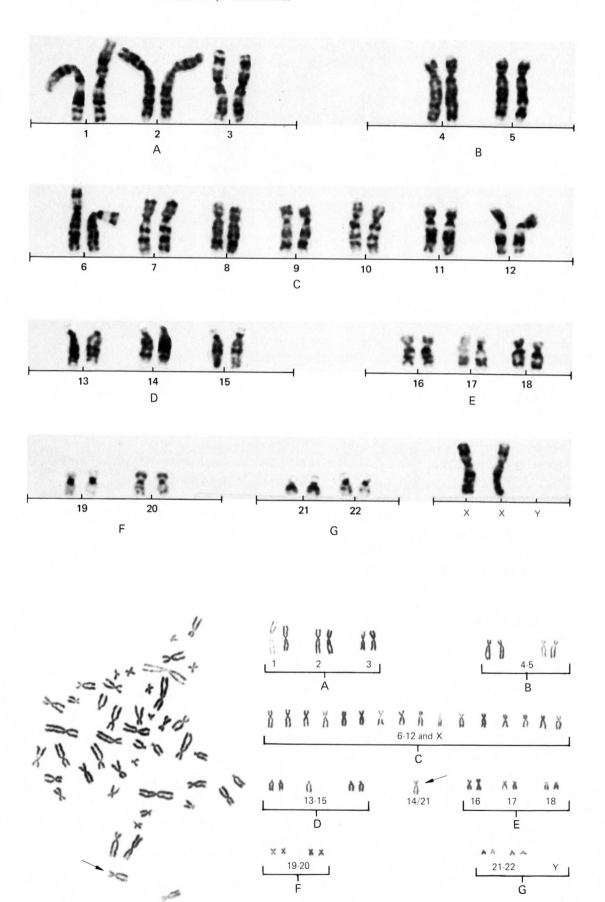

X Chromosomes occupy the second position in the C group

◄ **FIGURE 15-16**
Karyotype of a human female, showing the G-band patterns that allow
the unique identification of each
chromosome in the complement.

evidence is either unconvincing or highly ambiguous. Q bands appear
to result from binding between quinacrine dye and regions of DNA that
are AT-rich. Guanine and cytosine quench fluorescence, so GC-rich
regions of DNA probably remain unstained or lightly stained. It would
seem that a similar mechanism, or one that also stains AT-rich and
GC-rich regions differentially, would explain both Q-banding and
G-banding, because remarkably similar patterns are obtained with the
two methods. So far this appears to be untrue, and the mechanism of
G-banding remains a mystery. The practical advantages of G-banding,
however, lead to its widespread use, and the consistency and reproduci-
bility of banding patterns in anyone's hands make the method depend-
able and useful in numerous kinds of studies.

From comparative anatomy, the fossil record, and molecular evidence, we all know that the members of the great ape family (chimpanzee, gorilla, and orangutan) are our closest living relatives and that the
divergence leading to the great ape and human families took place about
5 to 10 million years ago, probably in Africa. Molecular hybridization,
DNA sequencing, and amino acid sequencing of various proteins suggest
that the two families have about 98% of their genes in common, many of
which have undergone no change in coding sequences during this period
of time. The close genetic relationship indicated by all these lines of
evidence is also reflected in the great similarities in G-banding patterns
of human and great ape chromosome complements (Fig. 15.18). These
patterns reveal that some restructuring of particular chromosomes has
occurred during evolution, including the apparent fusion of two short
acrocentrics present in apes to form the large metacentric chromosome 2
in the human complement.

◄ **FIGURE 15-17**
Metaphase chromosome spread (left)
and assembled karyotype (right) of the
chromosomes from a female with Down
syndrome. The nucleus contains
46 chromosomes, but karyotype
analysis reveals the presence of a
14/21 translocated chromosome.
This chromosome has one of the two
chromosomes 14 and one of the three
chromosomes 21 attached in a single
structure. Down syndrome develops
when three copies of chromosome 21
are present, whether these occur as
individual chromosomes in a person
with a total of 47 chromosomes in the
nucleus or one of the three copies is
part of a translocated chromosome,
as shown here. (Photograph courtesy
of T. R. Tegenkamp.)

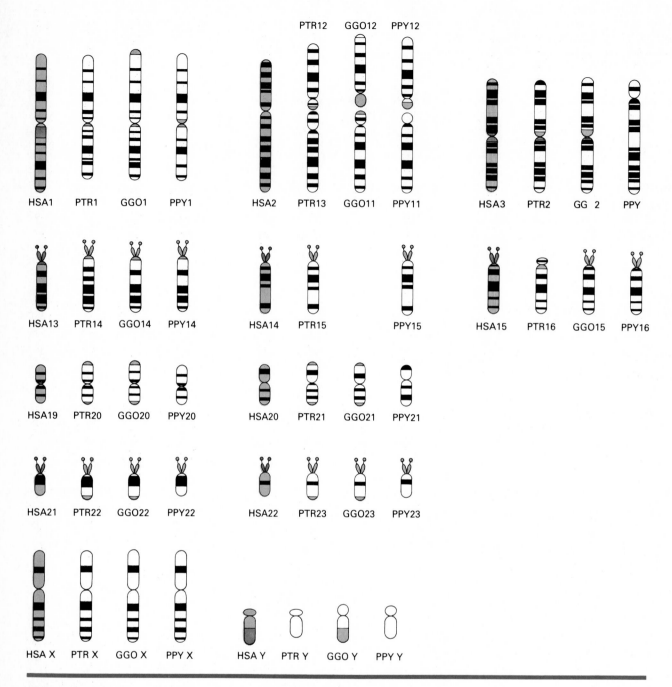

FIGURE 15-18

Comparisons of G-band patterns in selected human chromosomes (color; HSA = *Homo sapiens*) and their homologs in the three kinds of great apes (PTR = *Pan troglodytes*, the chimpanzee; GGO = *Gorilla gorilla*; PPY = *Pongo pygmaeus*, the orangutan). Each chromosome is numbered according to the karyotype of each species. The twelve selected human chromosomes are 1, 2, 3 (large metacentrics); 13, 14, 15 (large acrocentrics); 19, 20 (small metacentrics); 21, 22 (small acrocentrics); and the X and Y sex chromosomes. Note that human chromosome 2 is closely matched by two acrocentrics in all the great ape species and that some chromosomes are strikingly similar or even identical (X chromosome) in all four species. (From *Paris Conference (1971): Standardization in Human Cytogenetics*. Birth Defects: Original Article Series **14**: 9, 1975. The National Foundation, New York.)

Special Features of Chromosome Organization

Chromosomes are not simple strings of genes organized into chromatin fibers. Chromosomes are differentiated along their length into regions that perform unique functions, which cannot be taken over by substitute regions located elsewhere in the genome. In some cases, whole chromosomes in a genome may be unique and may perform some vital function for which no other chromosome can be substituted. The genome itself is differentiated into genetically active and inactive regions, only some of which can be explained by differential gene expression. In the next sections we will discuss some of these special features of chromosome organization and behavior in relation to cellular functions and development.

15.4
Heterochromatin and Euchromatin

In 1928 Ernst Heitz first pointed out the existence of interphase chromatin in two recognizably different states of condensation: **heterochromatin**, which remains condensed throughout interphase between nuclear divisions, and **euchromatin**, which is greatly extended and loosely distributed in the same nuclei (Fig. 15.19). From later genetic and autoradiographic studies, two additional features were found to distinguish these two forms of chromatin. First, very few gene mutations

FIGURE 15-19
Electron micrograph of a section through part of a rat osteoblast in interphase. Condensed heterochromatin is located mainly at the nuclear envelope, whereas dispersed fibrils of euchromatin fill most of the nuclear volume. ×24,000. (Photograph courtesy of M. Federman.)

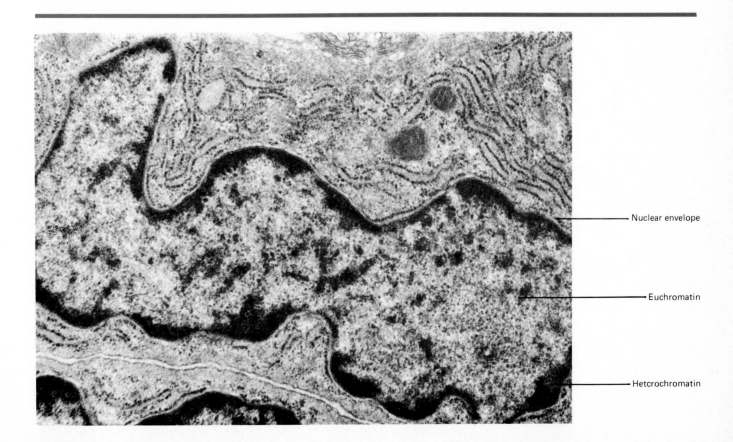

Nuclear envelope

Euchromatin

Hetcrochromatin

could be found in heterochromatic regions, whereas most of the gene map defined euchromatic chromosomal regions. These observations indicated that heterochromatin was more stable than euchromatin and contained far fewer polypeptide-specifying genes. Second, as was shown first in 1960 by J. Herbert Taylor and later by other investigators, heterochromatic regions of the chromosomes replicate considerably later than euchromatic regions during the S phase of the cell cycle. In autoradiographs of nuclei that have been pulsed with radioactive thymidine at different times in the S period, silver grains are distributed over euchromatin in cells given earlier pulses and over heterochromatin in cells provided with label later in the S period (Fig. 15.20). Heterochromatin is thus condensed during interphase, genetically stable or even inactive, and late-replicating.

These three features characterize **constitutive heterochromatin** at all times in the life of a cell, whereas **facultative heterochromatin** may revert to the euchromatic state at certain times in certain cells, in response to physiological or developmental conditions. The best characterized constitutive heterochromatin is located around the centromere region in higher eukaryotes. Such stable chromatin is desirable in a region required for chromosome movement to the poles during countless nuclear divisions in a lifetime. Constitutive heterochromatin is visualized cytologically by **C-banding**, a method of Giemsa staining that distinguishes between highly condensed chromatin, which is not substantially degraded during pretreatments with HCl and NaOH, and less condensed chromatin, which is largely degraded by pretreatment before staining (Fig. 15.21). The stain is nonspecific, but more of it is bound to constitutive heterochromatin because more of this chromatin remains undegraded and is thus present to be visibly stained. Centromeric

FIGURE 15-20
Light-microscope autoradiograph showing silver grains over chromosome regions that replicate late in the S period of the human cell cycle. These late-replicating regions are largely heterochromatic in nature. Note that only one of the two X chromosomes in this female cell is late-replicating. (Photograph courtesy of L. J. Sciorra.)

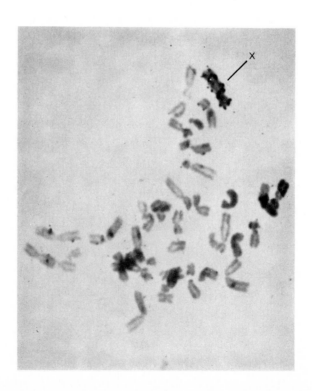

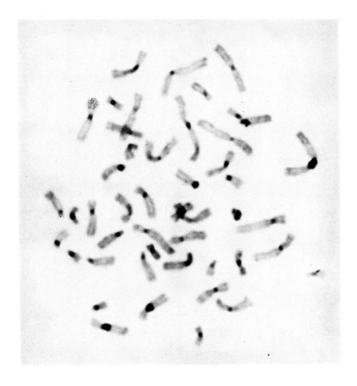

FIGURE 15-21
Human chromosome complement, showing C bands primarily at the centromere region of each chromosome. C bands identify constitutive heterochromatin, which is found at the centromere region in almost every eukaryotic species and at various other chromosome locations as well.

FIGURE 15-22
Densitometer tracings of purified DNAs from yeast, centrifuged to equilibrium in CsCl density gradients in an analytical ultracentrifuge. The buoyant density of DNA in CsCl is expressed in g/cc and is proportional to GC content of the DNA. Higher GC content produces proportionately higher buoyant density values. The reference DNA bands at 1.731 g/cc, bulk nuclear DNA at 1.700 g/cc, and three satellite DNAs at 1.688, 1.684, and 1.672 g/cc. Examination of the bottom tracing reveals that the 1.684-g/cc satellite consists of mitochondrial DNA. The other two satellites must be nuclear in origin because they appear in the middle tracing.

constitutive heterochromatin consists of highly repetitive DNA, which may include from 10^5 to 10^7 tandem repeats of short sequences of 2 to 10 base pairs each.

Centromeric constitutive heterochromatin can be isolated from *satellite DNA* peaks, which separate from bulk nuclear DNA in density gradients subjected to high-speed centrifugation (Fig. 15.22). Isolated satellite DNA can then be analyzed by renaturation kinetics to determine its chemical and kinetic complexity (see Section 12.12), by straightforward chemical analysis and sequencing, and by other means. Its location at the centromere region is readily established by the method of *in situ* **hybridization**, which we discussed briefly in Section 4.5. When labeled satellite DNA, or DNA or RNA copied from satellite DNA, is applied to pretreated chromosomes in microscope slide preparations, the location of the hybridized satellite DNA is revealed by the distribution of silver grains over relevant portions of the chromosomes. The results are particularly clear in mouse chromosomes, all of which are acrocentric and all of which therefore have their centromere near one end of the chromosome (Fig. 15.23).

The best-known example of facultative heterochromatin involves the mammalian X chromosome. The single X chromosome in males is almost entirely euchromatic, as is one of the two X chromosomes in females. The second X chromosome in females condenses to the heterochromatic state very early in embryonic development and remains condensed thereafter in all cell lineages; this phenomenon is called **X inactivation**, or **Lyonization** (in recognition of Mary Lyon, who first investigated the situation by systematic genetic analysis). From her studies and many others of various mammalian species, we know that only the euchromatic X chromosome is active in gene expression; the

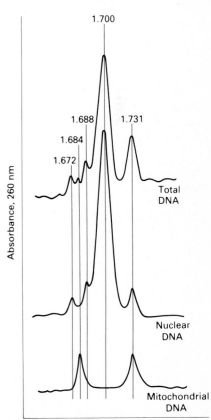

FIGURE 15-23
Light-microscope autoradiograph of mouse chromosomes hybridized *in situ* with radioactively labeled RNA copied from mouse satellite DNA. From the distribution of silver grains on the lightly stained chromosomes, it is evident that only centromeric heterochromatin has been labeled in these acrocentric chromosomes. The satellite DNA can therefore be identified as hetero-chromatin (repetitive DNA) from the centromere regions of all 20 pairs of chromosomes in this species. ×1420. (Photograph courtesy of M. L. Pardue and J. G. Gall.)

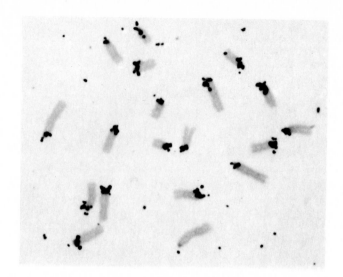

condensed X chromosome is inactive. Lyon showed by studies of female mice heterozygous for X-linked alleles that *either* one of the two X chromosomes might be randomly inactivated and that, once inactivated, that same X chromosome was inherited as an inactive chromosome in all descendant cells in a lineage. The heterozygous females developed patches of coat color, which showed that the wild-type or mutant X-linked color allele could be expressed in any one cell and that all the descendants of the cell (in a patch) expressed the same allele and must therefore carry the same euchromatic X chromosome and hetero-chromatic X. These studies further reveal that males and females have only one *active* X chromosome and are thus fully equivalent in their genetically expressed X-linked alleles, most of which govern traits unrelated to sex.

The heterochromatic X chromosome is visible as a dense blob in the interphase nucleus (Fig. 15.24). This blob is called **sex chromatin**, or a **Barr body**. From Barr body counts in humans and other mammals we can quickly determine the number of X chromosomes present, because

FIGURE 15-24
In this interphase nucleus from a human female, one of the two X chromosomes is condensed and is there-fore heterochromatic. The condensed X chromosome (at arrow) is called a Barr body, or sex chromatin. (Photograph courtesy of T. R. Tegenkamp.)

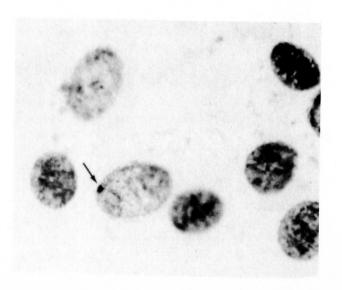

TABLE 15-1
Anomalous Sex Chromosome Constitutions Observed in Humans

Individual	Chromosome Constitution*	Number of Barr Bodies	Physical Sex
Normal male	46,XY	0	male
Normal female	46,XX	1	female
Turner female	45,X	0	female
Triplo-X female	47,XXX	2	female
Tetra-X female	48,XXXX	3	female
Penta-X female	49,XXXXX	4	female
Klinefelter male	47,XXY	1	male
	48,XXXY	2	male
	49,XXXXY	3	male
	48,XXYY	1	male
	49,XXXYY	2	male
XYY male	47,XYY	0	male

*The two-digit number indicates the total diploid chromosome number and is followed by the exact number and kind(s) of sex chromosomes present in the nucleus.

only one X chromosome remains euchromatic and any others appear as Barr bodies. Normal males have no Barr body, but males with one or more Barr bodies have one or more extra X chromosomes, which is correlated with the physical symptoms of **Klinefelter syndrome** (sterility, small testicles, enlarged breasts, torso disproportionate to limb length). XXY males may or may not be mentally retarded, but mental retardation is characteristic of males with three or more X chromosomes. Women with only one X chromosome (XO) exhibit the physical symptoms of **Turner syndrome** (sterility, small stature, underdeveloped breasts) but are not mentally retarded. Women with three X chromosomes are physically and mentally normal, but XXXX women are mentally retarded. In all these cases, the *number of Barr bodies plus one* provides a direct count of the number of X chromosomes in the nucleus. The Y chromosome is male-determining in mammals, so every male has a Y chromosome and one or more X chromosomes. Females have no Y chromosome but have one or more X chromosomes (Table 15.1). The complete absence of X chromosomes is a lethal condition because many essential genes are located in the X chromosome. The absence of a Y chromosome is obviously not lethal; every female lacks this chromosome.

The mammalian X chromosome is facultatively heterochromatic, because the condensed chromosome returns to the euchromatic state in the oocyte, or earlier, and remains so for a period of time in the embryo. This is evident from direct observations of such cells and from the fact that both X chromosomes in the young embryo must be euchromatic in order to explain why *either* one of them becomes condensed *at random* later on in development. X inactivation occurs early in mammalian embryo development. In humans, X inactivation takes place about the sixteenth day of embryo development. We know very little about the processes of X inactivation and reactivation, but we can be reasonably sure that they are unrelated to sex. X inactivation occurs in both males and females who have two or more X chromosomes, and it does not occur in males or females with one X chromosome.

Individual chromosomes are thus differentiated into active euchromatin and inactive heterochromatin. In some chromosomes or some portions of chromosomes, previously inactive facultative heterochromatin may be reactivated to the euchromatic state and participate in gene expression and development. The chromatin fiber is much more densely packed in heterochromatic regions than in euchromatic regions. In addition, as mentioned earlier, constitutive heterochromatin contains highly repetitive, simple-sequence DNA. It is less likely that all of the facultative heterochromatin has a distinctive DNA component, however, because both X chromosomes in a cell are genetically identical and either one may undergo X inactivation.

15.5
The Centromere Region

The **centromere region** includes the site of attachment of spindle fibers and thus serves as a device for controlled segregation of chromosomes during anaphase of mitosis and meiosis. The region is usually recognized as a prominent constriction of the chromosome, and, because of its importance in chromosome segregation, the centromere region is sometimes referred to as a **primary constriction**. Other constrictions on the same chromosomes are secondary by definition and are called **secondary constrictions** for that reason. The NOR is often recognized as a secondary constriction with a protruding satellite knob at the end of the chromosome, right next to the constriction (Fig. 15.25).

In most animals the centromere region includes a three-layered component sandwiched between constitutive heterochromatin of the two arms of a chromosome. The disk-shaped trilaminate component is the **centromere**, or **kinetochore**, and it consists of an outer, moderately dense layer, called the **centromere plate**, a relatively transparent middle layer, and an innermost layer composed of densely packed chromatin (Fig. 15.26). The centromere plate is the site of spindle fiber insertion, and it is present even when the other two layers are absent in species that have a *diffuse centromere region* extending all along the length of the chromosome instead of being localized in one specific site. In flowering plants the spindle fibers are inserted into a spherical centromere, which appears in electron micrographs as a roughly circular tangle of chromatin (Fig. 15.27).

We know virtually nothing about the proteins of the centromere and very little about the molecular interactions that lead to insertion of spindle fibers into the centromere. One or more of the microtubule associated proteins (MAPs) have been shown to bind to DNA, but until we know more about the centromeric proteins, we can say nothing about protein–protein interactions at the centromere. We do know that spindle fibers are inserted only into a centromere and that the centromere is essential for anaphase movement of chromosomes to the poles of the cell. *Acentric* chromosomes are not attached to the spindle and thus have no means by which to move directionally to the poles (see Fig. 11.34). A

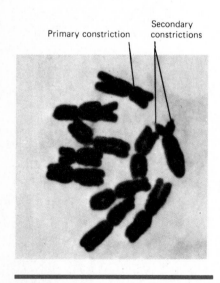

Primary constriction   Secondary constrictions

FIGURE 15-25
Light micrograph of 10 of the 16 metaphase chromosomes in an onion root-tip cell. The primary constriction (centromere region) is obvious in each replicated chromosome, and one of the chromosomes has a secondary constriction at its nucleolar-organizing end. ×4000.

FIGURE 15-26
Electron micrograph of the X chromosome of the Indian muntjac, a small Asiatic deer, showing the three-layered centromere (kinetochore). Spindle fibers are inserted into the moderately dense outer centromere plate. The pale middle layer of the centromere and the very dense layer closest to the chromosome are also clearly evident. ×41,500. (Photograph courtesy of B. R. Brinkley, from Brinkley, B. R., et al., 1984, *Chromosoma* **91**:1–11, Fig. 6C.)

FIGURE 15-27
Electron micrograph of a mitotic cell from the African violet, showing the spindle fibers (microtubules) inserted into the ill-defined centromere region of a dividing chromosome. This organization is typical of flowering plants. ×81,000. (Photograph courtesy of M. C. Ledbetter.)

Spindle fibers   Centromere region of chromosome   Spindle fibers

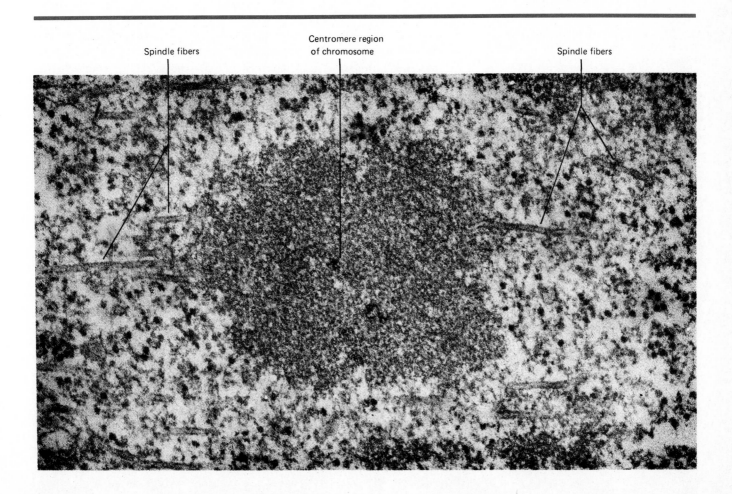

FIGURE 15-28
Base sequences (shown for the non-coding 5′ → 3′ DNA strand) of the centromere (CEN) region of yeast chromosomes 3, 4, 6, and 11 reveal three distinct regions of organization. Region I consists of 14 bases (base pairs (bp) in duplex DNA) that show some sequence variability; region II is a variable sequence of 82–89 base pairs that include 93%–94% AT; and region III is a highly conserved sequence of 11 base pairs.

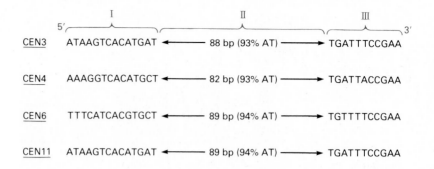

dicentric chromosome, with two centromeres, may be stretched as a bridge between the two anaphase nuclei if the inserted spindle fibers pull each centromere of the chromosome to a different pole.

Considerable progress has been made in recent years in the effort to define the molecular and organizational features of the centromere region in yeast (*Saccharomyces cerevisiae*). Particularly significant information has come from studies of yeast centromeres isolated from genomic libraries and cloned in spliced recombinant DNA with plasmid vectors. Identification of the centromere in the cloned DNA depends on gene markers flanking the isolated centromeres and on the orderly segregation of cloned centromeric DNA, as indicated by orderly segregation of the flanking allelic markers in mitosis and meiosis in host cells. The yeast centromere region is simpler than the equivalents in higher eukaryotes, because yeast lacks significant amounts of repetitive DNA and none is present on either side of its centromeric DNA. There is, however, more densely packed nucleosomal DNA around the centromeres than elsewhere in the genome.

Sequence analysis of centromeric DNA from yeast chromosomes 3, 4, 6, and 11 (*CEN3, CEN4, CEN6,* and *CEN11*) revealed the presence of common structural features, even though molecular hybridizations showed a lack of homology among these sequences. A common feature of all 4 centromeres was the presence of a central core sequence (region II) of 82 to 89 base pairs that were 93% to 94% AT, flanked by a short sequence on each side (regions I and III). Region III is a highly conserved sequence of 11 base pairs, varying from the consensus sequence by only one base pair in any case, and region I is a less highly conserved sequence of 14 base pairs (Fig. 15.28). Although the sequence of region II is not highly conserved, its length is similar in all the centromeres analyzed.

By progressive deletion analysis and by analysis of mutation induction at specific base-pair sites, centromeric function was shown to require that all of regions II and III and most of region I be intact; otherwise, aberrant segregations resulted. The chromatin structure of the yeast centromere region has been analyzed by mapping chromatin sites according to their sensitivity to cleavage by either micrococcal nuclease or DNAase I, and by the use of *CEN3* or *CEN11* hybridization probes to locate regions I to III within the chromatin fiber. These studies showed that regions I to III are contained within a segment that is 220 to 250 base pairs long protected from nuclease attack, and that they are flanked by highly phased (uniformly and densely packed) nucleosomes spaced at intervals of 160 base pairs. The remainder of the chromatin fiber consists of less densely packed nucleosomes, as shown by their

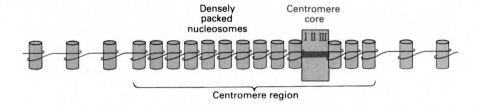

Densely
packed
nucleosomes

Centromere
core

I II III

Centromere region

FIGURE 15-29
Organization of the centromere region
in yeast chromosomes, based on
studies of chromatin sensitivity to
nuclease-induced cleavages. The
centromere core region of the DNA
duplex (color) is flanked by about 15
densely packed nucleosomes on one
side and by 3 packed nucleosomes on
the other side. Dense packing is
indicated by low sensitivity of these
chromatin regions to nuclease attack.
Less densely packed nucleosomes are
present elsewhere in the chromosome,
as indicated by the greater ease of DNA
cleavage (more exposed DNA) by
nucleases than for nucleosomes
around the centromere core region.

greater sensitivity to nuclease attack in being cut out and released more readily from the chromatin fiber. About 2000 base pairs of DNA (15 nucleosomes) on one side of *CEN11* and about 400 base pairs on the other side are densely packed and may be considered part of the centromere region (Fig. 15.29). Between regions I to III at the core of the centromere and the condensed chromatin on either side is a highly nuclease-sensitive site whose role in centromere function is unknown. It has been suggested that these sensitive sites may bind proteins, but we have no evidence on this matter at the present time.

Deletion studies have shown that removal of the phased nucleosomes around the centromere core had no effect on centromere function in directing orderly chromosome segregation. It is possible that this densely packed chromatin prevents transcription of centromeric DNA, because the introduction of a promoter into the centromere region of *CEN6* stimulated transcription of centromeric DNA and caused the abolition of *CEN6* function in chromosome segregation. The center of the centromere core is occupied by highly conserved region-III DNA. This fact, plus the observation that 220 to 250 base pairs are differentiated and protected from nuclease attack, has led to the suggestion that the whole protected segment may serve as a primitive kinetochore and may be the binding site for the single microtubule that attaches to each of the 17 chromosomes in the haploid (or 34 chromosomes in the diploid) nucleus (Fig. 15.30). Whether or not this is the case and whether any proteins are involved in spindle fiber attachment to the kinetochore remain to be determined.

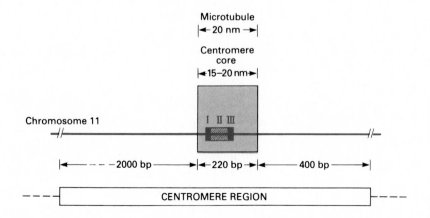

Microtubule
|← 20 nm →|

Centromere
core
|←15–20 nm→|

Chromosome 11

I II III

|←—— —2000 bp ———→|←—220 bp —→|←——— 400 bp ———→|

CENTROMERE REGION

FIGURE 15-30
General features of the centromere
region in yeast chromosome 11 are
typical of other yeast chromosomes
whose molecular features have been
analyzed. The 2000 base pairs (bp) on
one side and the 400 bp on the other
side of the centromere core were
defined by nuclease sensitivity studies
(and interpreted in terms of densely
packed nucleosomes; see Fig. 15.29).
Regions I-II-III (see Fig. 15.28) occupy
107–114 bp of the 220–250–bp stretch
of the centromere core, with region III
being centrally located in this stretch.
The width of the centromere core could
accommodate the single microtubule
(spindle fiber) that is inserted into the
chromosome during nuclear division,
and it may therefore be the binding site
of the spindle fiber in metaphase and
anaphase chromosomes in yeast.

The relationship between the relatively simple structure of the centromere region in the tiny yeast chromosomes and the more complex structures bordered by constitutive heterochromatin in higher eukaryotes remains unclear. Furthermore, the centromeres from the yeast *Saccharomyces cerevisiae* do not function when introduced on plasmids into cells of other yeast species, *Neurospora crassa* (another ascomycetous fungus), or cultured animal cells. The yeast *CEN* sequences thus appear to be species-specific, and we should be cautious in extending these data to explain centromere structure and function in other organisms. Despite these problems, the availability of molecular methods to analyze genetically favorable yeast strains should provide models and insights that should prove useful in analyses of centromere function in chromosome segregation in higher eukaryotes.

15.6
The Telomere Region

The **telomere region** can be functionally defined as that segment of DNA at the molecular end of a linear chromosome that is required for replication and stability of that chromosome. A telomeric region has a specialized DNA sequence and molecular structure that, together with associated proteins, may comprise as little as a few hundred base pairs at each chromosome terminus. We have known for 50 years that intact free ends of a chromosome will not fuse together, whereas broken ends will fuse to one another. From studies by H. J. Muller of x-ray–induced chromosome breaks in *Drosophila* and by Barbara McClintock of unstable chromosomes in maize, it was evident that the telomeres had special qualities. McClintock showed that, in maize, monocentric ring-chromosomes could recombine (fuse) to form dicentric ring-chromosomes that broke at anaphase and reformed as monocentric rings. This sequence of events constituted the "breakage–fusion–bridge" cycle of chromosome instability. The "healing" of broken ends to reconstitute functional telomeres and thus to stop the breakage–fusion–bridge cycle was shown by McClintock to be tissue-specific and stage-specific, occurring only in certain developmental stages of certain tissues.

Studies of cloned telomeres isolated from yeast and from a number of protozoan species have shown that all the telomeres of a given species share a common DNA sequence; the two ends of each chromosome are virtually identical. At each end of each chromosome there exist two kinds of DNA sequences: (1) **simple telomeric sequences**, which are at, or very close to, the extreme end of the chromosome arm and consist of very short, tandemly repeated DNA sequences; and (2) **telomere-associated sequences**, which are repeated but complex DNA sequences that may extend for many thousands of base pairs near the ends of the chromosomes. The simple telomeric sequences are probably the functional components of telomeric regions in that they are sufficient to supply a chromosome end with both stability (no fusion) and the ability to be completely replicated. The regular simple-sequence repeat in several species of protozoa is CCCCAA in some ciliates and CCCTAA in hemoflagellates, whereas in yeast the repeat is less regular and consists of $C_{1-3}A$.

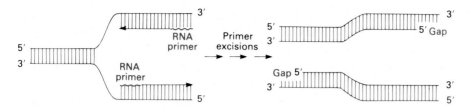

The need to know the DNA sequence at the ends of a chromosome is related to the problem of terminating replication of linear duplex DNA molecules. The excision of the terminal RNA primer creates a gap at the 5' end of each new DNA chain, which must be filled to complete the duplex semiconserved molecule (Fig. 15.31). No polymerase is known to extend a chain from the 5' end, however, which means that some special condition must prevail to allow the terminus of each new strand to be completed. Some viruses and all bacteria solve the problem by having a circular genome. Continued growth of the new strand around a circular template inevitably brings together the last-formed 3' end and the first-formed 5' end of the new strand, where they are joined by DNA ligase action (see Fig. 12.19 or 12.24). Other evolutionary solutions are also known in viruses. The presence of repeated sequences of DNA at the chromosome ends allows the formation of hairpin loops by base-pairing of single-stranded repeat regions, or perhaps some other means by which the incomplete 5' ends can be filled as the result of conformational changes that rely on redundancies in the sequence. Various suggestions have been made, and a number of different models are now available for experimental tests to determine the conformation of the simple telomeric sequence and the mechanism by which replication is successfully terminated (Fig. 15.32). The hairpin conformation required by several

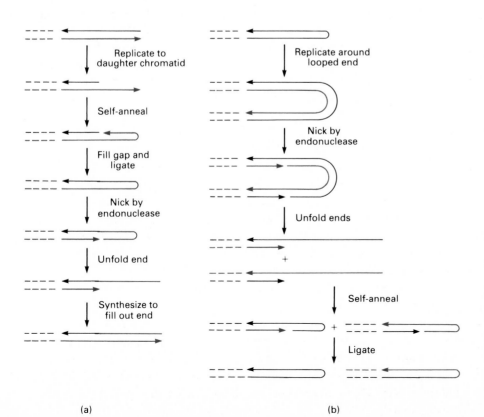

(a)　　　　　　　　　　(b)

FIGURE 15-31
Upon completion of DNA synthesis, each semiconserved daughter duplex has a gap at the 5' end of the new strand, which was left when the RNA primer in that location was excised. DNA chain growth requires a free 3'–OH end (see Fig. 12.10), which is absent at the gapped terminus. Special conditions are required to solve this problem of terminating the replication of new DNA strands.

FIGURE 15-32
Two of the hairpin-loop models proposed to explain the mechanism by which the gapped 5' end of the new strand in a semiconserved DNA duplex is filled in with redundant telomeric DNA sequences to terminate replication. The direction of the arrowheads on each strand indicates 5'→3' polarity. (a) The telomeric sequence in the parental strand (color) forms a hairpin loop and anneals to the gapped 5' end of the new strand (black). After gap-filling at the 3'–OH end of the parental strand, ligation joins the two strands into an uninterrupted looped sequence. The loop is nicked by an endonuclease, and the completed terminus of the new strand unfolds. The terminus of the parental strand (which was transferred to the new strand) is completed by the addition of DNA monomers complementary to the new-strand terminus. (b) The original strand has a terminal hairpin loop, and replication of the new strand (color) would follow the hairpin sequence. Separation of the original and new strands requires a nick at homologous sites on both strands. The nicked strands unfold and thereby separate, after which each strand undergoes self-annealing and ligation to regenerate a terminal hairpin loop.

of these models, has in fact been confirmed in several species. Various studies of telomere replication, function, and behavior are now in progress, all greatly aided by molecular methods that make possible DNA cloning and the incorporation and modification of different sequences in recombinant DNA.

Transcriptionally Active Chromatin

If some sequences are transcribed and others are not transcribed in the same chromosome, even at the same time, is there any difference in the chemistry or organization of the chromatin fiber in active and inactive regions? Are nucleosomes present in transcribing regions, and, if present, are they distinguishable in any way from nucleosomes in quiescent sites? If the DNA, the proteins, or both are different in transcribing chromatin, are these differences present before and after transcription, or are they transient modifications? We now have a variety of experimental data with which we can begin to answer these and other questions.

15.7
Studies at the Cytological Level

Transcription involves the unwinding of DNA, and we would therefore suspect that at least local unfolding of the chromatin fiber would be required for RNA polymerase to gain access to template DNA sequences. Mitotic chromosomes are biosynthetically inert, and ordinary interphase chromatin is so tangled and extended that we cannot usually distinguish one chromosome from another, much less one gene from another. Gene expression can be viewed in giant polytene chromosomes, particularly in dipteran insect larvae, because these chromosomes remain in a permanent interphase state and are rendered individually recognizable by their relative size and their unique, mappable band patterns (Fig. 15.33). Individual bands can be equated with individual gene loci in many cases, giving us a cytological basis for studying gene transcription directly in the intact chromosome.

As we discussed earlier in Section 14.4, locally unfolded regions, or puffs, are the sites of RNA synthesis. These puffs develop and regress at specific sites and specific times during development of the larva. Do these puffs truly represent actively transcribing sites of genes whose products are made only in some cells and not in others? In a singular study of differential gene expression in the midge *Chironomus*, Wolfgang Beermann showed that the *sz* locus was transcribed and translated only if that locus underwent the conformational act of puffing. In his preliminary studies, Beermann showed that the midge larva preparing to pupate produces a secretion of glue protein that later allows the pupa to stick to a solid surface while it metamorphoses to the adult form. Only four of the cells in the larval salivary gland produce this secretion, and in these same four cells a granular protein is made and incorporated into the glue protein secretion only if a particular puff forms near the end of

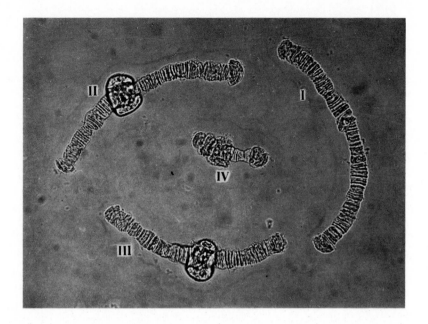

FIGURE 15-33
Phase-contrast light micrograph of the chromosome complement from interphase nuclei of salivary gland cells in the midge *Chironomus tentans*. The unstained chromosomes are identified by roman numerals. Each chromosome is recognizable by its morphology and banding pattern. A large Balbiani ring (very well-developed puff) is present in chromosomes II, III, and IV, and smaller puffs are distributed in various locations in all the chromosomes. The four pairs of chromosomes in these diploid cells appear to be four single chromosomes, because the homologs are very closely paired along their entire length. ×375. (Photograph courtesy of B. Daneholt.)

chromosome 4, and only if the wild-type allele of the *sz* gene is present (Fig. 15.34).

Beermann conducted a cytogenetic analysis to verify the apparent relationship between specific puff development and specific differential expression of the *sz* locus. The species *Chironomus pallidivittatus* is homozygous for the *sz*⁺ allele, the particular puff forms on chromosome 4, and the secretion contains the granular protein. In *Ch. tentans*, however, the genotype is *sz⁻/sz⁻*, the puff on chromosome 4 never develops, and the clear secretion lacks the granular protein. Would each chromosome 4 retain its activity or inactivity in the same cell? Beermann crossed the two species to obtain heterozygous *sz⁺/sz⁻* hybrid progeny, and each parental chromosome 4 was made visibly recognizable. The *Ch. tentans* chromosome 4 contained a large inverted segment, whereas the *Ch. pallidivittatus* chromosome 4 retained the standard noninverted band pattern. Homologous chromosomes pair in larval somatic nuclei, so the two chromosomes 4 in the hybrid progeny cells were held together only loosely because of the sequence differences between the inverted and noninverted regions.

Microscopic study revealed that only the *Ch. pallidivittatus* chromosome puffed at the expected terminus site in the four salivary gland cells and that only half the usual amount of granular protein was made in these *sz⁺/sz⁻* hybrids (Fig. 15.35). These results indicated that a local conformational change in the chromatin fiber was a concomitant of the expression of a transcribable gene. The *sz⁻* locus remained condensed and inactive even in the same nuclear and cytoplasmic environment as the hybrid cells. When conditions in the cell stimulate transcription, only certain loci will unfold and be transcribed and expressed. The nature of the unfolding process, however, remained to be investigated in other studies.

Chromosomes are also found in a greatly extended form in amphibian oocytes during a particular interval of meiosis (diplonema), which may continue for months in these cells. At this time the replicated

Chironomus pallidivittatus

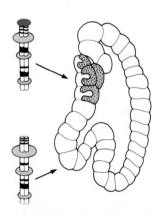

FIGURE 15-34
Drawing of the salivary gland from *Chironomus pallidivittatus*, showing that a granule-containing glue secretion is present in only four of the gland cells. Chromosome IV exhibits a terminal puff (color) only in these four cells. This particular puff is absent from chromosome IV in the other cells of the same salivary gland, but a number of other puffed sites are identical in all the gland cells. Differential action of the *sz*⁺ gene, which encodes the granular protein in the glue secretion, is inferred from these observations of genetically identical cells in an individual organism.

FIGURE 15-35
Diagrammatic summary of Beermann's experiments with *Chironomus*. Four cells in the salivary gland of *Ch. pallidivittatus* produce a granular secretion. A puff (color) is formed at one end of chromosome IV only in these four cells and not in the other cells of the gland (chromosomes shown to left of gland). The corresponding four cells in *Ch. tentans* produce a clear secretion lacking the granules, and no puff forms at the end of chromosome IV in any of its gland cells. In hybrids between these two species, half as many protein granules occur in the secretion as in the *Ch. pallidivittatus* parent. Because there are structural differences in chromosome IV in the two parent species, the two chromosomes in the hybrid chromosome pair are not closely held together, and the source of each can be identified. Only the chromosome in the hybrid that was derived from the *Ch. pallidivittatus* parent forms a puff in the four crucial gland cells. These experiments show that puffing is associated with gene action in directing synthesis of a protein that characterizes a phenotypic trait in the organism. (From W. Beermann. 1963. *Amer. Zool.* **3**: 23.)

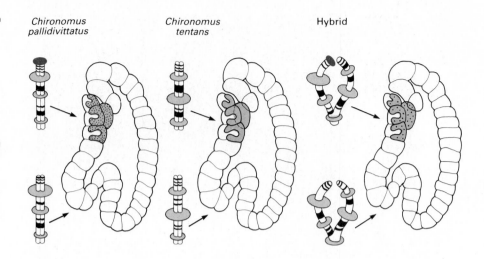

Chironomus pallidivittatus   Chironomus tentans   Hybrid

homologous chromosomes remain bound together in pairs only at certain sites (chiasmata) and are elsewhere separated enough for us to see each of the replicated homologues in some detail (Fig. 15.36). Some of these lampbrush chromosomes (so called because of their resemblance to the nineteenth-century lampbrushes) may be 800 μm long, whereas chromosomes in later stages of meiosis may be condensed to only 15 to 20 μm in length. Each chromosome has many hundreds of extended chromatin loops emerging from the axis, where the remainder of the chromatin is highly condensed. Each chromosome is a replicated structure, so pairs of loops extend at each decondensed site (Fig. 15.37). As shown by autoradiographic studies of [³H]uridine incorporation, transcription takes place along every loop but not at the condensed axial regions of the chromosomes, and it continues throughout the duration of this meiotic interval. Afterward, the chromosomes retract their loops as they condense, and biosyntheses stop for the remainder of meiosis.

The loops of lampbrush chromosomes represent fixed DNA sequences, because the same loops hybridize with the same probe DNAs or RNAs at all times during this meiotic interval. In this way, lampbrush chromosome loops correspond to polytene chromosome puffs; both represent localized decondensation of specific gene sequences undergoing active transcription. We know little about the nature of the lampbrush chromosome transcripts, however, because most of the mRNA is already stored in the oocyte after having been transcribed during the interphase preceding meiosis. Regardless of the function or fate of these meiotic transcripts, lampbrush chromosomes provide clear evidence that actively transcribing chromatin is decondensed and is thus conformationally altered from its transcriptionally inactive, condensed state.

Inasmuch as transcription involves a region of local unwinding generated by bound RNA polymerase in the area, it might require the displacement of nucleosomes or at least a loosening of the tightly wound DNA around the histone octamer. We believe this to be the case, because eukaryotic RNA polymerases are large proteins greater than 500,000 in molecular weight whereas nucleosomes have a molecular weight of only about half this amount. There hardly seems enough room for the polymerase to follow the wound DNA around the histone core. What is the nucleosomal organization of transcribed genes?

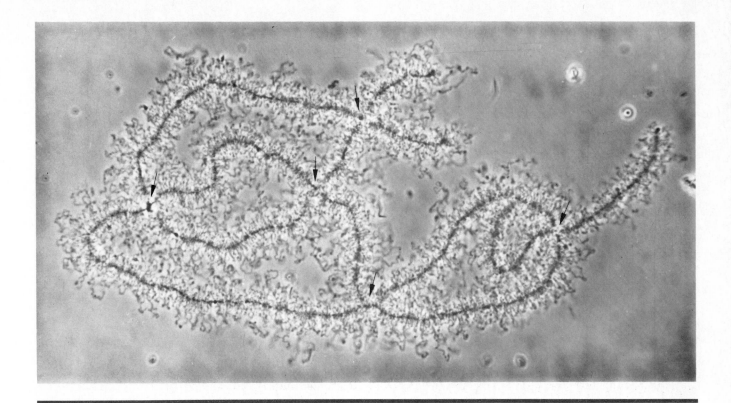

FIGURE 15-36
Phase-contrast light micrograph of a pair of homologous lampbrush chromosomes from diplonema-stage oocytes of a newt (*Triturus viridescens*). Numerous chromatin loops are evident along the axis of each of the two chromosomes, which have separated from each other everywhere except at five chiasma sites (at arrows). Transcription takes place at each chromatin loop in each chromosome during this stage of oocyte meiosis. ×440. (Photograph courtesy of J. G. Gall.)

FIGURE 15-37
Transcription of a pair of giant chromatin loops in the form of a double-loop bridge on (lampbrush) chromosome 6 from an oocyte of the newt *Notophthalmus viridescens*. (a) Phase contrast, unstained, unhybridized preparation, and (b) autoradiograph of the region after *in situ* hybridization with [³H]RNA. Both strands of the genetic region are transcribed, as is evident from the presence of hybridized labeled transcripts there. (Photographs courtesy of J. G. Gall, from Diaz, M. O., G. Barsacchi-Pilone, K. A. Mahon, and J. G. Gall, 1981, *Cell* **24**: 649, Fig. 3a, b. Copyright by M. I. T. Press.)

When rDNA is examined by electron microscopy, the lengths of transcribing rRNA genes and nontranscribing spacers indicate that all these regions are in a fully extended state and must thus be devoid of nucleosomes (see Fig. 13.26). The conformational state of these regions is difficult to see directly in these photographs, though, and it is possible that some nucleosomes are present, however few they may be. A more

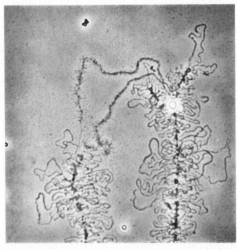

(a)

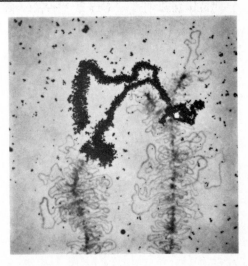

(b)

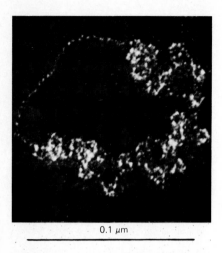

0.1 μm

FIGURE 15-38
Nucleosomal organization of the viral
SV40 minichromosome is evident
during transcription, except for a
nucleosome-free gap that is found in
about 20% of the genome preparations
examined. The gap is about 350 base
pairs long. (Photograph courtesy of M.
Yaniv, from Saragosti, S., G. Moyne,
and M. Yaniv, 1980, *Cell* **20**: 65, Fig.
2C. Copyright by M. I. T. Press.)

favorable transcription complex is present in the virus SV40, whose
minichromosomes can be extracted from infected cells. Electron
micrographs clearly show that the nucleosomes are present during
transcription but that a nucleosome-free gap may also be present (Fig.
15.38). The properties and composition of this denuded DNA region will
be mentioned later. The rRNA genes are transcribed at very high
frequency, whereas the SV40 genes are transcribed less intensively. To
determine whether the observed differences in chromosome organization
correspond to the different rates of transcription, other cellular genes
have been examined. In these cases, the transcribing chromatin is partly
extended and has fewer nucleosomes than nontranscribed regions.

The changes in structure of the chromatin fiber during transcription
have also been documented by comparing the nucleosomal units cleaved
by micrococcal nuclease in transcribing and nontranscribing preparations of the same set of genes. Heat-shock genes are transcribed
infrequently before the heat shock, but upon heat shock the genes are
activated and then they are intensely transcribed. Gels of digested
nontranscribing heat-shock genes display a few discrete bands, whereas
a smear of many different bands is found for digests of transcribing
heat-shock genes of *Drosophila melanogaster* (Fig. 15.39). These differences
indicate a change in nucleosomal organization when inactive genes
become transcriptionally active. Whether nucleosomes are displaced
and quickly replaced as the polymerase moves along the transcription
unit, or are not displaced at all, is uncertain. Nucleosomes clearly are
displaced in intensively transcribing rDNA, but this may be an exceptional situation.

15.8
Studies at the Molecular Level: Sensitivity to DNAase I

What causes the conformational change in transcribing chromatin that
leads to its unfolding, and what causes the change in nucleosomal
organization when genes become transcriptionally active? To answer
these questions we can examine all the kinds of molecular components
of the chromatin fiber—DNA, histone proteins, and nonhistone proteins—in transcribing and nontranscribing regions.

If nucleosomal organization has changed in some regions of nuclear
chromatin and not in others, then some portion of the DNA should be
more exposed and thus more likely to be digested by nucleases. When
the enzyme DNAase I is used over a period of time, DNA is eventually
degraded to very small fragments (acid-soluble material). When only
10% of the total DNA has been rendered acid-soluble, over 50% of the
DNA of active genes has already been degraded. To confirm that active
genes are preferentially degraded, active and inactive genes can be
compared by the use of probes to identify known sequences. In chicken
erythrocyte chromatin, β-globin genes are rapidly lost, whereas ovalbumin genes are degraded at the same low rate as bulk nuclear chromatin
(Fig. 15.40). In oviduct chromatin, however, the ovalbumin genes are
rapidly degraded and the β-globin genes respond as slowly as the bulk
chromatin. Preferential degradation thus correlates with the state of

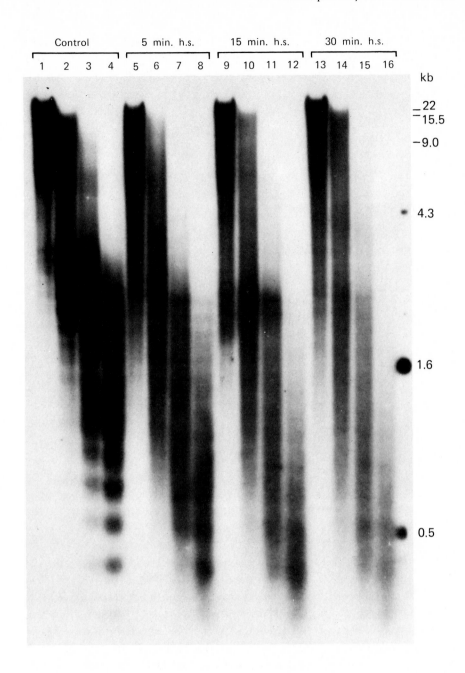

Control   5 min. h.s.   15 min. h.s.   30 min. h.s.

1 2 3 4   5 6 7 8   9 10 11 12   13 14 15 16   kb

— 22
—15.5

—9.0

— 4.3

1.6

0.5

FIGURE 15-39
Autoradiograph of a ^{32}P-labeled Southern blot of the gel pattern of DNA fragments recovered after micrococcal nuclease digestion of a chromosomal region encoded for the 70,000-dalton heat shock protein in chromatin from control and heat-shocked (h.s.) *Drosophila* tissue cultures. Preparations were subjected to 35°C heat shock for 0, 5, 15, or 30 minutes, and were then digested with the enzyme at each of four different concentrations (one lane per treatment). The progressively greater smearing of discrete DNA bands with longer-heat shock treatment at each nuclease concentration indicates the greater sensitivity to nuclease digestion of active versus inactive chromatin. These results are interpreted to mean that nucleosomal organization is disrupted upon activation of genes from a previously inactive state. (Photograph courtesy of S. C. R. Elgin, from Wu, C., Y.-C. Wong, and S. C. R. Elgin, 1979, *Cell* **16**: 807, Fig. 5. Copyright by M. I. T. Press.)

activity or inactivity of the gene; active genes are much more sensitive to DNAase I.

By using probes to determine whether all or part of the transcription unit and its flanking regions are equally sensitive to DNAase I, investigators have shown that the regions on either side are as sensitive as the transcription unit itself. The DNAase sensitivity test has been suggested to define a **chromosomal domain** (not equivalent to structural domains of chromosome loops; see Section 12.9). Such a domain is a region that includes all the components of a transcription unit and its bordering sequences that undergo structural change. A chromosomal domain may include more than one transcription unit, particularly in regions containing a cluster of related genes, such as the β-globin gene

FIGURE 15-40
Results of experiments designed to determine whether active genes are preferentially degraded by DNAase I under conditions in which only 10%–20% of total DNA is digested. Nuclei isolated from chicken fibroblasts and from 5-day-old and 18-day-old erythrocytes were briefly exposed to DNAase I, after which the DNA was isolated and tested for the presence of globin DNA and ovalbumin DNA by hybridization with labeled cDNA probes of these sequences. Fibroblasts (black triangles) served as a control system; these cells make neither globin nor ovalbumin. Another control consisted of undigested total DNA (colored triangles). In both controls, the globin and ovalbumin DNA probes hybridized to nuclear DNA to an equal extent, which indicated that the inactive genes were degraded to an equal extent. Furthermore, the globin and ovalbumin genes were degraded to a limited extent in fibroblast nuclei, which indicated their low sensitivity to DNAase I. In the case of erythrocytes, however, globin DNA was more susceptible than ovalbumin DNA to DNAase I attack, because less DNA remained in erythrocyte nuclei to hybridize with globin DNA probes than with ovalbumin DNA probes. Active globin genes and inactive ovalbumin genes in erythrocytes were therefore differentially sensitive to DNAase I, and the active genes were degraded to a significantly greater extent than the inactive genes from the same cells. (From Weintraub, H., and M. Groudine, 1976, *Science* **193**: 850. Copyright © by the American Association for the Advancement of Science.)

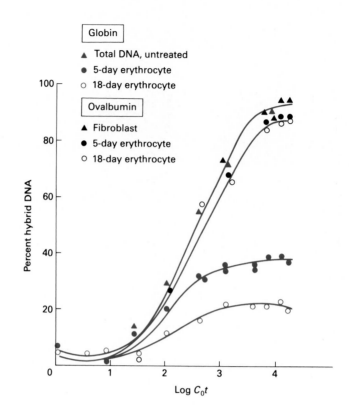

cluster or the ovalbumin-X-Y gene cluster. The sensitive flanking sequences may extend for thousands of base pairs on either side of the transcription unit(s). Such a large region of high sensitivity to DNAase I reflects a substantial structural change—and not only a change in a promoter or a region in the act of unwinding just ahead of the RNA polymerase during copying.

As we discussed in Section 12.10, the *nonhistone proteins* **HMG14** and **HMG17** (high-mobility group proteins) are loosely bound to the nucleosomes. When chromatin is digested with DNAase I, HMG14 and HMG17 are preferentially released from chromatin, and an active gene thereafter loses its high sensitivity to DNAase I. When the two nonhistone proteins are added back to the chromatin, the active gene regains its sensitivity. Significantly, removal and restoration of these two proteins have no effect on the same gene in a tissue in which that gene is not expressed. The globin genes are affected in erythrocyte chromatin, for example, but not in nonerythrocyte chromatin. When these same tests are applied to isolated nucleosomes, core particles, or cores alone, the same results are obtained. The HMG proteins must thus bind to the histone cores and somehow alter the conformation of the nucleosome, or perhaps they stabilize a conformational change that has already been established. In either case, HMG14 and HMG17 are responsible, at least in part, for DNAase sensitivity of active chromatin.

The histone proteins themselves are subject to transient modifications by the addition of acetyl, methyl, or phosphate groups to different portions of a few kinds of amino acids. By acetylation of lysine, methylation of arginine and histidine, or phosphorylation of serine and histidine, the positive charge is removed or reduced and the histones may thus be functionally altered (Fig. 15.41). When nucleosomal core

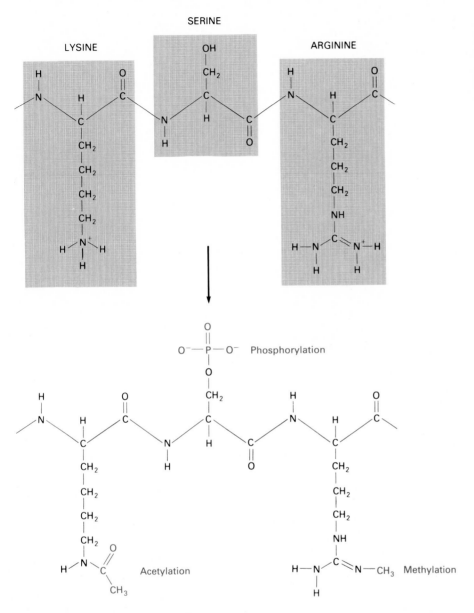

FIGURE 15-41
Histone proteins may be modified by phosphorylation (shown for serine), which increases the negative charge, or by acetylation (shown for lysine) or methylation (shown for arginine) which reduce the positive charge. Such electrical changes may alter histone function.

histones are acetylated, chromatin becomes more sensitive to DNAase I. We are uncertain of the significance of this induced structural change in chromatin, however, because both active and inactive genes become acetylated nonpreferentially.

Histone H2A is often recovered in a conjugate with the nonhistone protein **ubiquitin** (so named for its ubiquitous occurrence in prokaryotic and eukaryotic cells). In the conjugate, referred to as *UH2A*, the C-terminal glycine of ubiquitin is linked to lysine at position 119 of H2A (Fig. 15.42). The two components share a common C-terminus but each retains its original N-terminus. The acidic nature of ubiquitin lowers the basicity of the conjugate, so UH2A has different properties from basic H2A alone, although there is no noticeable structural difference between ubiquinated and nonubiquinated nucleosomes. Studies using probes of active and inactive genes, however, suggest that there is a tendency for UH2A to be concentrated in the nucleosomes of transcribed sequences. At the present time, we know little about the function of ubiquitin in the

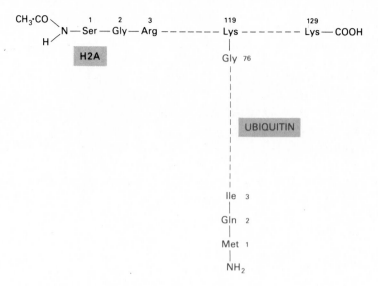

FIGURE 15-42
Histone 2A often exists in a conjugate (called UH2A) with the nonhistone protein ubiquitin. Each component of the conjugate retains its original N-terminus (which may be acetylated in the histone), but they share a common C-terminus. The conjugate tends to be concentrated in nucleosomes of transcribed DNA sequences.

nucleus, so little more can be said about its contribution to transcriptionally active chromatin.

The available evidence thus indicates that the domain constituting an active chromatin region becomes more sensitive to DNAase I as a consequence of some structural modification(s) of the nucleosomes in that region. Is there any difference in the DNA itself in these domains? If so, is the difference distributed throughout the domain or restricted to some portion(s) of the active region? In the next sections we will discuss the evidence bearing on these questions.

15.9
DNA Methylation and Transcriptional Activity

About 2% to 7% of the cytosine residues are methylated at carbon-5 in animal cell nuclei. Most of the **5-methylcytosine** (^mC) is found in highly condensed and often nontranscribed heterochromatic regions of the genome, but a scattering of ^mC residues is present in all parts of the nuclear euchromatin. These residues are principally found in CG doublets opposite each other in the DNA duplex, such that a *fully methylated* segment has the structure

$$5' - ^mCG - 3'$$
$$3' - GC^m - 5'$$

In a *hemimethylated* segment the ^mC residue is present in one strand but not in the complementary partner doublet.

The distribution of methylated CG doublets can be determined by the use of the restriction enzymes *Hpa*II and *Msp*I in restriction-fragment assays. Both enzymes cleave the same CCGG target sequences in DNA, but *Hpa*II cleaves only nonmethylated targets whereas *Msp*I cleaves both methylated and nonmethylated CCGG sequences (see Table 4.2). Gels of restriction fragments generated by *Msp*I reveal all the CG doublets present in the DNA, whereas gels of fragments generated by *Hpa*II indicate which of the fragments contain methylated CG doublets in the same DNA. Bands at the same position in the two gels indicate nonmethylated sites, and methylated sites are identified by bands that are unique in each gel. Unique smaller fragments in *Msp*I gels are replaced by larger unique fragments in *Hpa*II gels (Fig. 15.43).

Results of these restriction-fragment assays for various polypeptide-coding genes, rRNA genes, and some viral genomes showed that some sites in the DNA sequences are methylated in tissues in which the gene is not transcribed but are unmethylated or only partly methylated in tissues in which the gene is transcribed. In the case of the fetal γ-globin genes in the human β-globin gene cluster, many of the known CG sites are not methylated in fetal erythroid tissue where these genes are actively transcribed. More sites are methylated in γ-globin genes in adult erythroid tissue, and virtually all sites are methylated in nonerythroid tissues where these genes are not transcribed. A further correlation is found when methylated or nonmethylated DNA is injected into oocyte nuclei or some other suitable *in vivo* test system, and transcription is monitored. Methylated genes are inactive or barely active, whereas unmethylated genes are actively transcribed in the host system. When

FIGURE 15-43
Methylated and nonmethylated sequences containing the same CCGG target can be distinguished by restriction-fragment assays following the use of restriction enzymes *Msp*I and *Hpa*II. (a) Because *Msp*I cleaves both methylated and nonmethylated CCGG sequences, whereas *Hpa*II cleaves only nonmethylated CCGG sequences, any band(s) of restriction fragments present in the gels for both enzyme digests will represent non-methylated CCGG sequences. (b) Methylated CCGG sequences in the gel are represented by unique bands in the *Msp*I digest, which are replaced by one or more unique bands of larger fragments in the *Hpa*II digest.

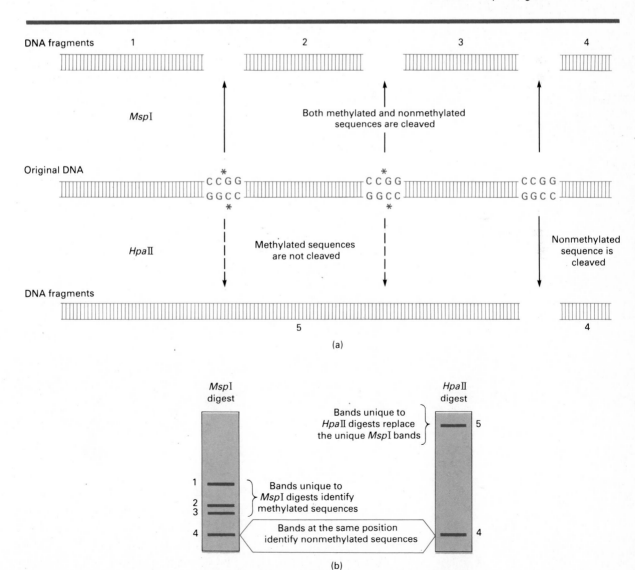

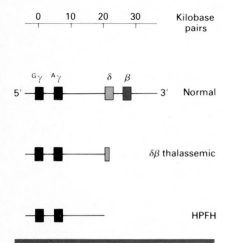

FIGURE 15-44
Deletions of δ-globin genes and
β-globin genes are responsible for
phenotypic expressions of human
blood disorders of the β-thalassemia
type. Individuals having δβ thalassemia
retain both $^G\gamma$- and $^A\gamma$-globin genes,
part of δ, and none of the β-globin gene.
In individuals with HPFH disorder, the
entire δ–β gene region is deleted. In
both disorders the γ-globin genes
guide synthesis of γ chains of fetal
hemoglobin, Hb F ($\alpha_2\gamma_2$), but normal Hb
A ($\alpha_2\beta_2$ or $\alpha_2\delta_2$) is not made because
the β-globin genes and the δ-globin
genes are missing.

unmethylated DNA is methylated prior to being introduced into the host cell, the methylated sequences fail to be transcribed or are transcribed at a greatly reduced rate. All these data indicate that active gene domains are undermethylated. Significantly, the distribution of under-methylated sites coincides with sites in active chromatin that are sensitive to DNAase I.

In another approach, the drug *5-azacytidine*, an analog of cytidine, was shown to activate globin genes that were turned off in a line of mouse leukemia cells. The analog cannot be methylated; cytidine can. When 5-azacytidine is incorporated into DNA during replication, it remains unmethylated whereas incorporated cytidine residues are converted to ^mC. The undermethylated DNA was selectively transcribed, because all the DNA was not activated in the mouse cells. Such results prompted clinical therapy on a trial basis for a few patients suffering from *sickle-cell anemia*, who make defective adult hemoglobin [Hb A ($\alpha_2\beta_2$)] because of a base substitution at position 6 in the β-globin chain. The defective Hb A is deficient in oxygen-carrying capacity, which leads to various debilitating symptoms of the blood disorder.

The aim of the clinical study was to determine whether the patients would produce functional fetal hemoglobin [Hb F ($\alpha_2\gamma_2$)] by the activation of γ-globin genes that are turned off shortly before or after birth. The treatments with 5-azacytidine indeed led to synthesis of Hb F, which helped to alleviate the distress of sickle-cell anemia in these patients. The effect was only temporary, however. Further clinical studies are clearly needed, and the therapy might be extended to individuals who suffer from one or more of the *β-thalassemias*. These inherited anemic disorders are characterized by reduced amounts of Hb A, or by its complete absence, as the result of deletions or structural alterations in the β-globin and δ-globin genes of the β-globin gene cluster [98% of adult hemoglobin is Hb A ($\alpha_2\beta_2$), and 2% is Hb A₂ ($\alpha_2\delta_2$)]. The promise of therapy to induce the synthesis of Hb F is evident in the fact that individuals who make only Hb F and no Hb A or Hb A₂ are healthy. Such individuals are characterized as having HPFH (hereditary persistance of fetal hemoglobin) syndrome, and both the β-globin genes and the δ-globin genes are deleted from chromosome 11 (Fig. 15.44, Table 15.2). The γ-globin genes remain transcriptionally

TABLE 15-2
Characteristics of β Thalassemias in Humans

Type of β Thalassemia	Clinical Symptoms	Genetic Defect	Hemoglobins in Adults
β⁺ thalassemia	mild to severe anemia*	little processing of globin pre-mRNA to mature mRNA	low Hb A ($\alpha_2\beta_2$) low Hb F ($\alpha_2\gamma_2$)
β⁰ thalassemia	mild to severe anemia*	improper regulation of gene expression	no Hb A low Hb F
δβ thalassemia	mild anemia	deletion of β globin gene and part of δ globin gene	no Hb A or Hb A₂ Hb F only, in low amounts
HPFH disorder	none	deletion of β and δ globin genes	no Hb A or Hb A₂ Hb F only, in adequate amounts

*The relative severity of clinical symptoms varies considerably and is presumed to be due to variability in the nature and/or extent of the genetic defect in the individual.

active throughout the life of such individuals, and they synthesize adequate amount of Hb F for red blood cell functions. It would be interesting to know whether these genes remain undermethylated in individuals with HPFH syndrome.

15.10
Hypersensitive Sites in Active Chromatin

When genomic chromatin is digested with *very low* concentrations of DNAase I, a set of specific fragments is generated and can be seen in gels as distinct bands whose positions indicate lengths of thousands of bases. These particular fragments result only when chromatin is digested, not when isolated DNA is digested under the same conditions. The sites of cleavage are referred to as **hypersensitive sites**, because they are cut by very mild DNAase treatment that otherwise has no effect on chromatin integrity. By probing different regions of fragments containing known genes, investigators have found that every active gene has a cleavage site at least in the region immediately upstream of the promoter. In fact, the hypersensitive upstream cutting site is present only in chromatin of cells in which the gene is active; the site is not present when the same gene is inactive. In appropriate cell systems, it has been shown that hypersensitive sites appear upon activation of a gene but may be retained for many generations after that gene has become inactive. The initiation of a hypersensitive site is thus separable from its perpetuation.

Hypersensitive sites are preferentially cleaved by a variety of nucleases when the gene can be transcribed, which indicates that such sites are structurally altered regions of chromatin. Each hypersensitive region extends over a span of 100 to 400 base pairs upstream of the transcribable gene, because such a length of chromatin is degraded by various DNA-cutting enzymes, including DNAase I, DNAase II, micro-coccal nuclease, and S1 nuclease (Fig. 15.45). In the SV40 minichromo-some engaged in transcribing the viral capsid genes late in the expres-sion cycle, the hypersensitive site occupies about 350 base pairs just upstream of the promoter for this transcription unit. Electron micro-graphs of these transcribing minichromosomes reveal a nucleosome-free gap of about 120 nm (about 350 base pairs), and digestion studies have shown that this gap corresponds to the nuclease-hypersensitive region (see Fig. 15.38). It may well be that other hypersensitive sites of active genes are also free of nucleosomes, which would help to explain their accessibility to nuclease attack over the whole length of the DNA sequence. This SV40 hypersensitive site contains the replication origin

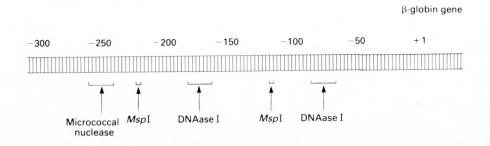

β-globin gene

-300   -250   -200   -150   -100   -50   +1

Micrococcal *Msp*I   DNAase I   *Msp*I   DNAase I
nuclease

FIGURE 15-45
The hypersensitive region of the human β-globin gene extends for a stretch of about 250 base pairs upstream of the startpoint of transcription (+1 nucleotide). The sites sensitive to the DNA-cutting enzymes micrococcal nuclease, DNAase I, and *Msp*I have been mapped and are indicated just below the DNA duplex.

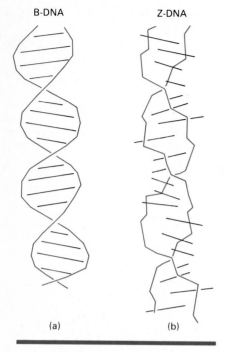

FIGURE 15-46

Duplex DNA may exist in a number of conformational states, including B-DNA with a right-handed spiral and Z-DNA with a left-handed spiral. Each model has been drawn to show the continuous helical lines of joined phosphate residues (color) in the backbone of each strand, and short horizontal lines show the positions of AT and GC base pairs (black) along the length of the helical axis. B-DNA is the principal conformational state of cellular DNA molecules, but short regions of Z-DNA may be interspersed with the predominating B form in DNA duplex molecules.

as well as promoter and enhancer sequences that regulate transcription. Specific proteins, such as initiation proteins and RNA polymerase, bind to these sites when they are accessible.

The mechanism that generates a hypersensitive site, like the mechanism of differential methylation of active and inactive genes, remains uncertain. One intriguing possible mechanism related to both of these phenomena involves the conformationally reversible states of DNA in its B-form and its Z-form. Sequences of alternating purines and pyrimidines, but particularly $(CG)_n$ sequences, tend to favor the left-handed spiral configuration of **Z-DNA** over the right-handed spiral configuration of B-DNA (Fig. 15.46). Z-DNA is very stable under physiological conditions if its C residues are methylated. If methylated Z-DNA sequences were present in a domain, the region would be transcriptionally inactive or less active. When demethylated, however, Z-DNA regions would revert more readily to their B-form and thereby become potentially transcribable. Conversion of Z-DNA to B-DNA would produce torsional stress leading to unwinding of the duplex and would thereby expose different protein-binding sites. Unwinding due to stress might break the DNA strand in one or more places, producing single-stranded regions that could be detected by S1 nuclease, which specifically degrades single-stranded DNA. The conformational change might also expose the DNA to attack by duplex-cutting nucleases, including DNAase I and II, micrococcal nuclease, and restriction enzymes. A hypersensitive site might thus be produced as a result of the conformational change from Z-DNA to B-DNA. Some preliminary evidence has been obtained in support of these events, particularly for the SV40 minichromosome.

By the use of fluorescent-tagged anti-Z-DNA antibodies, three segments of Z-DNA were identified in the SV40 minichromosome, and each segment was located by the use of restriction mapping. Each segment consisted of eight base pairs of alternating purines and pyrimidines, but two of the segments were identical and were situated in the 72-base-pair repeat *enhancer* sequences (Fig. 15.47). As mentioned in Section 13.4, enhancers stimulate transcription but are not considered

FIGURE 15-47

Three segments of Z-DNA in the 5243 base pairs of the SV40 genome have been located in a short region (see scale above) near the origin of replication. Two identical sequences of 8 alternating purine and pyrimidine residues are situated within the 72 base pairs of the enhancer repeats, and a third Z segment is located just upstream of the two enhancers. Conformational changes from the Z form to the B form of DNA in these segments may lead to the exposure of a hypersensitive site and thereby influence gene expression. (From Rich, A., et al., 1984, *Ann. Rev. Biochem.* **53**: 791–846, Fig. 12.)

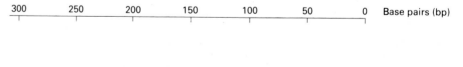

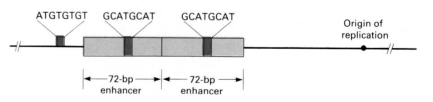

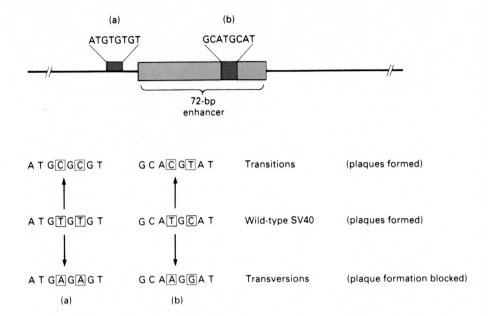

FIGURE 15-48
Effects of base substitution in Z-DNA
sequences [(a) and (b)] in SV40
variants containing only one of the two
enhancer repeats (see Fig. 15.48). Two
pyrimidines (boxed) were substituted
in each Z segment. When other
pyrimidines (T → C, C → T) were
substituted for pyrimidines T and G,
the Z-DNA conformation remained
unchanged because the sequence still
consisted of alternating purines and
pyrimidines. Such transitional mutants
retained their ability to reproduce and
form plaques. When purines A and G
were substituted for pyrimidines T and
C, however, the favored alternating
purine-pyrimidine sequence for Z-DNA
no longer existed. In such transversion
mutants viral reproduction and plaque
formation were blocked. These data
indicate that Z-DNA may play a role in
regulating gene expression. (From
Rich, A., et al., 1984, *Ann. Rev.
Biochem.* **53**: 791–846, Fig. 13.)

part of a promoter. In SV40 variants containing only one of the two enhancer repeats, the effects of base substitution in the Z-DNA sequence were tested by measuring the ability of the virus to reproduce and form plaques. When a purine was replaced by a pyrimidine or a pyrimidine by a purine (transversions), the alternating purine–pyrimidine sequence favored by Z-DNA was disrupted and the virus was inactivated. When a purine was replaced by another purine or a pyrimidine by another pyrimidine (transitions), the favored Z-DNA sequence was retained and there was no significant effect on viral activities (Fig. 15.48). These studies indicate the importance of Z-DNA in regulating transcriptional activity, but evidence that is more detailed and is obtained in a variety of other systems is required before specific conclusions can be reached about the cause-and-effect relationship of Z-DNA and the generation of a hypersensitive site. Some promising lines of study are now being pursued.

Transcriptionally active genes thus differ in at least three ways from their inactive state. (1) The nucleosomes of the active gene and its flanking regions, a chromosome domain, become highly sensitive to DNAase I. (2) The DNA of this domain is undermethylated. (3) One or more hypersensitive sites become established upstream of, but near to, the promoter. All these features accompany unfolding of the portion of a chromatin fiber carrying one or more active genes, due to local conformational changes involving nucleosome spacing, organization, and numbers. The accessibility and subsequent binding of catalytic, regulatory, and structural proteins to DNA is obviously influenced by the conformational information provided by the chromatin fiber.

The complexity of the eukaryotic chromosome is evident in its differentiated structures, nucleosomal organization, repetitive DNAs, and other features we have discussed in this and other chapters. The replication, stability, and accurate segregation of eukaryotic chromosomes require a minimum of three special regions in each chromosome of the genome: specific and unique origins of replication (see Section 12.2), one centromere, and two telomeres. Each of these regions of a chromosome is unique by virtue of its DNA sequence and proteins that are either permanently or transiently associated with the sequence. In addition, the structure and conformation of each region is unique, and no other part of the chromosome can be substituted for these three essential, differentiated regions. Transcriptionally active chromatin has no unique base sequence information, but conformational changes signal DNA-binding proteins to loosen or unbind and thereby allow transcription, or to bind tightly and stimulate transcription. Thanks to the precision, sensitivity, accuracy, speed, and flexibility of molecular methods for chromosomal analysis, astonishing progress has been made in a very short time. We can look forward to continued progress and a greater understanding of the eukaryotic genome in the immediate future.

Summary

The eukaryotic cell nucleus is essential for cell reproduction. It is surrounded by a nuclear envelope consisting of two membranes separated by a perinuclear space. The outer membrane is continuous with the rough endoplasmic reticulum and probably functions in protein synthesis and transport; the inner membrane is associated with the nuclear lamina, a protein meshwork that stabilizes nuclear form and to which chromatin binds. At intervals the two membranes may be fused. Nuclear pore complexes occur at these sites of membrane fusion, and they consist of annuli of 8 radially symmetric protein granules defining a 9-nm channel (nuclear pore) that promotes or hinders the passage of substances across the envelope between the nucleoplasm and the cytoplasm.

The nucleolus, a spherical structure associated with the nucleolar-organizing region (NOR) of specific chromosomes, is a center for the synthesis and processing of ribosomal RNA (rRNA) and the assembly of ribosomal subunits. Within the nucleolar matrix one can recognize the 10-nm-wide loops of nucleolar chromatin, the 5-nm-wide fibrils of ribonucleoprotein transcripts, and the 15-nm particles that correspond to maturing ribosome subunits. Nucleoli disappear at metaphase of nuclear division and reappear after telophase. They grow and merge to form the mature interphase structure with its concentrated activity of RNA polymerase III, the enzyme that transcribes rRNA genes (rDNA).

Chromatin is the stainable chromosomal material of all nuclei. In interphase, chromatin appears as an extended tangle of deoxyribonucleoprotein fibers, but at mitosis or meiosis, each deoxynucleoprotein molecule condenses to form a typical and recognizable chromosome structure. Each metaphase chromosome has a characteristic appearance determined by its size, the position of the centromere and secondary constrictions, and the pattern of G-banding after staining that allows the chromosomes to be analyzed in a karyotype.

Even in interphase, however, not all chromatin is functionally or structurally equivalent. Heterochromatin remains highly condensed, whereas euchromatin is more dispersed, which allows it to be transcribed. Facultative heterochromatin may become activated under certain environmental or developmental conditions. For example, in female mammals one of the two X chromosomes in each cell is inactivated after the early stages of embryogenesis, but in oocytes and early embryos the second X chromosome is reactivated. The inactive X forms a densely condensed heterochromatic body (Barr body), which is visible in interphase nuclei. By contrast, constitutive heterochromatin remains condensed at all times and is transcriptionally inactive. For example, the centromere region of vertebrate chromosomes consists of constitutive heterochromatin at each side of the kinetochore to which spindle fibers attach during nuclear division. Centromeric heterochromatin has an apparent genetic function, but it helps stabilize the region bounding the essential kinetochore. Cloning studies have revealed that yeast centromeres have a sequence of 107 to 114 base pairs of DNA with three characteristic regions essential for accurate chromosome segregation during nuclear division. The sequence and longer stretches on either side are organized in displays of phased nucleosomes, a means of nucleoprotein condensation. The telomere regions at the end of chromosomes ensure accurate completion of replication of the linear DNA molecules and prevent fusion of intact ends of different chromosomes.

Because transcription occurs at a phase when the chromosomes cannot be individually recognized, it is difficult to study the structural changes associated with gene activity. Studies have been made on the giant polytene somatic chromosomes of dipteran larvae and on lampbrush chromosomes of amphibian oocytes during meiosis. In both cases, specific regions of the chromosome that are serving as sites for RNA synthesis become unfolded (puffed) or looped out. It is not clear what happens to nucleosomes during transcription, but they seem to be less abundant in active regions.

Another approach correlates transcriptional activity of sequences with their sensitivity to mild treatment with nucleases such as DNAase I. Treatments that solubilize only 10% of the genome destroy 50% of active genes. This preferential degradation extends into the chromosomal domain around the active gene. There is substantial structural change in the DNA during gene activity. DNAase digestion also releases two high-mobility-group (HMG) proteins, implicating them in chromatin accessibility for transcription. Acetylation, methylation, or phosphorylation of histones increases the sensitivity of chromatin to digestion and may have functional significance. Binding of ubiquitin to histone H2A occurs selectively in active regions.

Methylation of cytosine residues in certain regions of the DNA is correlated with inactivity of those genes. Genes may be active and unmethylated at one development stage, whereas they are inactive and methylated at another. Inactive genes may be activated at least temporarily by treatments that prevent methylation. Just upstream from each active promoter is a region that is hypersensitive to DNAase digestion. The hypersensitivity exists only in chromatin with gene activity, but it may persist for many generations after the gene has become inactive, so some modification of the chromatin probably occurred during the activation process. One possible modification is a transition from inactive Z-DNA regions to regions that assume the right-handed helix shape of B-DNA.

Readings and References

Aaronson, R. P., and G. Blobel. 1975. Isolation of nuclear pore complexes in association with a lamina. *Proc. Natl. Acad. Sci. U. S.* **72**:1007.

Azorin, F., and A. Rich. 1985. Isolation of Z-DNA binding proteins from SV40 minichromosomes: Evidence for binding to the viral control region. *Cell* **41**:365.

Beermann, W., and U. Clever. April 1964. Chromosome puffs. *Sci. Amer.* **210**:50.

Bensaude, O., C. Babinet, M. Morange, and F. Jacob. 1983. Heat shock proteins, first major products of zygotic gene activity in mouse embryo. *Nature* **305**:331.

Berg, P. 1981. Dissections and reconstructions of genes and chromosomes. *Science* **213**:296 (Nobel lecture).

Bienz, M. 1985. Transient and developmental activation of heat shock genes. *Trends Biochem. Sci.* **10**:157.

Bird, A. P. 1984. DNA methylation—how important in gene control? *Nature* **307**:503.

Blackburn, E. H. 1984. Telomeres: Do the ends justify the means? *Cell* **37**:7.

Blackburn, E. H. 1985. Artificial chromosomes in yeast. *Trends Genet.* **1**:8.

Blackburn, E. H., and J. W. Szostak. 1984. The molecular structure of centromeres and telomeres. *Ann. Rev. Biochem.* **53**:163.

Bloom, K. S., *et al.* 1984. Chromatin conformation of yeast centromeres. *J. Cell. Biol.* **99**:1559.

Bonven, B. J., E. Gocke, and O. Westergaard. 1985. A high-affinity topoisomerase I binding sequence is clustered at DNAase I hypersensitive sites in *Tetrahymena* R-chromatin. *Cell* **41**:541.

Brown, S. W. 1966. Heterochromatin. *Science* **151**:417.

Busslinger, M., J. Hurst, and R. A. Flavell. 1983. DNA methylation and the regulation of globin expression. *Cell* **34**:197.

Caspersson, T., G. Lomakka, and L. Zech. 1971. The 24 fluorescence patterns of the human metaphase chromosomes—distinguishing characters and variability. *Hereditas* **67**:89.

Cavalier-Smith, T. 1983. Cloning chromosome ends. *Nature* **301**:112.

Church, G. M., and W. Gilbert. 1984. Genomic sequencing. *Proc. Natl. Acad. Sci. U. S.* **81**:1991.

Clarke, L., and J. Carbon. 1980. Isolation of a yeast centromere and construction of functional small circular chromosomes. *Nature* **287**:504.

Clarke, L., and J. Carbon. 1983. Genomic substitutions of centromeres in *Saccharomyces cerevisiae*. *Nature* **305**:23.

Cohen, J. S. 1980. DNA: Is the backbone boring? *Trends Biochem. Sci.* **5**:58.

Cold Spring Harbor Symposia on Quantitative Biology. 1983. *DNA Structures*, vol. 47.

De Lange, T., and P. Borst. 1982. Genomic environment of the expression-linked extra copies of genes for surface antigens of *Trypanosoma brucei* resembles the end of a chromosome. *Nature* **299**:451.

Dickerson, R. E., *et al.* 1982. The anatomy of A-, B-, and Z-DNA. *Science* **216**:475.

Dingwall, C. 1985. The accumulation of proteins in the nucleus. *Trends Biochem. Sci.* **10**:64.

Döerfler, W. 1983. DNA methylation and gene activity. *Ann. Rev. Biochem.* **52**:93.

Donelson, J. E., and M. J. Turner. February 1985. How the trypanosome changes its coat. *Sci. Amer.* **252**:44.

Drets, M. E., and M. W. Shaw. 1971. Specific banding patterns of human chromosomes. *Proc. Natl. Acad. Sci. U. S.* **68**:2073.

Ehrlich, M., and R. Y.-H. Wang. 1981. 5-Methylcytosine in eukaryotic DNA. *Science* **212**:1350.

Elgin, S. C. R. 1981. DNAase I-hypersensitive sites of chromatin. *Cell* **27**:413.

Felsenfeld, G. 1978. Chromatin. *Nature* **271**:115.

Felsenfeld, G., and J. McGhee. 1982. Methylation and gene control. *Nature* **296**:602.

Franke, W. W., U. Scheer, G. Krohne, and E.-D. Jarasch. 1981. The nuclear envelope and the architecture of the nuclear periphery. *J. Cell Biol.* **91**:39s.

Gall, J. G. 1967. Octagonal nuclear pores. *J. Cell Biol.* **32**:391.

Gall, J. G. 1981. Chromosome structure and the C-value paradox. *J. Cell Biol.* **91**:3s.

Gartler, S. M., and A. D. Riggs. 1983. Mammalian X-chromosome inactivation. *Ann. Rev. Genet.* **17**:155.

Gates, D. M., and I. Bekhor. 1980. Distribution of active gene sequences: A subset associated with tightly bound chromosomal proteins. *Science* **207**:661.

Gottschling, D. E., and T. R. Cech. 1984. Chromatin structure of the molecular ends of *Oxytricha* macronuclear DNA: Phased nucleosomes and a telomeric complex. *Cell* **38**:501.

Groudine, M., and K. F. Conklin. 1985. Chromatin structure and *de novo* methylation of sperm DNA: Implications for activation of the paternal genome. *Science* **228**:1061.

Hamkalo, B. A., M. R. Goldsmith, and J. B. Rattner. 1981. Higher-order structure in chromosomes. In *International Cell Biology 1980–1981*, ed. H. G. Schweiger, p. 152. New York: Rockefeller University Press.

Jähner, D., *et al.* 1982. *De novo* methylation and expression of retroviral genomes during mouse embryogenesis. *Nature* **298**:623.

Johnson, E. M., G. R. Campbell, and V. G. Allfrey. 1979. Different nucleosome structures on transcribing and nontranscribing ribosomal gene sequences. *Science* **206**:1192.

Jongstra, J., *et al*. 1984. Induction of altered chromatin structures by simian virus 40 enhancer and promoter elements. *Nature* **307**:708.

Kavenoff, R. L., L. C. Klotz, and B. H. Zimm. 1974. On the nature of chromosome-sized DNA molecules. *Cold Spring Harbor Sympos. Quant. Biol.* **38**:1.

Kerem, B.-S., *et al*. 1984. Mapping of DNAase I sensitive regions of mitotic chromosomes. *Cell* **38**:493.

Kolata, G. 1981. Z-DNA. *Science* **214**:1108.

Kolata, G. 1984. New clues to gene regulation. *Science* **224**:588.

Larsen, A., and H. Weintraub. 1982. An altered DNA conformation detected by S1 nuclease occurs at specific regions in active chick globin chromatin. *Cell* **29**:609.

Levinger, L., and A. Varshavsky. 1982. Selective arrangement of ubiquitinated and D1 protein-containing nucleosomes within the *Drosophila* genome. *Cell* **28**:375.

Levy, A., and M. Noll. 1981. Chromatin fine structure of active and repressed genes. *Nature* **289**:198.

Lewin, B. 1985. *Genes*. 2nd ed. New York: Wiley.

Ley, T. J., *et al*. 1982. 5-Azacytidine selectively increases γ-globin synthesis in a patient with β^+ thalassemia. *New Engl. J. Med.* **307**:1469.

Lyon, M. F. 1972. X-chromosome inactivation and developmental patterns in mammals. *Biol. Rev.* **47**:1.

Lyon, M. F. 1974. Evolution of X-chromosome inactivation in mammals. *Nature* **250**:651.

Maekawa, H., and Y. Suzuki. 1980. Repeated turn-off and turn-on of fibroin gene transcription during silk gland development of *Bombyx mori*. *Dev. Biol.* **78**:394.

Maniatis, T., *et al*. 1980. The molecular genetics of human hemoglobins. *Ann. Rev. Genet.* **14**:145.

Mardian, J. K. W., A. E. Paton, G. J. Bunick, and D. E. Olins. 1980. Nucleosome cores have two specific binding sites for nonhistone chromosomal proteins HMG 14 and HMG 17. *Science* **209**:1534.

Martin, G. R. 1982. X-chromosome inactivation in mammals. *Cell* **29**:721.

Miller, O. L., Jr. 1981. The nucleolus, chromosomes, and visualization of genetic activity. *J. Cell Biol.* **91**:15s.

Mohandas, T., R. S. Sparkes, and L. J. Shapiro. 1981. Reactivation of an inactive human X chromosome: Evidence for X-inactivation by DNA methylation. *Science* **211**:393.

Mondello, C., and P. N. Goodfellow. 1985. Methylation and expression of a housekeeping gene. *Trends Genet.* **1**:124.

Murray, A. W. 1985. Chromosome structure and behaviour. *Trends Biochem. Sci.* **10**:112.

Orkin, S. H., and A. Michelson. 1980. Partial deletion of the α-globin structural gene in human α-thalassemia. *Nature* **286**:538.

Papayannopoulou, T., *et al*. 1984. A haemoglobin switching activity modulates hereditary persistence of fetal haemoglobin. *Nature* **309**:71.

Pelham, H. 1985. Activation of heat-shock genes in eukaryotes. *Trends Genet.* **1**:31.

Razin, A., and A. D. Riggs. 1980. DNA methylation and gene function. *Science* **210**:604.

Reeves, R., and A. Jones. 1976. Genomic transcriptional activity and the structure of chromatin. *Nature* **260**:495.

Rich, A., A. Nordheim, and A. H.-J. Wang. 1984. The chemistry and biology of left-handed Z-DNA. *Ann. Rev. Biochem.* **53**:791.

Ris, H., and P. L. Witt. 1981. Structure of the mammalian kinetochore. *Chromosoma* **82**:153.

Roth, M., and D. M. Prescott. 1985. DNA intermediates and telomere addition during genome reorganization in *Euplotes crassus*. *Cell* **41**:411.

Sandeen, G., W. I. Wood, and G. Felsenfeld. 1980. The interaction of high-mobility proteins HMG 14 and HMG 17 with nucleosomes. *Nucleic Acids Res.* **8**:3757.

Schlesinger, M. J., G. Aliperti, and P. M. Kelley. 1982. The response of cells to heat shock. *Trends Biochem. Sci.* **7**:222.

Schlissel, M. S., and D. D. Brown. 1984. The transcriptional regulation of *Xenopus* 5S RNA genes in chromatin: The roles of active stable transcription complexes and histone H1. *Cell* **37**:903.

Schöler, H. R., and P. Gruss. 1984. Specific interaction between enhancer-containing molecules and cellular components. *Cell* **36**:403.

Sinibaldi, R. M., and P. W. Morris. 1981. Putative function of *Drosophila melanogaster* heat shock proteins in the nucleoskeleton. *J. Biol. Chem.* **256**:10735.

Smith, G. R. 1981. DNA supercoiling: Another level for regulating gene expression. *Cell* **24**:599.

Smith, H. O. 1979. Nucleotide sequence specificity of restriction endonucleases. *Science* **205**:455 (Nobel lecture).

Smith, R. D., and J. Yu. 1984. Alterations in globin gene chromatin conformation during murine erythroleukemia cell differentiation. *J. Biol. Chem.* **259**:4609.

Struhl, K. 1983. The new yeast genetics. *Nature* **305**:391.

Tjio, J. H., and A. Levan. 1956. The chromosome number of man. *Hereditas* **42**:1.

Van der Ploeg, L. H. T., *et al*. 1980. γ-δ-Thalassemia studies showing that deletion of the γ- and δ-genes influences β-globin gene expression. *Nature* **283**:637.

Van der Ploeg, L. H. T., S. H. Giannini, and C. R. Cantor. 1985. Heat shock genes: Regulatory role for differentiation in parasitic protozoa. *Science* **228**:1443.

Vlad, M., and H. C. Macgregor. 1975. Chromomere number and its genetic significance in lampbrush chromosome. *Chromosoma* **50**:327.

Wang, A. H.-J., *et al*. 1979. Molecular structure of a left-handed double helical DNA fragment at atomic resolution. *Nature* **282**:680.

Weintraub, H. 1983. A dominant role for DNA secondary structure in forming hypersensitive structures in chromatin. *Cell* **32**:1191.

Weintraub, H., and M. Groudine. 1976. Chromosomal subunits in active genes have an altered conformation. *Science* **193**:848.

Weisbrod, S. 1982. Active chromatin. *Nature* **297**:289.

Weisbrod, S., M. Groudine, and H. Weintraub. 1980. Interaction of HMG 14 and 17 with actively transcribed genes. *Cell* **19**:289.

White, M. J. D. 1973. *The Chromosomes*. 6th ed. London: Chapman & Hall.

Wood, W. I., and G. Felsenfeld. 1982. Chromatin structure of the chicken β-globin gene region. Sensitivity to DNase I, micrococcal nuclease, and DNase II. *J. Biol. Chem.* **257**:7730.

Wu, C. 1980. The 5′ ends of *Drosophila* heat shock genes in chromatin are sensitive to DNase I. *Nature* **286**:854.

Wu, C. 1984. Activating protein factor binds *in vitro* to upstream control sequences in heat-shock gene chromatin. *Nature* **311**:81.

Yuan, R., and D. L. Hamilton. 1982. Restriction and modification of DNA by a complex protein. *Amer. Sci.* **70**:61.

Yunis, J. J., and O. Prakash. 1982. The origin of man: A chromosomal pictorial legacy. *Science* **215**:1525.

Yunis, J. J., J. R. Sawyer, and K. Dunham. 1980. The striking resemblance of high-resolution G-banded chromosomes of man and chimpanzee. *Science* **208**:1145.

Zakian, V. A. 1984. Architecture of interphase nuclei. *Nature* **308**:406.

Zentgraf, H., *et al.* 1979. Mitochondrial DNA arranged into chromatin-like structures after injection into amphibian oocyte nuclei. *Exp. Cell Res.* **122**:363.

PART V

Reproduction and Development

CHAPTER 16

Cell Growth and Division

By the mid-nineteenth century it was firmly established that life comes from pre-existing life and cells from pre-existing cells, by the processes of **reproduction**. Each new cell receives a full set of genetic instructions, which means that the genome is faithfully replicated in parent cells and is then distributed to progeny cells by orderly processes that are repeated over countless generations. These events take place during a *cell cycle* and they involve the *replication of DNA* and the *orderly segregation of chromosomes* during *mitosis*. In addition, new macromolecules of all sorts must be synthesized as the parent cell grows and ultimately gives rise to two daughter cells. A multicellular organism is comprised of different kinds of cells in tissues and organs, and these may grow and divide at different rates and under different sets of conditions, even though they all contain the same genes. The controls over growth rate and division rate are among the least understood features of cell and developmental biology, and they provide some of the most challenging areas of cell study. We will address some of these phenomena and processes in this chapter and continue the discussion in the next chapter.

Cell Growth

Each one of us is made up of trillions of cells all of which are descendants of the initial fertilized egg. As the organism grows and develops, each tissue and every organ are formed in orderly progression, and each must function in its own way during the lifetime of the organism. Very few of the original embryonic cells remain in the individual, however, and the vast majority must be replaced or at least make new molecules and structures as the old parts wear out. Cell renewal can be studied in the intact organism, but certain kinds of studies are more easily accomplished in cell cultures where conditions can be standardized and manipulated. Some fundamental insights into controls over cell growth and division have been derived from studies of cells in culture.

16.1
Cell Renewal

Populations of cells in complex organisms undergo cell replacement and turnover of their macromolecular components, or **cell renewal**. Some kinds of cells, such as cardiac muscle and many nerve cells, are mitotically inactive, but even such differentiated cells replenish their molecules and structures under the influence of appropriate stimuli. Once lost, however, these cells cannot be replaced. For the great majority of differentiated tissues, new cells replace damaged or worn-out cells by mitotic divisions in either of two kinds of programs: (1) division of existing differentiated cells to produce pairs of daughter cells of the same type or (2) division of undifferentiated progenitor cells that give rise to a pair of dissimilar daughter cells; one daughter cell remains undifferentiated and functions like its parent cell, and the other daughter cell enters a pathway of differentiation and becomes capable of performing some other, unique function in the organism. Progenitor cells in animals are usually called **stem cells**, and in higher plants they are referred to as **meristematic cells**.

The liver is an organ composed of different tissues or cell types, all of which can be renewed by simple division to produce daughter cells like themselves. The principal cell in liver tissue is the **hepatocyte**, which performs the essential liver function of absorbing nutrients from the gut and transferring these substances to the bloodstream after processing. Nutrients and other materials are also degraded in the hepatocyte or are stored there for subsequent processing and use; glycogen is a major carbohydrate storage product in hepatocyte cytoplasm (Fig. 16.1). Like many other organs, the liver includes blood vessels, by which nutrients are provided and wastes removed, and fibroblasts that are part of the matrix of connective tissue. Cells in all these tissues of the liver are renewed by division of a differentiated parent cell to produce a pair of similar, differentiated daughter cells that are functionally and morphologically like the parent cell.

The liver normally displays a relatively slow rate of renewal and turnover, but the rate of cell proliferation can be increased substantially when a portion of the liver is damaged or surgically removed. Once the liver has regained nearly its original mass, the rate of cell growth and division returns to its previously slow rhythm. One or more factors circulated in the blood appear to stimulate mitosis, but we know virtually nothing about these components at the present time. Under normal conditions the various cell types and tissues are formed coordinately so that the mixture is properly organized and in balance, although we don't know how the situation is adjusted and the final mass controlled.

Regeneration may proceed abnormally if the liver is subjected to repeated abuse; the hepatocytes fail to regain their vitality for sustained division, and some other kind of cell increases and fills the available space. Repeated poisoning with alcohol, for example, leads to excessive increase in fibroblasts as hepatocytes become incapable of coping with and disposing of the alcohol. With the increase in connective tissue, the liver becomes less and less capable of handling its standard functions, and hepatocytes have little space in which to grow even when the toxic

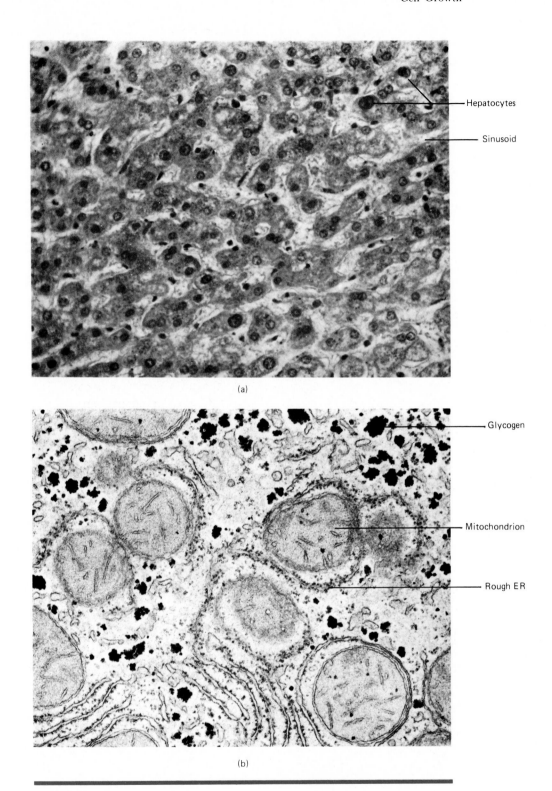

(a)

Hepatocytes

Sinusoid

(b)

Glycogen

Mitochondrion

Rough ER

FIGURE 16-1

Mouse liver hepatocytes. (a) Light micrograph of a liver section containing hepatocytes, the most abundant cell type, and anastomosing sinusoids through which blood circulates among the cells. ×400. (b) Electron micrograph of a rat liver hepatocyte containing glycogen, a storage form of glucose, in the form of granules deposited in the cytoplasm. ×25,000. (Photograph a courtesy of B. Babiarz, photograph b courtesy of M. Federman.)

agent is no longer supplied. This condition of the liver is called *cirrhosis*, and it is the result of chronic alcohol abuse.

Cell renewal through the agency of dividing stem cells or meristematic cells is characteristic of many tissues, including the mammalian epidermis, blood-forming tissues, and the vascular tissues of higher plants. A common feature of all these systems is that the derived tissue must be replenished continually but that the ultimate differentiated cells themselves cannot divide. The function of the stem cells, therefore, is to replenish damaged and worn-out cells of the differentiated tissue. Although the stem cells themselves are undifferentiated and nondescript in appearance, they are *committed* to produce only one or a few specific kinds of differentiated cells. Unlike early embryonic cells that can produce all the different cells of body and are therefore *totipotent* (see Section 14.1), stem cells are **unipotent** (produce one kind of cell) or **pluripotent** (produce two or more kinds of cells).

Cells of the mammalian epidermis arise from unipotent stem cells of the *basal cell layer* that abuts the basal lamina that separates the overlying epidermis from the underlying dermis. The various layers of epidermal tissue represent different stages of cellular progress to the surface of the skin and different stages of their transformation into keratinized *squamous cells* that lose their nucleus and ultimately flake off (Fig. 16.2). The rate of stem cell proliferation appears to be regulated by various growth factors and hormones, as well as by the thickness of the skin over the

FIGURE 16-2
Light micrograph of a section of skin from mouse embryo. Connective tissue containing fibroblasts in extracellular matrix (collagen, elastin, proteoglycans, and other components) lies beneath the layers of dermis and epidermis of the skin tissue. ×600. (Photograph courtesy of B. Babiarz.)

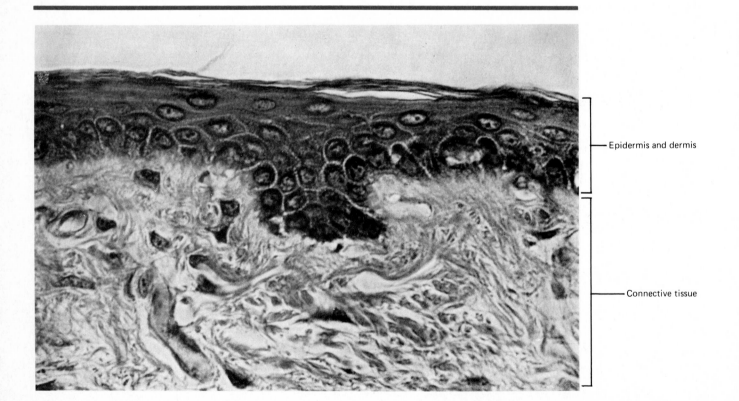

Epidermis and dermis

Connective tissue

TABLE 16-1
Types of Blood Cells and Their Functions

Type of Blood Cell	Principal Functions
Erythrocytes (red blood cells)	Transport of O_2 and CO_2
Leucocytes (white blood cells)	
Neutrophils (polymorphonuclear leucocytes)	Destroy bacteria
Eosinophils	Destroy larger parasites; influence allergic responses
Basophils	Release histamine in certain immune responses
B lymphocytes	Produce circulating antibodies
T lymphocytes	Interact with tumor cells, virally infected cells, and engage in other immune responses
Monocytes	Develop into macrophages in tissues
Megakaryocytes	Fragment to platelets, which initiate blood clotting

basal cell layer. When outer layers of the epidermis are removed, stem cells of the basal layer divide at a greater rate. The rate of division returns to normal when the new region of epidermis reaches approximately normal thickness. The nature of the stimulatory effect of epidermis removal and of the inhibitory effect of epidermis restoration are not well understood.

Pluripotent blood-forming (*hematopoietic*) stem cells in the bone marrow are of a single type, but they produce all the different kinds of blood cells. Red blood cells, or **erythrocytes**, carry hemoglobin throughout the body and engage in the exchange of O_2 and CO_2. **Megakaryocytes** are huge polyploid cells that fragment to "minicells" that become platelets and function in blood clotting and in repair of blood vessel walls. Various kinds of white blood cells, or **leucocytes**, provide different lines of defense against infection, immunogenic agents, and inflammation (Table 16.1). All these kinds of blood cells spend some part of their lifetime, which is generally rather brief, freely circulating in the body, and all must be renewed continually. Erythrocytes are the most abundant type of blood cell, and they are produced at the astonishingly high rate of about 2 million per second in human beings (Fig. 16.3). Mature human erythrocytes survive for about 120 days, devoid of virtually all their cellular structures; they are destroyed in the liver and spleen by being engulfed and digested by macrophages. Leucocytes are far less numerous than erythrocytes (they exist in a ratio of about 1 to 1000), and they have variable life expectancies. Neutrophils survive for a few days, whereas T and B lymphocytes may survive for years. The different kinds of blood cells, their different proportions in the body, and their different life expectancies necessitate complex sets of controls by which the balance is maintained and by which the production of any one or more of these cell types can meet the needs of the organism under different conditions of health and activity. We know that, in some cases, reproduction is hormonally regulated in cells that

FIGURE 16-3
Scanning electron micrograph of mammalian blood cells in a blood vessel. The flattened, smooth-surface erythrocytes are readily distinguished from the spherical, rough-surface leucocytes. ×3975. (Photograph courtesy of R. G. Kessel, from Kessel, R. G., and R. H. Kardon, 1979, *Tissues and Organs: A Text-Atlas of Scanning Electron Microscopy*. W. H. Freeman and Company. Copyright © 1979.)

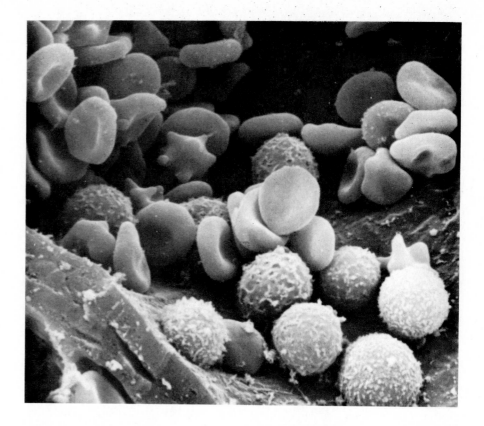

FIGURE 16-4
Stem cells of the bone marrow are pluripotent (they produce more than one kind of differentiated cell) and hematopoietic (all the cells are components of the blood system). Some of the precursor and differentiated blood cells that arise from bone marrow stem cells are illustrated here.

have already become committed to a particular pathway of differentiation but still occur in a precursor form (Fig. 16.4).

The glycoprotein hormone *erythropoietin*, produced chiefly in the kidney, is synthesized and secreted in large amounts in response to the loss of erythrocytes during bleeding. The hormone acts only on precur-

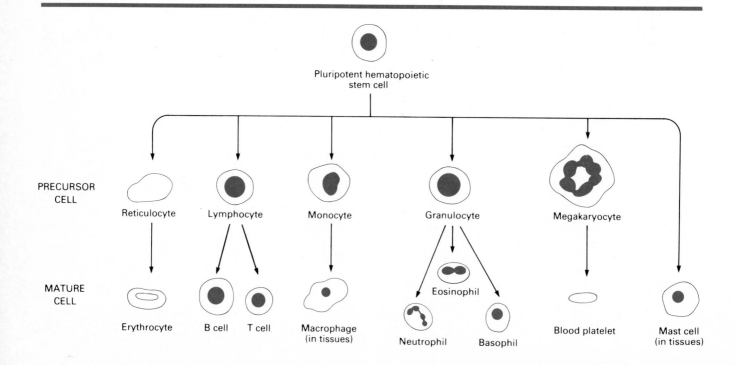

sor cells committed to become erythrocytes and stimulates only these immature cells to divide and replenish the red blood cell population. The production of other types of blood cells is not affected by the hormone, so erythropoietin provides a sensitive and specific control over red blood cell production. The proliferation of committed precursor cells for the various types of white blood cells also seems to depend on the response of each kind of cell to a glycoprotein factor specific for that committed cell type. In all these cases, it is the committed precursor cell that is capable of cell division and of being stimulated to divide. The end product of differentiation, red blood cell or white blood cell in these examples, is nondividing.

In higher plants a layer of pluripotent, meristematic **cambium** cells lies between the outer, food-conducting **phloem** tissue and the inner, water-conducting **xylem** tissue (Fig. 16.5). In woody plants the cambium is revealed when the bark is removed, and it is often wet to the touch because cells have been damaged by the peeling off of bark. Cambium cells give rise to xylem vessels and tracheids when the innermost daughter cell differentiates and to phloem sieve cells and companion cells when the outermost daughter cell differentiates. The remaining daughter cell of a pair retains its undifferentiated and mitotic features, thereby perpetuating the cambium. The increase in girth of perennial woody plants, such as trees, is due to the continued addition of new xylem cells to the interior, which accumulate and are visible as annual rings in cross-sectional cuts of the tree trunk or branches. Wood consists of these annual accumulations of xylem tissue, which lose their contents and die at maturity. Phloem cells are living, and they are substantially replaced rather than accumulated during the life of a perennial plant. The decision to differentiate as a xylem or a phloem cell

FIGURE 16-5
Light micrograph of a cross-section of woody stem, showing the cambium layer that produces food-conducting phloem tissue toward the outside and water-conducting xylem tissue toward the inside. (Photograph courtesy of R. Triemer.)

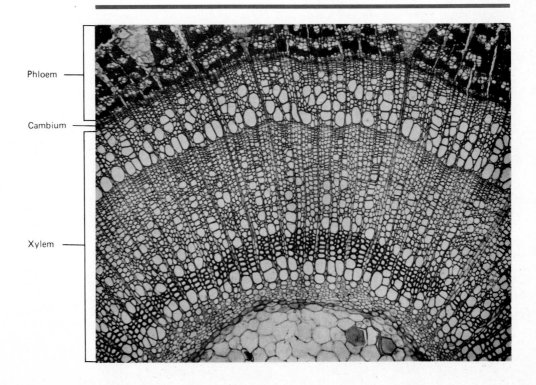

Phloem

Cambium

Xylem

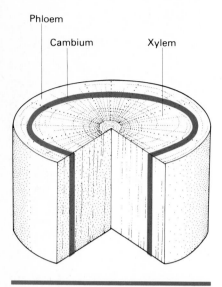

FIGURE 16-6
Drawing of a stem in three dimensions, showing the continuous cylindrical layer of meristematic cambium between the outer phloem and inner xylem tissues of the structure.

is coordinated in the entire cambial sheet, because the cambium layer is generally cylindrical and not invaginated or irregular (Fig. 16.6). Like the coordination and regulation of cambium cell divisions, the signal to produce xylem or phloem and the signal for these daughter cells to differentiate as one or the other type must be under stringent control.

It is often difficult or even impossible to analyze a progression of cellular events in the intact organism, because cells may not possess sufficiently distinctive features or may not be organized in recognizable patterns (and for various other reasons). In many cases the system can be better studied by transferring cells from one individual to another or by growing cells in culture. Cell culture methods enable us to analyze populations of cells from higher organisms by a variety of approaches previously available only for microorganisms.

16.2
Somatic Cell Cultures

Ordinary somatic (body) cells removed from an organism can be grown in *primary culture*, but these cells usually stop multiplying after a relatively few generations and are thus difficult to maintain for more than a brief time. Cells that can be selected from primary cultures and grown in *secondary culture*, however, may continue to produce clonal descendants indefinitely. Given supplies of nutrients and growth factors, secondary cultures may continue to grow and proliferate as virtually immortalized populations under appropriate conditions.

Various cell types can be cultured, including both differentiated and undifferentiated cells. Stem cells and their committed precursor derivatives can be maintained indefinitely in secondary cultures. Erythroblasts can be grown in secondary cultures, and their progress can be followed as they differentiate to the reticulocyte stage and finally to hemoglobin-filled erythrocytes, losing their nucleus and various organelles at first and ultimately losing their ribosomes as well. Lymphocytes and fibroblasts are the most frequently used cells for a wide variety of studies in culture.

Cultured mammalian cells have been studied for more than 25 years by the methods of **somatic cell genetics**, an invaluable approach to gene mapping and other studies of human chromosomes. In mapping human genes, investigators treat genetically marked human cells and rodent cells with *polyethylene glycol* to increase the frequency of cell fusions in the incubation mixture. The chemical agent modifies the cell surface and enhances cell–cell contacts so that membranes fuse and hybrid cells are formed. The initially binucleate **somatic cell hybrid** soon undergoes nuclear fusion, and uninucleate cell hybrids proliferate to form colonies on solid media once they are plated out. When human cells are fused with rodent cells, human chromosomes are lost at random in subsequent cell divisions, whereas all the rodent chromosomes are retained in the clone (Fig. 16.7). In this way, different clones of somatic cell hybrids can be established, each containing one or a few of the 24 different human chromosomes. These clones are then utilized in assigning genes to each human chromosome by comparing the retained DNA sequence or activity with the retained G-banded human chromosome(s). More than 600 human genes have been assigned to all of the chromosomes so far, and we estimate that an average of 4 new genes per month can be assigned in current and future studies (Fig. 16.8).

Somatic cell fusion is an infrequent event, and any hybrids would be swamped by growing parent cells once the incubation mixture was plated out. The problem is solved by plating the mixture on *selective* growth medium, which allows the hybrid cells to grow but simultaneously discourages or inhibits growth of the parental human and mouse cells. One of the most useful selective media is **HAT medium**, which includes the drug *aminopterin* to block the major pathway for synthesis of deoxyribonucleotides; *hypoxanthine*, a purine precursor; and *thymidine*. Cells can grow in the presence of aminopterin only if they have the enzymes **hypoxanthine-guanine phosphoribosyl transferase** (HPRT) and **thymidine kinase** (TK) to catalyze utilization of the two precursors in a "salvage" pathway of nucleotide synthesis (Fig. 16.9).

When TK-deficient mouse (or human) cells are mixed with HPRT-deficient human (or mouse) cells, neither parent can grow when plated out on HAT medium. The only cells that grow to produce colonies on HAT medium are $TK^+/HPRT^+$ somatic cell hybrids, which received a functional TK gene from one parent and a functional HPRT gene from the other parent (Fig. 16.10). Colonies or cells can be isolated from HAT medium, and these can be established separately in culture to provide materials for various studies, including gene mapping.

The development of tumors or of malignant cancerous growths in the organism can also be approached via studies of **cellular transformation** in cultured cells. Tumors *grow without restraint and invade tissues* near their site of origin; if the tumor is malignant, the cancer spreads to distant sites away from the original focus of growth, or undergoes *metastasis*. Transformed cells in culture display modified properties that distinguish them from normal cells, and they can be considered analogs of tumorous growths in the organism. Normal cells in culture stop moving and dividing upon making physical contact with each other, so that a confluent single layer of cells is produced in the culture dish. Transformed cells may continue to migrate and to multiply indefinitely, so that mounds of cells in disordered heaps are produced on solid substratum (Fig. 16.11). Normal cells do not multiply in media made semisolid by the addition of agar or methylcellulose, whereas transformed cells can proliferate in semisolid media. Because transformed cells produce descendant cells like themselves, the transformed phenotype is heritable.

Normal cells in culture stop moving and multiplying when they make physical contact because they are subject to *density-dependent regulation of growth*, often accompanied by *contact inhibition of movement*. Transformed cells are not subject to either of these phenomena, because the cells continue to move over one another despite their contacts and their continued growth yields high densities of cells in a finite space. The ability of transformed cells to penetrate and grow in semisolid media reflects their loss of *anchorage dependence*, a property that obliges normal cells to grow only when attached to a rigid surface. The mechanisms that

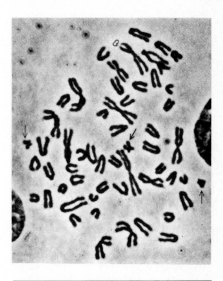

FIGURE 16-7
Three human chromosomes have been retained in this somatic cell hybrid derived from the fusion of a human cell and a mouse cell. Chromosomes 21 and 22 (light arrows) and chromosome 17 (dark arrow) are all that remain of the 46 human chromosomes present in the original cell hybrid, but all the mouse chromosomes have been retained. Although diploid mouse cells have 20 pairs of acrocentric chromosomes before being grown in culture, changes in chromosome number and morphology occur during long-term cell culture. These changes may be quite different from one culture to another for mice and other species. (Photograph from Ephrussi, B., and M.C. Weiss, 1969, *Sci. Amer.* **220**(4):26.)

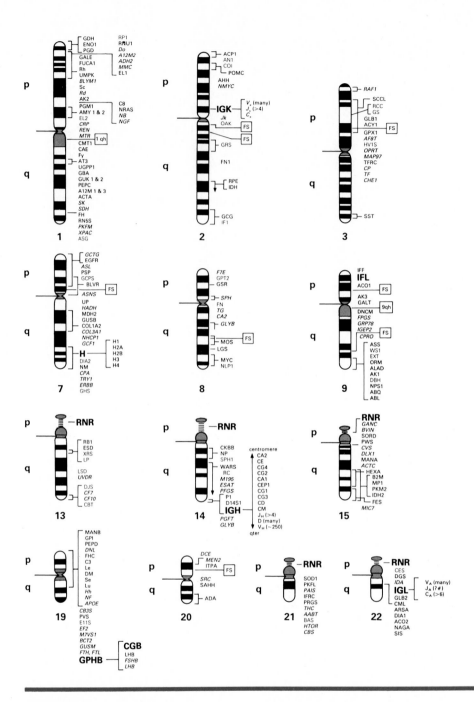

FIGURE 16-8
Gene maps of the human chromosome complement showing many of the important gene assignments (to the right of each chromosome). Gene location within a chromosome is indicated by reference to the shorter and longer arms (p and q, respectively) of the chromosome and to the band or interband number in that arm. For example, gene *HPRT*, which encodes the enzyme hypoxanthine-guanine phosphoribosyl transferase, is assigned to Xq27, or band 27 in the long arm of the X chromosome. (From McKusick, V. A., 1984, in S. J. O'Brien, ed., *Genetic Maps* **3**:417–428. Cold Spring Harbor, N.Y.: Cold Spring Harbor Laboratory.)

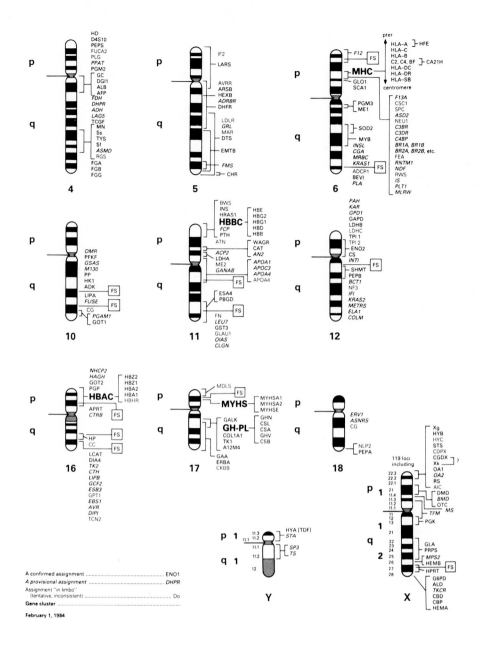

regulate all these properties are not well understood, but they involve the organization of the cytoskeleton and the availability and utilization of nutrients and growth factors in the medium. Whatever these mechanisms may be, transformed cells in culture, like cancer cells in the body, have escaped or lost the restraints over normal cell activities. Cells in culture thus provide readily accessible systems that can be manipulated, modified, and analyzed by the full repertory of genetic, biochemical, microscopical, and molecular methods now at our disposal. The insights provided by cell culture studies have considerably elucidated the relationships between cancer-inducing viruses and the disruptions in

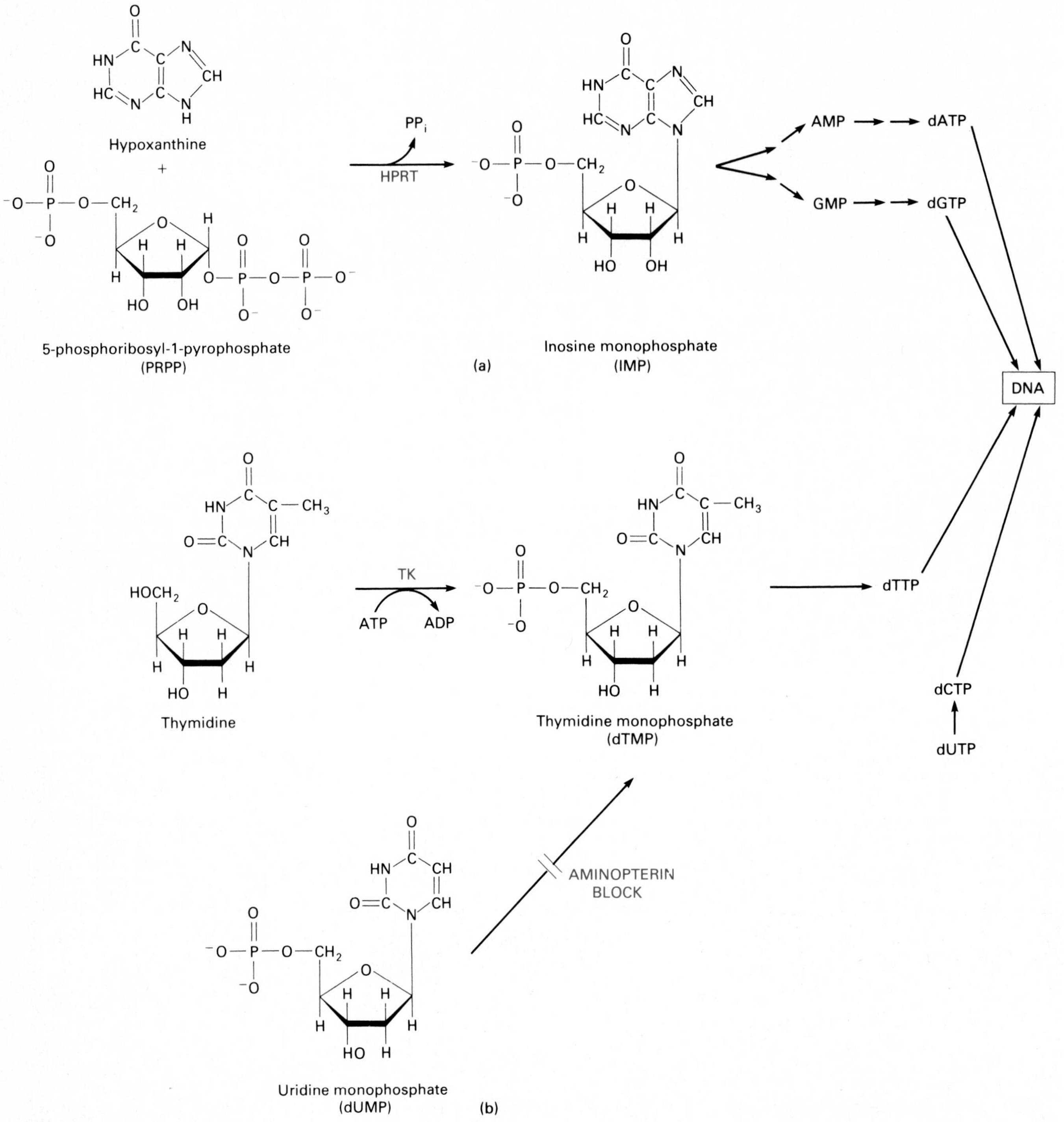

FIGURE 16-9

Deoxyribonucleotide precursors for DNA synthesis may be synthesized in salvage pathways or in major pathways in cells. (a) Purine precursors such as deoxyriboadenosine triphosphate (dATP) and deoxyriboguanosine triphosphate (dGTP) can be synthesized in a salvage pathway from hypoxanthine and phosphoribosyl pyrophosphate (PRPP) if the enzyme hypoxanthine-guanine phosphoribosyl transferase (HPRT) is present and functional. (b) Pyrimidine precursors such as deoxyribothymidine triphosphate (dTTP) can be synthesized from deoxyribouridine monophosphate (dUMP) in the major pathway, or directly from thymidine in the salvage pathway if the enzyme thymidine kinase (TK) is present and the major pathway is blocked by the drug aminopterin. The precursor deoxyribocytidine triphosphate (dCTP) is made from deoxyribouridine triphosphate (dUTP), which is not pictured here.

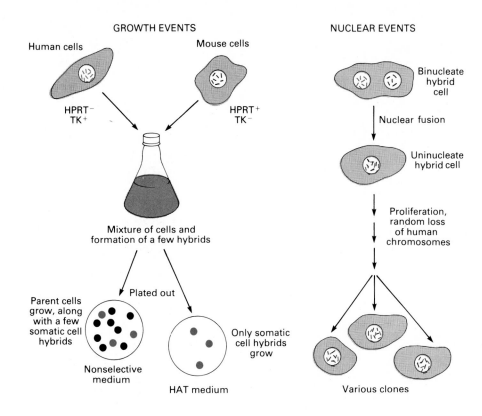

GROWTH EVENTS

Human cells   Mouse cells

HPRT⁻   HPRT⁺
TK⁺   TK⁻

Mixture of cells and
formation of a few hybrids

Plated out

Parent cells
grow, along
with a few
somatic
cell
hybrids

Only somatic
cell hybrids
grow

Nonselective
medium

HAT medium

NUCLEAR EVENTS

Binucleate
hybrid
cell

Nuclear fusion

Uninucleate
hybrid cell

Proliferation,
random loss
of human
chromosomes

Various clones

FIGURE 16-10
When mixtures of enzyme-deficient parent cells are plated out on ordinary growth medium, the few somatic cell hybrids are swamped by colonies of parental human cells and mouse cells. When plated out on HAT medium, however, the enzyme-deficient parent cells cannot grow, so the few somatic cell hybrids can be identified by colony growth on the selective medium. Such hybrids have the HPRT⁺ gene from one parent and the TK⁺ gene from the other parent and can therefore utilize the salvage pathways for deoxyribonucleotide synthesis. Once nuclear fusion has occurred in the somatic cell hybrid, human chromosomes are lost at random during cell divisions, but all the mouse chromosomes are retained. Different clones of somatic cell hybrids arise as a consequence of the random loss and retention of different numbers and kinds of human chromosomes, and such clones can then be used in studies to map genes in human chromosomes.

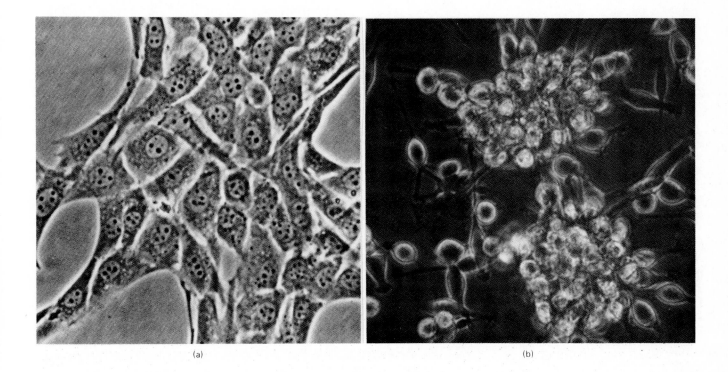

(a)   (b)

Mouse cells in culture. (a) Normal cells stop moving and multiplying when they make contact, so a confluent single layer of cells is produced on solid substratum. (b) Transformed cells continue to move and to multiply without restraint, so they produce disordered mounds of cells rather than a confluent monolayer on solid substratum. (Photographs by J. Lee.)

cellular activities and behaviors that characterize transformed cells in culture and cancerous growths in the organism. We will discuss some of these studies next.

16.3
Oncogenes and the Control of Cell Growth

A number of DNA and RNA viruses are known to be **oncogenic**—that is, to induce cancerous growths in the organism. Many of these viruses also elicit a transformation response in cultured cells. In the case of the RNA retroviruses, which are acutely transforming and are associated with specific kinds of cancers in specific tissues of specific hosts, genes responsible for the induction of abnormal growth have been identified in the viral genomes. These genes are **viral oncogenes** (v-*onc*). Nineteen *onc* genes have now been identified in retroviruses, and more probably remain to be discovered (Table 16.2). DNA sequences homologous to the retroviral *onc* genes have been found in normal untransformed cells and in normal tissues in all the vertebrate animals, from fish to primates, including humans. These **cellular oncogene** equivalents are referred to as c-*onc* genes. The c-*onc* genes appear to be the evolutionary progenitors of the v-*onc* genes and are therefore also referred to as **proto-oncogenes**. The virus is believed to have acquired the cellular genes via recombination events between the host genome and the infecting retroviral genome during relatively recent evolutionary time.

The initiation and maintenance of the abnormal growth response depends exclusively on the v-*onc* gene in the infecting virus. If the oncogene is defective or deleted, the virus can infect the cell but

TABLE 16-2
Characteristics of Retroviral Oncogenes

Oncogene	Retrovirus Source	Animal Origin*	Function of Oncogenic Protein Product
v–abl	Abelson murine leukemia virus	mouse	
v–fes	Feline sarcoma virus	cat	
v–fgr	Feline sarcoma virus	cat	
v–fps	Fujinami sarcoma virus	chicken	Tyrosine–specific protein kinase
v–ros	Avian sarcoma virus (UR2)	chicken	
v–src	Rous sarcoma virus	chicken	
v–yes	Avian sarcoma virus (Y73)	chicken	
v–erb–B	Avian erythroblastosis virus	chicken	
v–fms	McDonough feline sarcoma virus	cat	
v–mil	Avian carcinoma virus	chicken	Potential tyrosine–specific protein kinase
v–mos	Moloney murine sarcoma virus	mouse	
v–raf	Murine sarcoma virus	mouse	
v–sis	Simian sarcoma virus	wooly monkey	PDGF–like growth factor
v–ras^{Ha}	Harvey murine sarcoma virus	rat	GTP–binding
v–ras^{Ki}	Kirsten murine sarcoma virus		
v–fos	FBJ osteosarcoma virus	mouse	
v–myb	Avian myeloblastosis virus	chicken	
v–myc	Avian myelocytomatosis virus	chicken	DNA–binding**
v–ski	Avian sarcoma virus	chicken	
v–erb–A	Avian erythroblastosis virus	chicken	Unknown
v–rel	Avian reticuloendotheliosis virus	chicken	

*Animal from which the viral oncogene was first isolated (usually the normal host).
**The *B-lym* oncogene is DNA–binding, but the gene has not been found in retroviruses.

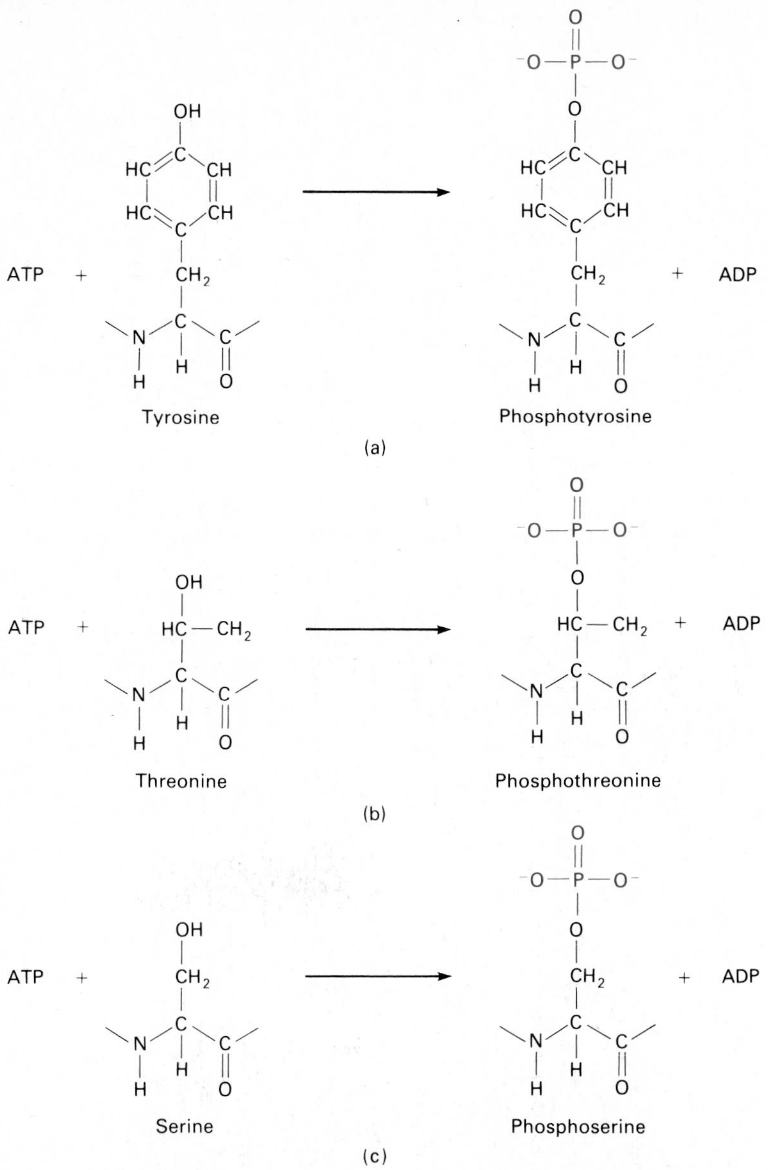

FIGURE 16-12
Protein kinases catalyze the phosphorylation of (a) tyrosine, (b) threonine, and (c) serine, the three amino acids that have a free hydroxyl group. The p60*src* kinase specifically catalyzes phosphotyrosine formation in certain target polypeptides.

abnormal growth will not occur. If a v-*onc* gene is present in the viral genome, most of the viral activity is devoted to maintaining the abnormal cellular state, because relatively few new viruses are made and released from the infected cell. Infected cells usually survive the viral challenge whether or not an oncogenic response has been initiated. The retrovirus infection cycle was illustrated in Fig. 12.22.

Given the sequence homologies between viral oncogenes and cellular proto-oncogenes, we might expect their protein products to be similar both in primary structure and in activity in the cell. The first step was therefore to characterize the oncogene protein product and then to determine which, if any, cellular protein had similar or identical structure and activity. The first breakthrough came in 1978 in studies of p60*src*, the 60,000-dalton protein product of the *src* oncogene in Rous sarcoma virus (RSV). Raymond Erickson and Marc Collett showed that p60*src* was a **protein kinase**, an enzyme that phosphorylates protein on hydroxyl groups of any of the three amino acids with a free OH group. It was later found that, instead of phosphorylating serine or threonine as several known protein kinases did, p60*src* phosphorylates the amino acid tyrosine (Fig. 16.12). Interestingly, in the subsequent search for tyrosine-specific protein kinases in normal cells, the first such enzyme to be identified turned out to be the protein product of the c-*src* proto-oncogene.

Phosphotyrosine accounts for only 1 in 2000 of the phosphate residues linked to proteins, whereas about 90% of the phosphate is present in serine residues and 10% in threonine residues of proteins. Although protein phosphorylation on tyrosine is a relatively rare event in normal cells, a tenfold increase over the normal level is found in cells transformed by oncogenic viruses whose v-*onc* sequence encodes a protein with tyrosine-specific protein kinase activity. In order to understand the mechanism by which such viruses transform cells, it was important to identify proteins that are targets for the protein kinases. Because transformed cells have an altered cytoskeletal organization, and because about ten different cytoskeletal proteins could be isolated from RSV-transformed cells for study, Tony Hunter and S. Jonathan Singer undertook an investigation of phosphotyrosine distribution in these cells. Only the protein **vinculin**, an agent that cross-links actin filaments to the plasma membrane, contained phosphotyrosine, but the amount was twenty times higher in RSV-transformed cells than in untransformed cells.

Vinculin is localized in adhesion plaques, and the protein may serve to bind groups of actin filaments, called stress fibers, and anchor them to the plasma membrane at adhesion plaque sites. The p60*src* protein is localized in adhesion plaques, too, and thus appears favorably situated to catalyze the phosphorylation of tyrosines in vinculin. The more highly

FIGURE 16-13
The relationship of stress fibers to adhesion plaques in cultured cells. (a) Diagram showing stress fibers bound to adhesion plaques at cell sites anchored to the solid surface of a culture dish. (b) Schematic view of one possible organization of various proteins in the adhesion plaque to which actin filaments of stress fiber groups are attached. In transformed cells the p60*src* protein kinase is situated close to vinculin, whose tyrosines may thus be available for phosphorylation by the enzyme. Phosphorylated vinculin may function less effectively in cross-linking actin filaments to the adhesion plaque and may thereby contribute to the disarray of stress fibers in transformed cells.

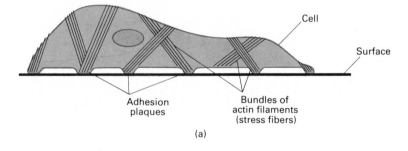

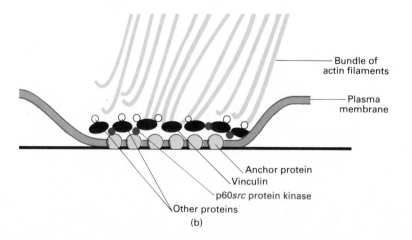

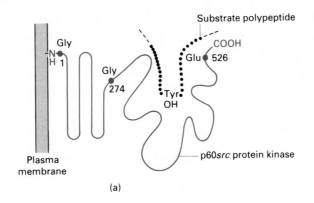

(a)

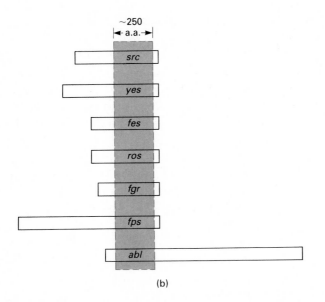

(b)

FIGURE 16-14
Tyrosine-specific protein kinases.
(a) The p60*src* protein kinase consists of 526 amino acids bound by its N-terminus to the plasma membrane. Tyrosines in the substrate polypeptides are phosphorylated by the enzyme at its catalytically active region, which occupies about 250 amino acids near its C-terminus. (b) Seven different v-*onc* genes encode a tyrosine-specific protein kinase. The genes vary in size (shown by bar lengths) but each gene encodes a very similar domain of about 250 amino acids (screened area) that corresponds to the catalytically active region of the kinase.

phosphorylated vinculin in RSV-transformed cells may act less effectively as a cross-linking agent and thus cause actin filament groups to become disorganized, contributing to the disarray of stress fibers in transformed cells (Fig. 16.13). Modifications in the cytoskeleton lead to alterations in the shape of transformed cells (see Section 11.21), and modifications in the composition of adhesion plaques may contribute to the loss of anchorage-dependence.

In addition to the *src* gene product, six other v-*onc* genes (*yes, fgr, abl, fps, fes,* and *ros*) encode a tyrosine-specific protein kinase. All seven of these proteins have a strikingly similar domain of about 250 amino acids, which is the catalytically active portion of the molecule (Fig. 16.14). Five other v-*onc* genes (*erb-B, fms, mil, raf,* and *mos*) also include this region, but none of these five proteins has been found to possess tyrosine-specific protein kinase activity. These amazing similarities suggest that at least these oncogenes share a common evolutionary progenitor gene from which each has arisen. In addition, all these proteins may possibly have functions that resemble protein kinases, although kinase activity has thus far been demonstrated in only seven of the twelve proteins.

Tumors and transformed cells show no restraints over proliferation, so it is highly significant that at least two v-*onc* protein products resemble a mitogenic growth factor or its membrane-bound receptor. Epidermal growth factor (EGF) and platelet-derived growth factor (PDGF) bind to their respective receptor molecules embedded in the plasma membrane and thereby stimulate mitosis. The EGF receptor has been purified and shown to be a transmembrane protein whose external domain binds EGF, which then stimulates its internal domain to exercise its catalytic function as a tryosine-specific protein kinase (Fig. 16.15). The PDGF receptor protein shows similar binding and catalytic functions. Sequence analysis of v-*onc* proteins revealed that the *erb-B* protein is a truncated form of the EGF receptor protein, lacking the binding region of the receptor but possessing the transmembrane segment and the catalytic domain that extends into the cytoplasm of the cell. The *sis* oncogene of simian sarcoma virus, however, is virtually identical to PDGF itself.

The strong implication of these sequence and functional homologies is that v-*onc* proteins promote unregulated growth by mimicking normal cell activities but in uncontrolled fashion. The *erb-B* protein may phosphorylate one or more proteins concerned with growth control and thereby activate mitosis, and the *sis* protein may be the PGDF growth factor itself because the c-*sis* gene appears to be the gene encoded for PDGF in normal cells. Both v-*erb-B* and v-*sis* could thus induce and maintain unregulated growth and division by tryosine-specific phosphorylations of proteins that are normally held in check by controls over the synthesis and activation of EGF and PDGF and their receptors in normal cells. Further investigations are required to verify these suggestions.

Studies by Raymond Erickson and Lewis Cantley have shown that the v-*src* and v-*ros* protein kinases may phosphorylate hydroxyl groups on *phosphatidylinositol*, a major component of the plasma membrane, as well as on proteins. The reaction produces a *polyphosphoinositide*, which

FIGURE 16-15
The receptor for epidermal growth factor (EGF) is a transmembrane protein whose external domain binds EGF. The binding of EGF stimulates the internal domain (with protein kinase activity) of the receptor to catalyze the phosphorylation of tyrosines in a substrate polypeptide. The v-*onc* gene *erb-B* specifies a kinase that is essentially identical to the transmembrane segment and catalytic internal domain of the EGF receptor, but it lacks the EGF-binding external region. The *erb-B* kinase mimics the activity of a normal cell protein (EGF receptor), but it may do so in an uncontrolled fashion.

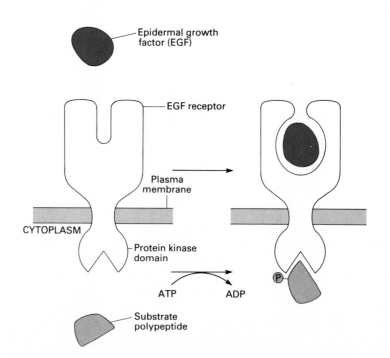

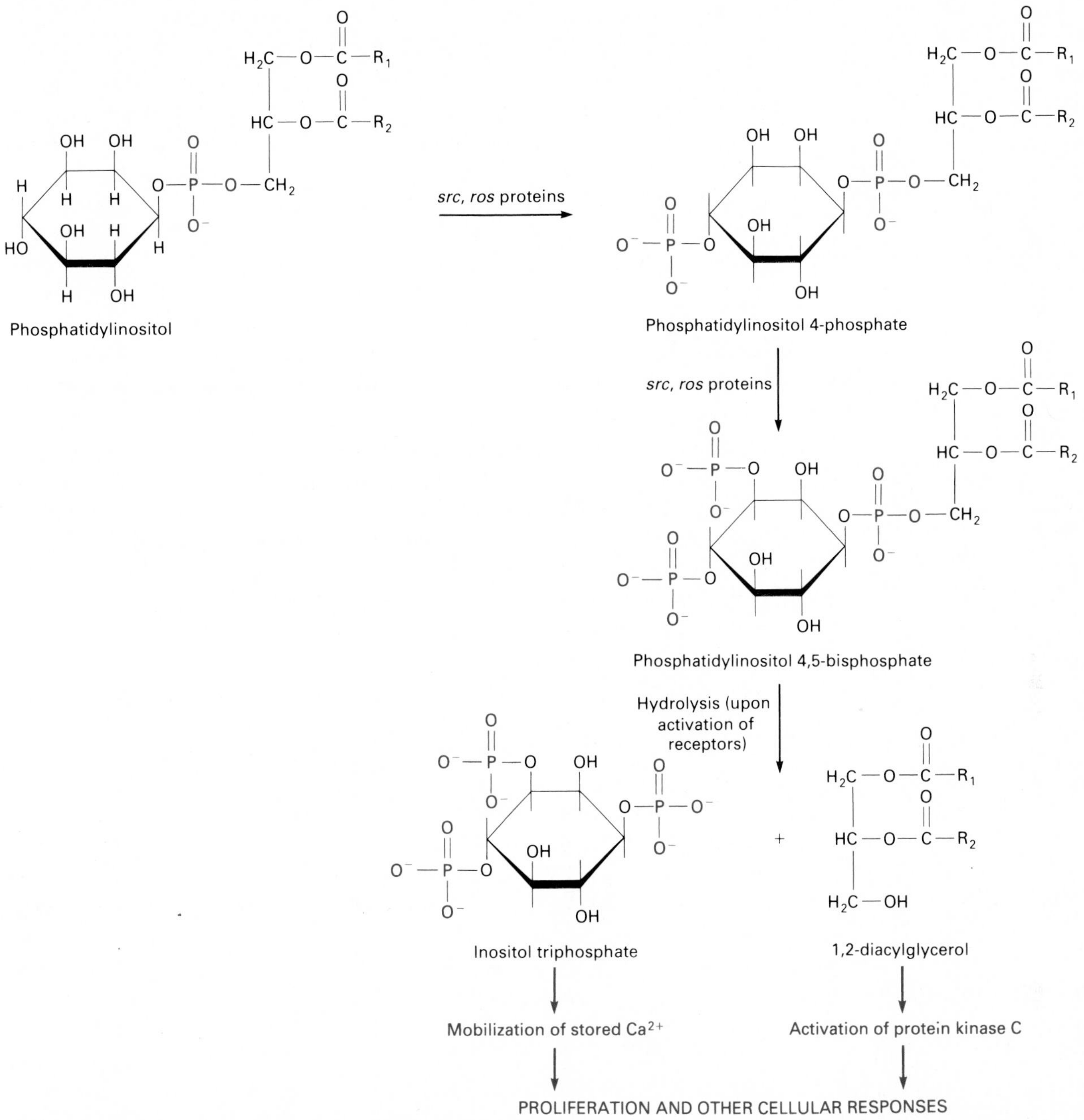

FIGURE 16-16
Both the *src* and *ros* gene products act as inositol lipid kinases and catalyze the phosphorylation of hydroxyl groups on phosphatidylinositol, a plasma membrane phospholipid, to produce the polyphosphoinositide compound phosphatidylinositol 4,5-bisphosphate. Activation of receptors for various growth factors, hormones, and other agents leads to hydrolysis of the polyphosphoinositide, which results in the release of 1,2-diacylglycerol and inositol triphosphate. Both products act as second messengers. Phospho-inositides may thus mediate signal transmission for growth factors, neuro-transmittors, and various hormones in the evocation of cellular responses.

mediates signal transmission for various hormones, neurotransmitters, and growth factors (Fig. 16.16). When growth factor and other receptors are activated, the phosphorylated membrane phospholipid is hydrolyzed and releases diacylglycerol and inositol triphosphate, which act as second messengers to evoke cellular responses (see Section 6.13). The effects of these two viral oncogenes in transformation and oncogenesis may therefore be involved with their mimicking growth-factor activity on the polyphosphoinositide system as well as on proteins at tyrosine residues.

In addition to their actions in relation to growth factors and their receptors, v-*onc* genes have been implicated as mimics of GTP-binding proteins that hydrolyze GTP to GDP and P_i at the plasma membrane and thereby act as coupling factors in systems that relay signals from adrenalin and other hormones to the cell interior. The p21*ras* proteins of the v-*ras* oncogene group not only bind GTP tightly but are also found associated with the inner face of the plasma membrane, which is where normal GTP-binding proteins are localized. Still other v-*onc* proteins bind tightly to DNA, including the *fos*, *myc*, and *myb* products, and may exert their influences directly on gene duplication and expression (Fig. 16.17). Localizations of v-*onc* proteins in the cell have been determined by immunofluorescence microscopy of fluorescent-labeled antibodies to the various proteins, and by the identification of these proteins in centrifugate subcellular fractions.

Viral oncogenes by definition are responsible for the induction of tumors and of cellular transformation. Do the structurally and functionally similar cellular proto-oncogenes also have oncogenic potential? At least four lines of evidence now support this possibility. First, when cloned c-*mos* or c-*ras*^Ha genes are spliced to a retroviral long-terminal-repeat sequence (see Fig. 14.29b) and introduced into a line of mouse fibroblast cells, transformation is induced. Second, the avian leukosis viruses lack an identifiable oncogene and induce malignancy only after long latent periods, presumably by a mechanism that involves activation of c-*myc* when the viral genome is inserted next to it on the chromosome. Third, c-*ras*^Ha and c-*ras*^Ki isolated from certain human tumors and tumor cell lines can induce transformation when introduced into a line of mouse cells. Fourth, in a study of fresh malignancies from human patients, the c-*myc*, c-*fos*, c-*ras*^Ha, and c-*ras*^Ki genes were expressed in all or nearly all of the tumors examined by DNA–RNA hybridization techniques, and these four genes (as well as c-*fms*) were expressed at significantly higher levels in malignant tissues than in normal tissues of

FIGURE 16-17
Protein products of v-*onc* genes have been localized in different regions of the cell via immunofluorescence and centrifugation studies. The particular locations of v-*onc* proteins provide information on the subcellular systems influenced by v-*onc* gene expression.

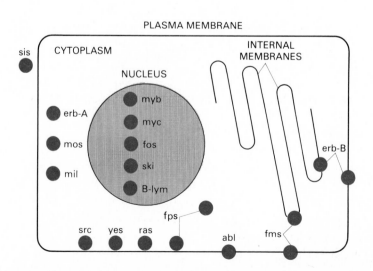

TABLE 16-3
Ratio of Differential Expression of c-*onc* Genes in Human Malignant and Normal Tissues, from Densitometry Measurements of Tumor to Control Preparations

Malignancy	Case Number	Probe				
		myc	*fos*	*ras*^{Ha}	*ras*^{Ki}	*fms*
Renal cell carcinomas	1	3.0	5.0	3.0	4.0	—*
	2	4.5	4.5	3.0	3.5	—
	3	3.5	3.0	3.5	3.0	—
	5	1.0	1.0	1.0	1.0	1.0
	6	1.0	1.0	1.0	1.0	1.0
	8	2.0	2.0	2.0	1.0	2.5
	9	2.0	1.0	1.0	1.0	6.0
Lung carcinomas	1	4.0	2.5	1.0	2.0	3.5
	2	1.0	1.0	3.0	1.0	3.5
Colon carcinomas	1	11.0	3.0	3.0	4.0	—
	2	4.0	4.5	2.5	2.0	5.5
Cecal carcinomas	1	2.0	1.0	2.0	1.0	1.0
Small-bowel adenocarcinomas	1	1.0	1.0	1.0	1.0	—
Ovarian adenocarcinomas	1	2.5	1.0	4.0	3.0	—
Percentage of cases with differential expression		71	50	64	50	62

*The symbol — means comparison not made.
(From Slamon, D. J., et al., 1984, *Science* **224**: 256–262, Table 3).

a given patient. In addition, more than one c-*onc* gene was transcriptionally active in all of the tumors examined (Table 16.3).

All these and other data on oncogene and proto-oncogene activities in normal and abnormal cells lead to useful ideas and hypotheses that are now under intensive investigation or are open to experimental tests. It would appear that proto-oncogenes play important roles in growth and development leading to differentiation of normal cells. These cellular genes are expressed in time-related and tissue-specific patterns in normal individuals, and products such as EGF receptors and PDGF are known to be involved in growth and division of normal cells. Furthermore, the c-*onc* gene sequences are highly conserved in vertebrates, and one or more homologous sequences have been found in *Drosophila* and yeast genomes. It is axiomatic that highly conserved genes encode products that are essential for many basic cell functions (histones, rRNAs, tRNAs, and others). When unperturbed, these genes guide normal processes under stringent cellular controls. When perturbed, these same genes may be induced to act or may become uncontrollably active and thereby induce proliferation and other malignant changes that characterize neoplastic growth.

How might c-*onc* genes be perturbed and become converted to oncogenic activity? Carcinogens such as UV, x-rays, and various chemical agents may induce mutations in c-*onc* genes and thereby alter the protein product. They may increase the rate of c-*onc* transcription and thereby cause the cell to be swamped with one or more proteins normally present in small amounts or not even present at certain stages of development. They may amplify the c-*onc* gene and cause excessive amounts of protein product to be produced. Or they may alter the

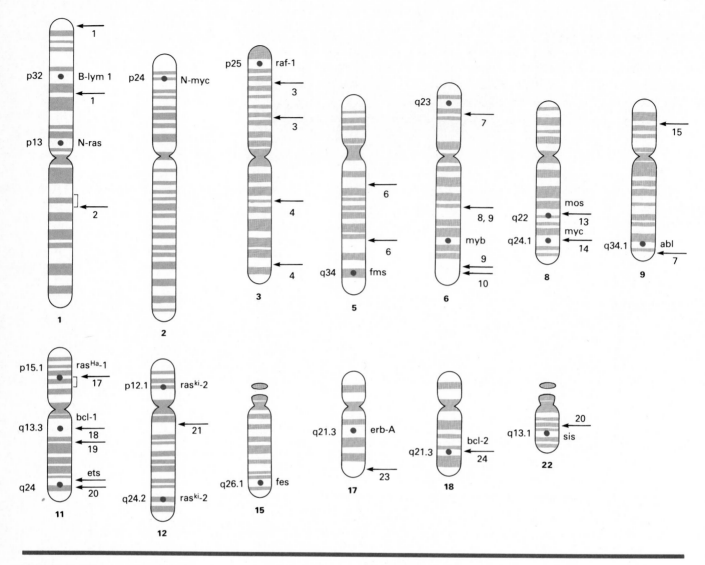

FIGURE 16-18
Standard diagrams of selected members of the human chromosome complement found in one study to undergo breakage and translocational rearrangement in human cancer cells and to carry cellular oncogenes (c-*onc* genes or proto-oncogenes) in mapped regions of the chromosomes. The identified chromosome band or interband is numbered at the left of each chromosome for the short arm (p) and the long arm (q). At the right of each chromosome is shown the breakpoint (arrow) and the number (below arrow) of the particular chromosome involved in the translocation at the breakpoint. Locations of the 17 c-*onc* genes are indicated by colored dots within the chromosomes, and the genes themselves are identified at the right of the dots. (From Yunis, J. J., and A. L. Soreng, 1984, *Science* **226**:1199–1204, Fig. 2. Copyright © 1984 by the American Association for the Advancement of Science.)

pattern of methylation so that one or more c-*onc* genes become undermethylated. Evidence is available in support of all these modifications in malignant tissue and in transformed cells. In addition, viruses may cause breaks in specific chromosomes at specific sites, which may be followed by translocational rearrangements of chromosome arms and by a perturbation of the activity of c-*onc* genes at or near the break sites and in the new location near different genes in the translocated chromosomes

(Fig. 16.18). In patients with Birkett lymphoma, c-*myc* may be included in the piece of chromosome 8 translocated to chromosome 14 near the gene cluster encoding the heavy chain of immunoglobulin. And in its new environment, c-*myc* transcription increases fivefold compared with mRNA synthesis in nontranslocated chromosome 8.

From studies of viral and cellular oncogenes, we hope to learn more about the normal processes and controls over cell growth and division and about the upsets that disturb these events and controls and thereby induce neoplastic growth and proliferation. From these studies we can also anticipate new approaches to cancer therapy, based on a detailed knowledge of the structure and function of proteins specified by viral oncogenes.

The Cell Cycle

The **cell cycle** consists of an interval of active biosynthesis and growth during which the cell doubles its mass and duplicates its contents, followed by a relatively brief episode of nuclear division that is usually accompanied by division of the cytoplasm and the formation of a new boundary to separate the nuclei and cytoplasm into a pair of daughter cells. The dramatic events of nuclear division, or *mitosis*, and of cell partitioning by *cytokinesis* have been known for 100 years through microscopic studies. Most of the activities that characterize the growth phase between mitotic divisions, which is called *interphase*, have been studied only in the last few decades. By the use of new and more sophisticated methods, we have gained considerable insight into the main events that occur at different times during interphase and into the manner in which the cell cycle is regulated. In some cases we have been aided by studies of cells that display one or more variations on the basic themes of a typical cell cycle. A certain amount of progress has been made in defining the genetic and biochemical controls over events in the cell cycle, but we are only just beginning to understand this important area of cell biology.

16.4
Activities During the Cell Cycle

The visible events of mitosis and cytokinesis were the principle focus of light-microscopic studies until the early 1950s. At this time the concept of DNA as the genetic material was being established, and new methods were developed and applied to analyze growth and reproduction at the cellular level. Microspectrophotometric methods and equipment were used to measure the amount of DNA in nuclei that were stained by the well-known Feulgen reagent. Apart from the distinctive magenta color imparted to stained chromosomes, it was possible to determine the amount of DNA per nucleus by measuring the amount of stain that was bound to the chromosomes. Autoradiography was another innovation of the 1950s, and this method enabled investigators to determine the sites and times of synthesis of DNA, RNA, and proteins in different cells and

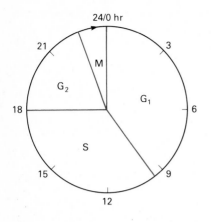

FIGURE 16-19
The cell cycle is divided into four consecutive phases: M phase is devoted to mitosis, and the G_1, S, and G_2 phases constitute the biosynthetically active time of interphase. DNA replication takes place during S phase, and it is separated from mitosis by the pre-replication G_1 phase and the post-replication premitotic G_2 phase, or time gaps. Although we have used a 24-hour cycle for convenience, intervals other than 24 hours are characteristic of different kinds of cells. The proportion of a cycle occupied by each phase also varies, but M is usually quite brief. The G_1 phase is the most variable in duration in different kinds of cells; it may even be lacking in some cell cycles.

FIGURE 16-20
Scanning electron micrographs of hamster cells in different phases of the cell cycle. (a) An M-phase cell, typically rounded up and covered with microvilli at the cell surface. (b) Late-M–early-G_1 daughter cells in the process of separation are typically covered with blebs rather than spikelike microvilli. (c) A late G_1 cell whose microvilli are confined to a rounded central region. By the time of S phase, the cell surface is relatively smooth and has few protruding microvilli. (Photographs from Goldman, R., 1975, *Cold Spring Harbor Sympos. Quant. Biol.* **39**:601.)

their parts. When it was found that vigorous biosynthetic activities occurred during interphase and not during mitosis, attention began to be paid to interphase.

Autoradiographic, microspectrophotometric, and other lines of study showed that DNA replicated during a portion of the interphase, but that some time elapsed between the end of mitosis and the onset of DNA replication and that another gap in time separated the end of DNA replication from the beginning of mitosis. Following the convention first suggested in 1953, the time devoted to mitosis is called the **M phase** and the interval of DNA synthesis is the **S phase**. The first time gap (between M and S phases) is the **G_1 phase** and the second time gap (between S and M phases) is the G_2 phase of the cell cycle (Fig. 16.19).

Different methods have been used to determine the number of hours spent in each phase of a cell cycle. Cells in culture provide a useful system for these determinations, particularly because we can synchronize the activities of a population of cells and thereby examine the population as an amplification of events occurring in a single cell. By adding inhibitors to stop protein synthesis, by arresting cells in mitosis with colchicine or in S phase with inhibitors of DNA replication, and by other means, investigators bring the population to a particular phase of the cycle. Upon release from inhibition, the cells resume activity at a common point and remain synchronous long enough for the studies to be performed. A simpler and perhaps more reliable method is to wash out cells undergoing mitosis, leaving behind cells in other phases of the cycle. This is readily accomplished because cells round up during mitosis and lose their firm attachment to the substratum, whereas interphase cells are flattened against the substratum and attached to it at numerous points (Fig. 16.20). Starting with a synchronous population of M-phase cells, it is possible to determine the duration of mitosis by

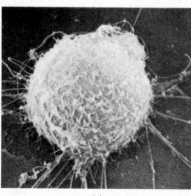
(a)

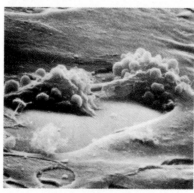
(b)

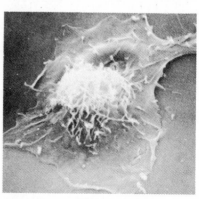
(c)

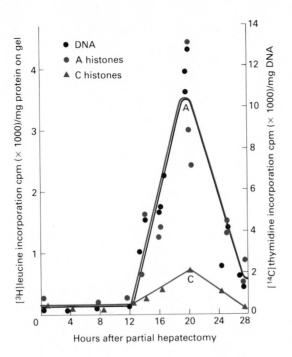

FIGURE 16-21
Double labeling with [³H]leucine precursors for protein synthesis and [¹⁴C]thymidine precursors for DNA synthesis show that DNA and histones are synthesized coordinately. Rat liver cells were stimulated to divide by removal of part of the liver (partial hepatectomy) and the animals were injected with labeled leucine and thymidine at various times after surgery. Livers were removed one hour later to determine the radioactivity in DNA and in two separable histone fractions (here designated as A and C). Synthesis of all three components occurred coordinately between 12 and 28 hours after surgery. (From Takai, S., et al., 1968, *Nature* **219**:861.)

microscopy, to determine the duration of S phase by autoradiographic data on [³H]thymidine incorporation, and by less direct means to estimate the G_1 and G_2 phases.

DNA replication is restricted to the S phase, but RNA and protein syntheses occur throughout interphase. All biosyntheses stop in M phase, when the sets of replicated chromosomes are distributed to daughter nuclei. If cytokinesis is synchronized with mitosis, the contents of the parent cell are apportioned to the daughter cells and these become separate, independent cells upon the formation of the new cell partition between them. Unlike all the other proteins that have been followed, the histone proteins are synthesized only during S phase (Fig. 16.21). In fact, histone mRNA is transcribed only during S phase. If DNA replication is inhibited, histone transcripts are degraded and translation cannot take place. The nature of control over synchronized DNA and histone synthesis is not known.

16.5
Variations in Cell Cycles

The G_1 phase is the most variable in duration, whereas the time spent in S and G_2 is remarkably constant in any particular kind of cell under a variety of conditions. Rapidly growing cells may dispense entirely with the G_1 phase and enter the S phase directly upon completing mitosis. Populations of protists, fungi, and other lower organisms retain a G_1 phase when growing under suboptimal conditions, but they dispense with G_1 under optimal conditions that sponsor rapid growth and division. The generation time is much shorter in rapidly growing cell populations as a consequence of their lack of a G_1 phase.

Similarly abbreviated cell-cycle times are typical of embryonic cells early in their development. The large fertilized egg divides rapidly and

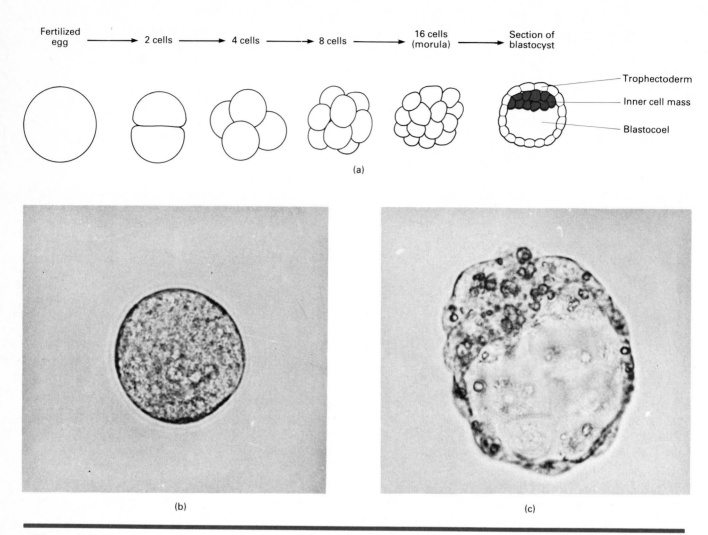

(a)

(b)

(c)

FIGURE 16-22

(a) The large fertilized animal egg undergoes mitotic divisions to produce 2-cell, 4-cell, 8-cell, 16-cell, 32-cell, and later stages in embryonic development. The total cellular mass remains unchanged, but the number of cells may increase from 1 to over 1000 in the blastula stage. (b) mouse fertilized egg, ×460, and (c) mouse blastocyst just before implantation in the uterine lining. ×460. (Photographs courtesy of B. Babiarz.)

repeatedly to produce the numerous smaller cells of the young embryo, all of which receive their portion of the egg cytoplasm as well as sets of chromosomes synthesized in S phase (Fig. 16.22). Adult *Xenopus* cells have a long S period lasting about 20 hours, whereas the young embryonic cells have a 25-minute cell cycle taken up primarily by S and M phases, with a very brief G_2 phase. DNA synthesis begins before mitosis has even been completed and occupies most of the 25-minute cycle. Cell cycles in invertebrate embryonic cells are similarly condensed and rapid. Sea urchin embryonic cell cycles last about 70 minutes; about 20 minutes of G_2 are sandwiched between 50 minutes of S and M phases.

These data indicate at least two important features of the cell cycle. First, the G_1 phase is a time of concentrated biosynthesis and growth in preparation for S phase. Cells that grow slowly require an extended G_1 phase in order to make all the molecules and structures required to enlarge the cell and complete the cycle. Rapidly growing cells and cells in embryos that do not grow between divisions already have a large store of materials that carry them directly from M to S, and they can dispense with G_1. Second, the time difference between S-phase duration in embryonic cells and in adult cells must be due to a difference in the pattern of DNA replication, not in the amount of DNA to be replicated, because all these cells are diploid. The difference in DNA replication pattern is evident from direct observations of replicating DNA in the two kinds of cells and from autoradiographic analysis. Relatively few replication "bubbles" are evident in S-phase DNA from adult cells, whereas virtually all the S-phase DNA from embryonic cells is covered with "bubbles" (Fig. 16.23). Clearly, all the origins of replication are engaged in embryonic chromosomes, but different replicons are active at different times in adult nuclei, leading to a lengthened S phase. These interpretations are verified by autoradiography, which shows widespread precursor incorporation throughout the genome in embryonic nuclei but a paced sequence of incorporation over many hours of DNA replication in adult nuclei. As we discussed in the previous chapter, euchromatic regions replicate earliest and heterochromatic regions of the chromosomes replicate later in S phase (see Fig. 15.20). It is not known whether the origins of replication are conformationally accessible throughout the genome in embryonic nuclei but not in adult cell nuclei, or initiation proteins occur in different amounts in the two kinds of nuclei, or there exists some other differential feature.

All cells do not recycle endlessly. Normal cells in culture stop dividing upon the development of a confluent single layer on solid substratum. If a patch of cells is scraped off, the cells bordering the opened space commence to divide and fill the space. Afterward, they return to their previous quiescent state. Cells in tissues may stop dividing, temporarily or permanently, but cells with the capacity to divide can be induced to resume division upon receipt of an appropriate stimulus, such as wounding, cell depletion, growth factors, hormones, and other means. Quiescent cells have the diploid amount of DNA, which indicates that they have not yet replicated since the last mitosis. Such cells are essentially stopped in G_1 and may reenter the cycle upon being stimulated to replicate their DNA. Quiescent cells are often said to be in **G_0 state** to distinguish it from the usual G_1 state in which cells prepare for, or are prepared for, DNA synthesis.

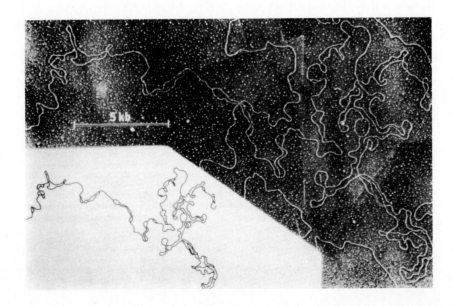

FIGURE 16-23
Electron micrograph and interpretive drawing of replicating DNA from embryonic nuclei of *Drosophila melanogaster*. The portion of the DNA molecule shown here is 119,000 base pairs (119 kilobase pairs) long and has 23 replication "bubbles." (Photograph courtesy of H. J. Kriegstein and D. S. Hogness, from Kriegstein, H. J., and D. S. Hogness, 1974, *Proc. Nat. Acad. Sci. U. S.* **71**:135, Fig. 1.)

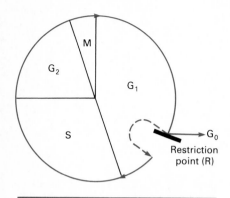

FIGURE 16-24
Cells may enter a quiescent state, or G$_0$ state, upon reaching a restriction point in G$_1$. G$_0$ cells may reenter the cell cycle if provided with appropriate stimuli or components that allow such cells to proceed past the restriction point and move on to the S phase and DNA synthesis.

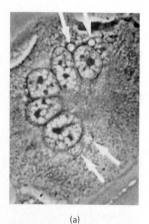

(a)

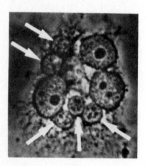

(b)

We are uncertain about the mechanism leading to cell quiescence and retrieval from that state. According to some experimental studies, an *unstable protein* (U protein) is required to take cells past a *restriction point* near the end of G$_1$ and to allow them to proceed into S phase (Fig. 16.24). According to other data, some one or more unknown cytoplasmic factors are in short supply or missing in G$_0$ cells, which cannot reenter the cycle unless such components are made or provided. The nature of the signal to complete G$_1$ and begin S phase is unknown, but we assume it is a positive signal. Various kinds of evidence point to such a turning on of activity, including cytological evidence. When hen erythrocytes are fused with human HeLa cells, the condensed and inactive erythrocyte nucleus enlarges and begins to transcribe RNA (Fig. 16.25). Some factor(s) present in the common cytoplasm may provide the signal that activates the quiescent nucleus or nuclei in the somatic cell hybrid. Studies by Potu Rao and Robert Johnson on fusions between mammalian cells in different phases of the cell cycle have provided dramatic evidence showing that DNA synthesis can be activated in cells at an appropriate stage of "readiness" to enter S phase. When cells in G$_1$ were fused with cells in S, the G$_1$ cells were stimulated to begin DNA replication earlier than they would have on their own. When G$_2$ cells were fused with cells in S, however, each nucleus remained unaffected by the presence of the other or the other's cytoplasm. The G$_2$ cells did not replicate again before proceeding to mitosis, and the S cells did not stop their DNA replication.

Cell fusion studies also revealed that the G$_2$-to-M transition is under positive control, just like the G$_1$-to-S transition. When mitotically dividing cells were fused with cells in any of the other three phases of the cycle, the interphase chromosomes of G$_1$, S, and G$_2$ nuclei underwent premature condensation in the presence of the M-phase nucleus. Changes in each nucleus of the cell hybrids could be observed unambiguously, because the human chromosomes in M-phase HeLa cells are numerically and morphologically distinguishable from the chromosomes in rat kangaroo cells (Fig. 16.26). In the cell hybrid, a G$_1$ nucleus or a G$_2$ nucleus did not replicate but the condensed chromosomes remained intact. An S-phase nucleus, on the other hand, underwent considerable fragmentation of its condensed chromosomes. In each case, therefore, a positive signal from the M-phase cell stimulated a response to condense in the interphase chromosomes. The decision to enter M phase from G$_2$ must therefore occur when the stimulating factor(s) for condensation are present and the G$_2$ cell becomes "ready" to begin mitosis.

FIGURE 16-25
Phase contrast light micrographs of HeLa (human) x chick-erythrocyte cell hybrids, whose nuclei are clustered together but unfused in the common cell cytoplasm. (a) At 18 hours after cell fusion the cell hybrid contains 4 chick-erythrocyte nuclei (at arrows) in an inactive state, and 5 larger, active HeLa nuclei with prominent nucleoli. (b) At 72 hours after cell fusion the cell hybrid shown here has 5 activated chick-erythrocyte nuclei and 3 larger, active HeLa nuclei, all with prominent nucleoli. The activation of chick-erythrocyte nuclei indicates positive control of transcription. (From Ringertz, N. R., et al., 1971, *Proc. Nat. Acad. Sci. U. S.* **68**:3228, Figs. 6 and 8.)

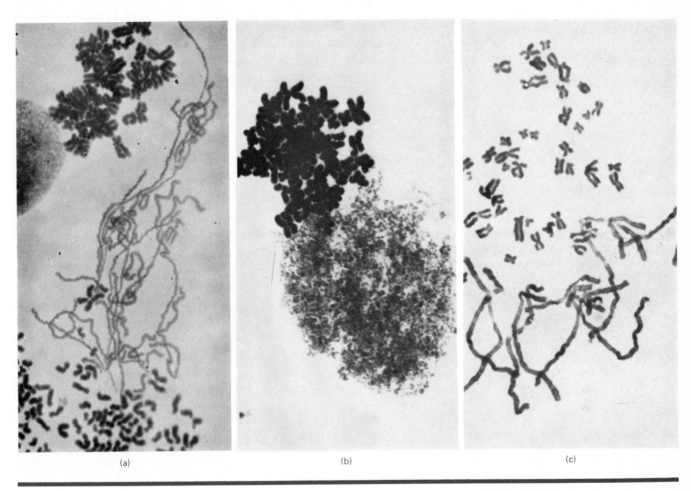

(a) (b) (c)

FIGURE 16-26
The results of fusion of an M-phase human HeLa cell nucleus (short, numerous, highly-condensed metaphase chromosomes) with rat kangaroo cell nuclei in (a) G_1, (b) S, and (c) G_2 phases of the cell cycle. The elongated rat kangaroo chromosomes in G_1 and G_2 nuclei undergo premature condensation, whereas S-phase chromatin becomes pulverized in the presence of the human M-phase nucleus. (Photographs courtesy of P. N. Rao, from Sperling, K., and P. N. Rao, 1974, *Humangenetik* **23**:237.)

16.6
Genetic Control of the Cell Cycle in Yeast

One approach to determining how the cell integrates and controls the diverse genetic, biochemical, and morphological processes that comprise the cell cycle is to isolate mutants that are defective or that vary in their reproductive activities. Using the yeast *Saccharomyces cerevisiae*, Leland Hartwell and co-workers have analyzed dozens of temperature-sensitive mutants that can undergo a normal cell cycle at the permissive temperature (23°C) but fail to complete the cycle at the higher restrictive temperature (36°C or 38°C). The particular mutation causes an accumulation of the cells at that point in the cell cycle where the product of the mutated gene would act at the permissive temperature. Mitosis and cytokinesis are analyzed together, so Hartwell has called the strains "cell division cycle" (*cdc*) mutants.

Different steps during the progression of a cell cycle in yeast have been correlated with morphological features and events that can be observed microscopically, such as emergence of a bud, migration of a daughter nucleus into the bud, and wall formation that separates the bud from the mother cell (Fig. 16.27). On the basis of the morphological features of the accumulated cells at the restrictive temperature, further studies can be more specifically directed toward describing the struc-

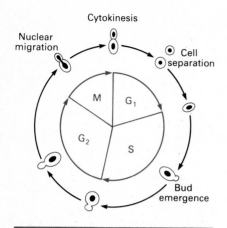

FIGURE 16-27
Various morphological features (outer circle) observed via microscopy serve as criteria to identify particular times during the progression of phases in the cell cycle (inner circle) in yeast.

tural, molecular, or biochemical events known (or expected) to characterize that time in the cell cycle. The failure of a newly emerged bud to grow, for example, would indicate some problem in S phase, and a search could then be made to determine the defect in DNA replication or some related process.

From these studies, Hartwell and others have determined the temporal order of gene expression during the cell division cycle and the process or event in which the genes are involved (Fig. 16.28). Unfortunately, relatively few *cdc* gene products have been identified so far. The task is somewhat simpler for genes involved in the initiation and synthesis of DNA, because we know of enzymes and other proteins that function at these times and can look for these molecules or functions encoded in *cdc* genes. The *cdc* 8 and *cdc* 21 mutations fail to proceed through DNA synthesis, which would indicate some problem in precursor availability or polymerases or binding proteins to make the single-stranded templates accessible to polymerases. Following these rationales, it was found that *cdc* 8 fails to make SSB protein and that *cdc* 21 is defective in thymidylate synthetase. These results also tell us that the wild-type alleles of each gene are encoded for single-strand binding protein and thymidylate synthetase, which was not known before.

Although cell-cycle mutants have been identified in several other fungi, as well as in protozoa, algae, and numerous mammalian cell lines, only a few gene products have been identified, and the biochemical basis for cell-cycle processes governed by their genes thus remains largely unknown. The task is enormous and difficult; we would expect *cdc* genes to be involved in central aspects of metabolism, energy-yielding processes, protein and structure assembly processes, regulation and coordination of activities, and a whole spectrum of processes that constitute and guide the growth and development of the cell. Various approaches to all these matters have recently been undertaken, including cloning of *cdc* genes to determine their base sequences and then conducting a compu-

FIGURE 16-28
Studies of cell division cycle (*cdc*) mutants provided data on the temporal order of gene expression during the cell cycle in yeast and data on the process or event in which the particular *cdc* gene (numbered) was involved. The spindle pole body (SPB) defines the poles of the spindle in dividing cells (see Fig. 16-38), and its duplication is a very early cell cycle event that is controlled by gene *cdc* 28. (From Hartwell, L. H., 1978, *J. Cell Biol.* **77**:627.)

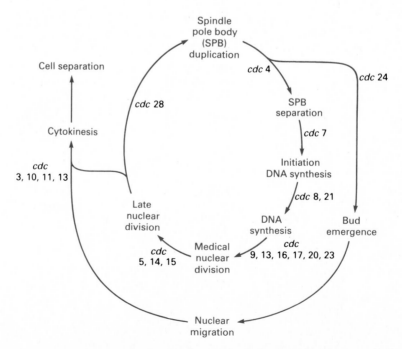

ter search for homologies with genes whose products are known. *In vitro* translation of these cloned genes has also been undertaken to learn their molecular product. Promising beginnings have already been reported, and we can expect progress in future studies—though at a somewhat slower rate than we have become accustomed to in this era of molecular biology.

Mitosis

Mitosis is a process of nuclear division that consists of a continuous sequence of events divided conventionally into five stages: prophase (*pro*: before), prometaphase, metaphase (*meta*: between), anaphase (*ana*: back), and telophase (*telo*: end). The principal morphological features of mitosis involve chromosome condensation, spindle formation and the alignment of chromosomes on the spindle equator, separation of replicated sister chromosomes and their movement to opposite poles of the cell, and nuclear reorganization (Fig. 16.29). Interphase is the interval

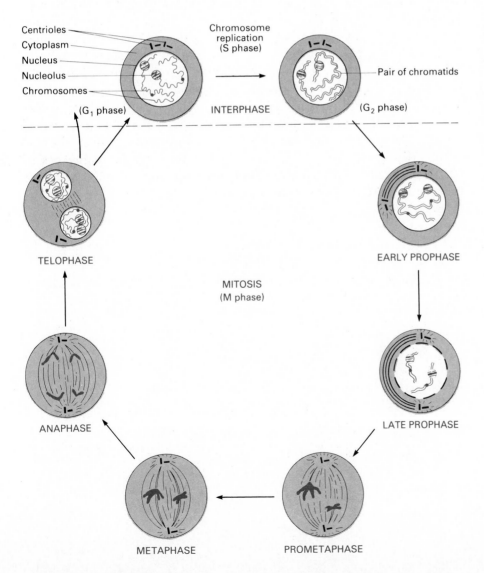

FIGURE 16-29
Interphase nuclei proceed through G_1, S, and G_2 phases of the cell cycle and then enter the M phase of mitosis. During mitosis, replicated chromosomes (pairs of sister chromatids) condense in prophase and line up on the spindle equator in metaphase. Sister chromatids separate from each other at anaphase. Nuclear reorganization occurs during telophase, and daughter cells may or may not proceed through one or more additional cell cycles, depending on the type of cell and its environment.

between successive divisions or the final condition of a nucleus that will not divide again. Mitosis is a mechanism for the distribution of chromosomes that have replicated earlier during interphase. Mitosis is a remarkably accurate mechanism that works just as well for a few chromosomes as for a few hundred, though mistakes are made occasionally. As in all biological systems, variations in one or more features of nuclear reproduction have been described in different organisms.

16.7
The Stages of Mitosis

The first visible sign of mitosis is condensation of the chromosomes, which signals the beginning of **prophase**. The chromosomes continue to become shorter and thicker throughout prophase, and eventually they become individually recognizable. Although each chromosome replicated in the preceding interphase, their doubled nature is not microscopically evident until about mid-prophase. At this time we can see that each chromosome is made up of two sister **chromatids** held together at the centromere region. The nucleolus begins to disappear as the chromosomes condense, and it is gone completely by the end of prophase.

Each centriole of the original pair in the cell has assembled a new centriole during interphase, so that two pairs of centrioles are present when mitosis begins. During prophase, each pair of centrioles becomes surrounded by the other components of the *mitotic center*—pericentriolar material, centrosome, and aster—in the cytoplasm adjacent to the nucleus at one pole of the cell. Spindle microtubules polymerize between the two mitotic centers, and the lengthening spindle fibers lead to separation of the two mitotic centers around the nuclear perimeter (Fig. 16.30). The mitotic centers sit at opposite poles of the cell by the end of prophase, with the spindle between them, but they remain outside the nuclear area until the nuclear envelope has disassembled completely in prometaphase.

The **prometaphase** stage begins with the complete disruption of the nuclear envelope and with erratic movements of the chromosomes in the nuclear space. Some of the chromosomes streak across the space, while others may stay put or just wiggle aimlessly. Chromosomal spindle

FIGURE 16-30
Spindle formation during mitotic prophase begins when spindle microtubules assemble between the two mitotic centers. Lengthening of the spindle leads to separation of the two mitotic centers in the cytoplasm outside the nucleus, until the two centers occupy opposite poles of the cell. The spindle moves to a more central location in the cell only after the nuclear envelope has disassembled at the conclusion of prophase.

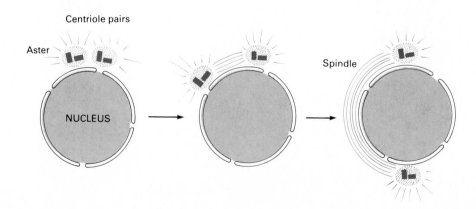

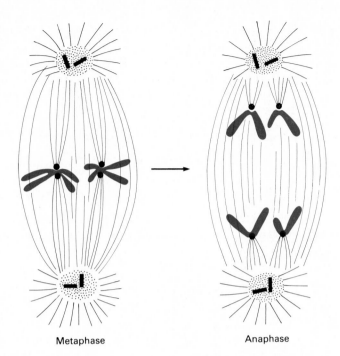

Metaphase   Anaphase

FIGURE 16-31
In metaphase the centromeres of sister chromatids face opposite poles of the cell, and the chromosomal spindle fibers extend from their insertion at the centromere to one pole of the cell for each sister chromatid of a pair. Separation of sister chromatids to opposite poles is more likely to be precise and accurate because of the spatial arrangement of their centromeres in relation to the poles of the cell.

fibers have not yet become attached to the centromere, or kinetochore, of each chromosome. As the nuclear envelope is disrupted, the entire spindle moves to occupy the nuclear space and becomes centrally located in the cell. Finally, as though a signal had been given, the chromosomes line up by their centromeres along the equatorial plane of the spindle figure, and metaphase begins.

Each **metaphase** chromosome becomes aligned on the spindle equator in such an orientation that the centromeres of each pair of sister chromatids face opposite poles of the cell. The chromosomal fibers have attached to each centromere by this time, and the stage is set for the precise separation of sister chromatids and their migration to opposite poles (Fig. 16.31). The forces that keep sister chromatids together from the time of their formation in interphase until the end of metaphase are not known. The situation is puzzling, because sister chromatids separate passively in metaphase cells that have been treated with colchicine, when the spindle fibers are absent or disorganized. In these drugged cells, a new nucleus is organized and it contains twice the number of chromosomes that were present in the parent nucleus (Fig. 16.32). Polyploid cells form spontaneously in liver and other tissues, where tetraploid and octaploid cells are not uncommon.

The relatively brief metaphase is followed by **anaphase**, which begins when sister chromatids of each replicated chromosome are pulled to opposite poles of the cell (see Section 11.14). Upon their separation, each chromatid becomes a full-fledged chromosome that acts independently of its sister. During anaphase movement each chromosome is pulled to the pole by its centromere-attached chromosomal spindle fibers, and these fibers gradually shorten as the poles are approached. At the same time that chromosomal fibers shorten, polar spindle fibers become gradually longer and the two poles of the spindle move farther and farther apart, presumably as a result of pushing forces exerted by the lengthening spindle.

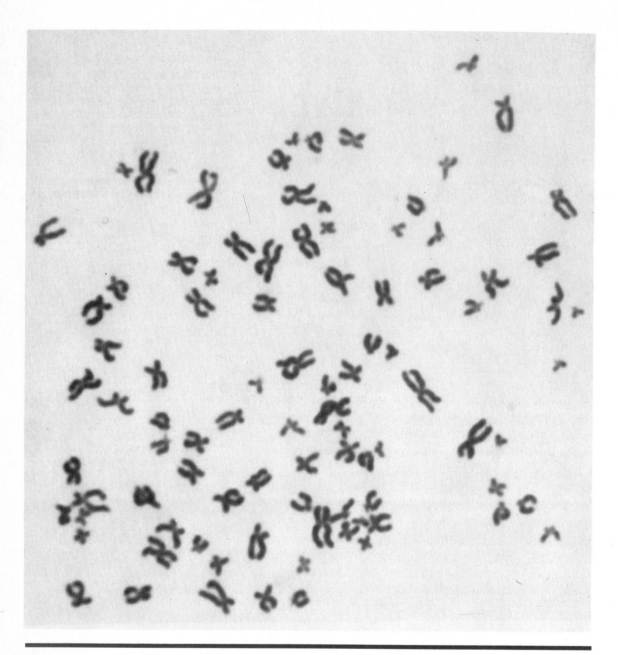

FIGURE 16-32
A tetraploid nucleus isolated from human cells contains 92 chromosomes rather than the usual diploid complement of 46 chromosomes. (Photograph by C. Hux.)

After a few minutes of anaphase separation, the two sets of chromosomes are assembled into separate nuclei as a new nuclear envelope forms around each of them during **telophase**. During nuclear reorganization in this final stage of mitosis, new nucleoli and nuclear envelope are assembled, the spindle gradually disappears, and the chromosomes unfold and gradually assume the extended appearance they had in interphase. When the pieces of nuclear envelope coalesce to form a complete boundary, mitosis ends and interphase begins.

16.8
Genetic Consequences of Mitosis

At the end of mitosis each daughter nucleus is genetically like the other and like the original parental nucleus (Fig. 16.33). By the mechanics of mitotic distribution, each nucleus is assured of receiving a complete set

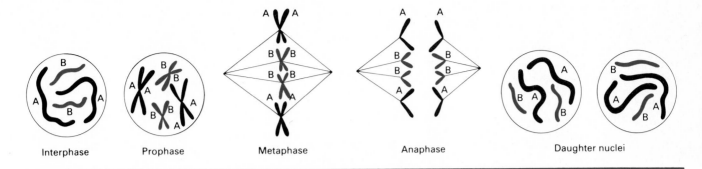

| Interphase | Prophase | Metaphase | Anaphase | Daughter nuclei |

FIGURE 16-33
Mitotic divisions, shown here for a diploid nucleus, produce daughter nuclei that are identical to each other and to the parental nucleus from which they arose. In this example, two pairs of chromosomes (A homologs and B homologs) replicate and proceed through precise alignment and separation into identical daughter nuclei.

of genetic instructions, which was duplicated in S phase. The fidelity of distribution accounts for genetic constancy in mitotic generations and leads to relatively uniform asexual populations of cells or organisms. Mutations and chromosome changes are faithfully transmitted to all the cells in a lineage, but because these genetic modifications are relatively rare events, it is more likely that genetic variability will characterize different asexual populations than any single population. By mitosis, virtually any genetic or chromosomal conditions, including aberrant numbers of chromosomes or sets of chromosomes, can be perpetuated within a population.

In bacteria the genome is contained in a single molecule of DNA, which is attached to the plasma membrane. After replication the genomic DNAs are separated passively to opposite ends of the cell as the plasma membrane lengthens during cell growth (Fig. 16.34). Logistical problems would certainly be encountered if the bacterial genome were subdivided into separate molecules, because the distribution mechanism provides no safeguards to ensure the separation of whole genomes into daughter nuclei. The safeguard lies in the organization of all the genes in one DNA molecule. On the other hand, genome organization may be very diverse in eukaryotes, and whole sets of chromosomes are segregated accurately and completely by virtue of the mitotic apparatus. The "invention" of mitosis during evolution permitted eukaryotes to exploit genome organizational diversity, leading to various chromosome numbers (linkage groups) and to the predominance of the diploid state in many species. These evolutionary innovations provide the foundations for eukaryotic flexibility in control mechanisms of gene expression, differentiation of the chromosomes, and gene reassortment in sexually reproducing species. We will discuss gene reassortment in the next chapter.

16.9
Modifications of Mitosis

As we should expect, variations in one or more features are characteristic of mitosis in eukaryotic species, particularly among the simpler organisms. Some of these variations have intrinsic interest of their own, but the greater value of comparative studies lies in our discerning evolutionary pathways by which organisms may have diversified and by which the current widely used mitotic apparatus may have arisen.

In ciliated protozoa such as *Paramecium* and *Tetrahymena*, two kinds of nuclei are present and each kind performs a different function in the life

FIGURE 16-34
Mode of distribution of the bacterial chromosome during cell division. (a) The replicating DNA molecule is attached at the site of replication (p_2) to the plasma membrane. Replication started at p_1 in the original parent cell. (b) When DNA replication is completed, each molecule has its own membrane attachment point bound to a newly formed portion of the plasma membrane (lightly stippled area). (c) Both DNA molecules undergo replication, and their attachment points separate as membrane growth takes place (new portions in gray). The chromosomes are carried apart as the membrane grows, not because of a special distribution process. (d) Two identical daughter cells are formed when cell division is completed.

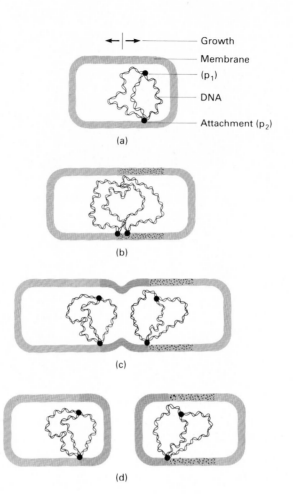

FIGURE 16-35
Light micrograph of *Paramecium tetraurelia*, showing the large macronucleus, which is responsible for metabolic and transcriptional activities, and two tiny micronuclei, whose functions are restricted to nuclear divisions. ×700. (Photograph courtesy of R. V. Dippell.)

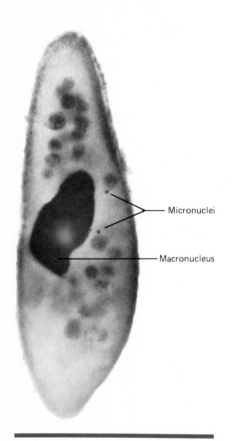

cycle. One or more small **micronuclei** carry out nuclear divisions by mitosis and meiosis but are otherwise metabolically inert. The large **macronucleus** does not undergo nuclear division, but it is highly polyploid and metabolically active in transcription, providing the instructions and molecules for translation in the cytoplasm (Fig. 16.35). The micronuclei can be lost without causing immediate damage, but such amicronucleate cells are asexual because the capacity for meiosis is also lost. New cells may be produced for a while by fission, which partitions cytoplasm and portions of the polyploid macronucleus to descendant cells. As the macronuclear genomes are separated into progeny cells, the genetic material is depleted gradually. After a while, new cells cannot be produced because of inadequate nuclear materials to maintain viability.

The *polytene* chromosomes of dipteran larval cells and other systems provide striking examples of the effects of repeated rounds of DNA replication without subsequent mitotic segregation of the replicated strands (see Fig. 15.33). Each chromosome is multistranded but acts as a unit in gene expression; the chromosome number remains at the diploid level, as does gene action. In other kinds of cells, one or more rounds of DNA replication may occur, but the chromatids remain associated at the centromere region and do not segregate into new nuclei. In Fig. 16.36, each chromosome apparently replicated once to produce two chromatids, and each chromatid replicated again to

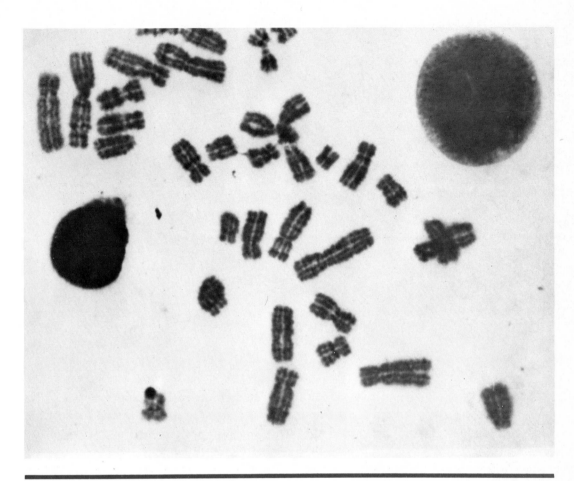

FIGURE 16-36
Endomitosis (replication without
subsequent separation of chromatids)
of these G-banded human chromosomes has produced diplochromosomes. Each chromatid of the first
replication event has replicated again,
making diplochromosomes that consist of two pairs of chromatids each.
(Photograph by C. Hux.)

produce *diplochromosomes* that consist of two pairs of chromatids each.
This process of chromatid replication without subsequent segregation
into separate nuclei is called **endomitosis** (*endo*: within). Endopolyploid
cells are often encountered in liver and other tissues, and they generally
have four or eight sets of chromosomes instead of the usual diploid
number.

Many protists and other lower organisms undergo **intranuclear
mitosis**, in which all the events of division take place in a nucleus whose
nuclear envelope remains intact at all times. In some of the dinoflagellates and protozoa, a central spindle consisting only of polar fibers
is formed between the mitotic centers at each pole of the cell, and the
bundle of fibers occupies a channel that runs through the intact nuclear
envelope. Chromosomes within the nucleus are attached to the nuclear
envelope but lack spindle fibers in the early stages of mitosis. As the
nucleus expands and approaches the two poles of the cell, chromosomal
spindle fibers are formed and become attached to the centromeres of the
chromosomes at the nuclear envelope (Fig. 16.37). Once they are
attached to spindle fibers, the sister chromatids are drawn to opposite
poles by an active process; their earlier separation results from passive
separation as the nuclear envelope expands poleward. In these organisms, the polar and chromosomal fibers clearly subsidize separate
activities. Polar fibers lead to spindle elongation and increasing separation of the two poles of the cell, whereas chromosomal spindle fibers

FIGURE 16-37
Drawing of anaphase during intra-nuclear mitosis in the protozoan *Barbulanympha*. Chromosomal spindle fibers extend from the aster at each pole to the centromere by which each chromosome is attached to the intact nuclear envelope. A spatially separate bundle of polar spindle fibers runs through a channel in the intact nuclear envelope and extends from pole to pole in the cytoplasm. None of the spindle fibers are found within the nucleus itself.

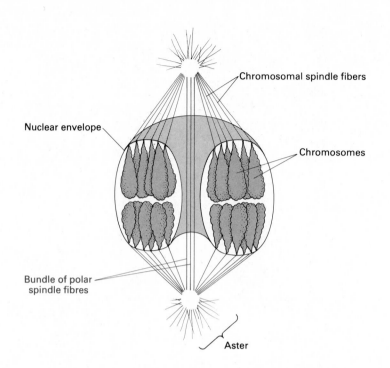

Chromosomal spindle fibers

Nuclear envelope

Chromosomes

Bundle of polar spindle fibres

Aster

pull the sister chromatids to opposite poles once the centromeres are near the poles and the spindle fibers extend from the mitotic centers to the centromeres attached to the expanding nuclear envelope. The push–pull differentiation of polar and chromosomal spindle fibers is particularly evident in these mitotic cells. In these cells, unlike those of higher organisms, the entire spindle figure is located in the cytoplasm outside the inact nucleus.

Intranuclear mitosis in the yeast *Saccharomyces cerevisiae* involves spindle formation within the intact nucleus. During nuclear preparations for division in the G_1 phase of the cell cycle, a structure called the *spindle pole body* (SPB) is duplicated and the two SPBs separate to become situated opposite each other at the nuclear envelope. The dense inner plaque of the SPB is a microtubule-organizing center from which spindle fibers assemble and aggregate into a spindle figure (Fig. 16.38). A single microtubule is attached to the simple centromere of the yeast chromosome, and anaphase movement to the poles involves centromere-directed events that pull the chromosomes toward the SPBs at the nuclear border. The SPB acts as a mitotic center, equivalent to the aster-bordered centrosome in animal cells. Each SPB in the G_1 cell must be important in other events as well as in spindle formation, because successful duplication and separation of SPBs are essential for subsequent initiation of DNA synthesis in S phase (see Fig 16.28).

In the simple dinoflagellate species *Gyrodinium cohnii*, an apparently primitive microtubule-aided mitotic mechanism was described by Hans Ris and Donna Kubai. During mitosis, channels appear in the cytoplasm and penetrate through the body of the intact nucleus without interrupting the continuity of the nuclear envelope. Bundles of microtubules appear within these cytoplasmic channels and provide rigidity to these regions. Chromosomes in the nucleus become attached by their centromeres to the inner nuclear membrane where the envelope abuts

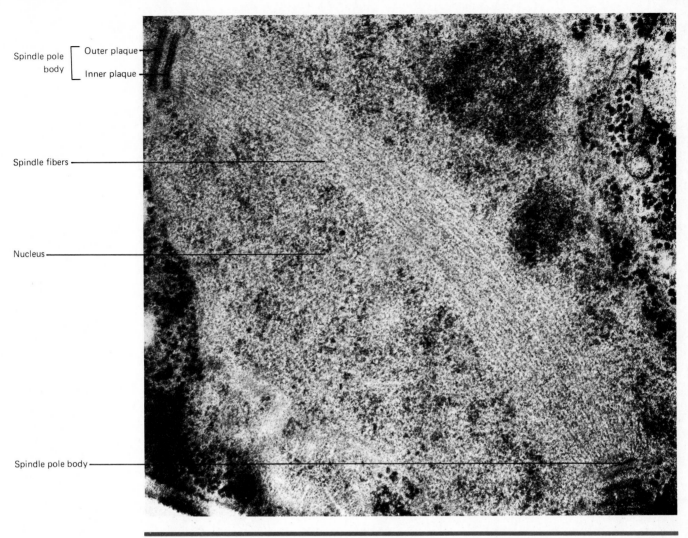

Spindle pole body { Outer plaque

Inner plaque

Spindle fibers

Nucleus

Spindle pole body

FIGURE 16-38
Spindle formation takes place entirely within the intact nucleus during intracellular mitosis (or meiosis) in the yeast *Saccharomyces cerevisiae*. The spindle pole body at each pole of the cell consists of a microtubule-organizing inner plaque, which is a differentiated region of the nuclear envelope, and an outer plaque adjacent to it in the cytoplasm bordering the nucleus. ×72,000. (Photograph courtesy of P. B. Moens.)

the cytoplasmic channels, but they are never attached to microtubules in the extranuclear channels (Fig. 16.39). Chromosomes are carried passively toward the poles of the cell as the nuclear envelope to which they are attached expands and itself approaches both poles. The microtubule-filled channels serve to define the plane of later cell division, just as a conventional spindle figure does, but the rigid, rodlike channels also serve to keep the nuclear envelope taut in regions where the chromosomes are attached by their centromeres; the spindle has no dynamic function in this species. Similarities to the bacterial system of genome separation during cell division are apparent. In bacteria the genomic DNA is attached by a special point to the plasma membrane that underlies the rigid cell wall, and the replicated DNA molecules are carried apart by expansion of the growing plasma membrane (see Fig. 16.34). In *G. cohnii* the rigid extranuclear channels lend support and draw the adjoining nuclear envelope taut, and the attached chromosomes are separated passively as nuclear enlargement occurs. Interestingly, dinoflagellate chromosomes consist almost entirely of tightly packed dulex DNA, with very little associated protein, and are thus similar in molecular organization to the bacterial chromosome.

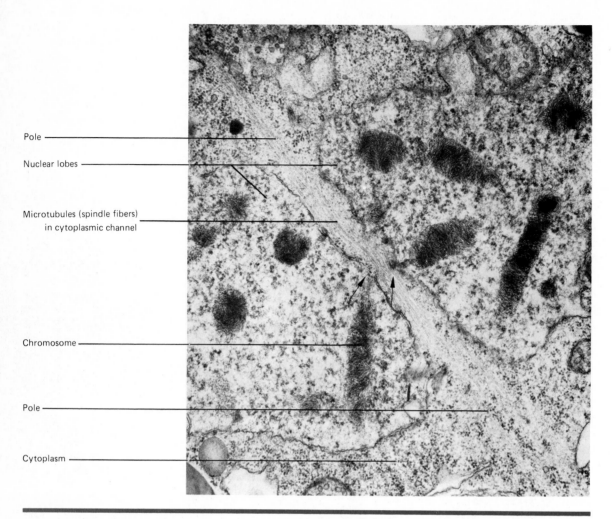

Pole

Nuclear lobes

Microtubules (spindle fibers)
in cytoplasmic channel

Chromosome

Pole

Cytoplasm

FIGURE 16-39
Electron micrograph through parts of
two lobes of a late-division nucleus
of the dinoflagellate *Gyrodinium
cohnii*. Microtubules are present only
in cytoplasmic channels between
lobes of the intact nucleus, and they
extend to the poles in the cytoplasm.
Chromosomes within the nucleus are
attached to the nuclear envelope
regions (at arrows) that border the
cylindrical channel of cytoplasm.
×26,200. (Photograph courtesy
of H. Ris, from Kubai, D. F., and H. Ris,
1969, *J. Cell Biol.* **40**:508–528,
Fig. 24.)

Various speculations and evolutionary scenarios have been proposed to trace the origins and subsequent modifications of the mitotic processes and structures that characterize eukaryotic organisms but are entirely absent in prokaryotes. It is clear that many different evolutionary modifications were instituted before the modern system was fully established in all the higher organisms and many lower eukaryotic forms. The sequence of events is unclear, but certain essential differences between prokaryotes and eukaryotes must be noted in relation to genome segregation patterns. In eukaryotes, the genome is subdivided into two or more independent chromosomes, the chromosomes are enclosed in a nucleus, a centromere or an equivalent differentiated structure is essential for attachment and directed movement to the poles of each chromosome, and spindle microtubules emerge from mitotic centers at the poles of the cell. Prokaryotes have no membrane surrounding their single chromosome equivalent, no microtubules, no special apparatus for segregating replicated DNA molecules, and a simple attachment point that hardly qualifies as a centromere but holds the genome firmly on the plasma membrane at all times.

Variations that have been described for spindle function in simpler eukaryotes provide a basis for possible evolutionary pathways leading to the modern spindle in higher organisms. On the assumption that the bacterial system of genome segregation is like the ancestral system, it seems reasonable to suggest that the first eukaryotes possessed a similar system. A single chromosome and its replica would be attached to the inner surface of the nuclear envelope and would separate as the envelope expanded. Once the genome was subdivided into more than one chromosome, a more precise segregation mechanism would be necessary to ensure the distribution of equal amounts of genetic material and thereby to direct a whole genome toward each end of the cell. Greater precision would be provided by a mechanism that guided the chromosomes toward opposite poles by establishing polarity of division. The simple system present in *Gyrodinium* may represent just such an early step in spindle evolution, in which cytoskeletal microtubules organize during division into a stiff, polarized, rodlike bundle that is not connected to the nuclear envelope and exerts no active force in moving the chromosomes. Still later, as we see in various protozoan species, the cytoplasmic bundle of polarized fibers become more regularly organized and oriented by mitotic centers of some sort at the poles of the cell. These mitotic centers, or microtubule-organizing centers, direct the assembly of fibers that attached to centromeres or centromere equivalents on the chromosomes, but contact is made between spindle fibers and centromeres at the nuclear envelope, to which the chromosomes have attached during the division process. In these cells the spindle exerts an active force in pulling the chromosomes directionally to the poles and in pushing apart the two halves of the dividing nucleus.

The nuclear envelope remains essential for mitosis in fungi and similar lower organisms in which the mitotic center (spindle pole body or equivalent) is a differentiated region of the nuclear envelope, even though chromosome centromeres themselves are no longer attached to the envelope. Intranuclear mitosis continues to be characteristic of lower organisms in all cases in which the nuclear envelope is a direct participant as a microtubule-organizing center. Later in evolution these centers are located in the cytoplasm, not in the nuclear envelope, so the entire mitotic apparatus can dispense with the nuclear envelope during division. The gradual disappearance of the nuclear envelope during division in higher organisms may well reflect such changing conditions during evolution. Ultimately, the centromeres themselves evolved as more complex differentiations of the chromosomes, in conjunction with repetitive DNA and nucleosomal organization. The simple yeast chromosome centromere (see Section 15.5) may be a remnant of an earlier stage in chromosomal evolution. Centromeres in higher organisms are surrounded by heterochromatin and are structurally more complex as well as more extensively differentiated regions. Some of these suggested evolutionary changes are illustrated in Fig. 16.40. Clearly, genetic modifications during evolution were responsible for these differences in the mitotic apparatus, and those changes that proved to be advantageous were incorporated into the genome. We have ample evidence from yeast and many other organisms that specific genes are responsible for specific structures, molecules, and processes that characterize mitosis.

FIGURE 16-40
Possible sequence of evolutionary changes in the mitotic apparatus of eukaryotes. (a) The ancestral cell may have had its chromosomal DNA attached to the plasma membrane, as in prokaryotes, and would therefore have had a replicated chromosome separation mechanism similar to the one known in modern bacteria (see Fig. 16-34). (b) Simple eukaryotes, like *Gyrodinium*, may have evolved a system in which chromosomes within a nucleus were attached to the nuclear envelope but not to spindle microtubules, which remained outside in the cytoplasm. The bundle of cytoplasmic microtubules would have provided tautness to the expanding nuclear envelope that passively separated replicated chromosomes into daughter nuclei. (c) Another evolutionary innovation was the development of mitotic centers from which chromosomal and polar spindle fibers were assembled in the cytoplasm. One set of polar spindle fibers defined the subsequent plane of cell division, and sets of chromosomal spindle fibers became attached to chromosomal centromeres at the nuclear envelope. Such a mechanism, as in *Barbulanympha*, more accurately directs one complete set of replicated chromosomes to each pole of the cell. (d) Confinement of the spindle to the interior of the nucleus, as in simple eukaryotes such as *Saccharomyces*, became possible when a portion of the nuclear envelope differentiated into a microtubule-organizing center (MTOC), from which microtubules assemble and become attached to chromosomal centromeres within the nucleus. (e) Once the mitotic centers assemble chromosomal spindle fibers that are inserted into centromeres of chromosomes that are not attached to the nuclear envelope, as well as polar spindle fibers, the nuclear envelope becomes dispensable for mitotic activities during metaphase and anaphase. In higher plants and animals, therefore, spindle formation and anaphase movement of chromosomes to the poles become cytoplasmic rather than intranuclear phenomena.

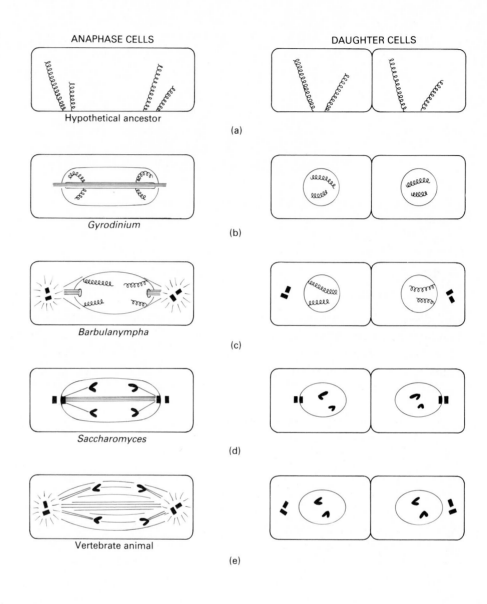

ANAPHASE CELLS — DAUGHTER CELLS

Hypothetical ancestor

(a)

Gyrodinium

(b)

Barbulanympha

(c)

Saccharomyces

(d)

Vertebrate animal

(e)

Cytokinesis

The formation of a new boundary that separates the daughter nuclei into two new cells and also apportions the mother-cell cytoplasm in relatively equal amounts to the daughter cells is called cell division, or **cytokinesis**. Cytokinesis is separable from mitosis, which is evident from multinucleated cells in a large variety of organisms. In higher organisms and some lower forms, cytokinesis is coordinated with mitosis and leads to the regular production of uninucleated cells. Cytokinesis usually starts during mitotic anaphase, and the mitotic spindle plays an important part in determining the position of the new cell boundary as well as the timing of its formation. Three major mechanisms of cytokinesis can be identified. Each is the predominant (or even the only) mode of cell division in different groups of organisms. Animal cells usually divide by the process of furrowing, or cleavage; higher plants divide by a process involving cell-plate formation; and algae and fungi

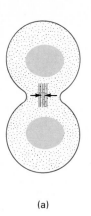
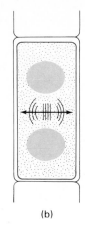
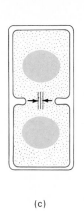

(a)   (b)   (c)

FIGURE 16-41
Drawings showing differences in the cell division processes of (a) furrowing and (b) cell plate formation in more advanced eukaryotes, and (c) new wall formation as it occurs in many algae, fungi, and bacteria.

undergo division by a process that somewhat resembles cytokinesis in bacteria (Fig. 16.41).

16.10
Furrowing in Animal Cells

Cell division in animals and some of the protists is first evident by a pinching-in of the plasma membrane at the midline of the spindle figure and at right angles to it. This process is called **furrowing**, or **cleavage**, and a progressively deeper cleavage furrow develops until the cell is divided in two (Fig. 16.42). Constriction around the midline of the

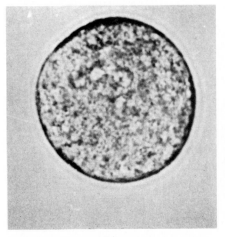
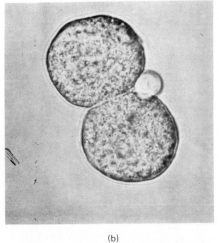

(a)   (b)

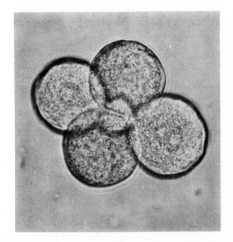
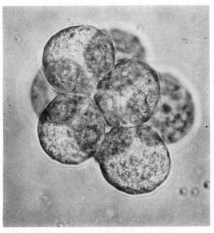

(c)   (d)

FIGURE 16-42
Successive cleavage divisions of the mouse (a) fertilized egg give rise to the (b) 2-cell, (c) 4-cell, and (d) 8-cell stages of the developing embryo. × 560 (Photographs courtesy of B. Babiarz.)

cell is accomplished by the contraction of an encircling group of actin filaments and myosin that assemble spontaneously into a **contractile ring**, which acts like a purse string being drawn tightly around the cell.

The force exerted by the contractile ring during furrowing is large and readily measured, and it is generated by a musclelike sliding of actin and myosin filaments. Cleavage can be stopped and the furrow relaxed by adding cytochalasin B, which disrupts actin filaments, or by injecting anti-myosin antibodies, which block actin-binding sites on myosin and thereby prevent sliding and the generation of force.

Electron microscopy has revealed that structural changes accompany furrowing, leading to the development of a **midbody** composed of the remnants of the polar spindle fibers to which some kind of dense material is added as furrowing proceeds (Fig. 16.43). The dense material of the midbody first appears in anaphase only at the spindle periphery, opposite the first inward site of furrowing around the midline of the cell. As telophase proceeds, more of this dense material is added until it fills the entire equatorial plane of the dividing cell. The midbody becomes smaller as constriction of the cell continues, and it usually disappears

FIGURE 16-43
Electron micrograph of a section through the elongated bridge of a human cell undergoing cytokinesis by furrowing. The midbody is a distinctive region of the bridge, and it includes numerous microtubules as well as densely staining material of unknown function. × 67,500. (Photograph courtesy of B. Byers, from Byers, B., and D. H. Abramson, 1968, *Protoplasma* **66**:413–435, Fig. 9.)

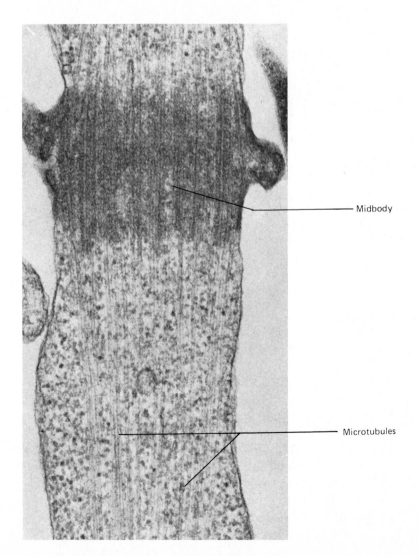

Midbody

Microtubules

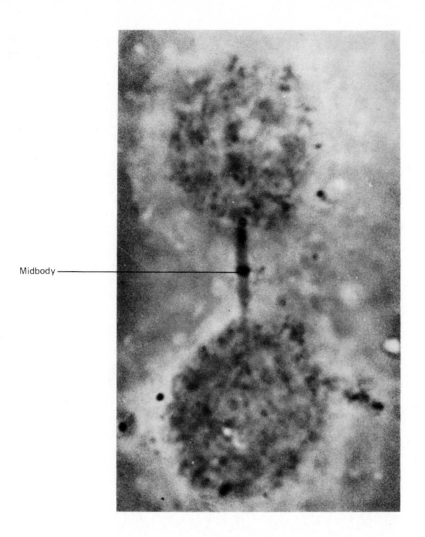

Midbody —

FIGURE 16-44
Phase-contrast light micrograph of a section through a human cell in the final stages of cytokinesis by furrowing. The constricted bridge between incipient daughter cells is considerably elongated and includes a prominent midbody. × 2100. (Photograph courtesy of B. Byers, from Byers, B., and D. H. Abramson, 1968, *Protoplasma* **66**:413–435, Fig. 8.)

before cleavage is completed. In some kinds of cells the midbody persists and may act as a connecting bridge between the two daughter cells (Fig. 16.44). The functional role of the midbody in animal cell division is unknown.

16.11
Cell Plate Formation in Plants

In plants, the new boundary that separates daughter nuclei into individual cells is called the **cell plate**, and it consists of plasma membranes and new primary cell walls that become continuous with the pre-existing membranes and cell wall of the original parent cell. Cell plate formation occurs through the agency of a **phragmoplast**, which consists of a growing collection of spindle fibers, secretion vesicles, and bits of endoplasmic reticulum that first appear around the midline of the cell near the inside perimeter. Beginning in anaphase and continuing until the cell plate has been completed in early interphase, the phragmoplast grows outward and inward until it extends entirely across the middle of the dividing cell (Fig. 16.45). When viewed from either pole, the phragmoplast first appears to have a doughnut shape because the

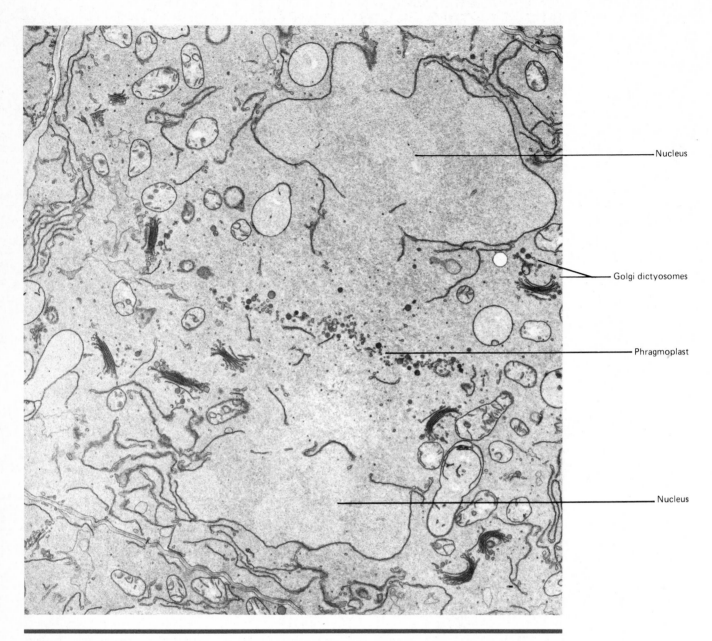

— Nucleus

— Golgi dictyosomes

— Phragmoplast

— Nucleus

FIGURE 16-45
Electron micrograph of a dividing maize root cell, showing the phragmoplast between daughter nuclei. The phragmoplast expands across the entire dividing cell as more and more spindle fibers, secretion vesicles (from the Golgi apparatus), and bits of endoplasmic reticulum are added. When the phragmoplast is completed and becomes continuous with the plasma membrane, the structure is called a cell plate. ×10,000. (Photograph courtesy of H. H. Mollenhauer.)

central region is incomplete. Late, its center is filled and the phragmoplast expands across the entire dividing cell.

During anaphase, spindle fibers begin to disappear in the polar regions but persist in the region around the midline of the cell. Membranous vesicles begin to appear around the persisting microtubules, and pieces of the endoplasmic reticulum also congregate in this area. The vesicles are filled with dense materials consisting of carbohydrate and lipid secretions that are the pectin, hemicellulose, and other precursor molecules of the new cell walls. In addition to the identical appearance of phragmoplast vesicles and vesicles still associated with dictyosomes of the Golgi apparatus, radioactive labeling has clearly established the Golgi apparatus as the source of the secretion vesicles.

As the phragmoplast grows, vesicles and bits of membrane coalesce to form the continuous plasma membranes that connect to existing plasma membrane of the daughter units. New cell wall material is deposited between the membranes separating the daughter cells, and thickening gradually takes place as new layers of fibrous materials are added to the originally thin, flexible partitions. With the completion of the cell plate, the daughter cells become independent entities, but connections between them are often retained as a result of the presence of cytoplasmic strands extending through openings (*plasmodesmata*), in the walls between adjacent cells (see Section 6.9).

The spindle fibers that persist during telophase and new microtubules that are added to the phragmoplast are believed to aid in the transport of vesicles within the structure; thus they actively contribute to cell plate formation. If cells are exposed to colchicine during phragmoplast formation, vesicles no longer accumulate at the midline of the dividing cell.

Like plant cells, algae and fungi possess rigid cell walls, but their cell division process more closely resembles cell wall formation in bacteria. As the plasma membrane invaginates and grows inward from the cell periphery, new cell wall materials are laid down along both sides of the growing membrane. As the edges of the inward-growing membranes and walls come together in the cell center, fusions are completed and each daughter cell has its own intact plasma membrane and cell wall (see Fig. 16.41c). The superficial similarity to inward movement of the new cell boundary in animals and in walled algal and fungal cells is deceptive: The mechanisms are basically different in these groups of organisms.

Summary

Cell renewal involves processes of repair and molecular turnover as well as division to produce new cells in a population. In some tissue and organ systems, such as liver, differentiated cells may produce new cells like themselves. In other systems, such as blood in animals and vascular tissues in plants, differentiated cells cannot divide but are renewed by division of unipotent or pluripotent stem cells. Stem cells produce others like themselves as well as products that differentiate into nondividing cells that carry out particular functions in the organism. Hormonal factors may regulate the route of differentiation of pluripotent stem-cell descendants, and they generally guide the rate and extent of cell renewal in tissues and organs.

The controls governing cell growth and division are best studied in cell culture. Primary cultures derived directly from an organism divide for only a limited number of generations, but from these, secondary cultures may be selected in which the cells grow indefinitely. Different cultured cells can be fused to form somatic cell hybrids that may proliferate in a selective growth medium (HAT) that prevents or discourages proliferation of the parental cells. Selective loss of chromosomes and correlated phenotypic traits in somatic cell hybrids permits gene assignment to particular chromosomes in the genome. Cells cultured directly from tumors or normal cells transformed by tumor viruses in culture exhibit a phenotype consistent with uncontrolled growth or malignancy—loss of contact inhibition and anchorage dependence, due to unresponsiveness to nutrients and growth regulating factors, and disorganization of the cytoskeleton.

Genes responsible for the transforming activity of certain viruses (v-*onc* genes) are homologous to sequences found in normal cells of all vertebrates (c-*onc* genes). A number of these viral oncogenes (and their cellular counterparts) encode protein kinase enzymes that specifically promote the phosphorylation of tyrosine residues in cytoskeletal proteins. Other oncogene products resemble growth factors or their receptors or mimic the activity of molecules that relay hormone signals from the cell membrane to the cell interior. Each of these activities could explain the unregulated phenotype of the transformed cell. When expression of cellular oncogenes is stimulated, the cells become transformed. The high degree of homology among cellular oncogenes from distantly related organisms suggests that these genes promote essential and highly regulated functions in normal growth and development. Tumor viruses may capture cellular oncogenes during infection and carry them to cells or chromosome locations where their expression would be inappropriate.

Macromolecules are actively produced in interphase, but not all are made continuously. In particular, DNA and histones are synthesized only during the S phase of the cell cycle, separated from mitosis (M) by G_1 before and by G_2 after synthesis. Studies on cultured cells, both synchronized and randomly growing, have revealed some of the factors that control these phases. Unlike G_2 and S, the duration of G_1 is strongly influenced by environmental conditions. It can be quite brief if nutrients are abundant, but under suboptimal conditions the G_1 phase can become prolonged, and if crowding induces quiescence, G_1 cells become arrested in a noncycling state referred to as G_0. The duration of S phase may also vary at different developmental stages, with embryonic cells of some species able to synthesize in 25 minutes what requires 20 hours in an adult. Cell-fusion studies suggest the presence of factors that promote the transition from G_1 to S and from G_2 to M. Once S phase has begun, however, fusion with G_2 cells cannot interrupt it, nor can fusion induce G_2 nuclei to synthesize more DNA until after they have divided. Using cell-division-cycle mutants in yeast and other organisms, investigators have identified and determined the order of action of a number of genes that regulate aspects of the cell cycle.

The M phase of the cell cycle, mitosis, is classically subdivided into 5 stages according to nuclear morphology:

1. Prophase. The chromosomes condense, the nucleolus disperses, and a spindle assembles.

2. Prometaphase. The nuclear envelope breaks down and the chromosomes attach to the spindle fibers.

3. Metaphase. The chromosomes are aligned at the equatorial plate of the spindle, with sister chromatids held together at their centromeres and facing opposite poles.

4. Anaphase. The centromeres separate and sister chromatids are pulled to opposite poles of the spindle as the chromosomal fibers shorten and the polar fibers elongate.

5. Telophase. The nuclear envelope re-forms around each daughter chromosome set, the spindle disperses, the chromosomes unfold, and nucleoli reappear.

This process ensures distribution of one copy of every chromosome to each daughter cell.

Various mitotic strategies exist in certain protists and other simple organisms. One possible sequence of evolutionary events derived from comparative studies of such organisms proposes that cells whose genome consisted of a single chromosome distributed it by expansion of the nuclear envelope to which the chromosome was attached. As genomes grew to include more than one chromosome, a more precise system of segregation was provided by microtubules. Once chromosomes were bound directly to spindle fibers, spindle microtubules promoted chromosome movement, and chromosome association with the nuclear envelope was less essential. With the development of highly evolved centromeres, the nuclear envelope was not required for the spindle-organizing function. Different known species of eukaryotic microorganisms exhibit many intermediate stages of this proposed scheme.

Cytokinesis, division of the cell, occurs by different mechanisms in animals, plants, and bacteria. In animals a furrow develops in the plasma membrane at the midline of, and at right angles to, the spindle. The membrane is drawn in by contraction of cortical actin and myosin filaments in the contractile ring, and the furrow progressively deepens, pinching off the two daughter cells. The remnants of spindle fibers collect at the neck to form a midbody that may disappear or persist as a bridge between daughter cells. In plants a cell plate forms from the phragmoplast, a collection of spindle fibers, secretion vesicles, and bits of endoplasmic reticulum in the cell center at the spindle midline. The collection of phragmoplast materials grows outward and eventually coalesces and forms a continuous membrane sheet that fuses with the existing parental plasma membrane. On each side of the phragmoplast a cell wall develops as vesicle contents are deposited. The wall gradually hardens and thickens. Plasmodesmata may remain and provide openings for cytoplasmic bridges between the daughter cells. In algae and fungi the plasma membrane invaginates, and new cell-wall material is laid down in the crevice on both sides.

Readings and References

Adlakha, R. C., C. G. Sahasrabuddhe, D. A. Wright, and P. N. Rao. 1983. Evidence for the presence of inhibitors of mitotic factors during G_1 period in mammalian cells. *J. Cell Biol.* **97**:1707.

Alitalo, K. 1985. Amplification of cellular oncogenes in cancer cells. *Trends Biochem. Sci.* **10**:194.

Armelin, H. A., *et al.* 1984. Functional role for c-*myc* in mitogenic response to platelet-derived growth factor. *Nature* **310**:655.

Bajer, A. 1968. Fine-structure studies on phragmoplast and cell-plate formation. *Chromosoma* **24**:383.

Baserga, R. 1981. The cell cycle. *New Engl. J. Med.* **304**:453.

Baserga, R., and W. E. Kisielski. August 1963. Autobiographies of cells. *Sci. Amer.* **209**:103.

Beams, H. W., and R. G. Kessel. 1976. Cytokinesis: A comparative study of cytoplasmic division in animal cells. *Amer. Sci.* **64**:279.

Birkenmeyer, L. G., J. C. Hill, and L. B. Dumas. 1984. *Saccharomyces cerevisiae CDC8* gene and its product. *Mol. Cell. Biol.* **4**:583.

Bishop, J. M. March 1982. Oncogenes. *Sci. Amer.* **246**:80.

Bishop, J. M. 1983. Cancer genes come of age. *Cell* **32**:1018.

Bloom, W., and D. W. Fawcett. 1975. *A Textbook of Histology.* 10th ed. Philadelphia: Saunders.

Byers, B., and D. H. Abrahamson. 1968. Cytokinesis in HeLa: Post-telophase delay and microtubule-associated motility. *Protoplasma* **66**:413.

Clemens, M. 1985. Interferons and oncogenes. *Nature* **313**:531.

Cohen, P. 1982. The role of protein phosphorylation in neural and hormonal control of cellular activity. *Nature* **296**:613.

Collett, M. S., and R. L. Erikson. 1978. Protein kinase activity associated with the avian sarcoma virus *src* gene product. *Proc. Natl. Acad. Sci. U.S.* **75**:2021.

Cooper, G. M. 1982. Cellular transforming genes. *Science* **218**:801.

Cooper, G. M., and M.-A. Lane. 1984. Cellular genes and oncogenesis. *Biochim. Biophys. Acta* **738**:9.

Cooper, S. 1979. A unifying model for the G_1 period in prokaryotes and eukaryotes. *Nature* **280**:17.

Croce, C. M., and G. Klein. March 1985. Chromosome translocations and human cancer. *Sci. Amer.* **252**:54.

Davis, M., S. Malcolm, and T. H. Rabbitts. 1984. Chromosome translocation can occur on either side of the c-*myc* oncogene in Burkitt lymphoma cells. *Nature* **308**:286.

D'Eustachio, P. 1984. Gene mapping and oncogenes. *Amer. Sci.* **72**:32.

Dickinson, J. R. 1984. The biochemical genetics of cell-cycle control in eukaryotes. *Trends Biochem. Sci.* **9**:269.

Dirksen, E. R., D. M. Prescott, and C. F. Fox, eds. 1978. *Cell Reproduction.* New York: Academic Press.

Doolittle, R. F., *et al.* 1983. Simian sarcoma virus *onc* gene, v-*sis*, is derived from the gene (or genes) encoding a platelet-derived growth factor. *Science* **221**:275.

Downward, J., *et al.* 1984. Close similarity of epidermal growth factor receptor and v-*erb-B* oncogene protein sequences. *Nature* **307**:521.

Duesberg, P. H. 1985. Activated proto-onc genes: Sufficient or necessary for cancer? *Science* **228**:669.

Ephrussi, B., and M. C. Weiss. April 1969. Hybrid somatic cells. *Sci. Amer.* **220**:26.

Fantes, P. A. 1981. Cell-division control: Why clocks are inadequate. In *International Cell Biology 1980–1981*, ed. H. G. Schweiger, p. 846. New York: Rockefeller University Press.

Feder, J., and W. R. Tolbert. January 1983. The large-scale cultivation of mammalian cells. *Sci. Amer.* **248**:36.

Garber, E. A., J. G. Krueger, H. Hanafusa, and A. R. Goldberg. 1983. Only membrane-associated RSV *src* proteins have amino-terminally bound lipid. *Nature* **302**:161.

Gilmore, T., J. E. DeClue, and G. S. Martin. 1985. Protein phosphorylation at tyrosine is induced by the v-*erbB* gene product *in vivo* and *in vitro*. *Cell* **40**:609.

Graf, L. H., Jr. 1982. Gene transformation. *Amer. Sci.* **70**:496.

Harrison, P. R. 1982. Stem-cell regulation in erythropoiesis. *Nature* **295**:454.

Hartwell, L. H. 1978. Cell division from a genetic perspective. *J. Cell Biol.* **77**:627.

Hartwell, L. H., J. Culotti, J. R. Pringle, and B. J. Reid. 1974. Genetic control of the cell-division cycle in yeast. *Science* **183**:46.

Hayward, W. S., B. G. Neel, and S. M. Astrin. 1981. Activation of a cellular *onc* gene by promoter insertion in ALV-induced lymphoid leukosis. *Nature* **290**:475.

Hoppe, J. 1985. cAMP-dependent protein kinases: Conformational changes during activation. *Trends Biochem. Sci.* **10**:29.

Hunter, T. August 1984. The proteins of oncogenes. *Sci. Amer.* **251**:70.

Hynes, R. 1982. Phosphorylation of vinculin by pp60[src]: What might it mean? *Cell* **28**:437.

Illmensee, K., and L. C. Stevens. April 1979. Teratomas and chimeras. *Sci. Amer.* **240**:121.

Inoué, S. 1981. Cell division and the mitotic cycle. *J. Cell Biol.* **91**:131s.

Jacky, P. B., B. Beek, and G. R. Sutherland. 1983. Fragile sites in chromosomes: Possible model for the study of spontaneous chromosome breakage. *Science* **220**:69.

John, P. C. L., ed. 1981. *The Cell Cycle.* Cambridge, England: Cambridge University Press.

Johnson, R. T., and P. N. Rao. 1970. Mammalian cell fusion: Induction of premature chromosome condensation in interphase nuclei. *Nature* **226**:717.

Johnson, U. G., and K. R. Porter. 1968. Fine structure of cell division in *Chlamydomonas reinhardi*. *J. Cell Biol.* **38**:403.

Johnston, G. C., and R. A. Singer. 1978. RNA synthesis and control of cell division in the yeast *S. cerevisiae*. *Cell* **14**:951.

Kay, R. 1981. How cells live together. *Nature* **294**:108.

Kessel, R. G., and R. H. Kardon. 1979. *Tissues and Organs: A Text–Atlas of Scanning Electron Microscopy.* San Francisco: Freeman.

King, S. M., and J. S. Hyams. 1982. The mitotic spindle of *Saccharomyces cerevisiae*: Assembly, structure, and function. *Micros* **13**:93.

Kirschner, M., J. Newport, and J. Gerhart. 1985. The timing of early developmental events in *Xenopus*. *Trends Genet.* **1**:41.

Kriegstein, H. J., and D. S. Hogness. 1974. Mechanism of DNA replication in *Drosophila* chromosomes. Structure of replication forks and evidence for bidirectionality. *Proc. Natl. Acad. Sci. U.S.* **71**:135.

Krontiris, T. G. 1983. The emerging genetics of human cancer. *New Engl. J. Med.* **309**:404.

Kubai, D. F., and H. Ris. 1969. Division in the dinoflagellate *Gyrodinium cohnii* (Schiller). A new type of nuclear reproduction. *J. Cell Biol.* **40**:508.

Kubai, D. F. 1975. The evolution of the mitotic spindle. *Internat. Rev. Cytol.* **43**:167.

Land, H., L. F. Parada, and R. A. Weinberg. 1983. Cellular oncogenes and multistep carcinogenesis. *Science* **222**:771.

LeBeau, M. M., and J. D. Rowley. 1984. Heritable fragile sites in cancer. *Nature* **308**:607.

Leblond, C. P. 1981. The life history of cells in renewing systems. *Amer. J. Anat.* **160**:113.

Leder, P., *et al.* 1983. Translocations among antibody genes in human cancer. *Science* **222**:765.

Lewin, B. 1980. *Gene Expression, 2: Eukaryotic Chromosomes.* 2nd ed. New York: Wiley.

Lo, C. W., and N. B. Gilula. 1980. PCC4azal teratocarcinoma stem-cell differentiation in culture. III. Cell-to-cell communication properties. *Dev. Biol.* **75**:112.

Lörincz, A. T., and S. I. Reed. 1984. Primary-structure homology between the product of yeast cell-division-control gene *CDC28* and vertebrate oncogenes. *Nature* **307**:183.

Majerus, P. W., *et al.* 1984. Phosphoinositide turnover provides a link in stimulus–response coupling. *Trends Biochem. Sci.* **10**:168.

Martin, G. R. 1980. Teratocarcinomas and mammalian embryogenesis. *Science* **209**:768.

Marx, J. L. 1984. What do oncogenes do? *Science* **223**:673.

Mazia, D. January 1974. The cell cycle. *Sci. Amer.* **230**:54.

McKusick, V. A. 1984. The human gene map. In *Genetic Maps 1984*, ed. S. J. O'Brien, vol. 3, p. 417. Cold Spring Harbor, N. Y.: Cold Spring Harbor Laboratory.

Miake-Lye, R., and M. W. Kirschner. 1985. Induction of early mitotic events in a cell-free system. *Cell* **41**:165.

Michell, B. 1984. Oncogenes and inositol lipids. *Nature* **308**:770.

Mitchison, J. M. 1971. *The Biology of the Cell Cycle.* Cambridge, England: Cambridge University Press.

Newmark, P. 1984. Cell and cancer biology meld. *Nature* **307**:499.

Newport, J. W., and M. W. Kirschner. 1984. Regulation of the cell cycle during early *Xenopus* development. *Cell* **37**:731.

Nicolson, G. L. March 1979. Cancer metastasis. *Sci. Amer.* **240**:66.

Nishizuka, Y. 1984. Protein kinases in signal transduction. *Trends Biochem. Sci.* **9**:163.

Nurse, P. 1985. Cell-cycle-control genes in yeast. *Trends Genet.* **1**:51.

O'Brien, S. J. 1984. Oncogenes and cancer loci. In *Genetic Maps 1984*, ed. S. J. O'Brien, vol. 3, p. 451. Cold Spring Harbor, N.Y.: Cold Spring Harbor Laboratory.

Pardee, A. B. 1974. A restriction point for control of normal animal cell proliferation. *Proc. Natl. Acad. Sci. U. S.* **71**:1286.

Pasternak, C. A. 1976. Surface membranes during the cell cycle. *Trends Biochem. Sci.* **1**:148.

Persson, H., *et al.* 1984. Antibodies to human c-*myc* oncogene product: Evidence of an evolutionarily conserved protein induced during cell proliferation. *Science* **225**:687.

Pickett-Heaps, J. D. 1969. The evolution of the mitotic apparatus: An attempt at comparative ultrastructural cytology in dividing plant cells. *Cytobios* **3**:257.

Pickett-Heaps, J. D., D. H. Tippit, and K. R. Porter. 1982. Rethinking mitosis. *Cell* **29**:729.

Pollack, R., ed. 1981. *Readings in Mammalian Cell Culture.* 2nd ed. Cold Spring Harbor, N.Y.: Cold Spring Harbor Laboratory.

Rao, P. N., and R. T. Johnson. 1970. Mammalian cell fusion: Studies on the regulation of DNA synthesis and mitosis. *Nature* **225**:159.

Rettenmier, C. W., J. H. Chen, M. F. Roussel, and C. J. Sherr. 1985. The product of the c-*fms* proto-oncogene: A glycoprotein with associated tyrosine kinase activity. *Science* **228**:320.

Riddle, V. G. H., and A. B. Pardee. 1980. Quiescent cells but not cycling cells exhibit enhanced actin synthesis before they synthesize DNA. *J. Cell. Physiol.* **103**:11.

Ris, H., and D. F. Kubai. 1974. An unusual mitotic mechanism in the parasitic protozoan *Syndinium* sp. *J. Cell Biol.* **60**:702.

Ruddle, F. H. 1981. A new era in mammalian gene mapping: Somatic cell genetics and recombinant DNA methodologies. *Nature* **294**:115.

Ruddle, F. H., and R. S. Kucherlapati. July 1974. Hybrid cells and human genes. *Sci. Amer.* **228**:82.

Schroeder, T. E. 1973. Actin in dividing cells: Contractile ring filaments bind heavy meromyosin. *Proc. Natl. Acad. Sci. U.S.* **70**:1688.

Shepard, J. F. May 1982. The regeneration of potato plants from leaf-cell protoplasts. *Sci. Amer.* **246**:154.

Slamon, D. J., J. B. deKernion, I. M. Verma, and M. J. Cline. 1984. Expression of cellular oncogenes in human malignancies. *Science* **224**:256.

Sluder, G., and D. A. Begg. 1983. Control mechanisms of the cell cycle: Role of the spatial arrangement of spindle components in the timing of mitotic events. *J. Cell Biol.* **97**:877.

Stein, G. S., *et al.* 1975. Cell cycle stage-specific transcription of histone genes. *Biochem. Biophys. Res. Commun.* **63**:945.

Stent, G. S. September 1972. Cellular communication. *Sci. Amer.* **227**:42.

Telzer, B. R., and J. L. Rosenbaum. 1979. Cell-cycle-dependent, *in vitro* assembly of microtubules onto the pericentriolar material of HeLa cells. *J. Cell Biol.* **81**:484.

Till, J. E. 1981. Cellular diversity in the blood-forming system. *Amer. Sci.* **69**:522.

Tucker, R. W., A. B. Pardee, and K. Fujiwara. 1979. Centriole ciliation is related to quiescence and DNA synthesis in 3T3 cells. *Cell* **17**:527.

Tunnacliffe, A., F. Benham, and P. Goodfellow. 1984. Mapping the human genome by somatic cell genetics. *Trends Biochem. Sci.* **9**:5.

Ullrich, A., *et al.* 1985. Human insulin receptor and its relationship to the tyrosine kinase family of oncogenes. *Nature* **313**:756.

Waterfield, M. D., *et al.* 1983. Platelet-derived growth factor is structurally related to the putative transforming protein p28^sis of simian sarcoma virus. *Nature* **304**:35.

Watt, F. M., and H. Green. 1982. Stratification and terminal differentiation of cultured epidermal cells. *Nature* **295**:434.

Weinberg, R. A. November 1983. A molecular basis for cancer. *Sci. Amer.* **249**:126.

Weinberg, R. A. 1984. Cellular oncogenes. *Trends Biochem. Sci.* **9**:131.

Wilson, E. B. 1928. *The Cell in Development and Heredity.* 3rd ed. New York: Macmillan.

Wyke, J. 1983. From c-*src* to v-*src*. *Nature* **304**:491.

Yunis, J. J. 1983. The chromosomal basis of human neoplasia. *Science* **221**:227.

Yunis, J. J., and A. L. Soreng. 1984. Constitutive fragile sites and cancer. *Science* **226**:1199.

Zimmerman, A. M., and A. Forer, eds. 1981. *Mitosis/Cytokinesis.* New York: Academic Press.

CHAPTER 17

Meiosis and Crossing Over

Sexual reproductive cycles are punctuated by the unique processes of meiosis and gamete fusion, which allow the generation of a great deal of genetic variability on a regular and continuing basis for the species. In meiosis the chromosome number of the parent cell is reduced by one-half in the daughter products, and many different combinations of alleles arise as a consequence of genetic recombination and independent assortment. Almost an infinite variety of genotypes are present in the gametes, which are the meiotic products, and any combinations of genomes may come together when the gametes fuse to initiate the next generation (Fig. 17.1). Asexual reproduction, on the other hand, perpetuates genetic uniformity; the daughter cells are identical to each other and to their parent cell. From observations of the fossil record and the relative diversity of life forms in existence today, we believe that the appearance of sexual reproduction among eukaryotic organisms marked

AaBbCc ♀ × AaBbCc ♂

Sperm

Eggs	ABC	ABc	AbC	Abc	aBC	aBc	abC	abc
ABC	AABBCC	AABBCc	AABbCC	AABbCc	AaBBCC	AaBBCc	AaBbCC	AaBbCc
ABc	AABBCc	AABBcc	AABbCc	AABbcc	AaBBCc	AaBBcc	AaBbCc	AaBbcc
AbC	AABbCC	AABbCc	AAbbCC	AAbbCc	AaBbCC	AaBbCc	AabbCC	AabbCc
Abc	AABbCc	AABbcc	AAbbCc	AAbbcc	AaBbCc	AaBbcc	AabbCc	Aabbcc
aBC	AaBBCC	AaBBCc	AaBbCC	AaBbCc	aaBBCC	aaBBCc	aaBbCC	aaBbCc
aBc	AaBBCc	AaBBcc	AaBbCc	AaBbcc	aaBBCc	aaBBcc	aaBbCc	aaBbcc
abC	AaBbCC	AaBbCc	AabbCC	AabbCc	aaBbCC	aaBbCc	aabbCC	aabbCc
abc	AaBbCc	AaBbcc	AabbCc	Aabbcc	aaBbCc	aaBbcc	aabbCc	aabbcc

FIGURE 17-1
In a standard cross between parents triply heterozygous for only 3 unlinked genes (*A/a, B/b,* and *C/c*), each parent produces 8 genetically different kinds of gametes ($2^3 = 8$). Random fertilization of eggs by sperm lead to 64 possible kinds of fusion ($4^3 = 64$), yielding 27 different genotypes ($3^3 = 27$) or allelic combinations among the progeny. Because of heterozygosity at hundreds or thousands of gene loci in sexual species, genetic variety is maintained at a very high level.

Animal

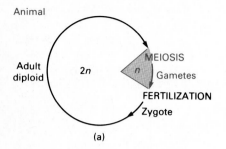

(a)

Plant

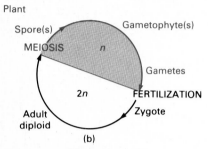

(b)

Various protists, fungi, and algae

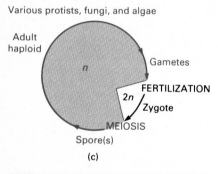

(c)

FIGURE 17-2
In every case the sexual cycle is punctuated by meiosis and fertilization, but their relative timing varies so that the haploid and diploid proportions of the cycle also vary. (a) In animals, meiosis is followed immediately by fertilization, so the diploid phase of the cycle is predominant. (b) A more extended haploid phase is typical of plants because of the gametophyte stage that occurs after meiosis and before fertilization. (c) Many protists, fungi, and algae usually have a very brief diploid phase because the diploid zygote undergoes meiosis and may therefore be the only diploid cell in the entire sexual cycle. Regardless of the duration of each phase, the chromosome number of the species remains constant. The reduction of chromosome number in meiosis and the doubling of chromosome number in fertilization are compensating processes in a sexual life cycle.

one of the significant steps in evolution. It provided the ongoing basis for continued genetic diversification at rates that far exceed those that characterize asexual life.

The Meiotic Process

Sexual life cycles include two alternating phases in which the chromosome number in one phase is twice the number in the other phase; typically, a life cycle consists of a *diploid phase* and a *haploid phase*. Diploidy is initiated by the **fusion of gametes**, or sex cells, and haploidy is initiated by **meiosis**, which immediately or ultimately produces the haploid gametes. Although we think of the large nonmotile **egg** as the typical female gamete and of the small motile **sperm** as the male sex cell, gametes come in all sizes and behavior patterns in eukaryotic species. Similarly, we think of **fertilization** as the standard act of gamete fusion, but the term specifically denotes the penetration of a large egg by a small sperm.

The remarkably orchestrated events of nuclear division by meiosis are relatively similar in sexual eukaryotes. During the 100 years since its initial discovery, the details of the meiotic process have come to light rather slowly. By the use of electron microscopy, genetics, and biochemistry, we have learned far more than was possible by light microscopy alone in earlier decades. We are just beginning to apply molecular methods to gain information on the many aspects of meiosis that continue to elude us to the present day.

17.1
Sexual Life Cycles

Eukaryotic species may have a predominant diploid phase or a predominant haploid phase in the life cycle, and the relative duration of each phase varies among different kinds of organisms (Fig. 17.2). Animals are diploid organisms whose haploid phase is restricted to the gametes, which are the immediate products of meiosis. Without further division or extensive development, two gametes fuse to become the diploid **zygote**, which is the initial cell of the next generation. In animals the *fertilized egg* is the zygote product of fusion of an egg cell and a sperm cell.

All the vascular plants (ferns and fern allies, gymnosperms, and flowering plants) also have a predominant diploid phase, but their haploid phase is more complex than in animals. The haploid phase in plants is initiated by meiosis, but the meiotic products are spores rather than gametes. These haploid spores develop into haploid gamete-producing structures called **gametophytes**, which ultimately produce the haploid gametes by ordinary mitotic divisions (Fig. 17.3). Gamete fusion produces the diploid zygote, which then develops into the spore-producing adult plant, or **sporophyte**. The familiar fern, pine tree, and rose bush are diploid sporophytes. The gametophytes are obscure structures that have been reduced in size and prominence during plant evolution. In gymnosperms and flowering plants, the

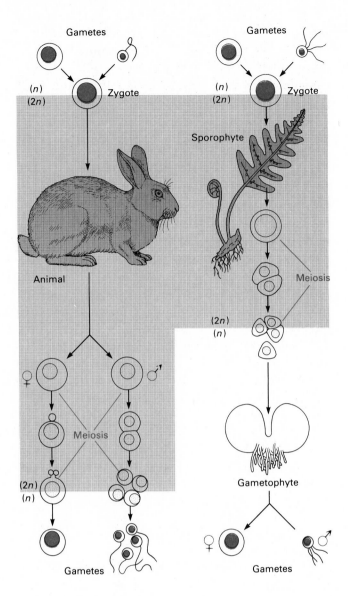

FIGURE 17-3
Comparison of animal and plant (fern) life cycles. The diploid animal produces gametes directly by meiosis, whereas spores are the products of meiosis in higher plants. The haploid plant spores develop into gametophytes, which then produce gametes. The haploid phase in animals is thus restricted to the gamete cells, whereas the haploid phase of the life cycle in plants involves spores and gametophytes as well as gametes.

gametophytes are microscopic structures entirely contained within and nourished by the diploid sporophytes.

A considerable amount of variation characterizes the diploid and haploid phases of the life cycle in protists, algae, and fungi. Often the diploid phase is brief and represented only by the zygote, which may undergo meiosis and produce haploid spores or gametes. If the meiotic products are spores they may develop to various extents, eventually producing gametes by mitosis, and the gametes fuse to produce the diploid zygotes of the next generation. If the meiotic products are gametes, they do not divide but fuse to restore the diploid phase. It should be clear by now that gametes and spores are not distinguished by whether they arise by mitosis or meiosis. Gametes are sex cells that have a single function and capacity—they fuse with a compatible gamete and produce a zygote, or they die. **Spores** can develop into a structure or an organism after mitotic divisions or differentiation, and they need not fuse with other cells to remain viable and productive. In the life cycle of unicellular *Chlamydomonas*, for example, zoospores or gametes may be produced by mitosis of the haploid adult cell. These two kinds of products look alike but behave quite differently. A zoospore may mature and produce other zoospores in asexual cycles of reproduction, but a gamete proceeds no further unless it fuses with a compatible gamete and produces a zygote. Meiotic division of the zygote produces new haploid cells that may mature to produce either gametes in a sexual cycle or zoospores in an asexual cycle (Fig. 17.4).

In multicellular organisms the gametes are produced in organs called **gonads**. The female gonad is an **ovary** or some equivalent structure in which the eggs, or ova, are produced. In males the **testis** or some equivalent structure is a gonad in which sperm or spermatozoa are produced. Only one kind of cell in a gonad is capable of undergoing meiosis; such a cell is called a **meiocyte**. In animals, the female produces **oocytes** in the ovary and the male produces **spermatocytes** in the testis. An oocyte produces four cells by meiosis, of which one becomes the functional egg cell and the other three abort. All four sperm cells produced by spermatocyte meiosis, however, develop into functional gametes (Fig. 17.5).

In plants, both the female and the male meiocytes are spore-producing cells, and they are therefore called **sporocytes**. The female structure is a *megasporangium* in which *megasporocytes* undergo meiosis and each produces one functional **megaspore** and three aborted cells. The megaspore in flowering plants develops into a gametophyte called the *embryo sac*, in which one of the eight nuclei is contained within the egg cell that constitutes the female gamete. The male structure is a *microsporangium* in which each *microsporocyte* produces four **microspores** by meiosis. The microspores develop into *pollen*, which is the male gametophyte, and when the pollen grain germinates on the female flower

FIGURE 17-4
Life cycle of the unicellular protist *Chlamydomonas*, which reproduces by both sexual and asexual means. In its sexual phase, a zygote is produced by gamete fusion (fertilization), and afterward the chromosome number is restored to the original level by meiosis. In its asexual phase, the organism multiplies by mitotic divisions of individual zoospores, which do not require a fusion event for reproduction to proceed.

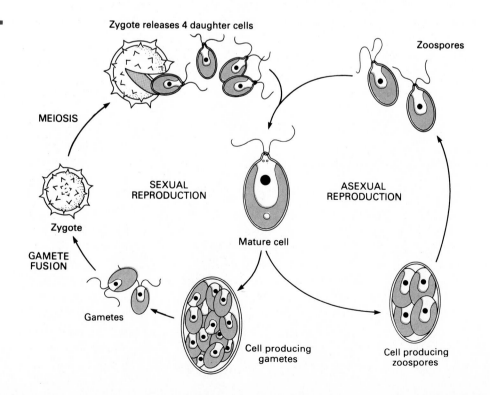

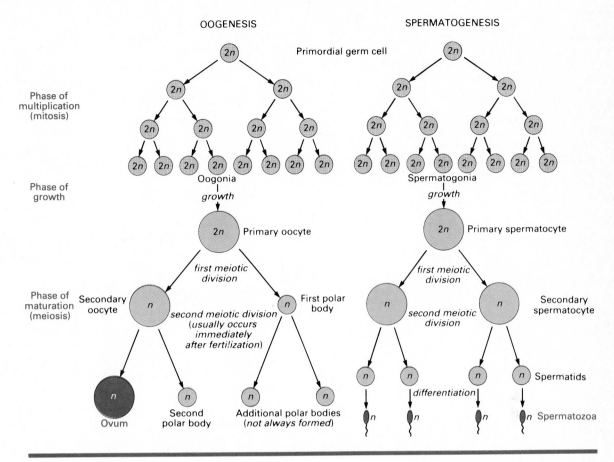

FIGURE 17-5

In higher animals (a) oogenesis leads to the production of one functional egg (ovum) per oocyte, whereas (b) spermatogenesis typically results in the production of four functional sperm (spermatozoa) per spermatocyte at the conclusion of meiosis.

structure, two sperm nuclei are delivered in the growing pollen tube to the embryo sac. One sperm nucleus fuses with the egg to produce the zygote, which develops into the embryo that grows to become the new adult sporophyte. The second sperm nucleus fuses with two polar nuclei in the embryo sac and gives rise to a triploid *endosperm* cell from which the nutritive endosperm tissue develops (Fig. 17.6). The seeds of flowering plants include the embryo and surrounding endosperm, which nourishes the developing embryo. Seeds are contained in fruits, which are matured ovaries and thus form from parent diploid tissues.

17.2
Why Two Divisions in Meiosis?

Each meiocyte, whether it produces gametes or spores, gives rise to a quartet of cells of which one or all are functional. The quartet of products results from two successive divisions of the nucleus, both of which are part of the sequence of meiosis. Why are there two divisions in meiosis but only one division in mitosis to yield the end products? The answer to this question lies in the amount of DNA per nucleus in the parent cell and its division products.

If we signify the DNA content by the arbitrary symbol X and reserve the symbol n for a set of chromosomes of some particular number, the interphase nucleus in diploid $(2n)$ organisms has the $2X$ amount of DNA before replication takes place. As the cell progresses to S phase from G_1,

FIGURE 17-6

Life cycle of maize *(Zea mays)*. Male flowers in the tassel and female flowers in the ear produce a succession of reproductive cells and structures that lead to fruit (kernal) formation. Each kernel contains a single seed, which includes the 2*n* embryo from which the new corn plant will develop and the 3*n* endosperm tissue that nourishes the growing embryo and young seedling during germination. The sporophyte (spore-producing plant) is conspicuous, whereas the male and female gamete-producing systems are microscopic in size.

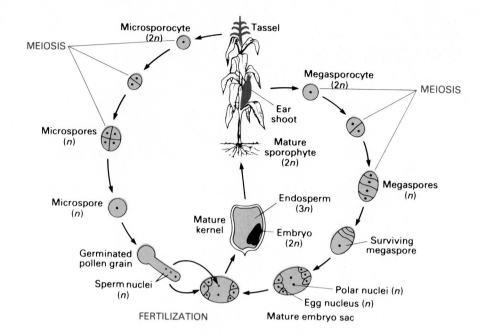

DNA replicates and the cell then has the 4X amount of DNA per nucleus. When mitosis occurs, the 4X amount of DNA is apportioned equally to the daughter nuclei, each of which receives the 2X amount of DNA distributed in 2*n* chromosomes. The chromosome number remains unchanged in the daughter nuclei, regardless of the number of sets of chromosomes originally present.

When DNA replicates in S phase of a premeiotic interphase nucleus, the 2X amount of DNA doubles to 4X and each chromosome in the 2*n* nucleus consists of a pair of sister chromatids. During the first meiotic division, the chromosome number is reduced by half as homologous replicated chromosomes move toward opposite poles during anaphase. The DNA content, however, is reduced from 4X to 2X, so each nucleus is

FIGURE 17-7

The amount of DNA per nucleus remains unchanged in mitotically dividing cells because replication from the 2X to the 4X amount of DNA is followed by the separation of replicated chromosomes at anaphase, thus restoring the 2X amount of DNA per nucleus. In meiosis, however, reduction from the parental 2X amount of DNA to the 1X amount in gametes requires two successive divisions. The 2X nucleus is reconstituted when two gametes, each having the 1X amount of DNA, fuse to form the zygote that initiates the new generation.

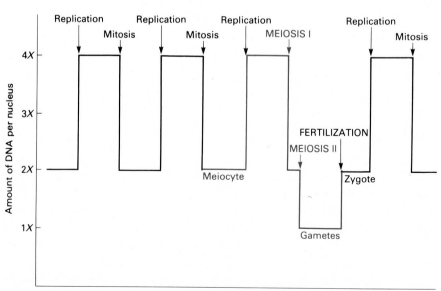

TABLE 17-1
Chromosome Numbers Found in Various Organisms

Organism	Diploid Number
human (*Homo sapiens*)	46
chimpanzee (*Pan troglodytes*)	48
rhesus monkey (*Macaca mulatta*)	42
dog (*Canis familiaris*)	78
cat (*Felis domestica*)	38
horse (*Equus caballus*)	64
toad (*Xenopus laevis*)	36
housefly (*Musca domestica*)	12
mosquito (*Culex pipiens*)	6
nematode (*Caenorhabditis elegans*)	11 ♂, 12 ♀
tobacco (*Nicotiana tabacum*)	48
cotton (*Gossypium hirsutum*)	52
kidney bean (*Phaseolus vulgaris*)	22
broad bean (*Vicia faba*)	12
onion (*Allium cepa*)	16
potato (*Solanum tuberosum*)	48
tomato (*Lycopersicon esculentum*)	24
bread wheat (*Triticum aestivum*)	42
rice (*Oryza sativa*)	24
baker's yeast (*Saccharomyces cerevisiae*)	34

still effectively like the meiocyte in having two copies of each gene (Fig. 17.7). During the second meiotic division, sister chromatids separate at anaphase, and each chromosome in the daughter nucleus has only $1X$ DNA. Each nucleus produced in the first division divides again, so four nuclei are produced by a meiocyte. Each of the four nuclei has one set of chromosomes $(1n)$ and, because these are unreplicated structures, the DNA content is $1X$ in each nucleus. When two haploid gametes fuse to form the zygote, each gamete nucleus is $1n$ and $1X$ and the fusion product is $2n$ and $2X$. If it were not for the second meiotic division, the amount of DNA would double in each successive generation. Such a system could not have supported life for very long during evolutionary time. Through the alternating events of meiosis and fertilization in the life cycle, each sexual species is characterized by a constant chromosome number from generation to generation (Table 17.1), and each chromosome carries one gene copy at each locus.

17.3

The First Meiotic Division _____

During interphase preceding meiosis, the meiocyte nucleus proceeds through a relatively typical sequence of G_1, S, and G_2 phases. Certain differences have been noted, however, between the interphases of mitotic divisions several cycles before meiosis and the interphase immediately preceding the onset of meiosis. In particular, DNA replication proceeds several times faster in the earlier interphases than in the premeiotic interphase. The rate of DNA synthesis is about the same per unit length of chromatin, but fewer replicons are active at any one time in premeiotic interphase than in earlier cycles. Apparently, fewer origins of

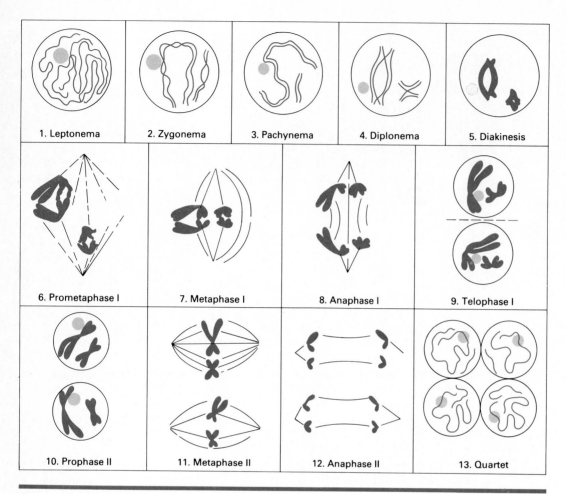

1. Leptonema 2. Zygonema 3. Pachynema 4. Diplonema 5. Diakinesis

6. Prometaphase I 7. Metaphase I 8. Anaphase I 9. Telophase I

10. Prophase II 11. Metaphase II 12. Anaphase II 13. Quartet

FIGURE 17-8

Meiosis. Chromosomes proceed through an extended prophase in division I (1–5), followed by movement to the spindle equator (6), alignment at the equator (7), and separation (8) and possible reorganization of the two nuclei (9) when meiosis I ends. During meiosis II, conventional prophase (10), metaphase (11), and anaphase (12) activities eventually lead to a quartet of nuclear products of the original meiotic cell. Significant events include chromosome pairing at zygonema (2), reduction of chromosome number by half at anaphase I (8), and reduction of gene numbers or DNA content in anaphase II (12) to half the level that was present in the premeiotic nucleus. In this example the chromosome number has been reduced from $2n = 4$ to $n = 2$.

replication become engaged in DNA synthesis in premeiotic interphase chromatin.

Once interphase is completed, the meiotic nucleus proceeds through a sequence of stages that constitute the first meiotic division, or **meiosis I** (Fig. 17.8). The continuous events of prophase, prometaphase, metaphase, anaphase, and telophase differ in certain significant features from the analogous stages of mitosis. Because the prophase of meiosis I is the most complex, protracted, and genetically significant interval, **prophase I** has been subdivided into the substages of leptonema ("slender thread"), zygonema ("yoked thread"), pachynema ("thick thread"), diplonema ("double thread"), and diakinesis ("divided across"). When referring to some feature of the first four substages, we will use the adjectives *leptotene*, *zygotene*, *pachytene*, and *diplotene*. For example, leptotene chromosomes pair during zygonema to produce pachytene bivalents consisting of four chromatids each.

Cells in **leptonema**, the first of the prophase I substages, are very difficult to preserve for microscopy and have therefore been studied in only a few organisms. Leptotene nuclei are highly hydrated and usually suffer severe alteration during preparation for microscopy. In those fixed and stained leptotene nuclei that have been studied, the chromatin appears as a hopeless tangle of fine threads with an obviously beaded aspect; each bead is called a **chromomere**. It is virtually impossible to follow any one chromatin thread for even a micrometer of its length without losing sight of it in a maze of twisted and interwoven threads. The replicated nature of leptotene chromosomes is not evident in the light microscope, but leptotene cells can be recognized by their considerably larger size than surrounding nonmeiotic cells and by the finely dispersed, beaded chromatin threads in the enlarged, hydrated nuclei.

The continuation of prophase I into **zygonema** is evident by the initiation of close pairing between scattered regions along homologous chromosomes. This pairing process, called **synapsis**, may begin anywhere along any of the chromosome pairs in the nucleus. As synapsis takes place, a three-layered structure called the *synaptonemal complex* begins to form in the space between paired chromosomes (Fig. 17.9). The synaptonemal complex develops only between paired homologous chromosomes and only in meiocytes. Even though homologous chromosomes are closely paired in certain kinds of somatic cells, such as the polytene nuclei of dipteran larval cells, no synaptonemal complex has ever been observed between paired somatic chromosomes. We will discuss the special features and significance of the synaptonemal complex later in this chapter.

FIGURE 17-9

The synaptonemal complex. (a) Electron micrograph of a section through a pair of homologous chromosomes from a pachytene nucleus of the fungus *Neottiella*. Sandwiched between the replicated homologs (each is a pair of chromatids) is a three-layered synaptonemal complex made up of a pale central region (which may have a dense central element down its center) flanked on each side by a banded lateral element. The synaptonemal complex develops only between synapsed chromosomes in meiotic prophase I. ×75,350. (Photograph courtesy of D. von Wettstein, from von Wettstein, D., 1971, *Proc. Nat. Acad. Sci. U. S.* **68**:851–855, Fig. 1). (b) An interpretive drawing of the photograph.

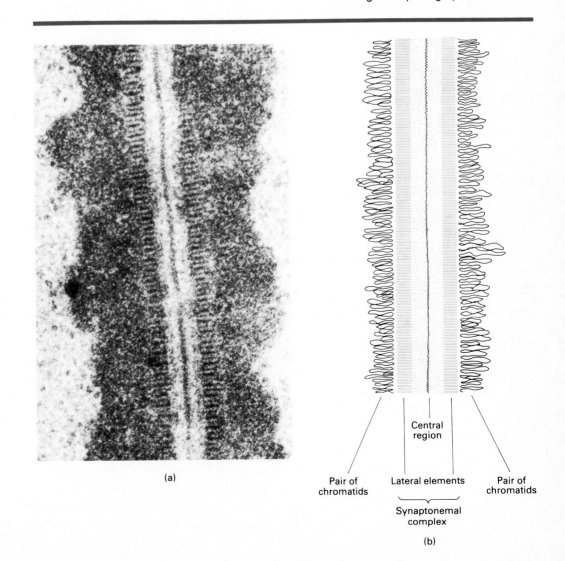

(a)

Pair of chromatids

Central region

Lateral elements

Pair of chromatids

Synaptonemal complex

(b)

When all the parts of all the homologous chromosomes are completely and closely synapsed, and the synaptonemal complex is fully formed along the entire length of each pair of homologous chromosomes, **pachynema** has begun. Although chromosome condensation has continued since leptonema, the replicated nature of each chromosome is still not visible by light microscopy. Each chromosome is composed of two sister chromatids, however, because DNA replication took place in interphase. The paired homologous chromosomes are referred to as **bivalents**, and each is composed of two pairs of sister chromatids—or a total of four chromatids per bivalent.

The bivalents continue to condense during pachynema but the homologous chromosomes remain closely synapsed. In favorable materials, such as maize, each pachytene bivalent can be recognized individually and the chromosomes can readily be counted. The ten chromosomes of the maize complement are visible as ten bivalents, each with distinctive length and morphology (Fig. 17.10). The pachynema substage is the time when *crossing over* takes place, leading to *genetic recombination*. By exchanges between homologous chromosome segments during crossing over, new allelic combinations are produced whereby the recombined chromosomes come to contain some of the alleles of each of the original parental homologous chromosomes. The highly significant process of crossing over and its profound genetic consequences will be discussed later in the chapter.

Pachynema ends and **diplonema** begins with the separation, or *opening out*, of paired chromosomes at various places along their length. The homologs remain associated only at sites of previous crossover exchanges, which are called **chiasmata** (sing.: **chiasma**). In favorable materials such as insect spermatocytes, it is clear that each chiasma involves only two of the four chromatids in a bivalent (Fig. 17.11). Bivalents with two or more chiasmata may have experienced crossover events involving two, three, or all four of the chromatids, but *each* chiasma represents one exchange event between two of the chromatids in a bivalent.

FIGURE 17-10
Pachynema of meiotic prophase I in maize, showing ten bivalents, one of which (chromosome 6) is attached at its nucleolar-organizing region to the nucleolus (dense circular structure). (Photograph courtesy of M. M. Rhoades.)

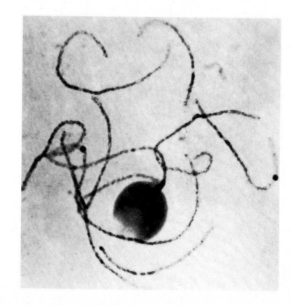

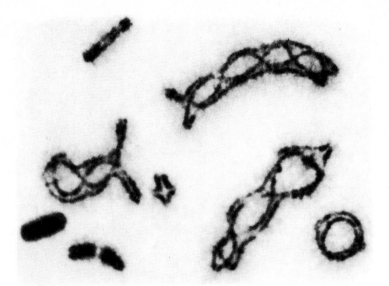

FIGURE 17-11
Diplotene bivalents in a grasshopper spermatocyte. Each chiasma (site of a previous crossover event) involves two of the four chromatids in a bivalent, but multiple exchange events may involve all four chromatids of a bivalent. (Photograph courtesy of B. John.)

During diplonema the synaptonemal complex is shed everywhere along the length of the chromosomes, except at the chiasmata. Even these fragments of the complex are usually shed before diplonema is over. In some species the oocyte may remain suspended in diplonema for weeks, months, or years. In amphibians the giant oocytes remain diplotene for weeks or months, and the chromosomes assume their distinctive lampbrush morphology at this time (see Fig. 15.36). Early in the development of the human embryo, the germ cells that will later develop into meiocytes migrate into the forming gonads. In the female fetus, the primordial germ cells develop into oogonial cells that begin meiosis and are thus in the primary oocyte stage long before birth has occurred (see Fig. 17.5).

All the oocytes that give rise to the eggs over a whole lifetime are therefore produced in the fetal ovaries, but the oocytes remain suspended in diplonema until the girl reaches puberty. During each menstrual cycle between puberty and menopause, when a woman is biologically capable of reproduction, a primary oocyte resumes the meiotic process and completes the first division. It is in this secondary oocyte stage that ovulation occurs during each menstrual cycle, when the immature oocyte (inaccurately called the egg or ovum at this stage) is released from the ovary and enters one of the two fallopian tubes (Fig. 17.12). If the secondary oocyte is penetrated by a sperm, the second meiotic division takes place to produce the single haploid egg nucleus. The fusion of egg nucleus and sperm nucleus results in the diploid nucleus of the fertilized egg, which is the initial cell of the new generation. When the cleaving fertilized egg enters the uterus from the fallopian tube and there becomes implanted in the uterine lining, embryogenesis proceeds. If it is successful, birth occurs about nine months later. If fertilization does not take place the oocyte soon dies, and another menstrual cycle begins as another primary oocyte resumes meiosis I and becomes the secondary oocyte of the next ovulation episode.

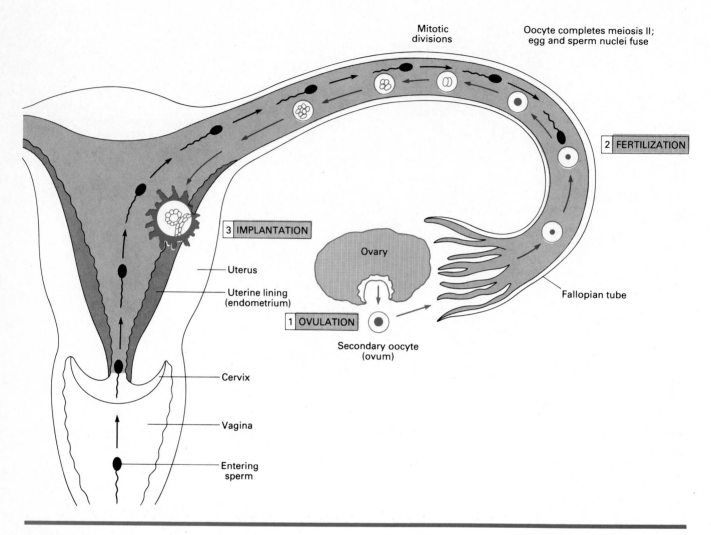

Mitotic
divisions

Oocyte completes meiosis II;
egg and sperm nuclei fuse

2 FERTILIZATION

3 IMPLANTATION

Uterus

Uterine lining
(endometrium)

Ovary

1 OVULATION

Secondary oocyte
(ovum)

Fallopian tube

Cervix

Vagina

Entering
sperm

FIGURE 17-12

During each menstrual cycle in the human female, a primary oocyte suspended in diplonema completes meiosis I and is released from the ovary (ovulation) as a secondary oocyte. The oocyte is swept into one of the two fallopian tubes and is moved by muscular contractions toward the uterus. If fertilized by a sperm, the secondary oocyte undergoes meiosis II and becomes a haploid ovum (see Fig. 17.5). The fertilized egg undergoes cleavages as it travels to the uterus. Once there, it becomes implanted in the uterine lining and continues its development for nine months *in utero*, after which time birth takes place.

In the human male, spermatogonia in the testes do not undergo meiosis until the boy reaches puberty. Between puberty and relative old age, spermatocytes develop and proceed through meiosis to produce hundreds of millions of sperm every day (Fig. 17.13). Most of these sperm are stored for a time in the epididymis adjoining the testes, but they die if not ejaculated. Several hundred million sperm may be present in an ejaculate, but only a small number reach the fallopian tubes in the female reproductive tract. Should a secondary oocyte be present in the fallopian tube, only one sperm of the 50 to 100 survivors fertilizes the oocyte (Fig. 17.14).

Whether continuing uninterruptedly or resuming meiosis, the diplotene bivalents condense still further and reach their most contracted size by the start of **diakinesis**. The short, thick bivalents are usually spread out within the nuclear space, making each readily visible and diakinesis the easiest stage for taking chromosome counts (Fig. 17.15). Near the end of diakinesis—and, therefore, of prophase I—the nucleoli and nuclear membrane disappear and the spindle figure is present in the nuclear region of the cell.

The bivalents move from one place to another during **prometaphase**, but they soon line up across the spindle equator and signal the

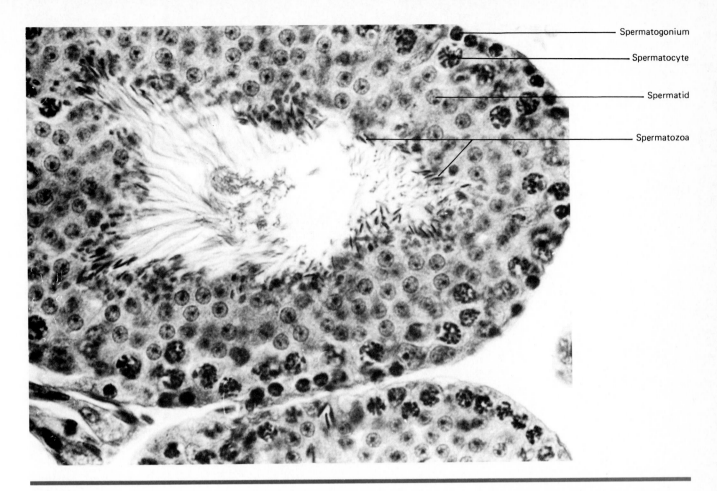

— Spermatogonium

— Spermatocyte

— Spermatid

— Spermatozoa

FIGURE 17-13
Light micrograph of a cross section through one of the seminiferous tubules in mouse testis. The gradient of differentiation and development proceeds from the peripherally located diploid spermatogonia which become the spermatocytes that undergo meiosis and produce haploid spermatids, which differentiate into motile spermatozoa. ×600. (Photograph courtesy of B. Babiarz.)

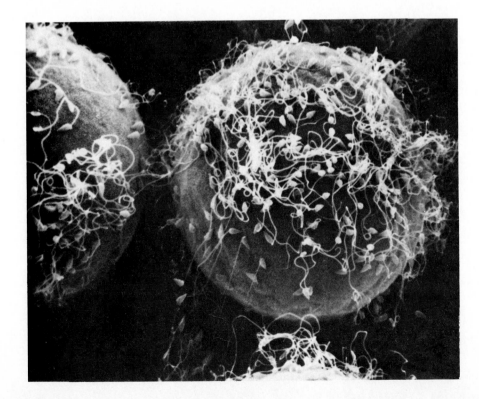

FIGURE 17-14
Scanning electron micrograph of numerous sperm attached to the surface of mollusc eggs. ×400. (Photograph courtesy of M. Tegner.)

Diakinesis in a maize meiocyte. Chromosome pairs are at their most contracted size and are greatly separated, all of which makes this stage of prophase I a most desirable one for counting chromosomes. Of the ten bivalents present, note that one (chromosome 6) is associated with the nucleolus. (Photograph courtesy of M. M. Rhoades.)

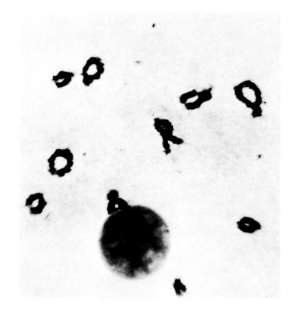

beginning of **metaphase I**. The ends of the chromosome arms are positioned at the equator, but the homologous centromeres of each bivalent are as far apart as is physically possible (Fig. 17.16). This orientation of chromosomes at the spindle equator is the opposite of the situation for mitotic metaphase chromosomes, which align by their centromeres at the spindle equator, whereas their arms wave about in all directions on either side of this zone.

Each chromosome of a bivalent consists of two chromatids, or a **dyad**. The centromeres of the sister chromatids in a dyad remain closely

Metaphase I in maize. (a) The ten bivalents are aligned on the spindle equator, and the centromeres of paired days are as far apart as possible, each being closer to a different one of the two poles of the cell. (Photograph courtesy of M. M. Rhoades). (b) Drawing of a bivalent, showing the spatial arrangement of chromosome ends on the spindle equator and the centromeres of paired dyads oriented toward opposite poles of the cell.

(a)

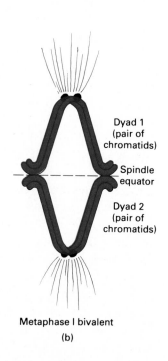

Dyad 1 (pair of chromatids)

Spindle equator

Dyad 2 (pair of chromatids)

Metaphase I bivalent

(b)

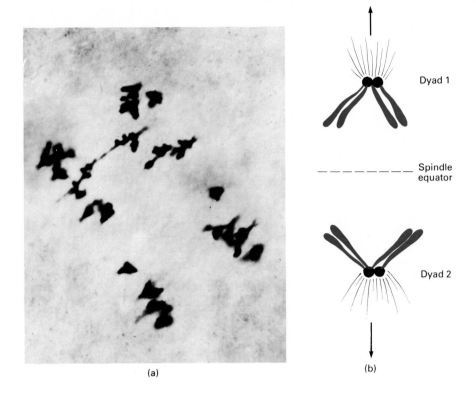

(a)

(b)

Dyad 1

Spindle equator

Dyad 2

FIGURE 17-17
Separation of homologous chromosomes at anaphase I in maize.
(a) Ten dyads move toward one pole and their homologs move toward the opposite pole of the cell. (Photograph courtesy of M. M. Rhoades). (b) Drawing showing the orientation of the centromeres of homologous dyads during anaphase. I.

associated on the same side of the spindle equator and therefore face the same pole. The other dyad of the bivalent is oriented such that its centromeres face the opposite pole of the spindle. By the simple device of centromere orientation, homologous dyads of each bivalent will move toward opposite poles during anaphase and thereby segregate one set of chromosomes from the homologous set.

During the relatively brief **anaphase**, homologous chromosomes (dyads) move to opposite poles of the cell, reducing the chromosome number in each group to half the diploid number. On the basis of chromosome number, haploidy is achieved during anaphase I. On the basis of DNA content, however, each haploid nucleus still has the $2X$ amount of DNA because each chromosome is a dyad (Fig. 17.17). The reduction by one-half of both chromosome number and DNA content is not achieved until completion of the second meiotic division.

In some species the anaphase nuclei may begin the second division almost immediately, whereas other species proceed through a stage of nuclear reorganization in **telophase** before beginning meiosis II. If telophase occurs, the chromosomes unfold and lengthen, nucleoli and nuclear membranes reappear, and daughter nuclei become evident. The reorganized nuclei may enter interphase (of variable duration) and then proceed through prophase and later stages of meiosis II. In some cases the telophase nuclei may proceed directly to metaphase II. In addition to the variability of events between telophase I and metaphase II, cytokinesis may take place following meiosis I, or it may be delayed until the end of meiosis II. In either event, the four haploid nuclei produced from each meiocyte are eventually enclosed in their own nuclear envelopes in their own cells at the conclusion of meiosis II.

(a)

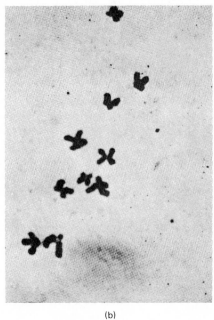

(b)

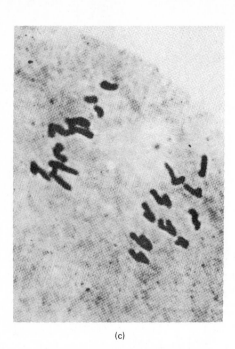

(c)

FIGURE 17-18

Stages of meiosis II in maize. Only one of the two nuclei is shown in each photograph, but the other nucleus in each dividing cell is engaged in identical activities. (a) Ten dyads at prophase II. (b) Ten dyads at metaphase II. (c) Ten single chromosomes moving toward each pole of the spindle at anaphase II. (Photographs courtesy of M. M. Rhoades.)

17.4
The Second Meiotic Division

The two nuclei produced in meiosis I proceed through all or some of the conventional stages of prophase, prometaphase, metaphase, anaphase, and telophase in **meiosis II**. Because these division events are similar in their mechanics to the sequence of stages in mitosis, meiosis II has often been described as a "mitotic" division. It is, of course, not a mitosis at all but rather the second of the two divisions needed to achieve the crucial reductions in chromosome number and DNA content that constitute the meiotic process.

During the second meiotic division the two chromatids of each dyad are separated into individual nuclei, at which time each chromatid becomes a full-fledged chromosome acting independently from other chromosomes (Fig. 17.18). The outcome of meiosis is the production of four nuclei, each of which is haploid in chromosome number and $1X$ in DNA content. The original meiocyte nucleus was diploid and $2X$, so reduction division is completed only when the four nuclear products of meiosis have been produced. The ultimate fate of these haploid cells and their contribution in the life cycle depends on the organism. Whether the meiotic products are spores or gametes, each meiotic division provides the haploid phase of the sexual cycle. The genetic significance of meiosis lies in the production of new combinations of alleles in each haploid genome. Not only are the allelic combinations different from one haploid cell to another, but they are also different from the combinations of alleles present in the maternal genome and the paternal genome of the original diploid meiocytes.

17.5
Genetic Consequences of Meiosis

No two individuals of a sexual species are genetically identical unless they were produced from a single fertilized egg. Except for identical twins or similar sets of siblings, each individual is genetically unique because each possesses a different **genotype**, or combination of alleles, of the genes that comprise a genome. All the members of a species share a common set of genes, but each gene may exist in one or more alternative forms (alleles). Production of the virtually infinite number of different genotypes in sexual species results from the reshuffling of existing allelic combinations during meiosis.

On the basis of his statistical analysis of the results in crossing pea plants with contrasting sets of characteristics, Gregor Mendel postulated two basic laws of inheritance: (1) there is a *segregation of the members of pairs of alleles* (unit factors) in reproduction, and (2) members of different pairs of alleles undergo *independent assortment* during reproduction. Meiosis was unknown in 1866 when Mendel's studies were published, but we now know that the two members of each pair of alleles in a meiocyte are segregated into different nuclei when the two members of each pair of homologous chromosomes separate in anaphase. Mendel's second law of inheritance is also explained by meiosis, because members of different pairs of alleles on nonhomologous chromosomes are aligned independently in metaphase I and assort independently in anaphase I of meiosis (Fig. 17.19).

If a meiocyte is heterozygous for only one pair of alleles (A/a), two kinds of gametes (A and a) are produced. If it is heterozygous for two pairs of alleles on different chromosomes (A/a B/b), four kinds of gametes (AB, Ab, aB, ab) are produced. If it is heterozygous for three pairs of alleles on different chromosomes (A/a B/b C/c), eight kinds of gametes (see Fig. 17.19) are produced. This simple relationship is expressed by 2^n kinds of gametes, where n is the number of different heterozygous allelic pairs on different chromosomes. In human beings with 23 pairs of chromosomes, 2^{23} different kinds of gametes may be produced when only one pair of alleles is heterozygous on each pair of chromosomes in a single oocyte or spermatocyte. If the chance that two gametes will be identical is 1 in 2^{23} (1 in 8,388,608) when each pair of chromosomes carries only one pair of heterozygous alleles and all the other alleles are the same (homozygous) on the 23 pairs of chromosomes, the chances that any two gametes will be identical is statistically so small as to be almost impossible in view of the many hundreds of heterozygous pairs of alleles normally present in the nucleus. When fertilization takes place involving any egg of any genotype and any sperm of any genotype, the chances that two different individuals will carry identical alleles in their diploid nuclei is essentially nil, on the basis of chance alone. Except for individuals produced from the same fertilized egg, therefore, no two people have, ever have had, or ever are likely to have the same genotype by chance alone. Considerations such as these illustrate that sexual reproduction essentially guarantees *genetic variety* in every generation. Because greater genetic variety offers the best chance that some inherited features will prove advantageous over the long run of evolutionary time under constantly changing conditions, sexual reproduction constitutes a mechanism most likely to lead to adaptive changes and to a greater probability of success during evolution.

Many thousands of different genes comprise the genome, but they are present in a relatively small number of chromosomes. How do alleles

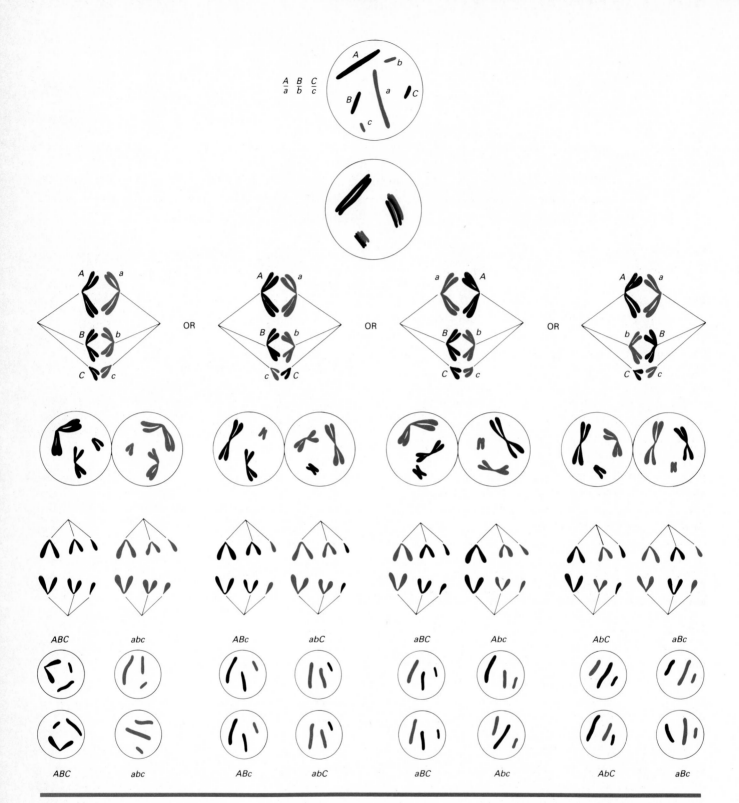

FIGURE 17-19
Illustration of Mendel's first and second laws of inheritance. During meiosis in meiocytes of a sexual diploid carrying alleles *A* and *a* on one pair of homologous chromosomes, alleles *B* and *b* on another pair, and alleles *C* and *c* on a third pair, there is segregation of the members of each pair of alleles (Mendel's first law) and independent assortment of the members of different pairs of alleles (Mendel's second law). The separation of members of each pair of homologous chromosomes in anaphase I accounts for the first law, and the second law is accounted for by the independent assortment in anaphase I of the pairs of homologous chromosomes. All eight possible genotypic combinations of alleles are produced in equal proportions in a population of haploid meiotic products of such triply heterozygous meiocytes.

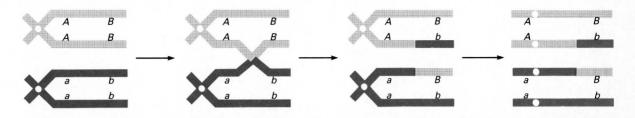

FIGURE 17-20
Crossing over in a pachytene bivalent heterozygous for two linked pairs of alleles (*AB/ab*). The two tightly synapsed homologous chromosomes (two pairs of chromatids) here undergo an exchange involving one chromatid of each homologous chromosome. The crossover event leads to new allelic combinations for the two exchanged chromatids (*Ab* and *aB*), but the noncrossover chromatids remain unchanged (*AB* and *ab*).

on the same chromosome become separated and recombined into new genotypic combinations? The production of recombinant genotypes that differ from the parental genotypes in **linked genes** (genes on the same chromosome) as well as in independently assorting genes is a standard observation in the analysis of genetic progeny. The fact that linked genes recombine with predictable regularity and frequency indicates the existence of some regular mechanism associated with meiosis, because meiosis is the time when members of each pair of alleles on all the chromosomes are segregated into different nuclei.

The process responsible for the **recombination** of alleles of linked genes is **crossing over**, which involves an exchange between homologous chromosome segments (Fig. 17.20). In the next sections we will deal specifically with the nature, timing, mechanism, and consequences of crossing over between linked genes in sexually reproducing species. In certain cases we have obtained vital information about crossing over from studies of viruses and bacteria. These experimental systems will be discussed when appropriate.

Crossing Over and Genetic Recombination

Genetic evidence showing that the alleles of some genes stay together in parental combinations more often than they are separated into new combinations was obtained very soon after Mendel's work was rediscovered in 1900. By 1911 Thomas Hunt Morgan had already suggested that allelic recombinations might arise via exchanges between homologous chromosomes in a process he called crossing over. Twenty years passed (1931) before convincing evidence was provided for physical exchanges leading to recombination, and an additional thirty years elapsed (1961) before the mechanism responsible for these physical exchanges was finally verified. Since 1961 we have been able to gain additional understanding of the molecular events of crossing over, and we now have testable hypothetical models of the process that are open to experimental analysis and verification.

17.6
Cytogenetic Evidence for Chromosome Exchanges in Crossing Over

Morgan's proposal that chromosome exchanges led to genetic recombination was verified in 1931 in two articles that were published quite independently of each other, each utilizing a different organism but a very similar experimental design. Both studies showed in the most elegant way that genetically recombinant individuals possessed physically exchanged homologous chromosomes. The major difficulty in obtaining such evidence is that homologous chromosomes ordinarily cannot be distinguished from one another by microscopy or other methods. In order to determine whether physical exchanges actually occurred, the homologous chromosomes had to be physically altered in such ways that each homolog was recognizable and readily related to the alleles each carried. By cytological studies with the microscope (to observe chromosome morphology directly) and by observation of the inherited features of the individual organisms (to ascertain which alleles they carried), the cytogenetic analyses of *Drosophila melanogaster* by Curt Stern and of maize (*Zea mays*) by Harriet Creighton and Barbara Mc-Clintock convincingly demonstrated the relationship between crossing over and genetic recombination. Both studies illustrate the general principles of the experiments; we will describe Stern's study of *Drosophila*.

Stern had come across unusual strains of *Drosophila*, including ones in which the X chromosome was physically altered and recognizably different from the normal X chromosome. In one strain the X chromosome had a piece of chromosome 4 attached in place of its own missing piece, but the chromosome was shorter than the normal X. In another strain a portion of the Y chromosome was attached to the X chromosome so that the altered X was longer than a normal X chromosome. Stern made the necessary crosses to obtain females with one each of the two kinds of altered X chromosomes instead of normal X chromosomes in their cells, and each physically distinguishable X chromosome carried different alleles of two genes governing eye characteristics. Stern could therefore determine parental or recombinant allelic combinations by direct observation of the eye traits in progeny flies, and he could correlate these genotypes with X chromosome morphology by direct microscopic observations of nuclei in fly cells.

The special females were crossed with males whose normal X chromosome carried the recessive carnation (*car*) mutant allele for eye color and the recessive wild-type allele (B^+) for eye construction. The dominant mutant allele for bar eyes (*B*) causes a reduced number of facets to develop in the compound eye of the insect, and a "bar" of color appears only in the faceted part of the eye. The dominant wild-type allele (*car*$^+$) governs red eye color. Female parents had red, bar eyes and male parents had carnation, nonbar eyes (Fig. 17.21).

In the progeny flies, Stern found that those with a parental allelic combination had X chromosomes that were morphologically identical to the X chromosomes in the parents. Progeny whose eyes indicated a recombinant genotype were found to have a physically changed X chromosome derived through the egg from the female parent. This correlation between physically exchanged chromosomes and new allelic combinations provided powerful evidence in support of the hypothesis that crossing over involves a physical exchange of homologous chromosome segments and that this exchange is responsible for genetic recombination involving linked genes.

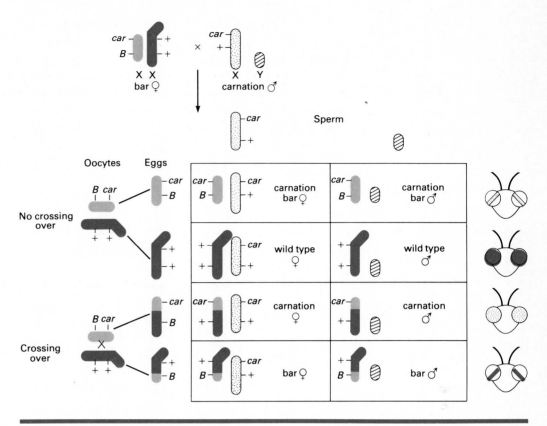

FIGURE 17-21
Diagrammatic summary of Curt Stern's
1931 cytogenetic experiments with
Drosophila melanogaster, in which he
obtained strains having physically
distinguishable X chromosomes that
were made allelically different for
eye color and eye facet number.
These classic studies relate physical
exchange between homologous
chromosome segments (crossing
over), as seen by microscopy, to
genetic recombination, as seen in progeny phenotypes and the genotypes
deduced from these.

17.7

Crossing Over Involves Chromosome Breakage and Reunion Events

In the 1930s two major hypotheses were proposed for the mechanism of chromosome exchange leading to genetic recombination. In 1931 John Belling proposed the **copy-choice** mechanism stating that the beadlike *chromomeres* "split" and were later joined together in different combinations depending on the way the new connecting strands switched back and forth during chromosome replication (Fig. 17.22). In 1937 Cyril Darlington proposed a **breakage and reunion** mechanism for crossing over, in which breaks in chromatids during prophase I were induced by torsional stresses and the subsequent rejoining of broken ends could produce recombined chromatids. Either one of these mechanisms would serve to explain the physically exchanged, genetically recombinant chromosomes that had been demonstrated in 1931 by Stern and by Creighton and McClintock, because their data indicated neither the time of meiotic crossing over nor the mechanism involved in the exchanges.

The crucial distinction in the *timing* of crossover events between copy-choice and breakage and reunion served as the basis for experimental analysis designed to determine which of the two mechanisms was correct. Copy-choice required exchanges to take place during DNA replication, whereas breakage and reunion required crossing over to take place after DNA had replicated. A third possibility (that crossing over

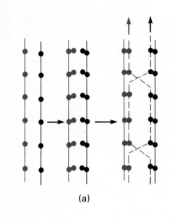

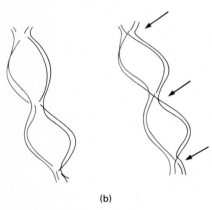

(a)

(b)

FIGURE 17-22
Mechanisms postulated in the 1930s to explain crossing over. (a) Copy choice. In 1931 John Belling suggested that the beadlike chromomeres of unreplicated meiotic chromosomes "split" and that different combinations of chromomeres (believed to be the sites of genes) might be joined together afterward as new connecting strands switched back and forth during replication. (b) Breakage and reunion. In 1937 Cyril Darlington suggested that stresses induced chromatid breaks and that subsequent rejoining could produce recombinant chromatids. Both mechanisms were based on the belief, widespread at that time, that replication occurred during prophase I of meiosis; we now know that replication takes place in premeiotic interphase.

occurred prior to DNA replication) had been disproved in the 1940s. As a matter of fact, various experimental data were collected in the 1940s that supported breakage and reunion and thus led to a decline in the plausibility of copy-choice. But in the 1950s there were many studies of genetic recombination in bacteria that were difficult to understand as consequences of breakage and reunion and were more easily interpreted by a copy-choice mechanism of crossing over. This revival of interest in copy-choice in the 1950s necessitated experimental tests by which one or the other mechanism of crossing over was firmly repudiated and the other firmly substantiated directly from data and not from interpretations of ambiguous observations. Such a stringent experimental analysis was provided in 1961 by Matthew Meselson and Jean Weigle; it abolished any further belief in the copy-choice mechanism.

Meselson and Weigle used a wild-type strain and a doubly mutant strain of phage λ (lambda), whose genome consists of a duplex DNA molecule. One strain was grown in *E. coli* on media containing the heavy isotope ^{15}N, and the other strain was grown in *E. coli* provided with ordinary ^{14}N. The reciprocal experiments utilized phage strains that were $+ +[^{15}N]$ and $c\ mi[^{14}N]$ or $+ +[^{14}N]$ and $c\ mi[^{15}N]$. Crosses were made by mixed infections of *E. coli* cells with both phage λ strains in $[^{14}N]$ medium. We will discuss the $+ +[^{15}N] \times c\ mi[^{14}N]$ cross, although similar results were obtained in the reciprocal cross of $+ +[^{14}N] \times c\ mi[^{15}N]$.

Each phage chromosome was *genetically* marked by two genes governing plaque characteristics, which permitted recombinants to be identified by the plaques produced by their infection, and each phage chromosome was *physically* distinguished by the presence of ^{15}N or ^{14}N in its DNA. We can interpret the results of this cytogenetic experiment by comparing the distribution of allelic markers with the distribution of isotopically distinguishable DNA molecules (chromosomes), in the same manner that Stern interpreted the results in his cytogenetic study of *Drosophila*.

If crossing over is by copy-choice, it must take place during DNA replication. If this were the case, all the recombinant phage should be "light" because only ^{14}N is available for new strand synthesis during infection. These $[^{14}N]$viruses would be genetically recombinant by virtue of new strands switching back and forth during replication, but they would be of only one isotopic composition. If crossing over occurs by the mechanism of breakage and reunion, however, at least some of the genetically recombinant progeny would have physically recombined DNA, part ^{15}N and part ^{14}N, because of rejoinings between new ^{14}N and parental ^{15}N strands that had been broken.

Progeny phage were collected from lysates of infected *E. coli* cells and were centrifuged in CsCl density gradients to separate lighter and denser phage (Fig. 17.23). Samples of these phage were removed from different parts of the density gradient to determine their genotype on the basis of plaque morphology produced in *E. coli* cultures infected by them afterward. Meselson and Weigle found that $c +$ and $+ mi$ genetic recombinants were also physically recombinant, according to their density positions in the CsCl gradients relative to fully light and fully heavy phage.

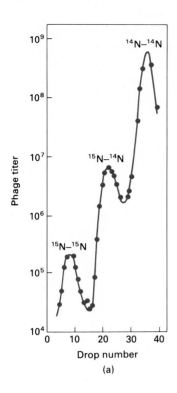

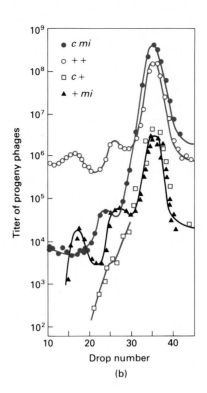

FIGURE 17-23
Evidence showing that crossing over occurs by the mechanism of breakage and reunion and not by copy choice. (a) Diagram showing the positions in a CsCl density gradient of lambda (λ) phage with unreplicated, fully labeled DNA (^{15}N–^{15}N), semiconserved DNA (^{15}N–^{14}N) after one replication, and unlabeled DNA (^{14}N–^{14}N) produced after two replications in *E. coli* growing in unlabeled [^{14}N]medium. The height of each peak reflects the amount (titer) of phage expected for 0, 1, and 2 replication cycles. (b) The results of mixed infection with $+$ $+$[^{15}N] and *c mi*[^{14}N] parental phage of *E. coli* in [^{14}N]medium. The $+$ *mi* genetic recombinants include phage with [^{15}N–^{15}N]DNA and [^{15}N–^{14}N]DNA, which must be due to breakage and reunion. If crossing over had occurred by copy choice, all the recombinants would have been ^{14}N–^{14}N, because parental (^{15}N) strands would be unchanged and only newly synthesized (^{14}N) strands would have switched back and forth to produce new allelic combinations. In addition, the unreplicated [^{15}N–^{15}N]DNA in one group of $+$ *mi* recombinants could not have been the result of copy choice in the [^{14}N]medium but could have arisen only if parental [^{15}N–^{15}N]DNA had undergone exchanges by breakage and reunion. (From Meselson, M., and J. J. Weigle, 1961, *Proc. Nat. Acad. Sci. U. S.* **47**: 857.)

Crossing over was thus shown to take place by a mechanism involving breakage and reunion of parental and newly synthesized DNA, and the way was opened to explore the molecular reactions involved in the process. In particular, enzymes associated with cutting the DNA duplex and the repair of broken ends upon rejoining could be sought. The enormous difficulties imposed by the organizational and molecular complexity of eukaryotic chromosomes have tended to limit their analysis and have spurred more varied and direct studies of crossing over in bacterial and viral systems, which are simpler and for which many useful mutants have been isolated. We will discuss relevant studies of all these systems in the next section.

17.8
Molecular Studies of Recombination Mechanisms

A number of different models now exist to account for genetic recombination via exchanges between DNA strands following their breakage and subsequent reunion in a new arrangement. It is very likely that some steps involved in recombination are different in different systems, such as exchanges during bacterial conjugation and transformation, viral integration into host genomes during transduction, and crossing over during meiosis in meiocytes or during mitosis in somatic cells.

Recombination in meiosis involves two chromatids of a bivalent, each with a single duplex DNA molecule, and it leads to the formation of a chiasma at the site of an exchange event. Pairs of sister chromatids are held close together by synapsis and stabilized by sharing a synaptonemal complex, so DNA molecules of nonsister chromatids are physically available to each other for crossing over. But we know of no forces that allow exchanges between intact, base-paired DNA molecules. Any model of recombination requires one or more steps by which a strand of each DNA duplex is cut, making single-stranded regions available for new base-pairing relationships. Nicking enzymes, such as endonucleases or a topoisomerase, can make such single-stranded cuts, and DNA ligase can seal the broken ends of rearranged strands by catalyzing covalent bonding of the sugar–phosphate backbones.

One of the models proposed to account for molecular recombination leading to chromatid exchange and chiasma formation was first proposed in 1964 by Robin Holliday, and a modified version still enjoys much favor. In this model, nicks are made by endonuclease action at corresponding sites on one strand of each DNA duplex in nonsister chromatids of a bivalent during prophase I of meiosis (Fig. 17.24). The

FIGURE 17-24
Summary of the Holliday model of crossing over between nonsister chromatids during meiosis in eukaryotes. Through a series of enzymatically catalyzed steps, reciprocally recombinant heteroduplex chromatid DNAs would be produced and a chiasma would be formed at the site of recombination. Only two of the four chromatids of a meiotic bivalent are shown here, and each chromatid has been represented as a duplex DNA molecule.

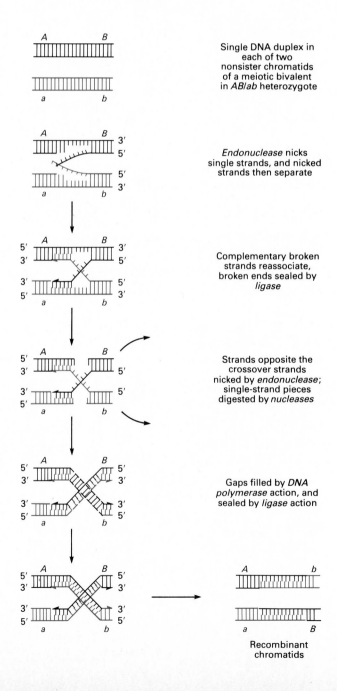

nicked strands loop out and the two strands reassociate into an exchanged arrangement, which is sealed by ligase action. The remaining intact strand of each duplex is nicked at a site opposite the crossover, the exposed ends are digested by exonuclease action, and the gap is filled in by DNA polymerase action to restore base-paired duplex segments. When these ends are covalently bonded by ligase, the two nonsister DNA duplexes exist as *heteroduplex* molecules whose alleles have been reciprocally recombined and whose strands are crossed over at a chiasma. When separated at anaphase I, each dyad includes one unchanged chromatid and one crossover chromatid. At anaphase II, the heteroduplex recombinant-DNA molecule in one chromatid is segregated from the unchanged DNA duplex in the sister chromatid (Fig. 17.25).

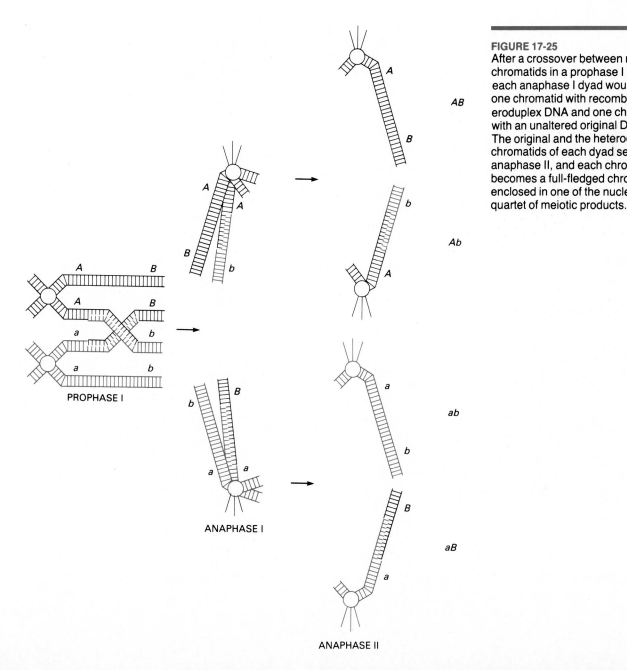

FIGURE 17-25
After a crossover between nonsister chromatids in a prophase I bivalent, each anaphase I dyad would consist of one chromatid with recombinant heteroduplex DNA and one chromatid with an unaltered original DNA duplex. The original and the heteroduplex chromatids of each dyad separate at anaphase II, and each chromatid becomes a full-fledged chromosome enclosed in one of the nuclei in the quartet of meiotic products.

Whether this model of crossing over and recombination or some other model proves to be correct, sufficient evidence exists to show that DNA replication enzymes are also involved in breakage-and-reunion events associated with recombination. Because a small amount of DNA is involved in recombination events, the reactions are usually referred to as **DNA repair synthesis**. Some of the most convincing evidence for DNA repair synthesis in recombination has come from studies of meiosis in lily plants by Herbert Stern and Yasuo Hotta. Similar evidence has also been obtained in studies of meiosis in the mouse and other species, which makes it very likely that DNA repair synthesis is fundamental to the processes of general recombination in eukaryotes. By *general* recombination we mean exchanges involving any of the nucleotide sequences in the genome, not necessarily those that require site-specific signals limiting the regions that may undergo exchange events (viral integration, transposition, and so on).

Lily flower buds of the same size are known to be in the same stage of meiosis, and all the meiocytes in these buds are also dividing synchronously. These features permit biochemical analysis of lily-bud meiocytes, because large quantities of identical material in known stages of meiosis can be collected and assayed. Stern and Hotta have shown that endonuclease, DNA polymerase, ligase, and other repair-enzyme activities appear early in prophase I, reach a peak at pachynema (the stage when recombination is presumed to occur), and decline afterward (Fig. 17.26). These activities coincide with the timing of synapsis, crossing over, and chiasma formation in meiotic cells.

By radioactive labeling, Stern and Hotta have shown that small amounts of DNA are synthesized during pachynema and that an equal amount is digested in the same substage. Because there is *no net change* in

FIGURE 17-26

DNA repair–synthesis during meiosis in lily flower buds. Early in prophase I there is a surge of endonuclease activity (breakage) and of ligase activity (rejoining) coincident with a small amount of DNA synthesis (color) during pachynema, the meiotic stage in which crossing over occurs by breakage and reunion. These activities decline during diplonema and diakinesis. (*Note*: The peak of DNA synthesis at zygonema represents new DNA replicating for the first time; it is not part of pachytene DNA repair–synthesis. See Section 17.9.)

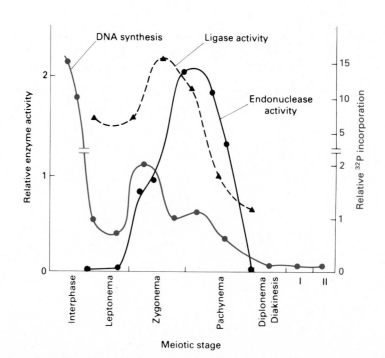

pachytene DNA, it would seem that DNA repair synthesis takes place at this time, replacing digested sequences with newly synthesized sequences of the same amount. Studies using inhibitors of DNA, RNA, and protein synthesis have consistently related DNA repair synthesis to genetic recombination and chiasma formation. All these data are consistent with the Holliday model of recombination, but they fit the requirements of other models, too, and we cannot choose a single recombination model from these studies alone.

Molecular analysis of mutants deficient in recombination have provided some important insights into the nature of exchange events in viruses and bacteria, whose naked DNA also undergoes physical and allelic rearrangement between linked genes. A number of these recombination-deficient mutants are also defective in DNA replication and in repair of DNA damaged by UV irradiation, further showing the activities of a common set of enzymes and other proteins in all these phenomena.

One highly regarded model of recombination applied to viral and bacterial systems and involving two interacting duplex DNA molecules is shown in Fig. 17.27. It is clear that portions of this model call on features of the mechanisms proposed by Holliday for eukaryotic DNAs, including single-strand nicks, strand exchange, and closure of recom-

FIGURE 17-27
Schematic summary of crossing over and its results according to the Holliday model as applied to paired DNA duplexes carrying alternative alleles of two genes (*A/a* and *B/b*). (a)–(f) Paired DNA duplexes experience breakage and rejoining, which lead to the formation of a joint molecule composed of four interlocked strands of DNA. (g) A planar molecule would arise by rotation of the joint molecule, and such a molecule would yield different products depending on the location of single-strand nicks. (h) Nicks in the two crossover strands would lead to (j) nonrecombinant duplexes containing heteroduplex regions, whereas (i) nicks in the two noncrossover strands would lead to (k) reciprocally recombinant DNA duplex molecules. (Adapted from Potter, H., and D. Dressler, 1977, *Proc. Nat. Acad. Sci. U. S.* **74**:4168.)

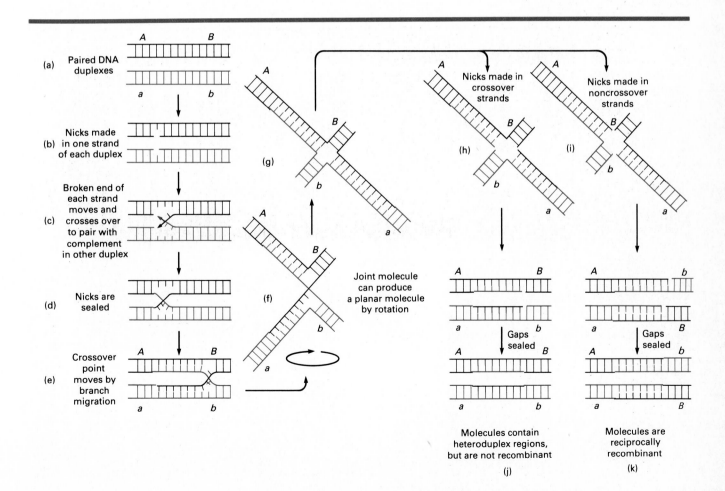

bined ends to generate a pair of heteroduplex molecules (Fig. 17.27a–d). Once the strand exchange has occurred, the crossover point can move along the duplex by a process called **branch migration**; movement may occur in either direction away from the original crossover site (Fig. 17.27e). The connected pair of duplexes, called a **joint molecule**, can rotate and thereby generate a planar molecule (Fig. 17.27f, g). In order to resolve the joint molecule into two separate duplex molecules, two additional nicks are required. If the same strands that were involved in the original crossover are nicked again, the two molecules that result are heteroduplex but not recombinant (Fig. 17.27h, j). If the nicks break the two noncrossover strands of the rotated joint molecule, however, two heteroduplex molecules arise that are reciprocally recombinant for allelic markers (Fig. 17.27i, k). This model and others like it differ in some details, but all of them rely on the formation of a heteroduplex **recombination intermediate** that can be extended by branch migration, because these features have been verified experimentally. Electron micrographs, among other kinds of data, show the predicted recombination intermediates in populations of DNA molecules. The photograph of a *chi figure* (resembling the Greek letter χ), as shown in Fig. 17.28, is exactly what is predicted by the model illustrated in Fig 17.27g.

From studies of the recombination-deficient *recA⁻* and *ssb⁻* mutants, among others in *E. coli*, and of similar mutants in some viruses and at least one fungus, another proposed scheme of recombination invokes the

FIGURE 17-28

Electron micrograph of a pair of DNA duplexes making up a recombination intermediate whose form resembles the Greek letter chi (χ). See Fig. 17.27 for steps leading to the formation of this planar joint molecule. (Photograph courtesy of D. Dressler and H. Potter, from Potter, H., and D. Dressler, 1977, *Proc. Natl. Acad. Sci. U.S.* **74**: 4168, Fig. 2C.)

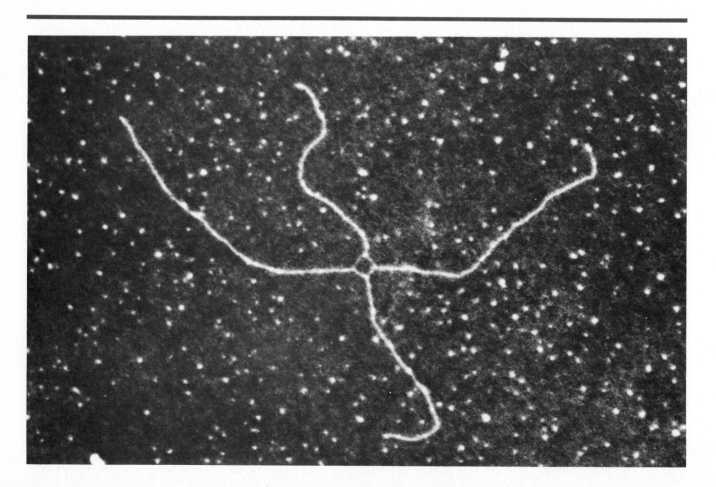

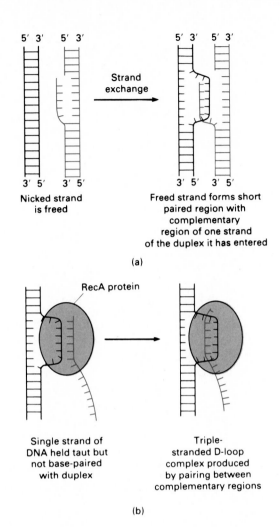

(a)

Nicked strand is freed

Freed strand forms short paired region with complementary region of one strand of the duplex it has entered

(b)

RecA protein

Single strand of DNA held taut but not base-paired with duplex

Triple-stranded D-loop complex produced by pairing between complementary regions

FIGURE 17-29
Recombination by strand exchange. (a) An exchange may occur when a nicked strand in one DNA duplex is freed and invades a homologous DNA duplex. The short freed region of the nicked strand may base-pair with an unwound D-loop region in the homologous duplex, and crossing over may thereby take place between homologous duplex strands. (b) RecA protein can bind tightly to single-stranded DNA or DNA regions, and it also has the ability to pull a single DNA strand into a D loop within the duplex. Base-pairing in the triple-stranded complex can take place and thereby provide a favorable situation for crossing-over events.

interaction of a single strand of DNA with a DNA duplex molecule. Both the SSB protein and **RecA protein** products of the *ssb* and *recA* genes, respectively, can bind tightly and cooperatively to single-stranded DNA regions and hold them taut and accessible for molecular interactions. The RecA protein has other properties as well, including the ability to pull a single strand into an intact duplex DNA molecule and hold these regions together in a base-paired triple-stranded complex (Fig. 17.29). Because the unwinding of one strand of the duplex causes it to loop out, new base-pairing can hold the single-stranded region together with its complement, whose original partner now exists in a so-called *D loop* conformation (it resembles the letter D) in the triplex structure.

RecA protein also has the property of a DNA-dependent ATPase, by which energy for these reactions may be provided. In the absence of ATP, the triple-stranded DNA structure will not be produced, nor is it produced in *recA⁻* mutants. It is also possible that RecA enzymatic activity sponsors branch migration. Though we are not sure of this, it is possible that the single-stranded DNA region required for RecA activity is provided by the **RecBC protein** product, which can generate single-stranded regions by unwinding DNA in the presence of SSB protein. The original identification of the RecBC protein was that of the potent enzyme exonuclease V, which degrades exposed ends of single-stranded DNA in uncontrolled fashion in *recA*⁻ mutants. Through the action of RecBC or other proteins, single strands for the RecA reaction may therefore be provided by nicks in duplex DNA and open the way to recombination between two duplex DNA molecules, as well as exchanges between single-stranded DNA and duplex DNA in virally infected cells.

The broad picture we have of molecular recombination ties together different biological processes (replication, recombination, repair) through the actions of many or all of the same enzymes and binding proteins that were first associated with DNA replication. Through the intervention of a common set of enzymes, therefore, the system can manage its DNA under different growth conditions and make new DNA, repair damaged DNA, and replace nucleotide sequences via heteroduplex intermediates in genetic recombination processes. The system can maintain itself, perpetuate itself, and generate genotypic variety from existing allelic combinations in a most economical fashion.

Chromosome Synapsis

The earliest significant event that distinguishes meiosis from mitosis is the precise pairing of homologous chromosomes, or **synapsis**. Many of the features of synapsis remain as mysterious today as they were many decades ago when the major tool available for analysis was the light microscope. By electron microscopy and by molecular methods, we have been able to dispel some of the mystery surrounding the phenomenon of homologous chromosome pairing, but much remains to be done.

17.9
The Synaptonemal Complex

The **synaptonemal complex** is a proteinaceous three-layered structure that begins to form along homologous chromosomes early in prophase I of meiosis, is fully formed in pachytene bivalents, and is shed during diplonema (Fig. 17.30). During leptonema, before synapsis begins, each replicated chromosome produces a long proteinaceous *lateral element*, which lies between the sister chromatids of the chromosome. When homologous chromosomes begin to pair in zygonema, a *central region* develops between paired lateral elements of the homologous chromosomes and holds them in register. The completed synaptonemal complex in pachytene bivalents consists of the two lateral elements and the shared central region, which may or may not include a more darkly staining *central element* (see Fig. 17.9). The chromatin of the paired chromosomes loops out from the bivalent complex, but only occasional chromatin strands can be seen traversing the 100-nm width of the complex between chromosomes.

The mechanism that leads to precise point-by-point pairing between homologous chromosomes is unknown. Several scattered items of information suggest that chromosome alignment leading to synapsis may be mediated somehow by the nuclear membrane. Pachytene bivalents in

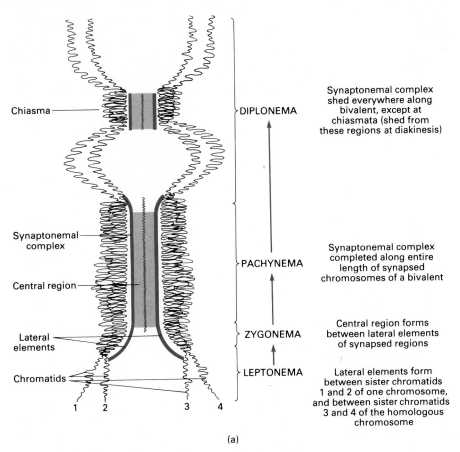

Chiasma

DIPLONEMA — Synaptonemal complex shed everywhere along bivalent, except at chiasmata (shed from these regions at diakinesis)

Synaptonemal complex

PACHYNEMA — Synaptonemal complex completed along entire length of synapsed chromosomes of a bivalent

Central region

ZYGONEMA — Central region forms between lateral elements of synapsed regions

Lateral elements

LEPTONEMA — Lateral elements form between sister chromatids 1 and 2 of one chromosome, and between sister chromatids 3 and 4 of the homologous chromosome

Chromatids

1   2   3   4

(a)

FIGURE 17-30
The synaptonemal complex. (a) Summary diagram of synaptonemal complex formation and removal during prophase I of meiosis. Beginning with lateral element formation in leptonema and the subsequent formation in zygonema of a central region between the two lateral elements of a bivalent, the synaptonemal complex is completed by pachynema in a sequence not unlike zippering. The diplotene bivalent sheds its synaptonemal complex everywhere except at chiasmata (sites of previous crossovers), and these last remnants are finally shed from the bivalents at diakinesis just preceding metaphase I. (b) Electron micrograph of a section through a meiotic cell of the fungus *Neottiella*. One of the pachytene bivalents has been sectioned favorably to display a synaptonemal complex between the paired chromosomes. ×16,000. (Photograph courtesy of D. von Wettstein, from Westergaard, M., and D. von Wettstein, 1970, *Compt. Rend. Lab. Carlsberg* **37**:239–268, Fig. 1.)

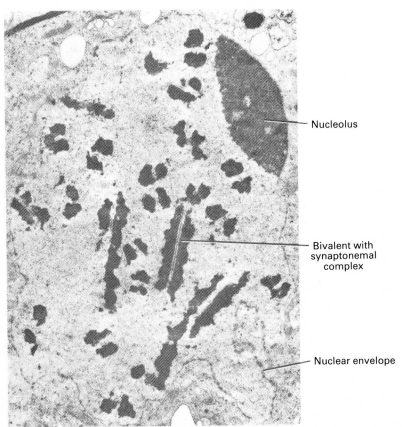

Nucleolus

Bivalent with synaptonemal complex

Nuclear envelope

(b)

eukaryotes are firmly attached to the inner nuclear membrane at both their termini (Fig. 17.31). Apparently, this attachment begins with unpaired leptotene chromosomes that have already developed a lateral element. Once attached, the leptotene chromosomes begin to synapse during zygonema only if new DNA is synthesized during this substage. Stern and Hotta showed that 99.7% of nuclear DNA replicated in premeiotic interphase in lily buds and that the remaining 0.3% replicated during zygonema (see Fig. 17.26). This *zygotene DNA* is synthesized from all the chromosomes, according to DNA–DNA hybridization assays, and it is isolated in a complex that includes membrane lipoproteins. This DNA is complexed with nuclear membrane only during zygonema, because the same DNA is isolated as part of total membrane-free nuclear DNA at later substages of prophase. If DNA synthesis during zygonema is inhibited, synapsis does not take place.

All these data are suggestive of some unique activity of zygotene DNA in the initial phases of chromosome synapsis, but we can only speculate at present about the nature of this activity. We do know that the membrane-attached ends of the chromosomes can be redistributed and ultimately come to lie as close as 300 nm apart. In some animal meiocytes all the chromosome ends come together in the nuclear envelope region opposite the centrioles; such a polarized display accounts for the description of a "bouquet" stage in the early literature on meiosis (Fig. 17.32). Just how zygotene DNA is involved in these events is not known, but perhaps these are telomere nucleotide se-

FIGURE 17-31
Electron micrograph of a longitudinal section through a pachytene bivalent from *Locusta migratoria* showing a well-developed synaptonemal complex between the paired homologous chromosomes and the attachment of one end of the bivalent to the inner membrane of the nuclear envelope. ×100,000. (Photograph courtesy of P. B. Moens.)

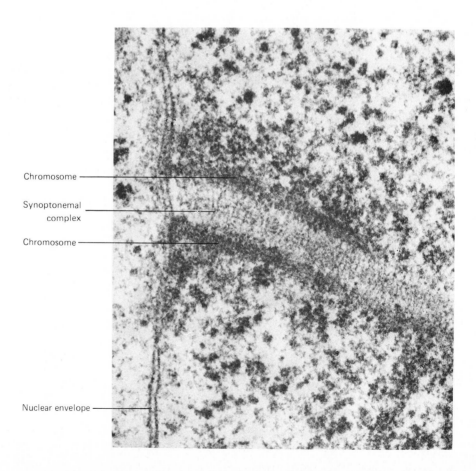

Chromosome

Synaptonemal complex

Chromosome

Nuclear envelope

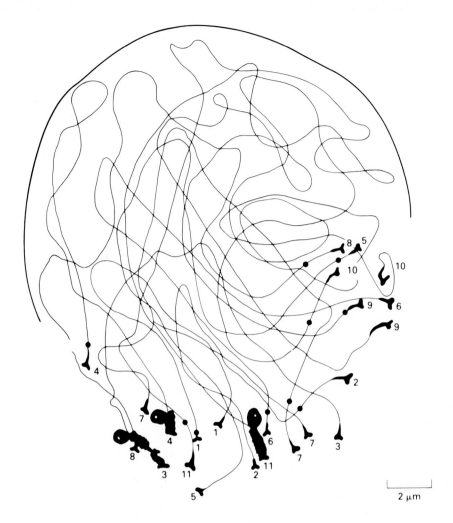

2 μm

FIGURE 17-32
Reconstruction of all the synaptonemal complexes in an early pachytene spermatocyte of *Locusta*, based on tracings of a series of electron micrographs through the nucleus. Each line represents a synaptonemal complex of a bivalent. The dot on each line represents the centromere in these acrocentric chromosomes. The larger dark areas beside the complexes for chromosomes 3, 4, and 11 represent the nucleoli, and the dotted areas nearby represent the heterochromatin associated with these nucleolar-organizing regions. The short line perpendicular to the end of a complex indicates the attachment point at the nuclear envelope. Both ends of each complex are attached to the same side of the nuclear envelope in a polarized "bouquet" arrangement. The single X chromosome in these spermatocytes is not shown because the unpaired chromosome does not produce a synaptonemal complex. At the time of preparation for electron microscopy, the pair of chromosomes 7 had not yet completed synapsis, so three ends are present instead of the two expected for a fully synapsed bivalent. (From Moens, P. B., 1974, *Cold Spring Harbor Sympos. Quant. Biol.* **38**:99–107, Fig. 3.)

quences that can somehow facilitate base-pairing of the identical chromosome ends (see Section 15.6). If this were the case, base sequence comparisons by molecular hybridization would provide definitive evidence of sequence locations and complementarity.

By whatever mechanism synapsis takes place, the formation of a synaptonemal complex is an absolute requirement for subsequent crossing over and recombination in meiocytes. We will briefly review some of the evidence for this relationship in the next section.

17.10
Recombination Nodules and Chiasmata of Synapsed Chromosomes

The active process of recombination is believed to be mediated by large, protein-containing **recombination nodules** that lie across the synaptonemal complex at widely spaced intervals along the length of a bivalent. These nodules are about 90 nm wide; they almost span the 100-nm space of synaptonemal complex between paired chromosomes. The nodules are presumed to include enzymes and other proteins that help bring together the loops of nonsister chromatin and sponsor the breakage-and-reunion events of crossing over and recombination. The

FIGURE 17-33
Recombination nodule. (a) Electron micrograph of a pachytene bivalent from a strain of mice in which one of the chromosomes has an inverted region and its homolog has the normal sequence. (b) Tracing of the photograph, showing the recombination nodule in the space between paired homologs in the looped region of the bivalent. (Photograph courtesy of M. J. Moses, from Poorman, P. A., et al., 1981, *Chromosoma* **83**:419.)

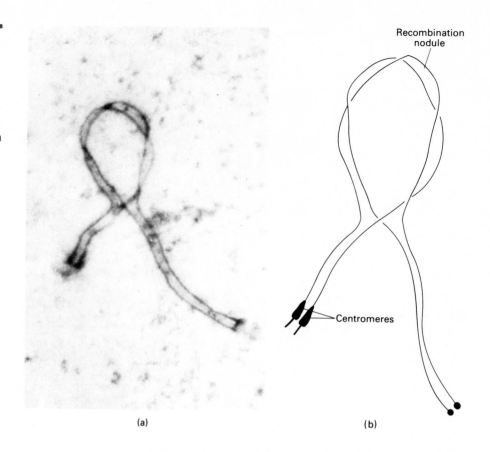

(a)   (b)

available data on the function of recombination nodules is indirect, but they form a strong body of circumstantial evidence nevertheless.

1. By electron microscope autoradiography it has been shown that labeled DNA precursors are preferentially incorporated into pachytene DNA at or near recombination nodules. These observations coincide with the evidence that DNA repair synthesis accompanies recombination during pachynema.

2. The number and distribution of recombination nodules coincide with the number and distribution of chiasmata, the presumed sites of crossing over in pachytene bivalents. Recombination nodules and chiasmata are both absent from heterochromatin, both diminish in frequency in recombination-defective mutants, and both are present in a few widely separated locations in normal bivalents. At present, however, we know little about the organization or action of the molecules that comprise a recombination nodule.

Many kinds of observations indicate that development of the synaptonemal complex is an essential prerequisite for chiasma formation and genetic recombination.

1. Asynaptic mutants, whose chromosomes do not pair, fail to produce synaptonemal complexes, they lack chiasmata, and genetic recombinants are absent from their progeny.

2. If protein synthesis is inhibited in zygonema after lateral elements have been formed, synaptonemal complex development stops,

synapsis does not take place, and neither chiasmata nor recombinants are produced.

3. If these inhibitors remain in the cell until late zygonema or early pachynema and are then washed out, synaptonemal complex formation does not resume and neither chiasmata nor recombinants are produced.

It would thus appear that, once begun, synapsis must be maintained without interruption if crossing over and chiasma formation are to take place. The synaptonemal complex itself does not initiate the pairing process, because pairing begins in zygonema *before* complex formation occurs. Instead, the synaptonemal complex stabilizes paired chromosomes in bivalent structures upon completion of synapsis, thereby increasing the opportunities for crossing over to occur. This feature is also apparent from studies of desynaptic mutants, which have fully formed synaptonemal complexes early in pachynema but whose bivalents separate precociously. Recombinations and chiasma frequency are sharply reduced in these mutants and may even fall to zero. The presence of a synaptonemal complex by itself does not guarantee that crossing over will take place; it only makes it more likely to occur in stably paired bivalents.

Genetic recombination studies reveal that mitotic cells undergo crossing over, but only irregularly and with much lower frequency than meiotic cells. This difference in the regularity of occurrence and the frequency of crossing over must be due in large measure to the presence of a synaptonemal complex between paired chromosomes in meiosis and to the absence of such a structure in mitotic nuclei. No such structure is present even in dipteran somatic cells in which homologous polytene chromosomes are closely paired.

Various kinds of evidence indicate that different processes or factors are at work in mitotic and meiotic recombination phenomena. For example, asynaptic *Drosophila* mutants undergo no crossing over or recombination during meiosis, but they continue to produce recombinants by mitotic crossing over at the same rate as wild-type somatic cells. Similarly, homologous chromosomes are loosely paired in *Drosophila* spermatocytes, and neither synaptonemal complexes nor chiasmata have been observed. All the sperm are genotypically nonrecombinant in normal males. At the same time, genetic recombinants are produced in the same frequency by mitotic crossing over in both males and females. Different controls or processes are clearly involved in meiotic and mitotic recombination phenomena.

In meiocytes, therefore, the synaptonemal complex stabilizes paired chromosomes during pachynema and makes it more probable that crossing over will take place during the interval of close physical proximity. We are still left with important unsolved problems, however, including the baffling question of how complementary strands of the nonsister chromatids gain access to each other across the 100-nm width of the synaptonemal complex. A detailed analysis of the recombination nodules should help to clarify the geometry of crossing over and should lead us to a better understanding of the molecular events that sponsor genetic recombination in complex eukaryotic chromosomes.

Summary

In different sexual organisms, different proportions of the life cycle are spent in the diploid and haploid phases. The former is initiated by fusion of haploid gametes, the latter by meiosis of a diploid meiocyte, but each of those events may be separated by extended periods of mitotic cell division and differentiation. In animals, the products of meiosis are the gametes themselves, which fuse to restore the predominant diploid phase. In some lower forms, meiosis of the zygote immediately follows fusion of gametes, and the bulk of the life cycle is represented by the haploid phase. In advanced vascular plants, the haploid structures (gametophyte) are contained and protected within the diploid sporophyte plant that is predominant in the life cycle. Meiocytes alone are capable of meiosis, and these unique cells are present in gonads— organs that produce and harbor the gametes or gamete-producing systems.

In meiosis each diploid meiocyte divides twice in succession to give four products, one or all of which may be functional. The meiotic divisions are initiated after DNA replication in interphase, so initially each replicated chromosome consists of two chromatids. In the first meiotic division, homologous chromosomes pair and later separate, so each nuclear product contains one set (haploid) of replicated chromosomes. In the second meiotic division the sister chromatids of each replicated chromosome separate to give daughter cells with one unreplicated copy of each chromosome. The first division yields nuclei whose chromosome number is one-half the meiocyte number, and the second division retains this haploid number but reduces the DNA content to the haploid level in each daughter nucleus. These daughter cells may divide mitotically as spores or produce somatic structure, or, without further division, they may differentiate as gametes, fuse with complementary gametes, and restore in the zygote the diploid chromosome number. One key advantage of sexual reproduction is the opportunity it affords for creating new combinations of parental genes regularly in each generation.

The first meiotic division is unlike mitosis and may last an extended period of time. It is preceded by an extended interphase that may involve fewer active replicons. The chromosomes then enter prophase I, in which various substages can be recognized:

1. Leptonema, in which the chromatin is dispersed as a tangle of beaded threads.

2. Zygonema, in which homologous chromosomes undergo close pairing, or synapsis, stabilized by a synaptonemal complex.

3. Pachynema, in which condensed bivalents but not their individual chromatids are distinguishable and in which crossing over and genetic recombination may occur.

4. Diplonema, in which bivalents open out and separate except at the points where the sites of crossing over (chiasmata) hold them in contact.

5. Diakinesis, the most contracted chromosome state, wherein the nuclear membrane breaks down, the chromosomes attach to spindle fibers, and the nucleoli disperse.

In prometaphase I the chromosomes move around and align themselves on the spindle to begin metaphase I. Unlike mitosis, in meiotic metaphase I the ends of the chromosomes are at the equator and the homologous centromeres are as far apart as possible. Within each dyad, the sister chromatids remain closely associated at the centromere. The replicated homologues (dyads) separate at anaphase I and the new nuclei undergo a variable degree of reorganization in telophase I. Cytokinesis may occur now, or it may follow meiosis II. The second meiotic division is superficially similar to a mitotic division. Dyads in both nuclei line up on both spindles at metaphase II, the two centromeres of each dyad uncouple at anaphase II, and the sister chromatids of each pair are pulled to opposite poles of their respective spindles. During telophase II, chromosomes unfold, a nuclear membrane forms around each of the four products, and cytokinesis occurs.

Even if the only gene reassortment in this process came from random combinations of parental chromosomes in any given gamete nucleus, sexual reproduction would allow vastly increased genotypic variability: Two choices for each of n chromosomes in a genome allow 2^n different chromosome combinations. In addition, however, the possibility of genetic recombination by crossing over allows new combinations even of the genes borne on a single chromosome (linked genes). Genetic recombination is the result of physical exchanges of homologous chromosome segments. Crossing over in eukaryotes and prokaryotes involves breakage and reunion of homologous DNA molecules or chromosomes, rather than switching of templates during replication (copy choice). In meiocytes crossing over takes place in synapsed bivalents during pachynema in prophase I and involves the introduction by endonucleases of single-strand breaks in nonsister chromatids, strand reassociation, and sealing of nicks with DNA ligase, such that the two dyads of a bivalent both have a parental chromatid and a cross-over chromatid. Nonsister DNAs exist as heteroduplexes. An analogous but not identical process occurs in bacteria and viruses; it involves single-stranded nicks, strand exchange, branch migration, and resolution by two more single-stranded nicks. The expected chi-figure recombination intermediate of the crossing-over process can be seen in electron micrographs.

The bivalents are held together in pachynema by a specialized structure, the synaptonemal complex. It begins to assemble after close pairing has begun in zygonema and is completed when pachynema begins. Without its continuous stabilizing influence, effective recombinational exchange cannot occur. Recombination nodules span the synaptonemal complex at sites later seen to contain chiasmata. In the absence of formation of the synaptonemal complex, meiosis proceeds as usual but recombination does not take place. Mitotic recombination is ordinarily much less frequent than meiotic recombination, and takes place in somatic cells, which do not develop synaptonemal complexes.

Readings and References

Arber, W. 1979. Promotion and limitation of genetic exchange. *Science* **205**:361 (Nobel lecture).

Baulieu, E.-E., F. Godeau, M. Schorderet, and S. Schorderet-Slatkine. 1978. Steroid-induced meiotic division in *Xenopus laevis* oocytes: Surface and calcium. *Nature* **275**:593.

Carpenter, A. T. C. 1979. Recombination nodules and synaptonemal complex in recombination-defective females of *Drosophila melanogaster. Chromosoma* **75**:259.

Chandley, A. C., Y. Hotta, and H. Stern. 1977. Biochemical analysis of meiosis in the male mouse. I. Separation and DNA labeling of specific spermatogenic stages. *Chromosoma* **62**:243.

Creighton, H. S., and B. McClintock. 1931. A correlation of cytological and genetical crossing-over in *Zea mays. Proc. Natl. Acad. Sci. U.S.* **17**:492.

DasGupta, C., R. P. Cunningham, T. Shibata, and C. M. Radding. 1979. Enzymatic cleavage of D loops. *Cold Spring Harbor Sympos. Quant. Biol.* **43**:987.

Dresser, M. E., and M. J. Moses. 1979. Silver staining of synaptonemal complexes in surface spreads for light and electron microscopy. *Exp. Cell Res.* **121**:416.

Dressler, D., and H. Potter. 1982. Molecular mechanisms in genetic recombination. *Ann. Rev. Biochem.* **51**:727.

Epel, D. November 1977. The program of fertilization. *Sci. Amer.* **237**:128.

Grell, R. F., E. F. Oakberg, and E. E. Generoso. 1980. Synaptonemal complexes at premeiotic interphase in the mouse spermatocyte. *Proc. Natl. Acad. Sci. U.S.* **77**:6720.

Grossman, L., S. Riazuddin, W. A. Haseltine, and C. Lindan. 1979. Nucleotide excision repair of damaged DNA. *Cold Spring Harbor Sympos. Quant. Biol.* **43**:947.

Hickson, I. D., and P. T. Emmerson. 1981. Identification of the *Escherichia coli* recB and recC gene products. *Nature* **294**:578.

Holliday, R. 1964. A mechanism for gene conversion in fungi. *Genet. Res.* **5**:282.

Hotta, Y., and H. Stern. 1977. Biochemical analysis of meiosis in the male mouse. II. DNA metabolism at pachytene. *Chromosoma* **62**:255.

Ikeda, H., and I. Kobayashi. 1979. recA-mediated recombination of bacteriophage λ: Structure of recombinant and intermediate DNA molecules and their packaging *in vitro. Cold Spring Harbor Sympos. Quant. Biol.* **43**:1009.

John, B., and K. R. Lewis. 1973. *The Meiotic Mechanism.* Oxford Biology Readers, ed. J. J. Head, no. 65. New York: Oxford University Press.

Kenyon, C. J. 1983. The bacterial response to DNA damage. *Trends Biochem. Sci.* **8**:84.

Knutton, S., and C. A. Pasternak. 1979. The mechanism of cell–cell fusion. *Trends Biochem. Sci.* **4**:220.

Lewin, B. 1980. *Gene Expression,* **2**: *Eukaryotic Chromosomes.* 2nd ed. New York: Wiley.

Lewin, B. 1985. *Genes.* 2nd ed. New York: Wiley.

Meselson, M., and C. M. Radding. 1975. A general model for genetic recombination. *Proc. Natl. Acad. Sci. U.S.* **72**:358.

Meselson, M., and J. J. Weigle. 1961. Chromosome breakage accompanying genetic recombination in bacteriophage. *Proc. Natl. Acad. Sci. U.S.* **47**:857.

Moens, P. B. 1966. Segregation of tritium-labeled DNA at meiosis in *Chorthippus. Chromosoma* **19**:277.

Moens, P. B. 1968. The structure and function of the synaptonemal complex in *Lilium longiflorum* sporocytes. *Chromosoma* **23**:418.

Moens, P. B. 1969. The fine structure of meiotic chromosome polarization and pairing in *Locusta migratoria* spermatocytes. *Chromosoma* **28**:1.

Moens, P. B. 1974. Quantitative electron microscopy of chromosome organization at meiotic prophase. *Cold Spring Harbor Sympos. Quant. Biol.* **38**:99.

Moens, P. B. 1978. The onset of meiosis. In *Cell Biology, A Comprehensive Treatise,* ed. L. Goldstein and D. M. Prescott, vol. 1, p. 93. New York: Academic Press.

Moens, P. B., and E. Rapport. 1971. Spindles, spindle plaques, and meiosis in the yeast *Saccharomyces cerevisiae* (Hansen). *J. Cell Biol.* **50**:344.

Moses, M. J. 1968. Synaptonemal complex. *Ann. Rev. Genet.* **2**:363.

Moses, M. J., S. J. Counce, and D. F. Paulson. 1975. Synaptonemal complex complement of man in spreads of spermatocytes, with details of the sex chromosome pair. *Science* **187**:363.

Nicklas, R. B. 1967. Chromosome micromanipulation. II. Induced reorientation and the experimental control of segregation in meiosis. *Chromosoma* **21**:17.

Potter, H., and D. Dressler. 1976. On the mechanism of genetic recombination: Electron microscopic observation of recombination intermediates. *Proc. Natl. Acad. Sci. U.S.* **73**:2000.

Radding, C. M. 1981. Recombination activities of *E. coli* recA protein. *Cell* **25**:3.

Radding, C. M. 1982. Strand transfer in homologous genetic recombination. *Ann. Rev. Genet.* **16**:405.

Rhoades, M. M. 1961. Meiosis. In *The Cell,* ed. R. Brachet and A. Mirsky, vol. 3, p. 1. New York: Academic Press.

Shibata, T., R. P. Cunningham, and C. M. Radding. 1981. Homologous pairing in genetic recombination. Purification and characterization of *Escherichia coli* recA protein. *J. Biol. Chem.* **256**:7557.

Shibata, T., C. DasGupta, R. P. Cunningham, and C. M. Radding. 1979. Purified *E. coli* recA protein catalyzes homologous pairing of superhelical DNA and single-stranded fragments. *Proc. Natl. Acad. Sci. U.S.* **76**:1638.

Shibata, T., *et al.* 1981. Homologous pairing in genetic recombination. The pairing reaction catalyzed by *Escherichia coli* recA protein. *J. Biol. Chem.* **256**:7565.

Simchen, G., Y. Kassir, O. Horesh-Cabilly, and A. Friedmann. 1981. Elevated recombination and pairing structures during meiotic arrest in yeast of the nuclear division mutant *cdc5*. *Mol. gen. Genet.* **184**:46.

Stahl, F. W., M. M. Stahl, and R. E. Malone. 1978. Rec-mediated recombination of phage lambda in a *recA⁻recB⁻* host. *Mol. gen. Genet.* **159**:207.

Stern, H., and Y. Hotta. 1977. Biochemistry of meiosis. *Phil. Trans. Roy. Soc.* (*London*) **B277**:277.

Taylor, J. H. 1965. Distribution of tritium-labeled DNA among chromosomes during meiosis. I. Spermatogenesis in the grasshopper. *J. Cell Biol.* **25**:57.

Vlad, M., and H. C. Macgregor. 1975. Chromomere number and its genetic significance in lampbrush chromosomes. *Chromosoma* **50**:327.

von Wettstein, D., S. W. Rasmussen, and P. B. Holm. 1984. The synaptonemal complex in genetic segregation. *Ann. Rev. Genet.* **16**:405.

Warner, R. C., R. A. Fishel, and F. C. Wheeler. 1979. Branch migration in recombination. *Cold Spring Harbor Sympos. Quant. Biol.* **43**:957.

West, S. C., E. Cassuto, and P. Howard-Flanders. 1981. Mechanism of *E. coli* recA protein directed strand exchanges in post-replication repair of DNA. *Nature* **294**:659.

Westergaard, M., and D. von Wettstein. 1972. The synaptonemal complex. *Ann. Rev. Genet.* **6**:71.

Williams, J. G. K., T. Shibata, and C. M. Radding. 1981. *Escherichia coli* recA protein protects single-stranded DNA or gapped duplex DNA from degradation by recBC DNase. *J. Biol. Chem.* **256**:7573.

Zickler, D., and L. W. Olson. 1975. The synaptonemal complex and the spindle plaque during meiosis in yeast. *Chromosoma* **50**:1.

PART VI

Evolution

CHAPTER 18

Cellular and Molecular Evolution

The remarkable diversity of life forms and processes has provided one focus of discussion in this book, but we have also seen repeatedly that various features occur in common or in similar patterns among this wealth of diversity. Both the similarities between and the distinctions among living systems are the outcome of evolutionary events that transpired over most of the 4.6 billion years that our planet has been in existence. In this concluding chapter, it seems appropriate to examine the underlying evolutionary processes on which life is based and to construct a framework in which the bewildering variety of life can be placed and in which relationships can be observed. We must restrict ourselves to selected aspects of evolutionary events and processes, because all of biology is a reflection of the past history of life on Earth and we can only touch on some of this drama in the space available.

Prebiotic Evolution

Whether or not life as we know it is all that exists in the universe, or represents the only forms possible should life also exist elsewhere, any consideration of life's origin and subsequent evolution on Earth must begin with the primeval conditions that set the stage for life on our planet. Some of the events we propose are more speculative than others, but all rest on observation and experiment in many different disciplines, including biology. We rely on our knowledge of current life and fossil forms in order to backtrack to earlier times and events, because our fundamental assumption is that all that is and all that was in the past are related by descent from common ancestral forms.

18.1
The Primeval Earth

According to our current belief (based on evidence from astrophysics and cosmology), the universe originated in a "**big bang**" some 15 to 20 billion years ago. We can say virtually nothing about the instant of the universe's origin, but we know enough physics and chemistry to outline the events from 10^{-43} seconds after the origin until 3 minutes later, when the universe had cooled sufficiently to allow neutrons and protons to stick together in atomic nuclei, once these had been formed by random collisions. Cooling continued to take place, and after 700,000 years the temperature dropped from 1 billion kelvins to a level that permitted electrons to bind to atomic nuclei. The universe that began to expand after the initial explosion is still expanding, and by now the background radiation from that explosion has cooled to a temperature of 3 K. The discovery of this predicted background radiation in 1965, by Robert Wilson and Arno Penzias, provided the first solid evidence for the big bang theory and simultaneously disposed of the alternative steady-state theory of a universe with no beginning and no end.

Only the elements hydrogen and helium were produced in the early phases of the evolution of the universe. Heavier elements were produced much later, after stars had been formed, and the elements still are being born in stars and in star explosions (supernovas). Stars themselves are formed from cold, turbulent **solar dust clouds**, under the influence of gravitational forces, and as they form and increase in density they heat up to temperatures that are high enough to sponsor thermonuclear reactions leading to element synthesis. In addition, depending on local conditions, the temperature of the nascent star, and various other factors, a solar dust cloud may give rise to one or more planets that orbit around the star. Our own solar system is comprised of a central star, the sun, and nine planets, of which Earth is third closest to the sun.

Planet formation probably began with the successive collision and clumping of tiny particles to form larger particles. They proceeded to enlarge into planetesimals, then protoplanets, and finally the planets themselves (Fig. 18.1). Different materials would be expected in the planetary bodies located at different distances along the steep temperature gradient from the center of the solar cloud outward. The inner planets would be predominantly rocky; rocky materials and frozen water would accumulate farther out; and rock, frozen water, and frozen ammonia and methane would be the main constituents of the most distant planets. The vast amounts of hydrogen and helium gases of the outer planets may have been swept up by gravitational forces exerted by their cores. The inner planets (Mercury, Venus, Earth, and Mars) probably were too small to attract any substantial amounts of these lighter gases, but they were large enough to attract heavier gases such as nitrogen, methane, and ammonia into their atmospheres. The rarity of many gases in our own atmosphere and the relatively high iron and silicate content of the solid phases may have resulted from local conditions prevailing in our region of the solar system very early in its formation.

We believe that, after the Earth was fully formed, the atmosphere was *nonoxidizing* and consisted of the original captured gases: some hydrogen, more nitrogen, carbon dioxide, methane, ammonia, hydrogen sulfide, and water vapor, but no oxygen. Such an atmosphere is a crucial feature of the chemical evolution and later biological evolution on Earth.

(a)

(b)

(c)

MARS   VENUS
MERCURY   SUN
EARTH

(d)

FIGURE 18-1
The solar system. (a) The solar system is believed to have begun as a diffuse cloud of dust and gases, which (b) contracted over a period of time to form the central sun (star) and whirling discs of preplanetary materials. (c) Whether by accretion of dust grains that broke up into planetesimals because of gravitational instability, or by progressive clumping of materials to produce planetesimals, protoplanets ultimately formed from these smaller bodies and later (d) became the planets and asteroid belt of the solar system we know today. The four inner planets are drawn to scale. The outer planets are not drawn to scale because it would require a width of four feet to place them at their proportionate distances apart.

The liquid hydrosphere of Earth probably was formed, or at least increased in amount, soon after planetary completion. The water may have originated by condensation from Earth's interior as well as from torrential rainfalls. Whatever its origins, water would have existed in liquid form, because the ambient temperature over much of the planet varied between 0°C and 100°C. Mercury and Venus have too high a surface temperature to maintain liquid water, and the farther planets, including Mars, are so cold all or most of the time that any water exists as permanent ice. In fact, the temperatures are low enough on Mars for carbon dioxide to exist in the frozen state (dry ice, at $-70°C$ and lower). No evidence of life on Mars was obtained from the two *Viking* spacecraft that landed there in 1976, but the project was launched because conditions in some parts of that planet theoretically could have supported some form of life.

The moon was probably completed about the same time as the Earth, or not long afterward. The oldest rocks collected by the lunar landing expeditions are 4.45 billion years old. The dating of meteorites, as representatives of the original solid materials of the solar system, has revealed that our Earth has existed in solid form for 4.6 billion years. Unfortunately, the violent events of the earliest history of the solar system and the subsequent erosion of surface materials have erased important clues that we would need to reconstruct the actual course of events during the formation of Earth and the solar system. The oldest existing surface rocks on Earth today are in Greenland, and these are only 3.8 billion years old. Even if it were possible to reconstruct the primordial history of Earth at the time when life originated, much of that history has been eroded away over eons of time. Enough of that primeval record still exists, however, for us to estimate the nature of the atmosphere and hydrosphere in which chemical reactions took place and in which, ultimately, life originated on Earth.

18.2
Chemical Evolution

If life did originate on Earth at some time in the past, as most scientists presume, we are obliged to understand how complex organic molecules arose here and how a chaos of chemicals and molecules evolved into organized living systems. It is clear from our observations of stars, planets, and meteorites that the organic molecules these systems contain must have been synthesized abiotically; we are certain that life cannot exist in any of these bodies. **Abiotic synthesis** of organic molecules could therefore have occurred on the primeval Earth, just as it can occur elsewhere in the absence of life.

The earliest hypotheses and evidence concerning abiotic syntheses on the young Earth were presented in the 1920s by the Soviet biochemist Alexander Oparin and the British biochemist and geneticist John B. S. Haldane. Their publications and subsequent reports stipulated the conditions most likely to have existed for the production and accumulation of organic molecules. The atmosphere was nonoxidizing, bodies of liquid water were present, ample amounts of small precursor molecules were available, and energy from various sources could sponsor the required endergonic reactions. Among the probable energy sources we can include solar radiation, particularly in the longer UV wavelengths of 300 to 400 nm; electrical energy from discharges during storms; thermal energy in volcanic regions; and perhaps energy released by radioactive decay of various elements in the rocky crust of Earth. Once formed, the organic molecules would accumulate in the waters of the planet, because no life was present to consume or use these compounds and because spontaneous reactions of organic synthesis and degradation are notoriously slow in the absence of enzyme catalysts.

One of the first experiments to impress the scientific community with the feasibility of abiotic synthesis and its accessibility to experimental analysis was reported in 1953 by Stanley Miller, who was a graduate student working with the prominent astronomer Harold Urey at the time. Miller assembled an apparatus that simulated the presumed conditions of the primeval Earth: (1) a gaseous phase containing reduced sources of carbon (CH_4, methane), nitrogen (NH_3, ammonia), oxygen atoms (H_2O), and hydrogen atoms from any or all of these

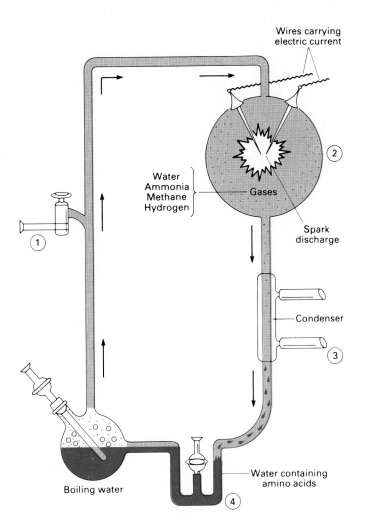

Wires carrying
electric current

Water
Ammonia
Methane
Hydrogen

Gases

②

Spark
discharge

Condenser

③

Water containing
amino acids

Boiling water

④

FIGURE 18-2
Diagram of the apparatus used by
Stanley Miller in experiments on abiotic
synthesis of organic compounds. Water
is added to the flask and the entire
apparatus is evacuated of air. Then
ammonia, methane, and hydrogen
gases are introduced through a valve
(1), and these gases circulate clockwise in a stream of steam produced
when water in the flask is heated
to boiling. The steam and gases
enter the sparking chamber (2), and
are subjected to spark discharges.
As the molecules move through the
vicinity of a water-cooled condenser
(3), condensations occur. Non-
gaseous substances accumulate
in the trap (4), while gaseous substances continue to circulate through
the apparatus and past the spark,
until the experiment is concluded.
Molecules collected from the trap
(4), or circulating gases removed
through the input valve (1), can be
analyzed during the experiment
and at its conclusion.

precursors as well as from hydrogen gas (H_2); (2) electrical energy
provided by spark discharge from electrodes wired to an electrical
current; (3) an ambient temperature between 0°C and 100°C in the
simulated atmosphere and hydrosphere; and (4) sterile conditions by
which any modern life forms were eliminated from the abiotic system
(Fig. 18.2).

The results of a week-long experimental run proved significant in
several respects. A small number of simple precursors accounted for a
large number of major organic products, including molecules characteristic of living cells today, and amino acids were produced at a relatively
constant rate throughout the experiments (Table 18.1). These amino
acids were shown to be produced in simple condensation reactions
involving hydrogen cyanide (HCN), aldehydes (R-CHO), and ammonia
in aqueous solution. A probable and well-known reaction sequence
would be

(a) $RCHO + HCN + NH_3 \rightleftharpoons \underset{\underset{NH_2}{|}}{RCH}-CN + H_2O$

(b) $\underset{\underset{NH_2}{|}}{RCH}-CN + 2\,H_2O \longrightarrow \underset{\underset{NH_2}{|}}{RCH}-COOH + NH_3$

TABLE 18-1
Biologically Significant Organic Molecules Produced in Two of the Experiments on Abiotic Synthesis Conducted by Stanley Miller and Reported in 1953.

Organic compound		Yield (micromoles)	
Name	Formula	Expt. 1	Expt. 3
Glycine	$H_2N—CH_2—COOH$	630	800
Alanine	$H_2N—CH(CH_3)—COOH$	340	90
Aspartic acid	$H_2N—CH(CH_2COOH)—COOH$	4	2
Glutamic acid	$H_2N—CH(C_2H_4COOH)—COOH$	6	5
β-alanine	$H_2N—CH_2—CH_2—COOH$	150	40
α-aminobutyric acid	$H_2N—CH(C_2H_5)—COOH$	50	10
α-aminoisobutyric acid	$H_2N—C(CH_3)_2—COOH$	1	0
Sarcosine	$HN(CH_3)—CH_2—COOH$	50	860
N-methylalanine	$HN(CH_3)—CH(CH_3)—COOH$	10	125
Formic acid	$H—COOH$	2330	1490
Acetic acid	$CH_3—COOH$	152	135
Propionic acid	$C_2H_5—COOH$	126	19
Glycolic acid	$HO—CH_2—COOH$	560	280
Lactic acid	$HO—CH(CH_3)—COOH$	310	43
α-hydroxybutyric acid	$HO—CH(C_2H_5)—COOH$	50	10
Succinic acid	$HOOC—CH_2—CH_2—COOH$	38	0
Iminodiacetic acid	$HOOC—CH_2—NH—CH_2—COOH$	55	3
Iminoacetic–propionic acid	$HOOC—CH_2—NH—C_2H_4—COOH$	15	0
Urea	$H_2N—CO—NH_2$	20	0
N-methylurea	$H_2N—CO—NH—CH_3$	15	0
Total yield of compounds listed*		15%	3%

* Percent yield based on the amount of carbon placed in the apparatus as methane.

Only a tiny amount of organic compounds formed in the control apparatus, which lacked an energy source, thus verifying that abiotic synthesis had indeed occurred in the experimental system and could, by analogy, have occurred on the primeval Earth.

For more than thirty years since Miller's pioneering studies, a large body of experimental evidence has been accumulated by many investigators, particularly by Cyril Ponnamperuma, Leslie Orgel, Sidney Fox, and others, to show that virtually all the kinds of biologically important organic molecules can be synthesized abiotically. Among these molecules are an assortment of proteins, nucleic acids, and energy-storing compounds such as ATP. These molecules would have accumulated in the primeval seas, and they would have increased in diversity and complexity as a result of condensation and polymerization reactions.

Despite general agreement on the synthesis and accumulation of organic molecules on the primeval Earth, there is little consensus on the manner in which these molecules were organized into interacting systems. The prevailing view is that interacting molecules must have been sequestered within structures that were separated by boundaries from one another and from the thermodynamic disorder in the surrounding waters. How else can we understand the orderly progress toward increasing interactions between molecules leading to longer

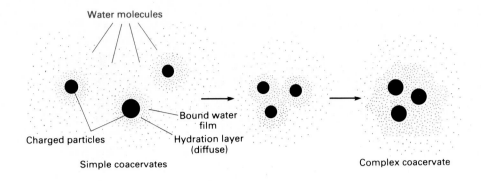

Water molecules

Charged particles

Bound water film

Hydration layer (diffuse)

Simple coacervates

Complex coacervate

FIGURE 18-3
Coacervation. Some of the electrically charged dipolar water molecules (color) become tightly bound to an electrically charged molecule or particle (gray) to become simple coacervate droplets, whereas water molecules at some distance away remain part of a free (unbound) water phase. Attractions between the electrically charged systems may lead to the fusion of two or more simple coacervates, which are then contained in a complex coacervate within a common film of bound water molecules. Such coacervates are separated from the external surroundings by the bound water film, which acts as a boundary.

survival time, increase in mass, and the ultimate development of life forms from pre-life systems?

18.3
Protobiont Models

Three major models of self-contained systems enclosed within a selectively permeable boundary have been proposed: the *coacervate model* of Alexander Oparin, the *proteinoid microsphere model* of Sidney Fox, and the *lipid bilayer model* proposed by Richard Goldacre. Each of these models of the **protobiont**, or pre-life form, represents a system that shows coordination of its activities in both space and time and can carry out these activities in the orderly and organized fashion typical of the true life forms, or eubionts, that eventually arose in the primeval seas. It is a basic premise of evolutionary phenomena that ancestral forms share certain features with their descendants, whether little or greatly modified.

A **coacervate** is a water droplet that forms spontaneously when polar water molecules are oriented around an electrically charged molecule or particle (Fig. 18.3). The film of bound water acts as a boundary between the interior of the coacervate and the disordered surroundings. Many different kinds of simple coacervates may form in the same medium, each perhaps containing different molecules, and such simple coacervates can merge to form complex coacervates with diverse molecular combinations. In addition to their having sequestered contents of high potential diversity, coacervates serve to concentrate molecules that may occur in dilute solution or suspension in the "organic soup" around them. For example, in a dilute solution of 1 part gelatin in 100,000 parts water (0.001%) more than 95% of the protein molecules may be drawn into the droplets formed by spontaneous coacervation.

When water-free mixtures of amino acids are heated at 160°C to 210°C, they polymerize into proteinlike molecules, or *proteinoids*, if the reactants are adsorbed to clay or another suitable surface. The adsorbed molecules penetrate into the layers of water that alternate with thin layers of silicates or other inorganic materials in clays; thus they may increase locally into concentrations that permit polymerizations to occur. Fox has reported the formation of polymers as large as 20,000 in molecular weight under anhydrous conditions at high temperatures.

Once formed, these proteinoids are unstable at high temperatures, and they persist only if cooled quickly. When proteinoids are cooled in water to 0°C to 25°C, spherical particles called microspheres precipitate out of solution (Fig. 18.4). These **proteinoid microspheres**, usually about 1 or 2 μm in diameter, show osmotic properties, weak catalytic activities, and budding or fragmentation superficially resembling cell division.

Various kinds of lipid molecules may segregate in aqueous media to form bilayers, which may form a continuous enclosure around a central space. These *lipid bilayers* resemble cellular membranes in various ways, including selective permeability properties and interactions with organic molecules next to or within the bounded vesicle or between the two lipid layers. Abiotically synthesized phospholipids may permit molecules to move selectively through the bilayer thickness and, depending on the substances moving in and out of an enclosed vesicle, biochemical reactions may take place and new compounds may be produced.

All three protobiont models provide the physical and chemical basis of a selectively permeable boundary, the sequestering of internal contents from external disorder, and the exchange of both energy and matter between the protobiont and its environment. Any of these forms would thus fulfill the requirement for an *open system* (perhaps existing in different *steady states*) which now characterizes life forms and permits repair and maintenance of parts and molecules, as well as reproduction and an increase in mass in living organisms. All of the models suffer from one or more limitations as the putative protobiont, however, and we cannot choose among these alternatives at the present time.

Coacervates are highly diverse systems, they can increase in mass, and they can incorporate more complex interactions into their repertory. For example, Oparin showed that coacervates containing the enzyme starch phosphorylase could synthesize and store starch if glucose 1-phosphate was provided in the medium. If the enzyme amylase was

FIGURE 18-4
When a hot solution of proteinlike polymers called proteinoids is cooled in water to 0°C–25°C, spherical structures called microspheres form very quickly. Because these spherical droplets contain proteinoids, they are referred to as proteinoid microspheres. ×900. (From Fox, S. W., ed., 1965, *The Origins of Prebiological Systems*, p. 347. New York: Academic Press.)

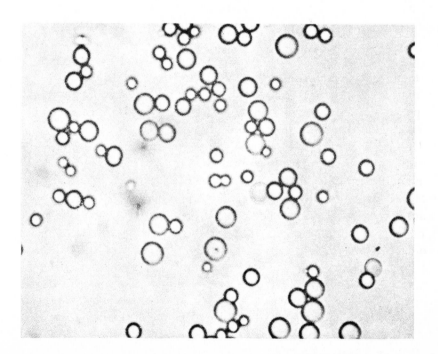

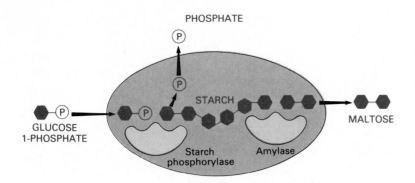

FIGURE 18-5
In experiments with coacervate droplet systems, A. Oparin showed that, under appropriate conditions, such systems might increase in mass and become biochemically more complex. Coacervates containing the enzyme starch phosphorylase can synthesize and store starch if glucose 1-phosphate is provided as a substrate. If the enzyme amylase is added, too, the starch is hydrolyzed by the amylase to produce maltose, which is released into the surrounding medium. The coacervate in this instance could thus increase in mass (due to storage of starch) or increase in biochemical complexity (a one-step reaction expands to a two-step reaction).

added to the coacervate, starch was hydrolyzed and maltose was released into the medium (Fig. 18.5). Such an exchange of energy and matter is characteristic of an open system, and a growing coacervate may fragment into smaller droplets in a crude form of reproduction. One major problem with coacervates, however, is their highly transient nature. Although some droplets may persist for several years under optimal conditions of pH, coacervates form and disintegrate rapidly in media of an inappropriate pH.

Proteinoid microspheres are also transient structures under anhydrous conditions, and high temperatures are essential for their formation. The major locations suitable for their formation and persistence are volcanic regions, where thermal springs occur and mud flats could provide clays for adsorption. Compared to coacervates or to lipid-bilayer vesicles, however, proteinoid microspheres are a relatively homogeneous population. Considering the exceedingly small probability that some particular collection of molecules contained within a bounded system would be just the right mixture to progress toward the living state under the best of conditions, the chances would be significantly lower in the case of a proteinoid microsphere. On the basis of its closer resemblance to living cells, along with diversity and biochemical activities, the lipid bilayer model may seem the most attractive possibility.

Regardless of the specific mode of its formation, a protobiont is a unique experiment in a nonliving world. Even if an appropriate protobiont did happen to include interacting molecules, its chances of evolving into a life form would depend on its existing long enough to incorporate all the necessary ingredients to sustain itself and, eventually, to reproduce others more or less like itself. Any protobiont that could retain more free energy would have a better chance to renew its components, to utilize the free energy in growth, and to adjust to changing internal and external conditions. Such a flexible, self-renewing protobiont would persist for a relatively longer time, perhaps increasing in numbers by passive fragmentation events, and would thereby be in existence and available for increases in the rate and efficiency of its chemical activities and for enhanced coordination of its reactions. Such a persisting and relatively successful protobiont population would be more likely to incorporate the final component needed to cross the border between nonlife and life; this final component is a self-replicating genetic program that can be transmitted to descendants and thereby perpetuate (and increase) the population.

18.4
Requirements for Life Forms _____

Cellular life as we know it has three basic components: (1) a boundary separating the living system from its environment, (2) metabolism consisting of coordinated sets of chemical reactions catalyzed by enzymes, and (3) a set of genes that makes possible information storage and flow and is capable of self-replication and transmission to descendants like itself. In our discussion of prebiotic evolution, we have taken the posture that the protobionts were bounded metabolizing systems lacking a genetic component. With the incorporation of a genetic system, protobionts would have evolved into **eubionts**, or true life forms. We really don't know the sequence of events that led to life, nor do we have workable experimental means by which to test any of the plausible hypotheses at the present time.

However life originated in the ancient past, eubionts must have been able to evolve via genetic modifications that could be transmitted to their descendants. By mutations of the few existing genes in the first life forms, and by new genes arising in enlarging genomes, early life forms must have enhanced their metabolism by including enzymes and energy-transferring molecules by which energy-releasing and energy-requiring reactions could be coupled. Modern cells engage in energy transfer through three principal pathways: the ATP–ADP cycle, oxidation–reductions, and electron transport via porphyrin-containing molecules such as cytochromes and chlorophyll, as we discussed in Chapter 3. From experiments in abiotic synthesis we have found that ATP and porphyrins are readily formed, so these substances are the prime candidates for the energy-transfer components of early life as well as of life today (Fig. 18.6).

Organic reactions are very sluggish in the absence of catalysts, mainly because of the stability of covalent bonding. Early life forms could easily have utilized inorganic catalysts that were plentiful in primeval environments, including H^+ and metallic ions such as Fe^{2+}, Mg^{2+}, Zn^{2+}, Mn^{2+}, and others. These catalysts are relatively nonspecific, however, compared with modern enzymes that contain these same metallic components. When Fe^{2+} coordinates with a porphyrin, the resulting heme molecule is 1000 times more efficient in catalyzing the breakdown of hydrogen peroxide than Fe^{2+} alone. With the further addition of protein to the heme group, the enzyme catalase sponsors H_2O_2 breakdown 10 million times faster than heme alone. Whereas Fe^{2+} and Fe^{2+}-porphyrins could easily have been utilized in primeval metabolism, any eubionts with a gene that specified a protein that would bind to heme and function as an efficient and selective catalyst would have enjoyed a selective advantage and thus would have been more likely to survive and to transmit its inherited trait to subsequent generations. Through *descent with modification*, new and more efficient and complex forms arise and become predominant in populations. By **natural selection**, the inherently better fit organisms are more likely to survive to reproductive age and thus to leave more descendants as well adapted as themselves to particular environments (Fig. 18.7).

Adaptive changes result from chance mutations and other random genetic alterations. Those inherited changes of greater adaptive value

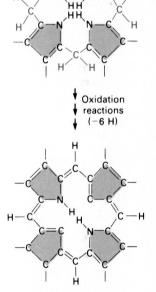

FIGURE 18-6
Experiments in abiotic synthesis have shown that multistep reactions produce (a) adenine from hydrogen cyanide and ribose from formaldehyde and that ATP is formed when a base, a sugar, and three phosphates combine into a single molecule. (b) Porphyrins are produced abiotically from formaldehyde and pyrrole precursors. Both ATP and porphyrins could well have served as energy-transferring components in primeval life forms, just as they do in modern life forms.

are likely to be transmitted in subsequent generations, slowly leading to new kinds of organisms and new kinds of biological capacities during evolution. Forms that are more poorly adapted to particular environments or less flexible under changing conditions are at a disadvantage; they may go extinct or become reduced in numbers and distribution. We would expect new functions to be incorporated into the existing framework of coordinated and interacting reactions and programs, by which these are enhanced but not disrupted. As life increased in its complexity, therefore, new capacities were included in existing systems. We therefore seek homologies amidst biological diversity in order to trace the evolutionary development of modern life from its ancestral

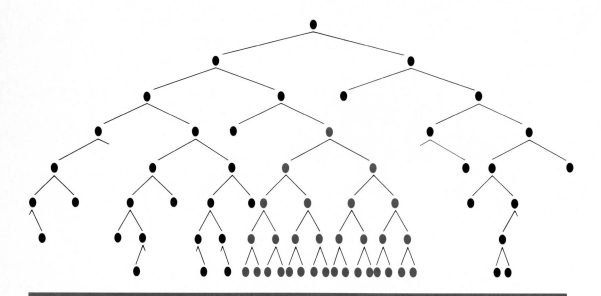

FIGURE 18-7
By natural selection, inherently better fit individuals (color) are more likely to survive to reproductive age and thus leave more descendants than are the less fit individuals (black), which produce fewer progeny or no progeny at all. Inherited traits that confer selective advantages on the better fit members of a population are thus transmitted to descendant generations, which are as well adapted as were their parents to particular life situations. The accumulation of adaptive traits in populations leads to evolutionary changes that may result in new biological capacities or lead to new kinds of organisms.

forms and to analyze particular pathways of evolutionary change over the vast expanse of time since life originated on Earth.

Cellular Evolution

What we see in the modern world are the end products, to date, of evolutionary pathways that produced an enormous variety of life forms from ancient primeval ancestors. Organisms differ in their sources of carbon and energy for metabolism, in their relative tolerance of or need for molecular oxygen, in their reproduction by sexual or asexual means, and in their cellular organization, among many other features. What were the probable evolutionary sequences by which primeval life diversified to produce the myriad life forms of today? In order to reconstruct some of these sequences, we compare fossil and living forms, lifestyles of more ancient and more recent organisms, and the geological record of ancient rock formations and those laid down later in the history of Earth. From many such comparative studies, all premised on the genetic continuity between past and present life, we glean at least the highlights of the dynamic panorama of evolutionary history.

18.5
Origin of the Information System

All cellular life today stores its genetic information in the form of a triplet code in linear or circular DNA molecules. The code itself is essentially universal, although some differences in codon meaning occur in mitochondrial genes (see Fig. 13.20). These observations indicate the common ancestry of all life forms, because it is virtually impossible for all these systems to have arisen independently and to have assumed identical features by chance alone. It has been suggested, however, that an RNA information-storage system may have existed earlier and have

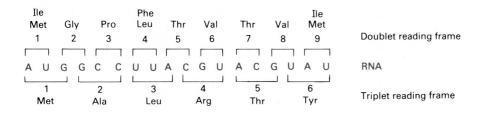

Doublet reading frame

RNA

Triplet reading frame

FIGURE 18-8
If a primeval doublet code had expanded to a triplet code during evolution, the entire reading frame would have become distorted and every protein encoded in the primeval genome would have changed. It is highly unlikely that such a profound modification would have been adaptive. Hence it is highly unlikely that the primeval genetic code evolved from a doublet to a triplet reading frame.

been replaced later by genic DNA. We know that RNA can function effectively as the material of many viral genomes, but whether RNA was used and later replaced in cellular organisms is entirely speculative.

The origin of the genetic code is hidden in the ancient past, but we can make some educated guesses about its beginnings by inspection of the existing code and by our knowledge of the reading frame for translation into polypeptides. As we discussed in Section 13.5, the codons that specify the same amino acid share an initial doublet and differ only in the 3' base. In half of the sixteen codon groupings, all four members of the codon family specify the same amino acid (Leu, Val, Ser, Pro, Thr, Ala, Arg, and Gly). By virtue of the anticodon wobble base in the 5' position, a single tRNA may recognize and interact with two related codons (see Fig. 13.18). Could the code have been based on doublets at first and then been altered to a triplet code later?

If the original code had been doublet and specified sixteen (4^2) amino acids, it may have served well enough for the construction of primeval proteins of greater simplicity. Once a doublet code was established, however, its expansion to a triplet code would have distorted the reading frame and thereby changed every protein encoded in a primeval genome (Fig. 18.8). It is unlikely that such a traumatic and pervasive change would have been tolerated—much less established as an adaptive modification. Similarly, we can reject the notion that a four-letter primeval code was later abbreviated to a triplet code. Such a change would also have destroyed the established reading frames of primeval genes.

The existence of common initial doublets in codons and of wobble in the tRNA anticodons suggests instead that the original triplet code may have utilized only the first two bases to specify an amino acid and that the third base may have been irrelevant in coding but important for other reasons. Perhaps steric requirements for binding between the tRNA anticodon and the messenger (or the gene directly?) mandated pairings of base triplets. If this were the case, the coding dictionary could be expanded from its original number of amino acids to the present twenty without disruption of the reading frame. In fact, from their presence and frequencies in ancient and modern proteins, there is reason to believe that certain of the amino acids (Gly, Ser, Asp, and others) were present in earlier codes and that other amino acids (Met, Trp) were added later.

Why are only twenty amino acids included in the genetic code when many others are not? According to the "frozen accident" hypothesis, the original allocation of codons was a matter of chance. As life forms became more complex, natural selection would have favored maintenance of the present code if it produced the fewest detrimental or lethal effects. Too much tampering with the code might cause disturbances in structure and metabolism that depend on specific proteins. Some modifications were tolerated, but large-scale changes were not adaptive.

The alternative "stereochemical" hypothesis states that the code is the outcome of specific chemical relationships between nucleic acid codons and amino acids. We know of no particular reasons, however, for specific codons to be associated with specific amino acids. In fact, all the available evidence shows that the interactions involve only tRNA and mRNA, regardless of the aminoacyl groups carried by the tRNA molecules (see Fig. 13.37). In experiments with microspheres that contained both proteins and nucleic acids, however, Fox reported that preferential absorption of amino acids was correlated with the nature of the nucleic acid polymer in the microspheres. Poly(A) favored the absorption of lysine into the microspheres, poly(U) favored phenylalanine, poly(C) favored proline, and poly(G) favored glycine. These correlations are meaningful because AAA is the codon for lysine, UUU for phenylalanine, CCC for proline, and GGG for glycine.

Our awareness of these features gives us little in-depth knowledge, however, because we can say virtually nothing about the development of a genetic system in which nucleic acids and proteins act interdependently in replication, transcription, and translation. The ribosome alone requires the precise activity of more than 80 different genes that specify ribosomal proteins and RNAs. Because of this impasse, various suggestions have been made for a primeval protein-synthesizing system in which tRNAs interacted directly with a nucleic acid template, in the absence of ribosomes. All these and other speculations are of some intellectual interest, but they remain mere suggestions until we can devise appropriate experimental tests. At present, we have many speculations and very few experimental data.

18.6
The Evolution of Metabolic Diversity

From the fossil record, the oldest cells yet discovered date back about 3.5 billion years. These bacterialike organisms must have been **anaerobic**. The geological record of iron-containing sediments indicates the existence of relatively reduced iron compounds until about 1.8 billion years ago and of relatively oxidized sediments by 1.5 billion years ago. The atmosphere was therefore nonoxidizing when life originated, and it continued to be nonoxidizing for about 2 billion years afterward. The introduction of molecular oxygen into the atmosphere is presumed to have begun after the appearance of photosynthetic blue-green algae, slowly at first and perhaps locally, and the present oxygen level of nearly 21% was not established until about 1 to 1.5 billion years ago (Fig. 18.9).

Primeval life must have been **heterotrophic** as well as anaerobic, gaining its energy and carbon from organic molecules for growth, repair, and reproduction. Modern heterotrophs are represented by animals, fungi, many protists, and most bacteria. Various bacterial groups are chemotrophic or autotrophic, and green plants, algae, many protists, and some bacteria are photosynthetic autotrophs. **Chemo-**

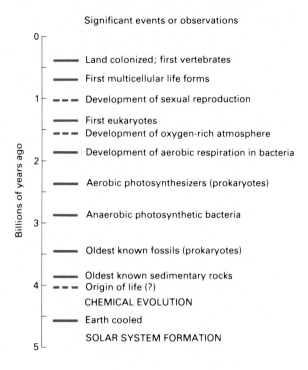

Significant events or observations

- Land colonized; first vertebrates
- First multicellular life forms
- Development of sexual reproduction
- First eukaryotes
- Development of oxygen-rich atmosphere
- Development of aerobic respiration in bacteria
- Aerobic photosynthesizers (prokaryotes)
- Anaerobic photosynthetic bacteria
- Oldest known fossils (prokaryotes)
- Oldest known sedimentary rocks
- Origin of life (?)
- CHEMICAL EVOLUTION
- Earth cooled
- SOLAR SYSTEM FORMATION

(y-axis: Billions of years ago, 0 to 5)

FIGURE 18-9
Selected highlights in the evolutionary history of Earth over the past 5 billion years, as interpreted from astrophysical, geological, biological, and fossil data. Certain events (dashed lines) clearly occurred, but the precise time of their occurrence is somewhat uncertain. For example, we don't yet know exactly when life originated (4.6 to 3.5 billion years ago), when the atmosphere became oxygen-rich (1.8 to 0.7 billion years ago), or when sexual reproduction arose in eukaryotes (1.2 to 0.7 billion years ago).

trophs derive energy by the oxidation of inorganic substances and carbon from organic molecules, whereas **autotrophs** obtain both energy and carbon from inorganic sources. Various subgroups, depending on the particular sources utilized, are recognized within these major groupings.

We might suppose that chemotrophs or autotrophs were the original primeval life forms, because their nutritional needs are simple compared with those of heterotrophs. But they are instead metabolically (hence genetically) complex with regard to the biochemical pathways required to make all their organic materials from simple precursors. Heterotrophy would have been the more likely nutritional mode for primeval life, because heterotrophs could absorb organic molecules directly from their environment and might need only simple biochemical processing to utilize these compounds in structure, function, and regulation of primeval systems. In modern life forms, each step in a biosynthetic or catabolizing sequence is governed by a specific enzyme, whose polypeptide chains are encoded in the genome. Complex biochemistry would thus require large numbers of genes, which primeval life must have lacked for a long period of evolutionary time.

How would primeval heterotrophic life have evolved toward greater complexity and to alternative nutritional modes? In 1945, Norman Horowitz proposed the idea of "*evolution backwards.*" His reasoning was based on the growing body of biochemical genetic evidence of genes specifying enzymes and of enzymes governing individual reaction steps in a sequence or cycle. In essence, Horowitz proposed that eubionts with simple nutritional needs and relatively few genes would have available in the "organic soup" a large number of molecules they could utilize directly and process in limited fashion. As these materials became scarce because life multiplied and used the resources produced so slowly by abiotic syntheses, any organism with the genetic capacity to make the necessary compounds from simpler precursors would have been at a selective advantage in depleted environments. If compound G was needed but unavailable, a mutant that could make G from its precursor F would survive and reproduce to leave descendants with the same enhanced metabolic capacity. Should F grow scarce, chance mutation allowing compound E to be processed to F and then G would become adaptive. By the expansion of such a sequence, with each step catalyzed by an enzyme under genetic control, more complex metabolism might have evolved.

$$
\begin{array}{ccccccc}
\text{gene:} & f & e & d & c & b & a \\
& \downarrow & \downarrow & \downarrow & \downarrow & \downarrow & \downarrow \\
\text{enzyme:} & f & e & d & c & b & a \\
\text{substrate:} & G \leftarrow F & \leftarrow E & \leftarrow D & \leftarrow C & \leftarrow B & \leftarrow A
\end{array}
$$

New metabolic pathways involving coupled reactions and common intermediates in energy transfer may have evolved in this way, leading to these basic features in modern organisms (see Sections 3.4 to 3.6). Intersecting biochemical pathways that utilized reaction products made internally, as well as substrates absorbed from the external environment, would have expanded the capacities of evolving life in various ways depending on the relationships and interactions between the organisms and their environments, just as we see in life forms today (Fig. 18.10).

Early life forms must have experienced genetic changes by which their genomes were enlarged from relatively few genes to the thousands that exist today in even the simplest cellular life. (We will return to this topic in Section 18.11.) Genome expansion clearly did not continue indefinitely, however, because a mammalian genome may include only about five to ten times as many genes as the genome of a bacterium like *E. coli* (see Section 12.11). In the great majority of cases that have been analyzed by molecular methods, as well as by other methods, existing genes are modified and produce modified products. Evolution has occurred largely via "tinkering" with existing systems rather than by new genetic systems arising, as suggested by François Jacob in his thoughtful publications. Modifications in the regulation of gene expression during development, as well as in the protein products themselves, must surely underlie much of the organismic diversity in the world

FIGURE 18-10
Intersecting biochemical pathways involving relatively few intermediate metabolites are a common feature in modern life forms. Reaction products made in these pathways, such as pyruvate, may be routed to different processing systems depending on internal and external conditions. Precursors need not be supplied only from the external environment in order to keep metabolism going.

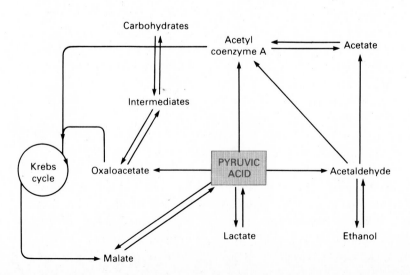

today. We will return to this theme at the end of the chapter, but we can illustrate some of these evolutionary premises in the development of two of the most important processes for life as we know it: oxygen-producing photosynthesis and oxygen-utilizing respiration.

18.7
The Evolution of Photosynthesis and Aerobic Respiration

During its evolution from anaerobic heterotrophy, primeval life developed modified electron transport pathways that were of the utmost significance for the subsequent appearance of eukaryotic organisms. From primitive beginnings, electron transport systems were modified in three particularly important respects: (1) the incorporation of a second photosystem by which water served as an electron donor for photosynthesis, (2) the release of large amounts of molecular oxygen into the air and waters when H_2O molecules were processed to release their electrons in expanded photosynthetic activity, and (3) the development of a respiratory electron transport pathway in which molecular oxygen served as the final electron acceptor.

Modern photosynthesis provides an unending food supply for all of life via green cells, and it continuously replenishes atmospheric oxygen for aerobic life, which now predominates on Earth. By aerobic respiration, large amounts of energy become available from a smaller food requirement in aerobes than in anaerobes, and sufficient energy is conserved in mitochondrial reactions and stored in ATP to subsidize the large organisms and vigorous activity that characterize eukaryotic life.

Richard Dickerson and others have proposed a highly plausible sequence of evolutionary events whereby changes in bacterial metabolism led from anaerobic heterotrophs to anaerobic photosynthetic autotrophs, and from these autotrophs to aerobically respiring bacterial groups that retained or lost their photosynthetic abilities in different lineages. The scenario is based on our knowledge of bacterial metabolism and on the analysis of cytochrome c and other components of photosynthetic and respiratory electron transport chains.

As we discussed earlier, primeval organisms were probably anaerobic heterotrophic scavengers of organic compounds, and free energy was extracted during fermentation reactions. Simple fermentations still characterize the catabolism of anaerobic bacteria such as *Clostridium*, and the ancient processes of glycolysis remain as hereditary vestiges of past ancestry in virtually all eukaryotic life, including our own species. Similar indications of past ancestry and evolutionary relationships are present in the electron transport systems, including cytochrome c, of bacteria and eukaryotes (Fig. 18.11).

Anaerobic photosynthesizers like the green and purple sulfur bacteria lack an aerobic respiratory pathway, but they have an electron transport chain by which electrons from H_2S or simple organic compounds are passed along to NAD^+ in the presence of light-activated bacteriochlorophyll, a porphyrin-based pigment. Heme and porphyrin compounds must have been present in early times, judging from the relative ease of their formation under abiotic conditions. During electron flow from the donor compounds to bacteriochlorophyll, ATP is synthe-

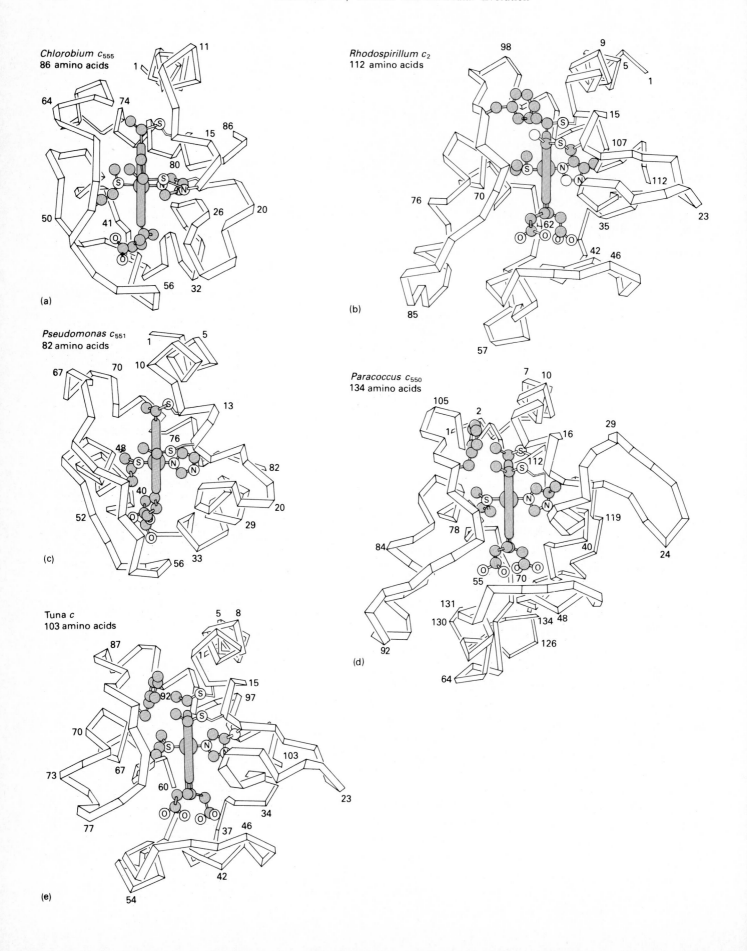

Chlorobium c$_{555}$
86 amino acids

(a)

Rhodospirillum c$_2$
112 amino acids

(b)

Pseudomonas c$_{551}$
82 amino acids

(c)

Paracoccus c$_{550}$
134 amino acids

(d)

Tuna c
103 amino acids

(e)

◄ FIGURE 18-11
Although varying considerably in the numbers of amino acids and their sequence, cytochrome c shows remarkably similar tertiary structure and heme-binding region in a spectrum of bacterial and eukaryotic species. Cytochrome c participates in (a) photosynthetic electron transport in Chlorobium, an anaerobic, photosynthetic green sulfur bacterium; (b) photosynthetic and respiratory electron transport in Rhodospirillum, a purple nonsulfur bacterium; (c) respiratory electron transport in Pseudomonas and (d) Paracoccus, both of which are nonphotosynthetic aerobic bacteria; and (e) mitochondrial electron transport in tuna and other eukaryotes. These homologies indicate the occurrence of evolutionary modifications in the cytochrome c gene and its polypeptide product during the development of aerobic photosynthetic and respiratory activities in prokaryotes and eukaryotes, which evolved from ancient anaerobic ancestry. (Data based on studies by R. E. Dickerson.)

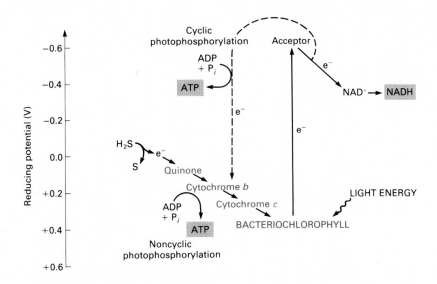

FIGURE 18-12
Bacterial photosynthesis involves photosystem I but not photosystem II (see Fig. 10.18). In the green and purple sulfur bacteria, electrons from H₂S are passed down an electron transport chain to light-activated bacteriochlorophyll and ultimately are accepted by NAD⁺ to produce NADH. The synthesis of ATP in noncyclic photophosphorylation is coupled to electron transport from H₂S to bacteriochlorophyll, and ATP synthesis in cyclic photophosphorylation is coupled to the transport of electrons passed back to the cytochromes in the chain. Anaerobic photosynthesizers are more efficient in their production of ATP and NADH than are the anaerobic nonphotosynthesizers, which rely principally on relatively inefficient fermentative reactions to extract and conserve fuel energy.

sized in a noncyclic photophosphorylation sequence. By cyclic photophosphorylation, energized electrons also can be passed back to the cytochromes and on to bacteriochlorophyll, and some of the free-energy difference is conserved in ATP synthesis (Fig. 18.12). These anaerobes have no C₃ cycle of CO₂ fixation, but they have an advantage over fermentative bacteria in being able to synthesize ATP and reduce NAD⁺ in the more efficient photosynthetic pathway.

The purple nonsulfur bacteria have both a photosynthetic and a respiratory capacity, and they utilize the same chain of electron carriers in both processes (Fig. 18.13). ATP can be synthesized by photophosphorylation during electron flow in the light, and by oxidative phosphorylation in reactions coupled to the transport of electrons to the cytochrome oxidase complex by which O₂ is reduced to H₂O. If the bacteriochlorophyll loop were to be deleted or suppressed, the respiratory chain would function more or less like the mitochondrial system in eukaryotes or the systems in nonphotosynthetic aerobic bacteria. The cytochromes c in all these systems are homologous, as is revealed in x-ray crystallographic studies of their structures (see Fig. 18.11).

The purple nonsulfur bacteria also possess a C₃ cycle of CO₂ fixation in photosynthetic dark reactions. Thus these organisms may

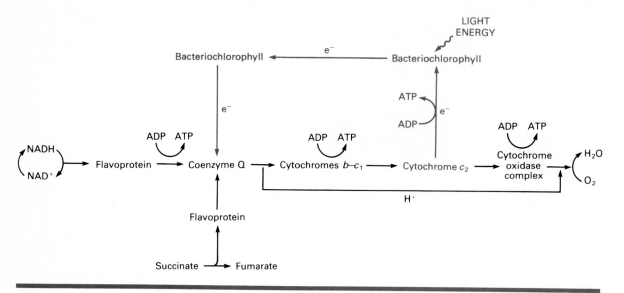

FIGURE 18-13

Rhodopseudomonas, a purple non-sulfur bacterium, uses the same chain of electron carriers in its photosynthetic activities, through the bacteriochlorophyll loop (color), as in its aerobic respiratory activities, in which electrons are passed to molecular oxygen via cytochrome carriers. ATP is synthesized by photophosphorylation during electron flow to bacteriochlorophyll in the light, as well as by oxidative phosphorylation during respiratory electron flow to cytochrome oxidase and oxygen. If the bacteriochlorophyll loop (color) were to be suppressed or deleted, the respiratory pathway would function very much the same as it does in nonphotosynthetic aerobic bacteria and in eukaryotic mitochondria.

have evolved from anaerobic purple sulfur bacteria and may have enhanced their metabolic capacities by the addition of a C_3 cycle in which ATP and NADH produced in the light reactions of photosynthesis were later utilized in carbohydrate synthesis in the dark reactions. The sharing of a common electron transport chain in photosynthesis and respiration further suggests that respiratory activities evolved after photosynthesis appeared and that they utilized parts of the photosynthetic apparatus that were a heritage from their anaerobic photosynthetic ancestors.

Respiration evolved independently in other bacterial lineages as well. The independently evolved respiratory patterns share many features in their reductase activities and differ predominantly in their terminal oxidases. These features suggest that the final steps in electron transport arose later in evolution and that different oxidases passed on electrons to different final electron acceptors, one of which was O_2. All these oxidases, however, received electrons from a cytochrome chain that included cytochrome *c*.

The appearance of aerobic respiration involving O_2 as the final electron acceptor could have occurred only if there were adequate supplies of dissolved oxygen in the waters and of gaseous oxygen in the atmosphere. The transition from an anaerobic to an aerobic environment must have depended largely on the photosynthetic activities of prokaryotic blue-green and grass-green algae, which derive electrons from H_2O and release O_2 as a by-product. This capacity relies on the presence of a second photosystem linked in series to the original photosystem of ancestral photosynthesizing bacteria (Fig. 18.14). Once present, the oxygenic photosynthesizers created an environment in which aerobic metabolism was possible and in which organisms with these efficient aerobic capacities were at a great selective advantage.

From the fossil record it seems that prokaryotic blue-green algal forms existed almost 2.5 billion years ago, but we believe they were preceded by anaerobic bacterial photosynthesizers. Photosynthesis thus evolved early in the history of life on Earth, but modern aerobic respiration must have been evolved much later (Fig. 18.15). The

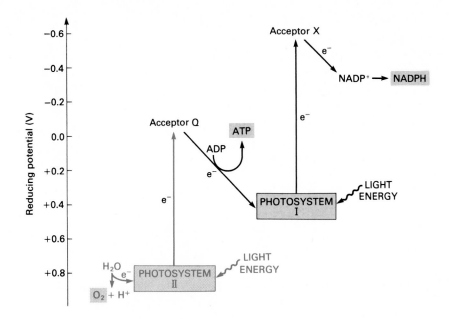

FIGURE 18-14
The evolution from anaerobic prokaryotic ancestry of oxygen-releasing
photosynthetic prokaryotes, such
as the blue-green and grass-green
algae, must have involved a number
of modifications and innovations. One
of these innovations featured the
addition of a photosystem II component linked to the electron transport
chain that funnels electrons to photosystem I. Because photosystem II
could obtain electrons from water,
oxygen was released as a by-product
of the reaction in which water molecules are "split" in the light. (Compare
with the anaerobic photosynthesis
shown in Fig. 18.12.)

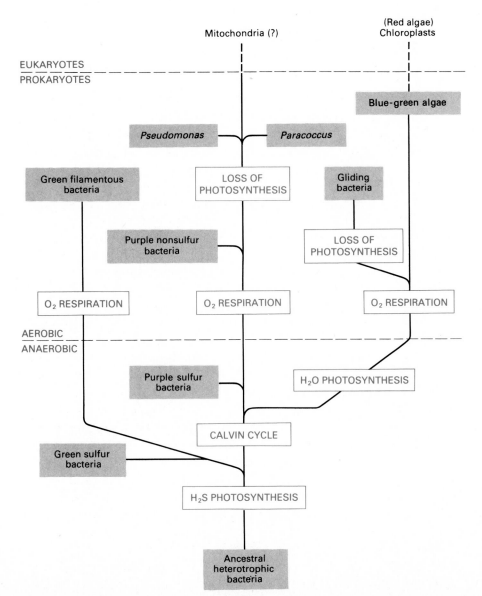

FIGURE 18-15
An evolutionary tree depicting possible pathways by which anaerobic,
heterotrophic ancestral bacteria gave
rise to anaerobic photosynthesizers
(green sulfur bacteria and purple sulfur
bacteria), from which aerobic respiratory lineages later were derived
independently. Photosynthesis was
retained in some lineages but was lost
in others. According to the endosymbiosis theory, modern counterparts or descendants in eukaryotes
are represented by mitochondria
and chloroplasts (see Fig. 9.37).

transition from an anaerobic to an aerobic atmosphere occurred very slowly, and large amounts of oxygen had collected only about 1 billion years ago, by which time eukaryotes had already evolved. The crisis that developed when the atmosphere became oxidizing must have led to the disappearance of, or a sharp diminution in, anaerobic life, which generally finds oxygen lethal. The few kinds of modern anaerobes inhabit those few pockets of the environment where oxygen is absent. whereas aerobic life is predominant and diverse.

With the change to an oxygenic atmosphere, an ozone layer developed in the upper atmosphere. Ozone (O_3) is produced from oxygen in the presence of the longer wavelengths of UV radiation from the sun

FIGURE 18-16
Excision repair is one of a number of known systems by which UV-damaged DNA is repaired. (a) UV absorption causes thymine–thymine dimer formation through C—C bonding (colored lines) in DNA. Dimerization causes the altered region of the DNA strand to bulge out. (b) By the process of excision repair, the thymine–thymine dimer (TT) region is excised and digested by nucleases, the gap is repaired accurately by DNA polymerase I, and ligase seals the strand to make an uninterrupted sugar–phosphate backbone (see Fig. 12.15).

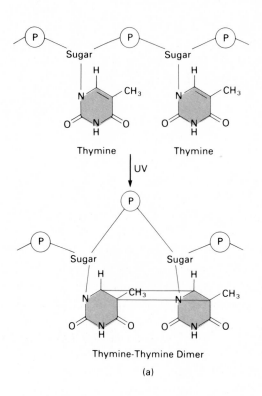

(a)

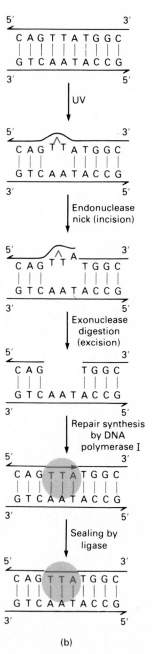

(b)

and from space; it is converted to oxygen under the influence of shorter wavelengths of UV radiation.

$$O_2 \xrightleftharpoons[\text{shorter UV }\lambda]{\text{longer UV }\lambda} O_3$$

The blanket of ozone absorbs much of the germicidal and mutagenic short-wavelength UV radiation, which is damaging to living systems, particularly to terrestrial life. Because of this feature, we are very much concerned today about the possible destruction of the ozone layer as a result of the widespread use of aerosol sprays containing fluorocarbons. Although we are not yet certain about the extent of these destructive effects, we have been cautious in recent years and have turned to the use of nonaerosol pump sprays wherever feasible.

It is interesting to note in this regard that virtually all organisms have more than one system by which UV-damaged DNA can be repaired (Fig. 18.16). It may very well be that these repair systems were adaptive inherited features of ancient life forms that received the full blast of mutagenic and germicidal UV radiation before the atmosphere became oxidizing and an ozone layer developed. These repair systems, or some of them at least, may be hereditary remnants of the ancient past.

18.8
Eukaryotes from Prokaryotes

From the fossil record and from extensive comparative studies of living organisms, we can be fairly certain that prokaryotes are by far the more ancient life forms and that eukaryotes arose about 2 billion years after Earth had been populated by many kinds of prokaryotic life. Because of the similarities or identities in the genetic systems, metabolic pathways, and molecular features of all life forms, we must infer that eukaryotes arose from prokaryotic ancestry rather than by independent pathways in which all these similarities and identities emerged by chance.

Whether we accept the traditional dichotomy of cellular life into prokaryotes and eukaryotes or prefer a phylogenetic tree in which archaebacteria and true bacteria exist independently alongside eukaryotes in a scheme that calls for three major evolutionary lineages (see Fig. 1.17), we can analyze eukaryotic origins by standard comparative methods and by studies of the fossil record. The earliest fossil evidence of eukaryotic cells, based on their relative size and internal organization, comes from different parts of the world in sedimentary rock formations dated to be 1.3 to 1.5 billion years old (Fig. 18.17). The atmosphere was still transitionally oxidizing at that time (it became maximally oxygenic only about 1 billion years ago).

The basic distinction between membrane-compartmented eukaryotic cells and noncompartmented prokaryotic cells, along with other features (see Table 1.3), provides the focus for evolutionary scenarios that have been proposed. These different proposals share some features, including the initial development of a nonrigid *mobile cell surface* in the presumptive prokaryotic ancestors of eukaryotic cells. Unlike existing prokaryotes, almost all of which have a rigid cell wall, these ancient wall-less prokaryotes would have been able to ingest solid foods by an endocytotic process. By similar membrane invaginations, the nucleus

FIGURE 18-17
Scanning electron micrograph of a fossil cell from 800-million-year old deposits in the Grand Canyon of Arizona. This Precambrian cell is believed to be eukaryotic because it is morphologically more complex and much larger (about 100 μm long) than any known prokaryote. (From "The Evolution of the Earliest Cells" by J. W. Schopf. Copyright © 1978 by Scientific American, Inc. All rights reserved.)

FIGURE 18-18
Internalization of membrane infolds has been proposed as an evolutionary phenomenon by which prokaryotic cells with a nonrigid mobile cell surface might have undergone endocytotic invaginations of plasma membrane regions. According to this hypothesis, these infolds were ultimately established in eukaryotes as internal membrane systems independent of the plasma membrane.

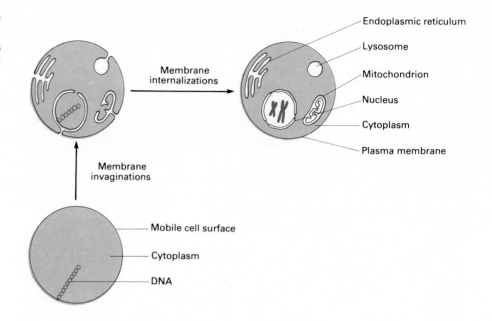

may have evolved as a delimited subcellular compartment, and other membranous systems may also have been established by a general process involving the *internalization of membrane infoldings* (Fig. 18.18). Although originally derived from the plasma membrane, these internalized membrane systems eventually became independent of the plasma membrane and developed in their separate ways under separate controls, as we see today.

Several features of a broad scheme for the origin of eukaryotic cells that was first proposed in the 1970s by Thomas Cavalier-Smith illustrate the way we can incorporate known processes into an evolutionary sequence. Once the mobile cell surface had appeared and ingestion became possible, solid foods could be utilized only after being digested to soluble forms. Modern eukaryotic cells sequester their powerful digestive enzymes primarily within lysosomes, but ancient cells may have packaged such enzymes in vesicles formed at the cell surface in response to the presence there of solid materials (Fig. 18.19). As evolution proceeded via the incorporation of beneficial mutations of positive selective value, lysosomes became internalized compartments—perhaps at first receiving solid materials and wrapping these into vesicles that migrated to the cell interior, and later retaining lysosomes as internal compartments that fused with incoming phagosomes and digested the materials in a secondary lysosome structure (see Fig. 8.3). The development of endoplasmic reticulum and Golgi membranes ultimately provided a system by which lysosome formation proceeded internally and by which membrane recycling involved the plasma membrane in exocytosis and endocytosis.

In prokaryotes the DNA molecule is attached to the plasma membrane, which would not be a safe place in a cell with an active and mobile cell surface. The DNA could be expelled by exocytosis or taken into the interior by endocytosis and perhaps digested there in lysosomes. Mutations leading to the detachment of DNA from the cell membrane might thus be adaptive, but the orderly segregation of replicated DNA

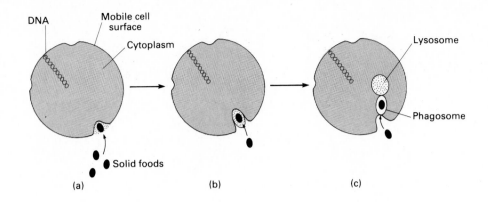

FIGURE 18-19
According to a proposal by T. Cavalier-Smith, the lysosome may have been the earliest membranous organelle to evolve. (a) Ingestion of solid foods would have been possible through the agency of endocytosis, but the powerful digestive enzymes (colored dots) would have been located in endocytotic pockets on the outer surface of the cell where they could not harm (digest) the internal cellular components. (b) Later in evolution, the solid foods might have been packaged along with the digestive enzymes in membranous vesicles formed at the cell surface, and foods would have been digested to soluble products outside the cell but in specialized enclosures. (c) Ultimately the digestive enzymes were packaged separately in internally located lysosomes, and foods in incoming phagosomes were solubilized after the lysosome and phagosome vesicles had fused, as in modern cells.

molecules during cell division would require some rigid substitute attachment system. In accordance with known eukaryotic mechanisms, Cavalier-Smith has postulated the emergence of a system of microtubules by which the DNA molecules are held taut and separate as they move toward opposite ends of the cell (Fig. 18.20). All eukaryotic cells possess microtubule and microfilament assemblies, suggesting the probability that such systems evolved very early in eukaryotic evolution and have been retained in all descendants ever since. In fact, microtubules have been discovered in a few highly specialized bacteria (spirochetes). Whether these organisms evolved a microtubular apparatus independently or have retained such a system from ancient times is uncertain.

The eventual enclosure of the genome and the development of a spindle in eukaryotes led to the major trademark of eukaryotic cells and to more sophisticated chromosome segregation mechanisms (see Section 16.9). These more accurate segregation devices in turn allowed partition of the genome into two or more DNA molecules, which were linear rather than circular, and ultimately to the development of chromosomes

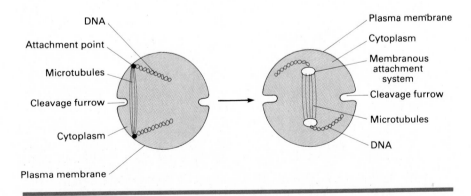

FIGURE 18-20
According to a proposal by T. Cavalier-Smith, detachment of DNA from the active and mobile cell surface would have reduced the probability of genes being expelled by exocytosis or taken in by endocytosis and being digested within the cells. The orderly segregation of replicated DNA would have been aided by the evolution of a rigid microtubular apparatus between the separating attachment points. Later in evolution, this system was dissociated from the mobile plasma membrane. All eukaryotes possess microtubules, which indicates that they appeared early in eukaryotic evolution and were retained in all descendant lineages.

as nucleoprotein structures with differentiated centromeres and other functional regions.

The origins of mitochondria and chloroplasts, each with a functioning genetic machinery, remain controversial. As we discussed in Section 9.15, we are not sure whether modern mitochondria are descendants of ancient aerobic endosymbiotic bacteria or are another one of the compartments formed by internalized membrane infolds. Chloroplast origins from endosymbiotic prokaryotic blue-green and grass-green algae are more certain, because recent molecular comparisons have strengthened the case for such evolutionary episodes (see Section 10.17).

18.9
The Appearance of Multicellular Organisms in Evolution

The familiar plants and animals we see around us are all multicellular—made up of millions, billions, or trillions of cells that may include more than 200 functionally different types. From the fossil record and from comparative studies of living species, it is clear that multicellular plants, animals, and fungi arose independently and at various times from various lineages of unicellular eukaryotic protists (Fig. 18.21). The adaptive advantages of multicellular construction include (1) replenishment of individual cells and a longer life expectancy because of cellular repair and replacement; (2) more reliable modes of reproduction through specialized cells set apart for this purpose; (3) larger body size, which leads to greater internal stability and to a variety of body plans and lifestyles; and (4) cellular differentiation whereby functional efficiency is increased for the organism as a whole.

The earliest evidence of multicellular eukaryotes is about 700 million years old and consists primarily of burrows made by marine animals that are not unlike the burrows made by some modern marine invertebrates. These ancient animals must already have developed a reasonably efficient hydrostatic construction in which fluid-filled body spaces worked against muscles, which allowed the animal to dig the kinds of tunnels found in fossiliferous sea beds. From the unusual Ediacaran region of South Australia and from other places have come fossils of soft-bodied marine organisms, some of which resemble modern groups like the jellyfish and annelid worms, but many of which are quite mysterious and unlike anything we know. The Ediacaran fossils of 680 to 580 million years ago and scraps of exoskeletal remains of larger animals dated to be about 580 million years old represent the only Precambrian animals we know. Beginning about 570 million years ago at the start of the Cambrian period of the Paleozoic era, and continuing for about 70

FIGURE 18-21 ▶

Multicellular plants, fungi, and animals evolved independently from various protist lineages, which in turn had evolved from various prokaryotic ancestors. The five-kingdom system shown here is widely accepted, but it is not the only evolutionary classification that has been proposed (see Fig. 1.17). (From "The Evolution of Multicellular Plants and Animals" by J. W. Valentine. Copyright © 1978 by Scientific American, Inc. All rights reserved.)

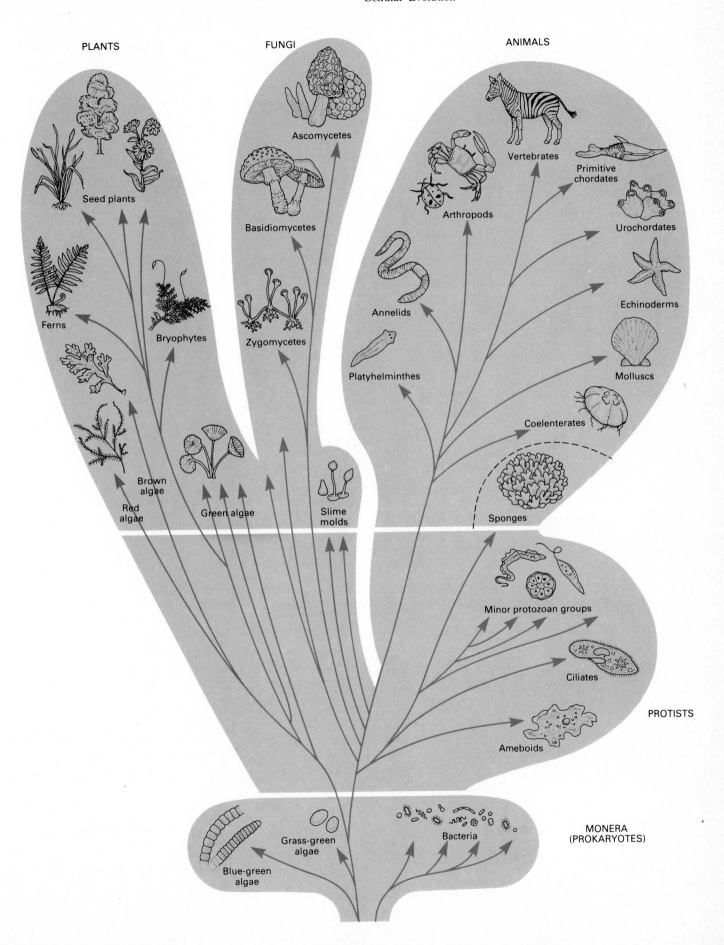

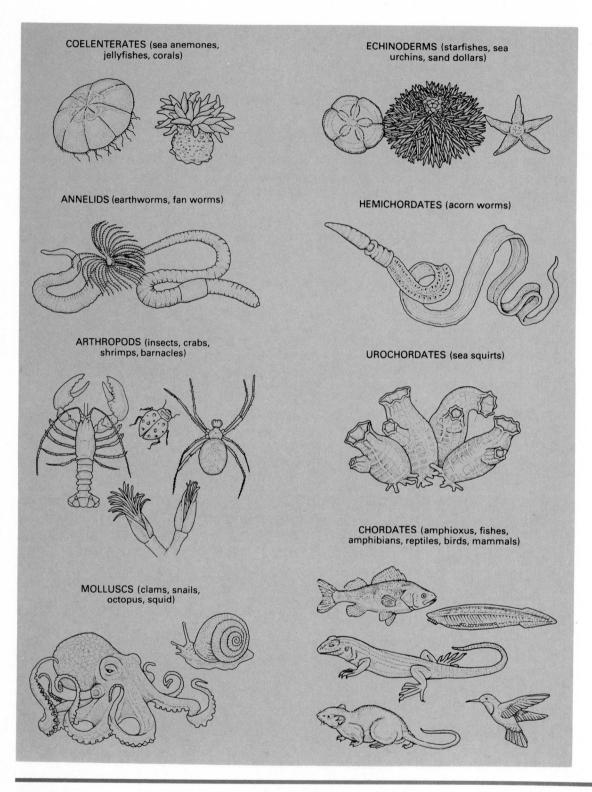

FIGURE 18-22

Eight selected animal phyla and representative members of each phylum are illustrated here. The chordates include the vertebrate classes of fishes, amphibians, reptiles, birds, and mammals. Hemichordates and urochordates are closely related to the chordates, and all these groups trace their ancestry back to the echinoderm group. Arthropods in general are considered more advanced than molluscs, coelenterates, annelids, and some other simple animal phyla (see Fig. 18.21). (From "The Evolution of Multicellular Plants and Animals" by J. W. Valentine. Copyright © 1978 by Scientific American, Inc. All rights reserved.)

million years of Cambrian times, ancestors of all the modern animal phyla evolved (Fig. 18.22).

For the last 500 million years at the dizzying pace that began with the first appearance of multicellularity, many families of metazoan animals appeared and diversified, and the land was colonized first by plants and later by animals. By the end of the Paleozoic era, reptiles were present but birds and mammals had not yet evolved (Table 18.2). Birds and mammals, including the first primates, first appeared in the Mesozoic era. The Cenozoic era in which we now live is characterized by the dominance of mammalian animals and flowering plants, the most highly evolved forms of life in the two kingdoms.

After its origin in the primeval seas, anaerobic heterotrophic life gave rise to photosynthetic forms that evolved in turn to extract electrons from water molecules and filled the air and seas with molecular oxygen. With fully functional aerobic respiration systems, prokaryotic life diversified metabolically but remained unicellular, asexual, and developmentally simple. Perhaps 1.5 billion years ago, eukaryotic forms

TABLE 18-2
Some Highlights in Organismic Evolution in the Last 700 Million Years.

Era*	Period*	Epoch	Evolutionary Events
Cenozoic (63 ± 2)	Quaternary (3 ± 2)	Recent	Appearance of modern humans
		Pleistocene	Appearance of *Homo* species
	Tertiary (63 ± 2)	Pliocene	Appearance of the human family
		Miocene	Anthropoid primates widespread
		Oligocene	First anthropoid primates
		Eocene	Diversification of modern mammals
		Paleocene	Modern mammals; woody plants
Mesozoic (230 + 10)	Cretaceous (135 ± 5)		Last dinosaurs; first flowering plants
	Jurassic (180 ± 5)		Dinosaurs abundant; early mammals; first birds
	Triassic (230 ± 10)		Reptile diversification; first mammals; seed ferns extinct
Paleozoic (580 ± 20)	Permian (280 ± 10)		Widespread extinctions; reptiles abundant
	Carboniferous (345 ± 10)	Pennsylvanian	Bony fishes abundant; insects abundant; land plants abundant; first reptiles
		Mississippian	Amphibians abundant; first insects; forests of tree ferns and their allies
	Devonian (390 ± 10)		Sharks and fishes abundant; first amphibians; many invertebrates; forests
	Silurian (425 ± 10)		First vascular land plants; first land invertebrates
	Ordovician (500 ± 10)		Metazoan diversification; aquatic life only
	Cambrian (580 ± 10)		First fishes; first chordates; abundant invertebrates; aquatic life only
Precambrian (4600)	Ediacaran (680 ± 20)		First metazoans; aquatic life only

* Numbers in parentheses indicate the approximate time that eras and periods began (millions of years ago).

FIGURE 18-23

From their beginnings about 4 billion years ago, life forms on Earth exhibited relatively little morphological diversity until the end of the long Precambrian era and the start of the Paleozoic era about 580 million years ago. The rapid increase in diversity of life forms during the past 680 million years coincides with the appearance of multicellular organisms. Prior to that time, all life forms were unicellular. In conjunction with the earlier evolutionary innovations of eukaryotic cellular organization, sexual reproduction, and other features, multicellularity appears to have stimulated rapid and significant evolutionary change and the exploitation of many different lifestyles and habitats by many kinds of organisms.

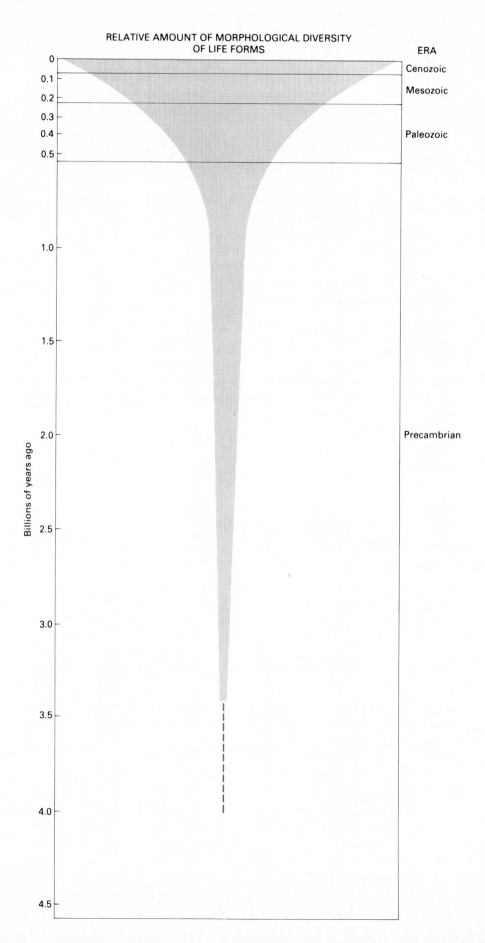

appeared and diversified during hundreds of millions of years into a variety of protists, all of which were unicellular. Some protist lineages became sexually reproducing and diversified genetically to a greater extent than was possible for asexual life. Beginning about 700 million years ago or earlier, different protist lineages gave rise to multicellular organisms in the seas. Once evolved, multicellular forms diversified at a relatively rapid rate. By contrast with the limited variety of life forms produced over billions of years earlier, multicellular organisms of many kinds and degrees of complexity appeared in the past 600 million years, and they have now filled virtually all the habitable environments on Earth (Fig. 18.23).

Evolving Genes and Proteins

As life evolved, the genome expanded and new kinds of functions appeared and became established. Although we cannot explain every evolutionary event in molecular terms, new methods of analyzing and sequencing nucleic acids and proteins have provided vital information on the nature of some kinds of genetic change. In this last part of the book we will discuss and illustrate some of the processes by which we believe genes and proteins have evolved in eukaryotic systems. Some of these processes almost certainly characterize genomic and metabolic evolution in prokaryotes as well.

18.10
Relationships Between Genes and Between Gene Products

It is possible to study evolutionary relationships between closely related species by interbreeding them and evaluating their progeny, if any, but organisms belonging to different kingdoms, phyla, classes, families, and genera cannot be interbred. We have utilized comparative studies of anatomy, physiology, biochemical pathways, and other features, in conjunction with the fossil record, to analyze these more distant relationships. Today, by using molecular methods to sequence nucleic acids and proteins and by putting these data into the perspective of secondary and tertiary structure of protein and RNA products of encoded genes, we can evaluate evolutionary relationships on a vast time scale. In addition, we are now aware of patterns of gene organization into exons and introns in eukaryotes, and we have found this perspective to be an essential component in evolutionary analysis.

Via amino acid sequencing, immunological cross reactions, and other methods, we can determine the degree of amino acid modification that has taken place in widely different organisms. The respiratory heme-protein cytochrome c is a common component of prokaryotic and eukaryotic organisms, but the molecule differs in amino acid composition in different species. Estimates of the number of nucleotide substitutions that have produced amino acid substitutions in the protein suggest that, the more distant the relationship between organisms, the greater

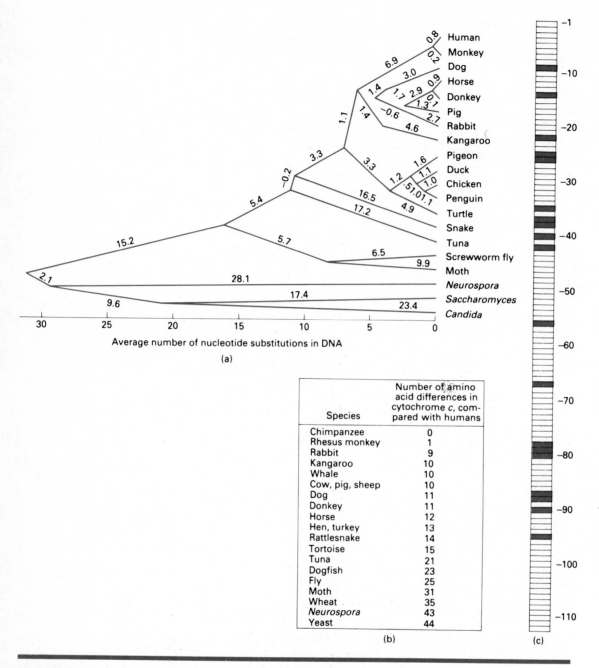

(a)

Species	Number of amino acid differences in cytochrome c, compared with humans
Chimpanzee	0
Rhesus monkey	1
Rabbit	9
Kangaroo	10
Whale	10
Cow, pig, sheep	10
Dog	11
Donkey	11
Horse	12
Hen, turkey	13
Rattlesnake	14
Tortoise	15
Tuna	21
Dogfish	23
Fly	25
Moth	31
Wheat	35
Neurospora	43
Yeast	44

(b)

(c)

FIGURE 18-24

Evolutionary changes in cytochrome c.
(a) A phylogenetic tree for 20 organisms based on amino acid differences in the protein. The numbers on the branches of the tree are the estimated numbers of nucleotide substitutions that have resulted in amino acid differences during evolution. (b) Amino acid substitutions distinguish human cytochrome c from many—but not all—other species. The more distant the relationship, the greater the number of amino acid differences

between us and other species. Cytochrome c in humans is identical to that in our closest relatives, the great apes, and it differs by only one amino acid (isoleucine at position 66) from the protein in Rhesus monkeys (threonine at position 66).
(c) Diagrammatic representation of the 112 amino acids of the human protein sequence, showing in color the amino acid sites that are identical in all the eukaryotes studied thus far.

the difference in their cytochrome *c* (Fig. 18.24). We infer a common origin for the gene in modern species because fully half the amino acids in the protein product occupy the same positions in the sequence in all aerobic life. Amino acid substitutions have been incorporated via mutations in codons, and the longer the evolutionary time interval between organisms the more extensive the modification of the gene and its product. Overall, the degrees of difference are correlated with the degrees of relationship and the time since divergence of each species in evolution. The evolutionary tree reflects the action of a "molecular clock" by which the amount of difference coincides with the time during which these differences accumulated in the genomes.

Despite substantial levels of amino acid substitution, the cytochrome *c* molecule has the same electron-transporting function and the same general three-dimensional structure (see Fig. 18.11). The same situation characterizes many other proteins that have been studied, but, whereas the rate of evolutionary divergence is relatively constant for any one type of protein, the rates vary from one functional type of protein to another (Fig. 18.25). The fastest rates of change occur in proteins with

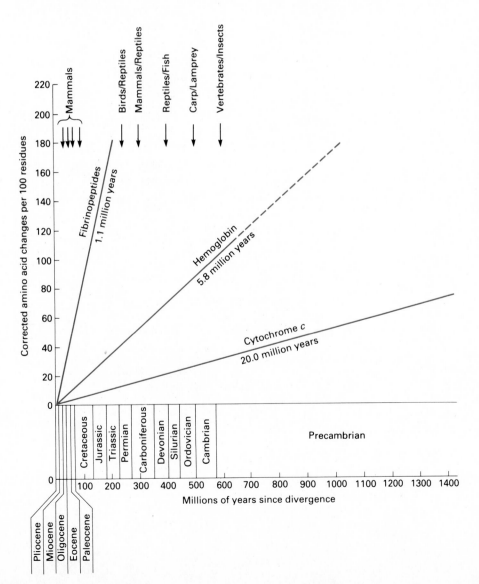

FIGURE 18-25
Rates of evolutionary change in fibrinopeptides, hemoglobins, and cytochrome *c*. Faster rates of change characterize the molecules most able to tolerate amino acid substitutions without undergoing change in vital functions. If the rate of change in histones were to be plotted, the line would be almost horizontal across the bottom of the graph. The time in millions of years for a 1% change in amino acid sequence to show up in evolutionary lineages is shown just under each plotted line. (From Dickerson, R. E., 1971, *J. Mol. Evol.* **1**:26.)

the fewest restraints on their function despite considerable modification in primary structure. Fibrinopeptides, for example, are enzymatically excised polypeptides from fibrinogen molecules that are converted to fibrin during blood clotting. Only a small portion of a fibrinopeptide molecule is involved in the clotting reactions, so the molecule can tolerate a substantial amount of modification without change in function. In histones, on the other hand, very little amino acid substitution has occurred during evolution in eukaryotes. Because histones bind securely at various sites to one another and to DNA in the chromosome, modifications almost anywhere in histone primary structure alter its binding specificities and nucleoprotein packaging. Although mutations continue to arise at random, most of these alterations must be maladaptive and selected against. The genes and their histone products are thus highly conserved in evolution.

From base composition analysis and nucleotide sequencing, we know that ribosomal RNAs and tRNAs are highly conserved products of eukaryotic genes but that differences between eukaryotic groups are greater than differences within any of these groups (Fig. 18.26). By the use of various methods to derive the secondary structures of these RNAs, however, investigators have found that, despite nucleotide deletions, additions, and substitutions over billions of years of evolution, the rRNAs and tRNAs have retained the same basic secondary-structural organization into functional domains of similar shapes. Among rRNAs, for example, similarities exist in molecules of such different lengths as 950 and 1550 bases in 12S and 16S rRNAs in human mitochondrial ribosomes, 1550 and 2900 bases in 16S and 23S rRNAs of *E. coli* ribosomes, and 1800 and 3400–4700 bases in 18S and 26–28S rRNAs in eukaryotic cytoribosomes (Fig. 18.27). Clearly we must take into account the structure as well as the nucleotide or amino acid sequence and composition of the gene product in order to evaluate homologies and

FIGURE 18-26

Evolutionary changes in the GC/AU ratio of rRNA in animals and certain protists. Numbers 1–6 are protists (*Euglena* = 6); 7–9, sponges and coelenterates; 10–12, nematodes and annelids; 13–25, arthropods; 26–30, molluscs; 31–32, echinoderms; 33–49, vertebrates (*Homo sapiens* = 49). Note the clustering of similar values for closely related organisms, such as the vertebrates (solid colored triangles), and note that differences are greater between groups than within a group of related organisms. The evolutionary pattern for rRNA base composition shown here coincides with patterns deduced from many other kinds of data. (From Lava-Sanchez, P. A., F. Amaldi, and A. La Posta, 1972, *J. Mol. Evol,* **2**:44.)

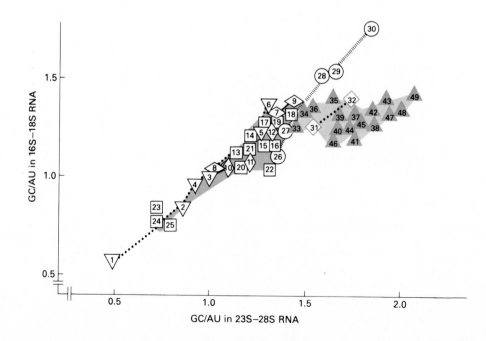

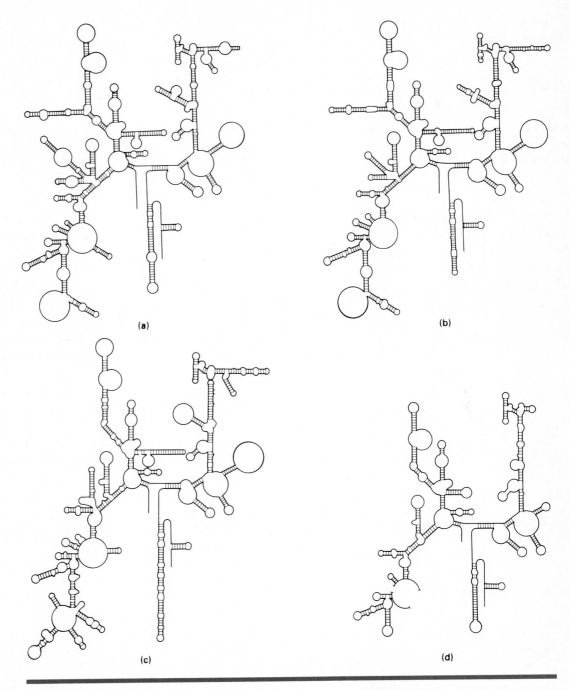

(a)

(b)

(c)

(d)

FIGURE 18-27
The secondary structure of 16S or 18S rRNA, from the small subunit of the ribosome, is strikingly conserved in (a) *E. coli*, a true bacterium, (b) *Halobacterium volcanii*, an archaebacterium, and (c) eukaryotic yeast (*Saccharomyces cerevisiae*). (d) Features common to all the sequenced 16S and 16S-like rRNAs, including those from mitochondrial ribosomes, are indicated. (From Noller, H. F., 1984, *Ann. Rev. Biochem.* **53**:119–162, Fig. 4.)

the magnitude and significance of evolutionary divergence in genes and their products.

18.11
Gene Duplication in Evolution

It is obvious that evolution does not proceed exclusively by the incorporation of adaptive mutations involving base substitutions, deletions, and insertions for a constant number of genes. Genome size varies considerably between prokaryotes and eukaryotes and between different eukaryotic groups (see Section 12.11). How do new genes arise and how

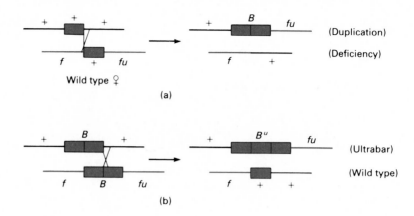

(a)

(b)

FIGURE 18-28
Unequal crossing over leading to gene duplication in *Drosophila melanogaster*. (a) Imprecise breakage and reunion of nonsister chromatid segments during meiosis in wild-type flies may lead to gametes containing a duplication of the eye-facet gene (colored box) or the reciprocal product carrying a deletion of that gene. Recombination of flanking marker genes (+/f and +/fu) provides evidence that unequal crossing over, rather than base substitution, has been responsible for the observed inherited modifications. Flies with the duplication develop bar eyes, and the duplicated locus is referred to as the *B* allele of the wild-type gene. (b) Unequal crossing over may produce other genetic modifications in phenotype, as in the case of homozygous bar-eye flies that produce gametes with three copies of the locus in one chromosome (much narrower bar, or ultrabar eye, is produced) and its reciprocal wild-type chromosome product. Here, too, the distribution of flanking gene markers indicates unequal crossing over, rather than base substitution, as the process responsible for the inherited modifications in progeny flies.

is the genome altered in its complexity (length of unique sequences) and overall size? By replication errors, transpositions, gross chromosomal changes in number and structure, and recombinational processes, large-scale changes in the genome take place. One of the processes leading to an increase in gene copies is recombination through **unequal crossing over**, whereby **duplication** of whole genes or of gene segments may result.

A classic example of duplication through unequal crossing over is provided by the bar-eye mutant of *Drosophila melanogaster*. By imprecise breakage and rejoining of nonsister chromatid segments, one chromatid acquires two copies of the wild-type gene and the other chromatid has none (Fig. 18.28). By following the recombination of gene markers flanking the eye-gene locus, it can clearly be shown that the mutation is the result of unequal crossing over and not of base substitution. As the number of gene copies on a chromosome increases from one in normal flies to two in bar-eye flies and to three in ultrabar-eye flies, the number of eye facets is diminished from the wild-type 800 per eye to as few as 45 per eye. Such a change in gene expression relative to the copy number and position of the gene loci is not always the result of gene duplication events.

From immunological cross reactions and amino acid compositional data, the α-globin genes and the β-globin genes in a vertebrate animal seem to be distantly related. When the amino acid sequences of the two globin chains are aligned in the most favorable way for comparisons, we find only 63 residues in the same locations among the 141 amino acids of α globin and the 146 amino acids of β globin from human hemoglobin molecules (Fig. 18.29). On the other hand, now that we know the exon–intron organization of these globin genes, we can see that both the α-globin genes and the β-globin genes are organized identically into three exons and two introns and that precisely the same exon–intron splice junctions are present in the two genes. Despite the divergence in coding sequence and modifications in the lengths of the intervening sequences between exons, the α-globin and β-globin genes are clearly the results of a gene duplication event in the ancient vertebrate past (Fig. 18.30). It is extremely unlikely that these corresponding features arose by chance in two different genes each of which just happened to encode one of the two globin polypeptides of the hemoglobin molecule.

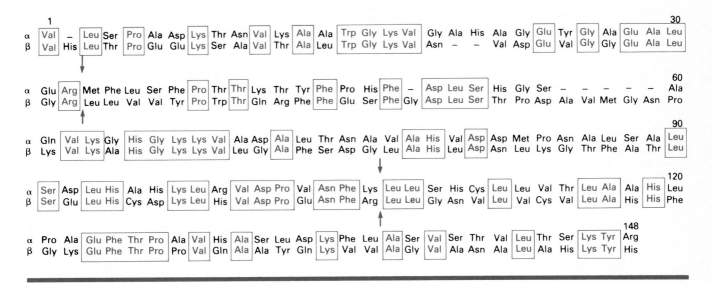

FIGURE 18-29

Amino acid sequences of alpha (α) and beta (β) globin chains in human hemoglobin. The 141 amino acids of α globin and the 146 amino acids of β globin have been aligned over 148 positions to enhance the similarities present. The exon–intron splice junctions (at arrows) are essentially the same in the two globins, even though the original gene duplicated and began to diverge about 500 million years ago. Only 63 amino acids (color) occupy the same locations in the two polypeptide chains. (Adapted from *Evolution* by T. Dobzhansky, F.J. Ayala, G.L. Stebbins, and J.W. Valentine, Fig. 9-17. W.H. Freeman and Company. Copyright © 1977.)

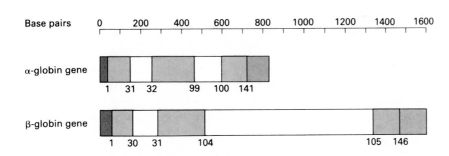

FIGURE 18-30

That the human α-globin gene and β-globin gene are products of evolutionary duplication is apparent from their similarity of organization. Each gene has three exons (color) of approximately the same length, separated by introns (white) and flanked at each end by leader and trailer segments (gray). The first intron is about the same in the two genes, but the second intron is much longer in the β-globin gene. The numbers below each gene refer to the amino acids in the polypeptides encoded at the sites shown. Additional evidence for duplication is furnished by the fact that the exon–intron splice junctions are virtually identical in the two genes (see Fig. 18.29). (From Maniatis, T., et al., 1980, *Ann. Rev. Genetics* **14**:145.)

We can trace back the evolutionary history of the human globin genes to the appearance of invertebrates about 600 million years ago. The ancestral gene may have encoded a polypeptide similar to the muscle protein *myoglobin*, which consists of a single polypeptide bound to a heme group. Duplication of the myoglobin gene was followed later, perhaps 400 million years ago, by duplication of the globin derivative to produce the forerunners of α-globin and β-globin genes. The β-globin gene duplicated several times afterward to produce ε globin (embryonic), γ globin (fetal), and most recently δ globin (Fig. 18.31). The γ-globin gene probably duplicated about 25 million years ago, but the $^A\gamma$-globin and $^G\gamma$-globin genes differ by only one nucleotide. The sequence of duplications and divergences is based on comparative studies of vertebrate species and the extent to which divergence has occurred in amino acid compositions as indicators of nucleotide modifications. We believe from these data that globin evolution has occurred at a relatively constant rate during evolution (see Fig. 18.25).

In humans, the five functional genes in the β-like globin cluster on chromosome 11 are spread over a DNA segment about 60,000 bases

FIGURE 18-31
A phylogenetic tree showing the relationships and origins of the human globin genes. Each duplication is indicated by an arrow, and the numbers along the branches indicate the numbers of nucleotide substitutions believed to have occurred over the past 600 million years of evolution from some (multicellular) ancestor to modern human beings.

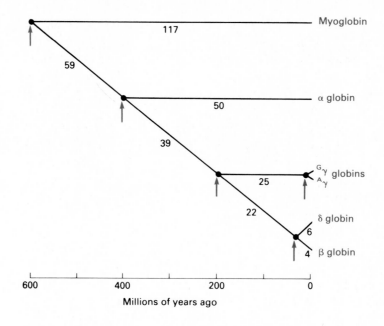

long. About 95% of this segment consists of noncoding DNA between genes and within the genic introns. The entire 60,000-base segment also occurs in the genomes of apes and Old World monkeys, which indicates that the segment has been conserved during the past 40 million years of primate evolution (Fig. 18.32). Data such as these emphasize that we must take into account the organization of sets of genes as well as that of individual genes during genome evolution.

Recent studies have provided evidence for duplication of parts of genes, presumably by recombination after unequal crossing over. The gene for chick α-2 (type I) collagen is organized into at least 52 exons alternating with 51 introns over a length of 38,000 base pairs. From

FIGURE 18-32 ▶

Changes in the cluster of β-like globin genes are shown for five primate species and the rabbit, as we believe them to have occurred during the past 90 million of the 180 million years of mammalian evolution. Reading upward from the rabbit, which belongs to a more ancient group of mammals than the more recent primates, it is clear that duplicate β-globin genes were present in the rabbit group at least 85 million years ago. The prosimians, the earliest primates, had already undergone differentiation of duplicate β-globin genes to harbor the embryonic ε-globin gene and the fetal γ-globin gene as well as a β-globin gene in a stretch of DNA about 25 kilobase pairs (kbp) long. The New World monkeys have ε-globin, γ-globin, and duplicate β-globin genes, present in DNA about 45 kbp long. The more closely related Old World monkeys, apes, and humans have virtually identical sets of β- and β-like globin genes spread over a DNA segment about 60 kbp long. Pseudogenes (prefixed by ψ) are inactive duplicates of functional genes, but pseudogenes are not transcribed or, at least, are not expressed. The pseudogene sites (marked by x) have been mapped for rabbit, lemur, and human chromosomes. It is significant that, despite divergence in morphology and in base sequences, the organization of the β-like gene cluster has remained unchanged during the 40 million years of monkey, ape, and human evolution. (From Lewin, R., 1981, *Science* **214**: 426–429.)

structural and sequencing analysis of the gene, it appears that many of these exons are 54 base pairs long. This coincidence suggests that the collagen gene evolved via many duplications of an initial coding sequence or gene that was 54 base pairs long (Fig. 18.33). It is highly unlikely that many exons of identical length arose by chance. We know that repeat sequences of various length are present between genes and within genes, and it is quite possible that mispairings of repeats could lead to unequal crossing over and to recombinant molecules with duplications and deficiencies (Fig. 18.34). Once the duplicated sequences were successfully established, divergence would occur because of the random nature of mutations. Different mutations in originally identical sequences would occur, and, depending on their relative adaptive value in the function of the gene product and as part of a larger dimension of interacting and interrelated functions in the organism in a particular environment, some of the modifications would be incorporated into the genome whereas others would be selected against.

Eukaryotic genes are organized into exons and introns, and polypeptides are folded into tertiary structures that consist of two or more compact regions, or **domains**, that function in a semi-independent manner but are linked together by more flexible hingelike portions of the chain. In 1978 Walter Gilbert suggested that the adaptive significance of the newly discovered interrupted gene organization in eukaryotes was related to the organization of domains in their polypeptide products. By rearrangements and recombinations of exons, new kinds of proteins

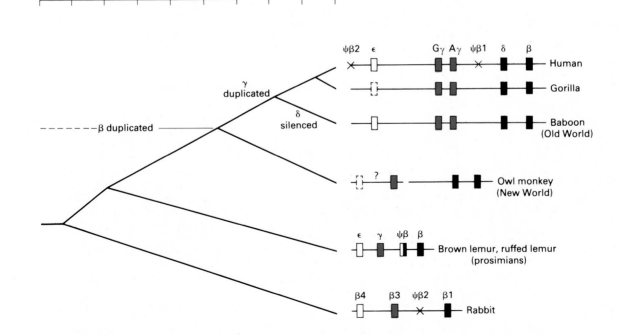

FIGURE 18-33
Organization of the chick α-2 (type I) collagen gene. (a) The gene consists of 52 exons (color bars) interspersed with 51 introns over a length of about 38,000 bases (38 kilobases). (b) Many of these exons are 54 base pairs long, which may represent the length of the ancestral coding sequence that duplicated many times during the evolutionary history of the gene. (From B. de Crombrugghe and I. Pastan. 1982. *Trends Biochem. Sci.* **7**:11–13, Figs. 1 and 2.)

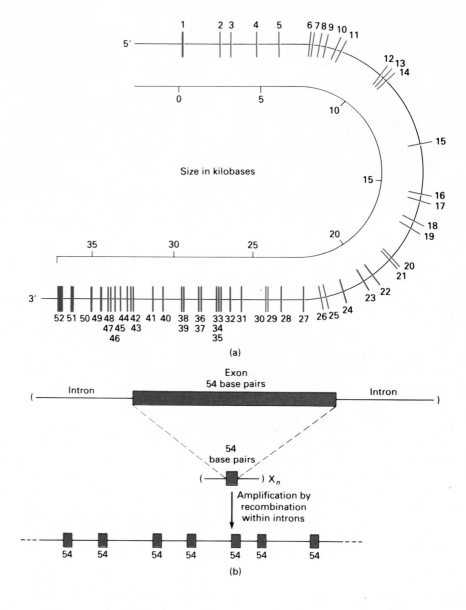

FIGURE 18-34
Consequences of recombination of coding sequences (color boxes) through unequal crossing over at homologous short repeated DNA sequences (black boxes) dispersed between or within genes. Duplication of a gene by unequal crossing over may occur (a) once or (b) repeatedly to produce two or more copies of the original coding sequence. (c) Unequal crossing over involving short DNA repeats in intervening sequences between exons (E_1–E_3) may similarly lead to a recombinant gene containing one or more duplicated coding segments. From A. J. Jeffreys and S. Harris, 1982, *Nature* **296**:9–10. Fig. 1. Copyright © 1982 Macmillan Journals Limited.)

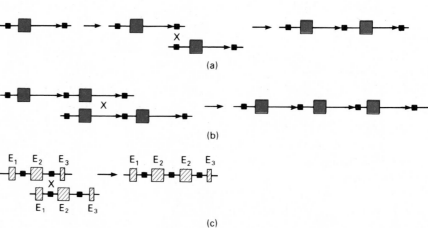

(a)   (b)

FIGURE 18-35
The three domains in a globin polypeptide appear to correspond to the
three exons in globin gene organization. (a) Two arrows show the points
at which the structure of a globin
chain is interrupted by the two introns in
the corresponding gene sequence.
(b) The exon–intron splice junctions
occur in the alpha-helical region of
the polypeptide, shown here in three
separated domains that correspond to
the three exons of the globin gene. The
product of the central exon surrounds
the heme component of the globin
chain. (From Gilbert. W.. 1981. *Science*
214:1311, Fig. 11. Copyright © by the
Nobel Foundation.)

might arise rapidly, and the retention of gene organization in a related family might be related to the retention of specific domains in molecular functions. We now have evidence in a number of cases to support Gilbert's original suggestion.

The remarkable conservation of globin gene organization is corre-lated with the conservation of functional domains in the polypeptides (Fig. 18.35). The central domain is heme-binding, and the domains on either side are largely concerned with binding together the two α chains and the two β chains of the hemoglobin molecule. This example and others have made us more alert to organizational homologies between genes and between polypeptides, and somewhat less concerned about amino acid compositional nonhomologies that are due to base substitu-tions by mutations. This new awareness has been important in various recent studies of the pathways by which particular genes and their protein products have evolved—for example, in determining the genetic basis for the origin of the related blood serum proteins *serum albumin* and *alpha-fetoprotein* (AFP).

Both serum proteins help to regulate the osmotic pressure of the intravascular fluid, but AFP is synthesized in the mammalian fetus whereas serum albumin becomes the major component at birth and replaces AFP. By comparisons of amino acid sequences in the two proteins, and of the organizational homologies in protein structure, Shirley Tilghman and co-workers found that 180 of the 584 residues were conserved in the two proteins and that each protein was organized into three domains that were similar in length (Fig. 18.36). These data provide strong evidence for a shared common ancestry of the two proteins and, by implication, of the genes that encode them. Molecular analysis of the exon–intron organization of the two genes indeed revealed their identical organization, although little sequence homology had been retained in individual segments. The lengths of the exons, however, were remarkably similar.

From these data Tilghman also sought information concerning the origin of the AFP and serum albumin genes. Each gene is organized into three major regions that correspond to the three domains of their polypeptide products. It was possible for these genes to have evolved by either one of two alternative pathways. By one alternative a single coding sequence may have duplicated, and each duplicate may then

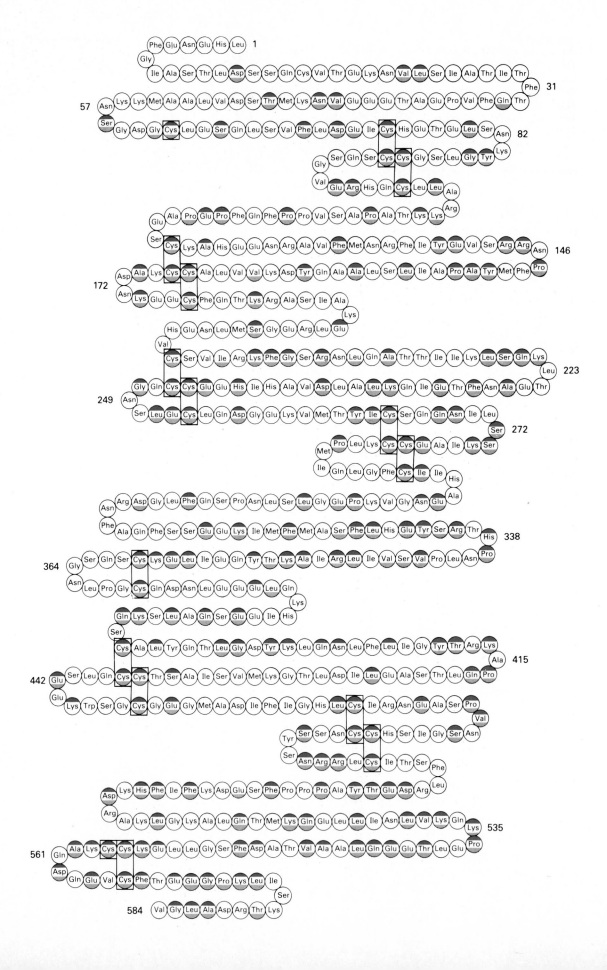

◄ **FIGURE 18-36**
The amino acid sequence of mouse
alpha-fetoprotein (AFP). Where
any of the 584 amino acids in the
mouse AFP sequence is the same as in
either human or bovine serum albumin,
the amino acid circle is colored above
(human) or blackened below (bovine)
the label. Amino acids are numbered to

the left and right of the large loops. A
total of 180 out of 584 amino acids
are the same in all three protein sequences, as seen in circles colored
above and blackened below the amino
acid name. (From M. B. Gorin et al.
1981 *J. Biol. Chem.* **256**:1954–1959,
Fig. 3.)

have gone on to evolve independently into tripartite genes consisting of three coding regions corresponding to the three protein domains in their respective products (Fig. 18.37). The alternative sequence involved the origin of a tripartite gene whose three segments were derived by duplications of a single coding sequence. This ancestral tripartite gene duplicated, and each copy later diverged to become the modern AFP and serum albumin genes.

This second alternative is the more plausible of the two possibilities. The three domains of each protein are functionally and organizationally similar to one another and to those in the other protein. The coding region for each domain in a protein is organizationally similar in all three parts of the gene. The similarities among all three coding regions in the gene and among all three domains in the protein argue for common ancestry from a single coding sequence. The high degree of organizational and functional similarity of AFP and serum albumin genes and proteins, in turn, argues for common ancestry *after* the appearance of a tripartite organization. Far more chance coincidence would be required to explain the evolution of two homologous tripartite genes from an original pair of duplicated single coding segments.

By studying individual domains of different proteins, we have also been able to glimpse possible evolutionary modifications leading to diversity of functions imposed on a common plan of organization. Some of these examples reflect the importance of tinkering with existing molecular regions to produce molecules with new but related functions. For example, cytochrome *c*, myoglobin, and globins are all heme-binding proteins that have important structural homologies that suggest an evolutionary relationship. Cytochrome *c* has its heme group so oriented to the polypeptide that the iron atom can readily pick up and release electrons and thus function in electron flow. In myoglobin the heme binds oxygen to its central iron atom and keeps it there because of the environment provided by hydrophobic regions of the polypeptide in which the heme is enclosed. In the absence of water, the iron atom is not oxidized, and, in its reduced ferrous form, the iron retains tightly bound molecular oxygen. Myoglobin acts as a storehouse of molecular oxygen and releases oxygen only in response to tissue requirement. In globins the heme group of a chain is oriented in such a way that the iron atom can readily bind molecular oxygen and readily release oxygen to all the body cells bordering the circulation stream. By these evolutionary changes it is very likely that tinkering with the cytochrome *c* that functioned originally in photosynthetic electron transport led to its mobilization in the modified function of respiration, an entirely new

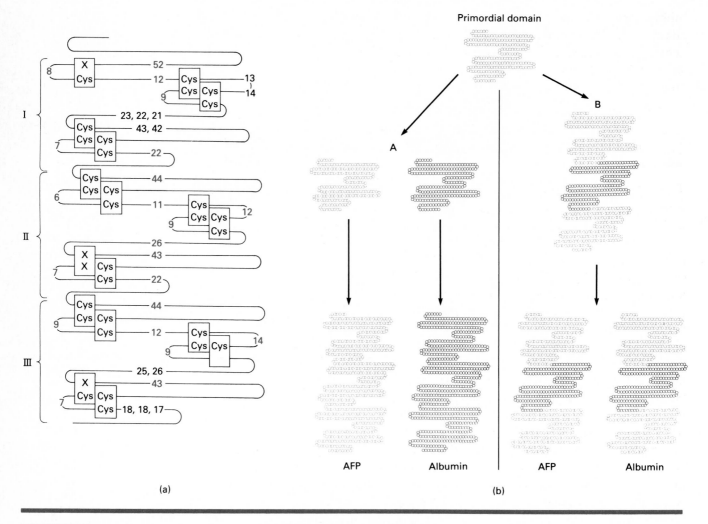

FIGURE 18-37
Comparison of alpha-fetoprotein (AFP) and serum albumin sequences.
(a) The lengths of amino acid sequences between cysteine–cysteine bonded residues are given for mouse AFP (numbers in color) and for human and bovine serum albumins. A single number indicates that all three proteins are identical, two numbers indicate the difference between AFP and the two albumins, and three numbers indicate the residues in AFP, human albumin, and bovine albumin, respectively, from left to right. The approximate borders of the three domains in these proteins are outlined on the left. (b) Two models (A and B) to explain the evolution of AFP and albumin genes from a single primordial gene, according to analysis of the proteins. Each of the models postulates the evolution of a tripartite organization from a single coding sequence. The data best fit model B, in which AFP and albumin genes diverged *after* the ancestral gene had evolved to a tripartite organization. (From M.B. Gorin et al. 1981. *J. Biol. Chem.* **256**: 1954–1959, Figs. 4 and 5.)

process that made possible an aerobic lifestyle. Myoglobin may be a modified cytochrome component that now provided a reservoir for the oxygen required by newly emerged aerobic life. The eventual appearance of globins in hemoglobin provided an efficient means for oxygen transport to the cells of multicellular organisms of increasing size and complexity in an aerobic world.

By the same sets of evolutionary processes acting on genetically diverse organisms with different requirements in different environments, millions of species have evolved and displayed an incredible spectrum of adaptations. Many of these adaptations involved tinkering with parts of genes, whole genes, and sets of genes, and many of these modifications were responsible for the genomes that today direct the expression of ancient abilities as well as new functions and developmental programs.

Summary

The universe probably originated in an enormous explosion (Big Bang), generating intense heat and clouds of cosmic dust and later forming hydrogen atoms. Much later, at various times in the ancient history of the universe, planets and their suns formed from solar dust clouds. Our own solar system includes nine planets, each with properties determined by its mass (and hence its gravitational field), its distance from the sun, and its chemical composition. The surface of the primitive Earth was covered with bodies of water and surrounded by a reducing atmosphere containing CH_4, and NH_3 that could support abiotic production of small organic molecules essential to living systems and subsidized by thermal, radioactive, electrical, and other energy sources. Model experiments have demonstrated synthesis of amino acids, nucleic acids and nucleotides (including ATP), porphyrins, proteins, and other compounds under conditions simulating those of the primitive Earth. Eventually the seas became rich soups of nutrients supporting protobiont formation.

Three of the possible types of protobionts whose formation has been envisioned have in common a selectively permeable boundary that provides them the opportunity to concentrate and sequester their contents while exchanging energy and matter with their environment. In the coacervate, one protobiont model, charged particles attract to themselves a layer of bound water that acts as a boundary between inside and outside. A second model proposes that protobionts were proteinoid microspheres, 1-to-2-μm protein-containing particles exhibiting osmotic properties, catalytic activity, and fragmentation. A third model is the vesicle formed by an enclosing lipid bilayer, a known configuration taken by phospholipids in aqueous solution that resembles cells with membranes; perhaps this model is the most attractive.

With a selectively permeable barrier established, a coordinated metabolism was required to mediate interactions with the environment. The major intermediates and energy-transferring molecules were probably found in the primordial soup, including ATP and ADP for phosphoryl group transfer, compounds mediating oxidation–reduction, and porphyrin for electron transport. The first catalysts were probably metal ions, later ions were stabilized by small molecules, and finally by these as prosthetic groups attached to proteins as in modern enzymes. Protobionts could only become eubionts with the development of a self-replicating genetic program. The triplet genetic code must underlie the programs of virtually all life forms. The third base of each triplet codon may have originally functioned other than as a coding element because that $3'$ position is often redundant in the modern code. It is unlikely that the triplet reading frame emerged from a doublet-based system in evolution. Whether the code was originally embodied in a sequence of RNA or of DNA and how it may have been originally translated are totally open to speculation.

Once eubionts existed, molecular diversity could evolve. Primordial heterotrophs relied on abundant pre-existing organic nutrients. Scarcity of a nutrient favored selection of those that could produce the nutrient from a precursor. By this process, progressively longer and more complex metabolic pathways evolved—first those such as glycolysis, later those that led in the direction of chemotrophy and autotrophy. Branching pathways and coupled reactions provided dramatic increases in efficiency and regulation. New catalysts that promoted new reactions were provided as the primordial genome expanded and as existing genomes underwent modification and rearrangement.

Chemotrophs probably derived their energy by receiving and transporting electrons from donors such as H_2S. A major development in photosynthetic autotrophs was the coupling of two light-harvesting photosystems by an electron transport chain and the photolysis of water to derive electrons for the conversion of light energy to chemical energy. Photosynthesis could generate ATP and reducing potential more efficiently than earlier systems, but incidentally it generated oxygen from water. Some autotrophs evolved respiratory chains (perhaps derived from photosynthetic pathways) that used oxygen as an electron acceptor, thereby generating far more ATP than could have been accomplished by other routes. Mechanisms to repair damage to nucleic acids by unfiltered ultraviolet (UV) radiation may also have evolved in this time, before atmospheric oxygen allowed development of the UV-filtering ozone layer.

Eukaryotes may have arisen from a wall-less prokaryote with a mobile plasma membrane. This membrane would permit the cell to engulf solid foods and process them first with extracellular digestive secretions and, later, by such enzymes stored in vesicles (ultimately lysosomes) near the plasma membrane. DNA was relocated to the cell interior from its attachment site on the plasma membrane, where it was not protected against digestive enzyme action. Microtubules provided a framework for DNA segregation, and a nuclear envelope developed. Additional opportunities were thereby provided for subdivision and rearrangement of the genome, proceeding from one circular DNA molecule to more than one chromosome harboring a set of genes.

Multicellularity gave organisms possibilities for structural and functional specialization that increased their life expectancy, stability, and efficiency. Multicellularity probably occurred independently in the plants, animals, and fungi. In the most recent 570 million years, all modern phyla emerged, first in the waters and later on the land that was made habitable for animals after being colonized by plants.

A great deal about evolutionary relationships can be learned from comparative morphological, biochemical, and molecular studies. The nucleotide sequences of genes and the amino acid sequences of their polypeptide products yield crucial data, but the three-dimensional conformation of a molecule often provides significant information about evolutionary directions taken over long periods of time. Molecules with similar function in distantly related organisms have preserved similarities in functional domains that are not obvious from analysis of primary structure. In addition to incremental changes brought about by point mutation and selection, evolutionary changes can arise through gene duplication, transposition, replication errors, recombination, or chromosomal rearrangements. Homologies among genes and proteins are best explained by duplication of an original gene, followed by divergence and further duplication of the first two gene copies, as exemplified in myoglobin and the families of globin genes in vertebrate animals. In several instances, clustering and distribution of introns in related genes are conserved more strikingly than the coding sequences themselves. Parts of genes have been duplicated, making larger units that have diverged to a greater or lesser degree in evolution as seems to have occurred in the chick alpha-2 collagen gene, the serum albumin and alpha-fetoprotein genes in mammals, and others.

Readings and References

Adams, J. G., III, W. T. Morisson, and M. H. Steinberg. 1982. Hemoglobin Parchman: Double crossover within a single human gene. *Science* **218**:291.

Akazawa, T., T. Takabe, and H. Kobayashi. 1984. Molecular evolution of ribulose 1, 5-bisphosphate carboxylase/oxygenase (RuBisCO). *Trends Biochem. Sci.* **9**:380.

Alexander, F., P. R. Young, and S. M. Tilghman. 1984. Evolution of the albumin: α-fetoprotein ancestral gene from the amplification of a 27-nucleotide sequence. *J. Mol. Biol.* **173**:159.

Almassy, R. J., and R. E. Dickerson. 1978. Pseudomonas cytochrome c_{551} at 2.0 Å resolution: Enlargement of the cytochrome c family. *Proc. Natl. Acad. Sci. U.S.* **75**:2674.

Ayala, F. J. September 1978. The mechanism of evolution. *Sci. Amer.* **239**:56.

Blake, C. C. F. 1981. Exons and the structure, function, and evolution of haemoglobin. *Nature* **291**:616.

Blake, C. C. F. 1983. Exons and the evolution of proteins. *Trends Biochem. Sci.* **8**:11.

Bodmer, W. F. 1981. Gene clusters, genome organization, and complex phenotypes. When the sequence is known, what will it mean? *Amer. J. Human Genet.* **33**:664.

Brandon, C.-I., H. Eklund, C. Cambillau, and A. J. Pryor. 1984. Correlation of exons with structural domains in alcohol dehydrogenase. *EMBO J.* **3**:1307.

Brimacombe, R. 1984. Conservation of structure in ribosomal RNA. *Trends Biochem. Sci.* **9**:273.

Calvin, M. 1975. Chemical evolution. *Amer. Sci.* **63**:169.

Cavalier-Smith, T. 1975. The origin of nuclei and of eukaryotic cells. *Nature* **256**:463.

Clarke, B. August 1975. The causes of biological diversity. *Sci. Amer.* **233**:50.

Cornish-Bowden, A. 1985. Are introns structural elements or evolutionary debris? *Nature* **313**:434.

Crick, F. H. C., S. Brenner, A. Klug, and G. Pieczenik. 1976. A speculation on the origin of protein synthesis. *Origins of Life* **7**:389.

Curtis, S. E., and M. T. Clegg. 1984. Molecular evolution of chloroplast DNA sequences. *Mol. Biol. Evol.* **1**:291.

de Crombrugghe, B., and I. Pastan. 1982. Structure and regulation of a collagen gene. *Trends Biochem. Sci.* **7**:11.

Dickerson, R. E. September 1978. Chemical evolution and the origin of life. *Sci. Amer.* **239**:70.

Dickerson, R. E. March 1980. Cytochrome c and the evolution of energy metabolism. *Sci. Amer.* **242**:136.

Dickerson, R. E., and I. Geis. 1983. *Hemoglobin: Structure, Function, Evolution and Pathology.* Menlo Park, Calif.: Benjamin-Cummings.

Doolittle, W. F. 1980. Revolutionary concepts in evolutionary cell biology. *Trends Biochem. Sci.* **5**:146.

Dover, G. A., and R. B. Flavell, eds. 1982. *Genome Evolution.* New York: Academic Press.

Echlin, P. June 1966. The blue-green algae. *Sci. Amer.* **214**:74.

Eiferman, F. A., *et al.* 1981. Intragenic amplification and divergence in the mouse α-fetoprotein gene. *Nature* **294**:713.

Eigen, M., W. Gardiner, P. Schuster, and R. Winkler-Oswatitsch. April 1981. The origin of genetic information. *Sci. Amer.* **244**:88.

Erwin, D. H., and J. W. Valentine. 1984. "Hopeful monsters," transposons, and Metazoan radiation. *Proc. Natl. Acad. Sci. U.S.* **81**:5482.

Folsome, C. E., ed. 1979. *Life: Origin and Evolution* (Readings from *Scientific American*). San Francisco: Freeman.

Frederick, J. F., ed. 1981. *Origins and Evolution of Eukaryotic Intracellular Organelles.* Ann. N.Y. Acad. Sci. **361**.

Gilbert, W. 1978. Why genes in pieces? *Nature* **271**:501.

Gilbert, W. 1981. DNA sequencing and gene structure. *Science* **214**:1305 (Nobel lecture).

Gilbert, W. 1985. Genes-in-pieces revisited. *Science* **228**:823.

Hardies, S. C., M. H. Edgell, and C. A. Hutchison, III. 1984. Evolution of the mammalian β-globin gene cluster. *J. Biol. Chem.* **259**:3748.

Hardison, R. C. 1984. Comparison of the β-like globin gene families of rabbits and humans indicates that the gene cluster 5′-ε-γ-δ-β-3′ predates the mammalian radiation. *Mol. Biol. Evol.* **1**:390.

Hill, A., *et al.* 1984. Two mouse early embryonic β-globin gene sequences. Evolution of the nonadult β-globins. *J. Biol. Chem.* **259**:3739.

Hoffman-Falk, H., P. Einat, B.-Z. Shilo, and F. M. Hoffmann. 1983. *Drosophila melanogaster* DNA clones homologous to vertebrate oncogenes: Evidence for a common ancester to the *src* and *abl* cellular genes. *Cell* **32**:589.

Horowitz, N. H. 1945. On the evolution of biochemical synthesis. *Proc. Natl. Acad. Sci. U.S.* **31**:153.

Jacob, F. 1977. Evolution and tinkering. *Science* **196**:1161.

Jaynes, J. M., and L. P. Vernon. 1982. The cyanelle of *Cyanophora paradoxa*: Almost a cyanobacterial chloroplast. *Trends Biochem. Sci.* **7**:22.

Jeffreys, A. J. 1982. Evolution of globin genes. In *Genome Evolution*, ed. G. A. Dover and R. B. Flavell, p. 157. New York: Academic Press.

Jeffreys, A. J., and S. Harris. 1982. Processes of gene duplication. *Nature* **296**:9.

Jukes, T. H. 1980. Silent nucleotide substitutions and the molecular evolutionary clock. *Science* **210**:973.

Kimura, M. November 1979. The neutral theory of evolution. *Sci. Amer.* **241**:98.

Kioussis, D., *et al.* 1981. The evolution of α-fetoprotein and albumin. II. The structures of the α-fetoprotein and albumin genes in the mouse. *J. Biol. Chem.* **256**:1960.

Lee, Y. M., D. J. Friedman, and F. J. Ayala. 1985. Superoxide dismutase: An evolutionary puzzle. *Proc. Natl. Acad. Sci. U.S.* **82**:824.

Lewin, R. 1982. On the origin of introns. *Science* **217**:921.

Lewontin, R. C. September 1978. Adaptation. *Sci. Amer.* **239**:212.

Lonberg, N., and W. Gilbert. 1985. Intron/exon structure of the chicken pyruvate kinase gene. *Cell* **40**:81.

Margulis, L. August 1971. Symbiosis and evolution. *Sci. Amer.* **225**:48.

Mayr, E. September 1978. Evolution. *Sci. Amer.* **239**:46.

Miller, S. L. 1957. The formation of organic compounds on the primitive Earth. *Ann. N. Y. Acad. Sci.* **69**:260.

Milner-White, E. J. 1984. Isoenzymes, isoproteins, and introns. *Trends Biochem. Sci.* **9**:517.

Mitchell, R. M., L. A. Loeblich, L. C. Klotz, and A. R. Loeblich, III. 1979. DNA organization of *Methanobacterium thermoautotrophicum*. *Science* **204**:1082.

Nei, M., and R. K. Koehn, eds. 1983. *Evolution of Genes and Proteins*. Sunderland, Mass.: Sinauer.

Rogers, J. 1983. Introns in archaebacteria. *Nature* **304**:685.

Robinson, I. B., and V. M. Ingram. 1982. Gene evolution in the chicken β-globin cluster. *Cell* **28**:515.

Schopf, J. W. September 1978. The evolution of the earliest cells. *Sci. Amer.* **239**:110.

Stanier, R. Y. 1970. Some aspects of the biology of cells and their possible evolutionary significance. *Sympos. Soc. Gen. Microbiol.* **20**:1.

Stebbins, G. L., Jr., and F. J. Ayala. July 1985. The evolution of Darwinism. *Sci. Amer.* **253**:72.

Südhoff, T. C., *et al.* 1985. The LDL receptor gene: A mosaic of exons shared with different proteins. *Science* **228**:815.

Südhoff, T. C., *et al.* 1985. Cassette of eight exons shared by genes for LDL receptor and EGF precursor. *Science* **228**:893.

Tajima, F., and M. Nei. 1984. Estimation of evolutionary distance between nucleotide sequences. *Mol. Biol. Evol.* **1**:269.

Tate, V., M. Finer, H. Boedtker, and P. Doty. 1983. Procollagen genes: Further sequence studies and interspecies comparisons. *Cold Spring Harbor Sympos. Quant. Biol.* **47**:1039.

Valentine, J. W. September 1978. The evolution of multicellular plants and animals. *Sci. Amer.* **239**:140.

Van Valen, L. M. 1982. Phylogenies in molecular evolution: *Prochloron*. *Nature* **298**:493.

Van Valen, L. M., and V. C. Maiorana. 1980. The archaebacteria and eukaryotic origins. *Nature* **287**:248.

Vidal, G. February 1984. The oldest eukaryotic cells. *Sci. Amer.* **250**:48.

Wetherill, G. W. June 1981. The formation of the Earth from planetesimals. *Sci. Amer.* **244**:162.

Whittaker, R. H. 1969. New concepts of kingdoms of organisms. *Science* **163**:150.

Woese, C. R. June 1981. Archaebacteria. *Sci. Amer.* **244**:98.

Woese, C. R., and G. E. Fox. 1977. Phylogenetic structure of the prokaryotic domain: The primary kingdoms. *Proc. Natl. Acad. Sci. U. S.* **74**:5088.

Wong, J. T.-F. 1981. Coevolution of genetic code and amino acid biosynthesis. *Trends Biochem. Sci.* **6**:33.

Glossary

α-actinin a long, flexible actin-binding protein that can cross-link actin filaments into loose networks with no particular orientation of the individual fibers

α-amanitin a compound isolated from the fungus *Amanita phalloides* that inhibits transcription of messenger RNA by eukaryotic RNA polymerase II

A band a region of a sarcomere in striated muscle that includes all the myosin filaments and part of the actin filaments at each end of the band

abiotic synthesis the formation of organic compounds in the absence of life

accessory fibers dense aggregates that lie outside and around the circle of microtubule doublets in the tail (flagellum) of sperm of many animal species, particularly those characterized by internal fertilization

acetyl coenzyme A (acetyl CoA) a high-energy intermediate in energy-transferring metabolic reactions; activated acetate linked to coenzyme A

α-chains of collagen stiff, cablelike polypeptides that are made up of about 1000 amino acids each and wind around each other in threes to form helical collagen molecules of the extracellular matrix in animals

acid hydrolases lysosomal digestive enzymes whose pH optimum is about 5.0

acrocentric designating a chromosome whose centromere is situated near one end, making one chromosome arm much longer than the other

acrosome a structure that covers the sperm head, is differentiated from the Golgi apparatus, and resembles a lysosome in its digestive enzyme content

actin the principal protein of microfilaments in striated muscle and many kinds of eukaryotic cells, involved in cell movements and part of the cytoskeleton

actin-binding proteins molecules that bind to actin in different ways and thereby regulate nonmuscle contractility; they may cross-link actin filaments, cap actin filaments by binding to one end of the fiber, or bind to actin monomers and prevent their assembly into polymers

activation energy the energy required for a chemical reaction to proceed. An enzyme binds transiently with a reactant to produce an enzyme–substrate complex that has a lower activation energy and thereby permits the reaction to take place more rapidly and at prevailing biological temperatures.

active site the region of enzyme surface to which substrate binds and then undergoes a specific chemical change in a metabolic reaction catalyzed by the enzyme

active transport the energy-requiring, assisted passage of molecules of a substance across a membrane in the direction of higher electrochemical gradient of the substance

adenine a cyclic nitrogenous purine base found in energy-transferring molecules and nucleic acids

adenosine triphosphatase *see* **ATPase**

adenosine triphosphate ATP; a nucleoside triphosphate that functions as a high-energy intermediate in energy-transferring reactions and as a precursor in nucleic acid synthesis

adenylate cyclase the enzyme that catalyzes the formation of cyclic adenosine monophosphate (cyclic AMP) from adenosine triphosphate (ATP)

adhering junction a differentiation of the cell surface that is a site of adhesion between adjacent cells or of a cell and basement layer; *see also* **desmosome**

ADP/ATP translocator a carrier protein in the mitochondrial membrane that is so regulated by the electrochemical proton gradient in mitochondria as to preferentially move ADP into the organelle and ATP out of it

aerobic respiration the major oxygen-dependent processes that produce ATP via the oxidation of glucose and other organic fuel molecules; *see also* **electron transport chain**, **Krebs cycle**, **oxidative phosphorylation**

α-helix   a major secondary structure in polypeptides, characterized by regularly repeated hydrogen bonding between C=O and N—H groups in the chain

allele   one of the alternative forms of a gene

allostery   the interaction between an enzyme at a site other than its active site and a compound that is not the substrate for this enzyme, causing inhibition or activation of the reaction catalyzed by the enzyme; *see also* **modulator**

ameboid movement   a mode of cellular motility characterized by crawling along a solid substratum using pseudopod surface extensions that form in response to an internal flow of cytoplasm

amide linkage   the covalent peptide bond between the C=O of the carboxyl group at the α-carbon of one amino acid and the N—H of the amino group at the α-carbon of the adjacent amino acid; the repeating covalent link between amino acids in a polypeptide chain

amino acid   the monomer building block of polypeptide and protein polymers; a carboxylic acid with one or more NH_2 groups

aminoacyl   an activated form of an amino acid, produced by a reaction with ATP

aminoacyl-tRNA   a complex of activated amino acid and its transfer RNA, which participates directly in the translation of encoded genetic information

aminoacyl-tRNA synthetase   one of a group of enzymes that catalyze the formation of aminoacyl compounds and the binding of the aminoacyl residue to a specific transfer RNA carrier

amphipathic   designating a molecule that contains both hydrophobic and hydrophilic residues

anabolism   the spectrum of energy-requiring synthesis reactions of metabolism; *see also* **catabolism**

anaerobic   designating conditions in which oxygen is absent, reactions that proceed in the absence of oxygen, or cells and organisms that function in the absence of oxygen

anaphase   a stage of mitosis or meiosis when sister chromatids or homologous chromosomes separate and move toward opposite poles of the cell

anaplerotic function   a characteristic action by which metabolites are replenished in accessory or nonmajor pathways

annulus   a ring or ring-shaped part of a cellular structure, usually referring to the eight-part protein border on each surface of the nuclear envelope at the site of a nuclear pore; *see also* **nuclear pore complex**

antibody   a protein secreted by plasma cells (activated B cells) that interacts with a specific invading antigen in an immune response; an immunoglobulin

anticodon   the triplet of nucleotides in a transfer RNA molecule that associates by complementary base-pairing with a specific triplet codon in the messenger RNA molecule during its translation at the ribosome

antigen   a foreign substance that stimulates the cellular production of specific neutralizing antibodies in an immune response

asexual reproduction   reproduction without the sexual process; vegetative propagation

A site   the region of a ribosome that accepts an incoming aminoacyl–tRNA unit during translation of a polypeptide from encoded genetic information

assembly–disassembly mechanism   the process proposed by Shinya Inoué to explain anaphase movement of chromosomes and spindle elongation during nuclear division, involving depolymerization of chromosomal microtubules by which fibers shorten and a force is generated to pull chromosomes to the pole at the same time that polar microtubules lengthen as tubulin monomers are added to the existing nonchromosomal fibers

assembly map   a summary of the order that ribosomal RNA and ribosomal proteins exhibit when they join in constructing ribosome subunits

ATPase   adenosine triphosphatase; the general term for enzymes that catalyze (1) the hydrolysis of ATP to produce ADP and inorganic phosphate and (2) the reverse reaction of ATP synthesis

ATP synthetase   the ATPase of the mitochondrial and chloroplast membranes in eukaryotes and the plasma membrane in prokaryotes that catalyzes ATP synthesis during oxidative phosphorylation in respiration and during photophosphorylation in photosynthesis; the $F_OF_1ATPase$

attenuation   a control mechanism that regulates gene expression through premature termination of the transcription of biosynthetic operons in bacteria

attenuator   a stem-and-loop secondary structure of messenger RNA that prevents the transcription by RNA polymerase of structural genes in biosynthetic operons in bacteria

autoradiography   a means of localizing radioactive atoms in biological materials by exposing a photographic emulsion laid over these materials and observing silver grains or darkened emulsion film where radioactive decays have occurred

autotroph   an organism that obtains its carbon and energy from inorganic sources

axoneme   the fibrous microtubular portion of a cilium or flagellum, exclusive of the enveloping cell membrane

bacteriochlorophylls   any of a group of light-absorbing pigments that are active in photosynthesis in particular groups of bacteria

bacteriophage   a virus whose host is a bacterium; phage

bacteriorhodopsin   a transmembrane transport protein of the "purple membrane" of the bacterium *Halobacterium halobium*, which functions as a light-driven proton pump that causes H^+ extrusion from the cell and thereby establishes an energy-rich voltage gradient across the membrane that drives the energy-requiring synthesis of ATP

Balbiani ring a large, well-developed puff at a site on a polytene chromosome of certain larval insect cells, such as salivary gland cells of dipteran larvae, and of some other kinds of cells and species

band 3 protein a transmembrane transport protein of the human erythrocyte plasma membrane that mediates the movement of polar molecules across the nonpolar lipid bilayer of the membrane

Barr body any condensed or inactivated X chromosome in the interphase nucleus; sex chromatin

basal body *see* **centriole**

base analogue a purine or pyrimidine base other than a standard nucleic acid base of similar molecular structure

base substitution a type of gene mutation in which the base or base pair at one site in the wild-type DNA sequence is different in the mutant sequence

β-carotene a particular carotenoid pigment that harvests light energy and can transfer excitation energy to other photosensitive pigments in a photosystem; the pigment that lends color to carrots, tomatoes, and other plant structures

belt desmosome an adhering junction that may encircle the cell and provide adhesion between adjacent cells

"big bang" the colloquial term that describes the theory that the universe originated in a massive explosion leading to the beginning of space and time and particulate matter

bioenergetics thermodynamics applied to living systems

bivalent a synapsed pair of homologous chromosomes typical of prophase I and metaphase I of meiosis

B lymphocyte the lymphoid blood-cell component that synthesizes and secretes antibodies after an antigenic stimulation that leads to its proliferation and differentiation into plasma cells; the immunoglobulin-producing cell of the humoral immune response system

branch migration the movement of an internal branch point in a recombination intermediate, as proposed in the Holliday model of crossing over between homologous DNA segments

breakage and reunion the mechanism of crossing over by physical breakage and subsequent reunion of broken nonhomologous segments of chromosomes or DNA molecules, leading to genetic recombination

CAAT box the -75 sequence of nine nucleotides with a consensus ordering of $GG_T^CCAATCT$ that is located in the promoter region of many eukaryotic genes, upstream of the $+1$ startpoint nucleotide, and may be required for high efficiency of transcription

calmodulin a ubiquitous calcium-binding protein that serves as an intracellular receptor of Ca^{2+} and, in its active form, mediates the intracellular response to Ca^{2+} as a second messenger after receptor activation by a bound ligand

cambium the lateral meristem that gives rise to phloem and xylem tissues in vascular plant stems and roots

cAMP *see* **cyclic AMP**

cancer a class of diseases characterized by uncontrolled growth, invasion of other tissues, and spread to distant sites (metastasis) in the body

cap the residue of 7-methylguanosine added to the $5'$ end of pre-messenger RNA

capping the addition of a 7-methylguanosine cap to the $5'$ end of pre-messenger RNA shortly after transcription begins

capping proteins a class of actin-binding proteins that bind to either end of an actin filament and thereby regulate the length of the actin polymer; gelsolin, fragmin, and villin are examples of capping proteins

carrier an integral membrane protein that assists ions and molecules across the lipid bilayer of a membrane; a transport protein in the membrane

catabolism the spectrum of energy-releasing breakdown reactions of metabolism; *see also* **anabolism**

catalase the enzyme that catalyzes the breakdown of hydrogen peroxide to water and oxygen, typically located in peroxisomes and other types of microbodies

catalyst any agent that affects the rate of a chemical reaction without altering the equilibrium point of that reaction; enzymes are proteinaceous catalysts in living systems

C-banding a method for staining chromosomes differentially to show constitutive heterochromatin as stained bands or regions and to show nonheterochromatic regions as unstained or weakly stained

C_3 cycle that part of the dark reactions of photosynthesis in which CO_2 is reduced to 3-phosphoglyceraldehyde, from which hexose sugars are produced and ribulose 1,5-bisphosphate is regenerated; also called the Calvin cycle

C_4 cycle an accessory CO_2-reducing pathway in photosynthesis by which CO_2 is taken from the air and used by PEP carboxylase to carboxylate pyruvate and form oxaloacetate, which later gives up its carboxyl as CO_2 to the C_3 cycle in underlying tissues of the same leaf; the Hatch–Slack pathway

cell the smallest membrane-bounded unit capable of independent reproduction

cell cycle the sequence of events between one mitotic division and another in a eukaryotic cell, consisting of the G_1, S, and G_2 phases of interphase and the M phase of mitosis proper

cell division formation of two daughter cells from a parent cell by enclosure of the individual nuclei or nucleoids in separate cell compartments; *see also* **cleavage**, **cytokinesis**, **furrowing**

cell plate   the new boundary that separates daughter nuclei into individual plant cells and consists of plasma membranes and new primary walls that become continuous with the pre-existing membranes and cell wall of the original parent cell; *see also* **phragmoplast**

cell surface   the cell covering, consisting of the exoplasmic layer of the plasma membrane and any external coats covering this membrane surface

cell theory   a generalization stating that the cell is the ultimate structural unit of the organism, first proposed in 1838–1839 by Schleiden and Schwann

cellular oncogene   any of a number of normal cellular gene equivalents of viral oncogenes responsible for tumor formation in organisms or transformation in cultured cells; proto-oncogenes; c-*onc* genes

cellular transformation   the alteration of normal properties of cells in culture, such that cells continue to multiply and to migrate indefinitely, producing mounds of disordered cells rather than a confluent single layer of cells on solid substratum

cellulose   a fibrous polymer of glucose units found in the plant cell wall and resistant to digestion in most cases because of its intramolecular β-glycosidic links between monomers; a structural polysaccharide

cell wall   the rigid or semirigid covering secreted by the living protoplast of plant, algal, fungal, and prokaryotic cells

centriole   a microtubular structure located at the spindle poles in most kinds of cells, or embedded at the cell periphery, and forming the basal-body portion of a cilium or flagellum, usually containing 9 sets of triplet microtubules that describe a cylinder

centromere   kinetochore; a disk-shaped trilaminate component of the centromere region of a chromosome, consisting of an outer dense layer (centromere plate), a relatively transparent middle layer, and an innermost layer of densely packed chromatin

centromere plate   the outermost dense layer of the centromere, in which spindle fibers are inserted during nuclear division and by which chromosomes are directed to the poles at anaphase of nuclear division

centromere region   primary constriction; the part of a chromosome that includes the site of attachment of spindle fibers and is thus essential for directed anaphase movement of the chromosome

centrosome   a relatively transparent region of cytoplasm at the poles of the dividing cell, surrounded by short microtubules of the aster and enclosing a pair of centrioles plus dense pericentriolar material

channel proteins   a group of transport proteins that form aqueous channels across the membrane and permit solutes of appropriate size and charge to move across the lipid bilayer by free diffusion

chemical signaling   a mode of intercellular communication by which chemical secretions signal target cells at a distance to undertake a particular activity inside the target cell or at its surface

chemiosmotic hypothesis   the proposition by Peter Mitchell that an electrochemical proton gradient is formed across the mitochondrial inner membrane or the chloroplast thylakoid membrane during electron transport, and that the energy stored in this gradient is used to drive ATP synthesis during oxidative phosphorylation in mitochondria or photophosphorylation in chloroplasts—that is, the means by which electron transport is coupled to oxidative phosphorylation or photophosphorylation

chemotroph   any organism that derives energy for metabolism from the oxidation of inorganic compounds and obtains carbon from organic compounds; *see also* **autotroph, heterotroph**

chiasma (*pl.*, **chiasmata**)   a site of exchange between two chromatids of a bivalent, visible as a crossover point in the bivalent during diplonema, diakinesis, and metaphase of meiosis I

chloramphenicol   an antibiotic produced by *Streptomyces venezuelae* that inhibits protein synthesis in prokaryotes, mitochondria, and chloroplasts, but not in eukaryotic cytoplasm, by binding to the large subunit of the ribosome and preventing the addition of an amino acid to the growing polypeptide chain

chlorophylls   the green photosynthetic light-capturing pigments of eukaryotic chloroplasts, located in thylakoid membranes of the organelle; *see also* **bacteriochlorophylls**

chloroplast   the chlorophyll-containing photosynthetic organelle in eukaryotes

chloroplast DNA   the genetic material encoding a number of chloroplast proteins and ribosomal and transfer RNAs, generally occurring as a single circular duplex molecule that is the organelle genome

cholesterol   a major lipid constituent of the plasma membrane of animal cells

chondronectin   a fiber-forming glycoprotein of the extracellular matrix that is a binding agent for chondrocytes to collagen in cartilage matrix

chromatid   one-half of a replicated chromosome and joined to its sister at the centromere region of the whole chromosome

chromatin   the deoxyribonucleoprotein material of the chromosomes

chromatin fiber   the continuous deoxyribonucleoprotein molecule of the chromosome

chromomere   a beadlike or knobby site on a eukaryotic chromosome resulting from local coiling of the chromatin fiber and best seen in relatively decondensed meiotic chromosomes during very early prophase I

chromosomal domain   a region of a chromosome that includes all the components of one or more transcription units and their bordering sequences that undergo structural change during active transcription, as shown by equally heightened sensitivity to DNAase I across the entire region engaged in transcription

chromosome   the gene-containing

deoxyribonucleoprotein structure in the eukaryotic nucleus, but sometimes used to refer to the genetically encoded nucleic acid molecule in bacteria, viruses, mitochondria, and chloroplasts

chromosome complement the set of chromosomes that constitutes the genome in eukaryotes

chromosome theory of heredity the proposition made by William Sutton in 1902 that the genes were located in chromosomes in the nucleus

cilia (*sing.*, **cilium**) a slender hairlike locomotor organelle produced by a centriole and composed of microtubules in a 9 + 2 arrangement, plus other proteinaceous components of the locomotor apparatus

cis **face** the portion of a stack of Golgi cisternae just formed or forming

cisterna (*pl.*, **cisternae**) a flattened membranous sac filled with fluid

clathrin the major polypeptide molecule of the fibrous meshwork coating the cytoplasmic face of the plasma membrane in invaginated pit regions, and the surface of vesicles derived from these pits or from regions of Golgi cisternae

cleavage furrowing; a cell-division mechanism most typical of animals, by which the cell is pinched in two to form daughter cells from a parent cell

closed system in thermodynamics, a self-contained unit that does not exchange matter and energy with its surroundings

CoA *see* **coenzyme A**

coacervate a fluid-filled droplet formed in dilute aqueous solutions, whose boundary develops as a film of bound water molecules; *see also* **protobiont**

coated pits invaginated sites of the plasma membrane that are lined on the cytoplasmic surface with a clathrin meshwork, or coat, and on the exoplasmic surface with receptors that become internalized by receptor-mediated endocytosis

coated vesicles fluid-filled droplets whose outer surface is coated with a clathrin meshwork, and that develop from clathrin-coated pits of the plasma membrane during receptor-mediated endocytosis or from clathrin-coated budding sites of Golgi cisternae

coding sequences exons; the segments of a split gene that are encoded for amino acids in the polypeptide or for nucleotides in the RNA molecule specified by that gene; *see also* **intervening sequences**

codons the triplets of nucleotides in a gene that specify the twenty amino acids and three punctuation signals included in the genetic code

coenzyme A a small organic molecule that participates in energy-transfer reactions as a carrier of activated metabolites, such as acetate or succinate

coenzyme Q ubiquinone; a lipid-soluble quinone that functions as both acceptor and donor of electrons and protons in the mitochondrial respiratory chain

colchicine an alkaloid drug, derived from the autumn crocus, that disrupts most existing microtubules and also prevents their assembly from tubulin monomers

colinear the spatial correspondence between the order of codons in DNA and the order of amino acids in the polypeptide translated from the encoded DNA

collagen one of a family of glycoproteins that make up the extracellular matrix in animals, and whose molecules consist of three α-chain collagen polypeptides wound into a three-stranded helix

collagen fibers assemblies of collagen fibrils in bundles that may measure several micrometers in diameter; part of the extracellular matrix in animals

collagen fibrils polymers assembled from collagen molecules in the extracellular matrix

communicating junctions sites on adjacent plasma membranes that allow ions and small molecules to move freely from one interacting cell to its joined neighbor cell and through the intercellular space; *see also* **gap junctions**

competitive inhibition a reversible inhibition of a catalyzed reaction in which the substrate and a structurally similar inhibitor molecule compete for the same active site of the enzyme; a reaction with unchanged V_{max} and increased K_M

complex oligosaccharides a class of N-linked oligosaccharides covalently added to polypeptides in the rough endoplasmic reticulum and modified later in the Golgi apparatus by the addition of terminal sugar units to a core of sugar residues; *see also* **high-mannose oligosaccharides**

complementary base-pairing specific hydrogen bonding between a particular purine and a particular pyrimidine component in duplex nucleic acid molecules, such that guanine pairs with cytosine and adenine pairs with thymine or uracil

complexity the total length of different or unique sequences in the genome, expressed in base pairs; *see also* **Cot value**

compound microscope an optical instrument whose total magnification capacity is the product of the individual magnifications of at least two different lenses

concatemer a nucleic acid molecule composed of multiple genome sequences covalently joined in tandem

connexon a component of the gap junction between adjacent cells, composed of six molecules of the protein connexin

consensus sequences conserved nucleic acid segments whose order of nucleotides is identical or virtually identical in genomes of a broad variety of organisms

conservative replication the discredited proposal that entirely new duplex DNA molecules are replicated from unaltered parental template duplexes

constant segment the portion of the heavy-chain or light-chain polypeptides of an immunoglobulin molecule that occurs in limited variety at the carboxy terminus of the chain

constitutive heterochromatin those regions of the

chromosomes, often around the centromere, that remain permanently condensed and are late-replicating and genetically stable or inert

contractile ring   a transient encircling system of microfilaments and other components formed under the plasma membrane in the furrow between cleaving cells and perpendicular to the plane of the furrow, which functions in the division of the two daughter cells during cytokinesis

cooperativity   a mechanism of regulation of enzyme activity characterized by greater or lesser responsiveness to substrate concentration by an enzyme composed of two or more subunits and evident in altered enzyme kinetics when compared with a noncooperative enzyme

copy choice   the discredited proposition that newly made strands switch back and forth along template parental strands during DNA replication and copy genes from both parental strands in new combinations (genetic recombinations)

core DNA   the length of 146 base pairs of DNA remaining in the octamer core particle of the nucleosome after all the rest of nucleosomal DNA has been digested by appropriate enzymes

core enzyme   the portion of *E. coli* RNA polymerase that can be separated from sigma (σ) factor and consists of four polypeptide chains ($\alpha_2\beta\beta'$)

corepressor   a metabolite that binds with repressor protein and blocks transcription of a messenger RNA that specifies a repressible enzyme polypeptide

core proteins   the set of proteins that remains with ribosomal RNA after the removal of split proteins from bacterial ribosome subunits treated with CsCl or LiCl to disrupt the particles

Cot value   in renaturation kinetics of DNA, the concentration or fraction of DNA that remains single-stranded at time *t*, expressed in nucleotide moles $\times$ sec per liter and indicative of the total length of unique sequences, or complexity of the genome

cotranslational transfer   transfer across the membrane into the periplasmic space in bacteria or into the lumen of the eukaryote endoplasmic reticulum of growing polypeptides during their translation at the ribosome bound to that membrane; *see also* **vectorial discharge**

covalent bond   interaction between atoms with shared electron shells

cristae (*sing.*, **crista**)   infoldings of the mitochondrial inner membrane

crossing over   physical exchange of homologous chromosome or DNA segments leading to recombination of linked genes; *see also* **breakage and reunion**

cross-linking proteins   a group of actin-binding proteins that link individual actin filaments into a network or bundle, or link actin filaments to the plasma membrane, and thereby regulate nonmuscle contractility; filamin, α-actinin, fimbrin, and vinculin are examples of cross-linking proteins

C value   the characteristic amount of DNA in the genome of a species, measured in picograms, daltons, or base pairs of DNA

C value paradox   referring to the lack of correlation between the size of the genome and the morphological or evolutionary complexity of different species

cyclic AMP   cAMP; adenosine monophosphate with its phosphate group bonded internally to form a cyclic molecule; a mononucleotide involved in the positive control of transcription; *see also* **adenylate cyclase**

cyclic photophosphorylation   the light-dependent synthesis of ATP in which electrons are recycled to the photosynthetic electron transport chain instead of being replenished by external electron donor molecules

cycloheximide   an organic molecule that inhibits protein synthesis at cytoplasmic ribosomes of eukaryotic cells but is ineffective in prokaryotes, mitochondria, and chloroplasts

cytochalasin B   a drug that selectively disrupts microfilaments but has little or no effect on microtubules

cytochemistry   a set of methods by which molecules or activities can be localized in cells or cell sections that process a substance in an assay mixture and produce a distinct reaction product that can be observed by microscopy

cytochrome $b-c_1$ complex   one of the four respiratory enzyme complexes of the mitochondrial inner membrane, which accepts electrons from reduced coenzyme Q and passes these to cytochrome *c*, with a sufficient drop in free energy to sponsor the synthesis of one ATP molecule per pair of electrons transported

cytochrome b_6-f complex   a respiratory enzyme complex of the photosynthetic electron transport chain that links photosystems I and II and is situated within the thylakoid membrane of the chloroplast

cytochrome oxidase   cytochrome $a-a_3$; the terminal enzyme of aerobic respiration, which transfers electrons directly to molecular oxygen

cytochrome oxidase complex   the last in the sequence of four respiratory enzyme complexes of mitochondrial electron transport to oxygen, situated in the mitochondrial inner membrane and able to sponsor the synthesis of one ATP molecule per pair of electrons that pass through the complex

cytochromes   a group of electron transport enzymes containing heme or related prosthetic group components that undergo valency changes of their iron atom in coupled oxidation–reduction reactions

cytokinesis   cell division; any process that separates daughter cells through the enclosure of individual nuclei in individual cells; *see also* **cleavage**

cytoplasm   the protoplasmic contents of the cell exclusive of the nucleus or nucleoid

cytoplasmic streaming   the directed flow of cytoplasm in cells with a rigid wall

cytoribosome   the 70S ribosome in prokaryote

cytoplasm or the 80S ribosome in eukaryote cytoplasm, as distinguished from mitochondrial and chloroplast ribosomes

cytoskeleton   the organized system of microfilaments, intermediate filaments, microtubules, and other fibrous structures in the cytoplasm of eukaryotic cells

cytosol   the unstructured portion of the cytoplasm; the cytoplasmic matrix in which the organelles occur

dark reactions   the light-independent photosynthetic reactions that reduce CO_2 to carbohydrates using the energy of ATP and NADPH made in the light reactions of photosynthesis

decamin filaments   a class of intermediate filaments composed largely of the protein decamin and found mainly in fibroblast cells

dehydrogenase   an enzyme that catalyzes the oxidation of a metabolite and whose NAD, FAD, or similar prosthetic group (1) undergoes reduction as the metabolite is dehydrogenated or (2) undergoes oxidation as the metabolite is reduced

denaturation   the weakening and disruption of the secondary or tertiary structure (or both) of proteins and nucleic acids, leading to loss of function; *see also* **melting**

denaturation mapping   the location of sequences high in A-T base pairs in duplex DNA subjected to mild conditions for partial melting. The sequences rich in G-C base pairs are more resistant to strand separation because they are held together by three hydrogen bonds per pair, whereas only two hydrogen bonds hold A and T together in a duplex molecule

2-deoxy-D-ribose   the pentose sugar unit in DNA and its nucleotide monomers

deoxyribonucleic acid *see* **DNA**

depolarization   discharge of the transmembrane potential in skeletal muscle fibers, caused by the flow of Ca^{2+}, K^+, and Na^+ ions across the sarcolemma

desmosome   an adhering cell junction that may encircle the cell (belt desmosome), be restricted to a localized site at adjacent plasma membranes (spot desmosome), or cause adhesion of a cell by its plasma membrane to a basement layer (hemidesmosome)

diakinesis   the last event of prophase I in meiosis

dictyosome   a stack of cisternae in the Golgi apparatus

differential gene expression   transcription and translation of some genes at the same time that other genes are inactive in the same cells, leading to different phenotypes in cells and organisms that are genetically identical

diplonema   the penultimate event of prophase I and the stage at which bivalents open out at all sites except at the chiasmata

dipole   a molecule carrying positive and negative charges spatially separated at opposite ends of the structure

disaccharides   carbohydrates made up of two sugar

units held together by an α- or a β-glycosidic bond

dispersive replication   a discredited model of DNA replication in which segments of parental and newly synthesized elements are interspersed in random fashion in all the duplex products

dissociation products of water H^+ and OH^- ions formed as water ionizes slightly

diversity segment   a sequence of amino acids situated between the variable and joining regions of an immunoglobulin heavy chain

D loop   a displacement loop consisting of the heavy strand of duplex mitochondrial or chloroplast DNA that bulges out as its partner light strand replicates a new duplex region

D-loop synthesis   a mode of replication of mitochondrial and chloroplast DNA that is characterized by early replication of the light strand and later replication of the heavy strand of the parental duplex

DNA   deoxyribonucleic acid; the genetic material comprised of the nitrogenous bases adenine, guanine, cytosine, and thymine covalently bonded to a chain of repeating deoxyribose and phosphate residues; usually in double helix (duplex) molecular configuration

DNAase   deoxyribonuclease; one of a group of enzymes that digest DNA

DNA double helix   the typical molecular form of the genetic material, existing as a duplex composed of two complementary polynucleotide chains helically wound around each other and joined by hydrogen bonds between paired bases

DNA ligase   the enzyme that catalyzes covalent bonding between free ends of the sugar–phosphate chain during DNA replication, recombination, and repair

DNA polymerase I   a gap-filling enzyme that adds monomer units to the 3'-OH end of another monomer or polymer of DNA

DNA polymerase III   the main replicating enzyme that catalyzes the synthesis of DNA polymers from deoxyribonucleoside triphosphate precursors, using single-stranded regions of duplex DNA as the template

DNA repair synthesis   replacement with new segments of nucleotides in damaged or recombinant molecules via synthesis reactions catalyzed by DNA polymerase and DNA ligase

dolichol   a membrane lipid that mediates the synthesis and processing of an oligosaccharide that is linked via asparagine to a polypeptide (*N*-glycosylation) in the lumen of the rough endoplasmic reticulum, after which the glycoprotein is transported through the ER lumen to the Golgi apparatus

domain   a compact region of a molecule or structure often associated with a particular function or capacity of that molecule or structure

downstream   referring to the region to the right of the startpoint of a gene; *see also* **upstream**

duplication   an extra copy of a nucleotide sequence,

gene, part of a chromosome, or whole chromosome in a cell or individual

dyad   a replicated chromosome consisting of two chromatids

dynein   a protein component with ATPase activity that is part of the arms of subfiber A in microtubule doublets of cilia and flagella in eukaryotes

ecdysone   a steroid hormone derived from cholesterol, produced in the prothoracic gland of insects, and required for molting and pupation

ectoplasm   the outermost gel-like layer of cytoplasm in amebas, *Nitella*, and certain other simple organisms; *see also* **endoplasm**

E face   the fracture face that occurs at the exoplasmic surface of a membrane; *see also* **P face**

egg   the female gamete

elastin   a fiber-forming protein of the extracellular matrix that has elastic properties and is rich in glycine and hydroxyproline but lacks hydroxylysine and neutral sugars

electrochemical gradient   a graduated series of differences in solute concentration and electrical charge along which molecules or ions move by means of diffusion or transport

electrochemical proton gradient   a graduated series of differences in proton (H^+) concentration and positive charge across a membrane, and a source of energy for mitochondrial and chloroplast ATP synthesis; *see also* **chemiosmotic hypothesis**

electron microscope   a magnifying system that uses beams of electrons focused in a vacuum by a series of electromagnetic lenses and that can provide much greater magnification and resolution than conventional light microscopes

electron transfer   a means of energy transfer in oxidation–reduction reactions

electron transport chain   a group of electron carriers, such as cytochromes, that transfers electrons from donor to acceptor along a gradient of decreasing energy and that sponsors the release of energy at each transfer step

electrophoresis   the movement of charged molecules in solution in an electrical field, the solution being held in a porous supporting medium such as cellulose nitrate or a gel made from polyacrylamide, starch, or agar

elongation factors   small molecules that mediate polypeptide chain growth during translation at the ribosome

endergonic   referring to a reaction that is energy-requiring and is characterized by a positive standard free-energy change ($\Delta G°$); *see also* **exergonic**

endocytosis   the intake of solutes or particles via their enclosure in a portion of plasma membrane and their movement into the cell in the resulting vesicles; *see also* **exocytosis**

endomitosis   chromosome replication without subsequent division of the nucleus

endonuclease   an enzyme that breaks one or both strands of a nucleic acid molecule by disrupting internal phosphodiester bonds of the sugar–phosphate chain; *see also* **restriction enzymes**

endoplasm   the more fluid, inner region of cytoplasm in amebas, *Nitella*, and other simple organisms; *see also* **ectoplasm**

endoplasmic reticulum   ER; sheet or sheets of folded membrane in eukaryote cytoplasm that functions as regions of protein synthesis and transport

endosome   an intracellular transport vesicle involved in sorting of proteins and in membrane recycling

endosymbiont theory   the proposal that mitochondria and chloroplasts in eukaryotic cells are evolutionary descendants of ancient free-living prokaryotic organisms

energy   the capacity to do work

energy of activation barrier   *see* **activation energy**

enhancer   a nucleotide sequence that exerts a stimulating influence on gene transcription regardless of its location in the genome

enzymes   the unique protein catalysts of biological systems

enzyme kinetics   the quantitative analysis of enzyme activity

equilibrium density gradient centrifugation   a method for separating macromolecules and cellular components according to differences that cause them to come to rest in regions of the gradient with solute densities corresponding to their own buoyant densities in the solute. The gradation of solute densities develops during centrifugation at very high speeds.

ER   the common abbreviation for endoplasmic reticulum

erythrocytes   mature red blood cells

etioplasts   transformed chloroplasts of dark-grown cells or organisms, lacking normal thylakoid organization and pigments; *see also* **prolamellar body**

eubionts   true life forms; *see also* **protobiont**

euchromatin   the noncondensed, active chromosomes or chromosome segments of the interphase nucleus; *see also* **heterochromatin**

eukaryote   an organism with a well-defined nucleus bounded by a nuclear envelope and usually having one or more membranous cytoplasmic organelles; *see also* **prokaryote**

excitation   a gain in energy by an atom that has absorbed sufficient energy to cause an electron to move to an orbital of higher accessible energy level, or an excited state

exergonic   referring to a reaction that is energy-releasing and is characterized by a negative standard free-energy change ($-\Delta G°$); *see also* **endergonic**

exocytosis   a mode of transport of substances out of a cell via the fusion of their membranous envelope with the plasma membrane and their subsequent expulsion to the outside; *see also* **endocytosis**

exon *see* **coding sequences**

exoplasmic fracture (EF) face the fracture surface of the split membrane bilayer that is closer to the cell exterior and farther from the cytoplasm; *see also* **protoplasmic fracture (PF) face**

extracellular matrix an organized external structure composed of protein and carbohydrate secretions from the cell or cells, which may be distributed within this matrix in animal connective tissue; *see also* **collagen**, **proteoglycans**

F actin the fibrous polymeric form of actin protein

FAD, FADH$_2$ the common abbreviations for the oxidized and reduced forms, respectively, of flavin adenine dinucleotide; *see also* **redox couple**

facultative heterochromatin condensed, late-replicating regions of the chromosomes that may revert to the euchromatic state under particular conditions; *see also* **constitutive heterochromatin**; **X inactivation**

fatty acids long hydrocarbon chain components of neutral fats, phospholipids, and various other lipids, having one or more double-bonded CH residues (unsaturated) or lacking these (saturated); fuel molecules whose oxidation provides free energy for the cell

feedback inhibition a control mechanism that regulates enzyme activity via inhibition of an enzyme catalyzing an early reaction in a multistep pathway by the end product of that pathway, thereby stopping further production of that end product

fermentation the oxidation of carbohydrate in oxygen-independent pathways; *see also* **glycolysis**

ferredoxin an iron–sulfur protein that has the high reducing potential of -0.6 volts and transfers electrons in various pathways, including the sequence from reaction-center chlorophyll *a* (P700) of photosystem I to NADP$^+$ in the light reactions of photosynthesis

fertilization the fusion of egg and sperm or other pairs of gametes to produce the zygote that initiates a new generation

F$_O$F$_1$ATPase the ATP synthetase of mitochondrial oxidative phosphorylation and of chloroplast photophosphorylation, that can also catalyze the hydrolysis of ATP under certain conditions

fibroblast a cell type of connective tissue in animals

fibronectin a fiber-forming glycoprotein of the extracellular matrix (cellular fibronectin) or of the blood and other body fluids (plasma fibronectin) that functions in blood clotting and, for cellular fibronectin, in cell adhesion

filamin a cross-linking, actin-binding protein that links together two or more individual actin filaments into a three-dimensional network of loose construction

fimbrin a small cross-linking, actin-binding protein that promotes tight bundling of actin filaments in parallel register

first law of thermodynamics energy can be neither created nor destroyed; statement of the principle of the conservation of energy in the universe

flagella (*sing.*, **flagellum**) whiplike locomotor organelles of very different chemical composition and construction in bacteria and eukaryotes; the microtubular-based eukaryotic appendages that are identical to cilia except that they are much longer and are usually, but not always, less numerous per cell

flagellin the protein monomer from which are formed the polymeric filaments that make up the bacterial flagellum

flavin adenine dinucleotide FAD; an electron-carrying molecule that participates in electron-transfer reactions as a coenzyme portion of an enzyme. FADH$_2$ is the reduced form of the redox couple.

flavin adenine mononucleotide FMN; riboflavin 5-phosphate; an electron-carrying molecule that participates in electron transfer-reactions, usually as the coenzyme portion of an enzyme. FMNH$_2$ is the reduced form of the redox couple.

flavoprotein a catalytic protein composed of one or more polypeptides and a flavin cyclic molecular component (such as NAD, FAD, FMN, and others) that can transfer electrons in oxidation–reductions

fluid mosaic membrane the generally accepted structural form of cell membranes, whose proteins are distributed in and on a phospholipid bilayer that has the consistency of a light oil and thus permits molecular mobility within the plane of the membrane

fMet the common abbreviation for *N*-formylmethionine, the initiator amino acid in prokaryotic and organellar protein synthesis at the ribosome

FMN the common abbreviation for flavin adenine mononucleotide

forming face the *cis* face of a stack of Golgi cisternae

fragmin an actin-binding capping protein that binds to one end or the other of an actin filament and thereby regulates the length of the actin polymer

free energy the energy that can be used to do work in biological systems

freeze-fracturing a method for preparing materials for electron microscopy by rapid freezing at very low temperatures and subsequent fracturing of the brittle material. The exposed fracture faces may or may not be etched before a platinum replica is prepared for microscopy.

fructose 6-phosphate a phosphorylated hexose sugar involved as an intermediate in the synthesis or breakdown of glucose and polysaccharides in the cell

furrowing a cleavage process of cell division in animals and many protists

fusion of gametes the act of sexual reproduction by which the zygote of the new generation is formed; *see also* **fertilization**

G actin   the protein monomer of polymeric F actin and microfilaments

gamete   a reproductive cell, such as egg or sperm, that can develop only after uniting with another, compatible reproductive cell to produce the new individual of the next generation

gametophyte   the haploid structure or individual that produces gametes in plants; *see also* **sporophyte**

gap junction   the principal form of communicating junction between cells in animal tissues, allowing ions and many molecules to move freely between joined cells and within the intercellular spaces

gated pore   a transport protein or protein complex that opens only in response to a particular stimulus and is otherwise closed

G-banding   a method of staining chromosomes with Giemsa stain to reveal patterns of deeply stained bands separated by lightly stained regions, permitting each chromosome in the genome to be uniquely identified

gel electrophoresis   *see* **electrophoresis**

gelsolin   an actin-binding capping protein that binds to one end or the other of an actin filament and thereby regulates the length of the actin polymer

gene   a unit of inheritance that occupies a particular site, or locus, on the chromosome and encodes the structure of a polypeptide or RNA molecule or regulates the activity and behavior of a structural gene, and that can mutate to one or more alternative allelic forms

gene amplification   repeated replications of some genes, producing many copies, at the same time that other genes do not replicate in the same cell

gene expression   the readout of encoded genetic information in DNA (or RNA) during transcription and translation, which leads to phenotypic development in the cell or individual

genetic code   the base triplets of DNA and RNA that specify the twenty amino acids used in protein synthesis during translation at the ribosome, plus START and STOP codons that punctuate the genetic message

genetic engineering   a set of methods by which genes from one species are spliced with genes from other species to form recombinant-DNA molecules that can enter a chosen host cell and be replicated and expressed in that cell and its clonal descendants

genome   all the genes present in the chromosome or set of chromosomes that specify all the inherited traits of a cell or individual

genomic flux   the concept of the genome existing in a dynamic and changing state rather than as a stable and passive set of genes occupying fixed locations and each gene destined only to be translated into a polypeptide or RNA encoded in the nucleotide sequence

genomic library   a collection of cloned DNA derived from restriction fragments of the chromosomes and including all or part of the genetic material of a species or strain of organisms

genotype   the genetic constitution of a cell or organism as distinguished from its expressed features (phenotype)

glial filaments   intermediate filaments composed of vimentin and an acidic protein, found in glial cells of the central nervous system in animals

gluconeogenesis   the synthesis of carbohydrates from such noncarbohydrate precursors as fats and proteins

glycolysis   the oxidation of sugar to pyruvate in fermentation reactions that are independent of molecular oxygen; the Embden–Meyerhof pathway

glycophorin   an integral glycoprotein that spans the thickness of the human erythrocyte plasma membrane and whose sugar residues are at the extracellular face of the membrane along with most of its 131 amino acid units

glycosidic bond   the link between monomeric sugars in disaccharides, oligosaccharides, and polysaccharides

glycosaminoglycans   GAGs; long, unbranched polysaccharide chains composed of repeating disaccharide units one of whose two monosaccharide residues is always the hexosamine (amino sugar) *N*-acetylglucosamine or *N*-acetylgalactosamine, occurring in the extracellular matrix of animals as covalently linked components of proteoglycans (except for hyaluronic acid)

glycosome   an organelle in trypanosomes that resembles a microbody in morphology but uniquely possesses glycolytic enzymes and lacks the flavin-oxidase–catalase system that is typical of microbodies

glycoprotein   a protein that contains one or more sugar residues

glyoxylate cycle   a set of reactions catalyzed by five enzymes, three of which are also Krebs cycle enzymes and two of which are unique to the cycle (malate synthase and isocitrate lyase), serving to provide or replenish intermediary metabolites

glyoxysome   a type of microbody characterized by a large repertory of enzymes, including enzymes of the glyoxylate cycle, and especially prominent in fatty seed endosperm and young seedlings of the same plants

Golgi apparatus   a region of smooth membranes organized as stacks of cisternae, anastomosing tubules, vesicles, and vacuoles, whose function is the processing and packaging of secretory proteins and lysosomal enzymes

gonads   the sex organs in which gametes are produced, such as ovary and testis in animals

G_1 phase   the portion of a cell cycle that begins after mitosis (M phase) and terminates when DNA replication begins (S phase); early interphase

G_2 phase   the portion of a cell cycle that begins with the termination of S phase and concludes when mitosis begins; late interphase

granum (*pl.*, **grana**)   a stack of flattened, coin-shaped sacs or grana thylakoids containing the components of the light reactions of photosynthesis

G_0 state   an interval when cells are not proceeding through the cell cycle; a noncycling state

gyrase a colloquial term for topoisomerase II, the DNA replication enzyme that sponsors supercoiling of duplex DNA via nicking and closing reactions

HAT medium a selective growth medium that contains the nucleic acid precursors hypoxanthine and thymidine and the drug aminopterin and that permits the growth of somatic cell hybrids carrying the alleles to produce hypoxanthine-guanine phosphoribosyl transferase (HPRT) and thymidine kinase (TK) to catalyze nucleic acid synthesis by a salvage pathway not blocked by aminopterin

heavy chain H-chain; the higher-molecular-weight polypeptide chain of the immunoglobulin molecule, comprised of variable segment, diversity segment, joining segment, and constant segment, each encoded by a different gene cluster; *see also* **light chain**

heavy-chain class switching during development of B lymphocytes, the rearrangement of constant-segment (*C*) genes such that one or more upstream genes are deleted and the downstream genes spliced to existing *VDJ* sequences to make a new *VDJC* combination encoding a different functional class of antibodies (immunoglobulins) due to the presence of a different constant segment in the heavy chain

heavy-chain gene assembly splicing of one *V* gene, one *D* gene, and one *J* gene from their respective gene clusters and joining of the *VDJ* sequence to the *C*-gene cluster to make a DNA template for the heavy chain of an immunoglobulin molecule in B lymphocytes

helicase a DNA replication enzyme with ATPase activity that moves ahead at the replication fork and disrupts hydrogen bonds between paired bases in the duplex molecule, thereby making each template strand accessible for synthesis of its complementary partner strand

hematopoietic referring to the capacity of stem cells to produce blood cells

heme an iron-containing porphyrin derivative in hemoglobins and in such enzymes as catalase and cytochromes

hemicellulose a branched polysaccharide that has no net electrical charge and is a molecular constituent of plant cell walls

hemidesmosome an adhering junction that binds the basal portion of a cell to an underlying basement substance, particularly in epithelium tissue

heterochromatin the chromosomes or parts of chromosomes that are condensed in the interphase nucleus, late replicating, and genetically stable or inert; *see also* **constitutive heterochromatin, facultative heterochromatin**, **euchromatin**

heteroduplex analysis the study by electron microscopy of homology and complementarity of single strands of DNA or of DNA and RNA in duplex molecules whose individual components come from different parts of the cell or from different strains or species of organisms

heterotrophic referring to a type of cell or organism that obtains its carbon and energy via the oxidation of organic molecules

highly repetitive DNA DNA consisting of millions of repeated short sequences of nucleotides, usually occurring in large clusters in eukaryotic genomes

high-mannose oligosaccharides a class of *N*-linked oligosaccharides whose terminal region consists exclusively of mannose residues and that is part of glycoproteins assembled in the rough endoplasmic reticulum but processed in the Golgi apparatus later on; *see also* **complex oligosaccharides**

high-mobility-group proteins HMG proteins; nonhistone chromosomal proteins with high electrophoretic mobility that appear to alter the conformation of chromatin or to stabilize altered conformations and are concentrated in actively transcribing regions of chromosomes

Hill reaction the generation of molecular oxygen in the light by green cells or by chloroplasts, with the concomitant reduction of $NADP^+$ but without the accumulation of CO_2 reduction products

histones any of five major types of basic chromosomal proteins that are characterized by high arginine and/or lysine content and are part of nucleosomes of the chromatin fiber

Hogness box TATA box; the -25 sequence in eukaryotic promoters that is involved in the binding of RNA polymerase in the initiation of messenger RNA transcription; the eukaryotic equivalent of the Pribnow box in prokaryotic promoters

hormone a chemical substance secreted by one organ and influential in the activities of other organs or tissues reached via the circulatory system

hybrid duplexes heteroduplexes; double-stranded nucleic acid molecules formed by annealing DNA strands or by DNA and RNA strands from different sources

hydrogen bond a weak chemical interaction between a hydrogen atom covalently linked to an oxygen or nitrogen atom in a molecule and a neighboring electronegative atom of oxygen or nitrogen covalently linked in a residue

hydrogenosome an organelle in trichomonatids that resembles a microbody in morphology but uniquely possesses a respiratory system and lacks the flavin-oxidase–catalase system that is typical of microbodies

hydrolysis the splitting of a molecule into two or more smaller molecules upon the addition of elements from water; one type of energy-releasing reaction

hydrophobic interaction a weak interacting force between water-repelling, nonpolar residues and molecules, such as between fatty acid chains of membrane phospholipids or between stacked aromatic bases in DNA

hyperchromic shift the increase in absorbance at 260 nm of single-stranded DNA compared with duplex DNA at the same concentration, thus an indication of melting

hypersensitive site in chromatin, a place of cleavage

by very mild DNAase digestion and an indicator of actively transcribing chromosome regions

hypoxanthine-guanine phosphoribosyl transferase   HPRT; the enzyme that catalyzes purine synthesis from hypoxanthine precursors of DNA; *see also* **HAT medium**

I band   a region of striated muscle myofibrils shared by two adjacent sarcomeres and bisected by a Z disc, containing only actin filaments and alternating with A bands in which the actin filaments terminate

immunoglobulins   Ig; any of five classes of antibody molecules, each consisting of two heavy and two light polypeptide chains, made in B lymphocytes and secreted when these become plasma cells after activation by antigens; the molecules that neutralize invading antigens in an immune response

impermeable junctions   those regions of the plasma membranes of adjacent cells that are fused and thus occlude the intercellular passageway; tight junctions

inducible enzyme   any of a type of catalyst that is synthesized only in the presence of its substrate (inducer) and is subject to transcriptional control

initiation codon   the nucleotide triplet AUG in messenger RNA, to which the initiating Met-tRNA or fMet-tRNA binds and starts polypeptide translation at the ribosome; the unit of the genetic code that specifies the *N*-terminal amino acid methionine or its derivative, *N*-formylmethionine; START codon

initiation complex   the aggregate of messenger RNA, a small ribosome subunit, and initiator aminoacyl-tRNA that marks the start of polypeptide translation from encoded genetic information

initiation factors   small molecules that bind to the small ribosome subunit of the initiation complex and aid in the initiation of polypeptide synthesis during translation

initiator aminoacyl-tRNA   the Met-tRNA or fMet-tRNA that binds to the initiation codon AUG in messenger RNA and starts polypeptide translation at the ribosome

inner mitochondrial membrane   the innermost of the two-membrane envelope of the mitochondrion; the membrane infolded into cristae. This structure contains enzymes and other components of the electron transport chain and is the site of ATP synthesis of aerobic respiration

inner sheath   the proteinaceous structure surrounding the two singlet microtubules of the ciliary or flagellar axoneme, to which the knobs of the radial spokes are bound

insertion sequence   IS; a transposable genetic element less than 2000 bases long that has inverted repeat base sequences at its termini and contains no other genes than those involved in its insertion and removal from DNA

***in situ* hybridization**   a cytological method for localizing chromosomal DNA regions that are complementary to specific added nucleic acid probes, by observing silver grain deposits in autoradiographs of the chromosome preparation on a microscope slide

integral protein   a molecular component of the fluid mosaic membrane, extending partly or completely through the lipid bilayer and protruding from one surface of the membrane or from both surfaces, respectively; *see also* **peripheral protein**

intermediate filaments   the 10-nm-wide, relatively inflexible fibers of the cytoskeleton in eukaryotic cytoplasm, composed of monomers of various proteins, such as decamin, vimentin, and others

intermembrane space   the region between the outer and inner membranes of the mitochondrion, and one of the four functional compartments of the organelle

interphase   the interval between mitotic or meiotic divisions of the eukaryote nucleus; the portion of the cell cycle that includes G_1, S, and G_2 periods

intervening sequences   introns; the transcribed noncoding segments of split genes that alternate with coding sequences (exons) but are excised from pre-messenger RNA during its processing to mature messenger RNA

intranuclear mitosis   the segregation of two sets of replicated chromosomes in a nucleus whose nuclear envelope remains intact throughout the division process

intron   an intervening sequence in split genes

ionic bond   an electrostatic bond

ionophores   a class of bacterial antibiotics that facilitate the transfer of monovalent and divalent cations across the membrane

iron–porphyrin   a molecular constituent, such as heme, that binds oxygen (in hemoglobins) or participates in electron transfer (in cytochromes) and is usually complexed with protein

irreversible inhibition   the irremediable cessation of a reaction because of the reduction or abolition of enzyme activity due to its binding with an agent (inhibitor) that alters the conformation of the catalyst sponsoring the reaction

IS   the common abbreviation for insertion sequence

isocitrate lyase   an enzyme of the glyoxylate cycle or bypass that catalyzes the formation of succinate (four carbons) and glyoxylate (two carbons) from isocitrate (six carbons)

isoelectric point   the pH at which equal numbers of positive and negative charges occur in a protein; the net charge is thus 0

isomers   alternative stereochemical forms of a molecule

isotopes   alternative forms of an element characterized by a different number of neutrons (atomic weight) but the same number of protons (atomic number) in the atomic nucleus. Heavy isotopes, such as ^{2}H and ^{15}N, are stable, whereas radioactive isotopes, such as ^{3}H, ^{14}C, and ^{32}P, are unstable and undergo beta decay (emit electrons)

isozymes   alternative molecular forms of an enzyme

joining segment J_H of the heavy-chain and J_L of the light-chain polypeptides of the immunoglobulin molecule that joins with the variable segment in light-chain assembly and with the variable-diversity segments in heavy-chain assembly before the V-J or V-D-J aggregate combines with a constant (C) segment of the two kinds of polypeptide chains to complete the sequence

joint molecule   a recombination intermediate produced by strand exchange during crossing over between two DNA duplex molecules and consists of the joined duplexes that can rotate to assume a planar form; chi figure

junctions   differentiated regions of the plasma membranes of adjacent cells, contributing to intercellular communication and cell adhesion; *see also* **adhering junctions, communicating junctions, impermeable junctions**

karyotype   a distribution of photographed chromosomes from a cell or individual, showing all the chromosomes arranged in homologous pairs in order of their centromere location and decreasing size

keratin filaments   a class of intermediate filaments whose main constituent is the protein keratin; tonofilaments of epithelial cells

kinetochore   centromere

Klinefelter syndrome   a clinical condition of human males having one or more extra X chromosomes

Krebs cycle   a common pathway for the complete oxidation to CO_2 of pyruvate or acetyl CoA derived from fuel oxidations in the cytosol, dependent on the presence of molecular oxygen and occurring in the mitochondrial matrix of eukaryotes and in the cytoplasm of prokaryotes

laminin   a fiber-forming glycoprotein in the underlying basal lamina (basement membrane) that serves as a binding agent for epithelial cells to collagen

lampbrush chromosomes   giant bivalents that have extensively looped-out regions of the chromatin fibers and are especially prominent in amphibian oocyte nuclei during the diplonema stage of meiotic prophase I

LDL   the common abbreviation for low-density lipoproteins

leader   a base sequence at the 5′ end of messenger RNA that is transcribed from the +1 startpoint nucleotide up to the initiation codon (TAC) of DNA but is usually not translated; a base sequence that is located between the promoter and structural genes in various biosynthetic operons in bacteria, and that, in its RNA transcript form, is involved in attenuation control of transcription

leader peptide   the translation of a sequence of leader codons that serves in attenuation control of the transcription of bacterial biosynthetic operons

leader sequence   the order of nucleotides in the region of RNA transcribed from the +1 startpoint nucleotide to the initiation codon in the template DNA

lectins   plant proteins, such as concanavalin A, that act as ligands and bind to particular sugar residues of membrane glycoproteins and glycolipids

leptonema   the first event of prophase I of meiosis

leucocytes   any of various kinds of white blood cells, such as lymphocytes, that function in various ways in the body's defense against disease

ligands   substances that bind to cellular molecules or structures

light chain   L-chain; the lower-molecular-weight polypeptide chain of the immunoglobulin molecule, consisting of a variable segment, a joining segment, and a constant segment, each encoded by a different gene cluster; *see also* **heavy chain**

light-chain gene assembly   splicing of one *V* and one *J* gene from their respective clusters, and joining of the *VJ* sequence to the *C*-gene cluster to make a template for the light chain of an immunoglobulin molecule in B lymphocytes

light reactions   a photosynthetic pathway by which light energy is transformed to chemical energy in the forms of ATP and NADPH

linked genes   genes that occur together on the same chromosome or DNA molecule

linker DNA   the portion of nucleosomal DNA that is most readily digested, in contrast to the 146 base pairs that remain unaltered in the core particle

low-density lipoproteins   LDL; the complex of esterified cholesterol molecules that is transported in the blood in LDL particles, taken into cells by receptor-mediated endocytosis, and rendered to free cholesterol molecules in lysosomes

lymphocyte   a type of white blood cell that functions in immune response systems and is either of the antibody-secreting B-cell (plasma cell) type or of the T-cell type that underwrites the cell-mediated immune response system

Lyonization   *see* **X inactivation**

lysosome   a membrane-bounded eukaryotic organelle that contains a variety of acid hydrolases capable of digesting virtually any biologically important organic compound

macronucleus   the larger nucleus of a ciliated protozoan, with all expected biological activities except for mitosis and meiosis; *see also* **micronucleus**

malate synthase   the unique enzyme of the glyoxylate cycle or bypass that catalyzes the synthesis of malate from glyoxylate and acetyl CoA

MAPs   the common abbreviation for microtubule-associated proteins

matrix   a semisolid suspension in the interior of mitochondria and chloroplasts and an organic medium of proteoglycans and other molecular secretions called the extracellular matrix

mature mRNA   the colinear copy of DNA-encoded information specifying the amino acid sequence in a polypeptide; spliced and processed pre-mRNA in eukaryotes

maturing face   the *trans* face of a stack of Golgi cisternae

Maxam–Gilbert base sequencing method   a set of procedures in which four equal aliquots of a preparation of single-stranded DNA restriction fragments are exposed to chemical agents that cause breaks at A, T, G, and C residues, and from which the exact sequence of bases can be read from the bands in autoradiographs of gels containing the electrophoretically separated broken fragments from each of the four aliquots

megakaryocytes   large blood cells in the bone marrow that give rise to platelets by a budding-like process

megaspore   a product of meiosis in plants that develops into the female gametophyte in which the female gamete (egg) arises by mitosis; *see also* **microspore**

meiocyte   a reproductive cell capable of meiosis, such as oocyte, spermatocyte, sporocyte, and others

meiosis   the reduction division of the nucleus in a sexual organism, which produces daughter nuclei having half the number of chromosomes and half the DNA content of the original meiocyte nucleus. The process consists of two successive divisions and results in the production of a quartet of gametes or sexual spores, only one of which may be functional in females

meiosis I, **meiosis II**   the first and second divisions of meiosis

melting   the dissociation of duplex nucleic acid molecules into single strands upon disruption of the hydrogen bonds that hold the strands together; *see also* **denaturation**

membrane recycling   the retrieval and re-use of existing membrane domains that retain their original specificity; for example, the intake by endocytosis of receptor-laden plasma membrane segments and their return to the cell surface during exocytosis

meristematic cells   stem-cell equivalents in plants that retain mitotic activity and give rise to daughter cells that differentiate into various types and to daughter cells that remain meristematic and thus maintain the system

meromyosin   the parts of a myosin molecule produced by trypsin digestion. One part is heavy meromyosin and has ATPase activity, and the other part is light meromyosin and lacks enzymatic activity.

mesosome   an extensively infolded region of the plasma membrane in bacteria, sometimes implicated in respiratory and cell-division processes

messenger RNA   mRNA; the complementary copy of the coding strand of DNA, made during transcription and containing the encoded genetic information for polypeptide synthesis during translation at the ribosome; *see also* **mature mRNA**, **pre-messenger RNA**

metabolism   the sum total of biochemical reactions in biological systems; *see also* **anabolism**, **catabolism**

metacentric   designating a chromosome whose centromere is centrally located and whose two arms are therefore of equal length

metaphase   the stage of meiosis or mitosis when chromosomes are aligned along the equatorial plane of the spindle

metaphase I   the metaphase stage of the first meiotic division

5-methylcytosine   a methylated derivative of the deoxyribonucleoside cytosine in DNA

7-methylguanosine   an unusual purine derivative that binds in its nucleoside triphosphate form to the 5′ terminus of eukaryote pre-messenger RNA and serves to "cap" that terminus

Michaelis–Menten equation   a quantitative means to determine the effect of substrate concentration on the velocity of reaction as an index of enzyme activity (rate of catalysis)

microbody   a membrane-bounded eukaryote cytoplasmic organelle with varied enzyme contents and functions but usually having a flavin-oxidase–catalase system; the general morphological equivalent for peroxisome and glyoxysome

microfilament   a long, 6-nm-wide, unbranched structure composed of two intertwined actin polymers and associated proteins, which is part of the cytoskeleton and one of the major components of the cellular contractile machinery

micronucleus   the smaller of the two kinds of nuclei in ciliated protozoa and the only one capable of undergoing mitosis and meiosis, but otherwise lacking biochemical functions; *see also* **macronucleus**

microsome   a vesicular membrane fragment of the endoplasmic reticulum produced during preparations for centrifugation or during centrifugation

microspore   a product of meiosis in plants that develops into the male gametophyte in which the male gametes are produced by mitosis; *see also* **megaspore**

microtrabecular lattice   a network of fine filamentous material dispersed throughout the cytoplasm as interconnecting links between cytoskeletal filaments and other fibrous structures

microtubules   25-nm-wide, hollow, unbranched, cylindrical assemblies of tubulin polymers (protofilaments) found as major structural elements of the cytoskeleton, the spindle, and cilia and flagella, and involved in chromosome and ciliary movement

microtubule-associated proteins   MAPs; molecules that bind to microtubules and guide their functions in motility phenomena

microtubule-organizing centers   MTOCs; sites of nucleation and assembly or disassembly of microtubules in the cell

microvilli (*sing.*, **microvillus**)   thin, fingerlike projections of the plasma membrane that have an internal core of actin filaments extending into the peripheral cytoplasm

midbody   dense materials and remnants of spindle fibers in the furrow between cleaving cells; forms during cytokinesis and disappears shortly before cell division is completed

middle-repetitive DNA   DNA consisting of hundreds or thousands of repeated nucleotide sequences encoding rRNA, tRNA, and certain proteins in eukaryotes

midpoint melting temperature T_m; the temperature at which 50% of DNA in solution is converted from duplex to single-stranded polynucleotides as the result of the disruption of hydrogen bonds between paired bases in the molecules; useful as an index of the GC content of the nucleic acid

misreading   the incorrect translation of one or more codons in messenger RNA, producing polypeptides with amino acid substitutions at the misread sites

mitochondrial DNA   mtDNA; the genome of the organelle carrying encoded information for organelle rRNA, tRNAs, and a selected group of polypeptides that are subunits of respiratory enzymes in the mitochondrial inner membrane; a circular (almost always), duplex DNA molecule in the organelle matrix

mitochondrion   the eukaryote cytoplasmic organelle that is bounded by an outer membrane and an inner membrane that infolds into cristae and is the center of aerobic respiratory activities and ATP synthesis in the cell

mitosis   the division of the nucleus that produces two daughter nuclei identical to each other and to the parent nucleus; somatic or vegetative nuclear division

modulator   an allosteric molecule that inhibits or stimulates a catalyzed reaction by binding to the enzyme surface elsewhere than the active site

molecular biology   a branch of modern biology concerned with explaining biological phenomena in molecular terms and often utilizing techniques of physical chemistry to investigate biological problems

molecular hybridization   the formation of DNA-DNA, DNA-RNA, or RNA-RNA duplex molecules by the hydrogen bonding of complementary single-stranded molecules or parts of molecules under suitable experimental conditions; a test for nucleic acid complementarity; *see also* **heteroduplex analysis**

monomer   the basic subunit of a larger functional molecule, particle, or cellular entity

monomer-stabilizing proteins   a class of actin-binding proteins that bind to G-actin monomers and prevent their assembly into actin polymers and microfilaments, thus stabilizing the monomer pool and controlling the monomer–polymer equilibrium in nonmuscle cells; *see also* **capping proteins, cross-linking proteins, profilin**

monosaccharide   a hexose or pentose sugar; the monomeric unit of disaccharide, oligosaccharide, and polysaccharide carbohydrate compounds

monosome   a single ribosome that may be one of an aggregate (polysome) engaged in translation

M phase   the portion of a cell cycle when mitosis occurs

mRNA   the common abbreviation for messenger RNA

mtDNA   the common abbreviation for mitochondrial DNA

multigene family   a set of genes derived by duplication

of an ancestral gene and varying from that gene and from each other in nucleotide sequence but still encoding functionally similar polypeptides or RNAs

muscle fiber   a multinucleate "cell" of striated muscle tissue that arises by the fusion of individual myoblasts during development and differentiation in the animal and contains many nuclei, sarcoplasmic reticulum, mitochondria, myofilaments, and other cytoplasmic components, all surrounded by a plasma membrane called a sarcolemma

mutagen   a physical or chemical agent that raises the rate of mutation of a gene significantly above its spontaneous mutation rate; a mutagenic agent

mutation   a process whereby a gene undergoes a change in its base composition, base sequence, or organization; a modified gene resulting from mutational events

myofibril   long, cylindrical bundles of actin filaments and myosin filaments in the sarcoplasm of a muscle fiber of striated muscle, and the fibrous contractile apparatus of the muscle

myosin   the protein monomer molecule of myosin filaments, with ATPase activity in the head or S1 region of the tailed molecule, itself composed of two subunit polypeptide chains that are helically wound around each other

myosin filaments   thick filaments; 15-nm-wide, long, fibrous structures composed of myosin molecules in polymers and prominent in striated muscle but present in smaller amounts in the cytoplasm of many kinds of cells, where they may be part of the cytoskeleton and participate in movement phenomena as contractile components

myosin light-chain kinase   in nonmuscle cells, an enzyme that phosphorylates one of the two pairs of light polypeptide chains in the head of myosin molecules, relieving the inhibition of myosin ATPase activity, and whose own activity is regulated by the calcium-binding protein calmodulin

NAD   the common abbreviation for nicotinamide adenine dinucleotide

NADH dehydrogenase complex   the first in the sequence of four respiratory enzyme complexes of the inner mitochondrial membrane that transfers electrons from NADH to subsequent components of the electron transport chain and sponsors a sufficient free-energy drop for the synthesis of one ATP molecule per pair of electrons passed to the next member of the chain

NADP   the common abbreviation for nicotinamide adenine dinucleotide phosphate, a redox-couple molecule that accepts and transfers electrons in many biosynthetic reactions (oxidized form, $NADP^+$; reduced form, NADPH)

Na^+–K^+ ATPase   a transmembrane catalytic protein that hydrolyzes ATP and provides the free energy for active transport of Na^+ out of the cell and of K^+ into the cell; an ion pump that generates and maintains the voltage gradient across the membrane, thereby providing energy for the active transport of sugars and amino acids into the cell

Na$^+$–K$^+$ pump   designation of the action of Na$^+$–K$^+$ ATPase as a system that pumps Na$^+$ out of the cell and K$^+$ into it, creating a voltage gradient across the membrane that provides the energy required to move sugars and amino acids into the cell against their concentration gradients

natural selection   the differential reproduction of genetically diverse types in populations, which results in individuals of greater fitness leaving more descendants than do others of lesser fitness and, therefore, leads to changes in gene frequencies over time; Darwinism

negative control   one of a class of mechanisms regulating gene expression, by which transcription is turned off through the blocking of an operator adjacent to one or more structural genes, or through attenuation, and transcription is turned on by removal of the block (repressor); *see also* **positive control**

neurofilaments   the term applied to intermediate filaments in nervous tissue

neutral fats   fatty acid esters of the alcohol glycerol, and a major storage form of lipids

nexin   the protein molecular component of links between microtubule doublets in eukaryote cilia and flagella

nicotinamide adenine dinucleotide   NAD; a redox-couple molecule that accepts and transfers electrons in many catabolic reactions, generally occurring as the coenzyme portion of dehydrogenases and various other enzymes (oxidized form, NAD$^+$; reduced form, NADH)

***N*-formylmethionine**   fMet; the formylated derivative of methionine that serves as the initiating amino acid in polypeptide synthesis at the ribosome in prokaryotes, mitochondria, and chloroplasts

***N*-linked oligosaccharides**   a class of short chains of sugars that are covalently linked via an asparagine residue to polypeptides synthesized in the endoplasmic reticulum. As glycoproteins, the conjugated molecules are transported via the ER to the Golgi apparatus. *See also* **complex oligosaccharides**, **high-mannose oligosaccharides**

30-nm fiber   the native chromatin fiber of the eukaryote nucleus, in contrast to the 10-nm-wide, stretched chromatin fiber or histone-depleted chromatin fiber

noncompetitive inhibition   a type of reversible inhibition of enzyme activity in which the inhibitor and substrate bind simultaneously to different sites of an enzyme, and that is kinetically evident by reduced V_{max} and unchanged K_M of the reaction; *see also* **competitive inhibition**

noncyclic photophosphorylation   the light-dependent synthesis of ATP that is coupled to electron transport between photosystems II and I in chloroplast photosynthesis and requires a continued external supply of electrons from water via chlorophyll of photosystem II

nonpolar   referring to chemical groups whose negative charge of symmetrically distributed electrons is shared equally by covalently bonded atoms; a characteristic of hydrophobic residues and molecules

nonrepetitive DNA   the unique, nonrepeated nucleotide sequences of a genome

NOR   the common abbreviation for a nucleolar-organizing region of the eukaryote chromosome, where ribosomal RNA genes are clustered and where the nucleolus is located or formed during telophase of a nuclear division

***N* terminus**   the amino-terminal end of a polypeptide and the first portion of the chain to be synthesized during translation at the ribosome, in contrast to the *C* terminus, which is the carboxy-terminal end of the chain and the last portion to be synthesized

nuclear envelope   the double-membrane boundary of the eukaryotic nucleus

nuclear lamina   a fibrous protein meshwork that forms a continuous sheath abutting the inner surface of the nuclear envelope on one side and bound to condensed chromatin on its inner surface

nuclear pore complex   a site of local fusion of the two membranes of the nuclear envelope, characterized by a narrow opening (pore) bordered on each surface of the envelope by an annulus of large protein granules arranged in a radially symmetric display

nuclear transplantation   the introduction of a diploid somatic nucleus into an egg whose own nucleus has been inactivated or removed in order to determine the genetic potential of the implanted nucleus in guiding normal development of the organism; *see also* **totipotent**

nuclease   any enzyme that breaks down nucleic acids

nucleic acids   a class of biologically important organic compounds existing in single-stranded or double-stranded polymeric forms called deoxyribonucleic acid (DNA) and ribonucleic acid (RNA); the genetic material in all life forms

nucleoid   a localized region of DNA in prokaryotic cells that is not separated by a membrane from the surrounding cytoplasm

nucleolar-organizing chromosome   one or more of the chromosomes in the genome, containing a localized region (NOR) of clustered ribosomal RNA genes (rDNA) and having the capacity to generate a nucleolus at the NOR

nucleolar-organizing region   *see* **NOR**

nucleolus   a discrete structure in the nucleus that is associated with ribosomal RNA synthesis and with the production of ribosome subunits and is formed at a particular nucleolar-organizing region of a nucleolar-organizing chromosome in the complement

nucleoprotein fiber   an aggregate of proteins and nucleic acid (generally the chromatin fiber, but the term is also applied to any aggregate of RNA or DNA and proteins)

nucleoside   a nucleic acid component consisting of a purine or pyrimidine base covalently linked to a ribose or deoxyribose sugar

nucleosome   the repeating nucleoprotein subunit of chromatin structure, consisting of a particular length of duplex DNA (156–260 base pairs) wound around an octamer made up of pairs of H2A, H2B, H3, and H4 histone molecules, and associated with histone H1 in a linker segment between core particles; *see also* **octamer core**

nucleus   the membrane-bounded compartment containing the chromosomes in eukaryotic cells; the major "trademark" of the eukaryotic cell

octamer core   the residual nucleosome particle consisting of 146 base pairs of DNA wound around two molecules each of H2A, H2B, H3, and H4 histone proteins. These base pairs remain unaffected by nuclease digestion of whole nucleosomes under controlled conditions

Okazaki fragment   a newly synthesized single-stranded DNA segment, about 2000 nucleotides long, that is covalently joined to similar segments during discontinuous DNA synthesis of a new partner strand along a complementary template strand of replicating DNA

oligosaccharide   residues or compounds composed of two to eight or nine sugar units or monosaccharides; *see also* **polysaccharide**

oncogene   a gene that can initiate and maintain the tumorous state in an organism or a transformed state in a cell culture and is found in oncogenic viruses (v-*onc* genes) and in their host cells, as well as in normal cells where they are designated c-*onc* genes; *see also* **cellular oncogene, proto-oncogene, viral oncogene**

oncogenic   the capacity to induce tumors in organisms or transformation in cell cultures; carcinogenic; tumorigenic

oocyte   the meiocyte that produces the egg or ovum by meiosis

oogenesis   the formation of eggs or ova from oocytes or from particular cells of the female gametophyte of plants

open systems   entities that can exchange energy and matter with their surroundings

operator   a nontranscribed regulatory nucleotide sequence that is capable of interacting with a specific repressor protein and thus of controlling the transcription of one or more structural genes adjacent to it in a bacterial operon

operon   a gene cluster consisting of a promoter, an operator, and one or more structural genes that function coordinately in bacterial gene expression; *see also* **repressor protein**

operon concept   the proposition of Jacob and Monod that structural gene expression in bacteria is controlled at the level of transcription by operator and repressor interactions

optimum pH   the particular level of acidity or alkalinity at which an enzyme activity occurs at its highest rate

origin of replication   a specific base sequence in DNA that is the site of initiation of replication, which then proceeds in one direction or in both directions away from the site

outer mitochondrial membrane   the outermost of the two enveloping membranes of the mitochondrion, readily permeable to ions and solutes and one of the four compartments of the organelle

ovary   the female gonad in which the eggs (ova) are produced for sexual reproduction

overlapping genes   different genes that share a common base sequence that is translated in two or three overlapping reading frames and thereby can specify different gene products

oxidant   an oxidizing agent that accepts electrons or hydrogens from a reductant, or reducing agent

oxidation   a reaction involving the loss of electrons or hydrogens from a reactant; *see also* **reduction**

oxidation–reduction   coupled reactions in which electrons or hydrogens lost in an oxidation reaction are picked up by components of a reduction reaction, thereby conserving energy; redox reactions

oxidative phosphorylation   the synthesis of ATP coupled to respiratory electron transport in eukaryote mitochondria or at the plasma membrane in prokaryotes

oxidizing agent   an oxidant

P700   the reaction-center chlorophyll *a* of photosystem I

P680   the reaction-center chlorophyll *a* of photosystem II

pachynema   the substage of meiotic prophase I when homologous chromosomes are fully synapsed, the synaptonemal complex is fully formed, and crossing over takes place

passive transport   the passage of substances across the membrane by free diffusion or by facilitated diffusion along a concentration gradient from higher to lower concentration of the substance, aided by transport proteins of the channel-forming or carrier types; *see also* **active transport**

PEP carboxylase   the enzyme that adds CO_2 from the air to phosphoenolpyruvate (PEP), making oxaloacetate, in the C_4 cycle of carbohydrate synthesis in C_4 photosynthetic plants

peptide bond   amide linkage; the universal link between amino acids in peptide and polypeptide chains; the covalent linkage formed when the amino group at the α carbon of one amino acid monomer joins with the carboxyl group at the α carbon of an adjacent amino acid monomer in a dehydration reaction

peptidoglycan   a network of individual polysaccharide chains connected by cross-links of four or five covalently bonded amino acid units and occurring in the form of a sheet that is the basic construction of the bacterial cell wall

peptidyl transferase   the ribosomal enzyme that catalyzes peptide bond formation between the existing peptidyl-tRNA at the P site and the newest aminoacyl-tRNA bound to the A site of the ribosome, making the growing peptidyl chain longer by one aminoacyl unit

pericentriolar material   densely staining material at the poles of both astral and anastral spindles, from which polar and chromosomal spindle fibers originate; the probable microtubule-organizing center (MTOC) of the spindle

peripheral protein   a membrane component loosely bound to a surface of the membrane, in contrast to integral proteins that are partly embedded in the membrane or that span it completely

peroxisome   a kind of microbody with a major function of degrading hydrogen peroxide by catalase action, upon its formation in a previous reaction catalyzed by a flavin oxidase; *see also* **glyoxysome**

P face   the fracture face that occurs at the protoplasmic (cytoplasmic) surface of a membrane; *see also* **E face**

phage   bacteriophage; a virus whose host is a bacterium

phagocytosis   the engulfment of solids by endocytosis at the cell surface

phloem   the food-conducting tissue of vascular plants

phosphocreatine   an energy-storing molecule in muscle, from which a phosphoryl group can be transferred to ADP to make ATP in a reaction catalyzed by phosphocreatine kinase

3′, 5′-phosphodiester bridge   the repeating covalent linkage in the sugar-phosphate backbone of a nucleic acid chain, formed as a diester link between a phosphate residue and the 3′ carbon of a pentose sugar at one side and the 5′ carbon of a pentose sugar on the other side of the phosphate residue

3-phosphoglyceraldehyde   the C_3-cycle product from which hexoses are made and ribulose 1, 5-bisphosphate is regenerated in the dark reactions of photosynthesis

3-phosphoglycerate   the first 3-carbon compound produced when the transient C_6 compound splits after its formation from the carboxylation of ribulose 1, 5-bisphosphate in the CO_2-fixing step of the C_3 cycle in the dark reactions of photosynthesis

phosphoglycolate   a phosphorylated 2-carbon compound formed in chloroplasts by the breakdown of oxygenated ribulose 1, 5-bisphosphate during photorespiration and subsequently processed in microbodies and mitochondria to become glycerate, which is phosphorylated to 3-phosphoglycerate and used in C_3-cycle reactions in the chloroplast and cytosol

phospholipid   an amphipathic membrane bilayer molecule with a polar hydrophilic head residue and two hydrophobic fatty acid chains in the "tail" region

phosphorylation   the addition of a phosphoryl group to a residue or compound, which raises the energy level of the molecule; an energy-transferring reaction

phosphoryl group transfer   one of the major modes of energy transfer in cells, mediated by the catalytic action of a kinase or by an ATPase

photon   a discrete package of electromagnetic radiation whose energy is measured in quantums

photophosphorylation   the light-dependent synthesis of ATP in photosynthesis, by a cyclic or a noncyclic pathway

photorespiration   the energy-inefficient uptake of oxygen and release of carbon dioxide by photosynthetic C_3 cells or individuals in the light

photosynthesis   the capture by chlorophylls and other light-sensitive pigments of light energy and its conversion to chemical energy in ATP and NADPH, and the subsequent use of this energy to make sugars from reduction products of CO_2; the processes of food manufacture in green cells and in certain bacteria, using light as the energy source and CO_2 as the carbon source for carbohydrate synthesis

photosystem I   PS I; a photochemical reaction complex in photosynthetic plants and bacteria through which $NADP^+$ is reduced but oxygen is not evolved

photosystem II   PS II; a photochemical reaction complex in chloroplasts to which water provides electrons, causing the release of O_2 molecules; the electrons are passed from reaction-center chorophyll *a* to an electron transport chain linked to photosystem I

phragmoplast   in plant cells undergoing cytokinesis, a growing collection of spindle fibers, secretion vesicles, and bits of endoplasmic reticulum that gradually enlarges across the center of the dividing cell and gives rise to the new cell plate that separates daughter nuclei into individual cells

pH scale   the biologically significant range of hydrogen ion concentrations in aqueous solutions, between $[H^+] = 1M$ at pH 0 and $[H^+] = 10^{-14} M$ at pH 14; $\log_{10}[H^+]$

phycobilins   accessory photosynthetic pigments found only in the chloroplasts of red algae and on thylakoids of blue-green algae

phycobilisomes   granules that are loosely attached to thylakoids in the cytoplasm of blue-green algae and in chloroplasts of red algae and that contain phycobilins

pinocytosis   the intake of fluids by endocytosis at the cell surface

plasma cells   antibody-secreting activated B cells (from B lymphocytes) of the humoral immune response system

plasmalemma   the plasma membrane

plasma membrane   the membrane that encloses the living protoplast of the cell, exhibits the properties of a boundary layer, differential permeability, intercellular communication, intercellular recognition, and other dynamic features, and may be coated with cell wall or extracellular matrix

plasmid   an extranuclear DNA genome that may influence the cellular phenotype and may exist integrated within the host chromosome or free and autonomously replicating in the host cytoplasm, often used as a vector sequence in recombinant-DNA molecules that are to be introduced into host cells and amplified there

plasmodesmata cytoplasmic channels between plant cells and, transiently, between cells in very early embryonic development in animals

plastid a general term for starch-storing or chlorophyll-containing organelles in protists and plants, but most often used to refer to a chloroplast

plastocyanin a small copper-containing protein at the end of the photosynthetic electron transport chain that transfers electrons to reaction-center P700 of photosystem I

plastoquinone a ubiquinone-like molecule that is the first member of the photosynthetic electron transport chain linking photosystems I and II in series

pluripotent designating a cell that can give rise to two or more kinds of differentiated cells; *see also* **totipotent, unipotent**

polar referring to chemical groups whose negative charge of electrons is closer to one atomic nucleus than to another in the electron-sharing (covalently bonded) unit; a characteristic of hydrophilic residues and molecules

polyadenylation the synthesis of a sequence of adenosine monophosphate residues as an extension of the 3′ terminus of a messenger RNA molecule during its post-transcriptional processing in eukaryotes and in certain mitochondria

poly (A) tail the polyadenylated sequence added to the 3′ terminus of messenger RNA during post-transcriptional processing

polymer an association of monomer units in a larger molecule

polymerase any of a group of enzymes that catalyzes the synthesis of polynucleotides from mononucleoside triphosphate precursors; *see also* **DNA polymerase, RNA polymerase**

polypeptide a polymer of amino acids linked together by peptide bonds in an unbranched chain; *see also* **protein**

polysome an aggregate of ribosomes bound to a messenger RNA molecule and actively engaged in translation of a polypeptide from encoded genetic information

polytene designating a multistranded chromosome whose many replicated DNA molecules remain associated in a single functional unit

poly (U) polyuridylic acid; an artificial RNA molecule consisting entirely of uracil residues bonded to a conventional sugar–phosphate "backbone"

P/O ratio a measure of the efficiency of oxidative phosphorylation, expressed in mole equivalents of inorganic phosphate (P_i) esterified per atom of oxygen consumed (reduced)

porphyrin any of a class of organic compounds in which four pyrrole units are connected in a ring structure with which a metal is associated; *see also* **heme, iron–porphyrin**

positive control a type of regulation mechanism by which transcription is turned on by the binding of a particular molecule or molecules to the promoter or operator adjacent to one or more structural genes; *see also* **negative control**

post transcriptional control any of a group of regulatory mechanisms that influences gene expression by acting on or modifying the RNA transcript rather than the process of transcription itself

pre-mRNA pre-messenger RNA; the precursor, primary transcript of a eukaryotic gene, which contains coding and noncoding sequences, is modified by the addition of a cap and a poly(A) tail, and is processed to mature mRNA in the nucleus

pre-rRNA pre-ribosomal RNA; the precursor, primary transcript of a eukaryotic ribosomal RNA gene, which is processed to mature rRNA before its incorporation into a ribosome subunit in the nucleolus

pre-tRNA pre-transfer RNA; the precursor, primary transcript of a transfer RNA gene, which is processed by modification of various bases and by other changes and becomes mature tRNA for binding to an aminoacyl residue

Pribnow box the TATA box in a prokaryote; the −10 sequence of a promoter upstream of the gene and is involved in the binding of RNA polymerase in the initiation of transcription

primary constriction the centromere region of a chromosome

primary lysosome the digestive organelle in eukaryotic cytoplasm that contains its acid hydrolases in latent form and has not yet encountered an appropriate substrate for its enzyme activities; *see also* **secondary lysosome**

primary structure the unique sequence of amino acids in a polypeptide or of nucleotides in a nucleic acid, as specified by genetic instructions

procollagen the triple-helical precursor, formed from three α chains, of mature collagen molecules of the extracellular matrix

profilin a monomer-stabilizing, actin-binding protein that binds to G-actin monomers and prevents their assembly into polymers

prokaryote a cellular organism lacking a membrane-bounded nucleus, typically a member of the bacteria or the blue-green algae; *see also* **eukaryote**

prolamellar body an aggregation of membranes in etioplasts transformed from chloroplasts in dark-grown cells, whose tubules give rise to reformed thylakoids when chloroplasts redevelop in the light

prometaphase the stage of mitosis or meiosis that is transitional between prophase and metaphase, before chromosomes are aligned on the spindle equator

promoter a specific nucleotide sequence in DNA, to which RNA polymerase binds and initiates transcription; a nontranscribed regulatory sequence upstream of the structural gene and essential for gene expression

prophase the first stage of mitosis or meiosis, occurring after DNA replication and before chromosome alignment on the equatorial plane of the spindle

prophase I   the prophase of meiosis I, consisting of leptonema, zygonema, pachynema, diplonema, and diakinesis

proplastid   an immature plastid

protein   one of a class of biologically important compounds, composed of one or more polypeptide chains in a functional molecule

protein kinase   any of a group of enzymes that phosphorylate proteins on free hydroxyl groups of the amino acids serine, threonine, or tyrosine; the protein product of seven or more viral oncogenes (v-*onc* genes) of retroviruses

proteinoid microsphere   a spherical particle formed when protein-like polymers are cooled in water and precipitate out of solution, and one of the proposed models of the protobiont that gave rise to the first life forms on Earth

proteoglycans   glycoproteins of the extracellular matrix, consisting of 90–95% carbohydrate in the form of numerous, long, unbranched glycosaminoglycan (GAG) chains covalently linked to serine residues of a very large core protein

protist   any member of the kingdom of eukaryotic unicellular organisms that are not included in the fungi, plant, or animal kingdoms

protobiont   a pre-life entity that ultimately evolved into a true life form, or eubiont; *see also* **coacervate**, **proteinoid microsphere**

protonmotive force   the energy source for ATP synthesis coupled to electron transport; the total protonic potential difference across the membrane, composed of components of the electrical gradient and the pH gradient produced by the pumping of protons across the mitochondrial inner membrane or the thylakoid in chloroplasts, and measured in volts

proto-oncogenes   normal cellular gene equivalents (c-*onc* genes) of retroviral v-*onc* genes; cellular genes presumably captured by retroviruses and acting as oncogenic sequences when reintroduced into cells during infection by these viruses

protoplasm   the living material of the cell, exclusive of its extracellular secreted coating or wall

protoplasmic fracture (PF) face   the fracture surface of the split membrane bilayer that is closer to the cytoplasm and farther from the cell exterior; *see also* **exoplasmic fracture (EF) face**

proviral DNA   the viral genome integrated into a host chromosome and transcribed in the host nucleus into virally specified RNA

pseudogene   a nonfunctional duplicate or derivative of a functional gene

P site   the region of the large ribosome subunit to which peptidyl-tRNA is bound during translation of a polypeptide from genetic information; *see also* **A site**

puff   an expanded chromosome region undergoing active transcription, usually observed in giant polytene chromosomes; *see also* **Balbiani ring**

pulse–chase   an experimental design in which a brief exposure to radioactively labeled substances is followed by an interval of exposure to a high concentration of the same substances in unlabeled form; functions as a means of determining precursor–product relationships in cells

punctuation processing   a mechanism whereby a polygenic transcript of mammalian mitochondrial DNA is cleaved at sites of tRNA termini, involving recognition signals for cleavage enzymes at looped secondary structures of the transcribed tRNA segments, thus liberating tRNA and mRNA sequences from the original transcript molecule

purine   parent compound of the nitrogenous bases adenine and guanine

puromycin   an antibiotic structurally resembling the terminal aminoacylated adenosine group of aminoacyl-tRNA; an inhibitor of protein synthesis at the ribosome. When incorporated into the growing polypeptide chain, puromycin causes the premature release of the uncompleted chain

pyridine nucleotide   any of a class of molecules that act as electron-transferring redox couples, such as $NAD^+/NADH$, and have a mononucleotide or dinucleotide component

pyrimidine   parent compound of the nitrogenous bases cytosine, thymine, and uracil

pyrrole   a ring-shaped compound containing one nitrogen atom and four carbon atoms, and is a precursor or component of porphyrin molecules such as heme and chlorophyll

Q-banding   a method of staining chromosomes with a fluorescent dye so that stained banded regions are differentiated from unstained interband regions when viewed by fluorescence microscopy

quantum   the energy of a photon, its amount being inversely proportional to the wavelength of emitted radiation

quaternary structure   specific assemblies in a protein composed of two or more polypeptide chains that have different properties in the protein molecule than they would as individual chains

r determinant   the portion of an R plasmid that includes genes for antibiotic resistance and, like other transposons, has typical insertion sequences (IS) at both termini

rDNA   the common abbreviation for ribosomal DNA; the ribosomal RNA genes clustered at a nucleolar-organizing region (NOR) of a nucleolar-organizing chromosome

reaction center   in a photosystem, the particular chlorophyll *a* that receives excitation energy from other light-harvesting pigments and can transfer electrons to an acceptor molecule; the site of conversion of light energy to chemical energy in photosynthesis

reanneal   renature; the reassociation of single-stranded nucleic acid molecules by complementary base-pairing to form duplex molecules or regions

receptor-mediated endocytosis   the intake of ligands bound to specific receptors of a coated pit region in the plasma membrane and the subsequent pinching off of a coated vesicle containing ligand–receptor complexes for processing inside the cell; *see also* **clathrin**

recombinant DNA   DNA molecules containing spliced segments derived from different sources, one segment being a vector sequence usually derived from a plasmid

recombinant DNA technology   the methods employed to amplify recombinant DNA in a suitable host in order to obtain large amounts of that DNA or its products

recombination   the combination of linked alleles in the progeny that differ from the parental sets because of crossing over between linked genes; the process or occurrence of new allelic combinations of linked genes in viruses, cells, or individuals

recombination intermediate   a molecular configuration of a pair of duplex DNA molecules believed to indicate a stage in crossing over leading to new combinations in DNA molecules or genotypes

recombination nodule   a large, protein-containing structure that is believed to mediate the processes of recombination and can be observed by electron microscopy within the 100-nm-wide space of the synaptonemal complex between paired chromosomes at pachynema

redox couple   a compound that can exist in both the oxidized and the reduced states and can act as an energy-transferring common intermediate in oxidation–reduction reactions

redox potential   the standard electrode potential

redox reactions   oxidation-reduction reactions

redox series   the quantitative expression of the different abilities of oxidants and reductants to accept or donate electrons, arranged in the order of the redox potential of these substances

reducing agent   reductant; a substance that can donate electrons or hydrogens to an oxidant, or oxidizing agent

reduction   a reaction involving the gain of electrons or hydrogens from a reactant; *see also* **oxidation**

regulatory gene   any gene or nucleotide sequence whose primary function is control over expression of other genes by modulating the synthesis of any products of those genes.

release factors   specific agents that cause the release of completed polypeptides from the ribosome at the conclusion of translation

renature   to reanneal or reassociate single-stranded nucleic acids by complementary base-pairing, forming duplex regions or whole molecules; *see also* **Cot value**

repetitive DNA   repeated nucleotide sequences of variable lengths occurring in the eukaryote genome in hundreds, thousands, or millions of copies; *see also* **highly**

repetitive DNA, **middle-repetitive DNA**

replication   a duplication process that requires copying from a template

replication fork   the Y-shaped region of duplex DNA at which replication is in progress

replicon   a unit of replication that has a unique origin sequence

repressible enzyme   any of a class of enzymes whose synthesis halts or decreases because of control over its transcription in the presence of a high concentration of a metabolite that is usually the end product of the biosynthetic pathway in which the enzyme acts

repressor protein   a repressor gene product that regulates bacterial operon transcription through binding to the operator, which prevents RNA polymerase from moving along the template to catalyze transcription of the adjacent structural genes

reproduction   the production, via sexual or asexual processes, of new cells or individuals by parent cells or individuals

resistance transfer factor   RTF; the portion of an R plasmid that mediates transfer of the plasmid from one cell to another; *see also* **r determinant**

respiration   *see* **aerobic respiration**

respiratory control   the inhibitory influence of the proton gradient across the inner mitochondrial membrane on the rate of electron transport down the chain of respiratory enzymes and carriers

respiratory enzyme complex   any one of four major assemblies of respiratory components of the mitochondrial inner membrane that transfer electrons from oxidized carbohydrates to molecular oxygen and provide sufficient free-energy change to sponsor the synthesis of three molecules of ATP per pair of electrons transported from NADH to O_2

restriction enzymes   a class of endonucleases that cut both strands of duplex DNA at specific sites of specific sequences composed of four to six base pairs showing rotational symmetry

restriction fragments   the cut pieces of duplex DNA produced by the action of a restriction enzyme

retrovirus   one of a class of RNA viruses of vertebrate animals, which copies DNA from RNA genomes using its own reverse transcriptase and is often oncogenic

reverse transcriptase   an RNA-dependent DNA polymerase that guides the synthesis of complementary DNA from RNA templates, which is a reversal of the usual situation in which RNA copies are transcribed from DNA sequences (hence the colloquial name of the enzyme)

reversible inhibition   the restoration of an enzyme's activity after its exposure to a competitive or noncompetitive inhibitor, by increasing the substrate concentration or by some other means, because the functional region of the enzyme undergoes no change during the interval of inhibition

rho protein   an *E. coli* gene product that binds to the terminator region of an informational DNA sequence and sponsors the dissociation of RNA polymerase from the DNA template, thereby ending transcription of that sequence

riboflavin   a component of flavin adenine dinucleotide (FAD) and of flavin mononucleotide (FMN); vitamin B_2

riboflavin 5-phosphate   flavin mononucleotide (FMN)

ribonucleic acid   RNA; one of the two major kinds of nucleic acids, characterized by the presence of uracil instead of thymine and by the presence of the pentose sugar D-ribose instead of 2-deoxy-D-ribose of deoxyribonucleic acid (DNA); *see also* **messenger RNA**, **retrovirus**, **ribosomal RNA**, **small nuclear RNA**, **transfer RNA**

ribophorin I, ribophorin II   two integral proteins of the rough ER membrane that help bind the ribosome to the membrane and thereby stabilize the signal receptor protein (SRP)–ribosome complex that is engaged in cotranslational transfer of nascent secretory proteins across the ER membrane into the ER lumen

D-ribose   a pentose sugar and a component of ribonucleotides in energy-transferring molecules (such as ATP, NAD, FAD, and others) and of ribonucleic acids

ribosomal DNA   rDNA; the clusters of ribosomal RNA genes at the nucleolar-organizing region of a nucleolar-organizing chromosome in eukaryotes

ribosomal RNA   rRNA; the particular ribonucleic acid molecules in the ribosomes of all cellular organisms and in mitochondria and chloroplasts, which function in the translation of polypeptides from genetic information in mRNA

ribosome   a complex structure consisting of a small subunit and a large subunit, each comprised of RNA and protein molecules, which is the site of translation (as polysome aggregates) in the cytoplasm and in mitochondria and chloroplasts; *see also* **cytoribosome**, **monosome**

ribosome subunits   two classes of structures making up the whole ribosome (monosome), one class of small subunits (30S in prokaryotes, 40S in eukaryotes), and one class of large subunits (50S in prokaryotes, 60S in eukaryotes), which as one small subunit and one large subunit together make up the 70S prokaryotic ribosome and the 80S eukaryotic ribosome

ribulose 1,5-bisphosphate   RuBP; the 5-carbon compound that fixes CO_2 in a reaction catalyzed by ribulose 1,5-bisphosphate carboxylase, which is the start of the dark reactions of photosynthesis in chloroplast stroma

RNA   the common abbreviation for ribonucleic acid

RNA polymerase   any of a group of enzymes that catalyze the synthesis of RNA molecules along DNA templates during transcription. In eukaryotes, RNA polymerase I guides transcription of ribosomal RNA, RNA polymerase II guides transcription of messenger RNA, and RNA polymerase III guides transcription of 5S rRNA and of transfer RNA

RNA primase   an RNA polymerase that guides the synthesis of a short segment of RNA primer during DNA replication

RNA primer   the short segment of RNA that is required to initiate DNA replication and is later excised and replaced by a DNA segment in a reaction catalyzed by DNA polymerase I

rolling circle mechanism   a process of duplex DNA replication in which multiple lengths of DNA sequences are synthesized and are then cut into specific lengths by endonucleases, after which the linear molecules are circularized through complementary base-pairing of their redundant termini ("sticky ends")

rough endoplasmic reticulum   rough ER; RER; the portion of the endoplasmic reticulum with ribosomes attached to one surface of the membrane sheet, and the system for synthesis and transport of many kinds of proteins in the eukaryotic cell; *see also* **smooth ER**

R plasmid   an autonomously replicating duplex DNA molecule that consists of a resistance transfer factor (RTF) and one or more transposable r determinants and can be transferred from one bacterial cell to another, influencing the phenotypic expression of the cells

rRNA   the common abbreviation for ribosomal RNA

RuBP   the common abbreviation for ribulose 1,5-bisphosphate

RuBP carboxylase   an abbreviation for ribulose 1,5-bisphosphate carboxylase

ruffled-membrane movement   a mode of locomotion along a solid surface exhibited by mammalian fibroblasts in cell culture and characterized by the alternating attachment and detachment of the leading edge of the cell to the solid surface. The undulating motion there accounts for a ruffled appearance in the advancing edge of the cell

S   a quantitative measure, expressed in Svedberg units, of the rate of sedimentation of a given substance in a centrifugal field, based on the sedimentation coefficient s, an s of 1×10^{-13} sec being defined as one Svedberg unit (1 S)

salivary gland chromosomes   giant polytene chromosomes in interphase nuclei of the salivary gland cells in larvae of dipteran insects such as *Drosophila* and *Chironomus*

sarcolemma   the plasma membrane of a striated muscle fiber

sarcomere   the contractile unit of striated muscle myofibrils, extending between adjacent Z-discs

sarcoplasm   the cytoplasm of a striated muscle fiber

sarcoplasmic reticulum   the endoplasmic reticulum of a striated muscle fiber

secondary constriction   any pinched-in site on a chromosome other than the primary constriction at the centromere region, but most often the site of a nucleolar-organizing region (NOR)

secondary lysosome   the active form of the eukaryotic

digestive organelle, which develops from a primary **lysosome** that has interacted with some appropriate substrate or vesicle containing such a substrate

secondary structure the local structure of a polypeptide or nucleic acid chain arising from chemical bonding between nearby residues to produce forms such as stem-and-loop or cloverleaf RNAs and α-helix or β-sheet configurations in polypeptides

second law of thermodynamics the statement that all systems tend toward an equilibrium, or minimal free-energy content

second messenger a receptor-generated intracellular signal activated by an extracellular ligand that acts as the first messenger on binding to receptor

secretion a substance produced in a cell but performing a function outside that cell or at its surface

secretory vesicle a membrane-bounded organelle containing secretions, and the means by which the secretions are delivered out of the cell by exocytosis

self-assembly the organization of structure in the absence of a template or parent structure, arising only from interactions between assembling components that contain all the information required to build the structure

semiconservative replication the usual mode of DNA synthesis in which each parental strand is a template for synthesis of a new complementary partner strand, producing two duplexes, each of which is comprised of one parental and one newly synthesized strand

sensory receptor a specialized cell that responds to light, sound, odor, or other environmental stimuli

septate junction a differentiated region shared by the plasma membranes of adjacent cells in invertebrates and characterized by a ladderlike arrangement of bars, or septa, in the intercellular space along the entire length of the junction

sex chromatin any condensed X chromosome, or Barr body, in the interphase nucleus

shuttle an indirect route for electron transfer across the mitochondrial membrane, by which electrons from NADH are taken across the membrane by a reduced metabolite and transferred to the respiratory chain, after which the reoxidized metabolite returns to the cytosol for another, repeating episode

sigma factor σ; a polypeptide subunit of the *E. coli* RNA polymerase, which is required to initiate transcription correctly and is released afterward, leaving the core enzyme ($\alpha_2\beta\beta'$) of the holoenzyme ($\alpha_2\beta\beta'$ σ) to carry out RNA polymerization

signal hypothesis the proposition stating that growing polypeptide chains of secretory proteins have an *N*-terminal signal peptide sequence that promotes attachment to the ER membrane or bacterial plasma membrane of the translating ribosomes of a polysome, leading to cotranslational transfer by vectorial discharge of the polypeptide into the ER lumen or out of the bacterial cell, respectively

signal peptidase the membrane-bounded enzyme that cleaves a signal peptide from the growing chain shortly after it has entered the bacterial periplasmic space or the ER lumen in cotranslational transfer events

signal peptide *see* **signal hypothesis**, **signal peptidase**

signal recognition particle SRP; an aggregate of six polypeptide subunits and a 7S RNA molecule that binds to a ribosome after the signal peptide sequence has been translated and mediates the binding of the ribosome to the ER membrane via interaction with an embedded SRP-receptor ("docking") protein

simple-sequence DNA a synonym for highly repetitive DNA

single-strand binding protein SSB protein; a noncatalytic molecule that binds cooperatively to single-stranded regions of DNA, leading to unwinding of the double helix at the replication fork and to tautness of the opened single-stranded regions, thus making them accessible to replication enzymes

sliding filament model the proposition that striated muscle contraction occurs via the sliding of actin filaments over myosin filaments, and a generalization applied to fiber interactions in nonmuscle cell movement phenomena

sliding microtubule mechanism the proposition that ciliary movement occurs via the sliding of microtubule doublets past one another, aided by a number of proteinaceous structures in the ciliary axoneme in eukaryotes

small nuclear RNAs snRNA; molecules believed to base-pair with consensus sequences at exon–intron junctions of pre-mRNA and give rise to secondary structures that facilitate the cutting out of introns and the splicing of exons during post-transcriptional processing to make mature mRNA in eukaryotes

smooth ER the portion of endoplasmic reticulum lacking attached ribosomes; *see also* **rough ER**

sodium–potassium ATPase *see* **Na$^+$–K$^+$ ATPase**

sodium–potassium pump *see* **Na$^+$–K$^+$ pump**

solar dust cloud the primordial nebula from which a solar system may develop

solute molecules dissolved in a solution

solvent the medium in which solutes are dissolved in a solution

somatic cell genetics genetic analysis of the genome using somatic (body) cells in culture and involving cell fusions and the random loss of particular chromosomes from the hybrid cell

somatic cell hybrid the product of fusion between somatic cells in culture

Southern blot assay a test in which electrophoretically resolved DNA segments are transferred from the gel to nitrocellulose filter paper and are then probed with radioactively labeled DNA or RNA to identify complementary sequences, which are evident by bands made visible in autoradiographs of the preparation (a similar technique called *northern blotting* is used to identify RNAs)

spectrin   the major protein that is isolated from erythrocyte plasma membrane preparations, is loosely bound at the inner surface of the membrane either as peripheral proteins or as components of the underlying cytoskeleton, and occurs as part of a fibrous meshwork that helps to restrain protein mobility within the membrane and to maintain cell shape

sperm   the male gamete(s) of sexual reproduction

spermatocyte   the meiocyte that produces sperm by meiosis

S phase   the portion of a cell cycle between G_1 and G_2 phases and the interval of DNA replication; mid-interphase

sphingosine   an aminated dialcohol that forms part of the hydrophobic tail (along with a fatty acid chain) of sphingomyelin, the most abundant of the membrane sphingolipids in brain and nervous tissue

spindle   an aggregate of microtubules and other components that is seen during nuclear division and functions in the alignment and movement of chromosomes at metaphase and anaphase, respectively

spindle fibers   the microtubules of the spindle extending from their origin at microtubule-organizing centers at the poles of the cell to the middle region of the spindle (polar fibers) or to their attachment points in the centromere of each chromosome (chromosomal fibers)

split genes   designating the organization of eukaryote genes into alternating coding sequences (exons) and noncoding intervening sequences (introns); also called interrupted genes or mosaic genes

spore   a single-celled reproductive unit that can give rise to a new individual directly upon germination

sporocyte   the meiocyte that produces spores by meiosis

sporophyte   the diploid structure or individual that produces megaspores and microspores in plants; *see also* **gametophyte**

spot desmosome   an adhering junction that occurs as an isolated point of contact between adjacent cells; *see also* **belt desmosome, hemidesmosome**

SRP   the common abbreviation for signal recognition particle

SRP receptor   "docking" protein; the protein embedded in the rough ER membrane that mediates the binding to that membrane of a ribosome engaged in translating a secretory polypeptide chain, via an interaction between a signal recognition particle (SRP) bound to that ribosome and the membrane receptor

SSB protein   *see* **single-strand binding protein**

standard electrode potential E_0; the oxidation–reduction (redox) potential of a substance relative to a hydrogen electrode, and expressed in volts

standard free-energy change $\Delta G°$; a thermodynamic constant representing the difference between the standard free energy of the reactants and the standard free energy of the products of a reaction; energy-releasing reactions have $-\Delta G°$ values, and energy-requiring reactions have $+\Delta G°$ values

start codon   the initiator codon AUG in messenger RNA

startpoint   the first nucleotide $(+1)$ to be copied into RNA from DNA; the initial point of transcription in a DNA sequence

steady states   different pairs of input–output rates in a system, but each steady state has a rate of input of matter and energy that equals the rate of output; a characteristic of living cells that maintains their nonequilibrium condition

stem cells   perpetually dividing, undifferentiated cells that give rise to more of themselves and to one or more differentiated cell types; *see also* **meristematic cells**

strand displacement   a replication mechanism in some viruses with linear duplex DNA genomes by which one DNA strand is displaced as a new strand is being synthesized, and by which each new strand has correct termini

streptomycin   an antibiotic produced by *Streptomyces griseus* that binds to the 30S ribosome subunit in bacteria and inhibits protein synthesis or causes misreading of the genetic message

striated muscle   skeletal muscle or voluntary muscle that is characterized by muscle fiber organization and by sarcomere contractile units in myofibrils

stroma   the unstructured matrix of the chloroplast, that bathes the grana and stroma thylakoids and enzymes of the dark reactions of photosynthesis

stroma thylakoids   large flattened sacs that occur singly or in small aggregates within the chloroplast stroma and are distinguished by their morphology from the small, coin-shaped grana thylakoids in the same space, often occurring as connections between separate stacks of grana thylakoids

structural genes   sequences of DNA that encode polypeptides or transfer RNAs and ribosomal RNAs; *see also* **regulatory gene**

submetacentric   designating a chromosome whose centromere is submedian in location, making one arm somewhat longer than the other

substrate   the molecule acted on and altered by interaction with a specific enzyme in a chemical reaction

succinate dehydrogenase complex   the respiratory enzyme complex of the electron transport chain in the mitochondrial inner membrane that receives electrons from the oxidization of succinate to produce fumarate in the Krebs cycle and then transfers these electrons from its $FADH_2$ component of the dehydrogenase to coenzyme Q of the transport chain

supercoiled DNA   a conformation of duplex DNA molecules in which a coil is superimposed on the helically coiled pair of polynucleotide chains

switch sites   tandemly repeated homologous regions immediately preceding almost every C_H gene in the cluster of constant-region genes for the heavy chain in immunoglobulin molecules and required for rearrangements and deletions of C_H genes during heavy-chain class switching in plasma cells (activated B lymphocytes, or B cells)

synapsis   the specific pairing of homologous chromosomes or regions, typically occurring during zygonema of meiotic prophase I but also evident in certain somatic cells, such as dipteran larval cells with paired polytene chromosomes

synaptonemal complex   a structural component that is situated between paired chromosomes in pachynema of meiotic prophase I and holds the chromosomes in register during crossing over

T$_m$ the symbol designating the midpoint melting temperature of a DNA sample

target cell   a cell that responds specifically to a given hormone or other agent

TATA box   Hogness box; in the eukaryote promoter, a −25 sequence of seven AT base pairs that provide a recognition site for the binding of RNA polymerase in the initiation of messenger RNA transcription; *see also* **Pribnow box**

tautomer   an isomer characterized by the location of a hydrogen atom that can move reversibly from one place to another and produce one tautomeric form or another of the molecule

telocentric   designating a chromosome whose centromere is at one terminus, so only one arm is present

telomere   the virtually identical segment of DNA at each end of each linear chromosome in a genome, consisting of very short, simple, tandemly repeated sequences at, or very close to, the extreme end of a chromosome arm, and much longer, complex sequences near the end of each arm, and all or part of which is required for the chromosome to be completely replicated and not to undergo fusion with other chromosome ends

telophase   the final stage of mitosis or meiosis, when nuclear reorganization occurs

termination codons   the stop codons UAA, UAG, and UGA, which mark the end of a genetic message specifying a polypeptide or a ribosomal or transfer RNA molecule

terminator   the terminal sequence that is at the end of a genetic region and is not transcribed into pre-messenger RNA

tertiary structure   the three-dimensional folding of a polypeptide or polynucleotide chain brought about by interactions among side-groups or other residues at some distance from one another in the primary structure of the molecule

testis   the male gonad in which the sperm are produced

thermodynamics   the branch of physical science that deals with exchanges of energy in collections of matter; *see also* **bioenergetics**, **first law of thermodynamics**, **second law of thermodynamics**

theta form   a circular replicating molecule of duplex DNA that resembles the Greek letter theta (θ); Cairns form

thick filaments   15-nm-wide myosin filaments, in contrast to 6-nm-wide microfilaments and 10-nm-wide intermediate filaments

thylakoid   a closed membrane sac that may be disk-shaped in a granum or greatly elongated in the stroma of a chloroplast, or may appear in prokaryotic cytoplasm as invaginations of the plasma membrane, and containing the light-requiring components of photosynthesis

thymidine kinase   TK; the enzyme catalyzing the phosphorylation of thymidine monophosphate to thymidine diphosphate or that of thymidine diphosphate to thymidine triphosphate in pathways of precursor synthesis for DNA

tight junction   an impermeable junction of epithelial tissue consisting of fused regions of plasma membranes from adjacent cells and occluding the intercellular passageway

Tn   the common abbreviation for a transposon

topoisomerase   any DNA replication enzyme that catalyzes reactions involving the nicking and closing of duplex DNA. Topoisomerase I is an unwinding enzyme that releases supercoils in duplex DNA, and topoisomerase II (gyrase) induces relaxed DNA to undergo supercoiling in a reaction that requires energy provided by ATP hydrolysis

totipotent   referring to the capacity of a nucleus to guide a complete program of development of an organism

trailer   the nucleotide sequence at the 3′ end of a messenger RNA molecule, just downstream of the encoded region and usually not translated at the ribosome

transcription   a process by which the nucleotide sequence of the coding strand of DNA is copied into a single-stranded complementary RNA molecule, under the catalytic direction of an RNA polymerase

transcriptional control   any mechanism by which regulation of gene expression is achieved via an influence over transcription (on, off, increase, decrease)

transcription unit   the region of a DNA sequence between the startpoint and the end of transcription and lying between the promoter and the terminator of that DNA sequence

***trans* face**   the maturing face of a stack of cisternae in the Golgi apparatus

transfer RNA   tRNA; the RNA molecule that carries an amino acid to a specific codon in messenger RNA during polypeptide translation at the ribosome

translation   the process by which amino acids are joined into a polypeptide chain at the ribosome, according to the nucleotide sequence of a messenger RNA transcript of encoded DNA

translocase   an enzyme component of the ribosome that catalyzes the relocation of the peptidyl-t-RNA from the A site to the P site and thereby opens the A site for the next incoming aminoacyl-tRNA unit in translation

transport protein   a channel-forming or carrier protein in the membrane that assists ions and molecules across the lipid bilayer of that membrane

transport vesicle   a bleb pinched from smooth membrane in the transitional region between rough and smooth ER, that encloses soluble proteins and delivers these contents to the interior of an organelle or to the extracellular side of the plasma membrane upon fusing with the specific target membrane; a component involved in the flow of membrane traffic in the cell and in membrane recycling

transposable genetic element   a unique DNA sequence that can move from one site to another in a genome, through insertions and excisions, and thereby influence gene expression; a movable genetic element

transposon   Tn; a transposable genetic element that is more than 2000 base pairs long and includes genes for insertion into a chromosome as well as genes unrelated to insertion; *see also* **insertion sequence**

tritium ^{3}H; the radioactive isotope of hydrogen

tropomyosin   in striated muscle, a regulatory protein bound to actin filaments and, together with troponin, involved in the control of muscle contraction

troponin   a regulatory protein that is bound to actin filaments in striated muscle, interacts with tropomyosin, and acts as a calcium-dependent switch in muscle contraction

tRNA   the common abbreviation for transfer RNA

T system   a series of transverse tubular infolds of the sarcolemma of striated muscle fibers that allows the rapid communication of electrical excitation to all the myofibrils in the fiber interior

tubulin α- and β-monomeric proteins that assemble as α, β-heterodimers into long polymeric protofilaments, which join side by side to describe a hollow cylindrical form for a microtubule in eukaryotes

Turner syndrome   a clinical condition of human females who have only one X chromosome (*45, X*) instead of the usual two

turnover number   an enzyme characteristic that is usually expressed as the number of substrate molecules that can be converted to product by one enzyme molecule per second

unequal crossing over   an exchange between chromosomes or DNA strands that produces one product with missing genes or sequences and the other product with duplicated genes or sequences

unipotent   designating the capacity of a nucleus to produce only one kind of differentiated cell

universe   the entire cosmos; the sum total of all known matter and energy in systems and surroundings

upstream   referring to the region to the left of the startpoint of a gene; *see also* **downstream**

uracil   the nitrogenous base in RNA that exists in place of thymine; a pyrimidine base in RNA that undergoes

complementary base-pairing with adenine in DNA or RNA molecules

vacuole   a region in the cytoplasm that is surrounded by a membrane and filled with molecules and particles in a watery medium and is particularly common in plant cells; a very large vesicle often associated with the Golgi apparatus

van der Waals bond   a nonspecific, weak chemical interaction resulting from attractive forces produced when two atoms or groups of atoms come near each other

variable segment   the *N*-terminal sequence of amino acids in the light and heavy chains of an immunoglobulin molecule, and the portion of the antibody that combines with a specific antigen in an immune response reaction

vector   an agent that transfers an item from one host to another

vectorial discharge   the mechanism by which nascent polypeptides are transferred across rough ER membrane into the ER lumen during translation (cotranslational transfer)

velocity of reaction   *V*; the rate of catalysis as determined by enzyme kinetics

vesicle   a small, membrane-bounded element filled with substances in aqueous solution

V-gene translocation   an immunoglobulin gene rearrangement that occurs during the differentiation of B lymphocytes from germ-line precursor cells and involves the association of a particular *V* gene from the *V*-gene cluster with the *C*-gene cluster to produce a functional and antigenically specific kind of immunoglobulin in a B lymphocyte and all its mitotic descendants, independently of any contact with the antigen

villin   an actin-binding capping protein that binds to one end or the other of an actin filament and thereby regulates the length of the actin polymer

vimentin filament   a type of intermediate filament composed primarily of the fiber-forming protein vimentin and present in many kinds of cells

vinculin   an actin-binding protein that cross-links actin filaments in belt desmosomes to the plasma membrane. In adhesion plaques it anchors stress fibers to the plasma membrane.

viral oncogenes   v-*onc* genes; genes in retroviral genomes that are not required for viral reproduction but that induce tumors in host organisms or cause the transformation of cells in culture after infection by the viruses carrying such genes; *see also* **cellular oncogenes**, **proto-oncogenes**

wobble hypothesis   the proposition by F. H. C. Crick that a tRNA may recognize two or more different codons in messenger RNA because the 5′ base in the anticodon triplet of such a transfer RNA is less restrained in its pairing with the 3′ base of the complementary codon in messenger RNA and can thus pair with more than one kind of base because of this property of reduced constraint, or ''wobble''

X inactivation   a phenomenon in which all the X chromosomes but one in a nucleus become genetically inactivated because they condense to the heterochromatic state, thus leaving one remaining euchromatic X chromosome to guide the expression of X-linked genes in the cell or individual; also called Lyonization in recognition of Mary Lyon, the discoverer of the phenomenon; *see also* **facultative heterochromatin**

xylem   the water-conducting tissue in vascular plants

Z-DNA   the left-handed helical configuration of duplex DNA, in contrast to the common right-handed helical configuration in B-DNA

Z disc   the protein structure that bisects the I band of a sarcomere and is the place to which the actin filaments bind

Z scheme   the photosynthetic pathway in which the flow of electrons from water terminates in the reduction of $NADP^+$; the light reactions of photosynthesis illustrated in the form of the letter Z when plotted along a redox scale

zymogens   digestive enzyme precursors secreted from pancreatic acinar cells in secretion granules packaged at the Golgi apparatus and delivered to the gastrointestinal system, where these enzymes function in their active form

zygonema   the second of the substages of meiotic prophase I and the interval when homologous chromosomes undergo synapsis

zygote   the product of gamete fusion in sexual reproduction and the initial cell of the new generation

zymogen granules   secretion vesicles containing digestive enzyme precursors (zymogens)

Index

Page numbers in **boldface** refer to figures and tables.